ANNUAL REVIEW OF
PLANT PHYSIOLOGY

ANNUAL REVIEW OF PLANT PHYSIOLOGY

WINSLOW R. BRIGGS, *Editor*
Carnegie Institution of Washington, Stanford, California

PAUL B. GREEN, *Associate Editor*
Stanford University

RUSSELL L. JONES, *Associate Editor*
University of California, Berkeley

VOLUME 25

1974

ANNUAL REVIEWS INC.   4139 EL CAMINO WAY   PALO ALTO, CALIFORNIA 94306

ANNUAL REVIEWS INC.
Palo Alto, California, USA

International Standard Book Number: 0-8243-0625-2
Library of Congress Catalog Card Number: A51-1660

Assistant Editor	Jean Heavener
Indexers	Mary A. Glass
	Susan Tinker
Subject Indexer	Hal Straus

PRINTED AND BOUND IN THE UNITED STATES OF AMERICA

CONTENTS

PREFATORY CHAPTER:
Reflections and Speculations, *F. W. Went*   1

CELL ORGANIZATION:
The C_4 Syndrome: A Structural Analysis, *W. M. Laetsch*   27
Microtubules and Microfilaments, *Peter K. Hepler and Barry
    A. Palevitz*   309

NUTRITION, ABSORPTION, AND TRANSPORT:
Uptake Mechanisms: Inorganic and Organic, *Per Nissen*   53
Phloem Transport: Physical Chemical or Impossible,
    Ian F. Wardlaw   515

BIOENERGETICS:
Metabolite Exchange Between Chloroplasts and Cytoplasm, *Ulrich
    Heber*   393
Energy Conservation in Photosynthetic Electron Transport of
    Chloroplasts, *A. Trebst*   423

METABOLISM:
Dinitrogen Fixation, *M. J. Dilworth*   81
Circadian Rhythms and Metabolic Patterns, *Orlando Queiroz*   115
Protein Turnover in Plants and Possible Means of its Regulation,
    R. C. Huffaker and L. W. Peterson   363
The Metabolism of Aromatic Compounds, *Helen A. Stafford*   459
Metabolism of Auxin in Higher Plants, *Elnora A. Schneider
    and F. Wightman*   487

DEVELOPMENT:
Plant Propagation Through Tissue Cultures, *Toshio Murashige*   135
Control of Seed Germination, *A. M. Mayer and Y. Shain*   167
Rapid Responses to Plant Hormones, *Michael L. Evans*   195
Isozymes in Development and Differentiation, *John G. Scandalios*   225
The Chemistry and Physiology of Abscisic Acid, *B. V. Milborrow*   259

SPECIAL TOPICS:
Phytotoxins Produced by Plant Parasites, *Gary A. Strobel*   541
Physiology of Mycorrhiza, *Franz H. Meyer*   567

REPRINT INFORMATION   587

INDEXES
Author Index   589
Subject Index   615
Cumulative Index of Contributing Authors, Volumes 21 to 25   624
Cumulative Index of Chapter Titles, Volumes 21 to 25   625

ANNUAL REVIEWS INC. is a nonprofit corporation established to promote the advancement of the sciences. Beginning in 1932 with the *Annual Review of Biochemistry,* the Company has pursued as its principal function the publication of high quality, reasonably priced Annual Review volumes. The volumes are organized by Editors and Editorial Committees who invite qualified authors to contribute critical articles reviewing significant developments within each major discipline.

Annual Reviews Inc. is administered by a Board of Directors whose members serve without compensation.

Annual Reviews are published in the following sciences: Anthropology, Astronomy and Astrophysics, Biochemistry, Biophysics and Bioengineering, Earth and Planetary Sciences, Ecology and Systematics, Entomology, Fluid Mechanics, Genetics, Materials Science, Medicine, Microbiology, Nuclear Science, Pharmacology, Physical Chemistry, Physiology, Phytopathology, Plant Physiology, Psychology, and Sociology (to begin publication in 1975). In addition, two special volumes have been published by Annual Reviews Inc.: *History of Entomology* (1973) and *The Excitement and Fascination of Science* (1965).

Fritz W. Went

Ann. Rev. Plant Physiol. 1974. 25:1–26

REFLECTIONS AND SPECULATIONS

❖7560

F. W. Went

Laboratory of Desert Biology, Desert Research Institute, University of Nevada System, Reno, Nevada 89507

CONTENTS

What Makes a Botanist?.	2
Botanical Problems of Yore.	3
AUXIN PROBLEMS.	4
Polar Auxin Transport.	6
Seed Dormancy.	7
Second Law of Thermodynamics.	7
Phototropism.	8
Auxin and Cofactors for Growth.	9
Translocation of Growth Factors Across Graft Unions.	9
CONTROL OF THE PLANT ENVIRONMENT.	10
Amateurs in Science.	11
Thermoperiodicity.	11
Productivity.	12
Circadian Rhythm.	13
The Nature of the Circadian Clock in Higher Plants.	14
Which Factors Ultimately Limit Growth?.	15
Variability and Air-Conditioned Rooms and Greenhouses.	16
ECOLOGY.	17
Desert Plants.	18
Mycorrhiza.	19
AIR POLLUTION.	20
Smog.	20
Natural Smog in Nature.	21
Quantity of Natural Smog on Earth.	23
Fate of the Natural Smog.	23
CONCLUSION.	24

When I was invited to write an introductory chapter for this Annual Review, I accepted with alacrity, especially since it was meant to be a "personal, philosophical, or historical essay." Present-day editorial policies do not allow a scientist to be

1

personal any more: an author should appear to be emotionally completely detached from his subject, which the born scientist of course never is. Just as the serenity of Vermeer and Delius, or the gigantic minds of Rembrandt or Beethoven are expressed in their creations, thus the personalities of the early botanists and those of the turn of the century became living persons in my mind, as they revealed themselves in their publications. It was a source of great satisfaction, when meeting them in person, to find that their physical appearance often resembled the mental image I had formed of them. It was probably no coincidence that the person of H. Fitting did not resemble his scientific image, for he seemed more detached in his writings than most other botanical authors. It is a source of regret that I never had a chance to meet N. Cholodny, A. Paal, nor P. Boysen Jensen to compare my mental image of them with reality. Yet a present-day meeting with Charles Darwin or Julius Sachs could hardly be satisfying because of the exalted image I have developed of them, based entirely on their writings and work.

What Makes a Botanist?

In my youth I had an extraordinary opportunity to become a botanist. I was born and grew up in a botanical garden. My father (F. A. F. C. Went) was professor of botany and director of the garden and botanical laboratory at the State University of Utrecht, a provincial town in the center of the Netherlands. His official residence, a very roomy 300-year-old house, was located in the botanical garden, just across from the newly rebuilt botanical laboratory, which under his guidance had become the model of a modern botanical installation, attracting visitors from all over the world. Just because of the obvious environmental pressure, my father was very careful not to push me into a botanical profession, and my early direct contacts with science and botany were: (a) my high school professors in biology, chemistry, and physics, who were all extraordinary teachers; and (b) a fellow high school student, C. G. G. J. van Steenis, with whom I regularly made bicycle trips to collect plants for our herbaria, and with whom I have been bound by a lifelong—and occasionally explosive—friendship. But it was not until I went as a student to the University of Utrecht that my fixation on botany became permanent.

What goes into the making of a professional biologist? Often it is environment, in which usually intellectually inquisitive parents and a plethora of plants or animals in garden or field produce the winning combination. If the home environment has not brought the stimulation, it usually is an inspiring high school or college teacher which produces a biologist. Any collecting activities resulting in herbaria, terraria, aquaria, or collections of insects or fossils are important too. And in the past as well as in the present, inquisitive minds became intrigued with the problems plants presented, such as their medicinal qualities (many of the 16th-18th century botanists were physicians), their diseases, their agricultural problems or horticultural possibilities. While all these factors contributed to my becoming a botanist, perhaps the most powerful was the fact that as a boy I spent many hours in the botanical laboratory. In the brightly lighted (or dark) rooms students could work the whole day with plants and discover their secrets, studying them under the microscope, or in the mysterious physiological darkrooms, or on the clinostat, or in a constant temperature waterbath, or in complicated machines. In the greenhouses of the botanical garden were sensitive plants, Venus fly traps and other insectivorous plants, cacti and desert plants, morphologically interesting forms, exotic flowers, and any number of other growing wonders, from algae to fungi to palms, which would whet the research appetite of any budding scientist. It is a pity that nowadays campus development has broken the close ties between students and teachers on the one hand and botanical gardens and biologically interesting plant collections on the other hand. In the old days botany professors profited by living in a botanical garden, and much of the work of J. Sachs, H. de Vries, K. von Goebel, E. Bünning, or Charles Darwin was based on the extensive plant collections they had growing next door. They verified their discoveries on a wide variety of plants, stressing the universal occurrence of a phenomenon rather than its presently overemphasized statistical significance. Many physiological problems can be solved with "oats, peas, beans, and barley," as the nursery rhyme says, even with their seedlings grown in physiological darkrooms, or their fruits or seeds bought in a supermarket, but for a balanced view of plant processes we need an overall view of the plant kingdom, which can be so inspiringly demonstrated in a botanical garden. Therefore, I consider myself lucky in having been connected most of my life with botanical gardens: I was born in the one of Utrecht, my first job was as a botanist at the famous botanical garden in Bogor, Java; then I was president of the California Arboretum Foundation, the sponsor of the Los Angeles State and County Arboretum, and for 5 years I was director of the Missouri Botanical Garden. In addition, extensive travels have given me a good overview of the plant kingdom. This gave me the advantage of coming close to the living plant, to acquaint myself not only with its appearance and occurrence, but also with its workings. And it has prevented me from becoming a narrow specialist, spending my life on the response of a single plant or organ.

Botanical Problems of Yore

When I look back on the problems that faced botanists 50 years ago, I realize the big ones are still with us. Although we know a lot more about the why and how of plant growth and development, about form and morphogenesis, about metabolism and nutrient uptake, or about response to the environment, the elemental problems remain basically the same, as enigmatic now as then. Only the emphasis has changed.

At the turn of the century there was an intense interest in tropic responses of plants, at least in European laboratories. It was thought that the response of a stem, a root, or a leaf of a plant to light or gravity could tell us much about inner processes controlling these responses. There was a curious duality in basic thinking on this subject. On the one hand it was thought, especially by the school of Pfeffer in Leipzig, that complex tropistic responses reflected an equally complex inner mechanism of stimulation and activation, to some extent the way Darwin compared the control of stem and root behavior by the stem and root tip with the action of the brain in lower animals. Thus Pfeffer was greatly puzzled by the basic experiment of P. Boysen Jensen on transmission of the phototropic stimulus across a cut surface, which was carried out in his laboratory in 1907. Later, in 1914, when A. Paal worked in his laboratory, Pfeffer let him repeat the transmission experiment, since the results were contrary to the extensive research of Fitting. But until his death in 1917, Pfeffer never drew the conclusion that a simple substance, not a complex stimulus, was involved in phototropism.

A different line of thought about tropism emanated from my father's laboratory, starting with the basic research of one of his students, A. H. Blaauw, on phototropism. The exceedingly clear mind of Blaauw could not accept the imprecise concept of "stimulation," and in some basic experiments he showed that a definite phototropic curvature was a response to a definite amount of light energy. Soon Blaauw, being a superb photographer, related the phototropic curvature to a photochemical process in the plant. Later, in a sensational series of experiments, Blaauw showed that the inhibitory effect of light on straight growth could—at least qualitatively—account for the phototropic curvature (since unilateral light produces a light gradient in the phototropically responding organ). He then pronounced his famous dictum: the problem of phototropism has become empty: only the problem of the effect of light on growth remains. During the next 10 years this resulted in a whole series of investigations for or against Blaauw's theory.

Curiously enough, this controversy was entirely bypassed in America. The practical New World botanists had very little interest in the tropistic behavior of plants to the extent that the word tropism was not even mentioned in the American textbook of plant physiology most used in the thirties, that of Miller.

Another burning question during my student days was that of limiting factors, a subject first broached by Liebig in the 1840s in the form of the "law of the minimum," and revived in 1905 by F. F. Blackman in a remarkable publication. In the U.S. this problem took the form of "master reactions" which were analyzed by means of their temperature sensitivity (e.g. by Crozier), or later by their differing chemical dependencies.

AUXIN PROBLEMS

The great advantage of working in my father's laboratory was not only (for those days) the superb instrumentation available (clinostats, Koningsberger auxanometer, thermostats, light sources, etc), but also the intellectual inquisitiveness of the entire staff and the broad range of scientific problems under investigation (temperature effects, respiration, photosynthesis, tropisms, growth responses, biochemistry, morphogenesis). There was a complete openness of discussion of each student's work, which resulted in a good deal of mutual stimulation and education. Perhaps most important in my father's laboratory were the availability of experimental techniques and material, the controlled temperature and controlled humidity chambers, and the oat coleoptile. Then as now, there were some students dissatisfied with too great an emphasis on the mechanistic approach towards life. I well remember endless discussions with some fellow students on why the growth-promoting principle of the oat coleoptile was not a spirit and weightless, ghostly and immaterial. It induced me to measure the diffusion constant of this "spirit," which indicated that auxin had a molecular weight ranging between 300 and 400, which made it impossible to classify it as a "spirit."

To get started in research in my father's laboratory, for the predoctoral degree (MS) a student had to repeat some work previously done for a PhD degree. So I started by remeasuring the growth response of oat coleoptiles to light with the auxanometer of Koningsberger. With a simple device to prevent the coleoptiles from circumnutating, I was able to obtain some excellent growth responses. They showed that the tip and the base of a coleoptile were differentially sensitive to light, the tip producing a much larger response. Discussing this result with my fellow students, it became clear that in some way this agreed with Boysen Jensen's and Paal's conclusions about the special function of the coleoptile tip in tropisms and growth. Since at that time I discharged my military obligations by attending a gas-warfare school in Utrecht during the day, I had my evenings and nights available for more productive activities, so I worked all night in the laboratory. After having established that decapitating coleoptiles did not basically abolish their ability to grow, I laid the basis for using such decapitated coleoptiles to test growth factors. When it was then established that a unilateral application of coleoptile diffusate caused a unilateral growth increase, the foundation for a quantitative growth hormone analysis was laid. The first experiment applying the diffusate of coleoptile tips into gelatin onto decapitated coleoptiles succeeded at 3 AM on April 17, 1926, and the next morning (when I had no military duties because it was Prince Consort Henry's birthday) I could repeat the experiment to my father's satisfaction. Then a whole series of experiments ensued, in which (a) the quantitative response of decapitated oat coleoptiles to the growth hormone could be established; (b) the thermostability of the growth substance was proved; (c) the light stability of auxin was evident; and (d) its significance in normal coleoptile growth was shown. This led to the dictum: no auxin—no growth.

After completing my military duties, I chose auxin (the word assigned by Kögl to the plant growth hormone) as my doctoral thesis subject. The newly developed technique of quantitative auxin analysis made it possible to study a number of other auxin and growth problems in a completely impartial and direct manner. I would like to stress that a number of facts thus turned up in my thesis work were complete surprises for me, such as the polar auxin transport and the lateral deflection of auxin transport under the influence of unilateral light. They definitely were not based on preconceived ideas or theoretical considerations, and in my later work as well, experimental facts rather than theoretical considerations have guided me. They also were supported by a number of studies by others, especially in my father's laboratory. Later in the 1940s and 1950s, not only the polar and lateral auxin transport, but also the light stability of auxin was challenged. Remarkably enough, this challenge was not based on facts, but founded on an artificial theoretical construction. Misused statistics were employed to show that my conclusions of 1927 were wrong, and it took considerable effort on the part of many investigators to reaffirm my original conclusions. This makes one wonder how often, in fields with which one is not familiar, wishful and clever theoretical constructions have warped facts or influenced their interpretation. And it is not even necessary to warp facts to reach completely erroneous conclusions, as the phlogiston and ether theories attest.

I would like to discuss some of the problems opened up by the development of a quantitative auxin test in more detail.

Polar Auxin Transport

The discovery of the polar transport of auxin was not only an unexpected phenomenon, but it promised a better insight into a puzzling morphogenetic problem, that of polarity in general. Why does an initially undifferentiated zygote produce a structure with head-tail or shoot-root differentiation? Grafting and cutting experiments had shown that the polarity exhibited by a stem or tuber or root in regenerating new roots or buds was a fundamental property of each tissue and each cell. All this came into the realm of polar auxin transport when I could show that the polarity in root initiation on stem cuttings should be attributed to polar auxin transport to the basal cut surface. Thus morphological polarity could be explained by the polar transport of a particular substance: the hormone auxin. At long intervals I have returned to this polarity problem.

First I found that dyes with chromophoric anions penetrated into a polar tissue (*Phaseolus* seedling stems) preferentially from the apex (like the acid auxin), whereas basic dyes penetrated over a greater distance from the base. This seemed to suggest that the polar auxin transport was based on an electrical polarity in the polar tissue.

I was able to attack another aspect of the polarity problem when radioisotopes became available. If auxin was moved polarly in coleoptiles by way of an electrical gradient, would other ions also show a tendency towards polar transport in coleoptiles? In my experiments, carried out in Berkeley with radioactive tracers, I applied agar blocks with radiophosphorus, radiosodium and radiobromine to the basal or apical cut surface of Avena coleoptile segments. I was unable to measure any differential transport in the two directions; actually these ions did not move at all, although simultaneous measurements showed polar auxin movement in the same coleoptile segments. Among the many possible interpretations of these results, I prefer the one that polar transport of auxin is only possible in a lipid medium in which an electrical gradient could be maintained.

Later I made another attempt at the polar transport problem in measuring auxin transport in upright and inverted *Tagetes* cuttings. When placed upside down in sand, they will root at the original apex, and the sprouts growing from a basal node will produce perfectly normal plants. Auxin transport in the inverted stem section of the cutting originally was strictly polar, but after several weeks a second, base-to-apex, auxin transport became superimposed on the original apex-to-base polar transport. The original intent of this experiment, planned jointly with E. J. Kraus to compare the physiological changes with anatomical studies, was never followed up because of Kraus' retirement. My own interpretation of these results is that in the course of several weeks, new vascular strands are produced in the inverted *Tagetes* stem, with an opposite polarity.

Seed Dormancy

A fully dormant seed retains its storage food for many years whether this dormancy is induced by complete dryness or otherwise, as, for example, *Amaranthus* seeds, which retain their viability for years after submergence in water, or *Lotus* seeds, buried for thousands of years in bogs. In the latter case it is obvious that the maintenance of the living condition—of the polarity of the cell structure, and of the accumulation of foods and salts inside the cells—does not require any metabolic activity. Yet as soon as a seed dies, it releases all its accumulated storage food. This is very obvious in germination tests. Viable seeds laid out on wet filter paper may remain dormant for many months, during which time they are not infected by fungi or bacteria. But the dead seeds among them within a few days are overgrown by mycelia, fed by the food oozing out of the dead cells. If the maintenance of the living membranes of 3000-year old buried *Lotus* seeds required any metabolic processes, then not more than one sugar molecule would have been available each minute per hundred million protein molecules, truly negligible for any maintenance work. Such dormant *Lotus* seeds obviously stay alive while fully saturated with water and maintain their semipermeability. Their cells must preserve all accumulated salts and nutrients without any appreciable energy expenditure. This can be accomplished in most seeds in the absolutely dry condition, as established in the first 20 years of a 1000-year experiment on seed longevity. These same seeds, when not maintained under vacuum, lose their viability in 5–10 years.

Second Law of Thermodynamics

Much biological work is directed at applying physical and chemical principles to biological systems, and—not surprisingly—in most cases these biological systems conform to physical laws or rules of chemical reactivity. This only proves that conventional physical and chemical processes prevail in biological systems, but it does not explain the basic problems of life. The Second Law of Thermodynamics, which requires that the equilibrium state is the state of maximum entropy (or randomness), cannot encompass the living condition, which is a continuous refutation of this second law, for living matter evades the decay to equilibrium. Life is not an equilibrium condition; it is not a condition of maximum entropy. Actually life is a question of increased enthalpy, in which energy is gathered at a greater rate than it is dissipated, building up more and more living cells, which only after death follow the general rule of increasing entropy. In the absence of life, in the absence of water, there are no energetic cycles, and the Second Law of Thermodynamics rules absolutely, as on the surface of the moon.

The dividing line between a living and a dead cell has not been found; as far as we know, the structure and configuration of an instantly killed cell remains unchanged, and the chemical constitution initially also is identical. These premises are the essential foundation for almost all biological and biochemical research carried out in the past.

A number of explanations have been given for this discrepancy between living and dead. It has been claimed that an essential part of the fine structure, not caught by the finest of our observational instruments, is destroyed. Thus the separation of the cellular components would be violated; enzymes and substrates would come into contact indiscriminately, and no proper sequence of reactions would be possible any longer. Another viewpoint is that certain higher levels of integration have been destroyed. Thus the death of a person usually involves only the nervous and functional integration of the body as a whole, whereas the individual cells remain alive for a considerable time; hair continues to grow. These two viewpoints are diametrically opposed: one seeks the problem of life on the molecular level; the other looks for it on the integrated level.

To me the most fundamental aspect of life is polarity or directedness, which we find on the molecular level in the synthesis of compounds, in the accumulation of ions, in the maintenance of a low level of entropy. We also find it in development, which is directed continuously towards increased size and differentiation or ontogenesis; it is unidirectional. And in evolution we find the same principle again: the tendency towards greater and greater complexity, which is often called orthogenesis.

The fact that any living organism is a refutation of the Second Law of Thermodynamics, which requires in all physical systems a continual increase in randomness, the entropy, is often glossed over by pointing out that the organism plus its environment as a totality follows the second law. This is essentially a reaffirmation of the first law. But this does not explain how parts of this system continuously violate this law up to the moment of death, when immediately the Second Law takes over again. That much more clarification and clear thinking is needed in the application of the Second Law of Thermodynamics to life phenomena is evident from the conclusions reached in two recent books on thermodynamics. Spanner, in his 1964 *Introduction to Thermodynamics,* questions the applicability of the Second Law to life. He claims that certainly memory, evolution, and life itself fall outside its bounds. Morowitz, in his *Entropy for Biologists* (1970), holds the opposite view: "At all levels life is very much subject to the Second Law of Thermodynamics. . . . Dissipative processes inherent in the random distribution of thermal energy act to constantly degrade biological structures. . . ." But this holds only when death supersedes life. Earlier Morowitz states: "The very ordered state of a biological system would, if left to itself, decay to the most disordered possible state." This, of course, is what happens after death. To counteract this leveling, "work must constantly be performed to order the system. The continuous performance of this work requires a hot source and a cold sink, which are ordinarily provided on the earth's surface by the heat of the sun and the cold of outer space." This is quite true, but Morowitz fails to add that just the existence of life makes the process go; on the moon the same sources of heat and cold exist, but without the ordering effects of life, no work can be performed and the moon surface remains completely inert.

Phototropism

I discovered another aspect of organismal polarity while trying to analyze phototropism in terms of auxin. Since coleoptile growth was completely limited by auxin supply and auxin was light stable, it should be possible to measure the phototropic curvature—a process involving growth—in terms of the amounts of auxin diffusing from the tip. When I measured the amounts of auxin produced by the coleoptile tip, I found that the total amount was only slightly decreased by illumination (16%), but that this auxin was redistributed by lateral illumination; compared with an oat seedling in darkness, during the first hour 54% diffused down the illuminated side and 114% diffused down the dark side, whereas in the second hour after illumination practically all auxin moved down the dark side. This was the experimental evidence for the Cholodny-Went theory of tropisms, for which Dolk provided the proof for geotropism. This evidence was completely clear cut, yet for almost two decennia it was attacked until work with radioactive indoleacetic acid fully confirmed our results. The fascination of radioisotope work was finally able to overcome prejudices against equally exacting pre-isotope work.

Auxin and Cofactors for Growth

One aspect of my thesis with which I felt most satisfied never has been commented on since. This was the analysis of the growth of the whole oat coleoptile. As in other plant organs, the region of maximal growth occurs at some distance from the stem tip. Since I could show that auxin was produced in the coleoptile tip only, there had to be some explanation of why the tip did not grow at the greatest rate. The explanation came by considering two sets of facts: (a) the region of maximum growth in the coleoptile shifts with age: when young its base has the fastest growth rate, but as it grows the zone of most rapid growth moves up and stays at an even distance from the tip; and (b) in the quantitative *Avena* test for auxin there is a sharp break in the auxin concentration-growth rate relationship; below a critical curvature angle there is a direct proportionality between applied auxin and curvature, and above this angle (17–20°) there is no effect of an increased auxin concentration at all. These two facts could be explained by a single assumption: auxin had to interact with another growth factor to produce growth, and this growth substance X was supplied from the base of the coleoptile. This meant that near the coleoptile tip auxin was in excess and did not limit growth, but nearer the base, where factor X was in excess, any variation in auxin concentration would show up in a variation in growth rate.

This two-factor model for growth has fascinated me all these years and has been the source of much frustration as well. After it was found that auxin was involved in many other growth and morphogenetic processes such as root initiation, it became very clear that one single substance could perform so many different functions *only* if it interacted with a whole array of different cofactors, which I referred to as calines. Indirect evidence for their existence was very clear, yet attempts to extract and to isolate them failed.

Translocation of Growth Factors Across Graft Unions

I then tried to approach the problem of the existence of other growth factors in a different way, namely by grafting. When stems are cut off, their growth stops almost immediately in spite of the fact that auxin production in the stem tip and leaves continues for some time. This cessation of growth is not due to lack of water or nutrients or any other materials which can be supplied to the cut stems. However, when new roots are produced on these cut stems growth resumes, and this also happens when the stems are grafted on a root stock, after vascular connections between stock and scion have become established. This seemed to indicate that a factor X was produced by roots, and was translocated to the growing point through the phloem.

Etiolated peas were used as experimental material since (a) they could be raised under the completely controlled conditions of a physiological darkroom (this was in the days before air-conditioned greenhouses); (b) many pea varieties were available, differing in leaf form and size and in morphological characters; and (c) their seeds have so much storage food that pea plants can grow for several weeks in darkness without running out of food. The outcome of these experiments, published with Hayward, was interesting for several reasons. In the first place, there were no differences between stem growth of the scions when put on stocks (their cotyledons attached) with different growth rates. This indicates that factor X, required to produce stem growth in conjunction with auxin, was not specifically stored in cotyledons, but was produced in sufficient quantities by the root systems regardless of variety or growth habit (dwarf, tall, and slender). In the second place, big differences were seen in leaf growth on the scions according to the genetic constitution of the stocks: pea varieties with large leaves (e.g. Daisy or Marvel) produced much larger leaves on the scions than small-leafed varieties like Alaska or Perfection. Leaf size of the scions apparently was determined by different amounts of stored phyllocaline in the cotyledons of the stocks. The third conclusion was perhaps the most interesting. Morphological characters such as multijugateness ("Acacia leaf") or "stipuleless" were not transmitted by grafting: they depended exclusively on the genetic constitution of the scion. Therefore the following statement seems pertinent: quantitative characters under genetic control are expressed through hormones, transmittable from organ to organ. Qualitative genetic characters are expressed through intracellular processes and are not hormonally controlled.

In the late 1930s, while I carried out these pea grafting experiments, I also tried my hand at grafting tomato varieties. My technique was poor, however, and I made only a few successful grafts between potato-leaf, wiry, and other tomato varieties, with a slight indication of transfer of leaf characters across the graft union. With a better technique I might have become just as famous as Lysenko, about whose grafting experiments I learned several years later.

CONTROL OF THE PLANT ENVIRONMENT

After Thimann and I had written *Phytohormones,* and when my quest for the elusive cofactors of auxins bogged down, a remarkable event occurred. Dr. H. O. Eversole, a retired physician, offered to build two air-conditioned greenhouses for me after he had succeeded in air-conditioning his own orchid house with the help of an engineer, A. J. Hess.

These first air-conditioned research greenhouses were financed by Miss Lucy Clark and built at Cal Tech in 1939. The preoccupation of the geneticists and plant scientists at Cal Tech with biochemistry kept them from realizing the extraordinary opportunities these Clark Greenhouses afforded for studying the environment and its role in plant development. Besides, they viewed heredity exclusively from the genic standpoint, disregarding a possible environmental involvement. This of course enabled me to use these greenhouses myself without any outside interference, and with a number of collaborators who came to employ these new facilities, many new facts were established. I could operate and modify these greenhouses without any objections, getting a very liberal education in air-conditioning and climatic control. And at the same time, having the greenhouses always full of plants, I learned a lot about the proper growing conditions for plants and the effects of temperature on them.

With the new greenhouses I had to develop new experimental plants. After comparing many plants I finally chose the tomato, which responded usually within 24 hours to changes in the environment. Their response could be measured easily in terms of stem length, provided they were kept pruned to a single stem. And their fruit set was very sensitive to the proper temperature regime: at 17°C night temperature fruit set was excellent, especially when combined with 26°C day temperature. This diurnal thermoperiodicity turned out to be one of the most important climatic responses of most other plants as well.

Amateurs in Science

When he offered to build the air-conditioned greenhouses for me, Dr. Eversole had expected such a specific temperature response, based on his experience with *Phalaenopsis* growing in his own air-conditioned greenhouse. Not being a practicing scientist himself and therefore not bound by the rigid rules of scientific experimentation, he had manipulated his thermostat until he found the ideal conditions for growing *Phalaenopsis,* and that was 26°C during the day and 20°C during the night. Only a person with the remarkable observational powers of Dr. H. O. Eversole could have thought of such decontrolling of a thermostat, and it violated all rules of a rigid scientific approach demanded by reviewers of papers to be published in scientific journals. This excludes most amateurs from contributing to science, which is a great loss, for we have to admit that all experimental science started through amateurs. It was not the official scholars, professors at universities, who started the era of the experiment. It was Francis Bacon, whose thinking stimulated men like R. Boyle and R. Hooke to carry out the first systematic experimentation, who originated a causal approach to nature and who started what now has become the Scientific Revolution. Transpiration, plant nutrition, and photosynthesis were discovered by country gentlemen and practicing physicians, and it was a country gentleman, Charles Darwin, who brought on the greatest change in biological thinking.

Thermoperiodicity

In the succeeding years I found more and more cases in which optimal growth and development of plants occurred at a higher daytime temperature and a cooler night, leading to the concept of diurnal thermoperiodicity. In the course of the next 30 years it became accepted with the same universality as photoperiodism, and any air-conditioned greenhouses or controlled environment growth rooms used for the routine growing of plants are now maintained at higher light and lower dark temperatures. The optimal daily temperature differential differs from plant to plant, but it is lowest for tropical rainforest plants (3°C for coffee), intermediate for most crop plants (6°C for tomato and corn), higher for dry region plants, and extreme for desert plants.

In addition to crop plants, about a dozen garden flowers were tested in the Clark greenhouses, and two dozen California wild flowers. The latter had not been selected for genetic uniformity, and varied considerably in their response, but all showed a preference for daily thermoperiodicity, and most were long-day plants.

In addition to thermoperiodicity, the experiments in the Clark greenhouses showed that greenhouse-grown plants would resemble field-grown plants in appearance, sturdiness, and productivity when the climatic regime in the greenhouse approximated that in the field. This became apparent when several tomato varieties grown in the field plots in coastal and inland locations in California were compared with the same varieties grown in the Clark greenhouses. I could estimate within close limits the night temperature in each field location by observing the appearance and fruit production of the different varieties, especially Beefsteak and Earliana, with whose behavior I was familiar from the greenhouse experiments.

When I had similar experiences with garden plants and wild California plants that also showed a correlation between greenhouse and field behavior, it obviously was time to launch a campaign for extending the air-conditioned greenhouse approach to plant growing in general. I convinced Dr. R. A. Millikan, chairman of the executive council of Cal Tech (equivalent to the position of president), of the importance of building a set of air-conditioned greenhouses and artifically lighted growing rooms in which the whole range of naturally occurring climates could be maintained. He in turn persuaded his friend, Mr. H. Earhart from Ann Arbor, Michigan, to provide the funds for them, and in June 1948 the building of the Earhart Plant Research Laboratory was started, to be completed a year later. Since nothing like this Pasadena phytotron (under which name the Earhart Plant Research Laboratory became known) had ever been built, it would have been very difficult to obtain tax funds for it. We can compare this situation with the first astronomical observatories and cyclotrons which also were privately financed.

Productivity

Of the many problems that have been investigated with the facilities of the phytotron, I would like to mention only a few. One of these is productivity, based on actual dry matter production over a period of 1–2 weeks' growth. The tomato plant was again the main experimental object, one reason being that it does not store food but uses all recently produced photosynthates for growth. Plants placed in darkness stop growing within 36 hours, when all available sugar has been consumed. After that, growth can resume upon sugar application in darkness. Sugar analyses had shown that in a tomato plant only sucrose is photosynthesized and metabolized; monoses remain constant and apparently are stored in the vacuole of the cells where they produce turgor but are unavailable for growth. During the first 7 hours in daylight, the sucrose content of a tomato leaf increases form 1% to 7% in a sigmoid way: first slowly, then for a few hours at a maximal rate, and in the final hour slowing to practically a standstill. The maximal photosynthetic sugar production within 7 hours of exposure to light was confirmed in a field experiment with tomato plots being covered with black cloth 5, 6, 7, and 8 hours after uncovering them in the morning. After 7 weeks, those receiving 7 hours of daylight were the heaviest and had produced 10 times the fruit weight of the uncovered controls.

Work based on dry matter production over a week's period showed that total photosynthesis was entirely limited by the amount of growth; for example, reducing growth by cutting off roots or stem tips reduced dry matter production to the same extent. Therefore, growth of the tomato plant is not controlled or limited by the amount of photosynthesis, but photosynthesis is limited by the amount of growth and the degree to which the plant can utilize its photosynthates. Under ideal growing conditions young tomato plants can transform 9.4% of the light energy falling on them into chemical energy, and this is only a fraction of the efficiency of the photosynthetic process.

This same limitation of photosynthesis by growth was found in experiments illuminating tomatoes with different colors of light. The efficiency of light utilization was the same for blue, red, and a combination of red and blue light. It was less for white light because of the poor absorption of the green part of the spectrum. But total growth was many times greater in a combination of red and blue light, and therefore, even though the efficiency at low light intensities was the same, maximal yield was low in either blue or red light.

In white light the saturating light intensity (when supplied at an 8-hour photoperiod per 24 hours over a 7–12 day growing period) for tomato plants was about 1200 fc. This means that even though for short periods the saturating light intensity for photosynthesis might be much higher, any light supplied for a week over an 8-hour photoperiod above 1200 fc is wasted. With the same experimental setup (young plants covering the pot surface fully with their leaves), the saturating light intensity was the same for sugar beets, strawberries, and other plants as it was for tomatoes. I believe that my experiments on efficiency of light absorption came closer to field conditions than short-term determinations obtained with gas-analytical methods. In this connection I showed that the geometry of leaf position greatly influenced the saturating light intensity of a leaf canopy, and that in most crop plants the leaf inclination was such that daylight was used at an optimal rate.

Circadian Rhythm

On the basis of the information presented earlier, I concluded that plant production could be improved by supplying the photosynthetic light in shorter bursts, allowing the sugar content to decrease in the photosynthetic cells between illuminations, and presumably having the plants make better use of the supplied light. This worked only when a 2 or 4-hour dark period was interposed between two 4-hour light periods, but growth and dry matter production was greatly reduced when the second 4-hour light period came 8 hours after the first. In the latter case the explanation obviously had to be Bünning's, namely that light during the skotophil phase was inhibitory. This brought me right into the problem of circadian rhythms, which were already under investigation in the Earhart laboratory. It had been found that tomato plants could grow well in a constant environment *only* if there were dark interruptions of the light on a 24-hour cycle; or if there was a temperature fluctuation on a 24-hour basis. Kristoffersen actually found that the optimal length of either the light interruption or the low temperature treatment was 6 hours per 24 hours. This strongly suggested that it was not a dark reaction or a low temperature process that was essential for normal growth of a tomato plant, but that an external *rhythm* could satisfy its circadian requirement.

This external rhythm could be treated quite quantitatively in experiments. When tomato plants were grown at 23°C, a light-dark succession of 12–12 hours was optimal; when the light-dark periods had a 22 or 27-hour cycle length, growth was less, and it was still less on a 20-hour cycle. When the optimal cycle length was determined at 15°, it was 27 hours, and at 30°C it was 20 hours. This indicates a Q_{10} of the circadian rhythm length of about 1.2–1.3. When other plants were investigated this way *(Baeria, Saintpaulia),* they showed the same response to a circadian rhythm in the environment, with a similar temperature dependence.

This is the first case in which it has been shown that an external circadian rhythm is essential for the normal functioning of an organism. This proves that in these plants an internal circadian rhythm exists that has to be driven by an external rhythm. Without this induced internal rhythm the plant cannot function properly. This is essentially what Bünning called the photophil and skotophil phases of a plant, and for which he showed that they could be "set" by an external clock. And it may well be this process that Brown stresses in his solar-day, lunar-day, and annual clocks controlling biological processes, which he shows being synchronized by an external clock.

The Nature of the Circadian Clock in Higher Plants

Throughout this work I have, of course, been speculating on the basis for the need of a plant for such an external circadian rhythm. When we observe tomato plants or African violets that did not receive the proper rhythm from an external clock being grown under constant conditions, we see several abnormalities. The first is a gradual general deterioration of the plant, a process that takes weeks or months, and if continued long enough leads to death. An African violet plant dies in 4–5 months when kept in a constant 10°C temperature, yet it grows well at 26°C, whereas an English daisy dies within 2 months when kept at 26°C but grows very well at a constant 13°C. The second deviation of the plant kept at the wrong constant temperature is a decrease in leaf size and the production of malformed and chlorotic leaves. And the third is a gradual decrease in stem growth rate, increase of the plastochron length, and an abnormal growing tip. These can all be reduced to one common denominator: a disturbed apical meristem. How can we imagine a mechanism for this disturbance?

For a long time investigators have looked for the process that regulated cell divisions in the apical meristem of plants. It was thought that it might be something like Spemann's organizer or at least some hormone controlling the sequence of cell divisions that leads to leaf differentiation and flower initiation. But no real evidence was found for the existence of such substances or hormones. The closest we have come to them is florigen. But active extracts have been found effective only on plants that need a single short-day cycle for induction, and the effect of these extracts never exceeds the response to a single inductive cycle.

Cytologists had known for a long time that to obtain good preparations of mitosis, growing points had to be fixed at a particular time of day, usually around midnight. This was measured quantitatively by Bünning, who showed that most mitoses in the stem apices of *Tradescantia, Perilla,* and spinach actually occurred just before or after midnight. As has been shown for algal and other cultures, such synchronization of mitosis can be induced by a rhythm in the environment. Therefore I assume that the cells in the meristem are synchronized by an environmental signal such as light-dark or high-low temperature rhythms. Thus the rhythm in the environment performs the same controlling role in a meristem as a hormone plays in stem elongation.

Taking this argument one step farther, I conclude that the photoperiodic stimulus in the apical meristem of a long or a short-day plant also is a rhythmic one. Since it comes from the leaves and can be transmitted by grafting, I further conclude that "florigen" or "anthocaline" is a factor periodically produced in the leaves of photoperiodically induced plants. This might be related to the daily periodicity of auxin production which Yin discovered in papaya leaves. And it suggests that extracts applied to induce flowering be supplied on pulses of 24 hours.

Which Factors Ultimately Limit Growth?

In our age of biochemistry we think of all biological processes as being controlled by chemical reactions, hormones, enzymes, or DNA. This cannot be the case in circadian rhythms, which have a Q_{10} of slightly above 1, indicating that a physical process such as diffusion is in control. This was found to be the case also for the "master" process in growth, under optimal growing conditions when no chemical processes limited growth. Ever since the Clark and Earhart greenhouses were built, I have been trying to increase the growth rate of tomato plants by changing their temperature and light regimes, water and chemical supply, genetic constitution, root environment, and CO_2 supply, and finally I reached a steady state rate of 42 mm/24 hr. This can be exceeded for a few days only when the plants are kept at a suboptimal night temperature, followed by nights at a supraoptimal temperature. Why can't a tomato plant grow at a greater rate? If a specific chemical were limiting, we should be able to supply this, either by application or by breeding, but no growth factors have been found to increase tomato stem growth beyond 42 mm/24 hr. If it were a chemical process, again a breeding program or a temperature treatment should be able to overcome this limitation, especially because the optimal temperatures for the growth of mature tomato plants (25° C during the day, 17° C during night) lie far below the optimum temperature of most physiological processes (at or above 40° C). Also, growth limits photosynthesis rather than photosynthesis limiting growth.

Taking these considerations and many other facts into account, I have come to the conclusion that it is the sugar supply to the growing tissues that becomes insufficient for faster growth. It would be interesting to breed a tomato variety with more and wider phloem tubes. But this might have to be done in a completely insect-free greenhouse where the plants could be fully protected from insect and mechanical injury, because any injury to such wide-vesseled phloem plants might be lethal if the sugar flow from a cut of the phloem could not be stopped.

Yet even if the sugar supply of the growing cells could be increased, there is another—and absolute—limitation on growth. This is an internal diffusion process inside the growing cells, where nucleic acids and messenger RNA have to interact with the cell constituents that do the growing. Since a diffusion process varies inversely with the second power of the linear dimension, one would expect that the maximum growth rate of 1μ bacterium would be 100 times as fast as that of a meristematic cell with a linear dimension of 10 μ. Since a mitotic division in the growing point of a higher plant occurs about once a day, a 1 μ bacterium should be able to divide every quarter hour (which actually has been found), whereas the growth rate of a tetraploid with bigger meristematic cells should be only half that of a diploid (although the overall size of the tetraploid could be more). This certainly would explain also why mature plant cells seldom divide.

My general conclusion is, therefore, that while the immediate control of plant growth is based on hormonal supply and metabolic processes, the ultimate control is by diffusion processes (including a circadian one), which are not as yet experimentally managable.

Variability and Air-Conditioned Rooms and Greenhouses

It is obvious that under well-controlled conditions the variability of plants should be less. But it is not generally recognized to what remarkable extent the variability is reduced in air-conditioned greenhouses. Significant treatment differences of only 10% in weight or size can be established with groups of 4–10 genetically uniform plants. Even more important is the degree to which reproducibility is improved. Since there are far fewer unintentional variables of temperature, light, nutrition, soil, pests, diseases and weeds, the response of plants under controlled greenhouse conditions is very much alike from experiment to experiment. An unexpected benefit from growing plants in air-conditioned rooms and greenhouses is that under optimal growing conditions variability of plant material is least. This has to be explained by the fact that even though growth rates are highest, it is not a single factor which controls growth, and therefore fluctuations in any one factor will have little effect on overall response. In general, the work under properly controlled conditions makes it possible to eliminate almost all variability deriving from the environment. This leaves only (a) the genetic variability, which can be reduced to very low levels either by using clonal material or by breeding; and (b) the basic variability within any physical system. Yet this innate statistical variability is unexpectedly low for a system as complicated as a living one, a fact on which both Bohr and Schrödinger have commented. Since it is possible to work so close to this low innate statistical variability of biological material, it is illogical and inefficient to continue using ordinary uncontrolled greenhouses for any research work. Commercial greenhouse growers have discovered this, and most rose or orchid or carnation growers have installed quite effective evaporative cooling systems in their greenhouses to control daytime temperatures, in addition to their heating systems for night temperature control. But too many university greenhouses are still uncontrolled, partly because of a lack of comprehension by administrators who consider money spent beyond salaries of research personnel as wasted, even though each research worker would be many times more efficient if he could carry out his experiments under controlled conditions. The National Science Foundation has recognized this fact by supporting the construction and operation of a number of phytotrons, but obviously it cannot underwrite the construction of every research greenhouse.

ECOLOGY

One of the major fields of research in the Earhart and Clark Laboratories obviously had to be ecology, since at last most of the environmental factors in the growth of a plant could be controlled, and their effect could be assessed. Thus the autecology of quite a number of plants, especially of cultivated ones, was determined to the extent that their behavior in the field could be predicted. Fortunately, in most plants only one or two environmental variables have an overriding effect on their climatic response, variables such as night temperature in tomatoes and day temperature in peas. This has not been realized by some ecologists who demand that all temperature fluctuations and photoperiods occurring in nature be religiously recreated in a phytotron to study the response of their plants. This defeats the purpose of a phytotron, for the significance of none of the factors or fluctuations can then be interpreted; such experiments should be conducted in nature, using the fluctuations of the natural environment. The facilities of the Pasadena phytotron and of most others were not designed to operate that way. Each greenhouse and each controlled environment room is being used by many investigators in many different experiments to study the effect of particular day and night conditions in many plants. The differences in response between tomato, potato, pea, sugar beet, strawberry, coffee, orchids, ecotypes of *Poa*, and *Mimulus* were thus dramatically illustrated and showed us many generalities, which would have been lost in the minutiae of exact climatic duplications.

In general it was found that the optimal growing conditions of a plant agree closely with the prevailing climate of the native habitat of the plant. Thus the range of plants being grown in field or garden gives an excellent idea of a local climate, provided their climatic responses are known. The further a plant is removed from its optimal climate, the more it has to be babied by the grower to keep it growing, and the more it has to be kept free from weeds. The work also showed the irrationality of maintaining separate orchid and fern and cactus greenhouses. What is needed are greenhouses in which specific climates are maintained, and plants with those climatic requirements should be grown together in them regardless of taxonomic relatedness. This was the basis for the air-conditioning arrangement in the climatron-greenhouse which I built in 1959-60 at the Missouri Botanical Garden in St.

Louis, where in different areas different climatic conditions could be maintained, resulting in optimal growth for plants from different regions of the world in the various sectors of the climatron.

The *Annual Review of Plant Physiology* is not the best place to discuss work on the ecology of plants. But since ecological studies have been an important part of my research work, I want to at least mention them. In Java, where for 5 years (from 1928–1932) I was employed at the Bogor Botanical Gardens, I started ecological work for two reasons: first, purely physiological studies can be carried out anywhere in the world, and the laboratories in temperate climates were better equipped for such work; and secondly, I wanted to lay a basis for more detailed physiological studies. I worked on a typically tropical subject, epiphytes, and found in a tropical rain forest that the different species of most trees harbored quite different communities of epiphytes. Only the epiphyte communities growing in humus accumulations in crotches of trees or in nest ferns were nonspecific. Especially orchids were very specific in their host tree, and I could identify trees by the orchid communities growing on them.

Desert Plants

While living in Pasadena (1933–1958) I soon became fascinated with the desert, and our family spent many weekends in the Mohave and Colorado deserts. A number of biological desert problems attracted my attention, none of which could be answered on the basis of available information. So I started to observe and measure desert plants, and after the Clark greenhouses were built, I could study the behavior of them under controlled conditions.

The first problem was their curious seasonal response. There are two periods when occasional rains occur in the Southern California deserts: midsummer, and late autumn and winter. And rain of more than an inch is followed by extensive germination. Most seedlings are annuals, and they occur in any one locality as two completely different communities: the summer and the winter annuals, with hardly a single species in common. Being reared on proper Darwinian principles, I looked for general germination of all species and survival of either summer or winter annuals. But in summer only the seedlings of summer annuals were found, and after an autumn or winter rain only winter annuals occurred. This could be confirmed in the air-conditioned greenhouses. The upper half centimeter of the desert soil with its normal seed complement was collected and this was spread thinly over containers with sand. When watered properly and placed in greenhouses at different temperatures, only summer annuals germinated at 26°C, only winter annuals at 8°C, and a combination of both at intermediate temperatures. Therefore, the species composition of the vegetation is not determined by selection and survival of those seedlings adapted to the prevailing temperatures, but by preferential germination. I also found that simple wetting of the desert seeds was insufficient for germination; a soaking rain was required. This was based on the leaching of inhibitors from the seeds by the rain. All this laboratory information was taken back into the field, and now it has become possible to predict desert blooming many months ahead, when the amount of rain and the temperatures following them are known. Conversely, it is possible to deduce the amount of rain and the date of its occurrence from the vegetation; it is even possible to tell summer rains many years after their occurrence, because of shrub germination and growth. Thus field observations led to laboratory analysis that could be taken back to the field to explain and understand what is happening in nature.

Mycorrhiza

Another subject that I first observed in the field and subsequently brought into the laboratory for further study was mycorrhiza. As a member of an expedition of the research vessel "Alpha Helix," I spent 1½ months in 1967 in the center of the Amazon basin. Impoundment of my laboratory equipment by Brazilian customs made it impossible to carry out my intended research program, so I spent my time in the Amazonian rain forest. There I found a tremendous activity of fungi in the upper soil layer where dead leaves, branches, and all other debris from the rain forest produced a litter layer completely pervaded by tree roots, fungal hyphae, and rhizomorphs. With this mass of hyphae digesting so much organic material, one might expect a very extensive development of mushrooms and other fungal fruiting bodies on the rain forest floor, but mushrooms are remarkably rare in the tropics. What I actually observed was an intimate network of hyphae and rhizomorphs between litter and tree roots, and most of these roots pervading the litter were mycorrhizal. Thus it became clear that mycorrhiza is not just a tree root-fungus association, but that it is part of a tripartite system. The fungi digest the litter and pass much of the extracted nutrients back to the tree roots, closing a nutrient cycle without which a rich rain forest never could exist on the very poor and leached soils of most of the Amazonian basin.

I hope that realization of this basic fact will become generally accepted by developers of the Amazonian rain forest. Utilization of temperate-zone agriculture (based almost exclusively on annual crops) has led to irreparable damage to untold Amazonian acres. If the original rich rain forest is replaced with an equally rich forest of economically useful plants such as Brazil nuts, oil palms, or cacao trees, the Amazon basin could become a real food basket of the world. But to this end a typical tropical agriculture must be developed based on leached soils, perennial crops, and mycorrhiza.

A somewhat similar situation was found in the desert, where most decomposition of plant litter is accomplished by fungi, and where mycorrhiza also occurs on the roots of a number of desert shrubs. And a considerable part of the consolidation of the desert sands, and even the fixing of dunes, is due to hyphae weaving sand grains together. But this is only possible, of course, when sufficient organic matter is present for fungal growth.

The realization of the overriding importance of litter in the mycorrhiza picture led me to a number of experiments in which pine seedling growth was quantitatively linked with the amount of decomposing litter in the pots. Humus, the end product of litter decomposition, had much less influence on the pine growth.

AIR POLLUTION

Much of my research work has been centered around effects of the environment on plant growth, and this brought climate to my attention. Then in the late 1940s another environmental factor, air pollution, started to require more of my attention. And ultimately this led to a realization that plants not only were passively responding to climatic factors, but actively changed them, in addition to their known role in energy transformation.

I have had occasional experience with toxic gases in the air. The first was SO_2 from a zinc smelter in Holland, then SO_2 from an undersea crater in Indonesia, and later SO_2 from a sulfuric acid factory in California. In all cases white bleached areas appeared on leaves between the main veins. Then I became acquainted with HF damage, caused by smoke stack emissions from a steel plant, an aluminum metal reduction plant, and superphosphate factories. This was typified by leaf-edge burn and brown discolored areas on corn and grape leaves. Then in the autumn of 1948 an entirely new type of plant damage started to appear on tomato seedlings and spinach plants in our Pasadena greenhouses. We first tentatively attributed it to fungicides. But this did not make much sense since (a) it occurred irregularly; (b) it never had occurred before; and (c) commercial spinach growers around Los Angeles suddenly started to complain about damage to their crops too, on the same days the spinach in our greenhouses was injured. This was not due to an emission of toxic materials from a point source, as in the case of SO_2 damage, but it was an areal occurrence including the whole Los Angeles metropolitan area. This was a new phenomenon. It occurred each time there had been an excessive number of complaints by the public of eye irritation, which was associated with dense blue hazes in the morning, the so-called Los Angeles smog.

Smog

Up to that time it had been assumed by the air pollution control authorities that the Los Angeles smog was just another form of SO_2 pollution. I rejected this assumption because (a) the plant injury symptoms did not agree with the intercostal bleaching of leaf areas caused by SO_2; (b) my nose had never alerted me to excessive SO_2 concentrations; and (c) SO_2 damage on plants normally had occurred only near concentrated SO_2 emission points, which hardly existed in the Los Angeles area. No SO_2 damage to vegetation had ever been observed in or near any city. Besides, my colleague, A. J. Haagen-Smit, a biochemist with a most remarkably sensitive nose, had identified Los Angeles smog with oxidants (ozonides and peroxides) produced when unsaturated hydrocarbons (olefins) react with ozone. He not only produced a product which looked and smelled like smog by reacting olefin vapors with ozone, but he showed how in the Los Angeles atmosphere these oxidants were produced by a photochemical process. This occurred whenever a high enough concentration of gasoline vapors or of exhaust gases from internal combustion engines was exposed to full sunlight in the presence of a catalyst such as nitrogen oxides. Such high concentrations of gasoline vapors could develop under low atmospheric temperature inversions, which were common in the Los Angeles area.

As a joint venture of Cal Tech, the University of California, and the Los Angeles County Air Pollution Control District, I organized a research team that used the facilities of the Earhart Research Laboratory (just inaugurated at that time) to identify the phytotoxic component of smog. In this team I was fortunate enough to combine the services of both A. J. Haagen-Smit, the later chairman of the important California Air Resources Board, and J. Middleton, the later U.S. Pollution Commissioner. In the specially designed gas chambers of the newly opened phytotron they tested all organic gases that were or could be present in the Los Angeles smog. Many different organic acids, hydrocarbons, aldehydes, ketones, and chlorinated compounds were tested singly or in combinations, but none produced smog injury symptoms on the five different test plants (spinach, endive, beets, alfalfa, and annual blue grass). It was not until we tried Haagen-Smit's olefin-ozone mixture that the typical smog injury symptoms developed on our test plants. This plant work signaled the change in attitude of air pollution control officials towards the identity of the toxic materials that had to be combatted in smog. Although more than half the SO_2 emissions had been removed from the Los Angeles atmosphere during the years that this gas was thought to be responsible for smog, the latter had not diminished. Combatting the oxidants, however, has prevented further deterioration of the smog situation in Los Angeles after 1954, which is more than can be said for most other metropolitan areas here and abroad.

The blue smog haze that accompanied eye irritation and the acrid smog smell apparently were due to the photochemical production of submicroscopic particles such as had been experimentally prepared by Tyndall a century ago. At that time he passed a beam of actinic light through air charged with organic vapors of amyl nitrite or allyl iodide. The developing "blue cloud" as he named it was due to the production of submicroscopic particles on which water vapor could condense and which could be measured conveniently with an Aitken condensation nucleus counter. This instrument is now available in a very convenient form, the Gardner small particle counter, which gives an excellent measure of the degree of air pollution.

We had thus a number of independent methods of measuring "smog": (a) an acrid smell and eye irritation due to oxidants; (b) a blue smog haze due to condensation nuclei; and (c) leaf damage to various plant species. By these criteria I estimated the amount of smog in different parts of the world, and I found typical photochemical smog in most of the metropolitan areas of the world: in all big North American cities, in South America (Sao Paulo, Rio de Janeiro and Bogota), in Australia (Melbourne, Sydney), and in Europe (London, Paris, Cologne, Copenhagen). An approximate analysis indicated that as soon as gasoline consumption in a city exceeded 12 tons per square mile per day, smog damage was visible.

Natural Smog in Nature

In my preoccupation with photochemical smog, I started to see smog hazes not only in cities, but also in the surrounding countryside. At first these were attributed to Los Angeles smog spilling over mountain passes. But when flying cross country I saw these blue hazes over the intermountain area and all over the east, becoming denser near big cities like Chicago and New York, but being essentially constant in between. Therefore, I had to conclude that there were sources other than gasoline vapors and exhaust gases that gave rise to the blue hazes in the countryside. Many geographical names were based on such hazes. Thus there are the "Blue Ridge" and the "Smoky Mountains" in Virginia and North Carolina, or the "Blue Mountains" in Australia. This blue haze is not a smoke (consisting of visible particles), since a smoke has the color of the actual material of which it consists, such as brown iron oxide, white calcium carbonate, black soot, or grey or yellow clay dust. And there are hardly any blue minerals. But submicroscopic particles of any kind will seem blue. On this basis it could be concluded that the blue "summer" or "heat" haze consisted of submicroscopic particles that did not arise by diminution of larger particles, but which only could arise from originally molecularly dispersed chemicals aggregating to particles with a molecular weight of millions. Therefore, I started to look for gases in the air which might react like the gasoline vapors that produce smog. And I found them in the aromatic substances given off by plants. Then it became clear that blue hazes were seen all over the world where vegetation occurred. In the Amazon basin I measured low numbers at ground level, but higher up in the atmosphere enormous numbers of Aitken condensation nuclei (ACN) occurred: over 1,000,000 ACN/cc. Over forested areas in the Midwest 30,000 ACN/cc occurred during summer, while in deserts the numbers were 2,000–10,000 and over oceans there were less than 1000/cc. There was also a strong positive correlation between ACN and the density of the vegetation in the desert. After a rainy winter, when lots of annuals had developed on the desert floor in March, the number of nuclei was at least double that of other years.

With a gas chromatograph the terpenes free in the country air can be measured. They fluctuate from about 2×10^{-9} g/liter of air in winter to 10×10^{-9} in summer and occasionally 20×10^{-9} in autumn. The pattern of their release by plants is much like that of transpiration: a maximum rate around noon, and a complete release upon death of the cell. In addition, ionone and irone are released in autumn upon decomposition of carotenoids in the fallen foliage. They provide the typical late-autumn smell of forests, and after condensation and coagulation of their photochemical reaction products they, together with terpenes released from the dying cells, are responsible for the dense autumn hazes.

Both in the laboratory and in nature I was able to reproduce the photochemical production of condensation nuclei, combining terpene vapors with ozone, or mixing terpenes and a catalyst (such as nitrogen oxides or iodine vapors) in strong light. There is no doubt about terpenes being able to produce ACN and blue hazes. In darkness, such as in caves or during night, no ACN are produced at all. But there are also other sources of ACN. In and around cities they come from combustion processes: exhaust from car engines, burning of coal, oil or gas, cigarettes, etc. And perhaps most of the pink haze one sees over the ocean consists of salt particles produced by bursting air bubbles. And a small amount of haze may be of volcanic origin. But otherwise all atmospheric hazes are derived from the vegetation. How does this fit quantitatively?

Quantity of Natural Smog on Earth

Photosynthesis produces yearly 2×10^{11} ton of organic matter. Upon decomposition most of this escapes as CO_2 into the air. But 0.2% of photosynthates are carotenoids and phytols, which probably after decomposition become terpenoids. The amount of terpenes produced by the vegetation is hard to estimate, because ultimately they all volatilize. It varies much from plant to plant, but probably is at least 0.5% of all dry matter formed. This would amount to 1×10^9 tons of terpenes, and together with the decomposition products of carotenoids, as much as 1.4×10^9 tons of volatile plant products are produced over the whole world per year. They are photochemically transformed into oxidants or free radicals which condense to particulate matter, first of a size of $10^{-2}\mu$, but gradually grow by coagulation to particles of $0.1-1\mu$ diameter. The latter particles can be filtered out by sucking air through "absolute" filters. The filter paper turns grey or greyish brown, and microscopically the filtered particles are brown droplets or black soot-like clusters. These have been named combustion nuclei and were supposed to be industrial smoke coming from coal and oil fires. Their concentration is actually twice as high in cities as in the countryside, but I collected them equally in southern Patagonia, the middle of the Amazon basin, Death Valley, the Sierra Nevada, eastern Nevada, and Point Barrow (the northernmost tip of Alaska). Therefore, I have to conclude that they are of natural origin and that they are the end products of photochemical terpene decomposition. This is supported by their quantity. In big cities the average particulate loading of the air is $150\gamma/m^3$, in smaller cities it is $100\gamma/m^3$, in the forested areas of southeastern USA it is $50\gamma/m^3$, and in the west and northwest it is $20\gamma/m^3$. The few data I have from the tropics indicate $100\gamma/m^3$ or more. Averaging this as $50\gamma/m^3$ for the land area of the world (90×10^6 square kilometers) to a height of 2 km, there are 9×10^6 tons of particulate matter of plant origin in the air at any one time. If we assume a dwelling time of 10 days for each particle, there would be 0.32×10^9 ton of particulates in the air over the world in one year, about one-fourth of all volatile matter produced by the vegetation.

Some of the major questions about this particulate matter concern what it is, what it does, and where it goes. In answer to the first question, chemical analysis of the aerial soot has shown it to be very high in carbon (80–90%) and hydrogen, with little oxygen or nitrogen. This agrees with its origin from terpenes (80% carbon). As to the function of the hazes, they contribute perhaps as much as a quarter of the total long-wave radiation of the atmosphere. This is many times as much as the CO_2 radiation, and therefore, together with water vapor, they are largely responsible for the greenhouse effect of the atmosphere; the effects of an increase in CO_2 caused by the combustion of fossil fuels can be disregarded.

Fate of the Natural Smog

As to the question, where this black air soot goes, this is partly answered by the black or grey color of drapes in windows, collars and cuffs of shirts, and the dark covering of older leaves of trees and shrubs, especially if they contain sticky oils. But this takes care of only a minute amount of all particulate matter. Most of it collects in the inversion layer of the atmosphere and in the surface of cumulus clouds, which especially in stagnant air masses become very dark. I have measured the condensation nuclei in cumulus cloud surfaces and found them to be concentrated 2–30 times. And we know from the dirt in rain and snow that much air soot is precipitated this way. The brown or black material that comes down by precipitation attaches itself to clay particles or accumulates under anaerobic conditions in bogs. The material on clay particles (microscopically visible on clay minerals in ponds and rivers) washes down rivers and accumulates in delta areas, which are the main source areas for oil accumulations. In bog areas the air soot is safe under anaerobic conditions and accumulates to produce anthracite or hard coal. If viewed this way, coal, which is largely an amorphous material, is an aerial product, and it is found in bogs not because it was formed there but because it is preserved there under anaerobic conditions. I was able to show that the high carbon content of fossil wood can be accounted for by impregnation of the fossil wood remains with high-carbon materials rather than decomposition of the low-carbon (cellulose) materials of wood. Thus I completely dissociate brown or soft-coal production (humifications of lignin) from bituminous coal formation.

I have no idea why either liquid drops or clusters of carbon particles result from the condensation of haze, but it is interesting that the major oil and coal forming periods in the world history coincide in time. And there are all intermediates between anthracites (low in bituminous material) through bituminous coals, asphalts, tars, and oil deposits.

CONCLUSION

Since I believe that my success as an investigator is partly due to qualities and training differing from those of my colleagues, I would like to analyze these. There is no doubt about the advantages I had in my early environment and training. Through teenage opportunity programs or high school summer training programs many young people have similar opportunities today as I had in my teens by associating as apprentices with mature scientists. And many children get a great deal of stimulation from science fairs or from a chance to work after school hours in high school laboratories. This may lay the motivation for their future careers and life. Children or students should be aware of the fact that their chosen profession will be with them throughout their lives, and that this choice better satisfy them. Let no one ever talk a child out of his own choice of a career, especially not if the objections are based on economic arguments. A dedicated scientist or technologist, no matter in what field, will find economically satisfactory employment.

Beyond opportunity, I was fortunate in my training. In Holland the high school training was very thorough, so that all language (French, German, and English) and humanities training, plus most of my chemistry, physics, and mathematics needs were satisfied when I left high school at 17 years of age. This meant that during my entire university training I could concentrate on biology. Its subject matter was certainly much more restricted than it is today, with only a little biochemistry, cytology, or genetics, but that was compensated for by physiological, taxonomical, and morphological training, even more than most physiologists, taxonomists, and morphologists receive today. This is inevitable with the increasing specialization today, but I greatly profited from the thorough knowledge my father had of botany in general. He knew the entire plant physiological literature, having read every important paper ever published (and remembering its content). He personally subscribed to most botanical journals. He knew and was friendly with most botanists all over the world, and thus I came to know many of them.

As to my own attributes, the most important is probably an insatiable curiosity about the world around me, not just about auxins or temperature effects on plants, but about nature in general. This extends beyond physiology to evolution, morphology, and ecology, and beyond that to climate and other elements of the physical world. When I can figure out why a particular plant grows in a particular place, or how some desert plant is able to take up enough water to survive, or why different plants in different habitats have the same shapes, or why there are no unbearably hot places in nature (outside of volcanoes, of course), then my intellectual curiosity is satisfied and I can go on to other problems. Yet all my most interesting and elusive problems are rooted in nature, and that is where I obtain my inspiration and motivation. The solution of these problems requires in most cases a laboratory, but ultimately my satisfaction comes when the answer I obtain in the laboratory is applicable in nature. In this way I am still basically a naturalist, or perhaps a biologist. A second and I think important quality I have is the inclination to generalize conclusions, but not to the extent of excluding facts which oppose these generalizations. Rather I tend to remember exceptions more than general rules. Thus I do not accept hypotheses or theories or even laws which disregard too many exceptions. Thus I reject the Second Law of Thermodynamics, or the concept of florigen as a specific substance, or the official theory of coal formation. This is not opposition to the establishment, but acceptance of exceptions.

As to work habits, I try many simple experiments. If these give positive results, I will try to follow them up, but if the results are equivocal, probably requiring intricate statistics, I drop them like a hot potato. It is of course very difficult to decide which problems will yield to an experimental approach, but I have been lucky in that respect.

I am very little impressed by complicated and clever theoretical or mathematical constructions; in fact, I don't understand many of them. Nor can I follow or accept statistical analyses: if the facts don't speak clearly for themselves, no statistical treatment will make them palatable. I still stand on my earlier criticism of the over-use of statistics in biology: statistics tend to smear variability evenly over an experiment; the good biologist should try to eliminate variability as much as possible.

Finally, I feel that research work should be fun, or rather that it should give me satisfaction. If a field becomes too controversial or too theoretical, I prefer to leave it, as I did the growth factor field in the early 1940s. After Thimann and I had written *Phytohormones,* I felt that I degenerated to a policeman, overseeing the auxin field, checking doubtful statements or questionable results. If they turned out to be correct, I had not achieved anything new, and if they were wrong, I had not discovered anything either.

This is a plea to change from time to time one's field of enquiry, to enter a new field where few preconceived ideas need to be fought, where little literature needs to be consulted, and where any discovery tends to be new. Besides, it is likely that discoveries in new fields can still be made with a minimum of sophisticated equipment. Such relatively new fields that I would like to enter are those of insect galls, sociology and physiology of ants, competition and other interrelationships between plants, evolution on an experimental basis, mimicry, symbiosis, and many other presently neglected fields which may not find their solution in DNA or RNA. Excessive preoccupation with this subject presently so popular has impoverished biology as a whole.

Ann. Rev. Plant Physiol. 1974. 25:27–52

THE C$_4$ SYNDROME: A STRUCTURAL ANALYSIS

♦7561

W. M. Laetsch

Department of Botany, University of California, Berkeley, California 94720

CONTENTS

INTRODUCTION 27
LEAF ANATOMY 28
    Stomata 30
    Structure of Mesophyll and Bundle Sheath Cells 30
    Starch Sheath 31
CHLOROPLAST STRUCTURE 34
    Dimorphic Chloroplasts and Light Reactions 36
    Peripheral Reticulum 37
        Peripheral reticulum and C₃ plants 39
        Function of the peripheral reticulum 41
STRUCTURE AND DISTRIBUTION OF MITOCHONDRIA AND MICROBODIES 43
C₃–C₄ INTERMEDIATES 44
STRUCTURAL BASIS FOR FUNCTION 45
FEEDBACK INHIBITION 47
C₄ PLANTS AS CRYPTO-SUCCULENTS 47

INTRODUCTION

The formation of C$_4$ dicarboxylic acids as primary products of photosynthesis in sugar cane was reported by Kortschak & co-workers in 1954 (70, 71). A series of reports were made by these workers over the next 5 years, but this work did not receive general notice until 1965 (72). In the meantime, Karpilov reported the same phenomenon in corn in 1960 (66), but his work was not generally recognized until after 1965. The experiments of the Hawaiians served as a basis for the series of investigations carried on in Australia by Hatch & Slack (50, 51) and their co-workers. This phenomenon is now called C$_4$ photosynthesis, and plants possessing this carbon fixation pathway are termed C$_4$ plants.

This field was first reviewed in 1968 (27b), and a series of subsequent reviews have tended to keep pace with the literature explosion in this field (17, 18, 49, 51, 111, 116). The two previous reviews on C$_4$ photosynthesis in this series (18, 51) concentrate on carbon metabolism. Walker's excellent review (111) contains a critical examination of C_4 photosynthesis and serves as an antidote to the sometime exuberant claims made by workers in a young and rapidly advancing field. These reviewers have emphasized the biochemical aspects of C_4 photosynthesis, but an important reason for interest in this phenomenon is the fact it is coupled with physiological features, specialized leaf anatomy, and organelle structure and distribution. These structural features and their possible adaptive significance have been emphasized in previous reviews (76, 77).

This review will emphasize structural features of leaves, cells, and organelles of C_4 plants. Primary emphasis will be upon relating structure with function, and how these structural and functional correlates might have evolved.

LEAF ANATOMY

Leaf anatomy of C_4 plants is similar to that of *Buchloe dactyloides* (buffalo grass) illustrated in Figure 1. The distinguishing feature is the radial arrangement of chlorenchyma around vascular bundles. The chlorenchyma in turn, is, differentiated into an inner layer of large, thick-walled, cylindrical cells containing prominent chloroplasts and one or more outer layers of palisade-like cells. Variations in this basic structure will be referred to below.

As with so many other things, German botanists identified this specialized anatomical pattern in a number of taxa and raised questions concerning its functional significance. Haberlandt called this anatomical pattern Kranz-type (halo or wreath) and called attention to a possible division of labor between chloroplasts of

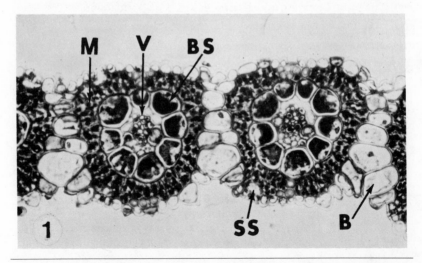

Figure 1   X section of leaf of *Buchloe dactyloides*. Bulliform cell (B), mesophyll (M), substomatal cavity (SS), bundle sheath (BS), vascular tissue (V). X 960.

the two cell types (47). Other contributions to the anatomy of leaves with Kranz anatomy were made by Moser (83), and Meyer reviewed the subject (82). Meyer stressed what he considered the direct and rapid transport of photosynthate from the assimilating tissue to the vessels. He felt that photosynthesis would be enhanced as a result of this rapid removal of end products. This relationship between leaf anatomy and the presumed inhibition of photosynthesis by accumulation of end products will be referred to later.

It is fascinating to note how studies on structural, physiological, and biochemical features of C$_4$ plants lead independent and parallel lives for so many years. The gradual convergence of these different lines of study with the resultant synergistic effect on all these disciplines is an intriguing aspect of the C$_4$ plant phenomenon. An investigation of leaf anatomy of the Australian salt bushes (*Atriplex*) by Black (20) stressed functional leaf anatomy of what we now know to be *Atriplex* species with C$_4$ photosynthesis. A particularly intriguing suggestion was that the bundle sheath is very important in the water economy of these xerophytic species and that these cells appear to function in wilted leaves when the surrounding mesophyll cells show signs of damage. Later considerations of adaptive aspects of Kranz anatomy have been concerned generally with carbon flow. The fact that this emphasis has possibly led us astray will be discussed later.

The anatomical similarity of many *Atriplex* species with the early C$_4$ plants, like sugar cane and maize, was not lost to the Australian workers, and *Atriplex* was one of the early and much studied C$_4$ plants. The relationship of Kranz anatomy with certain environmental conditions was also mentioned by Brown in his important paper of 1958 on leaf anatomy and grass taxonomy (23). His broad comparative study demonstrated that Kranz anatomy was found in tribes of the subfamily Panicoideae. This is in contrast with the dorsi-ventral anatomy of the leaves of tribes in the subfamily Festucoideae. The latter are considered to be of temperate origin while those taxa with Kranz anatomy are considered to be of tropical origin. There are taxa of tropical origin which do not possess Kranz anatomy, the bamboos being a prominent example.

Perhaps the first investigation linking Kranz anatomy with physiological aspects of photosynthesis was conducted by El-Sharkawy & Hesketh in 1965 (39). They found that species with high photosynthetic rates, which did not leak CO$_2$ to the environment in the light, had Kranz anatomy. These taxa are now known to be C$_4$ plants. The pieces of this structure-function puzzle were about to be joined. Subsequent to their initial work on C$_4$ photosynthesis in sugar cane, the Australian workers showed this pathway in other species (52), and these taxa were known to have Kranz anatomy. A little later, Downton & Tregunna (36) correlated Kranz anatomy and the possession of low CO$_2$ compensation points with plants known to have C$_4$ photosynthesis. At the same time, the list of such plants was extended to dicotyledonous species (63), and a concurrent study of leaf anatomy and cell ultrastructure of C$_4$ dicots was reported (74). The latter paper contained the first comprehensive hypothesis concerning the adaptive significance of the convergent physiological and morphological features in these diverse taxa. This hypothesis stated that the photosynthetic pathways and structural features of this group of plants are adaptations for efficient carbon fixation in regions with intermittent aridity. Subsequent reviews emphasizing Kranz anatomy and its possible role in C_4 photosynthesis have been written (53, 113).

The number of taxa with C_4 species was rapidly extended (30, 33, 95, 108, 112), and Smith & Brown (101) have recently published a compilation of grass species possessing the C_4 plant syndrome. It is now known that the following families have C_4 species: Amaranthaceae, Aizoaceae, Chenopodiaceae, Compositeae, Cyperaceae, Euphorbiaceae, Gramineae, Nyctaginaceae, Portulacaceae, Zygophyllaceae. The C_4 plants obviously have a polyphyletic origin, but they are concentrated primarily in the Gramineae and Caryophyllales. Common features of C_4 plants are their tropical origin and wide occurrence in xerophytic environments.

Stomata

The structure of the guard cells of C_4 grasses and C_3 grasses appears to be similar, and guard cell structure of C_4 dicot species is similar to C_3 dicots. If there is some aspect of the number, distribution, or function of guard cells of C_4 plants which sets them apart from C_3 plants, it has not been elucidated. It is important to describe the location of the stomata of C_4 plants relative to the underlying chlorenchyma, because a model for carbon metabolism in C_4 plants in the current literature states that CO_2 entering through the stomata passes through colorless cells before reaching chlorenchyma (28, 111). Coombs, Baldry & Brown (28) state that in *Pennisetum purpureum,* the stomata are located "between the vascular bundles opposite non-green tissue." The stomata of C_4 grasses are generally located such that the substomatal cavity is immediately adjacent to mesophyll cells (Figure 1). A cross-section of a *Pennisetum purpureum* leaf illustrated in (28) shows the stomata only on the abaxial side of the leaf, and the substomatal cavity appears adjacent to mesophyll cells. I have not observed any C_4 grass where CO_2 would have to go through bulliform cells before reaching mesophyll cells. The fact that initial fixation into C_4 organic acids in C_4 plants cannot be explained on the basis of cytoplasmic fixation in colorless cells is provided by the C_4 dicots. Leaves of these species do not have bulliform cells. The scheme proposed by the above authors must be discounted on anatomical grounds.

Structure of Mesophyll and Bundle Sheath Cells

The most common type of Kranz anatomy is that exhibited in Figure 1, where there is one bundle sheath layer and a surrounding layer of mesophyll. However, there are numerous exceptions, and any biochemical and physiological scheme based upon the most common type should explain these exceptions. These variations in monocots have been described recently (27a, 64). There can be two bundle sheaths containing chloroplasts such as possessed by the grass *Aristida.* Most interesting are variations in the Cyperaceae. There can be one bundle sheath with chloroplasts surrounded by a single layer of cells without chloroplasts. These two layers are surrounded by a layer of mesophyll cells with chloroplasts (19, 77). Some members of the Cyperaceae have two bundle sheaths separated by a layer of small cells without chloroplasts. This complex is in turn surrounded by a mesophyll layer. Very little is known about the physiology of C$_4$ plants with these more exotic anatomical patterns. An investigation might well modify some of the current models of the mechanism of C$_4$ photosynthesis.

There has been some confusion about Kranz anatomy as a criterion for the presence of C$_4$ photosynthesis (30). Many C$_3$ plants have a well developed bundle sheath, and in some cases this bundle sheath has chloroplasts. In no case, however, do C$_3$ plants have a radial arrangement of all of the chlorenchyma cells such as found in the C$_4$ plants. In few cases, if any, do they have a thick-walled bundle sheath with as many and frequently well developed chloroplasts as found in C$_4$ plants.

The relationship of chlorenchyma cells in C$_4$ plants is important in the light of models explaining C$_4$ photosynthesis on the basis of compartmentalization of carbon metabolism in mesophyll and bundle sheath cells. These relationships have been described in some detail for sugar cane and two dicot species (77). The bundle sheath cells tend to be cylindrical, with no air spaces between them. If the vascular bundle and the surrounding bundle sheath is considered as a unit, it can be seen that much of the leaf volume is composed of a series of long cylinders with a very low surface to volume ratio. In all species examined, there are fewer bundle sheath cells than mesophyll cells; the ratio is 1:5 in sugar cane and 1:11 in *Amaranthus edulis*. It will be seen that this ratio has been forgotten in discussions about relative numbers of organelles in mesophyll and bundle sheath cells. Mesophyll cells have substantial contact with each other, but they do have air spaces between them. The diffusion path for CO$_2$ from the leaf exterior to bundle sheath cells does not necessitate intervening cells. It is true, however, that air spaces in mesohyll of the species examined are smaller than those of the dorsi-ventral mesophyll in C$_3$ plant leaves. It is possible that in spite of these intercellular spaces, most CO$_2$ is incorporated by mesophyll cells. It has been stated that about 15% of the CO$_2$ entering a *Digitaria* leaf is fixed by bundle sheath cells (18). If this figure was determined from chemically fixed tissue or from tissue prepared for scanning electron microscopy, it is undoubtedly too high because of shrinkage of mesophyll cells in these processes. Examination of *Digitaria* leaf sections prepared from living leaves does not show air spaces abnormally larger than those in other C$_4$ grass leaves.[1]

Starch Sheath

The bundle sheath of leaves has long been recognized as a starch sheath or endodermis (40), and the role of this cell layer in serving as a starch "warehouse" has been stressed by many of the authors cited above. The fact that this tissue has some similar features to the endodermis of roots and some stems should not be lost sight of when models of the flow of carbon in C$_4$ plants are developed. It has long been known that the Casparian strips in the walls of endodermal cells and a layer in the walls of the mestome sheath and bundle or parenchyma sheath of many grasses was resistant to sulfuric acid digestion (96). Electron micrographs have shown that the walls of bundle sheath cells of many C$_4$ grasses have an electron opaque layer (27a,

[1]Author's unpublished data.

77, 78). This layer is very well defined in the walls bounding mesophyll cells (Figure 3), but appears to be absent from the walls adjacent to vascular tissue. O'Brien & Carr (86) have shown that this is a suberized layer, and that it can occur in walls of the mestome sheath of C_3 grasses as well as in bundle sheath cell walls of C_4 grasses. Authors reporting on this layer have also been impressed with the prominent plasmodesmata which extend through the pit fields. They have also discussed the possibility that this suberized layer "waterproofs" the bundle sheath and adjacent vascular tissue and that communication with the peripheral regions of the leaf are maintained through cytoplasmic connections. This layer might say something about how grasses make their living, but it does not seem to be correlated with C_4 photosynthesis. The fact that the suberized layer has not been observed in bundle sheath cell walls of C_4 dicots makes it increasingly difficult to establish any correlations with a particular photosynthetic pathway.

Bundle sheath cell chloroplasts accumulate great amounts of starch in the light, and this frequent observation has influenced thinking about the compartmentalization of function in C_4 photosynthesis. It has been assumed that initial fixation of carbon occurs in the mesophyll cells and that photosynthetic intermediates are transported to bundle sheath cell chloroplasts where they are converted to starch and eventually translocated to a carbon sink. Careful observations by Rhoades & Carvalho (93) provided irrefutable evidence that photosynthate was transported from the mesophyll cells to the bundle sheath cells. They observed chloroplasts in bundle sheath cells underlying chlorotic mesophyll cells in a variegated variety of maize. The chloroplasts in these bundle sheath cells did not form starch, whereas bundle sheath cells underlying green mesophyll cells did form starch in the light. These observations remain as the best proof that a photosynthate is transferred from mesophyll to bundle sheath cells, in spite of the many claims that have been made in recent years.

Storage of starch in bundle sheath cells has led to the impression that mesophyll cell chloroplasts cannot form starch in spite of many observations that mesophyll cells often contain small amounts of starch (19, 36, 74, 75, 78). It is important to recognize that mesophyll cell chloroplasts are perfectly capable of forming large amounts of starch, because several models for carbon flow in C_4 plants have indicated that only mesophyll cell plastids can form starch (28, 51, 60). It has been shown that mesophyll cell chloroplasts in maize will form starch when leaf tissue is incubated with sucrose (93), and mesophyll cell chloroplasts of sugar cane and *Digitaria decumbens* will form starch when export to a sink is inhibited. In the former case, this is done by isolating leaf tissue so that extensive translocation cannot take place (76). A mesophyll cell chloroplast from such an experiment is illustrated in Figure 2. The export of starch in *Digitaria* can be inhibited by low night temperatures (55). Mesophyll cell chloroplasts of *Digitaria* apparently form a considerable amount of starch during a normal period of illumination (19), but the condition illustrated in Figure 2 is unusual under normal circumstances for most C_4 plants. It is evidence that starch formation in the chlorenchyma of C_4 plants is a result of a source-sink gradient. If the sink is eliminated, the bundle sheath cell chloroplasts will first load with starch and subsequently mesophyll cell chloroplasts will do the same. The latter certainly possess all enzymes required for starch synthesis. The fact that these chloroplasts normally perform a certain function as a result of their position on a source-sink gradient and not because of qualitative differences in certain enzymes is perhaps indicative of other processes in C_4 plants which are thought to result from qualitative differences in the two cell layers.

Many of the earlier works concerned with Kranz anatomy focus on the effect this structural pattern might have on translocation of photosynthate into the vascular tissue. It was a particular concern of Silaeva (98) in addition to some of those works cited earlier. The discovery that C_4 photosynthesis was correlated with Kranz anatomy focused most of the attention of those interested in structure upon assimilation or retention of carbon, rather than upon its subsequent movement. Transport phenomena, however, have been emphasized by Laetsch (76, 77) and Smith (102). The importance of considering events "downstream" from carbon fixation in C_4 plants is reinforced by the intriguing results of Moss & Rasmussen (84) and Hofstra & Nelson (58). These authors report that translocation of ^{14}C from C_4 plants is more rapid than from leaves of C_3 plants. This area is ripe for further investigation, and it could well lead to a consideration of the much discussed CO_2 pump in leaves of C_4 grasses as a pump not to concentrate CO_2 in bundle sheath cells, but to effect the transport of carbon from bundle sheath to phloem. The question of whether rapid transport of photosynthate from the point of assimilation affects the rate of photosynthesis (74) will be discussed below.

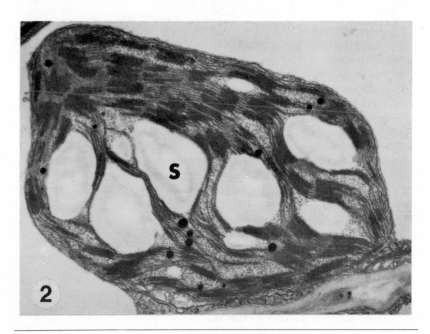

Figure 2   Mesophyll cell chloroplast of sugar cane. Starch (S). X 15,080.

CHLOROPLAST STRUCTURE

An assumed difference in chloroplasts of mesophyll and bundle sheath cells has been stated by authors since the time of Haberlandt. Most of this attention was directed to grass leaves, and the first ultrastructural observations of these chloroplasts was made by Hodge, McLean & Mercer (57). They observed that mesophyll cell chloroplasts in *Zea mays* had grana and were similar to other higher plant chloroplasts that had been seen previous to that time. They described bundle sheath cell chloroplasts, however, as being without grana. It was subsequently found that bundle sheath cell chloroplasts of *Zea mays* and closely related grasses possessed numerous rudimentary grana (76, 94, 97). In spite of this, the impression has remained that bundle sheath cell chloroplasts of maize are "agranal" (5). The ultrastructure of maize chloroplasts, along with chloroplasts from many other C_4 grasses, was investigated by Johnson in 1964 (65). Unfortunately, this doctoral thesis was not published, and many of her observations went unnoticed. A portion of this thesis, however, has been published recently (64). Much of the tissue used in Johnson's investigation was fixed with $KMnO_4$, so that features of the chloroplasts and cytoplasm in these plants subsequently observed by other authors were lost. The fascination with "agranal" bundle sheath chloroplasts evidenced by many workers in

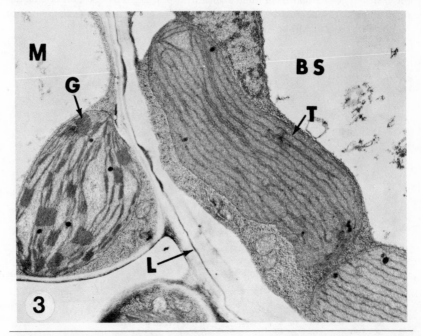

Figure 3 Mesophyll cell (M) and bundle sheath cell (BS) of sugar cane. Note grana (G) in the mesophyll cell chloroplast and generally unappressed thylakoids (T) in the bundle sheath cell chloroplast. An electron opaque layer (L) is the outer wall of the bundle sheath cell. X 12,480.

photosythesis undoubtedly derived from publications on the structure of sugar cane chloroplasts (75, 78, 79; Figure 3). The extreme structural dimorphism in chloroplasts from the two cell layers in sugar cane has led to the frequently stated notion that structural dimorphism of chloroplasts is a feature of all C$_4$ plants. This is in spite of the fact that the first paper correlating chloroplast structure and function in known C$_4$ plants was concerned with dicots in which there is no structural dimorphism (74; Figure 4). It has been observed that chloroplasts in mesophyll and bundle sheath cells in C$_4$ plants range all the way from no dimorphism to the extreme form found in sugar cane and other members of the Andropogoneae (14, 19, 76, 77). Extreme structural dimorphism is found in chloroplasts of C$_4$ dicots as well as monocots (77). There is no causal relationship between chloroplast structural dimorphism and C$_4$ photosynthesis.

Dimorphism usually does exist, but it is size dimorphism in addition to or rather than structural dimorphism. In cases where there is no structural dimorphism, there is a very pronounced size dimorphism. Size dimorphism is not always noticeable in sugar cane where there is a very marked structural dimorphism. The relationship between size and structural dimorphism and its possible physiological implications have been discussed in detail (76, 77). The most obvious hypothesis is that the

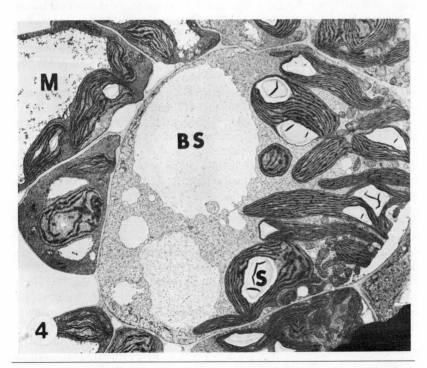

Figure 4   Mesophyll cell (M) and bundle sheath cell (BS) of *Portulaca oleracea.* Note large amounts of starch (S) in bundle sheath cell chloroplasts. X 2650.

increased amount of stroma in chloroplasts of the bundle sheath relative to meso-phyll chloroplasts is involved with starch synthesis. In spite of statements to the contrary (18), bundle sheath cell chloroplasts have to be considered as structural and/or functional amyloplasts.

The term "agranal" is commonly used in the literature, and this is probably unfortunate. It is not difficult to observe small overlaps and regions where thylakoids are appressed in chloroplasts of sugar cane, sorghum, and related genera. This is particularly common in peripheral regions of chloroplasts. The degree of thylakoid appression in sugar cane can be influenced by the temperature regime (77), and there are undoubtedly other environmental and physiological factors which influence the degree of appression. It has been shown that "agranal" bundle sheath cell chloro-plasts possess grana during their development (21, 78). The degree to which these grana are lost is probably a result of many variables. As will be discussed later, there is considerable evidence that bundle sheath cell chloroplasts in these species exhibit biochemical features which are thought to be correlated with appressed thylakoids in higher plant chloroplasts. These regions where thylakoids are appressed cannot be dismissed as being "functionally trivial" (64). It is also imperative for workers discussing chloroplasts which they claim to be "agranal" to present electron micro-graphs of a quality which permits observers to determine the validity of their claims. Unfortunately, it is all too common in the literature for a reader to be told that chloroplasts of one or the other cell layers have a particular feature and to be greeted with an illustration characterized by its fuzziness and almost complete lack of detail.

It has been claimed that C_4 plants can be divided into two groups, depending on whether the predominant primary product is malate or aspartate. These "malate and aspartate formers" (32) have been said to be correlated with the degree of granal development in bundle sheath cell chloroplasts, with location of chloroplasts in bundle sheath cells, and with size dimorphism of mitochondria in bundle sheath and mesophyll cells (33). It has been demonstrated that the relative amount of malate and aspartate formed can be a function of the age of the leaf and the time the leaf is exposed to $^{14}CO_2$ (69). It appears, therefore, that the term "malate and aspartate formers" is not a very useful one, since relative levels of primary products can be influenced by many factors.

Dimorphic Chloroplasts and Light Reactions

The demonstration that some C_4 plants possess bundle sheath cell chloroplasts essentially devoid of grana resulted in experiments testing the hypothesis that grana were correlated with photosystem II activity. It was reported that agranal chloro-plasts, such as those of *Sorghum*, lacked photosystem II activity (33a, 35, 115). It is unfortunate that because of work on photosystem II activity in the bundle sheath cell chloroplasts of a few grass species, it is assumed that bundle sheath cell chloro-plasts are "enriched in photosystem I relative to photosystem II" (10). Many C_4 plants have bundle sheath cell chloroplasts with well-developed grana, and there is little reason to expect that they are deficient in photosystem II. Other work on bundle sheath cell chloroplasts concerned with various aspects of the light reaction have been conducted (3–5, 10, 11, 41, 92, 103). A comprehensive work investigating photosystem II activity in bundle sheath cell chloroplasts of a wide variety of C$_4$ grasses and dicotyledonous species has been made by Elkin (38). All of these C$_4$ species had at least some photosystem II activity.

The work on "agranal" chloroplasts is undoubtedly of considerable interest to those correlating membrane structure with function, but this work tells us very little about C$_4$ photosynthesis. There is no evidence that there is any relationship between "agranal" chloroplasts with or without photosystem II and C$_4$ photosynthesis. Dimorphic chloroplasts bear no causal relationship with this process, and the degree of granal development in bundle sheath chloroplasts is probably involved in some fashion with their function in synthesizing and storing starch. The attempt to erect causal relationships on the basis of extreme chloroplast dimorphism has undoubtedly diverted us from investigating what might be real causal relationships.

Peripheral Reticulum

Structural dimorphism is not a feature possessed by chloroplasts of all C$_4$ plants, but all C$_4$ plant chloroplasts which have been observed to date possess a membrane system in the peripheral stroma which has been termed the peripheral reticulum (PR) (74, 94). This membrane system consists of anastomosing tubules contiguous with the inner membrane of the chloroplast envelope (74–78). It has been stated that it provides a connection between the thylakoid membrane system and the chloroplast envelope (94), but other authors have not been able to demonstrate clearly that this connection exists. The PR is illustrated in Figure 5. This membrane system has been observed in many C$_4$ plant species and a number of authors have commented on its role in C$_4$ photosynthesis (14, 19, 88). Effects of various fixation procedures on the peripheral reticulum have been investigated (77). It is not affected by fixation in glutaraldenhyde and/or OsO$_4$ at either room temperature or 4°C. It is destroyed or very considerably altered by KMnO$_4$ fixation. This is the reason it was never observed by earlier workers who studied chloroplast ultrastructure in plants such as maize. The fact that KMnO$_4$ fixation either destroys or disrupts this membrane system suggests that its composition differs from both the membranes of the plastid envelope and the thylakoid membrane system, since they do retain their morphological integrity with this fixative. It also disappears during senescence in leaves of *Portulaca oleracea.* This is further evidence that it has a composition different from that of the other chloroplast membrane systems.

Generally it has been found to be more highly developed in mesophyll cell chloroplasts than in bundle sheath cell chloroplasts, but it is not known if this is a constant feature in all C$_4$ plants. The PR retains its integrity during the isolation of chloroplasts of *Zea mays* (87). Isolated chloroplasts of spinach and *Portulaca oleracea* are compared in Figures 7–8. The PR is very well preserved in the isolated *P. oleracea* chloroplast, whereas the spinach plastid peripheral stroma is homogeneous just as it is in vivo. Fractionation studies on isolated chloroplasts of C$_4$ plants with the intent of obtaining information about the PR will probably prove difficult, since the PR fraction might be difficult to distinguish from the envelope fraction.

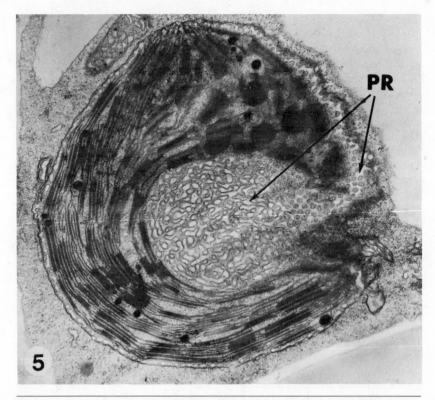

Figure 5   Mesophyll cell chloroplast of *P. oleracea*. This profile exhibits the complex system of anastomosing tubules termed peripheral reticulum (PR). X 14,000.

Additional information about the PR can be obtained from freeze-fracture studies of C_4 chloroplasts. The replica image of a freeze-fractured *P. oleracea* chloroplast is illustrated in Figure 6, and can be compared with the profile of a sectioned *P. oleracea* chloroplast in Figure 5. Fracture faces from that portion of the freeze-fractured chloroplast which is interpreted as the PR, exhibit particles averaging 84 Å. The size and distribution of these particles is similar to those of fracture faces of the inner membrane of the chloroplast envelope which average 80Å. These sizes are significantly different from those on the "B" and "C" faces of thylakoid membranes (90). The particles on the "B" faces of thylakoids average 134 Å, whereas those on the "C" face average 100 Å. Both the thylakoid membrane system and the PR originate from the inner membrane of the plastid envelope (77), but the PR continues to develop after the thylakoid membranes have formed, and it retains continuity with the inner membrane of the envelope. It follows, therefore, that the difference between this highly developed system of invaginations from the inner membrane of the envelope and the invaginations which give rise to the

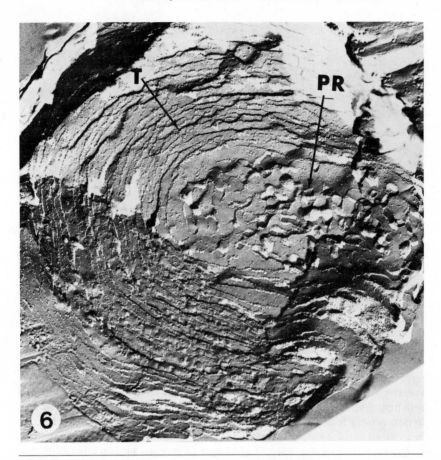

Figure 6 A profile of a replica obtained from a freeze-fractured *P. oleracea* chloroplast. Fracture face of peripheral reticulum (PR). Fracture face of thylakoid membrane system (T). X 25,600.

thylakoids during the normal development of the plastid represent a matter of degree.

The PR appears to influenced by light intensity in chloroplasts of *Amaranthus lividus* (81a). High light intensity inhibits its formation in this species. It has also been claimed that the PR is not observed in *Atriplex rosea* (34), but it has since been observed in chloroplasts of *A. rosea* by Goodchild (44) and by Laetsch (unpublished observations).

PERIPHERAL RETICULUM AND C₃ PLANTS It is generally accepted that PR is a characteristic of chloroplasts of C₄ plants, but reports of its occurrence in some C₃ plants has raised doubts about it being specifically correlated with C₄ photosynthesis. A

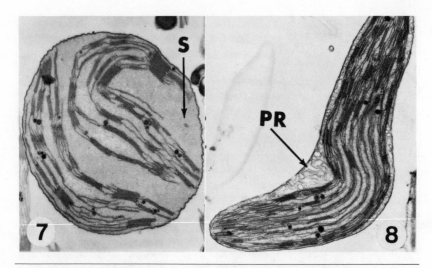

Figure 7   Profile of an isolated spinach chloroplast. Stroma (S). X 11,600.

Figure 8   Profile of an isolated *P. oleracea* chloroplast. Note peripheral reticulum (PR). X 11,000.

well-developed PR was observed in a wheat chloroplast profile (14), and it has been reported in chloroplast profiles of *Dactylis glomerata* (56). In the latter report, varieties with low rates of photorespiration are said to have a PR, whereas varieties with high rates do not. The PR profiles in this report are not highly developed and in fact, present fixation images which are not much different from those that can be observed in the peripheral stroma of chloroplast profiles of many C_3 plants. The peripheral stroma of two other *D. glomerata* chloroplast profiles reported in this paper do not have an accumulation of these vesicles. An electron micrograph of a portion of a chloroplast profile of the C_3 plant *Typha latifolia* purports to illustrate PR (45). This system is not highly developed and is absent from much of the peripheral stroma of this profile. In addition, a region identified as PR is actually a region where the cytoplasm has been digested between the plasmalemma and the chloroplast envelope. This report also contains errors in the "percent chloroplast with PR" and "percent chloroplast volume occupied by PR." The investigators really analyzed the percent of chloroplast profiles with PR. A profile without PR does not mean that the chloroplast does not have this membrane system. Information on the chloroplast volume occupied by PR has little meaning, because these calculations cannot be made unless they are derived from serial sections of the chloroplasts. They cannot be calculated with any accuracy from chloroplast profiles.

Another frequently cited example of PR in C_3 plant chloroplasts is that of soybean (106). The vesicles identified as PR occur in chloroplasts of leaves given 1.5

days of chilling treatment. It is not unusual for chloroplasts to develop a large number of peripheral vesicles when they are under stress. These vesicles can hardly be observed in the electron micrograph in this report, and authors citing this as an example of PR in a C_3 plant have not based their decision on a critical examination of the evidence presented. A further suggestion that the peripheral reticulum is found in chloroplasts of cells which do not carry out C_4 photosynthesis has been made (45). The authors feel that *Zea mays* bundle sheath cell chloroplasts with PR is evidence that this structure is not correlated with C_4 photosynthesis because bundle sheath cells supposedly have C_3 photosynthesis in contrast with mesophyll cells. As will be discussed later, it has not been firmly established that this division of labor between C_3 and C_4 carboxylation systems in these respective cell layers exists. It has been shown that the presence or absence of the PR is not necessarily determined by the type of carboxylation reaction that is going on within a cell type. Tissue cultures of the C_4 plant *Froelichia gracillus* conduct C_4 photosynthesis (77a), and pulse-chase experiments demonstrate that the label in the organic acids is transferred to sugar phosphates and subsequently to sucrose and starch.[2] These tissue cultures have relatively homogeneous cell and chloroplast populations. The chloroplasts, however, do not possess PR even though both C_3 and C_4 photosynthesis is carried on in the same cell. Similar results have been obtained by Usuda et al (109) in tissue cultures of *Amaranthus*. While it is clear that chloroplasts with PR are found in C_4 plants, it is not at all clear that this membrane system is associated with the prevalance of a particular carboxylating enzyme system in specific cell types.

Intriguing observations have been made on guard cell chloroplasts of a number of C_3 plants. Chloroplast profiles in guard cells of *Vicia faba* and *Allium porrum* demonstrate a membrane system that is morphologically very similar to the PR of chloroplasts of C_4 plants (2, 89). Chloroplasts in the mesophyll cells of these species do not have a PR-like membrane system. This fixation image is not found in guard cell chloroplasts of other C_3 plants such as tobacco and oats (67, 89). A PR-like membrane system observed in chloroplasts of *Nymphoides indica* (110) was found primarily in chloroplasts of epidermal cells. This is similar to the observations on guard cell chloroplasts, since guard cells are specialized epidermal cells. This membrane system in *Nymphoides indica* appears to respond in a similar fashion to $KMnO_4$ fixation and to senescence, as has been reported for PR in chloroplasts of C_4 plants (77). The occurrence of a PR-like membrane system in certain guard cell chloroplasts is particularly interesting in light of Allaway's (1) observation that malate accumulates in guard cells of *Vicia faba* during stomatal opening. These observations suggest the possibility that guard cells carry on C_4 photosynthesis, and the resultant anion accumulation could participate in the osmotic regulation of stomatal opening.

FUNCTION OF THE PERIPHERAL RETICULUM   It has been suggested that the PR is involved either in rapid transport of photosynthetic precursors or end products

[2]Laetsch and Kortschak, unpublished observations.

between cytoplasm and chloroplasts, or that it represents a site for enzyme systems involved in C_4 photosynthesis (74, 76). It has been shown that plants with crass-ulacean acid metabolism (CAM) possess carboxylation enzyme systems similar to those of C_4 plants and these plants have chloroplasts without PR (77). The fact that green cultured tissues also conduct C_4 photosynthesis and their chloroplasts do not have PR strongly suggests that this membrane system does not represent a site of enzymes specific to the C_4 pathway. The PR is an elaboration of the inner membrane of the chloroplast envelope, and it has been suggested that if the inner membrane of the envelope is the barrier limiting transport between the chloroplast and the cytoplasm, an increase in the surface of this membrane could facilitate transport (77a).

Current models for the mechanism of C_4 photosynthesis (Figure 9) dictate a rapid transport of photosynthetic precursors and products between chloroplasts and cyto-plasm. This is particularly true in the model which states that the initial carboxyla-tion reaction is in the cytoplasm. The PR is generally better developed in mesophyll cell chloroplasts. *Froelichia* tissue culture cells do both C_4 and C_3 photosynthesis, so transport between chloroplasts and cytoplasm might be less active than in leaves of a C_4 plant. As stated above, these chloroplasts do not have a PR. In addition, chloroplasts in senescing leaves of *Portulaca* lost the PR, and it is known that these senescing leaves of *Portulaca* produce substantial C_3 primary products during short-term exposure to $^{14}CO_2$ (69). This suggests a reduction in the shuttling of products between chloroplasts and cytoplasm. Bacteria are known to have an indu-cable and specific transport system for the uptake of C_4-dicarboxylic acids (68), and it would not be surprising if chloroplasts had a similar system. Although the present evidence is scanty and correlative rather than causal, it best supports the hypothesis that the PR is involved in transport of materials between chloroplasts and cyto-plasm. This hypothesis can be tested when intact and functional chloroplasts are isolated from C_4 plants.

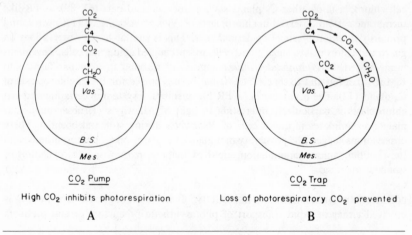

CO₂ Pump

High CO₂ inhibits photorespiration

A

CO₂ Trap

Loss of photorespiratory CO₂ prevented

B

Figure 9 Alternative models for the functional significance of C_4 plant leaf anatomy.

STRUCTURE AND DISTRIBUTION OF MITOCHONDRIA AND MICROBODIES

It was noted early that mitochondria in bundle sheath cells of C_4 dicots were larger and structurally more complex than those in mesophyll cells (74), and the occurrence of dimorphic mitochondria in C_4 plants and their possible function has been reviewed (33, 77). Dimorphic mitochondria are found in the C_4 dicots and in many C_4 monocots. In the latter group, they are found in those taxa possessing bundle sheath cell chloroplasts with reasonably well developed grana. In genera such as *Saccharum* and *Sorghum,* there is little, if any, mitochondrial dimorphism. The function of the large mitochondria with numerous and well-developed cristae is not known, but the evidence that there is rapid exchange of metabolites between mesophyll and bundle sheath cells and between bundle sheath and vascular tissue suggests that these mitochondria might be involved in producing energy utilized for transport. Caution must be used, however, in generalizing about the function of these dimorphic mitochondria, because they are not found in all C_4 plants.

Most reports on ultrastructure of C_4 plant leaf cells have made the point that bundle sheath cells seem to have a large number of organelles relative to mesophyll cells, and a number of these reports contain data on relative numbers of chloroplasts, mitochondria, and microbodies in bundle sheath cells and mesophyll cells (42, 54, 77, 80). All of these investigations show that there are more mitochondria and microbodies in a bundle sheath cell than in a mesophyll cell. This presumed concentration of organelles in bundle sheath cells has provided the basis for speculations that photorespiration in C_4 plants occurs primarily in bundle sheath cells, and that CO_2 generated in this process is reassimilated in mesophyll cells. The apparent lack of photorespiration in C_4 plants, therefore, has been ascribed to the reassimilation of CO_2 as a result of the Kranz anatomy (18, 42, 76, 107). It is important to realize that the data on relative numbers of organelles in bundle sheath versus mesophyll cells does not take into consideration the fact that there are more mesophyll cells than bundle sheath cells in the leaves of C_4 plants. Sugar cane, for example, has a mesophyll bundle sheath cell ratio of 5, while that of *Amaranthus* is 11 (77). These ratios were determined by examining disassociated cells and leaf sections by both light and electron microscopy. The ratio for *Sorghum* is probably very similar to that of sugar cane, and Huang & Beevers (59) have stated that the mesophyll bundle sheath cell ratio for maize is 3. Realizing that there are more mesophyll than bundle sheath cells, recalculation of the data provided in all the reports to date makes it clear that distribution of mitochondria and microbodies in these two cell layers is approximately even. This distribution of mitochondria is supported by the distribution of cytochrome oxidase in *Sorghum* and *Atriplex rosea* (59). It is still possible, however, that there is more mitochondrial activity in bundle sheath cells of many C_4 plants because their bundle sheath cells have both larger and structurally more complex mitochondria than those in mesophyll cells. Likewise, microbodies in the two cell layers might have a different function. This has been suggested by Frederick & Newcomb (42) on the basis of size, internal morphology, and staining reactions. This discussion emphasizes once again the absolute necessity of having a clear understanding of the architecture of leaves and the shapes, numbers, and sizes of cells and their organelles before attempts are made to correlate structure with function.

C_3–C_4 INTERMEDIATES

The C_4 plants represent a full syndrome of structural and functional characters clearly distinguished from those possessed by C_3 plants. Species have been assigned to either one or the other group, with leaf anatomy being considered a reliable indicator of the C_3 or C_4 syndrome. Since C_4 plants also have C_3 photosynthesis, and no angiosperms considered to be "primitive" are C_4 plants, it appears that C_4 plants are both polyphyletic and recent in their origin. A major question has been the lack of intermediates between these two groups. This lack of intermediates is particularly mysterious because a number of genera possess apparently closely related species which are either C_3 or C_4 plants. Until fairly recently, it was often stated that angiosperms presented a great mystery because they suddenly appeared in the fossil record possessed of all the characteristics that have come to be associated with the group. Likewise, C_4 plants appear to have arisen "full-blown" with hardly a trace of their evolutionary development.

It has been possible to produce hybrids between C_3 and C_4 plants in the laboratory (16). The C_4 plant *Atriplex rosea* was hybridized with the C_3 plant *Atriplex patula*. The F_2 and F_3 generations of such hybrids demonstrated various structural and functional conditions intermediate between the original parents, but these characteristics were uncoupled and a complete "$C_{3.5}$" plant was not obtained. Although this work has not told us very much about how C_4 plants might have evolved, it has been extremely valuable in providing information on the genetic relationship of elements of the C_4 syndrome.

A demonstration that structurally homogeneous tissue cultures can carry on C_4 photosynthesis (77a) and that senescent leaves of *P. oleracea* can simultaneously carry on C_3 and C_4 photosynthesis and yet retain Kranz anatomy suggests that the CO_2 fixation pathways and leaf anatomy of C_4 plants are not causally related. That C_3 and C_4 photosynthesis need not be spatially or temporally separated is also indicated by the observations of Avadhani et al (6) that CAM plants can also fix CO_2 into malate under short-term fixation in the light. These CAM plants do not have Kranz anatomy.

The CAM plants can be considered C_3-C_4 intermediates with respect to carbon fixation, and a taxon with a liberal sprinkling of C_3, C_4, and CAM plants should provide good prospecting for plants intermediate both in structure and function. The Aizoaceae is such a family, and it had been reported on the basis of leaf anatomy and cell ultrastructure that *Mollugo verticillata* might be such an intermediate (77). In contrast to *M. cerviana,* which has typical Kranz anatomy, *M. verticilata* has a well-developed bundle sheath with numerous chloroplasts, but the mesophyll is dorsi-ventral rather than centric. In addition, bundle sheath cell chloroplasts and mitochondria exhibited size dimorphism within the same cell. Those adjacent to vascular tissue were larger than those adjacent to mesophyll cells. It has recently been determined that *M. cerviana* is also C_4 with respect to primary products and photorespiration, while *M. verticilata* produces as much PGA and sugar phosphates under short-term exposure to CO_2 as it produces malate and aspartate (69a). It also exhibits photorespiration, and its rates are intermediate between those of *M. cerviana* and typical C_3 plants. It has also been found that other species in this family appear to have intermediate C_3-C_4 characteristics. Further work on these intermediates should provide much information which will revise our current ideas on the relationship between structure and function in C_4 plants. Such studies should help us to realize that carbon fixation and Kranz anatomy can be products of different selective pressures.

STRUCTURAL BASIS FOR FUNCTION

Biochemical features of C_4 plants have been well reviewed (18), and a detailed discussion of the evidence for biochemical compartmentalization in leaves is not in the scope of this review. I will, however, illustrate how one structure can provide the basis for several models of the mechanism of C_4 photosynthesis. Most of the current interpretations on structural and functional features of C_4 plants can be incorporated into models presented in Figure 9. The model in Figure 9 A is at the height of current fashion, and it states that the initial carboxylation reaction yielding C_4 acids takes place in mesophyll cell chloroplasts. Malate and/or aspartate are then transported to bundle sheath cells where decarboxylation occurs and CO_2 is refixed into PGA. Evidence from enzyme distribution studies (reviewed by Black, 18) has resulted in this model stating that there is a very significant quantitative, and perhaps even qualitative, difference between the carboxylation enzyme systems in mesophyll and bundle sheath cells, and that chloroplasts in the outer cell layer make organic acids whereas those in the inner cell layer make PGA. A fundamental tenet of this model is that CO_2 is concentrated in the bundle sheath cells as a result of the transport of malate and aspartate from the mesophyll cells. This CO_2 pump provides high CO_2 levels in bundle sheath cells and inhibits the production of glycolate and hence photorespiration. The actual transport of C_4 acids from the mesophyll cells to the bundle sheath cells has not been demonstrated, and it is unfortunate that this reasonable speculation has been elevated to a commonly expressed "fact" which has appeared in both professional and popular publications. According to the model in Figure 9A, Kranz anatomy is seen as an adaptation resulting in a high CO_2 concentration in the internal tissues which inhibits photorespiration and the subsequent loss of CO_2. The relatively greater efficiency of C_4 plants in utilizing CO_2 is ascribed to inhibition of photorespiration. This model does not explain why oxygen evolution would not occur in those large numbers of C_4 plants where the bundle sheath cell chloroplasts have normal or reasonably developed grana. There is no evidence that such chloroplasts do not evolve oxygen, and it is difficult to see why the oxygen concentration in these cells would be any lower than it would be in mesophyll cells.

Another current, if less popular, model is illustrated in Figure 9B. It states that the initial carboxylation reaction takes place in the cytoplasm of mesophyll cells and that C_4 acids probably are decarboxylated in the chloroplasts and CO_2 incorporated via the photosynthetic reductive pentose phosphate pathway. Photosynthetic intermediates are transported from mesophyll cell chloroplasts to bundle sheath cell chloroplasts where they are converted to starch. Some CO_2 could be fixed directly in bundle sheath cells. This model states that photorespiration goes on primarily in bundle sheath cells, and that the evolved CO_2 is reassimilated in the cytoplasm of mesophyll cells. In this model, the mesophyll cells act as a CO_2 trap rather than as the pump indicated in the first model.

Enzyme distribution studies also support this model, since a number of authors have reported the presence of ribulose diphosphate (RuDP) carboxylase in fractions derived from mesophyll cells (12, 15, 25, 85, 91, 99). In addition, authors who have strongly supported the model illustrated in Figure 9A have found that other enzymes involved in the photosynthetic reductive pentose phosphate pathway do not have a differential distribution between these two cell layers. This is particularly true of NADP-specific glyceraldehyde phosphate dehydrogenase (37, 51).

Enzyme distribution studies can be used to support either of these two models, and at present these studies present something of a buyer's market. The differential results that have been reported stem from the uncertainties of performing enzyme assays with plant extracts containing large amounts of inhibitors (8) and from the difficulty of insuring that particular fractions come from specific cell layers. Black (18) has pointed to the problems in this area and has correctly stated that cytological evidence to support results from differential grinding procedures has been modest to nonexistent. Attempts to isolate and separate chloroplasts from different cell layers has met limited success. It is difficult to prepare intact chloroplasts in either aqueous or nonaqueous media, and the use of the latter technique is further complicated by contaminating cytoplasmic proteins (13).

A final choice between models attempting to explain C_4 photosynthesis cannot be made until isolated chloroplasts can be induced to fix CO_2 in vitro. The greatest success in this endeavor has been enjoyed by O'Neal et al (87), whose results are perhaps the strongest evidence to support the model in Figure 9B. They obtained chloroplasts from 4 to 6-day-old maize seedlings which fixed CO_2 at reasonable rates. The photosynthetic products of these isolated chloroplasts were only those characteristic of C_3 plants. The leaves from which these plastids were isolated produced typical products of C_4 photosynthesis. Another study by this group (43) demonstrated that PEP carboxylase was found in their isolation medium and that isolated chloroplasts did not utilize malate or aspartate. Lyttleton (81) also found that intact isolated *Amaranthus* chloroplasts did not contain PEP carboxylase although it was in the supernatant. Cytological criteria have been used to criticize the work with maize. Chloroplasts from the young plants were not fully developed, although they did obtain grana. At this stage of development, however, bundle sheath cell chloroplasts could also have grana, but is likely that the isolation procedure would result in the release of a greater number of mesophyll cell plastids. The fact that there are many more mesophyll cell plastids in the leaf than bundle sheath cell plastids would ensure that the isolated chloroplasts would be enriched in mesophyll cell plastids. Conclusive proof that chloroplasts of a C_4 plant produce C_3

products must result from the use of fully developed chloroplasts, and it is hoped that improvements in isolation procedures will lead to a rapid resolution of this problem.

The latter evidence in combination with the rigorous application of "Occam's Razor" makes some variant of the model illustrated in Figure 9B most attractive to the author. It is attractive because it does not necessitate shuttling of metabolites between cell layers and the existence of two different kinds of chloroplasts in adjacent cell layers called for by the first model. Placing the C_4 carboxylation reaction in the cytoplasm would also be consistent with general thinking on where this reaction takes place in cells of other plants (111).

FEEDBACK INHIBITION

The most obvious evidence for compartmentalization of function in leaves of C_4 plants is accumulation of starch in bundle sheath cells. It has been suggested frequently that rapid removal of photosynthetic intermediates from mesophyll cells would prevent end-product inhibition resulting from starch synthesis in the mesophyll cells. This would enable mesophyll cell chloroplasts to photosynthesize at maximum rates at high light intensities. The relationship between starch accumulation and photosynthetic rates has been reviewed (85a, 111a). Haapala found that starch did not inhibit photosynthesis in the C_3 plant *Stellaria* (46). There is some confusion on this phenomenon in sugar cane (26), but Habeshaw has recently reported that photosynthetic rates in sugar beet are related to the rates of translocation from leaves (48). It has been shown that photosynthetic intermediates can regulate the activity of both PEP carboxylase and RuDP carboxylase (9, 24, 29). Both models illustrated in Figure 9 attempt to explain how Kranz anatomy permits C_4 plants to overcome the loss of carbon resulting from photorespiration, but it is also possible that this anatomy permits a division of labor between chloroplasts resulting in regulation of photosynthesis so that carbon fixation is carried on at a very high rate. The relative efficiency of C_4 plants in carbon fixation could then be due to initial carboxylation reactions rather than to a recyling of photorespiratory CO_2.

C_4 PLANTS AS CRYPTO-SUCCULENTS

The similarity between C_4 photosynthesis and CAM has long been noted (73, 74), and a comparison of spatial specialization of labor in CAM plants has been outlined (77). This relationship is expressed in Figure 10. Anatomy of C_4 plant leaves results, therefore, in compartmentalization of pieces of essentially the same biochemical machinery found in green cells of CAM plants. Variations of form and function among organisms are usually variations on a theme rather than distinct qualitative differences, and this relationship between CAM and C_4 plants reinforces this general principle.

The CAM plants are adapted to environments of more or less constant aridity, while C_4 plants are primarily found and apparently evolved in regions of intermit-

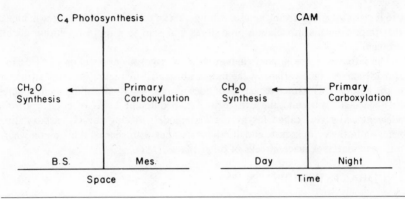

Figure 10   A model for the spatial and temporal compartmentalization of carbon fixation in C_4 and CAM plants.

tent aridity (74, 76, 77). Both CAM plants and C_4 plants have high CO_2 fixed per water use ratios (18). Aerial portions of CAM plants have low surface area to volume ratios, and while this is an optimal geometry for water retention, it is not efficient for gas exchange. Water, however, is the most limiting factor in the environment of CAM plants, and the greatest selective pressure would be for mechanisms facilitating water use efficiency. The C_4 plants, on the other hand, are adapted to habitats such as tropical savannas where periods of extreme drought alternate with periods of abundant water. They must be able to survive during periods of drought, and they must be able to compete with rapidly growing mesophytes during periods when water is not limiting. Kranz anatomy can be viewed as a structural compromise which restricts water loss and also permits efficient CO_2 fixation.

It was stated earlier that a feature of Kranz anatomy is the existence of a solid cylinder consisting of the vascular tissue and the large bundle sheath cells. These thick-walled bundle sheath cells do not have air spaces between them, and a C_4 plant leaf is really composed of rows of these cylinders. These cylinders, which make up at least half the volume of the leaf, provide a small surface area relative to volume. While it has not been proved, this geometry should minimize evaporative surfaces. It is known that transpiration rates in some C_4 grasses and C_4 species of *Atriplex* are considerably less than transpiration rates in C_3 grasses and C_3 species of *Atriplex* (31, 100). The surrounding mesophyll cells increase this favorable surface/volume ratio, although the intracellular spaces between adjoining mesophyll cells increase this ratio while at the same time permitting more efficient gas diffusion. The evolution of an efficient carbon-trapping system in the periphery of this cylinder results in rapid accumulation of dry matter and low water loss. This ability to grow rapidly, which is not generally shared by succulent plants, permits C_4 plants to compete successfully with mesophytes.

While most attention has been directed towards the relationship of C_4 plant leaf anatomy with carbon metabolism, it should be realized that any benefits in cutting down on photorespiratory CO_2 loss as a result of anatomy are very possibly secondary in terms of selective pressure. The major problem facing aerial regions of terrestrial plants is dessication, and it makes considerable sense to focus one's attention on adaptations for water retention when dealing with xerophytic plants. With this stricture in mind, it is reasonable to suppose that not only is the carbon-fixation mechanism of C$_4$ plants a variation upon a succulent theme, but that its specialized leaf anatomy is also a variation on a well-known succulent theme.

The similarity between carbon-fixation mechanisms in CAM plants and C$_4$ plants brings up the question of the basic significance of β-carboxylation in both types of plants. The CAM plants can fix CO$_2$ in the dark into C$_4$ acids, and they can fix CO$_2$ in the light into the same products (6). Winter (114) has shown that *Mesembryan-themum crystalinum* plants have CAM when subjected to NaCl, but are C$_3$ when not treated with NaCl. It is also known that malic acid synthesis can be greatly stimulated by subjecting barley roots to various levels of potassium (61). The latter phenomenon is interpreted as cation-induced anion synthesis. It is well known that both CAM and C$_4$ plants are frequently halophytes. A high concentration of cations is common in xerophytic environments, and higher plants can absorb large amounts of cations such as sodium and potassium. Terrestrial plants frequently maintain cation-anion equivalency with organic acids (27). Not only do C$_4$ plants accumulate sodium, but it has been reported as a required micronutrient (22). It is possible, therefore, that β-carboxylation was originally an adaptation for synthesis of anions to counterbalance the accumulation of cations resulting from existence in a saline environment. The C$_4$ plants apparently evolved on tropical savannas, river plains, and arid valleys where rainy seasons alternated with periods of extreme aridity, and a high tolerance for these saline environments would be necessary.

Accumulation of cations would most likely be localized in the tissue next to the vascular tissue, and it is possible that there is a relation between the large succulent-like bundle sheath cells and ion accumulation (62). If this were true, the purported transport of malate from the mesophyll cells to the bundle sheath cells could really be an anion pump rather than a carbon pump. In this scheme, the rather minor development of an enzyme system to regenerate phosphoenolpyruvate would result in C$_4$ photosynthesis.

The polyphyletic origin of C$_4$ plants provides a fascinating example of the convergence of morphological and biochemical features. It has been shown above that these features can be considered form and functional relatives of those observed in CAM plants. Both groups of plants have obviously adapted to aridity. Stebbins (104) has stressed the role that aridity can play in promoting rapid plant evolution, and an extremely provocative elaboration of this theme has been provided by Axel-rod (7). He describes conditions which might well have led to the evolution within diverse taxa of plants which we now associate with CAM and with C$_4$ photosynthesis.

The focus on photosynthesis in C$_4$ plants has been productive, but it is time to realize that plants do other things besides photosynthesize, and that the primary adaptations of C$_4$ plants were in response to selective pressures prevalent in xeric and saline environments. The evolution of structural and functional adaptations to these environments were very possibly pre-adaptive with respect to the evolution of efficient methods for assimilating and retaining carbon. This realization will make the study of structure and function in C_4 plants a far more interesting and rewarding endeavor.

ACKNOWLEDGMENTS

The author's research referred to in this review was largely supported by the National Science Foundation, and the preparation of the review was aided by NSF Grant GB–38672. Support was also provided by Tate & Lyle, Ltd. I am grateful to Ian Price, Barbara Brown, and the U.C. Berkeley Electron Microscope Laboratory for aid in preparing the illustrations.

Literature Cited

1. Allaway, W. G. 1973. *Planta* 11:63–70
2. Allaway, W. G., Setterfield, G. 1972. *Can. J. Bot.* 5:1405–13
3. Andersen, J. M., Boardman, N. K., Spencer, D. 1971. *Biochim. Biophys. Acta* 245:253–58
4. Andersen, J. M., Woo, K. C., Boardman, N. K. 1971. *Biochim. Biophys. Acta* 245:398–408
5. Andersen, K. S., Bain, J. M., Bishop, D. G., Smillie, R. 1972. *Plant Physiol.* 49:461–66
6. Avadhani, P., Osmond, C. B., Tan, K. 1971. See Ref. 49, 288–93
7. Axelrod, D. 1972. *Am. Natur.* 106: 311–20
8. Baldry, C. W., Bucke, C., Coombs, J., Gross, D. 1970. *Planta* 94:107–23
9. Bassham, J. A. 1973. *Soc. Exp. Biol.* 27:461–83
10. Bazzaz, M. K., Govindjee 1973. *Plant Physiol.* 52:257–62
11. Bishop, D. G., Andersen, K. S., Smillie, R. M. 1972. *Plant Physiol.* 49: 467–70
12. Berry, J. A., Downton, W. J. S., Tregunna, E. B. 1970. *Can. J. Bot.* 48: 777–86
13. Bird, I. F., Cornelius, M. J., Dyer, T. A., Keys, A. J. 1973. *J. Exp. Bot.* 24:211–15
14. Bisalputra, T., Downton, W. J. S., Tregunna, E. B. 1969. *Can. J. Bot.* 47:15–21
15. Bjorkman, O., Gauhl, E. 1969. *Planta* 88:197–203
16. Bjorkman, O., Nobs, M., Berry, J. 1971. *Carnegie Inst. Washington Yearb.* 70:507–11
17. Black, C. C. 1971. *Advan. Ecol. Res.* 7:87–113
18. Black, C. C. 1973. *Ann. Rev. Plant Physiol.* 24:253–86
19. Black, C. C., Mollenhauer, H. H. 1971. *Plant Physiol.* 47:15–23
20. Black, R. F. 1954. *Aust. J. Bot.* 2:269–86
21. Brangeon, J. 1973. *J. Microsc.* 16: 233–42
22. Brownell, P. F., Crossland, C. J. 1972. *Plant Physiol.* 40:794–97
23. Brown, W. 1958. *Bot. Gaz.* 119: 170–78
24. Buchanan, B. B., Schurmann, P. 1972. *FEBS Lett.* 23:157–59
25. Bucke, C., Long, S. P. 1971. *Planta* 99:199–210
26. Bull, T. A. 1969. *Crop Sci.* 9:726–29
27. Campbell, L. C., Pitman, M. G. 1971. *Salinity and Water Use*, ed. T. Talaman, J. R. Philip, 207–24. London: Macmillan
27a. Carolin, R., Jacobs, S., Vesk, M. 1973. *Bot. J. Linn. Soc.* 66:259–75
27b. Coombs, J., Ed. 1968. *Photosynthesis in Sugar Cane.* Proc. Int. Symp. London: Tate & Lyle. 81 pp.
28. Coombs, J., Baldry, C. W., Brown, J. E. 1973. *Planta* 110:121–29
29. Coombs, J., Baldry, C. W., Bucke, C. 1973. *Planta* 110:95–107
30. Crookston, R., Moss, D. 1970. *Plant Physiol.* 56:564–67
31. Downes, R. W. 1969. *Planta* 88:26–73
32. Downton, W. 1970. *Can. J. Bot.* 48:1795–1800
33. Downton, W. 1971. See Ref. 49, 419–25
33a. Downton, W., Berry, J., Tregunna, E. 1970. *Z. Pflanzenphysiol.* 63:194–98
34. Downton, W., Bisalputra, T., Tregunna, E. 1969. *Can. J. Bot.* 47:915–19
35. Downton, W., Pyliotis, N. 1971. *Can. J. Bot.* 49:179–82

36. Downton, W., Tregunna, E. 1968. *Can. J. Bot.* 46:207–15

37. Edwards, G., Black, C. 1971. See Ref. 49, 158–68

38. Elkin, L. 1973. *Bundle sheath and mesophyll chloroplasts of C$_4$ plants: An in situ comparison of their room temperature fluorescence.* PhD thesis. Univ. California, Berkeley. 565 pp.

39. El-Sharkawy, M., Hesketh, J. 1965. *Crop Sci.* 5:417–21

40. Esau, K. 1965. *Plant Anatomy.* New York: Wiley. 878 pp.

41. Faludi-Daniel, A., Dmeter, S., Garay, A. 1973. *Plant Physiol.* 52:54–56

42. Frederick, S., Newcomb, E. H. 1971. *Planta* 96:152–74

43. Gibbs, M., Latzko, E., O'Neal, D., Hew, C. S. 1970. *Biochem. Biophys. Res. Commun.* 40:1356–61

44. Goodchild, D. 1971. See Ref. 49, 426–27

45. Gracen, V., Hilliard, J., Brown, R., West, S. 1972. *Planta* 107:189–204

46. Haapala, H. 1969. *Planta* 86:259–66

47. Haberlandt, B. 1904. *Physiologische Pflanzenanatomie.* Leipzig: Engelmann. 616 pp.

48. Habeshaw, D. 1973. *Planta* 110: 213–26

49. Hatch, M. D., Osmond, C. B., Slayter, R. O., Eds. 1971. *Photosynthesis and Photorespiration.* New York: Wiley-Interscience. 565 pp.

50. Hatch, M. D., Slack, C. R. 1966. *Biochem. J.* 101:103–11

51. Hatch, M. D., Slack, C. R. 1970. *Ann. Rev. Plant Physiol.* 21:141–62

52. Hatch, M. D., Slack, C. R., Johnson, H. 1967. *Biochem. J.* 102:417–22

53. Hesketh, J. D., Baker, D. N. 1970. *Prediction and Measurement of Photosynthetic Productivity.* Wageningen: Centre Agr. Publ. Doc.

54. Hilliard, J. H., Gracen, V. E., West, S. H. 1971. *Planta* 97:93–105

55. Hilliard, J. H., West, S. H. 1970. *Science* 168:494–96

56. Hilliard, J. H., West, S. H. 1971. *Planta* 99:352–56

57. Hodge, A., McLean, J., Mercer, F. 1955. *Biophys. Biochem. Cytol.* 1:605–14

58. Hofstra, G., Nelson, C. D. 1969. *Planta* 103–12

59. Huang, A. H. C., Beevers, H. 1972. *Plant Physiol.* 50:242–48

60. Huber, W., Rongine de Fekete, M. A., Ziegler, H. 1969. *Planta* 87:360–64

61. Jacobson, L., Ordin, L. 1965. *Plant Physiol.* 40:70–75

62. Jennings, D. H. *New Phytol.* 67:899–911

63. Johnson, H. S., Hatch, M. D. 1968. *Phytochemistry* 7:375–80

64. Johnson, M. C., Brown, W. V. 1973. *Am. J. Bot.* 60:727–35

65. Johnson, M. D. 1964. *An electron microscope study of the photosynthetic apparatus in plants, with special reference to the Gramineae.* PhD thesis. Univ. Texas, Austin. 259 pp.

66. Karpilov, Yu. S. 1970. *Kazakhstan Agr. Inst.* 4:21

67. Kaufman, P. B., Petering, L., Yocum, C., Baic, D. 1970. *Am. J. Bot.* 57:33–49

68. Kay, W., Kornberg, H. L. 1971. *Eur. J. Biochem.* 18:274–81

69. Kennedy, R., Laetsch, W. 1973. *Planta*

69a. Kennedy, R., Laetsch, W. M. 1974. *Science.* In press

70. Kortschak, H. P., Hartt, C. E., Burr, G. O. 1954–1959. *Ann. Rep. Hawaii. Sugar Plant. Assoc.*

71. Kortschak, H. P., Hartt, C. E., Burr, G. O. 1957. *Proc. Hawaii. Acad. Sci.* Honolulu: Univ. Hawaii

72. Kortschak, H. P., Hartt, C. E., Burr, G. O. 1965. *Plant Physiol.* 40:209–13

73. Laetsch, W. M. 1968. See Ref. 27a, 415

74. Laetsch, W. M. 1968. *Am. J. Bot.* 55:875–83

75. Laetsch, W. M. 1969. *Progr. Photosyn. Res.* 1:36–46

76. Laetsch, W. M. 1969. *Sci. Progr. Oxford* 57:323–51

77. Laetsch, W. M. 1971. See Ref. 49, 323–49

77a. Laetsch, W. M., Kortschak, H. P. 1972. *Plant Physiol.* 49:1021–23

78. Laetsch, W. M., Price, I. 1969. *Plant Physiol.* 56:77–87

79. Laetsch, W. M., Stetler, D. A., Vlitos, A. J. 1966. *Z. Pflanzenphysiol.* 54: 472–74

80. Liu, A. Y., Black, C. 1972. *Arch. Biochem. Biophys.* 149:269–80

81. Lyttleton, J. 1971. See Ref. 49, 239–39

81a. Lyttleton, J., Ballantine, J., Forde, B. 1971. In *Autonomy and Biogenesis of Mitochondria and Chloroplasts,* ed. N. K. Boardman, A. Linnane, R. Smillie, 447–52. New York: Elsevier. 511 pp.

82. Meyer, F. J. 1962. *Das Trophische Parenchym.* Berlin: Befuder Borntaeger

83. Moser, H. 1934. *Beih. Bot. Zentr.* 52:378–88
84. Moss, D. N., Rasmussen, H. P. 1969. *Plant Physiol.* 44:1063–68
85. Nagy, A. H., Passery, M., Faludi-Daniel, A. 1971. *Plant Physiol.* 24:301–5
85a. Neales, T., Incoll, L. 1968. *Bot. Rev.* 34:107–25
86. O'Brien, T. P., Carr, D. J. 1970. *Aust. J. Biol. Sci.* 23:275–87
87. O'Neal, D., Hew, C., Latzko, E., Gibbs, M. 1972. *Plant Physiol.* 49:607–14
88. Osmond, C. B., Troughton, J. H., Goodchild, D. J. 1969. *Z. Pflanzenphysiol.* 61:218–37
89. Pallas, J. E., Mollenhauer, H. H. 1972. *Am. J. Bot.* 59:504–14
90. Park, R. B., Pfeifhofer, A. O. 1969. *J. Cell Sci.* 5:299–311
91. Poincelot, R. P. 1972. *Plant Physiol.* 50:336–49
92. Polya, G. M., Osmond, C. B. 1972. *Plant Physiol.* 49:267–79
93. Rhoades, M. M., Carvalho, A. 1944. *Bull. Torrey Bot. Club* 71:335–46
94. Rosado-Alberio, J., Weier, T., Stocking, C. 1968. *Plant Physiol.* 43:1325–31
95. Schoch, E., Dramer, D. 1971. *Planta* 101:51–66
96. Schwender, S. 1890. *Sb. Preuss. Akad. Wiss. Phys-Math. Kl.* 22:405–26
97. Shumway, L. K., Weier, T. 1967. *Am. J. Bot.* 54:773–80
98. Silaeva, A. M. 1966. *Fiziol. Rast.* 13:623–27
99. Slack, C. R. 1969. *Phytochemistry* 8:1387–91
100. Slatyer, R. O. 1970. *Planta* 93:175–89
101. Smith, B. N., Brown, W. V. 1973. *Am. J. Bot.* 60:505–13
102. Smith, F. A. 1971. See Ref. 49, 302–7
103. Smillie, R. M., Andersen, K. S., Tobin, N. F., Entsch, B., Bishop, D. G. 1972. *Plant Physiol.* 49:471–75
104. Stebbins, G. L. 1952. *Am. Natur.* 86:33–44
106. Taylor, A., Craig, A. S. 1971. *Plant Physiol.* 47:719–25
107. Tolbert, N. E. 1971. *Ann. Rev. Plant Physiol.* 22:45–74
108. Tregunna, E. B., Smith, B. M., Berry, J. A., Downton, S. 1970. *Can. J. Bot.* 48:1209–14
109. Usuda, H., Kanai, R., Takeuchi, M. 1971. *Plant Cell Physiol.* 12:917–30
110. Van Steveninck, M. E., Goldney, D. C., Van Steveninck, R. F. M. 1972. *Z. Pflanzenphysiol.* 67:155–60
111. Walker, D. A. 1970. *Ann. Rev. Biochem.* 39:389–428
111a. Wardlaw, I. 1968. *Bot. Rev.* 34:79–105
112. Welkie, G. W., Caldwell, M. 1970. *Can. J. Bot.* 48:2135–46
113. West, K. R. 1970. *The Biology of Atriplex,* ed. R. Jones. 11–15. Canberra, Aust.: CSIRO. 128 pp.
114. Winter, K. 1973. *Planta* 109:135–45
115. Woo, K. C. et al 1970. *Proc. Nat. Acad. Sci. USA* 67:18–25
116. Zelitch, I. 1971. *Photosynthesis, Photorespiration and Plant Productivity.* New York: Academic. 347 pp.

Ann. Rev. Plant Physiol. 1974. 25:53–79

UPTAKE MECHANISMS: INORGANIC AND ORGANIC

❖7562

Per Nissen

Botanical Laboratory, University of Bergen, Bergen, Norway

CONTENTS

INTRODUCTION 53
UPTAKE OF INORGANIC SOLUTES 54
    Phosphate and Sulfate. 54
    Mineral Cations, Chloride, and Boric Acid 57
    Diffusion Across the Plasmalemma? 61
    Multiphasic Series Model 62
    Complications and Limitations 63
        Diffusion in unstirred layer 63
        Variation along roots 64
        Microbial contamination 64
        Compartmentation and vesicles. 64
    Other Models and Interpretations. 65
    Experimental Factors and Phase Patterns 66
        Ca and phase patterns 66
        Counterions and phase patterns 66
        Aging and phase patterns 67
        Salt status and phase patterns. 68
        Long-term experiments and phase patterns 68
    ATPases and Binding Proteins 69
    Phase Transitions and Pattern Similarities. 71
UPTAKE OF ORGANIC SOLUTES 73
    Sugars. 73
    Amino Acids. 74
    Choline Sulfate 75

INTRODUCTION

The raison d'être for this review is the recognition of multiphasic mechanisms for uptake of sulfate and other inorganic ions by higher plants. The discussion is largely concerned with this development and some of its consequences and ramifications.

The concept of multiphasic uptake mechanisms has proved to be of particular value in resolving seemingly contradictory evidence for the parallel and the series models.

This restrictive approach seems permissible in view of the ubiquity of multiphasic uptake mechanisms and the recent availability of several excellent and comprehensive reviews. The point of departure for the present review is the discussion by Laties (99) of the series model. A recent review (100) incorporates the concept of multiphasic uptake mechanisms. The concept of dual mechanisms and the parallel model have been presented and discussed by Epstein (48, 52, 53). These and other kinetic models are also discussed in a recent book by Lüttge (114). Ion uptake in algae and higher plants has been reviewed by MacRobbie (127) and by Higinbotham (75). Recent reviews in this series include discussions of fluxes and compartmentation in giant algal cells and higher plant tissues (129), ion transport in cells of higher plants (2), translocation of inorganic solutes (102), salt transport and salinity (166), electropotentials of plant cells (76), and phosphate pools, transport, and availability (15). Aspects of transport and mineral metabolism have been reviewed yearly by Marschner (134–136). A recent symposium volume (3) contains a variety of papers on ion transport in plants.

The uptake of organic solutes by higher plants has received relatively slight attention. The discussion will center on the few systems where kinetic data are available. The mechanisms are in part multiphasic, in part not.

This review is to a large degree concerned with the results of a reanalysis of concentration-dependence data. Original data have preferably been used. If not available, the data have been estimated by careful measuring of points in published figures. A Fortran program in which the sum of squares of deviations in log v is minimized (cf 29, 30) has been used to avoid the weighting errors associated with the linear transformations of the Michaelis-Menten equation. For convenience the data have been plotted in the double reciprocal form (Lineweaver-Burk plot), but the choice of transformation is irrelevant. Bias and errors are introduced mainly in the choice of transition points. These are usually self-evident in the case of detailed and precise data (cf Figures 1, 2, and 4). Adjacent phases have been tested for fit to one or two phases. In the absence of other data, phases are not normally taken to be separate unless this provides a significantly better fit. Imprecise data, data representing the sum of two Michaelis-Menten terms, or data not obeying Michaelis-Menten kinetics will not give a good fit.

UPTAKE OF INORGANIC SOLUTES

Phosphate and Sulfate

Multiphasic uptake mechanisms were first recognized in a detailed study of uptake vs concentration in roots and leaf slices of barley (142). Uptake of sulfate in the range 10^{-5}–2.5×10^{-4} M can usually be represented by three phases (Figure 1). (The transition between phases 1 and 2 was in this particular experiment accompanied by a "jump.") A series of experiments in the range 10^{-9}–2.5×10^{-1} M yielded eight phases for roots and five phases for leaf slices. The following conclusions were drawn (142):

Table 2 Multiphasic uptake of mineral cations, chloride, and boric acid

Solute	Plant species and organ	Reference	Concentration range (M)[a]	Number of phases	Biphasic kinetics in low range[b]
K+	Barley, roots	Epstein et al (55, cf 143)	$2 \times 10^{-6} - 10^{-2}$	4	ns
K+	Barley, roots	Epstein & Rains (54, cf 146)	$10^{-3} - 5 \times 10^{-2}$	6	
K+	Barley, roots	Hiatt (71, cf 146)	$5 \times 10^{-6} - 10^{-2}$	4	**
K+	Barley, roots	Hiatt (72, cf 146)	$5 \times 10^{-6} - 5 \times 10^{-2}$	5	*
K+	Barley, roots	Hiatt (74, cf 146)	$10^{-5} - 2 \times 10^{-4}$	2	ns **
K+	Corn, roots	Lüttge & Laties (117, cf 144)	$10^{-5} - 4 \times 10^{-2}$	4	ns
K+	Corn, roots	Hiatt (73, cf 146)	$10^{-5} - 10^{-4}$	2	***
K+	Corn, leaf tissue	Smith & Epstein (180, cf 146)	$2 \times 10^{-6} - 2 \times 10^{-4}$	2	***
K+	Tall wheatgrass, roots	Elzam & Epstein (44, cf 146) Epstein (50, cf 146)	$5 \times 10^{-6} - 2 \times 10^{-4}$	2	* ns *
K+	Tall wheatgrass, roots	Elzam & Epstein (44, cf 146)	$5 \times 10^{-4} - 5 \times 10^{-2}$		
K+	Horse bean, roots	Salsac (178, cf 146)	$10^{-3} - 10^{-1}$	7	ni
K+	Red beet, discs	Osmond & Laties (151, cf 146)	$2 \times 10^{-3} - 5 \times 10^{-2}$	5	ns
K+	Red beet, discs	Osmond & Laties (152, cf 146)	$4 \times 10^{-5} - 5 \times 10^{-2}$	2	**
K+	Bean, stem tissue (fresh)	Rains (165, cf 146)	$2 \times 10^{-5} - 5 \times 10^{-2}$	3, 4	ni
K+	Avicennia marina, leaf tissue	Rains & Epstein (169, cf 146)	$10^{-4} - 1.5 \times 10^{-3}$	4	ni
K+	Avicennia marina, leaf tissue	Rains & Epstein (169, cf 146)	$2 \times 10^{-5} - 5 \times 10^{-2}$	2	ni
K+	Elodea densa, leaves	Jeschke (82, 83, cf 146)	$10^{-5} - 3 \times 10^{-2}$	3	
K+	Mnium cuspidatum, branches	Lüttge & Bauer (115, cf 146)	$7.5 \times 10^{-5} - 10^{-2}$	3, 4	

(i) The uptake of sulfate can be described by a single, multiphasic isotherm. (ii) The phases are separated by sharply defined inflection points. (iii) Each phase obeys Michaelis-Menten kinetics. (iv) The kinetic constants increase in a fairly regular manner, the increases in both V_{max} and K_m being small at low to intermediate concentrations of sulfate. (v) Only one phase functions at any one concentration. [The last conclusion] is evident from the good agreement with Michaelis-Menten kinetics and from the finding that extrapolation and subtraction of any one phase from the adjacent phases results in meaningless double reciprocal plots, often with negative values for V_{max}.

These kinetics were taken to indicate mediation by a single structure (site, carrier) which changes characteristics at certain discrete external concentrations of sulfate. The assertion (53) that the data reflect dual mechanisms of sulfate uptake is incorrect. The data cannot be resolved into two isotherms and are incompatible with the dual concept. The description of the highest phases in terms of Michaelis-Menten kinetics seems valid and meaningful despite claims to the contrary (appendix in 146).

A comprehensive reanalysis (145) of concentration-dependence data for uptake of phosphate and sulfate yielded regular and remarkably similar multiphasic patterns in a variety of plants and tissues (cf Table 1). For concentrations up to 5 $\times$ 10^{-2} M, five phases are thus evident in several experiments. The first transition,

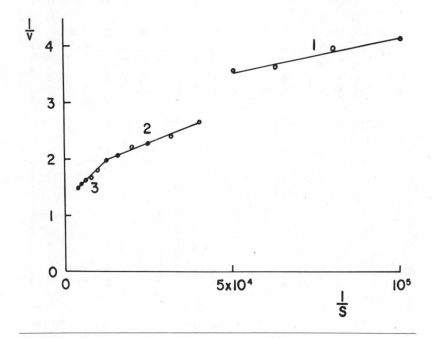

Figure 1 Double reciprocal plot for uptake of sulfate by barley roots in the range $10^{-5} - 2.5 \times 10^{-4}$ M. Redrawn from Figure 5B in (142).

Table 1 Multiphasic uptake of phosphate and sulfate

Solute	Plant species and organ	Reference	Concentration range (M)	Number of phases
$H_2PO_4^-$	Barley, roots	Barber (10, cf 145)	$2 \times 10^{-6} - 5 \times 10^{-2}$	5
$H_2PO_4^-$	Corn, roots	Carter & Lathwell (26, cf 145)	$8.6 \times 10^{-7} - 2.56 \times 10^{-4}$	2
$H_2PO_4^-$	Corn, roots	Weigl (189, cf 145)	$2.5 \times 10^{-3} - 7.25 \times 10^{-2}$	3
$H_2PO_4^-$	Subterranean clover, roots	Edwards (40, cf 145)	$5 \times 10^{-8} - 10^{-3}$	3
$H_2PO_4^-$	Wheat, seedlings	Edwards (41, cf 144)	$10^{-7} - 5 \times 10^{-2}$	5
$H_2PO_4^-$	Stylosanthes humilis, roots	Andrew (4, cf 145)	$10^{-6} - 5 \times 10^{-4}$	2
$H_2PO_4^-$	Phaseolus lathyroides, roots	Andrew (4, cf 145)	$10^{-6} - 5 \times 10^{-4}$	2
$H_2PO_4^-$	Desmodium uncinatum, roots	Andrew (4, cf 145)	$10^{-6} - 5 \times 10^{-4}$	3
$H_2PO_4^-$	Lucern, roots	Andrew (4, cf 145)	$10^{-6} - 5 \times 10^{-4}$	2
$H_2PO_4^-$	Barley, roots	Andrew (4, cf 145)	$10^{-6} - 5 \times 10^{-4}$	3
$H_2PO_4^-$	Celery, aged vascular bundles	Bieleski (14, cf 145)	$10^{-6} - 10^{-1}$	3
$H_2PO_4^-$	Elodea densa, leaves	Grünsfelder (66, cf 145)	$5 \times 10^{-6} - 5 \times 10^{-2}$	4, 5
$H_2PO_4^-$	Elodea densa, leaves	Grünsfelder (66, cf 145)	$10^{-3} - 10^{-1}$	4
$H_2PO_4^-$	Yeast (Saccharomyces cerevisiae)	Leggett (104, cf 145)	$2 \times 10^{-6} - 5 \times 10^{-4}$	2
$H_2PO_4^-$	Chlorella sp.	Jeanjean et al (81, cf 145)	$1.25 \times 10^{-6} - 2 \times 10^{-3}$	3
SO_4^{2-}	Barley, roots	Nissen (142)	$10^{-9} - 2.5 \times 10^{-1}$	8
SO_4^{2-}	Barley, leaf slices	Nissen (142)	$10^{-9} - 2.5 \times 10^{-1}$	5
SO_4^{2-}	Corn, roots	Berlier et al (13, cf 145)	$5 \times 10^{-5} - 10^{-2}$	3
SO_4^{2-}	Limnophila gratioloides, leaves	Penth & Weigl (155, cf 145)	$10^{-5} - 5 \times 10^{-2}$	5

between phases 1 and 2, almost invariably occurs between 10^{-5} M and 10^{-4} M.
for phosphate uptake by aged potato slices (39) can similarly be represented by
phases, probably phases 2–5, in the range $5 \times 10^{-5} - 2 \times 10^{-2}$ M. Most of the
in Table 1 were originally represented as the sum of two isotherms, but the existe
of dual mechanisms can be ruled out whenever sufficiently detailed and precise
are available. Extrapolation and subtraction of any one phase from the adja
phases result as before (142) in noninterpretable double reciprocal plots.

Mineral Cations, Chloride, and Boric Acid

A reanalysis (146) of data for alkali cations, metal ions (few data available), chlori
and boric acid has also been carried out (cf Table 2). Multiphasic isotherms are ag
obtained, but the patterns are not as regular as for phosphate and sulfate. Upta
in the low concentration range (below $5 \times 10^{-4} - 10^{-3}$ M) is often biphasic as sho
for boric acid in Figure 2. The kinetic constants for phase 2 are lower than th
for phase 1, and this may create a misleading impression of clearly separated di
uptake mechanisms.

The existence of two phases in the low concentration range is also, with excepti
of Na^+, the rule for alkali cations and Cl^- (143, 144, 146; Table 2). The anoma
noted for K^+ but not for Na^+ uptake (73, 74) may be caused by anomalies in t
time course for uptake by phase 2. The lowering of kinetic constants upon transiti
to a higher phase is, in a few experiments, repeated once or twice at higher conce
trations (146).

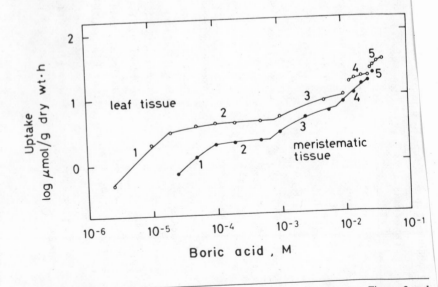

Figure 2 Uptake of boric acid by leaf and meristematic tissue of sugar cane. Figures 2 and 4 in (21) as reanalyzed in (146). Reproduced by permission of *Physiologia Plantarum*.

Rb^+	Barley, roots	Jackman (79, cf 146)	$2 \times 10^{-6} - 3.5 \times 10^{-2}$	3	**
Rb^+	Barley, roots	Bange & Meijer (7, cf 146)	$10^{-5} - 5 \times 10^{-4}$	2	ns ***
Rb^+	Barley, roots	Oertli (149, cf 146)	$10^{-5} - 3 \times 10^{-2}$	3	ni
Rb^+	Barley, roots	Hiatt (74, cf 146)	$10^{-5} - 2 \times 10^{-4}$	1, 2	*
Rb^+	Corn, roots	Torii & Laties (185, cf 144)	$5 \times 10^{-5} - 10^{-2}$	5	ns
Rb^+	Ryegrass, roots	Jackman (79, cf 146)	$3 \times 10^{-6} - 1.7 \times 10^{-2}$	2	ni
Rb^+	Mung bean, roots	Jackman (79, cf 146)	$2 \times 10^{-6} - 5 \times 10^{-2}$	3	ns
Rb^+	Subterranean clover, roots	Jackman (79, cf 146)	$3 \times 10^{-6} - 1.7 \times 10^{-2}$	3	ns
Rb^+	*Elodea densa*, leaves	Jeschke (83, cf 146)	$\sim 10^{-7} - 5 \times 10^{-2}$	4	ns
Rb^+	*Chlorella pyrenoidosa*	Kannan (90, cf 146)	$10^{-5} - 5 \times 10^{-2}$	2, 4	ni
Cs^+	Barley, roots	Bange & Overstreet (8, cf 146)	$2.5 \times 10^{-6} - 7.5 \times 10^{-2}$	4	**
Cs^+	Barley, roots	Bange & Meijer (7, cf 146)	$10^{-5} - 5 \times 10^{-4}$	2	***
Na^+	Barley, roots	Epstein & Rains (54, cf 146)	$10^{-3} - 5 \times 10^{-2}$	5	
Na^+	Barley, roots	Rains & Epstein (167, cf 146)	$5 \times 10^{-6} - 5 \times 10^{-2}$	4	ni
Na^+	Barley, roots	Rains & Epstein (168, cf 146)	$10^{-3} - 5 \times 10^{-2}$	5	
Na^+	Bean, stem tissue (fresh)	Rains (165, cf 146)	$2 \times 10^{-5} - 5 \times 10^{-2}$	3	ni
NH_4^+	Rice, roots	Fried et al (62, cf 146)	$2.5 \times 10^{-6} - 5 \times 10^{-3}$	4	*
NH_4^+	Durum wheat, roots	Picciurro et al (159, cf 146)	$7 \times 10^{-7} - 10^{-2}$	3	*
Ca^{2+}	Corn, roots	Maas (121, cf 146)	$10^{-5} - 10^{-3}$	1	ni
Mg^{2+}	Corn, roots	Maas & Ogata (123, cf 146)	$10^{-5} - 10^{-2}$	2, 3	**
Mn^{2+}	Barley, roots	Maas et al (122, cf 146)	$10^{-6} - 10^{-2}$	3	ns
Mn^{2+}	Sugar cane, leaf tissue	Bowen (23, cf 146)	$10^{-5} - 5 \times 10^{-3}$	2	***

Table 2 (Continued)

Solute	Plant species and organ	Reference	Concentration range (M)[a]	Number of phases	Biphasic kinetics in low range[b]
Zn^{2+}	Sugar cane, leaf tissue	Bowen (23, cf 146)	$10^{-5} - 2 \times 10^{-4}$	2	ns
Cu^{2+}	Sugar cane, leaf tissue	Bowen (23, cf 146)	$10^{-5} - 2 \times 10^{-4}$	2	* or **
Cl^-	Barley, roots	Elzam et al (45, cf 144)	$5 \times 10^{-6} - 5 \times 10^{-2}$	7	**
Cl^-	Barley, roots	Elzam & Epstein (43, cf 146)	$5 \times 10^{-6} - 2 \times 10^{-4}$	2	ns *
Cl^-	Barley, roots	Hiatt (71, 72, cf 146)	$5 \times 10^{-6} - 5 \times 10^{-2}$	4	ns
Cl^-	Corn, roots	Torii & Laties (185, cf 143, 146)	$2 \times 10^{-5} - 5 \times 10^{-2}$	5 – 7	ns ***
Cl^-	Corn, roots	Maas (121, cf 146), Maas & Ogata (123, cf 146)	$2 \times 10^{-5} - 2 \times 10^{-2}$	4	ns
Cl^-	Tall wheatgrass, roots	Elzam & Epstein (44, cf 146), Epstein (50, cf 146)	$5 \times 10^{-6} - 2 \times 10^{-4}$	2	*
Cl^-	Tall wheatgrass, roots	Elzam & Epstein (44, cf 146)	$5 \times 10^{-4} - 5 \times 10^{-2}$	7	
Cl^-	Wheat, leaf tissue	MacDonald & Macklon (124, cf 146)	$2.5 \times 10^{-3} - 4 \times 10^{-2}$	2	
Cl^-	Red beet, discs	Osmond & Laties (151, cf 146)	$2 \times 10^{-3} - 5 \times 10^{-2}$	2	
Cl^-	Carrot, xylem tissue	Lüttge et al (116, cf 146)	$10^{-3} - 8 \times 10^{-2}$	2	
H_3BO_3	Sugar cane, leaf tissue	Bowen (21, cf 146)	$2.5 \times 10^{-6} - 4.2 \times 10^{-2}$	5	***
H_3BO_3	Sugar cane, meristematic tissue	Bowen (21, cf 146)	$2.5 \times 10^{-5} - 3 \times 10^{-2}$	5	ns or *

[a]The range in which the phases have been resolved.

[b]ni = not indicated; ns = not significant (two phases indicated but $P > 0.05$; * = $0.01 < P \leqslant 0.05$, ** = $0.001 < P \leqslant 0.01$, *** = $P \leqslant 0.001$.

The kinetics of the dual and the multiphasic concepts are fundamentally different, and a choice can be made wherever sufficiently detailed and precise data are available (146). Two or more uptake mechanisms operating simultaneously should give continuously curved double reciprocal plots, whereas a series of straight lines is predicted for a single mechanism undergoing all-or-none transitions. The classical data of Epstein, Rains & Elzam (55), taken to indicate dual mechanisms for K^+ uptake by barley roots, have been shown to be better represented by a single, multiphasic isotherm (143). Given sufficiently detailed data, the kinetics can in no case be reasonably represented as the sum of two or more isotherms. Instead the data yield remarkably precise multiphasic isotherms *without* correction for "mechanism 1."

Discontinuous transitions and multiphasic isotherms are also revealed upon reanalysis (146) of experiments with competitive inhibitors (47, 123, 168, 180, 190). It has been claimed (53, 190) that uptake can be dissected into two components representing mechanisms 1 and 2 through studies of inhibition of Na^+ uptake by K^+ and vice versa. This interpretation cannot be correct since straightforward concentration-dependence data cannot be dissected into two components. It seems that the data reflect multiphasic rather than dual mechanisms (146). To be unequivocal, specificity studies of this type must be carried out in greater detail since several phases are involved.

The data for boron uptake were originally (21, 22) taken to represent uptake of the tetrahedral $B(OH)_4^-$ ion. Reanalysis (146) strongly indicates, however, that boric acid, $B(OH)_3$, by far the most predominant species, is being taken up. Oertli and co-workers (16, 150) conclude that boron rapidly diffuses into roots and leaves of barley and equilibrates with the external solution, whereas Bowen (21, 25) finds evidence for active uptake in sugar cane tissue. Uptake occurs against a concentration gradient at low external concentrations of boric acid; at high concentrations the plasmalemma is an apparent barrier to free diffusion. The differing viewpoints can partly be ascribed to differences in methodology, but the existence of a multiphasic mechanism for uptake of boric acid seems clear (Figure 2).

Diffusion Across the Plasmalemma?

An appreciable diffusive component across the plasmalemma was originally believed to be required for the tonoplast to become rate limiting (cf 99, 114). Strategies for measuring uptake across the plasmalemma alone include the use of relatively non-vacuolated root tips (185), bypassing of vacuoles by studies of long-distance transport (117), and use of short uptake and still shorter wash periods (36). The data do not, however, indicate a separate diffusive component above 10^{-3} M but rather a single, multiphasic mechanism.

Uptake of Cl^- and Rb^+ by both tips and proximal sections of corn roots (185) can be represented by precise and qualitatively similar multiphasic isotherms (143, 144, 146; Table 2). Isotherms for uptake and long-distance transport of K^+ in corn seedlings (117) are also multiphasic and not indicative of diffusion (143, 144). The same is true for phosphate uptake and long-distance transport in wheat seedlings

(41, cf 144). Studies involving short uptake and wash periods (36) are not sufficiently precise for the phases to be resolved.

The precise multiphasic kinetics tend to support Epstein's view (53) that appreciable free diffusion across the plasmalemma does not normally occur, even at relatively high salt concentrations. The maximal contribution of a diffusive component cannot, however, be estimated from available data. The postulation of a single, multiphasic mechanism for uptake across the plasmalemma does not necessarily imply that uptake should be similarly "active" over the entire concentration range. The concentration gradient (concentration inside/concentration outside) will decrease with increasing external salt concentrations, and the energy requirements and sensitivity to metabolic inhibitors may well be lowered for the higher phases (145). The higher phases may acquire some characteristics of facilitated diffusion as the affinities of the ions for their carriers or sites are decreased (appendix in 146). Evidence for diffusive exchange of Cl$^-$ across the plasmalemma has been obtained (33, 36), but the data are not detailed enough for kinetic analysis.

Multiphasic Series Model

The concept of dual mechanisms of ion uptake is well known and widely accepted. The two mechanisms have variously been placed in parallel at the plasmalemma or in series at the plasmalemma and the tonoplast (Figure 3). The controversy regarding the parallel vs the series model stems, it seems, mainly from the incorrect acceptance of the dual concept. Reasons for rejecting the parallel model have been given above. The series model (99) is not tenable in its original form and has been

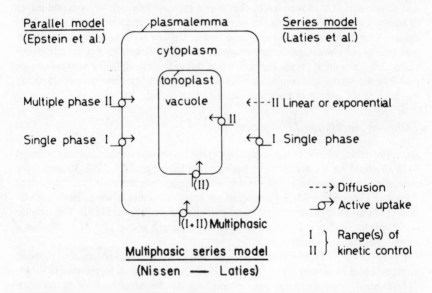

Figure 3 Localization of uptake mechanisms in vacuolated plant cells. Reproduced from (144) by permission of Academic Press.

supplanted by the multiphasic series model (100, 144), which involves a single, multiphasic mechanism at the plasmalemma and probably a similar mechanism at the tonoplast. Diffusion across the plasmalemma is neither required nor indicated.

There is no indication of a duality as implied in "mechanism 1" and "mechanism 2," and the use of these and similar terms should be abandoned. There is, furthermore, no fundamental distinction between the low and the high concentration range. The terms will, however, be retained in this review for reasons of comparison. The use of different concentration scales and the breaking of v vs S plots around 5×10^{-4} M are apt to be misleading. Logarithmic scales should be used.

Kinetic control may shift from the plasmalemma to the tonoplast at high salt concentrations and after filling of the cytoplasm. The values for V_{max} are distinctly higher for uptake across the plasmalemma than for tonoplast transport at high salt concentrations, and the plasmalemma does not restrain over-all uptake (143, 144, 146). Experiments with short-term vs long-term uptake of Cl⁻ by barley roots (36) indicate a change in control at about 10^{-2} M. Originally, tonoplast control was assumed in the range of mechanism 2, i.e. above 10^{-3} M. More detailed isotherms for long-term uptake above 10^{-2} M are needed to establish whether the tonoplast mechanism is multiphasic.

Complications and Limitations

The multiphasic series model seems consistent with all observations, but there may possibly be a few complications. Models of this type do also have certain inherent limitations.

DIFFUSION IN UNSTIRRED LAYER   Ion uptake from dilute solutions may, at least to some extent, be rate limited by diffusion in the unstirred layer around roots and other tissues. Polle & Jenny (164) found stirring to substantially increase Rb⁺ uptake by barley roots from a solution of 10^{-5} M RbCl, but not from a solution of about 10^{-4} M. The unstirred layer is presumably thinner with greater turbulence. At high pH, variations in Cl⁻ uptake with rates of aeration were likewise attributed to differences in stirring and to root-induced pH changes (80).

Jeschke & Simonis (85) found phosphate and sulfate uptake by leaves of *Elodea densa* to follow Michaelis-Menten kinetics in the low and intermediate concentration range. Activation energies and light stimulation tended to decrease below 10^{-6} M, and this was ascribed to rate limitation by diffusion in the unstirred layer. Active uptake was taken to be rate limiting at somewhat higher concentrations. Sulfate uptake by roots and leaf slices of barley from solutions of 10^{-7} M and 10^{-5} M K_2SO_4, however, was markedly and about equally inhibited by dinitrophenol (142).

Winne (191) has recently shown that the kinetics of carrier-mediated uptake systems will be distorted in the presence of an unstirred layer. Careful studies of phosphate (40, 41; cf 144, 145) and sulfate (142) uptake from dilute solutions (phase 1) do not indicate any deviations from Michaelis-Menten kinetics. Reanalysis of data for mineral cations, chloride, and boric acid (146) likewise reveals no kinetic evidence for an unstirred layer. Claims for rate limitation by diffusion in the unstirred layer should be supplemented by careful studies of uptake vs concentration.

VARIATION ALONG ROOTS Eshel & Waisel (56, 57) found marked variations in uptake of Na^+ and Rb^+ along corn roots and took this to imply the existence of different uptake mechanisms at various sites along the roots. Their call for caution should be heeded, but results obtained with entire roots are still very useful for characterizing uptake at the mechanism level. [See (53) for a discussion of methodology and advantages in using excised fibrous roots.] The postulation of different uptake mechanisms seems unwarranted and is not supported by reanalysis of concentration-dependence data.

Arrhenius plots for uptake in the 0–30°C range are biphasic (57) and indicate a change from a gel to a liquid-crystalline structure in the lipid portion of the membrane (see below). Differences in activation energies along roots may reflect differences in membrane lipids rather than different uptake mechanisms. The somewhat variable patterns for inhibition of Na^+ uptake by Rb^+ and vice versa can likewise be due to variations in membranes along roots rather than to different uptake mechanisms.

Uptake of Na^+ by low-salt barley roots was maximal near the tip, while uptake by high-salt roots had maxima at the tip and at the base (58). The isotherms for Rb^+ uptake along high-salt roots cannot, however, be analyzed in terms of multiphasic uptake mechanisms.

Uptake of Cl^- and Rb^+ by tips and proximal sections of corn roots (185) is characterized by qualitatively similar multiphasic isotherms (143, 144, 146). The only qualitative difference is in the inhibition of Cl^- uptake in the 1–5 mM range by Br^-, which changes from noncompetitive in tips to competitive in proximal sections (146). Whether this change reflects fundamentally different uptake mechanisms is questionable, however, in view of the strikingly similar multiphasic patterns in tips and proximal sections.

Barley roots yield precise multiphasic kinetics for uptake of sulfate (cf Figure 1) and, especially in the work of Epstein and co-workers, of alkali cations and chloride (146). The multiphasic patterns for entire roots would be blurred if the transition points varied along the roots. Furthermore these kinetics are similar if not identical with those obtained with more homogeneous tissues such as leaf slices, leaves of *Elodea*, discs of storage tissue, and algae (142, 145, 146). Mechanisms for ion uptake are not only similar along roots, but are also similar in a variety of plants and tissues. Variations along roots probably reflect quantitative rather than qualitative changes.

MICROBIAL CONTAMINATION Uptake of phosphate from very dilute solutions may be markedly affected by bacteria (9), but multiphasic kinetics are not caused by microorganisms associated with the roots. Experiments with sterile barley roots (10, 27) yield multiphasic isotherms for phosphate (145), and bacterial effects on uptake of alkali cations and chloride are normally insignificant (49, 51). Uptake of solutes by mycorrhizal associations is reviewed by Meyer (137) in this volume.

COMPARTMENTATION AND VESICLES The basic three-compartment model of cell wall, cytoplasm, and vacuole has recently been amended to include a direct pathway, possibly by way of vesicles, from the plasmalemma to the tonoplast (106, 118,

128, 138, 153). The evidence is somewhat indirect and has in part been disputed (59). Concentration-dependence data for ion uptake in a variety of plants and tissues are well accounted for by a single, multiphasic mechanism at the plasmalemma (and the tonoplast) and do not indicate rate limitation by organelles, vesicles etc. These entities surely participate in ion transport in various ways, but the multiphasic series model and similar models are limited in that they only provide information on the rate-limiting step.

Other Models and Interpretations

Several other models and interpretations have been proposed as alternatives to dual uptake mechanisms or as supplements to the parallel or series model.

Oertli (149) suggested that the parallel operation at the plasmalemma of an active uptake system and a passive carrier-mediated bidirectional mechanism could give rise to kinetics analogous to those of dual mechanisms. This pump and leak concept cannot, however, explain the kinetics since concentration-dependence data cannot be resolved into two components. The data in question are well represented by a multiphasic isotherm (146).

An alternative to carrier mechanisms was suggested by Hiatt (72). Ions were proposed to enter the cells by diffusion or exchange and to become associated with nondiffusible organic ions. Above 10^{-3} M, diffusion of neutral salts according to Donnan phenomena was thought to provide an additional component of ion uptake. The data cannot, however, result from two mechanisms, but are again well represented by single, multiphasic isotherms (146). Diffusion according to Donnan phenomena, furthermore, does not allow for selectivity between similar ions (166).

An electrokinetic interpretation of ion uptake involving an ohmic and a nonohmic component has been proposed (183, 184). Whether this formalism is relevant or offers advantages over Michaelis-Menten kinetics and the carrier concept seems doubtful (cf 53). The data used to support this interpretation are either not sufficiently precise to distinguish between the electrokinetic, dual, and multiphasic concepts (145) or can be accurately represented by multiphasic isotherms (146).

Gerson & Poole (63) proposed that dual mechanisms for uptake of anions could be attributed to a single uncharged carrier. The negatively charged ion-carrier complex would be sensitive to the membrane potential, and this could create influx kinetics resembling dual mechanisms. The authors point out that the model does not explain all aspects of dual mechanisms (cf 53), and it is clearly inadequate to explain multiphasic uptake.

Borst-Pauwels (19) recently developed rate equations for ion uptake via a two-site carrier. Na^+ uptake in yeast may occur via such a carrier (20), but it seems that multiphasic kinetics must result from all-or-none transitions in a single carrier or site since only one mechanism is operative at any one external salt concentration (142).

Pitman (160) used computer techniques to simulate Cl^- uptake by low-salt barley roots and arrived at a compromise between the parallel and the series models. In the high concentration range there was a need for active anion uptake at the plasmalemma to be larger than that provided by mechanism 1. An additional mechanism for active cation uptake was not required, but neither was it excluded. Active uptake of both anions and cations was required at the tonoplast. This model represents an improvement over the parent models. Active uptake at the plasmalemma has, however, been shown to be mediated by a single, multiphasic mechanism rather than by two mechanisms (cf Figure 3).

Barber has attributed mechanism 2 for uptake of Rb^+ and phosphate (10) and Tl^+ (Barber, submitted) by sterile excised roots to passive diffusion. The phosphate data (and probably also the other data) can, however, be represented by a single multiphasic isotherm in good agreement with data for phosphate and sulfate uptake by a variety of plants and tissues (Table 1).

The recent proposal (42) that mechanism 2 is restricted to multicellular organisms and reflects or is determined by diffusion in free space to internal cell layers is untenable. Examples of "dual" or rather multiphasic kinetics in unicellular organisms include uptake of phosphate by yeast (104, cf 145) and *Chlorella* (81, cf 145) and uptake of Rb^+ by *Chlorella* (90, cf 146). The concept seems also incompatible with the precise and consistent multiphasic isotherms observed both in relatively simple and in more complex plant tissues.

Experimental Factors and Phase Patterns

Ca AND PHASE PATTERNS   The influence of Ca^{2+} on ion uptake is pronounced and has been extensively studied (cf 166), but a detailed understanding of the underlying mechanisms is still lacking. The general agreement that Ca^{2+} is important for the structural integrity of cell membranes is borne out by an examination of its effect on multiphasic uptake patterns.

Uptake of Na^+ by barley roots in the presence of increasing amounts of K^+ (47) is characterized by different phase patterns in the absence and presence of Ca^{2+} (146). Biphasic kinetics for Cl^- uptake below 2×10^{-4} M were similarly indicated in the presence but not in the absence of Ca^{2+} (43, cf 146). However, isotherms for phosphate uptake by roots of subterranean clover were similarly multiphasic both in the absence and presence of Ca^{2+} (40, cf 145). Prior removal of Ca^{2+} by treatment of barley roots with water or a chelating agent has, however, been shown to abolish the lower phases for sulfate uptake (Holmern, Vange & Nissen, unpublished results). Uptake, and presumably also the phase pattern, was restored upon addition of Ca^{2+} or a number of other di- or trivalent cations. High pH (8.2) similarly reduced the number of phases, especially at low sulfate concentrations.

Precise studies of Cl^- uptake by barley roots (45) yielded somewhat higher affinities and lower values for V_{max} for the higher phases when the Ca^{2+} concentration was increased from 5×10^{-4} M to 10^{-2} M (144), indicating a tightening of the structure. Similar results were obtained for the highest phase for uptake of boric acid (21, cf 146).

COUNTERIONS AND PHASE PATTERNS   Cation uptake may be markedly influenced by concomitant anions. Uptake of K^+ is usually lower from solutions of K_2SO_4 than from solutions of KCl in the high but not in the low concentration range (55, ·72,

117). In contrast, SO_4^{2-} depressed Na^+ uptake both at low and high concentrations (167).

Examination of data for uptake of Rb^+ and K^+ by corn roots (117, 185; cf 144) and for Na^+ uptake by barley roots (167, cf 146) reveals that the general shape of the multiphasic isotherms is unaffected by the counterion. The use of SO_4^{2-} instead of Cl^- appears to cause a relative decrease in V_{max} values but not in K_m values for the higher phases. A small but highly significant ($P < 0.001$) "sulfate effect" has also been observed for phase 2 in the low concentration range (117, cf 144), and this effect can, accordingly, not be taken as evidence for the separate existence of "system I" and "system II."

The sulfate effect has been ascribed to diffusion according to Donnan phenomena (72), but this seems unlikely in view of the multiphasic kinetics (see above). Its localization at the plasmalemma (86) seems reasonable, especially since the effect is also found for long-distance transport (117, cf 144). An explanation wholly in terms of active anion uptake accompanied by passive K^+ influx (86, 182), however, seems difficult to reconcile with the precise multiphasic kinetics for K^+ uptake.

AGING AND PHASE PATTERNS   It is well known that slicing and washing storage and vegetative tissue may bring about enhanced uptake of ions and other solutes through rejuvenation and reactivation processes (53, 100), but detailed isotherms are available only in a few cases.

Diffusion kinetics were found for Cl^- uptake in fresh potato slices under rather nonphysiological conditions (101, cf 143). Uptake of K^+ and Cl^- by slices of red beet was probably multiphasic (151, cf 146). Aging generally increased affinities and V_{max} values, especially at low concentrations, but the transition points and phase pattern remained the same.

Phosphate uptake by fresh celery tissue seems to be mediated by a homogeneous low-affinity mechanism (14). Aging was taken to induce an additional, high-affinity mechanism, but the kinetics may be multiphasic rather than dual (145). Washing of bean stem segments was taken to induce a separate high-affinity mechanism for K^+ uptake (165). Reanalysis of the original data indicates, however, that a multiphasic mechanism was operative also in fresh tissue (146). Na^+ uptake decreased upon aging. As usual, K^+ uptake was biphasic and Na^+ uptake monophasic below 10^{-3} M. Hancock (67, 68) reported a low-affinity mechanism for uptake of 3-O-methyl glucose by fresh hypocotyl segments and the development of a high-affinity mechanism upon wounding or aging. Uptake by aged tissue is, however, probably mediated by a multiphasic mechanism (see below).

Roots may also undergo changes with time, but these may be mainly quantitative. Leonard & Hanson (109) found a doubling in uptake rates for various ions and solutes upon washing of plant roots for 2 hr. The washing seems to somehow augment or activate existing uptake mechanisms and was accompanied by an increase in $(Mg^{2+} + K^+)$-stimulated ATPase activity (110). Washing increased the V_{max} values for uptake of phosphate and K^+ in the low concentration range, while the affinities remained constant. Perusal of the original data (107) reveals that the phosphate pattern is multiphasic and does not change upon washing. A study of sulfate uptake likewise reveals only relatively minor differences in the multiphasic pattern upon washing of barley roots (Holmern, Vange & Nissen, unpublished results).

SALT STATUS AND PHASE PATTERNS   Roots grown in dilute Ca^{2+} solutions and thus low in internal ions have been used in most determinations of isotherms for ion uptake. It has been suggested by Pitman and co-workers (refs. in 105) and Johansen, Edwards & Loneragan (87) that system II may be an artifact of low salt tissue. The finding that system II merely represents the higher phases of a multiphasic mechanism indicates that the pattern should remain intact upon transition from low to high salt status (cf also 53).

Data of Leigh & Wyn Jones (105) for uptake of K^+ and Na^+ in the range $10^{-5}- 3 \times 10^{-2}$ M can thus be represented by three phases both for low- and high-salt corn roots. At least for Na^+, the values for V_{max} decrease upon transition to high-salt status, whereas the affinities $(1/K_m)$ remain essentially unchanged. K^+ uptake is probably biphasic and Na^+ uptake monophasic below 10^{-3} M. At least two mechanisms (or phases) for K^+ uptake by high-salt barley plants were also found by Johansen (86) by a more indirect approach. Dual or multiphasic isotherms are also indicated for Rb^+ uptake by high-salt barley roots (58).

An increase in salt status has generally been found to increase the specificity for K^+ uptake over Na^+ (163, cf 105). The difference in specificity for K^+ uptake at low and high concentrations observed in low-salt roots is not apparent in high-salt roots (but see 166).

Low-salt tissues will take up salts to a certain internal concentration where total efflux [across the plasmalemma and into the xylem (161)] will balance influx due to (a) increased efflux across the plasmalemma as found for Cl^- fluxes in carrot (33) or (b) a decrease in influx caused by feedback inhibition in some form. The inhibition has variously been found to be at the tonoplast (34, 160) or at the plasmalemma (36, 105). Salt status and feedback inhibition have recently been reviewed in greater detail by Laties (100).

Cram (35) found Cl^- influx in carrot and barley root cells to be regulated by the vacuolar concentration of $Cl^- + NO_3^-$, not by Cl^- or NO_3^- alone, nor by alkali cations, sugars, or malate. This suggests that Cl^- and NO_3^- are taken up by the same mechanism (but with different specificities) or that Cl^- and NO_3^- transports are under common control. This may be relevant to the discussion of a postulated common structure (see below).

LONG-TERM EXPERIMENTS AND PHASE PATTERNS   Epstein (53) cites evidence for the operation of dual mechanisms from long-term experiments. It seems, however, that multiphasic rather than dual mechanisms are indicated. Johanson & Joham (88) grew excised cotton roots for 14 days in a nutrient solution with varying concentrations of $CaCl_2$ and found a discontinuous relation between uptake and external Ca^{2+} concentration. Ca^{2+} uptake was approximately hyperbolic up to 0.2 mM and was described by two plateaus in the ranges 0.25–1.0 mM and 1.5–3.0 mM. The three phases were separated by marked jumps. Growth was mainly associated with the lowest phase. In later experiments (89) only one phase was observed below 0.8 mM, a difference which possibly may be attributed to the use of higher Na$^+$ levels in the nutrient solution.

Fageria & van Hai (unpublished data) grew rice plants in nutrient solutions over a wide range of phosphate concentrations (0.16–1288 μM). The P content, in percentage of dry weight, of both roots and shoots of 100-day old plants can be fairly accurately described by three phases of a multiphasic isotherm. The same number of phases is found for phosphate uptake in this range by a variety of plants and tissues (145). Due to differences in growth, phases 1 and 2 merge when the results are expressed as total P content of the plants. The transition between phases 2 and 3, however, is still evident for 25, 50, 100, and 125-day old plants and for the oldest plants is accompanied by a marked jump. Occasional depletion of phosphate may have occurred in the weaker solutions, but the correspondence between the kinetics of short- and long-term experiments is still probably meaningful and indicates that phase patterns and transition points remain fairly constant throughout the life of the plant. The phase patterns for sulfate uptake by young barley roots do, however, vary somewhat with the age of the seedlings (Vange, Holmern & Nissen, unpublished results).

The relationship between yield and amount of nutrient is generally taken to be a continuous function and is often described by various forms of the Mitscherlich equation, a first-order rate differential equation, or polynomial equations. This may not be strictly valid in view of the fact that ion uptake, a process fundamental for growth, is a discontinuous function of external salt concentration.

ATPases and Binding Proteins

It is well established that ATPases are involved in ion transport in animal tissues (179). The role of ATPases in ion transport in plants remains controversial (171), but good correlative evidence for the involvement of membrane-bound monovalent ion-stimulated ATPases is now emerging.

Good correlation was obtained between K$^+$ or Rb$^+$ uptake and K$^+$- or Rb$^+$-stimulated ATPase activity in roots of oat (61), barley, wheat, and corn (60), and the ATPase activity was adequate to account for the observed uptake rates. Double reciprocal plots for the range 5 X 10^{-3}– 5 X 10^{-2} M yield straight lines for ATPase activity, while an apparently curvilinear but presumably multiphasic relationship is indicated for Rb$^+$ uptake.

Analysis of more detailed data (111) for KCl-stimulated ATPase from plasma membranes of oat roots reveals, however, three remarkably precise phases in the ranges 2–4, 4.5–23, and 23–75 mM (Figure 4). There is a jump between the two lower phases, and the value for 100 mM KCl may represent a fourth phase. Phases cannot be unambiguously assigned in the range 0.01–2 mM because of somewhat erratic data. The data were originally represented by a continuously curvilinear isotherm and discussed in terms of negative cooperativity (see below), but the multiphasic interpretation provides a better fit. Both models suggest that multiphasic kinetics of ion uptake may reflect the operation of a single membrane-bound ATPase undergoing phase transitions. There are no dual ATPases; extrapolation

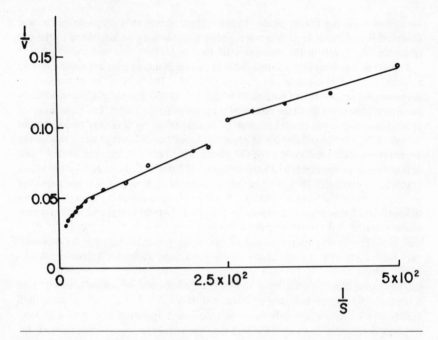

Figure 4 Double reciprocal plot for ATPase activity of plasma membrane fraction from oat roots in the range $2 \times 10^{-3} - 10^{-1}$ M KCl. Cf Figures 9–11 in (111). Original data kindly provided by Dr. T. K. Hodges.

and subtraction of the contribution of a high-affinity mechanism result, as for ion uptake, in a noninterpretable double reciprocal plot in the high concentration range.

Hodges and co-workers (108, 177) have recently made important progress in the separation and purification of membrane-associated ATPases from plant roots. At least five ATPase activities could be separated by centrifugation of membrane fractions from oat roots (108). One of the ATPases is associated with plasma membranes and has been partially purified (77).

Ecological reasoning has aided in the finding of $(Na^+ + K^+)$-stimulated ATPases in plants (95). Specific ratios of Na^+ to K^+ were found to stimulate ATPases in sugar beet seedlings (70) and in leaves of the mangrove *Avicennia nitida* (96), i.e. in halophytes which have to protect themselves from Na^+ in the cytoplasm. Qualitative correlations between salt accumulation characteristics and ATPase stimulation were obtained for a series of inbred strains of sugar beet (97). Negative charges are needed to bind the monovalent cations to the membrane, and this may be the reason for the correlation between sulfolipid and $(Na^+ + K^+)$-stimulated ATPases (69, 98). An ATPase from turnip has recently been suggested to be involved in the transport of anions across the tonoplast (177).

Ratner & Jacoby (171) found Mg^{2+}-dependent ATP hydrolysis by ATPases from grass roots to be stimulated by at least one of the monovalent organic cations tris, choline, and ethanolamine. This stimulation was equal to that in the presence of KCl or NaCl, but uptake of the organic cations by corn roots was much slower than uptake of K^+. The correlation between Rb^+ or K^+ uptake and Rb^+- or K^+- stimulated ATPase activity in roots (60, 111) cannot therefore be extended to organic cations. An explanation of these findings may be that the organic cations can stimulate the energy transducing moiety of the uptake system but cannot be transported by specific carrier proteins (cf 154).

The concept of carriers has remained purely kinetic, but recent studies of bacterial binding proteins may also provide a breakthrough in our understanding of the molecular nature of uptake mechanisms (refs. in 1). It remains to be seen to what extent the information gained from bacterial systems applies to higher plants, but promising starts have been made.

Nieman & Willis (139) treated carrot discs with ice-cold solutions of NaCl and found exchange of tissue Ca^{2+} and Mg^{2+} for Na^+, release of protein, and suppression of active uptake of glucose and phosphate. Attempts to restore uptake by adding back the released materials were unsuccessful. They propose that linkages between the outer cell surface and proteins required for active solute uptake are maintained by divalent cations and disrupted by monovalent cations. Osmotic shock may also be a factor in their experiments (1). A binding protein for α-aminoisobutyric acid is indicated in studies with bean leaves (see below).

Ighe & Pettersson (78) found a dinitrophenol-sensitive binding of Rb^+ in the free space of wheat roots. The amount actively bound was directly proprotional to the rate of active uptake. The specificity of initial binding of sulfate and phosphate (156–158) matches that of uptake across the plasmalemma (cf 53). The metabolism-linked component is too large to represent binding to carrier sites, but its close correlation with active uptake is intriguing.

These studies should be extended to other plant systems. It may, however, be difficult to prove specific binding of a solute to its binding protein without suitable controls, preferably mutants lacking the moieties being sought.

Phase Transitions and Pattern Similarities

Discontinuous transitions seem an invariant feature of inorganic ion uptake in higher plants (142–146). Uptake of sugars (112) and possibly amino acids (see below) is also multiphasic. Jumps occur only sporadically (cf Figures 1 and 2), and there must be some form of control ensuring that phase transitions are not normally accompanied by abrupt changes in uptake rates (146).

The molecular basis for phase transitions remains unknown. Linask & Laties (112) discuss their results in terms of Ling's (113) concept of cardinal adsorbents and envisage the multiphasic isotherm for glucose uptake as representing interacting protein or lipoprotein structures which undergo all-or-none transitions as the external glucose concentration is raised. The transitions increase the number of binding sites or at least represent configurational changes which increase uptake rates. Whether these concepts apply to ion uptake is not clear. The kinetics for alkali cations, chloride, and boric acid are more complex (cf Figure 2), and the highest phases for phosphate and sulfate uptake have K_m values which are high relative to the external concentration, i.e. transitions occur long before saturation, in fact before half-saturation (142, appendix in 146). V_{max} increases 100–1000-fold when the external concentration of phosphate or sulfate is raised from a low to a high level (142, 145). This seems to indicate an increase in turnover instead of, or in addition to, an increase in the number of sites.

Sulfate uptake by barley roots is competitively inhibited by analogs in the order $S_2O_3^{2-} > CrO_4^{2-} > SeO_4^{2-} > MoO_4^{2-} > WO_4^{2-}$ (Vange, Holmern & Nissen, unpublished results) in fair agreement with data for *Neurospora* (187). Addition of analogs will also cause sulfate uptake to be shifted to higher phases. The analogs are equally effective in this respect; i.e. the transition points are determined only by the total concentration of sulfate and analog. The difference in specificity for uptake and transition indicates that phase transitions are not caused by binding of ions to uptake sites or carriers since this would require higher external concentrations of weakly bound analogs. The structure undergoing transition must have receptor sites of about equal affinity for all analogs (sulfate included) if transitions are in fact caused by binding of ions to a structure. Transitions in a postulated common structure (see below) may lead to conformational changes in uptake sites or carriers.

The structure undergoing transition must, as part of the membrane, obviously be either a protein, lipid, or lipoprotein. More specifically it may be part of a membrane-bound ATPase (cf Figure 4), and further studies of this enzyme may also yield important information on the phenomenon of discontinuous transitions. A galactose-binding protein from *Escherichia coli* has been found to undergo a conformational change upon binding of substrate (18, 93), but this change may not be discontinuous. Discontinuous transitions have been observed in certain lipid systems, e.g. for the binding of Mn^{2+} to micelles of lecithin (64). A succession of negative and positive cooperativity results in sharp breaks in double reciprocal plots for glutamate dehydrogenase (38, 46), but the breaks are not true discontinuities and jumps do not occur (Dalziel and Engel, private communication). Voltage-resistance relationships may change in the 0.1–1 mM range (Higinbotham, private communication), but the uptake patterns seem too complex to be explained on an electrochemical basis.

Arrhenius plots (log v vs $1/T$) for uptake processes (28) or membrane-bound enzymes (120, 170) are usually biphasic and clearly discontinuous. This reflects a change from a gel to a liquid-crystalline structure in the lipid portion of the membrane (94, 119). Transitions as a function of temperature may, however, have little in common with concentration-dependent transitions. The multiphasic isotherm for sulfate uptake seems to be the same in the gel and the liquid-crystalline state (Holmern, Vange & Nissen, unpublished results). Uptake from solutions of 2.5 × 10^{-4} M sulfate gave biphasic Arrhenius plots, whereas uptake from 10^{-1} M solutions gave monophasic plots. This probably reflects the change from high to very low affinity as the sulfate concentration is raised (142).

The multiphasic patterns for uptake of K^+, Cl^-, and $B(OH)_3$ are very similar (146) and may in fact be identical, as indicated by isotherms for K^+ and Cl^- uptake by roots of tall wheat grass (44, cf 146). The more regular patterns for phosphate and sulfate uptake (145) may also be identical (Vange, Holmern, & Nissen, unpublished results). The identity of the transition points indicates, as do specificity studies (see above), that transitions do not primarily occur in specific uptake sites or carriers, but in a structure common to all solutes with the same phase pattern. However, even a large excess of phosphate, at least as the singly charged species $H_2PO_4^-$, does not influence the sulfate pattern (Vange, Holmern, & Nissen, unpublished results). This indicates that, alternatively, there may be separate but very similar structures for the various ions. A general loosening or tightening of the structure may also explain why the kinetic constants increase or decrease in step. If ATPases are indeed involved, this line of reasoning indicates that a single ATPase may somehow mediate uptake of several different solutes. Mediation of uptake by polyvalent carriers or structures has been proposed by several workers (e.g. 6, 7, 188, 192).

Phase patterns are not influenced by the charge on the solute. Cations (K^+/Rb^+ and probably other alkali cations), anions (Cl^- and probably other halide ions), and at least one uncharged solute, boric acid, yield the same pattern. Silicic acid, $Si(OH)_4$, is also actively taken up by plant roots (11). This indicates that phase transitions may not be caused by electrostatic binding to the postulated common structure. At least kinetically, the charge on the solute seems irrelevant. This may have consequences for the interpretation of ion uptake on the basis of electrochemical principles (75, 76).

The similar kinetics also indicate that the energy source may be the same for uptake of cations and anions. MacRobbie (125, 126) concluded for *Nitella translucens* that the energy for K^+ uptake was provided by ATP formed by cyclic photophosphorylation, whereas Cl^- uptake depended upon electron transport of noncyclic photophosphorylation. Raven (172, 173) reported similar results for ion fluxes in another fresh water alga *Hydrodictyon africanum* (but see 84). Unfortunately, concentration-dependence data are not available for these algae. For higher plants the energy form seems to be linked to ATP formation both for cations and anions, as shown for barley leaf tissue (91) and *Elodea* leaves (84).

The multiphasic patterns are not only similar for various ions but are, as already noted, similar or identical for uptake and long-distance transport. This strongly indicates that uptake across the plasmalemma of root cortical cells is rate-limiting transport to the shoot. Active secretion of ions into the xylem by stelar parenchyma cells (two-pump hypothesis, cf 2, 100, 103, 162), if in fact it does occur (5), is not reflected in the kinetics of long-distance transport.

UPTAKE OF ORGANIC SOLUTES

Sugars

A multiphasic mechanism for uptake of glucose and 3-O-methyl glucose by aged potato slices has been reported by Linask & Laties (112). Uptake in the range $10^{-6} - 10^{-1}$ M could be precisely represented by four phases with regularly increasing kinetic constants. These authors interpreted the three lower phases to reflect events at the plasmalemma and the highest phase (above 1.5×10^{-2} M) to possibly represent transport to the vacuole. Subsequent studies (Linask & Laties, in preparation) are taken to suggest that the multiphasic isotherm reflects binding of the sugars to both membrane and cytoplasmic proteins. It is gratifying to note that uptake of 3-O-methyl glucose by aged carrot root slices in the range $5 \times 10^{-4} - 5 \times 10^{-2}$ M (174) is multiphasic and that the patterns for the two tissues are very similar. Other data (65) for uptake of monosaccharides by carrot tissue are also in part biphasic within the range $5 \times 10^{-3} - 10^{-1}$ M. Similarly, uptake of 3-O-methyl glucose by Hypomyces-infected (67) and aged (68) squash hypocotyls may be mediated by multiphasic rather than dual mechanisms.

Uptake of sucrose (186) and of glucose and fructose (181) by vascular bundles from leaf petioles of sugar beet was resolved in the high concentration range into a hyperbolic and a linear isotherm, indicating the simultaneous operation of an active and a passive process. Uptake of several monosaccharides into immature parenchyma tissue of sugar cane (24) is active, monophasic, and apparently mediated by the same carrier sites in the range $10^{-3} - 1.5 \times 10^{-2}$ M. Maretzki & Thom (131–133) have described a high-affinity (A) and a low-affinity (B) system for uptake of glucose by sugar cane cells. System A is tentatively located at the plasmalemma and system B at the tonoplast, but they may also be in parallel at the plasmalemma or part of the same bi- or multiphasic system (private communication).

Sugars may be rapidly phosphorylated or undergo other alterations, and it is not always clear whether they are transported across membranes in an unchanged form (75). Phosphorylation of glucose by hexokinase from corn (32) may be represented by a bi- or triphasic isotherm in the range $10^{-5} - 5 \times 10^{-3}$ M while the data for fructose are monophasic. The multiphasic kinetics for glucose uptake cannot, however, be ascribed to metabolic complications since the nonmetabolizable analog, 3-O-methyl glucose, shows the same pattern (112).

Amino Acids

Studies of amino acid uptake in higher plants are relatively few, but include several amino acids and widely different plant cells and tissues.

Uptake of various amino acids by carrot root cells was found to occur against a concentration gradient and to be inhibited by metabolic inhibitors (17). Competition studies indicated a common carrier. The affinities were higher for L-amino acids than for the corresponding D-amino acids and higher for amino acids with more lipophilic side chains. Uptake was monophasic in the range $10^{-3} - 5 \times 10^{-2}$ M but was not studied at lower concentrations. Uptake of glycine, alanine, and phenylalanine by wheat roots over a wider concentration range ($10^{-5} - 10^{-2}$ M) was taken to be mediated by two carriers (37), but the isotherms may be multiphasic rather than dual.

Uptake of the basic amino acids arginine and lysine by sugar cane cells appeared to be active and mediated by separate mechanisms with K_m values of about 10^{-4} M and 2.4×10^{-3} M, respectively (130). The kinetics were monophasic at low concentrations, but competition studies indicated the existence of a less specific low-affinity mechanism for arginine uptake, possibly identical with the lysine mechanism. The existence of a single, multiphasic mechanism for arginine uptake cannot, however, be excluded. Alanine uptake by soybean root cells was slow and nonsaturable when the cells were grown with NH_4^+ (92). Uptake into cells starved for 12 hr, i.e. into cells with low levels of NH_4^+ and amino acids, was rapid and apparently saturable, but the external concentration of alanine did not exceed 10^{-5} M.

Glutamic acid uptake by segments of sunflower hypocotyl was represented by a slightly curved line in the range $2 \times 10^{-3} - 8.7 \times 10^{-2}$ M (175), but may be equally well represented by a biphasic isotherm. Uptake of the amino acid analog α-aminoisobutyric acid by fresh and aged leaf strips of barley was represented by the sum of two mechanisms in the range $10^{-5} - 1.5 \times 10^{-2}$ M (176). Diffusion was found by free space considerations to play no or only a minor role. The data can, however, be equally well represented by a single biphasic mechanism. Experiments over a larger concentration range indicate in fact that there are probably more than two phases (Shtarkshall & Reinhold, in preparation).

Amar & Reinhold (1) found that cold osmotic shock, i.e. transfer from 0.5 M sucrose at 25° C to water at 2° C, of aged strips of bean leaves severely reduced their uptake of α-aminoisobutyric acid. A reduction in influx rather than nonspecific membrane damage was indicated. The shock also brought about the release of about 4% of the cell protein. Addition of shock fluid restored the uptake capacity in some but not all experiments. Attempts to detect binding of α-aminoisobutyric acid to shock protein in vitro by equilibrium dialysis were unsuccessful, probably because of the relatively high K_m for amino acid uptake in this system.

Amino acid uptake by bacteria in many instances can be accurately represented by multiphasic isotherms (cf 31, 143). This survey indicates that higher plants may also take up amino acids via multiphasic mechanisms, but more detailed and precise data are needed to unequivocally determine the kinetics.

Choline Sulfate

Uptake of choline sulfate by barley roots was found to be mediated by dual mechanisms (148). More detailed studies have confirmed that the uptake of this organic zwitterion is indeed mediated by dual or multiple mechanisms as opposed to the multiphasic mechanisms for inorganic ions and glucose. Double reciprocal plots for choline sulfate uptake by roots and leaf slices of barley are continuously curvilinear. The data can be precisely represented by the sum of a high-affinity, low-V_{max} mechanism and a mechanism with very low affinity and a high V_{max}. A third component, apparently of very high affinity, is observed at 10^{-7}–10^{-6} M choline sulfate. In contrast, uptake of choline sulfate by filamentous fungi is mediated by a single mechanism in the range 10^{-9}–10^{-1} M (12).

The dual (or triple) mechanisms for choline sulfate uptake are very different from the dual mechanisms postulated for uptake of inorganic ions. Both mechanisms are homogeneous and their K_m and V_{max} values differ by several orders of magnitude.

Plants can also take up choline sulfate through the mediation of certain Gram-negative rhizosphere bacteria (140, 141, 147). This complex and still very puzzling interaction involves a sequence of three induction processes: 1. induction of a bacterial permease for choline sulfate; 2. induction of bacterial "effectiveness" (surface changes); and 3. induction of an uptake mechanism in the plant. Plants in contact with effective bacteria will take up choline sulfate rapidly. The bacteria can be removed after completion of the final induction process with no loss in uptake rates. The specificity of induced plant uptake is identical with the specificity of the bacterial permease and much higher than that of the constitutive plant uptake mechanisms. Transfer of information in some form from the bacteria to the plant remains a distinct possibility. Further investigations have been hampered by the failure to obtain induction with cell-free preparations from effective bacteria.

ACKNOWLEDGMENTS

I thank all who have generously cooperated in providing original data, comments, preprints etc and regret that important matters had to be excluded from this review. Dr. C. Johansen critically read the manuscript, and Dr. G. G. Laties has provided continued encouragement and advice.

Literature Cited

1. Amar, L., Reinhold, L. 1973. *Plant Physiol.* 51:620–25
2. Anderson, W. P. 1972. *Ann. Rev. Plant Physiol.* 23:51–72
3. Anderson, W. P., Ed. 1973. *Ion Transport in Plants.* London, New York: Academic. 630 pp.
4. Andrew, C. S. 1966. *Aust. J. Agr. Res.* 17:611–24
5. Baker, D. A. 1973. *Planta* 112:293–99
6. Bange, G. G. J. 1972. *Acta Bot. Neer.* 21:145–48
7. Bange, G. G. J., Meijer, C. L. C. 1966. *Acta Bot. Neer.* 15:434–50
8. Bange, G. G. J., Overstreet, R. 1960. *Plant Physiol.* 35:605–8
9. Barber, D. A. 1968. *Ann. Rev. Plant Physiol.* 19:71–88
10. Barber, D. A. 1972. *New Phytol.* 71:255–62
11. Barber, D. A., Shone, M. G. T. 1966. *J. Exp. Bot.* 17:569–78
12. Bellenger, N., Nissen, P., Wood, T. C., Segel, I. H. 1968. *J. Bacteriol.* 96:1574–85
13. Berlier, Y., Guiraud, G., Sauvaire, Y. 1969. *Agrochimica* 13:250–60
14. Bieleski, R. L. 1966. *Plant Physiol.* 41:447–54
15. Bieleski, R. L. 1973. *Ann. Rev. Plant Physiol.* 24:225–52
16. Bingham, F. T., Elseewi, A., Oertli, J. J. 1970. *Proc. Soil Sci. Soc. Am.* 34:613–17
17. Birt, L. M., Hird, F. J. R. 1958. *Biochem. J.* 70:286–92
18. Boos, W., Gordon, A. S., Hall, R. E., Price, H. D. 1972. *J. Biol. Chem.* 247:917–24
19. Borst-Pauwels, G. W. F. H. 1973. *J. Theor. Biol.* 40:19–32
20. Borst-Pauwels, G. W. F. H., Schnetkamp, P., van Well, P. 1973. *Biochim. Biophys. Acta* 291:274–79
21. Bowen, J. E. 1968. *Plant Cell Physiol.* 9:467–78
22. Ibid 1969. 10:227–30
23. Bowen, J. E. 1969. *Plant Physiol.* 44:255–61
24. Ibid 1972. 49:82–86
25. Bowen, J. E. 1972. *Plant Cell Physiol.* 13:703–14
26. Carter, O. G., Lathwell, D. J. 1967. *Plant Physiol.* 42:1407–12
27. Cartwright, B. 1972. *Soil Sci. Plant Anal.* 3:313–22
28. Charnock, J. S., Cook, D. A., Opit, L. J. 1971. *Nature New Biol.* 233:171–72
29. Cleland, W. W. 1963. *Nature* 198:463–65
30. Cleland, W. W. 1967. *Advan. Enzymol.* 29:1–32
31. Cosloy, S. D. 1973. *J. Bacteriol.* 114:679–84
32. Cox, E. L., Dickinson, D. B. 1973. *Plant Physiol.* 51:960–66
33. Cram, W. J. 1968. *Biochim. Biophys. Acta* 163:339–53
34. Cram, W. J. 1968. *Abh. Deut. Akad. Wiss. Berlin* 4a:117–26
35. Cram, W. J. 1973. *J. Exp. Bot.* 24:328–41
36. Cram, W. J., Laties, G. G. 1971. *Aust. J. Biol. Sci.* 24:633–46
37. Cseh, E., Böszörményi, Z. 1964. *Proc. 6th Hung. Meet. Biochem.,* 277–92
38. Dalziel, K., Engel, P. C. 1968. *FEBS Lett.* 1:349–52
39. Diouris, M., Penot, M. 1972. *C. R. Acad. Sci. Sér. D* 275:2647–50
40. Edwards, D. G. 1968. *Trans. 9th Int. Congr. Soil Sci. Adelaide* 2:183–90

41. Edwards, D. G. 1970. *Aust. J. Biol. Sci.* 23:255–64
42. Ehwald, R., Sammler, P., Göring, H. In press
43. Elzam, O. E., Epstein, E. 1965. *Plant Physiol.* 40:620–24
44. Elzam, O. E., Epstein, E. 1969. *Agrochimica* 13:196–206
45. Elzam, O. E., Rains, D. W., Epstein, E. 1964. *Biochem. Biophys. Res. Commun.* 15:273–76
46. Engel, P. C., Ferdinand, W. 1973. *Biochem. J.* 131:97–105
47. Epstein, E. 1961. *Plant Physiol.* 36:437–44
48. Epstein, E. 1966. *Nature* 212:1324–27
49. Epstein, E. 1968. *Experientia* 24:616–17
50. Epstein, E. 1969. In *Ecological Aspects of the Mineral Nutrition of Plants*, ed. I. H. Rorison, 345–55. London: Blackwell
51. Epstein, E. 1972. *New Phytol.* 71:873–74
52. Epstein, E. 1972. *Mineral Nutrition of Plants: Principles and Perspectives.* New York: Wiley. 412 pp.
53. Epstein, E. 1973. *Int. Rev. Cytol.* 34:123–68
54. Epstein, E., Rains, D. W. 1965. *Proc. Nat. Acad. Sci. USA* 53:1320–24
55. Epstein, E., Rains, D. W., Elzam, O. E. 1963. *Proc. Nat. Acad. Sci. USA* 49:684–92
56. Eshel, A., Waisel, Y. 1972. *Plant Physiol.* 49:585–89
57. Eshel, A., Waisel, Y. See Ref. 3, 531–37
58. Eshel, A., Waisel, Y. 1973. *Physiol. Plant.* 28:557–60
59. Findlay, G. P., Hope, A. B., Walker, N. A. 1971. *Biochim. Biophys. Acta* 233:155–62
60. Fisher, J. D., Hansen, D., Hodges, T. K. 1970. *Plant Physiol.* 46:812–14
61. Fisher, J. D., Hodges, T. K. 1969. *Plant Physiol.* 44:385–95
62. Fried, M., Zsoldos, F., Vose, P. B., Shatokhin, I. L. 1965. *Physiol. Plant.* 18:313–20
63. Gerson, D. F., Poole, R. J. 1971. *Plant Physiol.* 48:509–11
64. Gomperts, B., Lantelme, F., Stock, R. 1970. *J. Membrane Biol.* 3:241–66
65. Grant, B. R., Beevers, H. 1964. *Plant Physiol.* 39:78–85
66. Grünsfelder, M. 1971. *Die Kinetik der Phosphataufnahme bei Elodea densa.* PhD thesis. Univ. Würzburg. 134 pp.
67. Hancock, J. G. 1969. *Plant Physiol.* 44:1267–72
68. Hancock, J. G. 1970. *Can. J. Bot.* 48:1515–20
69. Hansson, G., Kuiper, P. J. C., Kylin, A. 1973. *Physiol. Plant.* 28:430–35
70. Hansson, G., Kylin, A. 1969. *Z. Pflanzenphysiol.* 60:270–75
71. Hiatt, A. J. 1967. *Plant Physiol.* 42:294–98
72. Ibid 1968. 43:893–901
73. Ibid 1970. 45:408–10
74. Ibid 1970. 45:411–14
75. Higinbotham, N. 1973. *Bot. Rev.* 39:15–69
76. Higinbotham, N. 1973. *Ann. Rev. Plant Physiol.* 24:25–46
77. Hodges, T. K., Leonard, R. T., Bracker, C. E., Keenan, T. W. 1972. *Proc. Nat. Acad. Sci. USA* 69:3307–11
78. Ighe, U., Pettersson, S. 1974. *Physiol. Plant.* In press
79. Jackman, R. H. 1965. *N. Z. J. Agr. Res.* 8:763–77
80. Jacobson, L., Cooper, B. R., Volz, M. G. 1971. *Physiol. Plant.* 25:432–35
81. Jeanjean, R., Blasco, F., Gaudin, C. 1970. *C. R. Acad. Sci. Sér. D* 270:2946–49
82. Jeschke, W. D. 1970. *Planta* 91:111–28
83. Jeschke, W. D. 1970. *Z. Naturforsch.* 25B:624–30
84. Jeschke, W. D. 1972. *Planta* 103:164–80
85. Jeschke, W. D., Simonis, W. 1965. *Planta* 67:6–32
86. Johansen, C. 1971. *Mechanisms of Potassium Absorption in High-Salt Plants.* PhD thesis. Univ. Western Australia
87. Johansen, C., Edwards, D. G., Loneragan, J. F. 1968. *Plant Physiol.* 43:1722–26
88. Johanson, L., Joham, H. E. 1971. *Plant Soil* 34:331–39
89. Ibid 1971. 35:323–36
90. Kannan, S. 1971. *Science* 173:927–29
91. Kholdebarin, B., Oertli, J. J. 1972. *Z. Pflanzenphysiol.* 66:352–58
92. King, J., Oleniuk, F. H. 1973. *Can. J. Bot.* 51:1109–14
93. Kreishman, G. P., Robertson, D. E., Ho, C. 1973. *Biochem. Biophys. Res. Commun.* 53:18–23
94. Kumamoto, J., Raison, J. K., Lyons, J. M. 1971. *J. Theor. Biol.* 31:47–51
95. Kylin, A. See Ref. 3, 369–77
96. Kylin, A., Gee, R. 1970. *Plant Physiol.* 45:169–72
97. Kylin, A., Hansson, G. 1971. In *Potassium in Biochemistry and Physiology.* Int. Potash Inst. Coll., Skokloster, Sweden

98. Kylin, A., Kuiper, P. J. C., Hansson, G. 1972. *Physiol. Plant.* 26:271–78
99. Laties, G. G. 1969. *Ann. Rev. Plant Physiol.* 20:89–116
100. Laties, G. G. 1974. Cornell Univ. Press. In press
101. Laties, G. G., MacDonald, I. R., Dainty, J. 1964. *Plant Physiol.* 39: 254–62
102. Läuchli, A. 1972. *Ann. Rev. Plant Physiol.* 23:197–218
103. Läuchli, A., Spurr, A. R., Epstein, E. 1971. *Plant Physiol.* 48:118–24
104. Leggett, J. E. 1961. *Plant Physiol.* 36:277–84
105. Leigh, R. A., Wyn Jones, R. G. 1973. *J. Exp. Bot.* 24:787–95
106. Leigh, R. A., Wyn Jones, R. G., Williamson, F. A. See Ref. 3, 407–18
107. Leonard, R. T. 1971. *Induction of Increased Ion Absorption in Corn Root Tissue.* PhD thesis. Univ. Illinois, Urbana. 132 pp.
108. Leonard, R. T., Hansen, D., Hodges, T. K. 1973. *Plant Physiol.* 51:749–54
109. Leonard, R. T., Hanson, J. B. 1972. *Plant Physiol.* 49:430–35
110. Ibid 1972. 49:436–40
111. Leonard, R. T., Hodges, T. K. 1973. *Plant Physiol.* 52:6–12
112. Linask, J., Laties, G. G. 1973. *Plant Physiol.* 51:289–94
113. Ling, G. N. 1970. *Proc. Nat. Acad. Sci. USA* 67:296–301
114. Lüttge, U. 1973. *Stofftransport der Pflanzen.* Berlin, Heidelberg, New York: Springer. 280 pp.
115. Lüttge, U., Bauer, K. 1968. *Planta* 78:310–20
116. Lüttge, U., Cram, W. J., Laties, G. G. 1971. *Z. Pflanzenphysiol.* 64:418–26
117. Lüttge, U., Laties, G. G. 1966. *Plant Physiol.* 41:1531–39
118. Lüttge, U., Pallaghy, C. K. 1972. *Z. Pflanzenphysiol.* 67:359–66
119. Lyons, J. M. 1972. *Cryobiology* 9: 341–50
120. Lyons, J. M., Raison, J. K. 1970. *Plant Physiol.* 45:386–89
121. Maas, E. V. 1969. *Plant Physiol.* 44:985–89
122. Maas, E. V., Moore, D. P., Mason, B. J. 1968. *Plant Physiol.* 43:527–30
123. Maas, E. V., Ogata, G. 1971. *Plant Physiol.* 47:357–60
124. MacDonald, I. R., Macklon, A. E. S. 1972. *Plant Physiol.* 49:303–6
125. MacRobbie, E. A. C. 1965. *Biochim. Biophys. Acta* 94:64–73
126. MacRobbie, E. A. C. 1966. *Aust. J. Biol. Sci.* 19:363–70
127. MacRobbie, E. A. C. 1970. *Quart. Rev. Biophys.* 3:251–94
128. MacRobbie, E. A. C. 1970. *J. Exp. Bot.* 21:335–44
129. MacRobbie, E. A. C. 1971. *Ann. Rev. Plant Physiol.* 22:75–96
130. Maretzki, A., Thom, M. 1970. *Biochemistry* 9:2731–36
131. Maretzki, A., Thom, M. 1972. *Plant Physiol.* 49:177–82
132. Maretzki, A., Thom, M. 1972. *Biochem. Biophys. Res. Commun.* 47:44–50
133. Maretzki, A., Thom, M. 1973. *Plant Physiol.* 53S:#339
134. Marschner, H. 1970. *Fortschr. Bot.* 32:43–54
135. Ibid 1971. 33:85–94
136. Ibid 1972. 34:113–22
137. Meyer, F. H. 1974. *Ann. Rev. Plant Physiol.* 25:567–86
138. Neirinckx, L. J. A., Bange, G. G. J. 1971. *Acta Bot. Neer.* 20:481–88
139. Nieman, R. H., Willis, C. 1971. *Plant Physiol.* 48:287–93
140. Nissen, P. 1968. *Biochem. Biophys. Res. Commun.* 32:696–703
141. Nissen, P. 1971. In *Informative Molecules in Biological Systems,* ed. L. G. H. Ledoux, 201–12. Amsterdam: North-Holland
142. Nissen, P. 1971. *Physiol. Plant.* 24:315–24
143. Ibid 1973. 28:113–20
144. Nissen, P. See Ref. 3, 539–53
145. Nissen, P. 1973. *Physiol. Plant.* 28:304–16
146. Ibid 1973. 29:298–354
147. Nissen, P. 1973. *Sci. Rep. Agr. Univ. Norway* 52(20):1–53
148. Nissen, P., Benson, A. A. 1964. *Plant Physiol.* 39:586–89
149. Oertli, J. J. 1967. *Physiol. Plant.* 20:1014–26
150. Oertli, J. J. 1969. *Agrochimica* 8:212–19
151. Osmond, C. B., Laties, G. G. 1968. *Plant Physiol.* 43:747–55
152. Osmond, C. B., Laties, G. G. 1970. *J. Membrane Biol.* 2:85–94
153. Pallaghy, C. K., Lüttge, U., von Willert, K. 1970. *Z. Pflanzenphysiol.* 62:51–57
154. Pardee, A. B. 1968. *Science* 162:632–37
155. Penth, B., Weigl, J. 1969. *Z. Naturforsch.* 24B:342–48
156. Persson, L. 1969. *Physiol. Plant.* 22:959–76
157. Pettersson, S. 1966. *Physiol. Plant.* 19:459–92
158. Ibid 1971. 24:485–90

159. Picciurro, G., Ferrandi, L., Boniforti, R., Bracciocurti, G. 1967. In *Isotopes in Plant Nutrition and Physiology*, 511–26. IAEA, Vienna
160. Pitman, M. G. 1969. *Plant Physiol.* 44:1417–27
161. Pitman, M. G. 1971. *Aust. J. Biol. Sci.* 24:407–21
162. Ibid 1972. 25:243–57
163. Pitman, M. G., Courtice, A. C., Lee, B. 1968. *Aust. J. Biol. Sci.* 21:871–81
164. Polle, E. O., Jenny, H. 1971. *Physiol. Plant.* 25:219–24
165. Rains, D. W. 1969. *Plant Physiol.* 44:547–54
166. Rains, D. W. 1972. *Ann. Rev. Plant Physiol.* 23:367–88
167. Rains, D. W., Epstein, E. 1967. *Plant Physiol.* 42:314–18
168. Ibid, 319–23
169. Rains, D. W., Epstein, E. 1967. *Aust. J. Biol. Sci.* 20:847–57
170. Raison, J. K., Lyons, J. M., Mehlhorn, R. J., Keith, A. D. 1971. *J. Biol. Chem.* 246:4036–40
171. Ratner, A., Jacoby, B. 1973. *J. Exp. Bot.* 24:231–38
172. Raven, J. A. 1967. *J. Gen. Physiol.* 50:1627–40
173. Raven, J. A. 1968. *J. Exp. Bot.* 19:233–53
174. Reinhold, L., Eshhar, Z. 1968. *Plant Physiol.* 43:1023–30
175. Reinhold, L., Powell, R. G. 1958. *J. Exp. Bot.* 9:82–96
176. Reinhold, L., Shtarkshall, R. A., Ganot, D. 1970. *J. Exp. Bot.* 21:926–32
177. Rungie, J. M., Wiskich, J. T. 1973. *Plant Physiol.* 51:1064–68
178. Salsac, L. 1970. *Absorption du calcium par les racines de Feverole (calcicole) et de Lupin jaune (calcifuge).* PhD thesis. Univ. Paris. 146 pp.
179. Skou, J. C. 1965. *Physiol. Rev.* 45:596–617
180. Smith, R. C., Epstein, E. 1964. *Plant Physiol.* 39:992–96
181. Sokolova, S. V. 1972. *Fiziol. Rast.* 19:1282–91
182. Tadano, T., Baker, J. H., Drake, M. 1969. *Plant Physiol.* 44:1639–44
183. Thellier, M. 1970. *Ann. Bot. London* 34:983–1009
184. Thellier, M., Thoiron, B., Thoiron, A. 1971. *Physiol. Vég.* 9:65–82
185. Torii, K., Laties, G. G. 1966. *Plant Physiol.* 41:863–70
186. Turkina, M. V., Sokolova, S. V. 1972. *Fiziol. Rast.* 19:912–19
187. Vallée, M., Segel, I. H. 1971. *Microbios* 4:21–31
188. Weigl, J. 1967. *Fortschr. Bot.* 29:50–67
189. Weigl, J. 1968. *Planta* 79:197–207
190. Welch, R. M., Epstein, E. 1968. *Proc. Nat. Acad. Sci. USA* 61:447–53
191. Winne, D. 1973. *Biochim. Biophys. Acta* 298:27–31
192. Wong, J. T. 1965. *Biochim. Biophys. Acta* 94:102–13

Ann. Rev. Plant Physiol. 1974. 25:81–114

DINITROGEN FIXATION ❖7563

M. J. Dilworth[1]

Department of Soil Science and Plant Nutrition, University of Western Australia, Nedlands, Australia

CONTENTS

THE NITROGENASE ENZYME AND ITS PROPERTIES. 82
   Purification. 82
   Components and Subunits 84
   Cross-reactions. 86
   Enzymatic Properties 88
   ATP Binding and Electron Transfer. 90
   Molybdenum Function within Nitrogenase 92
ELECTRON DONOR SYSTEMS FOR NITROGENASE. 93
ROUTES OF AMMONIA ASSIMILATION IN DINITROGEN-FIXING SYSTEMS. 95
   Tracer Studies 95
   Glutamate Dehydrogenase, Glutamine Synthetase, Glutamate Synthase 96
   Ammonia Uptake in Nitrogen-Fixing Organisms 98
GENETIC REGULATION OF NITROGENASE 100
   Genetics 100
   Control of Nitrogenase Synthesis. 102
PHYSIOLOGICAL CONTROL OF NITROGENASE ACTIVITY 104
EVOLUTION WITHIN NITROGEN-FIXING SYSTEMS. 107

Since the subject of dinitrogen fixation was last considered in this series (18), a number of reviews (11, 38, 71, 252, 258) and books dealing with the subject in considerable detail (51, 219, 220, 222) have appeared. The author's main interest in dinitrogen fixation is centered on the process occurring in the legume root nodule, and the physiological and genetic control of the ancillary metabolism necessary for it to occur. Selected data relating to the nitrogenase enzyme are summarized, where possible, in relation to the situation in the nodulated legume. Some extrapolation from the properties of nitrogenase to natural situations is made, particularly as they apply to genetic and physiological control of enzyme production and activity. Progress in the inorganic chemistry of N_2 fixation is not discussed.

[1]Written while on sabbatical leave in the Department of Botany. University of Durham, England.

Dinitrogen fixation is a property of only prokaryotic organisms—bacteria, blue-green and otherwise. The distribution within the bacteria ranges from obligate aerobes through facultative to obligately anaerobic organisms. The N_2-fixing aerobes are in discrete taxonomic groups; the incidence in the facultative organisms is scattered, whereas the anaerobes have a wide range of N_2-fixing types (220). A recent table of the N_2-fixing prokaryotes and the symbiotic associations in which they participate can be found in the same review.

Since 1971, considerable progress has been made in the purification and study of the chemical character of the nitrogenase (N_2ase) components from a range of organisms, with reliable data on the metal, inorganic sulphide, amino acid composition, and subunit size and molecular weights becoming available. Answers to questions about which of the two components of N_2ase interacts with N_2, ATP, and reductant, and about the sequence of electron transfer within the enzyme complex, appear at last to be forthcoming. The electron donor systems supplying electrons to nitrogenase have been at least partially elucidated in a number of different systems, with interesting implications for the evolution of nitrogenase activity.

Nitrogenase activity can be controlled in at least two main ways—by physiological manipulation of the existing enzyme, and by genetic control of the rate of its synthesis and destruction. Some of the main environmental influences on N_2ase activity have been identified, but the control of enzyme synthesis and degradation is still far from clear. In particular, it has become obvious that we need to understand not only the control of N_2ase itself, but also the control of the enzyme systems responsible for incorporating the fixed nitrogen into amino acids. Progress has been relatively rapid in defining the genetic system responsible for the structure of N_2ase.

Probably the least progress has been made in understanding how the legume (or indeed the nonlegume) nodule works, although the methods of anaerobic growth of rhizobia on nitrate seem promising for studying the possible changes that occur when free-living rhizobia become symbiotic.

Overshadowing all the effort being applied to N_2 fixation in all its facets, is the problem of population increase. N_2 fixation is as fundamental to the biosphere as photosynthesis, and dwindling world reserves of fossil fuels point up the difficulties for the future of the alternative chemical production of fertilizer nitrogen. The nodulated legume producing either grain or leaf protein is independent of applied fertilizer nitrogen with all its ecological, economic, and environmental disadvantages. It is my view that in the short term at least, the future for alleviating world shortage of protein lies with the nodulated grain legume. While it is also vital to explore the possibilities of genetic inclusion of nitrogen-fixing capability in non-nitrogen-fixing angiosperms, the work on legumes must remain a major concern.

THE NITROGENASE ENZYME AND ITS PROPERTIES

Purification

Nitrogenase has been purified from a range of bacteria: *Azotobacter vinelandii* (46, 53, 233), *A. chroococcum* (149), *Bacillus polymyxa* (150), *Clostridium pasteurianum* (186, 187, 266), *Chromatium* (278), *Klebsiella pneumoniae* (97), *Myco-*

bacterium flavum (27), *Rhizobium japonicum* (24, 101, 140), *R. lupini* (154, 275), and *Rhodospirillum rubrum* (27), and from the blue-green alga, *Anabaena cylindrica* (247). In all cases, the activity is resolved by chromatography into two components, the first containing nonheme iron and molybdenum, and the second containing iron as the metal component. Inorganic (acid-labile) sulfide has also been invariably associated with both components. In this review, the nomenclature for the components is that of Eady et al (97). Reports of requirements for more than two components for active N_2ase (146, 260) apparently are erroneous (142, 233); in one case the components isolated appear to be an Mo-containing subunit and an Mo-free Av 1^1 (147, 148).

Nitrogenase purification involves (*a*) an extraction from the bacterial cell; (*b*) some form of preliminary purification, usually not involving chromatography; (*c*) resolution of the complex into two proteins and their separation by various chromatographic procedures; and (*d*) their storage. Procedures will not be given in detail here, as many are well documented, but the absolute requirement for O_2-free conditions should be emphasized.

Extraction from the bacterial cell is preceded in symbiotic systems by isolation from the plant tissue, usually entailing blending in the absence of O_2 in the presence of soluble or insoluble polyvinylpyrrolidone [to remove phenolic compounds (173)] in buffers containing a reducing agent (23, 24, 154, 161). Extraction of N_2ase from isolated bacteroids then follows lines similar to those used in other bacteria. Although effective in isolating active nitrogen-fixing bacteroids from legume nodules, these methods seem to have been unsuccessful with nonlegume nodules. Disruption of bacteria uses either autolysis of cells vacuum dried at 45° (186, 266, 268), sonication (154, 251), osmotic lysis (204, 234), or passage through various forms of pressure cell (23, 27, 46, 53, 97). A special problem with certain bacteroid preparations is the sudden drop in pH accompanying depolymerization of bacteroid poly-β-hydroxybutyrate on disruption. While this has been noted for soybean (161) and snake bean (275), lupin (154, 275) and serradella (275) present no such problem.

Preliminary purification is accomplished using differential protamine sulfate precipitation (46, 53, 101, 186), heat treatments (24, 53), fractional precipitation with polypropylene glycol (101, 161), and various other procedures. A number of the more recent methods (97, 154, 233, 265, 275) dispense with preliminary purifications.

Separation of the two components by chromatography on DEAE-cellulose uses a variety of buffer systems and salt gradients (NaCl or $MgCl_2$) for elution, and is followed by gel filtration methods suited to the size of the particular component. Only the Av 1 protein has been crystallized (54, 233), the insolubility of Av 1 in dilute (40–60 mM) salt solutions being used to achieve crystallization. The crystals in the former case were white, and spectral data have been reported to indicate cytochrome *c* contamination (233); the latter were brown but had an activity not significantly different from the white.

¹See Table 1 for definitions of bacterial abbreviations.

Components and Subunits

Criteria of purity include behavior during ultracentrifugation and during electrophoresis in polyacrylamide gel, with or without sodium dodecyl sulfate (SDS). Exclusion of oxygen during electrophoresis (234) is essential to avoid the production of apparently multiple bands, particularly with component 2 (97, 216, 233). Production of the correct number of subunit bands in SDS gels, a single band in free electrophoresis, and single ultracentrifuge peaks are rated in that order (71). Even then, active and inactive forms of components may be purified together; Cp 1 has been shown to contain a protein of identical subunit composition and electrophoretic mobility, but with no Mo, much less Fe, and no activity (187). Presence of such contaminants will cause erroneous values for metal content, substrate activity, or stoichiometry of subunit or component interactions. Table 1 summarizes some representative data for purified components.

Earlier variability for the molecular weight of Cp 1 has been attributed to its derivation as a weight average molecular weight with partly dissociated enzyme (134).

One feature which emerges is the apparent splitting of components 1 into one- and two-Mo proteins, apparently without relation to organism. The acetylene-reducing activities of components 1 are relatively constant per unit of Mo (71, Table 1), ranging from about 200 mol C_2H_2 reduced/min/mol Mo for Rj 1 and Rl 1 to 260 for Cp 1 and Kp 1, thus suggesting that all the enzymes have a similar environment for Mo, and that it is involved in substrate reduction. In Cp 1, Mo is found in association with a dimer (one of each type of subunit) after anaerobic dialysis at ' low pH where iron and sulfide have largely been lost (60). Treatment of Cp 1 with mersalyl, a thiol-complexing reagent, releases the Mo, sulfide, and most of the iron (71). It remains to be seen whether the one-Mo components 1 will prove to have lost Mo during purification or will still contain inactive protein, in view of the results with Cp 1 (134, 298).

Higher apparent activity per unit protein has been reported where a purified component is assayed with a crude complementary component. Since a range of proteins activate A. vinelandii N_2ase (286), such values must be interpreted cautiously in comparing purified nitrogenase components but may nevertheless be significant in vivo.

Of the symbiotic systems, Rj 1 and Rl 1 appear to have almost the same molecular weight and both differ from other systems in having apparently identical subunits (140, 275). After carboxymethylation, Rl 1 shows only one N-terminal amino acid (serine), consistent with identical subunits (276). Rl 2 subunits behave identically in SDS electrophoresis and have the same N terminus (serine). Although the Rl 1 and 2 values for molecular weight so far are only from gel electrophoresis and gel filtration, both components give single bands in anaerobic gel electrophoresis and have therefore been included.

An analysis of the pattern of amino acid composition in Cp 1, Av 1, and Kp 1 shows considerable overall similarity (60). The lower tryptophan content of Cp 1 compared to Kp 1 and Av 1 seems to be in disagreement with its markedly lower helix content when compared to Kp 1 (97). Both Cp 1 and Cp 2 have very low helix

Table 1 Some selected properties of bacterial nitrogenase components

Organism and refs.	Code	Molecular weight	Subunits	Mo	Fe	Labile sulfide	C_2H_2 reducing activity when saturated with other component (n moles/min/mg)	Ala	Arg	Asx	Half Cys	Glx	Gly	His	Ile	Leu	Lys	Met	Phe	Pro	Ser	Thr	Trp	Tyr	Val
Clostridium pasteurianum (71,134,186, 187,266)	Cp 1	210,000– 220,000	2 x 59,500 2 x 50,700	2	18	17–19	2200–2600	140	62	192	40	196	182	46	160	138	160	60	68	86	92	120	6	84	148
(194,266)	Cp 2	55,000– 56,000	2 x 27,500	0	4	4	2200–3100	40	24	45	34	70	60	4	34	52	32	16	11	18	24	24	0	18	12
Azotobacter vinelandii (53,54,233)	Av 1	270,000	2 types, both about 40,000	2	32–36	26–28	1640	169	108	249	34	250	206	55	134	190	177	86	102	101	134	115	50	79	173
(53,119, 233)	Av 2	40,000		0	2–3		1800–2100																		
Klebsiella pneumoniae (97,98)	Kp 1	218,000	2 x 50,000 2 x 60,000	1	17	17	1200	158	122	210	38	206	152	48	100	182	102	76	96	92	110	104	56	68	124
(97,98)	Kp 2	66,800	2 x 34,600	0	4	4	980	60	24	60	18	84	60	6	48	42	36	36	12	18	24	36	0	18	42
Rhizobium japonicum (140)	Rj 1	200,000	4 x 50,300	1.3	29	26	1000	162	94	182	23	179	170	53	112	136	122	39	80	89	109	89	29	65	126
(18)	Rj 2 (im- pure)	51,000		0																					
Rhizobium lupini (275)	Rl 1	200,000	one type, 57,000	1	18–20		1000	136	88	176	30	166	154	66	106	122	118	50	84	91	98	92		73	104
(275)	Rl 2	65,000	2 x 32,500	0	3		430	63	29	64	10	72	59	14	45	57	30	14	9	22	35	23		22	36

content (13–15%) (60). The amino acid compositions of Cp 1 subunits are relatively very similar, as they are for Av 1 subunits (53). The low histidine content and the absence of tryptophan from components 2 is yet another point of similarity to the ferredoxins (292) already indicated (71, 97, 205, 206).

The results of a wider comparison of nitrogenase components with each other and with other iron-sulfur proteins by statistical comparison of their amino acid compositions (124, 177) are presented in Table 2. In the method used, 98% of all proteins known to be related by sequence homology give an index less than 100 (177); a number of 70 (based on 18 amino acids) is considered to represent a nonfortuitous similarity of composition (124). Table 2 excludes data for cysteine and tryptophan and counts glutamine + glutamate together and asparagine + aspartate together.

The following broad generalizations can be made:

1. Components 1 appear to be a very closely related group of proteins, related to each other more closely than they are to the components 2.

2. Components 2 (very restricted data) also appear closely related to each other.

3. Neither component 1 nor 2 shows any likely relation to bacterial ferredoxins, despite specific similarities such as absence or low levels of tryptophan or histidine.

4. Nitrogenase components are much more similar to bacterial and algal flavodoxins than they are to ferredoxins. In specific cases, the similarity is particularly marked, e.g. to *E. coli* flavodoxin.

5. The nitrogenases are more like bacterial rubredoxins and plant ferredoxins than bacterial ferredoxins, but the relatedness appears to be less than with the flavodoxins. Ferredoxin and flavodoxin from the same organism appear to be unrelated (109).

Cross-reactions

Combination of nitrogenase components from different sources leads, in a majority of cases, to active nitrogenase, whether the activity measured is reduction of N_2, H^+, or another substrate (68). Table 3 illustrates these relationships (27, 68, 78, 150, 192, 220). Interactions between *Anabaena cylindrica* components and those of "*Chloropseudomonas ethylica*" have been omitted, owing to doubt about ownership of the latter nitrogenase (116, 247). The lack of interaction of either *A. vinelandii* or *K. pneumoniae* components with *C. pasteurianum* components, and the interaction of *A. vinelandii* and *K. pneumoniae* components, parallels the amino acid compositional differences (60). Whether interaction is associated with overall composition or more directly with helix content determined by composition remains to be determined. On very limited information, rhizobial N_2ase seems most closely related to those from aerobes and facultative anaerobes. It seems safe to generalize that N_2ases are very similar functionally, with a gradation in properties from strict aerobes to strict anaerobes. Differences between extremes are difficult to assess due to noninteraction. As pointed out by Postgate (220), the evolutionary divergence indicated is small; whether this is due to a short evolutionary history or very rigid structural requirements for nitrogenase activity cannot yet be decided.

Table 2 Relationships between nitrogenase proteins and other iron-sulfur proteins

	C. pasteurianum N₂ase 1	C. pasteurianum N₂ase 1-1	C. pasteurianum N₂ase 1-2	K. pneumoniae N₂ase 1	R. japonicum N₂ase 1	R. lupini N₂ase 1	A. vinelandii N₂ase 1	C. pasteurianum N₂ase 2	K. pneumoniae N₂ase 2	R. lupini N₂ase 2	C. pasteurianum ferredoxin	C. butyricum ferredoxin	M. aerogenes ferredoxin	Chromatium ferredoxin	B. polymyxa ferredoxin	A. vinelandii ferredoxin I	C. pasteurianum flavodoxin	D. vulgaris flavodoxin	D. gigas flavodoxin	E. coli flavodoxin	A. vinelandii flavoprotein	R. rubrum flavodoxin	Chlorella flavodoxin	C. pasteurianum rubredoxin	D. desulfuricans rubredoxin	P. elsdenii rubredoxin	M. aerogenes rubredoxin	P. oleovorans rubredoxin	Medicago ferredoxin	Leucaena ferredoxin
1. C. pasteurianum N₂ase 1	0										266	248	309	182	237	164	114	106	74	55	103	82	68	301	177	150	163	59	110	127
2. C. pasteurianum N₂ase 1-1	4	0									250	226	299	173	221	154	99	102	75	51	101	92	60	272	156	137	147	58	102	125
3. C. pasteurianum N₂ase 1-2	8	11	0								307	292	328	193	255	173	136	137	104	67	107	107	94	301	169	167	174	54	132	131
4. K. pneumoniae N₂ase 1	43	48	50	0							290	267	334	202	245	159	117	87	74	61	73	79	75	357	214	186	153	62	120	101
5. R. japonicum N₂ase 1	31	37	36	13	0						286	273	317	232	246	177	94	71	58	57	55	55	55	377	210	179	170	56	112	100
6. R. lupini N₂ase 1	20	22	20	15	13	0					270	253	295	203	235	173	122	93	88	57	83	81	73	326	172	151	156	45	119	121
7. A. vinelandii N₂ase 1	15	16	21	13	12	15	0				273	256	319	188	248	148	84	92	60	54	65	79	60	309	181	162	140	52	99	95
8. C. pasteurianum N₂ase 2	72	76	72	65	60	75	61	0			404	374	408	197	265	213	135	92	115	43	78	98	98	430	263	245	191	105	99	91
9. K. pneumoniae N₂ase 2	42	39	63	59	66	73	45	51	0		266	242	325	151	223	158	105	91	76	49	126	112	68	379	198	171	169	108	96	119
10. R. lupini N₂ase 2	49	52	66	40	28	43	54	38	37	0	239	242	265	191	194	171	83	43	59	36	82	67	49	413	227	188	182	84	77	91
Refs.	60	60	60	97	140	275	275	60	97	275	77	77	77	293	293	289	162	96	96	271	99	63	300	77	77	77	77	14	77	77

Table 3 Cross-reactions of nitrogenase components from bacteria

References		Av 1	Ac 1	Rj 1	Kp 1	Rr 1	Mf 1	Bp 1	Cp 1	Dd 1
(78, 192)	Av 2	⊕		+	+			−	−	
(27, 150)	Ac 2		⊕		+	±	±	+		
(192)	Rj 2	+		⊕						
(27, 78, 150, 220)	Kp 2	+	+		⊕	+	+	+	−	+
(27)	Rr 2					⊕				
(27)	Mf 2		+		+	+	⊕	+		
(27, 78, 150, 192, 220)	Bp 2	+	tr	+	+	+	+	⊕	±	+
(27, 78, 150, 192)	Cp 2	−		−	−	−	−	+	⊕	

Ac = *Azotobacter chroococcum*
Av = *Azotobacter vinelandii*
Bp = *Bacillus polymyxa*
Cp = *Clostridium pasteurianum*
Dd = *Desulfovibrio desulfuricans*
Kp = *Klebsiella pneumoniae*
Mf = *Mycobacterium flavum*
Rj = *Rhizobium japonicum*
Rr = *Rhodospirillum rubrum*

+ = activity from about 50% to 100%.
± = activity over 20% but less than about 50%
tr = trace.
− = no complementation.

Enzymatic Properties

All nitrogenases studied require a source of electrons ATP and Mg^{2+} for the reduction of N_2 or any other substrate. The dependence on ATP is absolute; other nucleoside triphosphates are inactive (49, 97, 122, 189). Mg^{2+} can be replaced by Mn^{2+} Co^{2+}, Fe^{2+}, or Ni^{2+}, but with decreased activity (49, 85, 97, 123, 138). ATP is hydrolyzed to ADP and P_i (49, 55, 156). The stoichiometry of ATP utilization during reduction of substrates has been widely discussed; lowest estimates quoted per electron pair (uncorrected for reductant-independent ATPase activity) are 4.3 and 3 for *A. vinelandii* and *C. pasteurianum* preparations, respectively (71, 266). Although ATP hydrolysis occurs in the absence of reductant, both N_2ase components are required (43, 143). The apparently higher requirement for *A. vinelandii* N_2ase has been attributed to a second mechanism of ATP hydrolysis that does not result in electron transport (118).

A wide range of substrates besides N_2 is reduced by N_2ase, including N_2O, C_2H_2 and higher alkynes, cyanide, various nitriles and isonitriles, and azide. For a discussion of the reaction products and suggested mechanisms, see references 53, 71, 120, and 121. ATP consumption per electron pair transported to substrate varies widely with a minimum value for C_2H_2 reduction (137). In the presence of ATP and reductant, but in the absence of other substrates, H^+ is reduced to H_2 (44, 48, 123). Since there is no isotope effect on H_2 evolution (141), it has been suggested that ATP hydrolysis is the limiting reaction, with electron flow partitioned between other substrates (when present) and H^+ according to the properties of the other substrate (49, 122). Although ATP hydrolysis has been considered independent of substrate (see 120), substantial enhancement of hydrolysis by a range of substrates has been reported (137, 149), particularly with cyanide and isocyanide. Only C_2H_2 appears to accept the electrons sufficiently rapidly to virtually prevent H_2 evolution (53, 137). Interrelationships between the substrate analogs have been analyzed for *A. vinelandii* and *K. pneumoniae* N₂ases (138, 210). CO inhibits all reductions except that of H^+ but is not reduced; H_2 inhibits only N_2 reduction. From the pattern of inhibition, N₂ase substrate-binding sites were classified into several types: for N_2 or H_2; for azide, cyanide, or isocyanide; for C_2H_2; for CO and for H^+. However, while cyanide inhibits C_2H_2 reduction, C_2H_2 does not effect cyanide reduction and may stimulate it, implying different sites for N_2, C_2H_2, and cyanide (98). Multiplicity of binding sites appears improbable, but substrates may interact with variable combinations of the same group of sites. Reduction of cyanogen, thiocyanate, and cyanate has recently been listed (see 220); products include methane.

A. vinelandii, C. pasteurianum, and *R. japonicum* N₂ases also catalyze an ATP- and reductant-dependent exchange of D_2 with H_2O. Exchange occurs only in the presence of N_2 and not with other substrates, and is inhibited by CO (71, 141, 267). Hydrogenase activity cannot explain this action since it does not catalyze the exchange reaction in *A. vinelandii* or in pea nodule bacteroids (90). Contradictory reports (26, 150) query the requirement for N_2 for D_2-H_2O exchange by *A. vinelandii* N₂ase, although supporting it for nodule N₂ase. The mechanism behind D_2-H_2O exchange remains obscure, although the occurrence of an exchange catalyzed by Pt-diimide and Pt-hydrazine complexes has prompted the suggestion that enzyme-bound diimide or hydrazine on N₂ase is involved (141). In bacteroid extracts, CO inhibits N_2 reduction competitively and D_2-H_2O exchange noncompetitively, whereas identical kinetics of CO inhibition would be expected if intermediates of N_2 reduction are involved (267).

The ratio of the components required for optimal N₂ase activity has been estimated for *C. pasteurianum* and for *K. pneumoniae*. A value of one 220,000 mol wt Cp 1 to two 55,000 mol wt Cp 2 has been suggested (71, 187, 268). For *K. pneumoniae* components, the ratio of Kp 1 (218,000) to Kp 2 (67,000) for optimal reduction of N_2 or H^+ was 1:1 (97). Excess Cp 1 over Cp 2 (172) or Kp 1 over Kp 2 (97) inhibits electron transfer to N_2, C_2H_2, or H^+, but not ATP hydrolysis. The ratio for optimal activity also varies with substrate (97, 149, 150).

Nitrogenases from a wide variety of organisms are inactivated by O_2; only crude N₂ase from *A. vinelandii* and *A. chroococcum* are at all resistant (44, 150). Blue-green algal (32, 127, 245) and rhizobial (18, 102, 275) N₂ases are completely O_2-sensitive. Generally, components 2 are much more sensitive than components 1, and storage in liquid N_2 (151) is the only safe method, although components 1 can be stored at $-15°$.

In addition, various components 2 are also cold-labile and inactivated at around
$0°$ even with added reducing agent; thus crude *A. cylindrica* N_2ase (126), crude
R. rubrum N_2ase (50), Av 2 (45), Ac 2 (149), Cp 2 (190), and Mf 2 (27) are
cold-labile; Kp 2 (97), Rj 2 (102), and crude *Chromatium* N_2ase are not (278). The
mechanism of cold inactivation and the structural features of N_2ases permitting or
preventing cold lability are not understood.

ATP Binding and Electron Transfer

Early studies of ATP binding to N_2ase components produced conflicting results.
Whereas binding of ATP to Cp 2 was shown to require Mg^{2+} while ADP binding
did not (42), ATP and cyanide binding to Kp 1, Kp 2, and other proteins was found
to be nonspecific (26). From the kinetics of C_2H_2 reduction as a function of ATP
concentration, two sites for ATP interaction with N_2ase were inferred (189), and
ADP, known to be an inhibitor of N_2ase (42, 44, 112, 241), was shown to block
N_2ase reactions once the ATP/ADP ratio fell to less than 0.5. Multiple binding sites
for ATP and ADP have also been suggested for rhizobial N_2ase (154). ATP and
other nucleoside triphosphates sensitize crude *A. chroococcum* N_2ase to O_2 (287).
Mg^{2+} is antagonistic, suggesting that bound metal is important in structure maintenance, a view reinforced by sensitization to O_2 after anaerobic treatment with
Chelex-100 or EDTA. Anaerobic ATP treatment followed by dialysis does not
result in sensitivity to O_2. The effects are on Ac 2; Hill plots again suggest at least
two sites of ATP action for C_2H_2 reduction, for $MgCl_2$ action, and for induction
of O_2 sensitivity. The evidence is considered consistent with ATP altering the ligand
conformation around a metal in such a way as to potentiate interaction of Ac 2 with
Ac 1 along lines suggested earlier (240). ADP inhibition of N_2ase from *K. pneumoniae* is competitive with respect to N_2 (210), while the rhizobial N_2ase is more
sensitive to ADP than any others (154). In crude N_2ase preparations, AMP appears
to be inhibitory (189, 210); in purified preparations (156) it has no effect, suggesting
that phosphorylation to ADP occurs in the less purified systems. Control of N_2ase
activity via the ATP/ADP ratio is an obvious possibility for intracellular regulation
(154, 189), but remains to be demonstrated directly in vivo. The fact that the growth
yield in NH_3-limited *C. pasteurianum* cultures is not less than in N_2-grown cultures
(66) while the N_2ase is present at three times the concentration (67) suggests a
control of this type over ATP hydrolysis.

Electron paramagnetic resonance (EPR) spectra of purified N_2ase components
have recently clarified some of the partial reactions catalyzed by each type. The EPR
spectra of Cp 1, Av 1, and Kp 1 are very similar, if not identical, with signals at
$g = 2.01, 3.68$, and 4.33 (76, 205, 206, 242). Previous reports of $g = 1.94$ signals
akin to those for ferredoxins appear due to impurities (71, 76, 233). Since no
broadening or additional lines occur when Cp 1 contains 76% ^{95}Mo, and because
no hyperfine structure is seen corresponding to natural Mo isotopes, the EPR
spectrum is attributed to a polynuclear Fe system rather than Mo (206). The EPR
spectra of Av 2, Cp 2, and Kp 2 (205, 206, 242) are also closely similar, with g values
2.05, 1.94 (mid-point), and 1.88, closely resembling EPR spectra for ferredoxins
(207).

Addition of Mg^{2+}/ATP to Av 2 or Cp 2 changes the resonance to an axial form, increases or produces a $g = 4.3$ split signal, and reduces intensity in the $g = 2$ region (205, 299). Titration with ATP indicates a binding of nearly 2 mol ATP per mol of Cp 2 (299). Mg^{2+} with either ADP or ATP produces similar effects, as does β,γ-methylene-ATP, but not α,β-methylene-ATP. An effect of Mg^{2+}/ATP in creating a second environment for Fe is suggested (205); an alternative is a conformational change because $5M$ urea mimics the Mg^{2+}/ATP effect on Cp 2 (299). Of course, the two are not mutually exclusive. Addition of Mg^{2+}/ATP to Cp 1 or Av 1 produces either no change (299) or a slight quantitative change (205) in EPR spectrum; mixture of Cp 1 with Cp 2 without either Mg^{2+} or ATP produces only a slight change. On addition of ATP/Mg^{2+} to Cp 1 + 2 in dithionite, the Cp 1 signal decreases or disappears almost completely, to return again when either dithionite is exhausted or ADP inhibition occurs (188, 205). Exhaustion of reductant causes the Cp 2 signal to disappear. Estimates of half time show that the Cp 2:Mg^{2+}/ATP complex forms before the Cp 1 signal disappears (188). Similarly the $g = 3.68$ resonance disappears when Kp 1 + 2 are incubated under steady state conditions (Mg^{2+}/ATP/dithionite/ATP generator), but not if any of the first three components is omitted (242). Exhaustion of dithionite causes the reappearance of the Kp 1 EPR spectrum. Lauth's Violet oxidizes Kp 1 to a form with no EPR spectrum and without inactivation; dithionite slowly restores the spectrum alone, the restoration being unaffected by Kp 2 or ATP/Mg^{2+} alone but occurring with $t_{1/2} = 10$ msec when both are added together. Kp 2 reduced with dithionite and separated from it by gel filtration causes very rapid regeneration of the Kp 1 EPR spectrum when added with Mg^{2+}/ATP (242). The data are all consistent with Mg^{2+}/ATP acting on component 2 to cause electron transport to component 1 with substrate (H^+, N_2, or analog) then being reduced.

The EPR spectrum reported for *C. ethylicum* 1 is quite unlike those for Av 1, Cp 1, or Kp 1; its $g = 1.94$ signal suggests contamination with ferredoxin-like proteins or a vastly different component 1 (103). Since ATP and cyanide affect the spectrum directly, the presence of inactive component 2 might explain the results.

The rate-limiting reaction in the sequence is open to question, and its identity depends on the oxidation state of the EPR-negative component 1. If indeed this is an oxidized state induced by electron transfer to H^+ or N_2, and the EPR-negative species is 90 percent of the total, the implication is that electron transfer to substrate is not limiting. With ATP/Mg^{2+} activation of Cp 2 preceding electron transfer to Cp 1 and being faster, electron transfer from Cp 2 to Cp 1 would then be the limiting reaction. If, however, Lauth's Violet (242) or phenazine methosulfate (188) do not produce the same species as the EPR-negative form of Cp 1, the EPR-negative species might be a reduced one, and substrate reduction would then be rate-limiting (242). The lack of an isotope effect on ATP-dependent H^+ reduction might imply that the latter is not the case (141). Disappearance of the EPR signal from Kp 2 is reported (243) to occur at the same fast rate as the appearance of the Kp 1 signal while the reducing agent (dithionite) is being exhausted, strongly indicating that in the functional complex the EPR-negative form of Kp 1 is a reduced state.

Analysis of kinetic data for variable ratios of Rj 1 and Rj 2 also leads to the conclusion that Rj 1 binds the substrate and Rj 2 carries the ATP-binding site (24).

Direct effects of H^+ and C_2H_2 on the EPR spectrum of Kp 1 indicate that this component binds the substrate (243).

ATP (or ADP)/Mg^{2+} in the presence of dithionite induces a form of Kp 2 in which –SH groups titratable with DTNB are more accessible, and in which association is demonstrable in the ultracentrifuge; dithionite prevents this association (263). Again the implication of conformational change induced by ATP is obvious, but whether this is its only function remains open. An interesting parallel is the ATP-dependent DNAase (259, 269) involved in bacterial DNA recognition processes, where one suggestion for ATP function is maintenance of a specific conformational state able to discriminate between homologous and foreign DNA (294). Electron activation in this hydrolytic enzyme activity is obviously not involved.

Molybdenum Function within Nitrogenase

The function of the Mo in nitrogenase has been the subject of much study in view of the analogies to inorganic Mo complexes with cysteine (230–232), 2-aminoethane-thiol (129), and glutathione (273) in capabilities for ATP-stimulated reduction of N_2 or its analogs. Certain strains of *Azotobacter* known to grow in media where V replaced Mo (7) were also found to have significant N_2ase activity. Many of the features of this N_2ase were similar to normal Mo-N_2ase, but activity and stability to heat, O_2, and storage appeared decreased (9, 52). The affinity of V-N_2ase for N_2, C_2H_2, CO, and other substrates was lower (52, 174), a greater proportion of electrons went to H^+ rather than to other substrates, and the ratio of C_3H_6:C_3H_8 from acrylonitrile reduction changed (52). The inference that Mo was directly involved in substrate reduction (52) led to a model of a dinuclear Fe-Mo system for N_2 reduction (119, 120). The N_2ase activity in V-grown cultures was later attributed to contaminant Mo (9), and the V found in Ac 1 was suggested to cause conformational modification of Mo-Ac 1 to increase its stability. However, others (52) consider that Mo contamination could account for only 10 percent of the observed N_2-ase activity from V-grown cells. If the apparent V-N_2ase is due to contaminant Mo, which competes very efficiently with V for incorporation into N_2ase (9), the kinetic differences may only be due to changes in the ratio between Mo-containing component 1 and component 2, since normal Ac 2 formation occurs during growth on V (9). With *R. japonicum* N_2ase, increasing the ratio of Rj 2 to Rj 1 does increase the K_m for N_2 and C_2H_2 reduction (24).

Tungsten is also incorporated into N_2ase, producing a catalytically inactive enzyme (10), a parallel to the case for nitrate reductase in plants (201, 208) and *A. chroococcum* (117).

Fragments of Mo-containing enzymes produced by acid (pH 2.0–2.5) treatment of xanthine or aldehyde oxidases complement the NADH-cytochrome *c* reductase fragment of *Neurospora crassa* nitrate reductase to restore nitrate-reducing activity (158). Nitrogenase, Cp 1, Av 1, or Rj 1 will do the same, in some cases without acid treatment, with Rj 1 the most effective on a protein basis (196). It is possible that an appreciable protein unit is incoporated; with xanthine oxidase, the molecular weight of the cytochrome *c* reductase was 50,000 (195), while that of the reconstituted nitrate reductase was 235,000 (158). The unit derived from Cp 1 probably resembles that (60) from which iron and sulphide, but not Mo, have been lost. Controlled enzymatic digestion of component 1 should indicate the minimum requirements for the complementation to occur.

Alteration of the basicity of protons on ligands coordinated to Mo as a result of alteration of the Mo oxidation state has been suggested as the common mechanism behind oxidation-reduction reactions catalyzed by Mo- enzymes (254). In the case of N_2, which was postulated to be bound end-on to an Fe site, reduction of Mo causes ligands to become protonated, so that coupled electron and proton transfer to N_2 can occur to produce bound diimide. Reduction of Mo and reprotonation of its ligands were proposed so that the reduction of N_2 continued. If a similar process is involved in nitrate reductase and nitrate is not bound to Mo, the electron transfer section of both enzymes might well be rather similar, as the complementation studies with *N. crassa* nitrate reductase suggest. It would also imply that Mo is involved not only with reduction of N_2, but may be involved with C_2H_2 binding as well, and with H_2 evolution. Reduction of bis-N_2 complexes of Mo and W (59) to produce hydrazine complexes, taken with the reduction of Mo-hydrazine complexes (273), clearly implicates Mo as the probable binding site for N_2 throughout its reduction by N_2ase.

Bacteroid nitrate reductase and nodule N_2ase appear strongly correlated (61); taken with the above results this may mean a structural common denominator between N_2ase and nitrate reductase, particularly in the rhizobia (102). Presumably any such structural common denominator should be demonstrable immunologically. That nitrate reductase is high in nodule bacteroids is probably due to anaerobiosis, since anaerobic nitrate-grown *R. japonicum* and bacteroids both contain comparable levels while air-nitrate cells have much lower activity (74). It seems possible that *Rhizobium* ferredoxin (164), which is also induced during anaerobic-nitrate growth (216), might also be involved with both nitrate reductase and N_2ase.

ELECTRON DONOR SYSTEMS FOR NITROGENASE

The sources of electrons for N_2 reduction and the metabolic pathways they follow to N_2ase have been considered extensively in three recent reviews (11, 251, 258). Because of the author's bias, only the symbiotic legume system will be considered here.

A system of H_2, hydrogenase, and ferredoxin from *C. pasteurianum* will support C_2H_2 reduction by bacteroid N_2ase with an added ATP-generating system (281).

The general occurrence of high concentrations of poly-2-hydroxybutyrate (PHB) in nodule bacteroids (62, 107, 114, 281) and the high activities of 2-hydroxybutyrate dehydrogenase (36, 281) are compatible with an electron transfer sequence

$$\text{2-hydroxybutyrate} \longrightarrow NAD^+ \longrightarrow FAD\ (FMN) \longrightarrow N_2\text{ase} \longrightarrow N_2$$
$$\text{dyes}$$

With FMN or FAD, NADH dehydrogenase from bacteroids markedly increased the reduction rate; however, activities were low in relation to dithionite, flavin concentrations relatively unphysiological, and a correlation between N_2ase activity and PHB or 2-hydroxybutyrate dehydrogenase activity lacking (281).

A system generating NADPH could be coupled to bacteroid N_2ase (282) with bacteroid iron-sulfur protein (164), azotoflavin (12, 132, 288), and ferredoxin-NADP reductase, with electron flow

glucose 6-phosphate $\longrightarrow$ bacteroid iron-sulfur protein $\longrightarrow$ N_2ase $\longrightarrow$ N_2
$+$ azotoflavin

Addition of FAD or FMN removed any requirement for bacteroid iron-sulfur protein or azotoflavin, short-circuiting electron flow between NADP-ferredoxin reductase and N_2ase (282). It was shown that although bacteroid iron-sulfur protein and azotoflavin accelerated C_2H_2 reduction with dithionite in a similar way to that found for *Azotobacter* N_2ase (286), their effects in increasing electron transfer from $NADP^+$ to N_2ase were relatively much greater although the absolute rates were low (282).

With spinach chloroplast fragments lacking photosystem II, light was shown to energize electron transfer from ascorbate-2:6-dichlorophenolindophenol to *Azotobacter* N_2ase or crude bacteroid N_2ase, and C_2H_2 reduction was increased by adding an electron carrier from bacteroids (290). Purification of this factor (164) showed it to be a very O_2-labile iron-sulfur protein. Its status as a ferredoxin remains in doubt owing to its inactivity in light-driven $NADP^+$ reduction with ferredoxin-$NADP^+$ reductase, or in the clostridial phosphoroclastic reaction. Some evidence is available that a second electron carrier, perhaps analogous to azotoflavin, occurs in bacteroids (11, 164, 216) but its nature is uncertain. Such carriers are not detected in normal laboratory cultures of rhizobia.

Anaerobic nitrate growth of *R. japonicum* produces cells with many of the characteristic cytochrome changes from the laboratory form usually associated with bacteroids (74). Growth under such conditions is slow and very restricted among rhizobial strains (74). From extracts of such cells a protein with similar properties to bacteroid iron-sulfur protein can be isolated; the identity of the two cannot be assumed yet (216). The spectra were similar but not identical; if they are the same, anaerobic nitrate growth produces less than one percent of the bacteroid level (216). Other factors found in the anaerobic nitrate cells apparently transfer electrons to N_2ase; one at least seems not to be present in bacteroids and may not normally be involved with N_2 reduction.

Anaerobic nitrate growth of rhizobia does not induce synthesis of N_2ase components (217), a fact that is not surprising in view of a likely high pool of ammonia from nitrate reduction repressing N_2ase biosynthesis. Soybean bacteroids, however, will slowly reduce N_2 or C_2H_2 anaerobically in the presence of nitrate (226), the rate being related to the nitrate-reducing capacity of the bacteroids. C_2H_2 reduction activity due to endogenous electron donors is approximately doubled by adding glucose or succinate, but only succinate is effective for nitrate reduction. Nitrite inhibits N_2ase activity, probably accounting for the short period of linear C_2H_4 production. The system is artificial in that nodules do not normally contain nitrate, and nitrate reductase appears to be induced by the absence of O_2 rather than the presence of nitrate (74); however, it does indicate that the nitrate reductase involved is probably dissimilatory and presumably coupled to oxidative phosphorylation. The complex cytochrome chains in rhizobia (4) may well be involved in electron transport to nitrate.

It appears likely that the specific electron carriers for N_2 reduction in rhizobia differ from those in other organisms in being inducible by anaerobiosis; production in other organisms appears to be constitutive in relation to ammonia (220), but the situation with respect to O_2 cannot be readily resolved in the anaerobes, and in the facultative and aerobic N_2-fixing bacteria low effective intracellular O_2 concentration is a necessary requirement for N_2ase function and probably biosynthesis. Production of the electron carriers in relation to O_2 concentration seems not to have been examined in detail. If, as in *Azotobacter*, the carriers are specific for N_2ase (220), mutants may be found which are phenotypically *nif⁻* but where the lesion lies in the electron transport system.

Bacteroid hydrogenase (88, 89) has been shown to resemble that of *Azotobacter* in being particulate, having a similar range of electron acceptors, not evolving H_2, having a very low rate of catalysis of D_2–H_2O exchange, and being associated with ATP production coupled to O_2 reduction (90). Strains of pea rhizobia differ in the hydrogenase activity of their bacteroids, and the activity of any individual strain is host-regulated. The function most favored is improvement of energetic efficiency by reuse of H_2 evolved from N_2ase to reduce O_2 and thereby produce ATP (90). Hydrogenase occurrence may be more widespread than presently known for rhizobia, since if its activity is less than that of ATP-dependent H_2 evolution from N_2ase, it is not detected without mass spectrometric methods. The *Azotobacter* enzyme (139, 227) may have a similar function.

Evidence is accumulating that $NADP^+$ may be a key electron carrier from which electrons are channeled to N_2ase in *Azotobacter* (13), nodule bacteroids (282), and blue-green algae (32, 111) from a general metabolic pool. In the blue-green algae, ferredoxin may be a central compound for N_2ase electron supply, accepting electrons from NADPH, other substrates, and possibly directly from photosystem I (138, 170, 245, 246). Phytoflavin may also be involved (32). At the moment the direct photoreduction of ferredoxin and subsequently N_2ase is a controversial topic, recently reviewed by Stewart (251), but it seems safe to assume that no one reducing system is responsible for N_2ase activity in blue-green algae, and that different systems probably function under different conditions. In a similar way ATP may well be generated from photosynthetic phosphorylation in the light, and from oxidative or substrate-level phosphorylation in the dark.

ROUTES OF AMMONIA ASSIMILATION IN DINITROGEN-FIXING SYSTEMS

Tracer Studies

It is well documented that the initial stable product of N_2 reduction is ammonia. This conclusion is derived from the similarity of labeling patterns produced from $^{15}NH_3$ and $^{15}N_2$ (1, 47, 272, 296) and by the production of $^{15}NH_3$ from $^{15}N_2$ by whole cells (1, 296), nodules (16, 152, 153), or cell-free N_2ase (58). Incorporation of NH_3 into organic form was often assumed to result directly in glutamate by reductive amination of 2-oxoglutarate catalyzed by glutamate dehydrogenase (GDH) because glutamate and glutamine contained the highest amino acid label from either $^{15}N_2$

or $^{15}NH_3$ (1, 5, 47, 152, 153, 296, 297). The alternative possibility (165) that the primary route might well be through the amide-N of glutamine seems to have lapsed from lack of a mechanism for cyclic glutamate formation from glutamine, although several studies (1, 167, 298) had shown enrichments of ^{15}N in the amide group of glutamine that equalled or exceeded the enrichment in the amino group of glutamate. In alder nodules, where citrulline appears to be the main nitrogen storage and translocation compound, the carbamyl-N has a higher ^{15}N content from $^{15}N_2$ than does glutamate (166). In other nonlegume nodules where asparagine and glutamine are the main storage and transport amino acids (29), the amide-N of glutamine also had the highest amino acid labeling (167). In legumes, however, tracer evidence is not available to support the idea that NH_3 might be bound first as glutamine.

Glutamate Dehydrogenase, Glutamine Synthetase, Glutamate Synthase

In bacteria, amino acid dehydrogenases are not the only, nor indeed even the main, mechanism for ammonia incorporation into amino acids. Salient observations include the following:

(a)   Mutants of *E. coli* are known which grow normally on ammonia but lack glutamic dehydrogenase (GDH) (270).

(b)   No GDH activity can be detected in extracts of *C. pasteurianum,* although amino acid biosynthesis appears to involve glutamate as the central compound (70); other clostridia do, however, contain GDH (277).

(c)   In *Klebsiella aerogenes* cultures growing on limiting ammonia, the NADP-linked GDH falls to less than 3 percent of the level found with high NH_3, and the internal pool ammonia is then 0.5 mM, less than one tenth the Michaelis constant for the GDH for NH_3. No other pathway of ammonia assimilation known at that time accounted for the observed rate of ammonia utilization (182). Low activities for GDH during ammonia limitation are recorded for *Erwinia carotovora, Pseudomonas fluorescens, Bacillus subtilis,* and *B. licheniformis* (183, 262).

(d)   In *K. aerogenes,* ammonia limitation leads to an increase in glutamine synthetase (GS) activity, although it is not clear whether this is achieved by derepression of synthesis or activation of existing enzymes (180). A brief pulse of ammonia then leads to a 25-fold increase in pool glutamine in 2 min, but other amino acids receive the bulk of incorporated ammonia (262).

(e)   A reductive step has been demonstrated which results in the transfer of the amide-N of glutamine to 2-oxoglutarate with concomitant oxidation of NAD(P)H (183, 261) and appears to be a major route for NH_3 incorporation into amino acids. The enzyme catalyzing this transfer, glutamine (amide):2-oxoglutarate amino-transferase (oxidoreductase) (GOGAT), is a specific enzyme and not an artifactual combination of glutaminase and GDH. In each organism where the GS/GOGAT system is claimed to operate, it is necessary to establish that both enzymes are present and that the oxidation of NAD(P)H occurring when glutamine is added to the system is due to GOGAT and not to coupled action of glutaminase and GDH.

The control of these enzymes and pathways has been discussed in detail by Brown et al (37); only a brief summary is presented as background to N_2-fixing systems.

Glutamate dehydrogenases exist with dual coenzyme specificity (110) and with single coenzyme specificity but biosynthetic or catabolic roles (38, 39). In many organisms, the biosynthetic GDHs are repressed when environmental (or pool) ammonia is at low concentration and are at high activity when pool ammonia is high. However, in others one GDH may serve a dual role and be under complex control (38); and in yet others with both NAD- and NADP-linked enzymes, the former behaves as a catabolic enzyme relatively unresponsive to ammonia concentration, while the NADP enzyme is biosynthetic and repressed in low ammonia conditions (39).

The control of GS is complex; in *Escherichia coli* a complicated pattern of control of enzyme synthesis (284), cumulative feedback inhibition of enzyme activity (135, 283), and chemical modification of enzyme structure and activity (238) exist to modulate overall activity. Overall, low pool ammonia appears to correlate with high enzyme activity, the GS activity also appearing to be low when amino acid pools are high in *E. coli* (179), *B. subtilis* (225), *K. aerogenes* (180), *Lactobacillus arabinosus* (224), and *Pseudomonas* spp. (38, 39).

In *E. coli,* for which the most complete picture of GS control exists, feedback inhibition occurs with endproducts of glutamine metabolism (283), and the degree of inhibition is cumulative (135). *E. coli* GS exists in two interconvertible forms—GSa (or GS I) which is active with Mg^{2+} but not with Mn^{2+} and resistant to feedback inhibition, and GSb (or GS II) which has an opposite metal specificity and is sensitive to feedback inhibition. Conversion of GSa to GSb is enzymatic, involving an adenyl transfer from ATP to one or more tyrosyl hydroxyls of GS$a,$ a reaction stimulated by glutamine and its products (237) and inhibited by 2-oxoglutarate and high ATP levels (133). Deadenylation requires at least two proteins and is inhibited by glutamine and AMP and stimulated by ATP and 2-oxoglutarate (236). This pattern serves to facilitate glutamine synthesis when energy charge and 2-oxoglutarate concentration are high and glutamine and its products low, as occurs during ammonia limitation.

In *Bs. subtilis,* however, no adenylation control system occurs, and GS activity is directly sensitive to glutamine, AMP, and glutamine products as feedback inhibitors (79). The K_m for NH_3 for bacterial GS is usually low (less than 0.5 mM), in contrast to values for GDH (5–40 mM), a difference of obvious importance for NH_3 assimilation.

GOGAT has been found in many prokaryotes, including several N_2 fixers. It has a low K_m for glutamine (0.2–0.5mM) and 2-oxoglutarate (2–7 mM) and specificity for glutamine, 2-oxoglutarate (185), and either NADH or NADPH. The GOGAT in an organism seems to be of only single coenzyme specificity (37, 193), although the situation in *C. pasteurianum* may be clouded by transhydrogenase activity (69). GOGAT is constitutive in some organisms lacking GDH (69, 70, 100, 183) but ammonia limitation generally produces the highest activities (37). Although ammonia or glutamate limitation produces similar pool levels of these compounds in *K. aerogenes,* GOGAT activity is high in the former and low in the latter, implying that neither compound alone is the repressor. Glutamate accumulated as an osmotic regulator in NaCl- or glutamate-stressed *K. aerogenes* or *B. licheniformis* does not cause repression of GOGAT (181, 183). Alanine addition to carbon-limited *B. licheniformis* cultures containing a high glutamate pool results in GOGAT repression. GOGAT is inhibited by a wide range of amino acids when purified from *E. coli* (185).

In *K. aerogenes, E. carotovora,* and *Pseudomonas* spp., GS, GOGAT, and GDH are controlled independently (38–40), while in *E. coli* two independent mutations affecting GS and GDH are required before glutamate auxotrophs are produced (15). Coordinate linkage of the genes for these enzymes appears unlikely, although an organization of GS and GOGAT into a functional complex is possible. Cyclic adenosine 3', 5'-monophosphate (cAMP) is also involved in regulation of NH_3 assimilation in *E. coli*; it causes increases in GDH and GS activities while repressing glutaminase A (221).

The GS/GOGAT system achieves precisely the same end result as GDH—reductive amination of 2-oxoglutarate—but the increase in ability of an organism to grow at low ammonia concentrations is paid for as increased energy cost in using one ATP per glutamate formed. In comparisons of the energetics of growth on N_2 with growth on unlimited ammonia (66, 67, 72, 73, 131, 145) this extra cost must be included if indeed ammonia is generally assimilated via this route in N_2-fixing organisms.

Ammonia Uptake in Nitrogen-Fixing Organisms

Among N_2-fixing organisms, GOGAT has been demonstrated in *K. pneumoniae* (193), *A. vinelandii* (193), *A. chroococcum* (95), *C. pasteurianum* (69, 193), *Chromatium* (193), *Chlorobium thiosulfatophilum* (193), and *R. rubrum* (193). Bacteroids of *R. lupini* (36, 155), *R. japonicum* (36, 193), and *Rhizobium leguminosarum* (36) have GOGAT activity, but those of *Rhizobium meliloti* from lucerne and *Rhizobium phaseoli* from red runner bean do not (36). Laboratory cultures of *R. leguminosarum, Rhizobium trifolii,* and *R. japonicum* have GS and GOGAT activities under appropriate conditions (36). In very few cases, however, are the data conclusive for the operation of the GS/GOGAT pathway for NH_3 assimilation from N_2, mainly because full data indicating levels of GS and GOGAT compatible with N_2ase activity have not been presented.

In batch cultures of *K. pneumoniae* grown on N_2, the GOGAT level was slightly lower than in those grown on NH_3, but the GOGAT/GDH ratio changed from 0.4 to 22, indicating that control was exerted on GS and GDH. In the same cultures, the apparent adenylation value for GS (250) decreased from 11 on NH_3 to 2–3 on N_2 (193). In sulfate-limited chemostat cultures of *A. chroococcum,* GOGAT and GDH levels remain constant irrespective of the nitrogen source, amino acid or ammonia pools (95), implying that any control must have been on GS, although this remains to be demonstrated. *Chromatium* GS may also be regulated by enzyme modification (193). In *C. pasteurianum,* GOGAT activity is unaffected by ammonia concentration, but GS activity was repressed by growth on NH_3 instead of N_2, and GDH has not been identified at all (69, 70).

In the lupin nodule system, GS is present in both plant and bacteroid fractions with sufficient NAD-linked GOGAT to match N_2ase activity (36, 155). The K_m for

2-oxoglutarate for GOGAT is very low (<1 μM), and aspartate at 0.5 mM inhibits it by 50%; asparagine and glutamate, two of the principal nodule amino acids (152), do not. The ^{15}N labeling pattern in serradella is at present inconsistent with operation of the GS/GOGAT system, since amide-N contains less newly fixed ^{15}N than glutamate (152).

In laboratory cultures of *R. japonicum,* NADP-linked GDH is repressed by aspartate and glutamate (36, 108) but induced by high NH_3 (36, 108). NAD-linked GOGAT is hardly affected by NH_3 or glutamate concentration; GS is repressed by high NH_3 but not by glutamate (36). Nodule bacteroids, from which NADP-linked GDH is absent, contain NAD-linked GDH and NAD-linked GOGAT, but the GS activity appears inadequate to allow for NH_3 incorporation at observed rates of N_2 fixation. Plant GS is very much the major part of total GS activity. From the chemostat evidence, the occurrence of high GOGAT activities may indicate only that GOGAT is not regulated, rather than that it is necessarily functional in the nodule.

In the fast-growing *R. leguminosarum,* both GS and NADP-linked GOGAT are repressed by high NH_3 or nitrate, and GOGAT by high glutamate, under chemostat conditions (36). GDH is partially repressed by glutamate, while in the nodule bacteroids from broad bean (*Vicia faba*) and pea it is absent altogether, and the GDH activity is NAD-linked (36). GS and GOGAT activities are both inadequate to account for NH_3 incorporation from N_2, and again plant GS is very high (36). In *R. trifolii,* chemostat studies indicate that high NH_3 represses GS and GOGAT and induces GDH; high glutamate represses all three. Data for bacteroids are not available. In the bacteroids of *R. phaseoli* and *R. melitoti* apparently lacking GOGAT, GDH is significantly higher than in those containing GOGAT activity (36).

Since the main exported nitrogen compounds from nodules appear to be glutamine and asparagine (predominantly the latter) (212), further work is needed to clarify where and how NH_3 is actually assimilated into organic form, and where it is subsequently converted or reconverted to glutamine and asparagine. Indeed it still remains possible that ammonia, the main product of fixation by bacteroid suspensions (22, 163), may be excreted into the plant system for conversion to glutamate, glutamine, and asparagine. The higher atom percent excess ^{15}N found in bacteroids (157, 160) may only represent rapid saturation of the amino acids synthesized by the bacteroids for their own maintenance, and the high activities of GOGAT found in lupin and soybean bacteroids may well be due to inherent lack of regulation of this enzyme. The conditions responsible for repression of the NADP-linked GDH of bacteroids are still not identified, but the pattern otherwise is consistent with a high NH_3 concentration within the bacteroid. Perhaps the NH_3 pools of bacteroid and plant are the two NH_3 pools postulated in serradella (153) and soybean (16).

In the blue-green algae, the route of NH_3 assimilation has received considerable attention. The free amino acid pools of *Anabaena cylindrica, A. flos-aquae,* and *Westelliopsis prolifica* are largely aspartate, glutamate, and glutamine, a condition typical for organisms incorporating via the GS/GOGAT pathway (81). ATP-dependent NH_3 incorporation in *A. cylindrica* extracts (32) is associated with GS activity (80, 81, 126), which appears adequate to account for published rates of N_2 fixation (128). That its activity is higher in heterocysts than in vegetative cells (126) suggests its involvement in assimilation of NH_3 from N_2, although the evidence for its regulation is not clear. From the relatively modest increase in activity from NH_3 uptake to N_2 fixation (80), it appears likely to be involved in both processes. The presence of GOGAT was reported (81), but the activity was extremely low and almost certainly due to combined action of glutaminase and GDH (126). Other assays for GOGAT in N_2-fixing strains were made in *tris* buffer (197), which proved to be strongly inhibitory to bacterial GOGAT (36). Even assays in noninhibitory buffers (41) have proved negative, however. Accordingly, the presence of GOGAT in blue-green algae appears at present improbable.

GDH is well documented in blue-green algae (214), alanine dehydrogenase (AlaDH) and GDH being found in most unicellular forms, while in the filamentous forms AlaDH occurs in six out of ten but both AlaDH and GDH in only one (197). In the N_2-fixing strains, growth on N_2 increased AlaDH and decreased GDH levels compared to growth on nitrate (197).

It is therefore possible that NH_3 from N_2 flows through glutamine and is transported as such away from the N_2ase so that it can be hydrolyzed elsewhere by glutaminase to provide NH_3 for other reductive aminations and glutamate for transamination (126). Such a scheme, which is expensive in terms of ATP, will require demonstration by ^{15}N labeling from $^{15}N_2$ of the appropriate amino acids of both heterocysts and vegetative cells.

In summary then, the GS/GOGAT pathway is likely to function in many free-living N_2-fixing bacteria, with the probable exception of the blue-green algae. While its occurrence in laboratory-grown rhizobia and some nodule bacteroids is clear, its functional significance in the nodule is uncertain. In nonlegume nodules, ^{15}N labeling patterns suggest rapid incorporation of NH_3 into the glutamine amide-N, but whether this occurs via an endophyte GS/GOGAT system or a plant GS remains to be established.

GENETIC REGULATION OF NITROGENASE

Genetics

A number of mutants apparently unable to fix N_2 have been isolated in past years, but their characterisization has not always been achieved. As yet even a definite number of structural genes for N_2ase itself cannot be specified; a minimum of three is obvious for *C. pasteurianum* and *K. pneumoniae* from component subunit structure, but there may be two in *R. lupini* (275) and *R. japonicum* (140), where Rl 1 and Rj 1 appear only to have one type of subunit. The number of regulator genes involved, the specificity of the genes for electron carriers to N_2ase to N_2 fixation, and the possible effects of indirectly involved genes remain to be defined. Mutations in uptake genes for Mo might produce an apparently *nif⁻* phenotype if cells were tested on NH_3 media; growth in virtually Mo-free conditions does occur on NH_3, but such mutants should also not grow on nitrate. In view of the possible common

Mo protein between N_2ase and nitrate reductase, however, nif^- mutants could in some cases be nit^- as well.

Initial studies of the nif genes have been made in $K.$ $pneumoniae$. Generalized transducing phage P1 for $E.$ $coli$ and $Shigella$ was used to transfer genes for N_2 fixation from fixing to nonfixing mutants of $K.$ $pneumoniae$ M5A1 with a frequency of about 1–4 x 10^{-5} (256); two-point transductional crosses between nif^- mutants indicate a requirement for "several genes scattered across one region of the chromosome" for N_2 fixation. At least one mutant, nif-23, appears to have lost nitrate reduction as well. Cotransductional analyses indicate that nif and histidine (his) genes are closely linked (256), and later work indicates that the nif region corresponds to about 15–20 average gene lengths (257). However, at least two nif^- mutants appear to have lesions unlinked to his, and one regulator mutant blocks both his and nif, but the overwhelming majority are linked to his. Deletions produced by phage 2 extend through gluconate-6-phosphate dehydrogenase (gnd), nif, and his (257). There is no apparent involvement of cAMP as nonproducing mutants show normal N_2ase induction independent of exogenous cAMP. For $A.$ $vinelandii$, cAMP does not alleviate ammonia repression of N_2ase (95). Mutants in glutamate synthase (GOGAT) do not grow on N_2 although N_2ase is induced at a lowered level in $K.$ $pneumoniae$, possibly because NH_3, whose incorporation may be limited by the high K_m GDH, accumulates and represses N_2ase synthesis (193).

Conjugating strains of $K.$ $pneumoniae$ do not fix N_2 (86), but the introduction of a derepressed R factor into strain M5A1 from $E.$ $coli$ allows it to transfer chromosomal material. Crosses between nif^+ M5A1 carrying the R factor and streptomycin-resistant (str^r) nif^- M5A1 produces nif^+str^r cells with a 1 X 10^{-5} frequency. A close linkage of nif to his was also confirmed (86). Intergeneric transfers of nif, with a high frequency his-transferring R-factor system in str^s M5A1 as donor, and a nonrestricting, nonmodifying his^-str^r $E.$ $coli$ as recipient were selected for by screening for his^+str^r cells; in two experiments 10 of 12, and 2 of 6, his^+ hybrids were also nif^+ (87). Ammonia repression of N_2ase synthesis in the $E.$ $coli$ hybrids show that regulatory and structural genes are probably transmitted together. The question of whether $Klebsiella$ or $Escherichia$ electron carriers to N_2ase were being used remains to be answered.

Identity of the N_2ase synthesized in $E.$ $coli$ hybrids with $K.$ $pneumoniae$ N_2ase has been demonstrated immunologically (56, 57). It appears that while the nif genes are chromosomal in $K.$ $pneumoniae$, they are often plasmid-borne in $E.$ $coli$ hybrids (56, 57), a finding possibly explaining the instability of the hybrids in N_2ase production. However, the N_2ase appears to be integrated into the chromosome in some of the $E.$ $coli$ hybrids (56, 57).

Undoubtedly the genetic manipulation of the nif genes offers interesting possibilities for wider transmission of nif within bacteria and, perhaps, via phages or extracted DNA into eukaryotic systems by various methods (93, 168, 169). Some sense of perspective for practical agricultural exploitation of N_2ase genetics needs to be maintained; we cannot afford to neglect the proven potential of symbiotic systems while pursuing new opportunities for incorporating N_2 fixation into agricultural crops where it does not at present occur.

Control of Nitrogenase Synthesis

In batch cultures of N_2-fixing organisms grown on NH_3, N_2ase activity only appears after NH_3 is exhausted, and then after a lag period of variable length (95, 176, 215, 234, 255). Amino acid additions shorten this lag, the explanation being offered that amino acid pools are required for N_2ase synthesis (213, 291). Where the cultures were not N-limited during most of their growth, it is highly probable that derepression or activation of the GS/GOGAT pathway is the limiting step, although this has not been shown. In chemostat cultures limited by NH_3 or urea, N_2ase activity is derepressed to levels above those in normal cultures growing on N_2 (30, 66, 67, 73, 191), and the NH_3 pool size in cells growing on N_2 alone, while significant, is still markedly lower than under repressed conditions (81, 95). Internal NH_3 varies as expected for the corepressor for N_2ase synthesis, but cannot yet be identified as such because any one of its many derivatives may be the active species. Repression and derepression are coordinate in $A.$ $vinelandii$ (76, 234) and $A.$ $chroococcum$ (95) for the two N_2ase components. In partially derepressed conditions, the intracellular membranous network observed in N_2-fixing cultures but absent from NH_3-grown cultures (204) is present to a moderate extent in all cells (95). A different pattern of lipid composition is associated with the N_2-fixing cultures, although no change in total lipid occurs (178).

A number of phenotypically nif^- mutants of $A.$ $vinelandii$ are defective in functional Av 1, Av 2, or both (235), and complementation between appropriate extracts occurs (106, 235, 249). Curiously, however, Av 1 activity is never completely absent in any mutants assayed with Av 2, and this residual activity is genuine in being completely suppressible with antibody to Av 1 (235). In some cases, the EPR signal at $g = 3.65$ from Av 1 is 10–20 times stronger than expected for the C_2H_2-reducing activity, suggesting defective synthesis of the protein. Where no functional Av 2 activity occurs, immunological assay sometimes reveals cross-reacting but obviously inactive protein (235).

In blue-green algae, N_2ase activity in N_2/CO_2 or air-grown cells is increased two- to tenfold by a period of N starvation (198, 244), which also decreases the NH_3 and glutamate pools (81). It is repressed by growth on NH_3 (252) or urea (31). Nitrate, which produces effects similar to NH_3 in $A.$ $vinelandii$ (95), has a variable effect of N_2ase synthesis in blue-green algae (30, 198, 202), probably depending on whether nitrate reduction opposed to NH_3 assimilation produces a high or low internal NH_3 pool. The situation is complicated by effects of combined nitrogen on heterocyst production, which also appear to vary with different organisms. In many cases, ammonia or nitrate represses heterocyst formation; in others, particularly with nitrate, variable results are reported (105, 198, 251, 280), and this may again reflect an ammonia (or its derivatives) pool situation.

Constitutive mutants for N_2ase have been found in $A.$ $vinelandii$ (115, 248). Reversion of nif^- strains producing neither Av 1 nor 2 leads, in about one third of the cases, to constitutive mutants (115), which produce lowered N_2ase activities when grown on N_2 but are only about 50% repressible by the NH_3 concentrations reported. The effects of higher NH_3 concentrations on such mutants are not known; it is possible that an altered repressor protein still would be able to cut off N_2ase synthesis at higher NH_3 concentrations. 2-Methylalanine, which inhibits growth of *A. vinelandii* on N_2 almost completely, on nitrate partially, and on NH_3 not at all, has been suggested as a possible corepressor (248). The 2-methylalanine effect is seen only in cultures using glucose or maltose (228). A partly constitutive mutant is as much inhibited by 2-methylalanine as a wild type, implying that NH_3 or its metabolites and 2-methylalanine do not work at the same site, although they might still affect the same repressor protein (115). A nonmetabolizable compound like 2-methylalanine seems an unlikely candidate for a corepressor.

Attempts to determine whether N_2ase is induced by presence of N_2, virtual absence of NH_3 or some metabolite from it, or both, have not been resolved completely because of the technical difficulties in removing N_2 from gases. Thus, when *K. pneumoniae* cultures exhaust their supply of NH_3 and are incubated under 0.7 atm He containing only 0.044 ppm N_2, N_2ase induction occurs (209) even though a maximum of 20–100 molecules of N_2 per cell could have been present. With *A. vinelandii*, incubation of cultures which have exhausted NH_3 under He/O_2 allows N_2ase induction (255), but N_2 in the gases is still a significant factor. It has been pointed out (71) that for *A. chroococcum* induced under Ar/O_2 of known purity (73), N_2 would need to be effective at 10 nM, or about 0.1% of that required for induction of β-galactosidase in *E. coli* by isopropylthiogalactoside. While specific N_2 binding at this dilution appears improbable, it would be interesting to see if added C_2H_2 would perhaps interfere with N_2ase induction as it does with N_2ase activity.

Addition of fixed nitrogen (as NH_3, urea, or nitrate) to N_2-fixing cultures has effects which vary with the organism. In *C. pasteurianum* (66, 67) and *K. pneumoniae* (176) N_2ase remains active when NH_3 is added, and dilutes out through growth. In *A. vinelandii* (95, 234), simple dilution occurs for about half a generation, followed by active destruction, with 95% of enzyme either destroyed or inactive in two generations. An inhibitory effect of added NH_3 on N_2ase in resting cells has been noted (122). Urea repression of N_2ase in *A. flos-aquae* also appears to cause active destruction (31). In *A. cylindrica*, nitrate-grown cells derepressed under N_2/CO_2 produce a peak of C_2H_2-reducing activity which rapidly declines as growth resumes, apparently due to a buildup of combined nitrogen (198).

Highly significant from the ecological aspect is the finding that the concentration of NH_3 required for complete repression of N_2ase synthesis is directly related to population density (95). NH_3 concentrations in the soil solution, and in many natural waters are usually low and appear inadequate to repress N_2ase activity. It appears that in many situations, with the possible exception of root rhizospheres and similar specialized locales, carbon limitation to growth must usually limit N_2 fixation. Under these conditions of very slow and restricted growth, internal ammonia concentrations in N_2-fixing organisms may still be sufficiently high to repress N_2ase biosynthesis.

Of the genetics of N_2ase and its control in legume nodules we know very little with certainty, not even the location of the N_2ase genes. A suggestion (84) that some part of the nodule N_2ase might be plant-specified has been tested by examining the properties of component 1 from nodules where either the plants or the rhizobial strains have been varied independently. The results show no discernible differences in electrophoretic properties attributable to either variable, but there were significant differences in the content of four amino acids due to varying rhizobial strain, and in two amino acids by varying the plant species (217). The preliminary conclusion that only rhizobial variation is significant is not established; the plants chosen (*Vigna sinensis* and *Phaseolus aureus*) admittedly show different leghemoglobin (Lb) types but are nevertheless both from the tribe Phaseolae of the Leguminales (136), and therefore they do not constitute the most appropriate comparison in view of the obviously greater conservatism of N_2ase amino acid composition compared to that of Lb (Table 2, 35). In these circumstances, the significant difference in two amino acids attributable to the plant type may well be important, even though the major influence under these experimental conditions comes from the rhizobia. However, the apparent identity of the subunits within Rj 1 (140), Rl 1, and Rl 2 (275) leaves little room for plant-specified material unless still smaller subunits occur in the N_2ase components. The same type of experiments are still to be done with component 2, and are currently in progress in our laboratory. An alternative approach is that of introducing into rhizobia a derepressible N_2ase operon capable of turning on rhizobial N_2ase genes as well, perhaps in conjunction with anaerobic conditions. If rhizobial N_2ase is completely specified genetically by bacterial DNA, it follows that repression in *Rhizobium* is either achieved by lower NH_3 concentrations than in other N_2-fixing bacteria, or by an entirely different mechanism, since it does not fix N_2 apart from the plant even during N Starvation.

Lb, whose production in legume nodules is normally correlated with N_2 fixation, is genetically defined by the plant (65, 82). The possibility that variations due to rhizobial genes had been missed because both studies had used similar rhizobial strains was eliminated when typical fast- and slow-growing rhizobia nodulating the same legume were shown to produce indistinguishable Lbs (34). Heme synthesis by the nodule system also seems to involve a joint rhizobial-plant pathway, whose partitioning appears to vary with the plant (64, 113). Properties, synthesis, and possible functions of Lb have been reviewed recently (3, 4).

PHYSIOLOGICAL CONTROL OF NITROGENASE ACTIVITY

Physiological control of existing N_2ase seems to be mediated by several probably interacting factors, each of which can presumably interact directly with the enzyme or influence supply lines for ATP or electrons. In symbiotic systems where the prokaryote is dependent on its photosynthetic host for carbohydrate, light will obviously be a major factor if the system has no oxidizable reserves for dark periods. It appears likely that light and other influences on photosynthesis and translocation will be seen with rhizosphere associations such as *Paspalum notatum-Azotobacter paspali* (91) and corn-*Enterobacter* (223) just as with many nodulated legumes (175) and nonlegumes (274).

Products of N_2 fixation (NH_3 and amino acids) consistently have no effect on cell-free N_2ase preparations (58, 66, 67, 154), so product inhibition is improbable as a control. Ammonia repression has already been considered in the genetic regulation of N_2ase formation.

The ATP/ADP ratio has been mentioned as a potential regulator of N_2ase activity and appears the most probable one, although little direct evidence for its operation in vivo is available. There is an obvious advantage to an organism in not consuming all available ATP via N_2ase if its energy charge is low (189) and being able to fix N_2 when its energy charge is high. Direct analysis for intracellular concentrations of ATP and ADP in cells growing on either N_2 or limiting NH_3 with high derepressed N_2ase levels should clarify the point, although the constant growth yields of *C. pasteurianum* under these conditions indicate that N_2ase is controlled by energy supply (66). The physiological factors affecting ATP/ADP ratios are obviously complex in whole organisms and even more so in symbiotic systems.

O_2 has long been known to inhibit N_2 fixation even in aerobic organisms such as *Azotobacter* (184). Its inhibitory effect on all N_2ases except crude extracts of *A. vinelandii* and *A. chroococcum* indicates that natural protective mechanisms must operate, particularly in the blue-green algae with their O_2-evolving photosynthesis. A number of possible mechanisms for this protection have been suggested, some morphological and some physiological.

Slime production, often a characteristic of N-limited bacterial cultures (131), may play a role in reducing the diffusion of O_2 into *Derxia* (130), *Azotobacter* (218), *Enterobacter* (223), and blue-green algae.

Physical barriers to O_2 and specific metabolic changes to prevent O_2 access to N_2ase are clear in the blue-green algae. Here the development of thick-walled heterocysts occurs as a probable physical barrier (104, 280) and the repression of photosystem II formation (33, 92) presumably prevents O_2 evolution in the light. Higher respiratory activity in the heterocyst (105) may also aid in keeping the O_2 concentration down. Sensitivity to exogenous O_2 can, however, still be demonstrated (253). N_2 fixation in nonheterocystous filamentous blue-green algae is possible only at low pO_2 (252) with a normal soluble and O_2-sensitive N_2ase (127). *Gloeocapsa*, a unicellular form, appears to fix aerobically (285), but the extracted N_2ase is still O_2-sensitive (112). Its mode of protection, apart from slime outside the cells, is obscure, although its reported association with particles may be significant (112). The suggested compartmentation implies that the heterocyst receives carbon compounds from the undifferentiated cells and exports nitrogen compounds to them. The question of whether undifferentiated cells in heterocystous species can also synthesize N_2ase remains controversial, but under microaerophilic conditions it appears probable. If indeed N_2ase can be introduced into a plant cell then the chloroplast appears the least likely place to put it, and the mitochondrion the best available place.

In the aerobic azotobacters, two mechanisms of protection have been postulated (72, 73) and reviewed recently (131, 218)—respiratory and conformational. The evidence for respiratory protection, conferred by respiration consuming O_2 before it can reach the N_2ase, is compelling and is also important in facultative anaerobes such as *K. pneumoniae* (159). Respiration at high pO_2 appears to be uncoupled at site I; there is increased synthesis of NAD (P)H dehydrogenase and of cytochrome a_2, which may terminate a chain of low energy conservation efficiency (144). Because of respiratory protection, cultures grown at high pO_2 have high ATP/N_2

ratios (131); at low pO_2 the figure of 5.2 ATP/N_2 based on the difference in growth yield between C-limited cultures supplied N_2 or NH_3 may need correction downward by 2 if the former is incorporated via the GS/GOGAT pathway and the latter via GDH. In view of the much greater apparent consumption of ATP in *C. pasteurianum* (66, 67), *K. pneumoniae,* and *Desulfovibrio desulfuricans* (131), the N_2- and NH_3-grown *A. chroococcum* cultures appear not to be truly comparable in energy conservation, in respiration, ATP generation coupled to H_2 oxidation after evolution from N_2ase, or in some other way.

The evidence for conformational protection—assumption of a shape excluding O_2 and substrates from the N_2ase in response to O_2 concentrations above those consumable by respiration—is by contrast circumstantial. Much rests on whether the O_2-insensitive N_2ase isolated from *Azotobacter* is a true physiological entity or an artifact of disruption in which the membrane found with the N_2ase (203) has protected it accidentally. A lag time in reactivation of N_2ase occuring on removal of excess O_2, a possible objection to a mechanism involving direct removal of electrons by O_2 from N_2ase or one of its carriers (131), may only represent reduction of slightly damaged component 2, which on prolonged oxygenation would become inactive (94). Both respiratory and conformational protection seem to imply an intracellular localization of N_2ase internal to the respiratory membrane.

In the legume-*Rhizobium* system, compartmentation appears to have been coupled to synthesis of a specific O_2 transport system to facilitate N_2 fixation. The failure to fix N_2 in the absence of O_2 (17) and the obligatory respiratory habit of *Rhizobium* in laboratory culture imply that ATP formation for N_2ase in the bacteroid is probably coupled to respiration. A requirement for these densely bacteria-packed cells is to transport O_2 at low tension (2) but at high flux (4). Aeration pathways through the nodule (19) and Lb to facilitate O_2 diffusion are the apparent solutions evolved. A localization of Lb between bacteroid membrane and membrane envelope (20, 83, 265) is consistent with this role for Lb, although localization of Lb is still in question (75).

Lb addition to dense bacteroid suspensions at low pO_2 stimulates acetylene reduction up to fortyfold, but respiration only up to twofold (25). The implication that respiration coupled to ATP generation for N_2ase has a higher K_m for O_2 than does general respiration is the reverse of what might be expected, since the reverse arrangement of K_m values would seem more favorable to guarantee ATP for N_2ase without endangering it by a higher O_2 concentration. Respiratory protection by the bacteroids is probably involved. Higher ATP/ADP ratios in the bacteroids should be demonstrable in the presence of Lb. The effect is mediated through a higher effective oxygen concentration at the bacteroid membrane and not through direct transfer of superoxide between oxyLb and the bacteroid terminal oxidase (279). The nodules formed on the nonlegume *Trema* by a typical cowpea *Rhizobium* (264) should logically be found to contain an analogous protein to Lb. Why nonlegumes, which are also dependent on O_2 for activity (28), are independent of Lb-like pigments awaits isolation of the endophyte and characterization of the systems supplying ATP and electrons to N_2ase, since these may still be essentially anaerobic.

The rhizosphere associations between free-living N_2-fixing organisms and higher plants are also O_2-sensitive (91, 125), and the isolates from them also show O_2 sensitivity of N_2 fixation to varying degrees. To manipulate these associations to our advantage requires much better understanding of their physiology than we have, at present, but increasing the root excretion to create an N-deficient, C-rich, and almost anaerobic environment seems a likely possibility. Such an environment should favor growth of N_2-fixing organisms with a ready sink for the NH_3 resulting from their eventual death.

EVOLUTION WITHIN NITROGEN-FIXING SYSTEMS

A possible paradox in the evolution of N_2ase would occur if primitive anaerobes evolved the enzyme during the stage of biotic evolution when plentiful NH_3 was available anaerobically (218). If N_2ase did evolve in organisms not fixing N_2, the most likely function suggested is that of detoxification of substrate analogs such as cyanide, azide, or acetylene (239). If the exhaustion of fixed nitrogen compounds occurred anaerobically, or if the original anaerobic atmosphere was N_2/CO_2 rather than NH_3/CH_4, the paradox vanishes, and N_2ase could have evolved initially in the anaerobes, subsequent cellular modifications allowing it to survive later aerobic conditions. Geochemical data relating the time when N_2ase evolved to the time when fixed nitrogen was exhausted and O_2 appeared would resolve the question, but are unlikely to be available.

Much of the above argument rests on N_2ase being an ancient enzyme because of its reductive character and requirement for anaerobiosis. A consideration of relatively late evolutionary emergence of N_2ase leads to a suggestion that its subsequent distribution may have been limited to those species still having suitable internal environments or electron carriers for its function (220). The very wide and unpredictable occurrence of N_2ase in the bacteria (blue-green and otherwise), and in particular its very limited occurrence in anaerobic groups, may have arisen for this reason (220). The close relatedness of the N_2ase proteins (Table 2), which might be interpreted as favoring recent evolution, was recognized as equally likely to support an ancient origin and conservatism for functional reasons (220), as for cytochrome c. It was pointed out that since *nif* genes can be plasmid-borne, their very scattered occurrence in the enterobacteria might be accounted for by the frequent loss or gain of the genes.

The problem of why eukaryotes have never acquired N_2ase is explained by a late evolutionary origin, evolution having already taken the eukaryote too far towards genetic rigidity and aerobiosis for it to be accommodated (220). It is also suggested that blue-green algae, which are often thought to have given rise to chloroplasts by endosymbiosis, and which still form symbiotic associations with plant groups up to the angiosperms, acquired N_2ase only after chloroplast development had proceeded too far for it to function. Objections to a late emergence of N_2ase can be found; if N_2 fixation has always been the function of heterocysts in blue-green algae and if *Gunflintia minuta* (171) was a fossil heterocystous species, N_2 fixation would date to 2×10^9 years ago. Another objection concerns the function for *Azotobacter* ferredoxins and flavodoxin before N_2ase was transferred to it, since no function other than electron transport to N_2ase is known for them today, and selection prior to N_2ase acquisition would have been expected to eliminate them. It is nevertheless somewhat easier to explain the absence of N_2ase from eukaryotes on an assumption of late evolution, though in the bacteria and blue-green algae it seems no more likely than an ancient origin.

The first stages of evolution of nodular N_2-fixing systems, postulated as rhizosphere associations of varying specificity (211), are now well established (91, 125, 233), although the intermediate stage of an intercellular bacterial symbiosis remains to be found in angiosperms. Leaf nodules in *Psychotria,* an obvious possible example, seem to fix no N_2 (8), although intercellular blue-green algae in cycads undoubtedly do (21). Root nodulation by bacteria is restricted to relatively primitive plant families, raising questions of whether these families developed some special characteristics, or whether the more advanced families lost some characteristics necessary for establishment of symbioses. Discovery of nodulation within the more advanced families would imply that such characteristics did persist, and perhaps heighten hopes for artificially inducing symbiosis in such plants.

Genetic transfer of N_2ase to higher plants, a possibility which may no longer be science fiction, requires that we understand why eukaryotes have no N_2ase despite a probable 2×10^8 years of contact in the same plant cell of plant genomes with blue-green algal, rhizobial, or actinomycete genomes. It seems highly probable that the major obstacles to such transfers, aside from DNA restriction systems and other problems of gene incorporation, maintenance, and expression, lie in protecting N_2ase from cellular O_2, supplying it with ATP, finding or introducing electron carriers for it, and organizing a regulatory system for the disposal of its product and for its synthesis. A simple derepressed N_2ase system could be disastrous for the plant's chance of matching its requirements of carbon and nitrogen.

In assessing the chances of achieving N_2 fixation in other plants by inducing a complete nodular symbiosis, one is forced to consider the restriction of root nodule symbiosis to families generally considered primitive, and the reasons for it. Inducing a new symbiosis when we do not understand the genetics and control systems of the ones we have is a very difficult undertaking, that seems to offer even less chance of success that the direct introduction of N_2ase. The author is impressed by the fact that the would-be transferrer of N_2ase to a plant must succeed where nodulated legumes have been trying for some 2×10^8 years in however many nodule cells have been produced per year with some 10,000 bacteroid genomes per nodule cell, all without apparent success. Unfortunately, this does not absolve us from trying for either scientific or practical reasons, but it does require us, for very good practical reasons, to make the best possible use of the N_2-fixing associations we already have, and particularly the root nodule and rhizosphere associations.

ACKNOWLEDGMENTS

I am indebted to the colleagues in several countries who made manuscripts available to me, and to the various people in the University of Durham, who by their tolerance made this review possible.

Literature Cited

1. Allison, R. M., Burris, R. H. 1957. *J. Biol. Chem.* 224:351–64
2. Appleby, C. A. 1969. *Biochim. Biophys. Acta* 188:222–29
3. Appleby, C. A. 1974. See Ref. 222
4. Appleby, C. A., Dilworth, M. J. 1974. See Ref. 51
5. Aprison, M. H., Magee, W. E., Burris, R. H. 1954. *J. Biol. Chem.* 208:29–39
6. Bachmayer, H., Yasunobu, K. T., Peel, J. L., Mayhew, S. 1968. *J. Biol. Chem.* 243:1022–30
7. Becking, J. H. 1962. *Plant Soil* 16:171–201
8. Becking, J. H. 1971. In *Biological Nitrogen Fixation in Natural and Agricultural Habitats*, ed. T. A. Lie, E. G. Mulder. *Plant Soil*, special vol. 361–74
9. Benemann, J. R., McKenna, C. E., Lie, R. F., Traylor, T. G., Kamen, M. D. 1972. *Biochim. Biophys. Acta* 264:25–38
10. Benemann, J. R., Smith, G. M., Kostel, P. J., McKenna, C. E. 1973. *FEBS Lett.* 29:219–21
11. Benemann, J. R., Valentine, R. C. 1972. *Advan. Microbial Physiol.* 8:59–104
12. Benemann, J. R., Yoch, D. C., Valentine, R. C., Arnon, D. I. 1969. *Proc. Nat. Acad. Sci. USA* 64:1079–86
13. Benemann, J. R., Yoch, D. C., Valentine, R. C., Arnon, D. I. 1971. *Biochim. Biophys. Acta* 226:205–12
14. Benson, A. et al 1971. *Biochem. Biophys. Res. Commun.* 42:640–46
15. Berberich, M. A. 1972. *Biochem. Biophys. Res. Commun.* 47:1498–503
16. Bergersen, F. J. 1965. *Aust. J. Biol. Sci.* 18:1–9
17. Bergersen, F. J. 1966. *Biochim. Biophys. Acta* 115:247–49
18. Bergersen, F. J. 1971. *Ann. Rev. Plant Physiol.* 22:121–40
19. Bergersen, F. J., Goodchild, D. J. 1973. *Aust. J. Biol. Sci.* 26:729–40
20. Ibid, 741–56
21. Bergersen, F. J., Kennedy, G. S., Wittmann, W. 1965. *Aust. J. Biol. Sci.* 18:1135–42
22. Bergersen, F. J., Turner, G. L. 1967. *Biochim. Biophys. Acta* 141:507–15
23. Ibid 1970. 214:28–36
24. Bergersen, F. J., Turner, G. L. 1973. *Biochem. J.* 131:61–75
25. Bergersen, F. J., Turner, G. L., Appleby, C. A. 1973. *Biochim. Biophys. Acta* 292:271–82
26. Biggins, D. R., Kelly, M. 1970. *Biochim. Biophys. Acta* 205:288–99
27. Biggins, D. R., Kelly, M., Postgate, J. R. 1971. *Eur. J. Biochem.* 20:140–43
28. Bond, G. 1961. *Symp. Soc. Exp. Biol.* 8:59–72
29. Bond, G. 1971. See Ref. 8, 317–24
30. Bone, D. H. 1971. *Arch. Mikrobiol.* 80:234–41
31. Ibid, 242–51
32. Bothe, H. 1970. *Ber. Deut. Bot. Ges.* 83:421–32
33. Bradley, S., Carr, N. G. 1971. *J. Gen. Microbiol.* 68:xiii
34. Broughton, W. J., Dilworth, M. J. 1971. *Biochem. J.* 125:1075–81
35. Broughton, W. J., Dilworth, M. J. 1973. *Biochim. Biophys Acta* 317:266–76
36. Brown, C. M., Dilworth, M. J. 1973. Unpublished results
37. Brown, C. M., Macdonald-Brown, D. S., Stanley, S. O. 1972. *J. Mar. Biol. Assoc. UK* 52:793–804
38. Brown, C. M., Macdonald-Brown, D. S., Meers. J. L. 1973. *Advan. Microbial Physiol.* 11:1–52
39. Brown, C. M., Macdonald-Brown, D. S., Stanley, S. O. 1973. *Antonie van Leeuwenhoek* 39:89–98
40. Brown, C. M., Stanley, S. O. 1972. *J. Appl. Chem. Biotechnol.* 22:363–89
41. Brown, C. M., Whitton, B. A. 1973. Unpublished results
42. Bui, P. T., Mortenson, L. E. 1968. *Proc. Nat. Acad. Sci. USA* 61:1021–27
43. Bui, P. T., Mortenson, L. E. 1969. *Biochemistry* 8:2462–65
44. Bulen, W. A., Burns, R. C., LeComte, J. R. 1965. *Proc. Nat. Acad. Sci. USA* 53:532–39
45. Bulen, W. A., LeComte, J. R. 1966. *Proc. Nat. Acad. Sci. USA* 56:979–86
46. Bulen, W. A., LeComte, J. R. 1972. *Methods Enzymol.* 24:456–70
47. Burma, D. P., Burris, R. H. 1957. *J. Biol. Chem.* 225:287–95
48. Burns, R. C. 1965. In *Non-Heme Iron Proteins: Role in Energy Conversion*, ed. A. San Pietro, 289–97. Antioch Press
49. Burns, R. C. 1969. *Biochim. Biophys. Acta* 171:253–59
50. Burns, R. C., Bulen, W. A. 1966. *Arch. Biochem. Biophys.* 113:461–63
51. Burns, R. C. 1974. *Dinitrogen Fixation*, Vol. 1, pt. 2. New York: Wiley. In press
52. Burns, R. C., Fuchsman, W. H., Hardy, R. W. F. 1971. *Biochem. Biophys. Res. Commun.* 42:353–58
53. Burns, R. C., Hardy, R. W. F. 1972. *Methods Enzymol.* 24:480–96

54. Burns, R. C., Holsten, R. D., Hardy, R. W. F. 1970. *Biochem. Biophys. Res. Commun.* 39:90–99
55. Burris, R. H. 1971. See Ref. 218, 106–60
56. Cannon, F. C., Dixon, R. A., Postgate, J. R., Primrose, S. B. 1973. *J. Gen. Microbiol.* In press
57. Ibid. In press
58. Carnahan, J. E., Mortenson, L. E., Mower, H. F., Castle, J. E. 1960. *Biochim. Biophys. Acta* 44:520–35
59. Chatt, J., Heath, G. A., Richards, R. L. 1972. *J. Chem. Soc. Chem. Commun.* 1010–11
60. Chen, J.-S., Multani, J. S., Mortenson, L. E. 1973. *Biochim. Biophys. Acta* 310:51–59
61. Cheniae, G., Evans, H. J. 1957. *Biochim. Biophys. Acta* 26:654–55
62. Craig, A. S., Greenwood, R. M., Williamson, K. I. 1973. *Arch. Mikrobiol.* 89:23–32
63. Cusanovich, M. A., Edmondson, D. E. 1971. *Biochem. Biophys. Res. Commun.* 45:327–36
64. Cutting, J. A., Schulman, H. M. 1969. *Biochim. Biophys. Acta* 192:486–93
65. Ibid 1971. 229:58–62
66. Daesch, G., Mortenson, L. E. 1968. *J. Bacteriol.* 96:346–51
67. Ibid 1972. 110:103–9
68. Dahlen, J. V., Parejko, R. A., Wilson, P. W. 1969. *J. Bacteriol.* 98:325–26
69. Dainty, R. H. 1972. *Biochem. J.* 126:1055–56
70. Dainty, R. H., Peel, J. L. 1970. *Biochem. J.* 117:573–84
71. Dalton, H., Mortenson, L. E. 1972. *Bacteriol. Rev.* 36:231–60
72. Dalton, H., Postgate, J. R. 1969. *J. Gen. Microbiol.* 54:463–73
73. Ibid 1969. 56:307–19
74. Daniel, R. M., Appleby, C. A. 1972. *Biochim. Biophys. Acta* 275:347–54
75. Dart, P. J. 1968. *Proc. 4th Eur. Reg. Conf. Electron Microsc. Rome,* 69–70
76. Davis, L. C., Shah, V. K., Brill, W. J., Orme-Johnson, W. H. 1972. *Biochim. Biophys. Acta* 256:512–23
77. Dayhoff, M. O. 1972. *Atlas of Protein Sequence and Structure.* Washington, D.C.: Nat. Biomed. Res. Found.
78. Detroy, R. W., Witz, D. F., Parejko, R. A., Wilson, P. W. 1968. *Proc. Nat. Acad. Sci. USA* 61:537–41
79. Deuel, T. F., Stadtman, E. R. 1970. *J. Biol. Chem.* 245:5206–13
80. Dharmawardene, M. W. N., Haystead, A., Stewart, W. D. P. 1973. *Arch. Mikrobiol.* 90:281–95
81. Dharmawardene, M. W. N., Stewart, W. D. P., Stanley, S. O. 1972. *Planta* 108:133–45
82. Dilworth, M. J. 1969. *Biochim. Biophys. Acta* 184:432–41
83. Dilworth, M. J., Kidby, D. K. 1968. *Exp. Cell Res.* 49:148–59
84. Dilworth, M. J., Parker, C. A. 1969. *J. Theoret. Biol.* 25:208–18
85. Dilworth, M. J., Subramanian, D., Munson, T. O., Burris, R. H. 1965. *Biochim. Biophys. Acta* 99:486–503
86. Dixon, R. Q., Postgate, J. R. 1971. *Nature* 234:47–48
87. Ibid 1972. 237:102–3
88. Dixon, R. O. D. 1967. *Ann. Bot.* 31:179–88
89. Dixon, R. O. D. 1968. *Arch. Mikrobiol.* 62:272–83
90. Ibid 1972. 85:193–201
91. Döbereiner, J., Day, J. M., Dart, P. J. 1972. *J. Gen. Microbiol.* 71:103–16
92. Donze, M., Haveman, J., Schiereck, P. 1972. *Biochim. Biophys. Acta* 256:157–61
93. Doy, C. H., Gresshoff, P. M., Rolfe, B. G. 1973. *Proc. Nat. Acad. Sci. USA* 70:723–26
94. Drozd, J. W., Postgate, J. R. 1970. *J. Gen. Microbiol.* 63:63–73
95. Drozd, J. W., Tubb, R. S., Postgate, J. R. 1972. *J. Gen. Microbiol.* 73:221–32
96. Dubourdieu, M., LeGall, J. 1970. *Biochem. Biophys. Res. Commun.* 38:965–72
97. Eady, R. R., Smith, B. E., Cook, K. A., Postgate, J. R. 1972. *Biochem. J.* 128:655–75
98. Eady, R. R., Smith, B. E., Thorneley, R. N. F., Ware, D. A., Postgate, J. R. 1973 *Biochem. Soc. Trans.* 1:37–38
99. Edmondson, D. E., Tollin, G. 1971. *Biochemistry* 10:124–32
100. Elmerich, D., Aubert, J.-P. 1971. *Biochem. Biophys. Res. Commun.* 42:371–76
101. Evans, H. J., Koch, B., Klucas, R. V. 1972. *Methods Enzymol.* 24:470–76
102. Evans, H. J., Russell, S. A. 1971. See Ref. 218, 191–244
103. Evans, M. C. W., Telfer, A., Cammack, R., Smith, R. V. 1971. *FEBS Lett.* 15:317–19
104. Fay, P. 1973. In *The Biology of Blue-Green Algae,* ed. N. G. Carr, B. A. Whitton, 238–59. Oxford: Blackwell
105. Fay, P., Walsby, A. E. 1966. *Nature* 209:94–95
106. Fisher, R. J., Brill, W. J. 1969. *Biochim. Biophys. Acta* 184:99–105

107. Forsyth, W. G. C., Hayward, A. C., Roberts, J. B. 1958. *Nature* 182:800–1
108. Fottrell, P. F., Mooney, P. 1969. *J. Gen. Microbiol.* 59:211–14
109. Fox, J. L., Smith, S. S., Brown, J. R. 1972. *Z. Naturforsch.* 27b:1096–1100
110. Frieden, C. 1965. *J. Biol. Chem.* 238:3286–99
111. Gallon, J. R., Kurz, W. G. W., LaRue, T. A. 1973. *Can. J. Microbiol.* 19: 461–65
112. Gallon, J. R., LaRue, T. A., Kurz, W. G. W. 1972. *Can. J. Microbiol.* 18: 327–32
113. Godfrey, C. A. 1972. *Leghaemoglobins and Haem Synthesis in Lupin and Serradella Root Nodules.* PhD thesis. Univ. Western Australia
114. Goodchild, D., Bergersen, F. J. 1966. *J. Bacteriol.* 92:204–13
115. Gordon, J. K., Brill, W. J. 1972. *Proc. Nat. Acad. Sci. USA* 69:3501–3
116. Gray, B. H., Fowler, C. F., Nugent, N. A., Fuller, R. C. 1972. *Biochem. Biophys. Res. Commun.* 47:322–27
117. Guerrero, M. G., Vega, J. M., Leadbetter, E., Losada, M. 1973. *Arch. Mikrobiol.* 91:287–304
118. Hadfield, K. L., Bulen, W. A. 1969. *Biochemistry* 8:5103–8
119. Hardy, R. W. F., Burns, R. C., Hebert, R. R., Holsten, R. D., Jackson, E. K. 1971. See Ref. 8, 561–90
120. Hardy, R. W. F., Burns, R. C., Parshall, G. W. 1971. *Advan. Chem. Ser.* 100: 219–45
121. Hardy, R. W. F., Burns, R. C., Parshall, G. W. 1973. In *Inorganic Biochemistry,* ed. G. Eichhorn. Amsterdam: Elsevier
122. Hardy, R. W. F., Holsten, R. D., Jackson, E. K., Burns, R. C. 1968. *Plant Physiol.* 43:1185–1207
123. Hardy, R. W. F., Knight, E. 1966. *Biochim. Biophys. Acta* 132:520–31
124. Harris, C. E., Teller, D. C. 1973. *J. Theoret. Biol.* 38:347–62
125. Harris, D., Dart, P. J. 1973. *Soil Biol. Biochem.* 5:277–79
126. Haystead, A., Dharmawardene, M. W. N., Stewart, W. D. P. 1973. *Plant Sci. Lett.* 1:439–45
127. Haystead, A., Robinson, R., Stewart, W.D.P. 1970. *Arch. Mikrobiol.* 74: 235–43
128. Haystead, A., Stewart, W. D. P. 1972. *Arch. Mikrobiol.* 82:325–36
129. Hill, R. E. E., Richards, R. L. 1971. *Nature* 233:114–15
130. Hill, S. 1971. *J. Gen. Microbiol.* 67: 77–83
131. Hill, S., Drozo, J. W., Postgate, J. R. 1972. *J. Appl. Chem. Biotechnol.* 22:541–58
132. Hinkson, J. W., Bulen, W. A. 1967. *J. Biol. Chem.* 242:3345–51
133. Holzer, H. et al 1969. *Fed. Eur. Biochem. Soc. Symp.* 19:171–77
134. Huang, T. C., Zumft, W. G., Mortenson, L. E. 1973. *J. Bacteriol.* 113: 884–90
135. Hubbard, J. S., Stadtman, E. R. 1967. *J. Bacteriol.* 94:1016–24
136. Hutchinson, J. 1964. *The Families of Flowering Plants,* Vol.1. Oxford: Clarendon
137. Hwang, J. C., Burris, R. H. 1972. *Biochim. Biophys. Acta* 283:339–50
138. Hwang, J. C., Chen, C. H., Burris, R. H. 1973. *Biochim. Biophys. Acta* 292: 256–70
139. Hyndman, L. A., Burris, R. H., Wilson, P. W. 1953. *J. Bacteriol.* 65:522–31
140. Israel, D. W., Howard, R. L., Evans, H. J., Russell, S. A. 1973. *J. Biol. Chem.* In press
141. Jackson, E. K., Parshall, G. W., Hardy, R. W. F. 1968. *J. Biol. Chem.* 243: 4952–58
142. Jeng, D., Devanathan, T., Mortenson, L. E. 1969. *Biochem. Biophys. Res. Commun.* 35:625–33
143. Jeng, D., Morris, J. A., Mortenson, L. E. 1970. *J. Biol. Chem.* 245:2809–13
144. Jones, C. W., Brice, J. M., Wright, V., Ackrell, B. A. C. 1973. *FEBS Lett.* 29:77–81
145. Jungermann, K., Thauer, R. K., Leimenstall, G., Decker, K. 1973. *Biochim. Biophys. Acta* 305:268—80
146. Kajiyama, S., Matsuki, T., Nosoh, Y. 1969. *Biochem. Biophys. Res. Commun.* 37:711–17
147. Kajiyama, S., Nosoh, Y. 1972. *Arch. Mikrobiol.* 85:181–92
148. Kajiyama, S., Nosoh, Y. 1973. *J. Biochem.* 73:889–91
149. Kelly, M. 1969. *Biochim. Biophys. Acta* 171:9–22
150. Ibid 1969. 191:527–40
151. Kelly, M., Klucas, R. V., Burris, R. H. 1967. *Biochem. J.* 105:3C–5C
152. Kennedy, I. R. 1966. *Biochim. Biophys. Acta* 130:285–94
153. Ibid, 295–303
154. Ibid 1970. 222:135–44
155. Kennedy, I. R. 1973. *Proc. Aust. Biochem. Soc.,* 33
156. Kennedy, I. R., Morris, J. A., Mortenson, L. E. 1968. *Biochim. Biophys. Acta* 153:777–86

157. Kennedy, I. R., Parker, C. A., Kidby, D. K. 1966. *Biochim. Biophys. Acta* 130:517–19
158. Ketchum, P. A., Combier, H. Y., Frazier, W. A., Madansky, C., Nason, A. 1970 *Proc. Nat. Acad. Sci. USA* 66:1016–23
159 Klucas, R. 1972. *Can. J. Microbiol.* 18:1845–50
160. Klucas, R. V., Burris, R. H. 1966. *Biochim. Biophys. Acta* 136:399–401
161. Klucas, R. V., Koch, B., Russell, S. A., Evans, H. J. 1968. *Plant Physiol.* 43:1906–12
162. Knight, E., Hardy, R. W. F. 1967. *J. Biol. Chem.* 242:1370–74
163. Koch, B., Evans, H. J., Russell, S. A. 1966. *Plant Physiol.* 41:1748–50
164. Koch, B., Wong, P., Russell, S. A., Howard, R., Evans, H. J. 1970. *Biochem. J.* 118:773–81
165. Leaf, G. 1959. *Advan. Sci.* 15:386–92
166. Leaf, G., Gardner, I. C., Bond, G. 1958. *J. Exp. Bot.* 9:320–31
167. Leaf, G., Gardner, I. C., Bond, G. 1959. *Biochem. J.* 72:662–67
168. Ledoux, L., Huart, R. 1969. *J. Mol. Biol.* 43:243–62
169. Ledoux, L., Huart, R., Jacobs, M. 1971. *Eur. J. Biochem.* 23:96–108
170. Lex, M., Stewart, W. D. P. 1973. *Biochim. Biophys. Acta* 292:436–43
171. Licari, G. R., Cloud, P. E. 1968. *Proc. Nat. Acad. Sci. USA* 59:1053–60
172. Ljones, T., Burris, R. H. 1972. *Biochim. Biophys. Acta* 275:93–101
173. Loomis, W. D., Battaile, J. 1966. *Phytochemistry* 5:423–38
174. McKenna, C. E., Benemann, J. R., Traylor, T. G. 1970. *Biochem. Biophys. Res. Commun.* 41:1501–8
175. Mague, T. H., Burris, R. H. 1972. *New Phytol.* 71:275–86
176. Mahl, M. C., Wilson, P. W. 1968. *Can. J. Microbiol.* 14:33–38
177. Marchalonis, J. J., Weltman, J. K. 1971. *Comp. Biochem. Physiol.* 38B:609–25
178. Marcus, L., Kaneshiro, T. 1972. *Biochim. Biophys. Acta* 288:296–303
179. Mecke, D., Holzer, H. 1966. *Biochim. Biophys. Acta* 122:341–51
180. Meers, J. L., Tempest, D. W. 1971. *Biochem. J.* 119:603–5
181. Meers, J. L., Kjaergaard-Pedersen, L. 1972. *J. Gen. Microbiol.* 70:277–86
182. Meers, J. L., Tempest, D. W., Brown, C. M. 1970. *J. Gen. Microbiol.* 60: x
183. Ibid 1970. 64:187–94
184. Meyerhof, O., Burk, D. 1927. *Z. Physiol. Chem.* 139A:117–42
185. Miller, R. E., Stadtman, E. R. 1972. *J. Biol. Chem.* 247:7407–19
186. Mortenson, L. E. 1972. In *Methods Enzymol.* 24:446–56
187. Mortenson, L. E., Zumft, W. G., Huang, T. C., Palmer, G. 1973. *Biochem. Soc. Trans.* 1:35–37
188. Mortenson, L. E., Zumft, W. G., Palmer, G. 1973. *Biochim. Biophys. Acta* 292:422–35
189. Moustafa, E., Mortenson, L. E. 1967. *Nature* 216:1241–42
190. Moustafa, E., Mortenson, L. E. 1969. *Biochim. Biophys. Acta* 172:106–15
191. Munson, T. O., Burris, R. H. 1969. *J. Bacteriol.* 97:1093–98
192 Murphy, P. M., Koch, B. L. 1971. *Biochim. Biophys. Acta* 253:295–97
193. Nagatani, H., Shimizu, M., Valentine, R. C. 1971. *Arch. Mikrobiol.* 79:164–75
194. Nakos, G., Mortenson, L. E. 1971. *Biochemistry* 10:455–58
195. Nason, A., Antoine, A. D., Ketchum, P. A., Frazier, W. A., Lee, D. K. 1970. *Proc. Nat. Acad. Sci. USA* 65:137–44
196. Nason, A., Lee, K., Pan, S., Ketchum, P. A., Lamberti, A., De Vries, J. 1971. *Proc. Nat. Acad. Sci. USA* 68:3242–46
197. Neilson, A. H., Doudoroff, M. 1973. *Arch. Mikrobiol.* 89:15–22
198. Neilson, A. H., Rippka, R., Kunisawa, R. 1971. *Arch. Mikrobiol.* 76:139–50
199. Newman, D. J., Postgate, J. R. 1968. *Eur. J. Biochem.* 7:45–50
200. Newton, J. W., Wilson, P. W., Burris, R. H. 1953. *J. Biol. Chem.* 204:445–51
201. Notton, B. A., Hewitt, E. J., Fielding, A. H. 1972. *Phytochemistry* 11:2447–49
202. Ohmori, M., Hattori, A. 1972. *Plant Cell Physiol.* 13:589–99
203. Oppenheim, J., Fisher, R. J., Wilson, P. W., Marcus, L. 1970. *J. Bacteriol.* 101:292–96
204. Oppenheim, J., Marcus, L. 1970. *J. Bacteriol.* 101:286–91
205. Orme-Johnson, W. H. et al 1972. *Proc. Nat. Acad. Sci. USA* 69:3142–45
206. Palmer, G., Multani, J. S., Cretney, W. C., Zumft, W. G., Mortenson, L. E. 1972. *Arch. Biochem. Biophys.* 153:325–32
207. Palmer, G., Sands, R. H. 1966. *J. Biol. Chem.* 241:253–54
208. Paneque, A. et al 1972. *Plant Cell Physiol.* 13:175–8
209. Parejko, R. A., Wilson, P. W. 1970. *Can. J. Microbiol.* 16:681–85
210. Parejko, R. A., Wilson, P. W. 1971. *Proc. Nat. Acad. Sci. USA* 68:2016–18

211. Parker, C. A. 1957. *Nature* 179:593–94
212. Pate, J. S., Walker, J., Wallace, W. 1965. *Ann. Bot.* 29:475–93
213. Patil, R. B., Pengra, R. M., Yoch, D. C. 1967. *Biochim. Biophys. Acta* 136:1–5
214. Pearce, J., Leach, C. K., Carr, N. G. 1969. *J. Gen. Microbiol.* 55:371–78
215. Pengra, R. M., Wilson, P. W. 1958. *J. Bacteriol.* 75:21–25
216. Phillips, D. A., Daniel, R. M., Appleby, C. A., Evans, H. J. 1973. *Plant Physiol.* 51:136–38
217. Phillips, D. A., Howard, R. L., Evans, H. J. 1973. *Physiol. Plant.* 28:248–53
218. Postgate, J. R. 1971. *The Chemistry and Biochemistry of Nitrogen Fixation.* London: Plenum
219. Postgate, J. R. 1972. *Biological Nitrogen Fixation.* Watford: Merrow
220. Postgate, J. R. 1974. *Symp. Soc. Gen. Microbiol.* 24: In press
221. Prusiner, S., Miller, R. E., Valentine, R. C. 1972. *Proc. Nat. Acad. Sci. USA* 69:2922–26
222. Quispel, A. 1974. *Biological Nitrogen Fixation.* Amsterdam: North Holland
223. Raju, P. N., Evans, H. J., Seidler, R. J. 1972. *Proc. Nat. Acad. Sci. USA* 69:3474–78
224. Ravel, J. M., Humphreys, J. S., Shive, W. 1965. *Arch. Biochem. Biophys.* 111:720–26
225. Rebello, J. L., Strauss, N. 1969. *J. Bacteriol.* 98:682–88
226. Rigaud, J., Bergersen, F. J., Turner, G. L., Daniel, R. M. 1973. *J. Gen. Microbiol.* 77:137–44
227. Rose, I. A., Ochoa, S. 1956. *J. Biol. Chem.* 220:307–14
228. St. John, R. T., Brill, W. J. 1972. *Biochim. Biophys. Acta* 261:63–69
229. Sasaki, R. M., Matsubara, H. 1967. *Biochem. Biophys. Res. Commun.* 28:467–73
230. Schrauzer, G. N., Doemeny, P. 1971. *J. Am. Chem. Soc.* 93:1608–18
231. Schrauzer, G. N., Schlesinger, G. 1970. *J. Am. Chem. Soc.* 92:1808–9
232. Schrauzer, G. N., Schlesinger, G., Doemeny, P. 1971. *J. Am. Chem. Soc.* 93:1803–4
233. Shah, V. K., Brill, W. J. 1973. *Biochim. Biophys. Acta* 305:445–54
234. Shah, V. K., Davis, L. C., Brill, W. J. 1972. *Biochim. Biophys. Acta* 256:498–511
235. Shah, V. K., Davis, L. C., Gordon, J. K., Orme-Johnson, W. H., Brill, W. J. 1973. *Biochim. Biophys. Acta* 292:246–55
236. Shapiro, B. M. 1969. *Biochemistry* 8:659–70
237. Shapiro, B. M., Stadtman, E. R. 1968. *J. Biol. Chem.* 243:3769–71
238. Shapiro, B. M., Stadtman, E. R. 1970. *Ann. Rev. Microbiol.* 24:501–24
239. Silver, W. S., Postgate, J. R. 1973. *J. Theoret. Biol.* 40:1–10
240. Silverstein, R., Bulen, W. A. 1970. *Biochemistry* 9:3809–15
241. Slepko, G. I. et al 1969. *Dokl. Akad. Nauk SSSR* 184:473–76
242. Smith, B. E., Lowe, D. J., Bray, R. C. 1972. *Biochem. J.* 130:641–43
243. Ibid 1973. 135:331–41
244. Smith, R. V., Evans, M. C. W. 1970. *Nature* 225:1253–54
245. Smith, R. V., Evans, M. C. W. 1971. *J. Bacteriol.* 105:913–17
246. Smith, R. V., Noy, R. J., Evans, M. C. W. 1971. *Biochim. Biophys. Acta* 253:104–9
247. Smith, R. V., Telfer, A., Evans, M. C. W. 1971. *J. Bacteriol.* 107:574–75
248. Sorger, G. J. 1968. *J. Bacteriol.* 95:1721–26
249. Sorger, G. J., Trofimenkoff, D. 1970. *Proc. Nat. Acad. Sci. USA* 65:74–80
250. Stadtman, E. R. et al 1970. *Advan. Enzyme Regul.* 8:99–118
251. Stewart, W. D. P. 1973. See Ref. 104, 260–78
252. Stewart, W. D. P., Lex, M. 1970. *Arch. Mikrobiol.* 73:250–60
253. Stewart, W. D. P., Pearson, H. W. 1970. *Proc. Roy. Soc. London Ser. B* 175:293–311
254. Stiefel, E. I. 1973. *Proc. Nat. Acad. Sci. USA* 70:988–92
255. Strandberg, G. W., Wilson, P. W. 1968. *Can. J. Microbiol.* 14:25–31
256. Streicher, S. L., Gurney, E., Valentine, R. C. 1971. *Proc. Nat. Acad. Sci. USA* 68:1174–77
257. Streicher, S. L., Gurney, E., Valentine, R. C. 1972. *Nature* 239:495–99
258. Streicher, S. L., Valentine, R. C. 1973. *Ann. Rev. Biochem.* 42:279–302
259. Takagi, Y., Matsubara, K., Anai, M. 1972. *Biochim. Biophys. Acta* 269:347–53
260. Taylor, K. B. 1969. *J. Biol. Chem.* 244:171–79
261. Tempest, D. W., Meers, J. L., Brown, C. M. 1970. *Biochem. J.* 117:405–7
262. Tempest, D. W., Meers, J. L., Brown, C. M. 1973. In *Enzymes of Glutamine Metabolism,* ed. S. Prusiner, E. R. Stadtman, 167–82. New York: Academic

263. Thorneley, R. N. F., Eady, R. R. 1973. *Biochem. J.* 133:405–8
264. Trinick, M. J. 1973. *Nature* 244:459–60
265. Truchet, G. 1972. *C.R. Acad. Sci. Paris* 274:1290–93
266. Tso, M.-Y.W., Ljones, T., Burris, R. H. 1972. *Biochim. Biophys. Acta* 267: 600–4
267. Turner, G. L., Bergersen, F. J. 1969. *Biochem. J.* 115:529–35
268. Vandecasteele, J.-P., Burris, R. H. 1970. *J. Bacteriol.* 101:794–801
269. Van Dorp, B., Ceulen, M. T. E., Heijneker, H. L., Pouwels, P. H. 1973. *Biochim. Biophys. Acta* 299:65–81
270. Vender, J., Rickenberg, H. V. 1964. *Biochim. Biophys. Acta* 90:218–20
271. Vetter, H., Knappe, J. 1971. *Hoppe-Seyler's Z. Physiol. Chem.* 352:433–46
272. Wall, J. S., Wagenknecht, A. C., Newton, J. W., Burris, R. H. 1952. *J. Bacteriol.* 63:563–74
273. Werner, D., Russell, S. A., Evans, H. J. 1973. *Proc. Nat. Acad. Sci. USA* 70:339–42
274. Wheeler, C. T. 1969. *New Phytol.* 68: 675–82
275. Whiting, M. J., Dilworth, M. J. 1973. Unpublished observations
276. Whiting, M. J., Richardson, M., Dilworth, M. J. 1973. Unpublished results
277. Winnacker, E. L., Barker, H. A. 1970. *Biochim. Biophys. Acta* 212:225–42
278. Winter, H. C., Arnon, D. I. 1970. *Biochim. Biophys. Acta* 197:170–79
279. Wittenberg, J. B., Bergersen, F.J., Appleby, C. A., Turner, G. L. 1973. *J. Biol. Chem.* Submitted
280. Wolk, C. P. 1973. *Bacteriol. Rev.* 37: 32–101
281. Wong, P., Evans, H. J. 1971. *Plant Physiol.* 47:750–55
282. Wong, P., Evans, H. J., Klucas, R., Russell, S. 1971. See Ref. 8, 525–43
283. Woolfolk, C. A., Stadtman, E. R. 1967. *Arch. Biochem. Biophys.* 118:736–55
284. Wu, C., Yuan, L. H. 1968. *J. Gen. Microbiol.* 51:57–65
285. Wyatt, J. T., Silvey, S. K. G. 1969. *Science* 165:908–9
286. Yates, M. G. 1970. *FEBS Lett.* 8: 281–85
287. Yates, M. G. 1972. *Eur. J. Biochem.* 29:386–92
288. Yoch, D. C. 1972. *Biochem. Biophys. Res. Commun.* 49:335–42
289. Yoch, D. C., Arnon, D. I. 1972. *J. Biol. Chem.* 247:4514–20
290. Yoch, D. C., Benemann, J. R., Arnon, D. I., Valentine, R. C., Russell, S. A. 1970. *Biochem. Biophys. Res. Commun.* 38:838–42
291. Yoch, D. C., Pengra, R. M. 1966. *J. Bacteriol.* 92:618–22
292. Yoch, D. C., Valentine, R. C. 1972. *Ann. Rev. Microbiol.* 26:139–62
293. Yoch, D. C., Valentine, R. C. 1972. *J. Bacteriol.* 110:1211–13
294. Yuan, R., Heywood, J., Meselson, M. 1972. *Nature* 240:42–43
295. Zelitch, I. 1951. *Proc. Nat. Acad. Sci. USA* 37:559–65
296. Zelitch, I., Rosenblum, E. D., Burris, R. H., Wilson, P. W. 1951. *J. Biol. Chem.* 191:295–98
297. Zelitch, I., Rosenblum, E. D., Burris, R. H. 1951. *J. Bacteriol.* 62:747–52
298. Zumft, W. G., Cretney, W. C., Huang, T. C., Mortenson, L. E. 1972. *Biochem. Biophys. Res. Commun.* 48:1525–32
299. Zumft, W. G., Palmer, G., Mortenson, L. E. 1973. *Biochim. Biophys. Acta* 292:413–21
300. Zumft, W. G., Spiller, H. 1971. *Biochem. Biophys. Res. Commun.* 45: 112–18

Ann. Rev. Plant Physiol. 1974. 25:115–34

CIRCADIAN RHYTHMS AND METABOLIC PATTERNS

♦7564

Orlando Queiroz

Laboratoire du Phytotron, Centre National de la Recherche Scientifique,
Gif-sur-Yvette, France

CONTENTS

INTRODUCTION 116
CIRCADIAN METABOLIC RHYTHMS 116
  Background Considerations 116
  Circadian Rhythms in the Activity of Liver Enzymes 117
  Circadian Rhythms in Chloroplasts of Unicells 118
  Crassulacean Acid Metabolism (CAM) 119
    Rhythm of CO₂ fixation 120
    Storage step 120
    Rhythm of CO₂ output 121
    Induction of CAM by photoperiodism 121
    Effect on the phase of enzyme rhythm by change of photoperiod 121
    Effect of short days 121
SOME GENERALITIES ON MODELS 123
  Physiological Validity of Models 123
  Models of Circadian Rhythms 124
FEEDBACK AND METABOLIC CIRCADIAN PERIODICITY 124
  Basic Characteristics of Feedback Models 124
  The Problem of Circadian Periodicity 125
LIGHT AND METABOLIC CIRCADIAN PERIODICITY 126
  Light as a Circadian Timer in Models: The Case of CAM 126
  Enzyme Control 127
COMPARTMENTATION AND METABOLIC RHYTHMS 129
PHYSIOLOGICAL SIGNIFICANCE OF CIRCADIAN METABOLIC RHYTHMS 130
  Metabolic Coherence and Rhythms 130
  The Case of CAM 130
  Adaptive Signification of Circadian Rhythms 131
CONCLUDING REMARKS 131

[1]The author would like to thank Dr. B. M. Sweeney for stimulating discussions on this subject. An important part of the literature search for this paper was made while the author was an invited lecturer in the department of biology on the Riverside campus of the University of California, and he is deeply indebted for the remarkable working and library facilities put at his disposal during that period.

INTRODUCTION

This review is not intended to be an exhaustive coverage of the literature, but rather a workshop on the structural and coordinating role of circadian oscillators in temporal operation of the metabolic network. Circadian rhythms, and their obviously highly provocative connection to climatic factors, have received strong theoretical and experimental attention substantiated by a number of reviews, treatises, and symposia (1, 12, 22, 61, 83, 84, 102–104, 114). Short-period biochemical oscillations have also been reviewed recently (41). Experimental data on circadian variations are available for a number of enzymic reactions, but the concept of metabolic pattern has seldom been considered in the sense of temporally coordinated multireaction operation. It is along these lines that the present review will be directed. Discussion will be centered on areas for which information on several circadian metabolic functions is already dense enough to enable time maps to be drawn and, in some cases, to be connected to variations in day-night cycles.

Special attention will be paid to models. Circadian rhythms are present at all biological levels, undoubtedly contributing to coordination of life processes (71, 135). This ubiquity implies an overwhelming variety of specific oscillatory systems, making very difficult the search for the basic general laws that eventually rule this class of phenomena. Abstract, associative models can then be valuable tools to hierarchize interconnected functions, to predict the properties expected to be dominant in a complex system, and to formalize the relationships between temporal and structural organization.

This chapter will be restricted to metabolic circadian behavior. The nature and intrinsic properties of the so-called biological clocks and of timing mechanisms will not be discussed in any detail beyond the limits of their immediate connection to metabolic events. Temperature effects will also be omitted.

CIRCADIAN METABOLIC RHYTHMS

Background Considerations

Circadian rhythms are biological oscillations displaying a 24 hr period under natural environmental conditions. Under experimental constant conditions (constant temperature and continuous light or darkness) the period of the rhythms usually changes slightly and stabilizes at a value more or less close to 24 hr. Nowadays these rhythms are generally supposed to reflect the behavior of an endogenous system or property called a biological clock. As a matter of fact, some systems displaying typical characteristics of endogenous, clock-dependent circadian rhythms (definite entrainment limits, phase response curves) will damp very fast under constant conditions. This probably can be explained in most cases by metabolic poisoning or starvation resulting from the suppression of the necessary balance between light and dark reactions. It would be more realistic to consider [extending Cumming's considerations on flowering (21)] that sustained rhythmic operation of some pathways can only be obtained in daily photoperiodic cycles that will provide the necessary supply of substrates and removal of products.

A number of reports on metabolic 24 hr oscillations lack information on the characteristics of the observed rhythm. Nevertheless, such characterization, necessary to decide whether the rhythm actually is a clock-dependent rhythm or merely an oscillation dependent on a passive light-sensitive reaction, is of basic importance for the interpretation of the data.

There are very few examples of studies on the rhythmic behavior of an entire pathway considered in an integrated manner. Two examples of this approach are the work on the short-period rhythmic operation of yeast glycolysis and on the circadian rhythm of CAM in *Kalanchoe*. Research on the former, mainly carried on in Chance's laboratory (15, 16), achieved a good understanding of the underlying mechanism (42, 76, 77), and has been recently reviewed by Hess & Boiteux (41). Circadian rhythm of acid metabolism in *Kalanchoe* will be discussed in this section.

Convergence in different lines of research in the study of a specific organ or a specific function has proved to be fruitful. Information on a specific organ can be illustrated by work on circadian rhythms in liver. An impressive picture on rhythms correlated to the photosynthetic function is afforded by work of different authors on *Euglena* and *Acetabularia*, both at the metabolic and epigenetic levels. In higher plants it is paradoxical that despite the extensive knowledge on the reactions of carbon metabolism in photosynthesis, only a small amount of information is published on the variations of carbon flow through those reactions with respect to the time of day (e.g. 67, 99). However, knowledge of diurnal variations in pools of organic and amino acids is basically necessary to study the influence of environmental factors on carbon metabolism (99). It is striking that studies on the action of light or darkness on photosynthetic enzymes and products have been carried generally in terms of dark to light or light to dark changes followed by short-time observation of the obtained effects. Almost nothing is known about the behavior of enzyme capacity and about the balances between metabolic pools during the whole length of the normal photosynthesizing period. A somewhat similar situation can be found concerning enzymic reactions controlled by phytochrome.

Circadian Rhythms in the Activity of Liver Enzymes

Circadian variations have been reported since 1966 (74, 88) for the measurable total activity of several liver enzymes. The most intensively studied has been tyrosine aminotransferase, which proves to be an inducible enzyme (136). Effects of temperature (31), of different light/dark cycles (7), and of dietary treatments (30, 74) on the circadian periodicity and the inducibility of the enzyme have been reported. Possible causal relationships between the rhythm of enzyme activity and availability of cofactors (8, 139), activity of the sympathetic nervous system (8), or hormonal activity (17) have been discussed. Attempts have been made to correlate the circadian variations in activity of this and other enzymes to circadian variations in metabolites: e.g. rhythm of tyrosine aminotransferase in respect to rhythm in plasma tyrosine or glucose contents (32); or rhythm in polysome profiles (30); rhythm of phosphorylase in respect to rhythm in glycogen content (120); rhythm of tryptophan pyrrolase in respect to rhythm of plasma corticosterone content (88). At the epigenetic level, circadian variations in liver nucleic acids have been reported (23, 26, 48,

74), showing well-defined phase relationships with other oscillatory parameters. Thus a map of liver circadian functions is being progressively established. Further research on phase relationships could provide a comprehensive insight on physiological timing and metabolic coherence in this organ.

Such techniques as the treatment of the tissues with tetraphenylboron, which results in dissolving the tissue into suspensions of isolated cells (38), would provide the means of studying the characteristics of these rhythms independently of hormonal, nervous, or dietary controls.

Circadian Rhythms in Chloroplasts of Unicells

A number of circadian rhythms are known in unicellular organisms, both in populations and isolated cells. A thoughtful review on the subject has been presented recently by Sweeney (103). Acute and well-documented discussion on the possible role of nucleic acids in circadian mechanisms has been published by Vanden Driessche (114), who also published a monograph on rhythms in chloroplasts of *Acetabularia* (115). Discussion and an extended bibliography on rhythms of photosynthesis in *Euglena* can be found in a recent paper from Edmunds' laboratory (122). Within the scope of this review, attention will be focused on photosynthesis and connected or supposedly connected chloroplast functions.

Work from Vanden Driessche's laboratory established that the shape of chloroplasts vary according to a circadian periodicity in *Acetabularia mediterranea* (112). These results suggested further research on the behavior of chloroplastic structures in time, and it has been shown that the spatial organization of the lamellae, their degree of association in pseudograna, and the swelling of the thylakoids vary in circadian manner (119). Cyclic changes in thylakoid membranes have also been reported for *Chlamydomonas* (95). Concomitantly, stroma density and the number of carbohydrate granules (and their contour line) follow a daily variation (75, 119). Photosynthesis and photosynthetic capacity also display circadian oscillation in these algae (40, 89, 97, 105, 106, 111), the maximum occuring at the middle of the light period. This rhythm can be reset by changes in the dark/light cycle and persists for at least several cycles in constant light and constant temperature (105); the endogenous nature of the rhythm is thus established. A circadian variation in ATP content was shown also to be of endogenous nature (113); content is higher at the beginning than at the middle of the light period. Synthesis of RNA, mainly chloroplastic (23 S and 16 S rRNA), shows a circadian rhythm, the peak taking place at about 3 hr after the middle of the light period and the minimum at about the end of the dark period (118). The rhythm occurs also in continuous light, but with strong damping. This fact is not a sufficient reason to suppose that this rhythm would be independent of the other rhythms; it simply can be more sensitive, directly or indirectly, to some critical level of metabolites attained in continuous light with consequent faster damping than the other observed oscillations. Polysaccharide content of the chloroplasts varies also in circadian manner, the maximum occuring about 3 hr after the middle of the light period (117). The apparent decrease in ATP when RNA and carbohydrate contents increase can be understood in terms of balance between production and utilization of ATP (2, 9), a factor probably of great importance in the relationships between the different rhythms.

It is interesting to note the differences in phase for some of these rhythms and synchrony for others, but speculation on their eventual metabolic meaning must wait for more data on the exact localization of the different peaks, mainly for photosynthesis and ATP rhythms, and on their shape (asymmetry between the ascending and descending parts of the waves could be meaningful). It appears from the present data that all these rhythms are very probably ordered in time with defined phase relationships and that the hypothesis of internal coordination by a basic single or multiple oscillator must be considered.

The circadian rhythm of photosynthesis in synchronously dividing or nondividing cultures of *Euglena* also has received broad attention (122). This rhythm does not correlate with variations in chlorophyll nor to light reactions, and it appears that reactions in photosystems I and II are not causal parameters of the rhythmicity. Concerning dark reactions, the rhythm of photosynthesis shows no correlation with variations in ribulose diphosphate carboxylase but is closely followed by diurnal changes in glyceraldehyde-3-phosphate dehydrogenase, even after uncoupling from the dark-light rhythm. It must be noted that these results by Walther & Edmunds (122) are not in agreement with those of Codd & Merrett (18), who found a rhythm of ribulose diphosphate carboxylase in *Euglena*. Relationships between the rhythm of cell division, entrainment by light-dark cycles, and circadian rhythms of enzyme capacity have been studied in Edmunds' laboratory for a wide series of enzymes (24, 100, 122).

Gonyaulax has also been subjected to intensive study, as well as day-active (rhythm of photosynthesis) or night-active organisms (rhythm of luminescence) (103). Experiments with a number of metabolic inhibitors and inhibitors of protein synthesis did not afford definitive information about the basic rhythmic variable. On the other hand, relationships between changes in photosynthetic capacity and changes in enzyme activity (ribulose diphosphate carboxylase) proved to be difficult to establish (102, 103). This aspect of the problem certainly would deserve further investigation.

Crassulacean Acid Metabolism (CAM)

The circadian rhythm of organic acids in Crassulaceae was classically defined as a night/day two-step mechanism: schematically, malate is produced from CO_2 fixation and accumulates during the night; the major part of it subsequently will be depleted during the following day, with the production of CO_2. The leaves tend to an overall increase in malate content, except during senescence. Control by photoperiodic conditions was demonstrated in 1954 (37). A number of reviews have dealt with the biochemical and gas-exchange mechanisms and with the ecological aspects of CAM (3, 5, 54, 57, 65, 83, 84, 87, 108, 109, 121, 131). The basic features of the malate pathway system are summarized in Table I. Recent studies, confirming earlier results obtained after $^{14}CO_2$-feeding experiments in different light and temperature conditions (14, 50, 54, 91), show that two transaminases (aspartate aminotransferase and alanine aminotransferase) are connected to the main pathway (64, 85). Malate and aspartate are allosteric inhibitors of P-enolpyruvate carboxylase (80, 85, 107), and malate is an activator of malic enzyme (33).

Table 1 Features connected to the malate pathway in *Kalanchoe*

	Darkness		Light
CO_2	*Fixation*	*Storage*	*Output*
Enzymes concerned	P-enolpyruvate carboxylase	malate dehydrogenase	malic enzyme
Reactions	CO_2 + PEP ⟶ OAA ⟶ malate (NADH)		⟶ CO_2 + pyruvate + NADPH
Control	phytochrome (37, 81) inhibition by malate (56, 80) inhibition in long days by tannin-type substance (11)		phytochrome ? (81, 133) light ? (86) activation by malate (33)

Both the rhythms of CO_2 output and of CO_2 fixation display characteristics of endogenous rhythms. Wilkins developed systematic research on the effects obtained by light and temperature signals on the phase and the period of the CO_2 output rhythm in *Bryophyllum* (127–134). Working with CO_2-free air, which may have influenced some particular points of his results (83), Wilkins clearly established that the rhythm involves the operation of a biological clock. The essential features of his results in this connection have been repeated with leaves of *Kalanchoe blossfeldiana* in normal air for both the CO_2 output and the CO_2 fixation rhythms (83). Both rhythms damp after a few cycles in continuous light or dark conditions (83), but this damping can very likely result from the biochemical characteristics of this pathway.

Some confusing interpretations can be found in the literature concerning the interrelations between the components of the system and its behavior. Following is a summary of these interrelations, obtained mainly from results with *K. blossfeldiana*.

RHYTHM OF CO_2 FIXATION   (*a*) This rhythm is an overt indicator of the actual activity of P-enolpyruvate carboxylase. (*b*) A circadian rhythm of P-enolpyruvate carboxylase capacity (total activity as measured in the extracts) has been demonstrated (66, 81, 82); this rhythm is synchronous to the rhythm of CO_2 fixation. (*c*) The relationship between the phase of this rhythm and the phase of the oscillation of total content in malate will depend on factors influencing the latter [timing of malate utilization, temperature, degree of photoperiodic effect (78, 79)].

STORAGE STEP   (*a*) Malate seems to be produced at any time from oxaloacetate immediately after this latter is synthesized through dark CO_2 fixation. (*b*) Malate is transferred to a storage pool (vacuole ?); it will be made available for the following decarboxylative step generally at the beginning of the following day.

RHYTHM OF CO_2 OUTPUT   (*a*) This rhythm is an overt indicator of the actual activity of malic enzyme. (*b*) Malate decarboxylation starts massively at the beginning of the light period under day-night cycles. The effect of light could be to make malate [which is also an activator (33)] available for the enzyme's activity (see p. 127 of the present review). (*c*) The complexity of the intermediary malate storage steps, implying transfer and permeability parameters, makes it difficult to speculate on direct relationships between the rhythm of CO_2 output and the initial P-enolpyruvate carboxylase step. Moreover, there is no simple relationship between the phase of the rhythm of P-enolpyruvate carboxylase and the phase of the rhythm observed in malic enzyme capacity (85, 86).

Phytochrome controls the activity of P-enolpyruvate carboxylase and hence the rhythm of CO_2 fixation; its effect on malic enzyme and the rhythm of CO_2 output has not been clearly established (81, 133).

INDUCTION OF CAM BY PHOTOPERIODISM   The mechanism of CAM induction can be followed in young leaves of *Kalanchoe blossfeldiana* (11). In long days these leaves show no net dark CO_2 fixation, no accumulation of malate, and low enzyme capacity. Transfer into short days acts on a double mechanism: (a) progressive disappearance of an inhibitor; this substance, of the tannin type, has been isolated and proved to be highly inhibitory for P-enolpyruvate carboxylase, aspartate aminotransferase, and malate dehydrogenase at concentrations which do not affect malic enzyme (11); (b) induction of enzyme activity, after a lag-time of about 7 short days (11).

EFFECT ON THE PHASE OF ENZYME RHYTHM BY CHANGE OF PHOTOPERIOD   Current work in this laboratory shows that under long days P-enolpyruvate carboxylase displays a circadian oscillation of small amplitude. In a typical experiment the peak was at about 5 P.M. in long days; after 4 short days the peak was shifted to 7 A.M.; after 7 short days to 12 noon; after 10 short days to 6 P.M.; after 16 short days to 8 P.M. The fastest shift occurred during the lag-time of enzyme induction (7 short days).

EFFECT OF SHORT DAYS   (*a*) If the plants are kept under short days, the activity of the pathway will increase exponentially after about the 7th short day up to about the 50th, and then it decreases sharply. (*b*) Enzyme capacity displays circadian oscillations whose characteristics depend, for each enzyme, on the number of short days and on the thermoperiod (64, 81, 85). (*c*) The phase of the rhythms shifts continuously with the number of short days (Figure 1), concomitantly with changes in mean value and correlated amplitude (64, 86). In the experiment diagrammed in Figure 1, phase shifting is similar (about 0.3 hr/cycle) for the four enzymes during about 50 short days, suggesting the action of a single common basic oscillator. At that stage of the experiment the phase of malic enzyme starts shifting faster (0.7 hr/cycle); after about 60 short days, the phase of P-enolpyruvate carboxylase jumps (1 hr/cycle during a few cycles) and then resumes the preceding value. It must be noted that this phase jump coincides with the beginning of the sharp decrease in CAM activity (85).

Discussion on some regulatory problems in CAM operation will be developed in following sections (see p. 126 and 130).

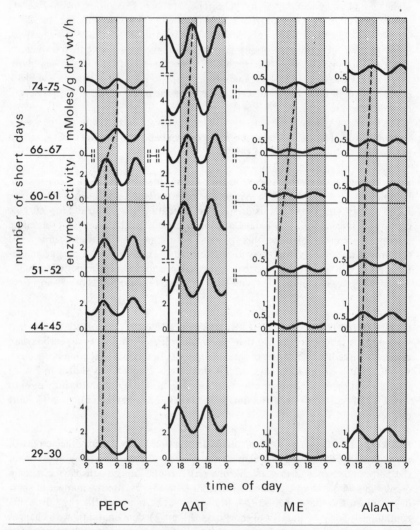

Figure 1 Rhythms of enzyme capacity in *Kalanchoe blossfeldiana,* a CAM plant, under short days, for P-enolpyruvate carboxylase (PEPC), aspartate aminotransferase (AAT), malic enzyme (ME), and alanine aminotransferase (AlaAT). Oscillations are drawn during two successive cycles at different moments of a 75 short-day experiment. The broken lines join corresponding phases to accentuate similarities or differences of shifting as a function of the number of short days (modified from 85).

SOME GENERALITIES ON MODELS

Because of the diversity of biological rhythms, a single general formulation has not been found as yet, so each model is able to grasp only some of their essential features. A direct mathematical approach implies that physiological functions are assumed to behave like rather simple mathematical functions. In spite of this oversimplification, some of the resulting models can display basic properties very similar to some properties of biological processes and afford suggestions on the inner physiological oscillatory mechanisms. Another frequent and more behavioral type of approach is based on the fact that allosteric feedback appears to be a very general tool in metabolic operation. Because a feedback mechanism produces oscillatory outputs, a number of theoreticians propose "box" models influenced by the engineering way of treating feedback loops. According to the real features of these outputs, i.e. their actual utilization by the organism, quantitative information will be sent back to the "box" which will correct their production according to this signal. The biological nature of the processes involved is not defined. The basic assumption in this approach is that evolution has tended to optimize the operation of metabolic systems (90). The components of the model will then be tentatively modified until their behavior simulates more or less closely the overt biologic rhythm; the properties of this elaborated model will then be interpreted in terms of analogy with possible biological parameters.

Physiological Validity of Models

The use of "boxes" in modeling can lead to a somewhat realistic approach of physiological organization. Let us consider an overt circadian rhythm—for example, flower induction, insect eclosion, phototaxis, and also photosynthesis or CO_2 rhythms in *Lemna* or in Crassulaceae. These final circadian processes integrate the operation of a complex underlying mechanism supposed to contain a basic oscillator and a nondefined number of intermediate metabolic steps. The action of external effectors (light, temperature, chemicals) on the clock can be evaluated through changes observed in the overt final rhythm without taking into consideration the details of the intermediary steps. These latter can then be blocked into a "box," i.e. an associative element. This method is not only designed to obtain technical simplification, but it probably corresponds also to a realistic approach of physiological mechanism. It is likely that living matter is organized as an interrelated succession of functional levels. This would in part result from the fact that different time scales are present and superimposed in biological operation (35, 59). In other terms, the basic condition (simultaneous presence of widely different time scales) for contraction mechanisms to be operative in a system (110) exists in the biological structures. Hence the physiological operation of the complex machinery of each subsystem, internally time coherent, would be integrated into a small set of physiologically efficient variables, its final outputs. Relative to the machinery of level B, which utilizes the outputs of level A, this latter behaves exactly like a "box," and vice-versa, as the organization of biological systems presents a bidirectional continuable hierarchy (6, 68). As suggested by Markowitz, it follows that the study of *classes* of elements could be of great significance (59). As circadian rhythms imply interconnections between very different biological subsystems, their study through this type of models appears to be valid.

The problem of synchronization of the individual oscillators must be faced before one tries to apply to physiological processes the suggestions provided by the model, because the overt measurable rhythm is actually the result of the operation of populations of molecules. In some cases the models deal already with collective oscillators, and the rationales will directly concern "physiological functions" in the usual sense of the term. The output of the individual oscillators could be an enzyme (69, 70), or the oscillator could be a metabolic reaction chain (59); the model will deal with variations in total enzyme activity or in final product. In the case of these models, changes in time of balances between pools of effectors, substrates, and enzymes will become fundamental data for the interpretation of changes in amplitude and phase of the rhythms. Nevertheless, these factors generally are not included in the models.

Models of Circadian Rhythms

Phenomenological models attempting to describe circadian rhythms fall into two broad categories. One includes models of biochemical systems displaying sustained oscillation either through the effects of cross-coupling between reactions or through the effects of feedback, or both; in this category, the achievement of a 24 hr periodicity is not inherent in the structure of the model and requires a specific constraint or additional assumptions. The other category includes models that attempt to simulate directly the shape of the overt rhythm and its typical responses to exogenous signals without referring to the biochemical detail of the system; the property of circadian periodicity is carried by the structure of the model through a convenient choice of parameters.

FEEDBACK AND METABOLIC CIRCADIAN PERIODICITY

Basic Characteristics of Feedback Models

Analog computer simulation defined the necessary relationships between the characteristics of the oscillation and the characteristics of the enzymic feedback control (63) in the case of a Yates-Pardee type of feedback (138). Form of the wave, amplitude at each step of the pathway, changes in amplitude, and phase relationships between oscillations in concentration of intermediate metabolites depend on the rates of enzymic reactions and on the degree of cooperativity by the allosteric effector. Cross-coupled systems of two reactions or chains of reactions, in which the product of each component is an effector of the other, was shown (43, 98) to display an oscillatory behavior, self-sustained over a reasonably wide range of parameter values; there is no intrinsic factor favoring a 24 hr periodicity.

$$A_0 \longrightarrow A$$
$$A + E_1^+ \longrightarrow E_1^+ A \longrightarrow E_1 + B$$
$$B + E_2 \longrightarrow E_2 B \longrightarrow E_2 + P$$
$$B + E_1 \rightleftharpoons E_1^+$$

Illustrated above is a linear version, presented by Higgins (43), that could be applied successfully to the short-period oscillations reported in yeast glycolysis by Chance and colleagues (15, 41). Pye could demonstrate that the key enzyme of the process E_1 was phosphofructokinase, A_0 being glucose, A being fructose-6-phosphate, and B, activator of E_1, being ADP, produced by its operation (76). A remarkable point is that the oscillations are self-sustained only when glucose is present in convenient amounts. If excess glucose is added to the culture, there are no oscillations until this excess is used up, and then oscillations appear spontaneously; but if trehalose, precursor of glucose, is added in excess, oscillations continue to occur. The explanation is that the enzyme trehalase would maintain the production of glucose at the proper rate to produce oscillations. In other words, the rate of entry of the initial substrate into the compartment is a basic factor for oscillation. Pavlidis & Kauzmann (72) pointed out that in the kinetic equations describing the model, most of the rate constants enter under the form k_i/k_j, which would justify a certain degree of temperature compensation typical of endogenous rhythms. This property of the model would be improved if it is assumed that the first reaction of the system depends on a diffusion process for substrate availability. On the other hand, other fundamental characteristics of light-sensitive endogenous rhythms, like phase response curves, can be simulated by the model if the second reaction is supposed to be photoactivable. Hence the probable importance for metabolic rhythmicity of processes like diffusion and photoactivation is brought to light through the study of this Higgins-Pavlidis model.

The Problem of Circadian Periodicity

Paradoxically, a determinative cause for a 24 hr period oscillation does not emerge convincingly from the models. The usual relaxation time of enzymic reactions is too short for a final circadian oscillation to arise directly from their operation. In the case of the Pavlidis-Kauzmann model, the authors consider that a very slow diffusion process or a very low concentration of enzymes probably would be needed in order to change the time scale of the system. Inhibitory coupling between a large number of oscillators in such a way that the overall oscillation at the level of the population would display a much lower frequency than the individual oscillators has been considered by several authors. Pavlidis proposed a modified model on these lines (69, 70). In his extensive theoretical work on feedback control at epigenetic level, Goodwin evaluates, for higher organisms, a period of about 4 hr for the feedback controlled oscillation in protein synthesis, but coupling would easily lengthen the period (35). Winfree tried another approach, based on weakly coupled relaxation oscillators, displaying dissipative, limit-cycle behavior (135). Vanden Driessche published a survey of the "multi-unit" theory, based mainly on Pavlidis's model, in relation to experimental data on light and temperature effects and RNA variations in unicells (116). The complex model elaborated by Ehret & Trucco (25) was based on regulation of cycling sequential transcription of template RNA from DNA; this model contains also a diffusion term capable of slowing down the cycling mechanism.

In other words, these different models tacitly require the presence of a factor introducing a "delay" in their cyclic operation, a kind of standstill intermediary step, so that the cycle would be closed only after about 24 hours.

This question is faced directly in a flexible and relatively simple model recently proposed by Johnsson & Karlsson (49) and applied to petal circadian movements (52). The model explicitly contains a "delay block," and it appears that the free-running period of the final oscillation would be strongly dependent on the values of the delay function, much more than on the relationship between input and corrected output signals.

In Wever's model for circadian rhythms (124, 125), a second order differential equation of the Van der Pol type, with convenient parameters, simulates a behavior more or less close to experimental data on circadian phenomena. One very interesting point in Wever's equation is that besides the oscillating variable (which could be enzyme capacity) the equation contains an independent controlling variable analogous to an environmental *Zeitgeber,* such as photoperiod. It is shown that in a very realistic way the intensity and amplitude of the *Zeitgeber* can modify the amplitude, the mean value, and also the shape of the overt rhythm, and also that the *Zeitgeber* can entrain the rhythm and modify its period within a well-defined range (126).

In summary it appears that the models do not really afford an explanation of why a broad category of rhythms displays a periodicity so close to 24 hr. The authors either express the hope that the biological equivalent of some slowing down mechanism will in vivo bring the period precisely around that value, or they impose it by adjusting mathematical parameters without clear physiological counterpart. On the other hand, the preceding discussion on models pointed out the probable importance, for metabolic oscillations, of factors such as diffusion mechanisms (which would control substrate availability), more abstract "delay" mechanisms (not necessarily implying diffusion), and light-activated steps (of chemical or physical nature).

LIGHT AND METABOLIC CIRCADIAN PERIODICITY

It is beyond the scope of this review to discuss the role of light as a biological timing agent or its action on endogenous clocks. The discussion will be restricted to some aspects of the connections between light (or photoperiod) and rhythmic changes in metabolism.

Light as a Circadian Timer in Models: The Case of CAM

Among the extensive literature on the effects of light signals on circadian rhythms, the spectacular results obtained by Pittendrigh (73) and Hillman (44–47) with "skeleton" photoperiods afford considerable information on entrainment phenomena in vivo.

As endogenous circadian rhythms are sensitive to light signals in a very specific way, light appears to be a good candidate for the role of imposing a circadian operation to systems like those described by the preceding models. In models of the Higgins-Pavlidis type, if we assume that enzyme E_2 can operate only under light, the concentration of B would be—for a high ratio between the activities of E_2 and E_1 ($E_2 > E_1$)—very low during the day, and hence its action on E_1 would be weak; during the dark period E_2 would not operate, B would accumulate with increasing and continuous action on E_1. Thus the rhythm in the amount of B and in the activity of E_1 would be entrained towards a 24 hr periodicity. This type of photoperiodic effect could be one of the timing factors in the circadian oscillation in malate content and enzyme capacity in CAM plants. In this case the biochemical model contains a negative feedback by malate on P-enolpyruvate carboxylase. In vivo malate accumulates mainly during the night, in spite of the presence of malic enzyme, and this latter enzyme starts depleting massively the accumulated malate only after light is turned on (or only if temperature is suddenly increased in darkness). It does not seem that the malic enzyme is directly photoactivated. Another hypothesis is that light would act on some permeability barrier (55) or viscosity barrier and make malate available for enzyme action. In any case this step would be sufficient to entrain the operation of the whole pathway towards a 24 hr period. In other words, utilizing the Johnsson-Karlsson terminology, a "delay block" would intervene at this stage of the CAM system, maintaining malate unavailability until the end of the dark period.

A more general discussion of this scheme combining light action through phytochrome, permeability phenomena, and positive or negative metabolic effectors on enzyme activity has already been developed in another review (84).

As Hillman (46) emphasizes, the study of the entrainment range could afford clear distinction between a clock-dependent rhythm and an imposed oscillation. If the rhythm involves a circadian clock, it would be able to synchronize only to a limited range of light-dark periodicities; in contrast, a simple light-activated reaction would "follow" any light schedule. Hence, when attempting to simulate photoperiodism-type behavior, models must be able to meet the condition of limited entrainment range. The model proposed by Wever appears to have such possibilities (125, 126). More particularly, it shows when and how relative coordination appears between a self-sustained oscillation and a *Zeitgeber* too strong or too weak to produce full entrainment. Changes in the amplitude of the rhythm and periodically changing phase relationships between the rhythm and the *Zeitgeber* can then be observed. It is interesting to note a remarkable formal analogy between Wever's theoretical solutions and the behavior of P-enolpyruvate carboxylase in *Kalanchoe blossfeldiana* kept in short days (Figure 2).

Enzyme Control

The most immediate way of conceiving a role of light and metabolic circadian rhythms is through enzyme photoactivation or induction. A recent paper by Zucker reviews this subject (143), and the reader is invited to refer to this work for extensive information on the matter. See also a recent review by Filner, Wray & Varner (29), and a review on connections to phenolic compounds by Zucker, Hanson & Sond-

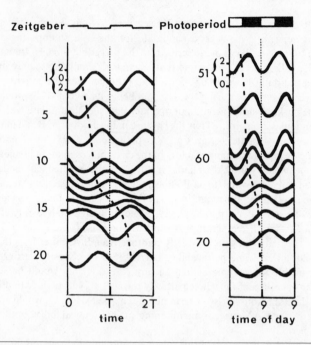

Figure 2   At left, example of oscillations showing the phenomenon of "relative coordination" at the limits of the range of entrainment by a *Zeitgeber,* according to Wever's model for circadian rhythms. Two periods are drawn successively at different moments of a 20-period series. Ordinates: number of periods; inserted scale: values of the oscillatory variable. *Zeitgeber:* forcing oscillation, drawn at the same scale (modified from 126).
At right, experimental oscillations of P-enolpyruvate carboxylase capacity in the leaves of *Kalanchoe blossfeldiana,* measured under increasing number of short days (see Figure 1). (Modified from 85.)

heimer (144). Schopfer listed the enzymes controlled or suspected of control by phytochrome (94). He emphasizes an interesting point: it appears from the survey that P_{fr} would control mainly enzymes involved in anabolic metabolism in a wide diversity of pathways.

In particular, synthesis of NADP-glyceraldehyde-3-phosphate dehydrogenase is controlled by phytochrome in higher plants, and the activity of the enzyme is increased by light (140, 142). Activation appears to be correlated with photosynthetic non-cyclic electron flow (141) and to correspond to a reversible increase in V_{max} of the enzyme, expressed on a protein basis, measured in crude extracts (62). The localization of the synthesis of this enzyme outside the chloroplasts in *Euglena* (93) could be of interest in connection with observations on the characteristics of the circadian rhythm in activity and also in connection with the possible role of compartmentation in rhythms (see next section).

Control by phytochrome and by photoperiodism of the activity of key-enzymes linked to photosynthesis, such as NADP-glyceraldehyde-3-phosphate dehydrogenase and ribulose diphosphate carboxylase (28, 143), could obviously be a determinant factor in circadian rhythms of photosynthesis and connected pathways, and of other energy-dependent physiological functions (21). This field is at present widely open for research.

COMPARTMENTATION AND METABOLIC RHYTHMS

Causal connection between compartmentation and biological rhythms could be of outstanding physiological and evolutionary significance. As yet only indirect evidence has been obtained and the problem has been explored more deeply by theoretical studies than by direct experiments. It has been shown that treatments with heavy water increase the period of different biological rhythms (10, 13, 27, 101); such effect implies that rhythms are generated at a metabolic level and also suggests a role of membranes or of cytoplasm density in the rhythms. It is known that photoperiodism controls the viscosity of cytoplasm in the leaves of *Kalanchoe blossfeldiana* (96), a plant in which number of circadian rhythms has been shown to depend on photoperiodism. As pointed out by Sweeney (103), a number of results clearly show that metabolism as a whole is not involved in the clock system and the hypothesis of a discrete oscillation-generating system must be considered. Such hypothesis obviously implies at least functional, and possibly structural, compartmentation. Moreover, Sweeney argues that the failure to observe a circadian rhythm in any procaryote supports the hypothesis that rhythms may depend on interactions between organelles, taking place across membrane barriers. She notes, however, that no relationship has been found between phase of rhythm and variation in ion exchange in *Gonyaulax* (103). Yet the possibility of a role of ion transfer deserves further research, mainly in the case of rhythms of metabolites, like malate, known for their role in ion exchange mechanisms.

The localization in membranes of the site for phytochrome action appears at present to be a highly plausible hypothesis (39). It would be consistent with a strong link between circadian phytochrome-controlled metabolic rhythms and compartmentation (83, 84), and would meet the condition of tight control through initial substrate concentrations emphasized by some of the models presented in the preceding sections.

The "delay block" in the model of Johnsson and Karlsson means that oscillations can be modulated by the effective time delay between stimulation and final measurable reaction; compartmentation could then be an important factor (see also the discussion on CAM, p. 127). A model by Goodwin & Cohen (36) and a later version by Cohen (20) give the first clear formulation of how feedback mechanisms and compartmentation could merge in order to transmit information and to achieve functional organization in developing systems. Glass & Kauffman (34) studied the dynamics of a pathway in which an enzyme presents cooperative, sigmoidal response to the concentration of a metabolite produced in another compartment by a later step of the pathway. The characteristics of the resulting rhythm will reflect the degree of compartmentation of its cooperative components. Convenient methodology must be developed for the study in vivo of this important and promising problem.

PHYSIOLOGICAL SIGNIFICANCE OF CIRCADIAN METABOLIC RHYTHMS

Metabolic Coherence and Rhythms

Key enzymes in intermediary metabolism are very often placed in branch points which command the delicate balance between connected pathways (19) or the metabolic switches required for readjustment in the responses to external changes (64, 83, 85). Periodic switches are needed for the normal day-night operation (4) and also for developmental and seasonal readjustments. The ability of metabolic systems to strongly modify the balances between pathways are also necessary for fast responses to environmental events [Weber's "acute adaptation" (123)]. In most cases anaplerotic mechanisms are then triggered with strong increase in metabolic flow. It can be expected that switches will generally produce, at least in a transient way, metabolic pulses propagating in wavelike fashion along the pathway (58). Changes in flow require control in order to attain a new optimized level; feedback in such instances is the operative mechanism, and it tends to introduce oscillatory modes in the pathway. On the other hand, if an enzyme showing circadian rhythmicity, or having a tendency to undergo it, is also easily inducible by chemical or other effectors, a connection can be expected between the rhythmic ability of the enzyme and its key position in metabolic strategies (17).

Coordinated circadian operation of the intricate bundle of metabolic rhythms could be achieved by common effectors. It has been suggested that content of ATP could be the underlying clock for many enzyme rhythms, owing to its sensitivity to light as a *Zeitgeber* (51). A similar role has been proposed for NADP under phytochrome control (137). It has not been proved that such effectors could justify all the typical characteristics of circadian rhythms.

The Case of CAM

The causes of rhythmicity in CAM appear to be very complex. Allosteric inhibition of P-enolpyruvate by malate could be a good candidate for the role of originating the oscillations (56, 81, 83). However, more recent results have shown that this hypothesis could scarcely account for all the known characteristics of the rhythms of enzyme and CO_2 exchange, mainly phase resetting by change in photoperiod (85, 86) and the suggested relative coordination (see Figure 2). Moreover, it could not explain the rhythms in transaminases; these could be expected to depend on a common effector (glutamate or pyridoxal phosphate), but phase synchronization with P-enolpyruvate carboxylase would remain unexplained. The possibility of periodic enzyme synthesis (53, 60, 100) would hardly explain synchrony in phase patterns (Figure 1) or circadian periodicity for all enzymes. In conclusion, all available data on CAM rhythms suggest that even if malate feedback operates under certain conditions in vivo, this effect should be superposed on a basic oscillator (of unknown nature) which underlies the coherent operation of several enzymes of the pathway (86).

The shift in phase of all the enzymes (Figure 1) would tend to produce a progressive change in the day-night metabolic patterns (see Figure 3 in 85). This would illustrate a very important consequence of slow metabolic readjustment, which can be expected in systems containing several connected circadian rhythms.

Adaptive Signification of Circadian Rhythms

It is generally thought that metabolic synchronization to the day-night rhythm confers a selective advantage in plants. At first sight it appears that this result could be obtained through simple photoactivation of convenient key reactions. On the contrary, biological adaptation has evolved a much more complex and mysterious solution: the biological clock mechanism. A strong advantage of this solution probably lies in its apparent coordinating ability. Moreover, its characteristics appear to be very similar in very different organisms. It is possible that the so-called clock is not an identifiable entity but a biological property (47) probably related to homeostasis (125). In other words, it is a type of ubiquitous, flexible, and adaptively efficient mechanism, present under different specific forms at all organizational levels. It has not been proved whether feedback has a central role in the mechanism or is superposed on it. It has been demonstrated that feedback tends to "buffer" the variability arising from fluctuations or perturbation in the initial steps of a pathway (92); this means that feedback increases homeostatic efficiency (90). In this connection, the preceding discussion on CAM would support the working hypothesis that control by feedback could be more efficient if applied to an already oscillating system.

CONCLUDING REMARKS

Enzyme regulation is generally better known in terms of test tube kinetics than in terms of physiological timing. We know in most cases the kinetic characteristics of an enzyme, but we know almost nothing about its behavior as a population of molecules during physiological continuous operation. The ubiquitous presence of circadian rhythms shows that metabolic patterns are continuously changing relationships between enzymic reactions, pathways, and compartments. The best physiological description of a pathway containing a feedback control is given by a spectrum of rhythms showing the phase relationships between its components under different environmental conditions. Metabolism is multilevel machinery, its operation is "goal-seeking" in adaptive terms and highly integrative. The multitude of variables intervenes at each level through a small number of degrees of freedom, and the behavior of such a complex system cannot be deduced from the simple sum of the behavior of its components considered individually. For all these reasons models can be very useful and appropriate tools. It could be of outstanding interest to develop our knowledge about the connections between metabolic regulation and circadian rhythms in areas such as compartmentation, balances at branch points, or isoenzyme patterns. Experimentation under accurately controlled conditions is imperative.

   Note added in proof: Interesting results communicated by E. Wagner (to appear in *Can. J. Bot.*) concern circadian rhythmicity of energy charge in *Chenopodium rubrum*. Hence energy charge could have a role in coherent circadian variations of a number of metabolic reactions. An important recent survey by C. S. Pittendrigh (to appear in *The Neurosciences; Third Study Program,* ed. F. O. Schmitt, MIT Press, 1973) pays most attention to the çouplings, mutual and hierarchical, or circadian oscillators. Particularly relevant to the preceding discussions are his considerations of the part played by circadian rhythms in the organization of internal timing and the fact that experimental disruptions of the organism's circadian oscillatory organization results in impairment of its normal growth and longevity.

Literature Cited

1. Aschoff, J. 1965. *Circadian Clocks.* Amsterdam: North-Holland
2. Atkinson, D. E. 1966. *Ann. Rev. Biochem.* 35: 85–124
3. Avadhani, P. N., Osmond, C. B., Tan, K. K. 1971. In *Photosynthesis and Photorespiration,* ed. M. D. Hatch, C. B. Osmond, R. O. Slatyer, 288–93. New York: Interscience
4. Bassham, J. A. 1971. *Science* 172: 526–34
5. Beevers, H., Stiller, M. L., Butt, V. S. 1966. In *Plant Physiology,* ed. F. C. Steward, 4B:119–262. New York: Academic
6. Bianchi, L. M., Hamann, J. R. 1970. *J. Theor. Biol.* 28:489–96
7. Black, I. B., Axelrod, J. 1968. *Proc. Nat. Acad. Sci. USA* 61:1287–91
8. Black, I. B., Axelrod, J. 1970. *Arch. Biochem. Biophys.* 138:614–19
9. Bomsel, J-L., Pradet, A. 1967. *Physiol. Veg.* 5:223–36
10. Bruce, V. G., Pittendrigh, C. S. 1960. *J. Cell. Comp. Physiol.* 56:25–31
11. Brulfert, J., Guerrier, D., Queiroz, O. 1973. *Plant Physiol.* 51:220–22
12. Bünning, E. 1967. *The Physiological Clock.* New York: Springer Verlag
13. Bünning, E., Moser, I. 1968. *Naturwissenschaften* 55:450–51
14. Champigny, M. L. 1960. *Rev. Gen. Bot.* 67:65–216
15. Chance, B., Estabrook, R. W., Ghosh, A. 1964. *Proc. Nat. Acad. Sci. USA* 51:1244–51
16. Chance, B., Hess, B., Betz, A. 1964. *Biochem. Biophys. Res. Commun.* 16: 182–87
17. Civen, M., Ulrich, R., Trimmer, B. M., Brown, C. B. 1967. *Science* 157: 1563–64
18. Codd, G. A., Merrett, M. J. 1971. *Plant Physiol.* 47:635–39
19. Cohen, G. N. 1967. *Le Métabolisme Cellulaire et sa Régulation.* Paris: Hermann
20. Cohen, M. H. 1972. In *Lectures on Mathematics. Some Mathematical Questions in Biology, II. Proc. 4th*

Symp. Math. Biol. Boston, ed. J. D. Cowan, 1–32. Providence, R. I.: Am. Math. Soc.
21. Cumming, B. G. 1972. *Proc. Int. Symp. Circadian Rhythmicity Wageningen 1971,* 33–85
22. Cumming, B. G., Wagner, E. 1968. *Ann. Rev. Plant Physiol.* 19:381–416
23. Echave Llanos, J. M., Epele, M. E., Surer, J. M. 1970. *J. Interdisciplinary Cycle Res.* 1:2–9
24. Edmunds, L. N. Jr., Walther, W. G., Sulzman, F. M. 1972. *J. Interdisciplinary Cycle Res.* 3:107–8
25. Ehret, C. F., Trucco, E. 1967. *J. Theor. Biol.* 15:240–62
26. Eling, W. 1967. See Ref. 61, 105–14
27. Enright, J. T. 1971. *Z. Vergl. Physiol.* 72:1–16
28. Feierabend, J., Pirson, A. 1966. *Z. Pflanzenphysiol.* 55:235–45
29. Filner, P., Wray, J. L., Varner, J. E. 1969. *Science* 165:358–67
30. Fishman, B., Wurtman, R. J., Munro, H. N. 1969. *Proc. Nat. Acad. Sci. USA* 64:677–82
31. Francesconi, R. P., Mager, M. 1970. *J. Interdisciplinary Cycle Res.* 1:239–50
32. Fuller, R. W., Jones, G. T., Snoddy, H. D., Slater, J. H. 1969. *Life Sci.* 8:685–91
33. Garnier-Dardart, J., Queiroz, O. 1974. *Phytochemistry.* In press
34. Glass, L., Kauffman, S. A. 1972. *J. Theor. Biol.* 34:219–37
35. Goodwin, B. C. 1963. *Temporal Organization in Cells.* London, New York: Academic
36. Goodwin, B. C., Cohen, M. H. 1969. *J. Theor. Biol.* 25:49–107
37. Gregory, F. G., Spear, I. Thimann, K. V. 1954. *Plant Physiol.* 29:220–29
38. Hardeland, R. 1972. *J. Interdisciplinary Cycle Res.* 3:109–14
39. Haupt, W. 1972. In *Phytochrome,* ed. K. Mitrakos, W. Shropshire Jr., 349–68. London, New York: Academic
40. Hellebust, J. A., Terborgh, J., McLeod, G. C. 1967. *Biol. Bull.* 133:670–78
41. Hess, B., Boiteux, A. 1971. *Ann. Rev. Biochem.* 40:237–58

42. Hess, B., Brand, K., Pye, K. 1966. *Biochem. Biophys. Res. Commun.* 23: 102–10
43. Higgins, J. 1964. *Proc. Nat. Acad. Sci. USA* 51:989–94
44. Hillman, W. S. 1964. *Am. Natur.* 98: 323–28
45. Hillman, W. S. 1970. *Plant Physiol.* 45:273–79
46. Hillman, W. S. 1972. *Proc. 4th Int. Photobiol. Congr.* Bochum
47. Hillman, W. S. 1972. *Plant Physiol.* 49:907–11
48. Jerusalem, C. 1967. See Ref. 61, 115–23
49. Johnsson, A., Karlsson, H. G. 1972. *J. Theor. Biol.* 36:153–74
50. Jolchine, G. 1959. *Bull. Soc. Chim. Biol.* 41:227–34
51. Jones, P. C. T. 1972. *J. Theor. Biol.* 34: 1–13
52. Karlsson, H. G., Johnsson, A. 1972. *J. Theor. Biol.* 36:175–84
53. Klevecz, R. P. 1969. *Science* 166: 1536–38
54. Kluge, M. 1971. See Ref. 3, 283–87
55. Kluge M. Personnal communication
56. Kluge, M., Osmond, C. B. 1972. *Z. Pflanzenphysiol.* 66:97–105
57. Lioret, C., Moyse, A. 1963. In *Comparative Biochemistry,* ed. M. Florkin, H. S. Mason, 5:203–6. New York, London: Academic
58. Markowitz, D. 1971. *J. Theor. Biol.* 31:475–92
59. Ibid 1972. 35:27–53
60. Masters, M., Donachie, W. D. 1966. *Nature* 209:476–79
61. Mayersbach, H. von 1967. *The Cellular Aspects of Biorhythms.* Berlin, Heidelberg, New York: Springer Verlag
62. Melandri, B. A., Pupillo, P., Baccarini-Melandri, A. 1970. *Biochim. Biophys. Acta* 220:178–89
63. Morales, M., McKay, D. 1967. *Biophys. J.* 7:621–25
64. Morel, C., Celati, C., Queiroz, O. 1972. *Physiol. Veg.* 10:743–63
65. Moyse, A. 1965. In *Travaux dédiés à Lucien Plantefol,* 21–45. Paris: Masson et Cie
66. Mukerji, S. K. 1968. *Ind. J. Biochem.* 5:62–64
67. Noguchi, M., Tamaki, E. 1962. *Arch. Biochem. Biophys.* 98:197–205
68. Pattee, H. H. 1970. In *Towards a Theoretical Biology,* Vol. 3. Chicago: Aldine
69. Pavlidis, T. 1969. *J. Theor. Biol.* 22:418–36
70. Ibid 1971. 33:319–38
71. Pavlidis, T. 1971. In *Proc. Symp. Biochronometry,* ed. M. Menaker, 110–16. Washington, D.C.: Nat. Res. Counc.
72. Pavlidis, T., Kauzmann, W. 1969. *Arch. Biochem. Biophys.* 132:338–48
73. Pittendrigh, C. S. 1965. See Ref. 1, 276–97
74. Potter, V. R., Gebert, R. A., Pitot, H. C. 1966. *Advan. Enzyme Regul.* 4: 247–65
75. Puiseux-Dao, S., Gilbert, A. M. 1967. *C. R. Acad. Sci. Paris D* 265:870–73
76. Pye, K. 1969. *Can. J. Bot.* 42:271–85
77. Pye, K., Chance, B. 1966. *Proc. Nat. Acad. Sci. USA* 55:888–94
78. Queiroz, O. 1965. *Physiol. Veg.* 3: 203–13
79. Ibid 1966. 4:323–39
80. Queiroz, O. 1967. *C. R. Acad. Sci. Paris* 265:1928–31
81. Queiroz, O. 1968. *Physiol. Veg.* 6: 117–36
82. Queiroz, O. 1969. *Phytochemistry* 8: 1655–63
83. Queiroz, O. 1970. *Physiol. Veg.* 8:75–110
84. Queiroz, O. 1972. See Ref. 39, 295–316
85. Queiroz, O., Celati, C., Morel, C. 1972. *Physiol. Veg.* 10:765–81
86. Queiroz, O., Morel, C. 1974. *Plant Physiol.* In press
87. Ranson, S. L., Thomas, M. 1960. *Ann. Rev. Plant Physiol.* 11:81–110
88. Rapoport, M. I., Feigin, R. D., Bruton, J., Beisel, W. R. 1966. *Science* 153: 1642–44
89. Richter, G. 1963. *Z. Naturforsch.* 18b: 1085–89
90. Rosen, R. 1967. *Optimality Principles in Biology.* London: Butterworths
91. Saltman, P., Kunitake, G., Spolter, H., Stitts, C. 1956. *Plant Physiol.* 31: 464–68
92. Savageau, M. A. 1972. In *Curr. Top. Cell. Regul.* 6:63–130
93. Schiff, J. A. 1970. *Symp. Soc. Exp. Biol.* 24:277–302
94. Schopfer, P. 1972. See Ref. 39, 486–514
95. Schor, S., Siekevitz, P., Palade, G. E. 1970. *Proc. Nat. Acad. Sci. USA* 66: 174–80
96. Schwabe, W. W., Wilson, J. R. 1965. *Ann. Bot. N. S.* 29:383–406
97. Schweiger, E., Wallraff, H. G., Schweiger, H. G. 1964. *Science* 146: 658–59
98. Spangler, R. A., Snell, F. M. 1961. *Nature* 191:457–58
99. Steer, B. T. 1973. *Plant Physiol.* 51: 744–48
100. Sulzman, F. M., Edmunds, L. N. Jr.

1972. *Biochem. Biophys. Res. Commun.* 47:1338–44
101. Suter, R. B., Rawson, K. S. 1968. *Science* 160:1011–14
102. Sweeney, B. M. 1969. *Rhythmic Phenomena in Plants.* London, New York: Academic
103. Sweeney, B. M. 1972. *Proc. Int. Symp. Circadian Rhythmicity Wageningen 1971,* 137–56
104. Sweeney, B. M., Hastings, J. W. 1960. *Cold Spring Harbor Symp. Quant. Biol.* 25:87–104
105. Sweeney, B. M., Haxo, F. T. 1961. *Science* 134:1361–63
106. Terborgh, J., McLeod, G. C. 1967. *Biol. Bull.* 133:659–69
107. Ting, I. P. 1968. *Plant Physiol.* 43: 1919–24
108. Ting, I. P. 1971. See Ref. 3, 169–85
109. Ting, I. P., Johnson, H. B., Szarek, S. R. 1972. In *Net Carbon Dioxide Assimilation in Higher Plants,* ed. C. C. Black, 26–53. Cotton Inc.
110. Uhlenbeck, G. 1968. *Fundamental Problems in Statistical Mechanics.* Ames: Iowa State Univ.
111. Vanden Driessche, T. 1966. *Biochim. Biophys. Acta* 126:456–70
112. Vanden Driessche, T. 1966. *Exp. Cell Res.* 42:18–30
113. Vanden Driessche, T. 1970. *Biochim. Biophys. Acta* 205:526–28
114. Vanden Driessche, T. 1971. *J. Interdisciplinary Cycle Res.* 2:133–45
115. Vanden Driessche, T. 1971. See Ref. 71, 612–22
116. Vanden Driessche, T. 1973. *Chronobiology.* In press
117. Vanden Driessche, T., Bonotto, S. 1968. *Arch. Int. Physiol. Biochim.* 76:205–6
118. Vanden Driessche, T., Bonotto, S. 1969. *Biochim. Biophys. Acta* 179:58–66
119. Vanden Driessche, T., Hars, R. 1972. *J. Microsc.* 15:85–90
120. Vilchez, C. A., Saffe de Vilchez, I. E.

1971. *J. Interdisciplinary Cycle Res.* 2: 55–62
121. Walker, D. A. 1962. *Biol. Rev.* 37: 215–56
122. Walther, W. G., Edmunds, L. N. Jr. 1973. *Plant Physiol.* 51:250–58
123. Weber, G. 1962. *Advan. Enzyme Regul.* 1:1–35
124. Wever, R. 1965. See Ref. 1, 47–63
125. Ibid, 74–83
126. Wever, R. 1972. *J. Theor. Biol.* 36: 119–32
127. Wilkins, M. B. 1959. *J. Exp. Bot.* 10:377–90
128. Ibid 1960. 11:269–88
129. Wilkins, M. B. 1960 *Cold Spring Harbor Symp. Quant. Biol.* 25:115–29
130. Wilkins, M. B. 1962. *Proc. Roy. Soc.* 156:220–41
131. Wilkins, M. B. 1965. See Ref. 1, 146–63
132. Wilkins, M. B. 1967. *Planta* 72:66–77
133. Wilkins, M. B. 1973. *J. Exp. Bot.* 24:488–96
134. Wilkins, M. B., Holowinsky, A. W. 1965. *Plant Physiol.* 40:907–9
135. Winfree, A. T. 1967. *J. Theor. Biol.* 16:15–42
136. Wurtman, R. J., Axelrod, J. 1967. *Proc. Nat. Acad. Sci. USA* 57:1594–98
137. Yamamoto, Y. 1972. See Ref. 39, 407–29
138. Yates, R. A., Pardee, A. B. 1956. *J. Biol. Chem.* 221:757–70
139. Yuwiler, A., Geller, E., Eiduson, S. 1971. *Biochim. Biophys. Acta* 244: 557–66
140. Ziegler, H., Ziegler, I. 1965. *Planta* 65:369–80
141. Ibid 1966. 69:111–23
142. Ibid 1967. 72:162–69
143. Zucker, M. 1972. *Ann. Rev. Plant Physiol.* 23:133–56
144. Zucker, M., Hanson, K. R., Sondheimer, E. 1967. In *Phenolic Compounds and Metabolic Regulation,* ed. B. J. Funkle, V. C. Runeckles, 68–93. New York: Academic

Ann. Rev. Plant Physiol. 1974. 25:135–66

PLANT PROPAGATION THROUGH TISSUE CULTURES[1]

❖7565

Toshio Murashige

Department of Plant Sciences, University of California, Riverside, California 92502

CONTENTS

THE ORCHIDS 138
STAGES OF THE TISSUE CULTURE METHOD 138
   Stage I: Establishment of the Aseptic Culture 139
   Stage II: Multiplication of Propagula 140
   Stage III: Preparation for Reestablishment of Plants in Soil 140
REQUIREMENTS OF EACH STAGE 140
   The Explant of Stage I 148
   The Nutrient Medium 150
      Chemical composition of the medium 150
      Physical qualities of the medium 154
   The Culture Environment 156
   Light Requirements 156
      Light intensity 156
      The daily light period 156
      Light quality 157
   Influence of Temperature 157
THE PLANTS FROM TISSUE CULTURE 158
   Reproduction of the Selected Plant 159
   Disease-Free Plants through Tissue Culture 160
FUTURE PROSPECTS 160

When Haberlandt attempted the first plant cell culture, his intentions were to develop a more versatile tool to explore morphogenesis and to demonstrate totipotentiality of plant cells. He probably did not suspect that the cell culture technique

[1]The following abbreviations have been used: BA (N_6-benzyladenine); CMP (cytidine 5'-monophosphate); CPA (4-chlorophenoxyacetic acid); 2, 4-D (2,4-dichlorophenoxyacetic acid); GA_3 (gibberellin A_3); IAA (indole-3-acetic acid); IBA (indole-3-butyric acid); 2iP (N_6-(2-isopentenyl)-adenine); MS (Murashige & Skoog salt formula); NAA (β-naphthaleneacetic acid); UMP (uridine 5'-monophosphate).

would become a valuable aid in economically oriented activities. There are four areas in which applications of plant tissue culture are possible, either presently or in the near future: 1. production of pharmaceuticals and other natural products; 2. the genetic improvement of crops; 3. the recovery of disease-free clones and preservation of valuable germ plasm; and 4. rapid clonal multiplication of selected varieties. Although there has been substantial research on the use of cell and organ cultures as sources of pharmaceuticals, a successful commercial application remains unrealized. The technique of embryo culture has served plant hybridizers for many years. Test-tube pollination with ovary and ovule cultures may similarly find utilization in plant breeding. Two recent developments in cell culture techniques have been stirring considerable excitement. One has been the attainment of haploid plants through anther and microspore cultures. Haploid plants will minimize hybridization steps considerably and help markedly in the recovery of mutants, either the naturally or the artificially induced. The other development has been the fusion of protoplasts of genetically distinct species and the achievement of somatic hybrid plants. Soon we may expect genetic transformation of higher plants, and it is conceivable that ultimately an alternate and much abbreviated procedure for developing a new crop variety will involve the introduction of desired cistron units from one variety into the protoplast of another, followed by the reconstitution of the plant from the transformed protoplast. The use of cell and organ culture methods in the reestablishment of pathogen-free clones has been reviewed recently.[2] These methods result in the restoration of vigor and yield lost due to infection. Furthermore, they provide a means to expedite the movement of plants from one country or region to another; they could greatly relieve quarantine pressures. If combined with freeze preservation methods, cell and organ cultures will also provide a method for the conservation of valuable pathogen-free germ plasm.

The application of cell and organ cultures to plant propagation is the topic of this review and is therefore covered in detail. The review may seem premature, inasmuch as extensive information directed specifically at the use of tissue cultures in the propagation of a host of crops is still lacking. Nevertheless, it has been undertaken with the hope that it will provide useful guidance to researchers concerned with the propagation of plants through tissue culture.

At the outset, certain terms or concepts which have been grossly misused require clarification. Foremost among these are "meristem culture," "meristemming," and "mericlones." The two latter terms were coined by the orchid trade and were derived from the first. These terms have created serious confusion in the practical employment of plant tissue cultures. With respect to rapid asexual multiplication, they are misleading and inappropriate and their use should be discouraged. The term "tissue culture" is simpler and more accurate. The true meristem culture signifies an explant whose dimensions are much too small to be of practical value in rapid clonal multiplication. The explant of the shoot apical meristem culture is restricted to the terminal dome and measures less than 0.1 mm in height. Such an explant cannot be obtained without considerable difficulty, and results in very poor

[2]Murashige, T., Jones, J. B. *Proc. 3rd Int. Symp. Virus Diseases Ornamental Plants.* In press.

survival and a slow rate of plant multiplication in vitro. Therefore, it has never been used in conjunction with tissue culture propagation of plants. The true meristem culture has significance in the recovery of pathogen-free plants, however. Commercial propagators of orchids have routinely used stem tip sections as long as 5–10 mm. These large explants hasten multiplication but do not necessarily exclude pathogens that may be infecting the stock plants.

A widespread misconception is that plant cell or tissue cultures are composed of uniform and undifferentiated cells. In fact, cells of most plant cultures are not uniform or undifferentiated. Variations in size, degree of vacuolation and cytoplasm content, cell wall characteristics, and shape usually characterize the cells of a cultured tissue, callus included. Moreover, the constituent cells are highly differentiated, and clearly so when compared to cells of an apical meristem or an embryo; the latter serve as useful reference for the undifferentiated state. In contrast to meristem or embryo cells, tissue culture cells, especially callus cells, are highly vacuolated, thin in cytoplasm, very large, of diverse shapes, and contain only faintly visible nuclei. These cells are indeed differentiated, but perhaps unorganized. The confusion is due partly to the use of the term undifferentiated when one really means unorganized.

The available information on tissue culture propagation of plants has been obtained from experiments with herbaceous, but not woody, genera. Accordingly, the conclusions of this review should not be viewed as applicable to the propagation of woody perennials, except perhaps as a foundation for their research. The successful manipulation of plant or organ regeneration processes has thus far been confined to those plants whose cuttings can be rooted without difficulty. Hence, even some tree species such as the aspen have been propagated successfully through tissue culture, although most have not. A reasonable guide is that any herbaceous plant whose cuttings can be rooted readily is multipliable through tissue culture following a minimum of experimentation.

The goal of asexual propagation is to produce uniform plants of a selected genotype. Vegetative propagation usually assures that the desired characteristics of the selected plant is retained throughout its clone. In contrast, there is no certainty that seedlings will reproduce even some of the parental characteristics. Nevertheless, seed propagation has been used in many instances for economic reasons, and major characteristics of a variety have been reproduced with sufficient consistency, e.g. many flowers and vegetables.

It is possible to achieve diverse objectives through the tissue culture method of plant propagation. It is most often sought as an alternative in the propagation of cultivars when conventional methods permit only slow increases in clonal plants, e.g. the orchids. Tissue culture propagation is particularly helpful when used in conjunction with plant breeding programs. It enables the timely increase and hastens the availability of new varieties. Even with cultivars that are propagated readily through cuttings, divisions, and other conventional asexual techniques, the tissue culture method can be utilized to enhance substantially the rate of multiplication. A millionfold increase per year in the rate of clonal multiplication over conventional methods is not unrealistic. Hence, with plants such as chrysanthemums and others that are already propagated quite rapidly by stem cuttings, tissue culture may be a desirable aid in meeting special needs. In commercial nurseries, tissue cultures can also be used to minimize the growing space usually provided for the maintenance of stock plants. Furthermore, when properly executed, the method can be used in the reproduction and maintenance of relatively disease-free plants.

THE ORCHIDS

Marston (130, 131) has published useful reviews on the research associated with tissue culture propagation of orchids; thus the orchids are treated only lightly and separately from other plants. General interest in the use of tissue cultures in plant propagation is attributable to the commercial success achieved with orchids. Unfortunately, research with orchids has not produced substantial information of a fundamental nature which can be applied to all plants. The more generally applicable principles have been obtained from investigations of tobacco and some other species.

The potential of propagating orchids through tissue culture was observed first by Morel (143) and incidentally in his attempt to recover virus-free cymbidiums from infected plants. He used explants composed of the shoot apical meristem together with a few primordial leaves. The explant was small enough to result in a plant free of the virus in question. Moreover, the culture proceeded through stages in which protocorms were differentiated, and after a number of recultures the protocorms were multiplied substantially. Further development from the protocorms resulted in the production of numerous clonal cymbidium plants in a short time. Morel subsequently described similar observations with other orchid genera (144, 145). . Commercial orchidologists quickly exploited Morel's observations and made a profitable venture of orchid tissue cultures. But they also modified his technique drastically, and orchid tissue culture as practiced today is not applicable to recovering pathogen-free clones, as Morel originally intended.

Table 1 contains a list of the orchid genera that can be propagated asexually through tissue cultures. The most frequently used explant has been the shoot tip, measuring 0.5–5 mm in height. Leaf and root tips of some genera have also manifested plant regenerating characteristics, e.g. *Cattleya* (28), *Epidendrum* (31, 32), *Laeliocattleya* (31, 32), and *Neottia* (25). In the absence of a suitable source of shoot tips, young inflorescences have served satisfactorily as explants in still other genera, e.g. *Ascofinetia, Neostylis,* and *Vascotylis* (81). For the most part, orchid cultures have been achieved without significant variations in the nutrient medium formulation. The major emphasis has been on discovering a suitable explant and developing an appropriate art. More thorough investigation of nutrient media, light, and temperature may substantially increase benefits from the procedure.

STAGES OF THE TISSUE CULTURE METHOD

While it has been recognized that the propagation of a plant through tissue culture must proceed through a sequence of steps, it has not been the general practice to systematically explore specific requirements of each step. As a commercial proce-

Table 1 Orchid genera that can be propagated through tissue culture

Genus	Explant	Reference
Ascofinetia	Young inflorescence	(81)
Calanthe	Shoot tip	(13)
Cattleya	Young leaf tip, shoot tip	(26, 28, 114, 191, 204)
Cymbidium	Shoot tip	(44, 45, 143–145, 199, 228–230, 242, 243)
Dendrobium	Shoot tip	(94, 145, 198)
Epidendrum	Leaf tip	(31, 32)
Laeliocattleya	Leaf tip	(31, 32)
Lycaste	Shoot tip	(145)
Miltonia	Shoot tip	(145)
Neostylis	Young inflorescence	(81)
Neottia	Root tip	(25)
Odontoglossum	Shoot tip	(145)
Odontonia	Shoot tip	(13)
Oncidium	Shoot tip	(13)
Ophrys	Embryo	(13, 27)
Phaius	Shoot tip	(145)
Phalaenopsis	Inflorescence node	(62)
Rhynchostylist	Shoot tip	(221)
Vanda	Shoot tip	(107, 221)
Vascotylis	Young inflorescence	(81)
Vuylstekeara	Shoot tip	(13)
Zygopetalum	Shoot tip	(13)

dure, the sequential steps must be identified and virtually optimum conditions of each should be established. In principle, there are three major steps, hereafter referred to as stages for the purpose of emphasis, each with a different objective and possibly different requirements.

Stage I: Establishment of the Aseptic Culture

The objective of Stage I is simply to attain an aseptic tissue culture of the plant in question. The culture may result as enlarging shoot tips, rooted shoot tips, callus, etc. It is only necessary that the culture be free from obvious infection, that a suitable proportion of explants survive culture, and that there is rapid growth among the explants.

Stage II: Multiplication of Propagula

In Stage II a rapid increase of organs and other structures which can ultimately give rise to plants is the aim. The increase can be achieved in most instances by either inducing adventitious organ or embryo formation or by enhancing axillary shoot initiation. Table 2 contains a list of plants and the methods by which their asexual multiplication might be accomplished. With most species the more likely method of multiplication would be adventitious organogenesis, either of shoots or of asexual embryos. In many cases an intermediary callus has been involved. The orchids have been multiplied through adventitious protocorm formation (26). Whereas the method of adventitious organogenesis may enable a substantially faster increase in propagula, it can have serious disadvantages. For example, a high incidence of genetically aberrant plants has not been uncommon with this method. The method of axillary shoot multiplication may be slower, but genetically deviant plants have been virtually absent when it has been used, e.g. *Asparagus officinalis* (69, 155) and *Gerbera jamesonii.*[3]

Stage III: Preparation for Reestablishment of Plants in Soil

A successful tissue culture method of propagation must result in reestablishment in soil of a high frequency of the tissue culture derived plants. Stage III is intended to prepare the propagula for their successful transfer to soil. Research on Stage III has been largely neglected. This stage involves the rooting of shoot cuttings, hardening of plants to impart some tolerance to moisture stress, conferring of a degree of resistance to certain pathogens, and conversion of plants from the heterotrophic to the autotrophic state. With certain plants, e.g. bulbs and others adapted to the temperate climate, it may be necessary to satisfy dormancy-associated requirements. Bulbs, corms, and tubers may undergo dormancy when transferred from test tube to soil without having fulfilled their chilling requirements.

Common conditions with respect to nutrient medium and culture environment may sometimes be applicable to two stages. Thus, it has been possible to proceed through Stages I and II by utilizing nutrient media of the same composition and form and the same light and temperature provisions. For maximum success Stage III conditions should be distinct from the other two, however. Orchid tissue culturers have consistently published procedures where only one stage has been recognized. It is probable that even the orchid process can benefit from refinements in terms of two or three stages in vitro.

REQUIREMENTS OF EACH STAGE

The requirements of each stage in vitro can be categorized as nutrient medium characteristics and culture environment qualities. The study of Stage I must also consider the explant. In Stage II it may be helpful to first determine the method by which the multiplication is to be achieved, i.e. adventitious shoots, asexual embryos,

[3]Unpublished experiments of author.

Table 2 Plants with demonstrated potential for clonal multiplication through tissue cultures[a]

Plant and Reference	Explant Source	Method of Multiplication
Agavaceae		
Dracaena sp.[b]	Shoot tip	Adventitious shoots
Yucca sp.[b]	Shoot tip	Adventitious shoots, asexual embryos
Alliaceae		
Allium cepa L. (46)	Aerial bulb scale	Callus, adventitious bulb
Amaryllidaceae		
Amaryllis sp.[b]	Bulb scale	Adventitious bulbs
Aquifoliaceae		
Ilex aquifolium L. (79)	Cotyledon	Asexual embryos
Araceae		
Philodendron sp.[b]	Shoot tip	Adventitious shoots
Araliaceae		
Panax ginseng C.A. Mey (22)	Leaf, root	Callus, asexual embryos
Asclepiadaceae		
Pergularia minor Andr. (37)	Stem	Callus, asexual embryos
Tylophora indica Merr. (186)	Stem	Callus, asexual embryos
Asteraceae		
Chondrilla juncea L. (91)	Root	Adventitious shoots
Chrysanthemum morifolium Ram. (12, 76)	Stem, shoot tip	Callus, adventitious shoots
Cichorium endivia L. (231, 233)	Embryo	Callus, adventitious shoots, asexual embryos
Cichorium intybus L. (129)	Root	Adventitious shoots
Crepis capillaris Wallr. Beitr. Fl. Hercyn. (84, 253)	Hypocotyl, leaf	Callus, adventitious shoots
Gerbera jamesonii Bolus[b]	Shoot tip	Axillary shoots
Lactuca sativa L. (38)	Cotyledon, hypocotyl, root	Adventitious shoots
Begoniaceae		
Begonia rex Putz. (208)	Leaf	Adventitious shoots
Begonia sp.[b]	Shoot tip	Adventitious shoots
Blechnaceae		
Woodwardia fimbriata[b]	Rhizome tip	Adventitious shoots
Brassicacea		
Brassica oleracea L.		
var. acephata (78, 116)	Leaf, root stem	Adventitious shoots
var. botrytis (126, 236)	Inflorescence	Adventitious shoots
var. gongylodes (250)	Corm	Adventitious shoots

Table 2 (Continued)

Plant and Reference	Explant Source	Method of Multiplication
Bromeliaceae		
Aechmea fasciata Baker[b]	Lateral bud	Adventitious shoots
Ananas comosus Schult.[b]	Lateral bud	Adventitious shoots
Cryptanthus bivittatus Regel[b]	Lateral bud	Adventitious shoots
Cryptbergia sp.[b]	Lateral bud	Adventitious shoots
Dyckia sulphurea C. Koch[b]	Lateral bud	Adventitious shoots
Caryophyllaceae		
Dianthus caryophyllus L. (61)	Shoot tip	Callus, adventitious shoots
Chenopodiaceae		
Beta vulgaris L. (21, 127)	Leaf, root hypocotyl, cotyledon, flower bud	Callus, adventitious shoots
Convolvulaceae		
Convolvulus arvensis L. (15, 16, 39, 75)	Root, stem	Callus, adventitious shoots
Ipomoea batatas Poir. Encyc. (57)	Root	Adventitious shoots
Crassulaceae		
Crassula sp.[b]	Leaf	Adventitious shoots
Echeveria elegans Rose (179)	Leaf	Adventitious shoots
Kalanchoe sp.[b]	Leaf	Adventitious shoots
Cruciferae		
Amoracia rusticana (250)	Hypocotyl, stem	Adventitious shoots
Cheiranthus cheiri L. (93)	Seedling	Callus, asexual embryos
Isatis tinctora L. (36)	Root	Adventitious shoots
Lunaria annua L. (175)	Leaf	Callus, adventitious shoots
Nasturtium officinale R. Br. (9, 10)	Stem	Adventitious shoots
Sinapis alba L. (7)	Hypocotyl	Callus, asexual embryos
Cucurbitaceae		
Cucurbita pepo L. (85, 203)	Hypocotyl, cotyledon, fruit	Callus, asexual embryos
Cupressaceae		
Biota orientalis Endl. (104)	Cotyledon	Asexual embryos
Cuscutaceae		
Cuscuta reflexa Roxb. Pl. Corom. (118)	Seedling	Callus, asexual embryos
Cyatheaceae		
Alsophila australis R. Br.[b]	Rhizome tip	Adventitious shoots

Table 2 (Continued)

Plant and Reference	Explant Source	Method of Multiplication
Cycadaceae		
Cycas sp. (169)	Megagametophyte	Callus, asexual embryos
Zamia integrifolia Ait. (168, 170)	Megagametophyte, embryo	Asexual embryos
Cyperaceae		
Pterotheca falconeri Hook. (134)	Seedling	Callus, asexual embryos
Davalliaceae		
Nephrolepis bostoniensis[b]	Rhizome tip	Adventitious shoots
Nephrolepis exultata[b]	Rhizome tip	Adventitious shoots
Euphorbiaceae		
Euphorbia pulcherrima Willd. (159) ·	Seed	Callus, adventitious shoots, asexual embryos
Geraniaceae		
Pelargonium hortorum Bailey (1, 30, 176–178)	Stem, shoot tip, anther	Callus, adventitious shoots
Gesneriaceae		
Gloxinia sp.[b]	Shoot tip	Axillary shoots
Saintpaulia ionantha Wendl. (106)	Leaf	Callus, adventitious shoots
Iridaceae		
Gladiolus hortulans (73, 210, 240, 256)	Corm, shoot tip, flower stalk	Callus, adventitious · corms
Leguminosae		
Lotus caucasicus Kupr. (163)	Anther	Asexual embryos
Lotus corniculatus L. (163)	Anther	Asexual embryos
Vigna sinensis Endl. (157)	Cotyledon	Adventitious shoots
Liliaceae		
Asparagus officinalis L. (5, 54, 69, 155, 216, 220, 251)	Spear, shoot tip, embryo	Callus, adventitious shoots, asexual embryos
Haworthia angustifolia V. Polln. (90)	Inflorescence	Adventitious shoots
Haworthia atrofusca G.G. Smith (90)	Inflorescence	Adventitious shoots
Haworthia chloracantha Haw. (90)	Inflorescence	Adventitious shoots
Haworthia maughanii V. Polln. (90)	Inflorescence	Adventitious shoots
Haworthia retusa L. (90)	Inflorescence	Adventitious shoots
Haworthia turgida Haw. (121)	Ovary	Adventitious shoots
Haworthia variegata L. (90, 122, 123)	Inflorescence, stem	Callus, adventitious shoots

Table 2 (Continued)

Plant and Reference	Explant Source	Method of Multiplication
Liliaceae (Continued)		
Iris hollandica (47)	Lateral bud	Adventitious shoots
Lilium longiflorum Thunb. (60, 207)	Bulb scale, shoot tip	Adventitious bulbs
Lilium speciosum Thunb. (192)	Bulb scale	Adventitious bulbs
Loranthaceae		
Dendrophthoe falcata Blume (86)	Embryo	Callus, asexual embryos
Meliaceae		
Azadirachta indica A. Juss. (182)	Seedling	Callus, adventitious shoots
Musaceae		
Musa cavendishii Lamb. (117)	Shoot tip	Adventitous shoots
Myrtaceae		
Eucalyptus citritodora Hook. (6)	Lignotuber	Adventitious shoots
Papaveraceae		
Macleaya cordata R. Br. (98, 99)	Leaf	Asexual embryos
Passifloraceae		
Passiflora caerulea L. (158)	Stem	Callus, adventitious shoots
Plumbaginaceae		
Plumbago indica L. (165)	Stem	Adventitious shoots
Poaceae		
Avena sativa L. (23)	Seedling	Callus, adventitious shoots
Bromus inermis Leyss. (48)	Mesocotyl	Callus, asexual embryos
Hordeum vulgare L. (169)	Embryo	Asexual embryos
Oryza sativa L. (164, 200)	Seed	Callus, adventitious shoots
Saccharum sp. (11, 70)	Stem, shoot tip, leaf, inflorescence	Callus, adventitious shoots
Sorghum bicolor Moench. (132)	Stem	Callus, adventitious shoots
Triticum aestivum L. (209)	Root, stem	Callus, adventitious shoots
Triticum dicoccum Schrank, Baier. Fl. (209)	Root, stem	Callus, adventitious shoots
Triticum monococcum L. (209)	Root, stem	Callus, adventitious shoots
Polymoniaceae		
Phlox drummondii Hook. (100)	Flower bud	Callus, adventitious shoots

Table 2   (Continued)

Plant and Reference	Explant Source	Method of Multiplication
Primulaceae		
Cyclamen persicum Mill. (133, 218, 250)	Seedling	Adventitious shoots
Pteridaceae		
Adiantum cuneatum Langs & Fisch[b]	Rhizome tip	Adventitious shoots
Microlepia strigosa[b]	Rhizome tip	Adventitious shoots
Pteris argyrea[b]	Rhizome tip	Adventitious shoots
Pteris cretica L. (19)	Leaf, stem	Aposporic gametophytes, sporophytes
Ranunculaceae		
Ranunculus sceleratus L. (101–103)	Flower bud	Callus, asexual embryos
Rosaceae		
Rosa sp. (82)	Stem	Adventitious shoots
Rubiaceae		
Coffea arabica L. (215)	Stem	Callus, asexual embryos
Coffea canephora Pierre ex Froehner (215)	Stem	Callus, asexual embryos
Coffea liberica Hiern (215)	Stem	Callus, asexual embryos
Rutaceae		
Citrus aurantium L. (41)	Nucellus	Asexual embryos
Citrus grandis L. (41, 180)	Nucellus	Asexual embryos
Citrus hystrix D. C. (41)	Nucellus	Asexual embryos
Citrus ichangensis Swing. (41)	Nucellus	Asexual embryos
Citrus jambhiri Lush. (41)	Nucellus	Asexual embryos
Citrus kharna Rafin. (41, 211)	Nucellus	Asexual embryos
Citrus lansium Lour. (41)	Nucellus	Asexual embryos
Citrus limon L.		
cv. Eureka (41)	Nucellus	Asexual embryos
cv. Meyer (41)	Nucellus	Asexual embryos
cv. Ponderosa (41, 180)	Nucellus	Asexual embryos
Citrus limonia Osbeck (41)	Nucellus	Asexual embryos
Citrus madurensis Lour. (41, 55)	Nucellus, seedling stem	Asexual embryos, adventitious shoots
Citrus medica L. (41)	Nucellus	Asexual embryos
Citrus microcarpa Bunge (181)	Nucellus, ovule	Callus, asexual embryos
Citrus paradisi Macfad. (41, 97)	Nucellus, ovule	Asexual embryos
Citrus reticulata Blanco		
cv. Algerian (41)	Nucellus	Asexual embryos
cv. Cleopatra (41)	Nucellus	Asexual embryos
cv. Nagpuri (195)	Nucellus, ovule	Asexual embryos
cv. Ponkan (41)	Nucellus,	Asexual embryos

Table 2 (Continued)

Plant and Reference	Explant Source	Method of Multiplication
Rutaceae (Continued)		
Citrus sinensis Osbeck (41, 97, 141)	Nucellus, ovary, ovule	Asexual embryos
Eremocitrus glauca Swing. (41)	Nucellus	Asexual embryos
Fortunella crassifolia Swing. (41)	Nucellus	Asexual ambryos
Microcitrus australasica F. Muel. (41)	Nucellus	Asexual embryos
Microcitrus warburgiana F.M. Bail. (41)	Nucellus	Asexual embryos
Poncirus trifoliata L. (41, 211)	Nucellus	Asexual embryos
Salicaceae		
Populus tremula L. (247)	Root	Adventitious shoots
Populus tremuloides Michx. (244-247, 249)	Root sprout	Adventitious shoots
Santalaceae		
Santalum album L. (183)	Seed	Asexual embryos
Saxifragaceae		
Saxifraga sp.[b]	Shoot tip	Axillary shoots
Scrophulariaceae		
Linaria vulgaris Mill (29)	Root	Adventitious shoots
Mazus pumilus Murm. F. (187)	Stem	Callus, adventitious shoots
Torenia fournieri Lind. (33)	Leaf, stem	Adventitious shoots
Verbascum thapsus L. (24)	Stem	Adventitious shoots
Solanaceae		
Atropa belladona L. (222, 254)	Leaf, root	Callus, adventitious shoots, asexual ambryos
Datura inoxia Mill. (40, 56)	Anther, stem	Callus, adventitious shoots, asexual embryos
Lycopersicon peruvianum L. (171)	Root	Adventitious shoots
Nicotiana longiflora Cav. (2)	Stem	Callus, adventitious shoots
Nicotiana rustica L. (235)	Shoot tip	Callus, adventitious shoots
Nicotiana suaveolens Lehn. (174)	Stem	Callus, adventitious shoots
Nicotiana sylvestris[b]	Stem	Callus, adventitious shoots
Nicotiana tabacum L. (58, 59, 119, 147-153)	Leaf, stem	Callus, adventitious shoots
Petunia hybrida Hort. (68, 184)	Leaf, stem	Adventitious shoots

Table 2 (Continued)

Plant and Reference	Explant Source	Method of Multiplication
Solanaceae (Continued)		
Petunia inflata R.E. Fries (68, 184)	Leaf, stem	Adventitious shoots
Physalis peruviana L. (255)	Leaf	Adventitious shoots
Salpiglossis sinuata L. (80)	Anther	Callus, adventitious shoots
Solanum dulcamara L. (255)	Leaf	Adventitious shoots
Solanum melongena L. (252)	Embryo	Callus, asexual embryos
Solanum nigrum L. (255)	Leaf	Adventitious shoots
Solanum tuberosum L. (42, 250)	Tuber	Adventitious shoots
Solanum xanthocarpum Scrad. & Wendl. (185)	Stem	Adventitious shoots
Taxodiaceae		
Sequoia sempervirens Endl. (8)	Stem	Callus, adventitious shoots
Thelypteridaceae		
Cyclosorus dentatus Forsk. (135)	Root tip	Callus, aposporic gametophytes, sporophytes
Ulmaceae		
Ulmus campestris L. (51, 83)	Stem	Adventitious shoots
Umbelliferae		
Ammi majus L. (205)	Ovule	Callus, asexual embryos
Anethum graveolens L. (87)	Embryo	Callus, asexual embryos
Apium graveolens L. (189)	Hypocotyl	Callus, asexual embryos
Conium maculatum L. (161)	Hypocotyl	Callus, asexual embryos
Daucus carota L. (63, 64, 66, 67, 89, 113, 115, 146, 162, 188, 217)	Leaf, hypocotyl, root	Callus, asexual embryos
Foeniculum vulgare Mill. (120)	Stem	Callus, asexual embryos
Petroselinum hortense Hoffm. (232)	Leaf	Callus, adventitious shoots
Sium suave Walt. (4)	Embryo	Callus, asexual embryos

[a] Excludes orchids.
[b] Unpublished data of author.

axillary shoots, etc. Stage III must consider any special physiological needs of the species or variety in question, such as chilling requirements, high intensity light for cladophyll differentiation, etc. As illustrations, the three stages during the propagation via tissue cultures of *Asparagus, Gerbera,* and some bromeliads are shown in Table 3.

The Explant of Stage I

In deciding on a suitable explant, the investigation should consider (a) the organ that is to serve as tissue source; (b) the physiological or ontogenetic age of the organ; (c) the season in which the explant is being obtained; (d) the size of the explant; and (e) the overall quality of the plant from which explants are to be obtained. Table 2 shows that virtually every organ or tissue can be used as a source of explants. Nevertheless, the degree of success has been variable, and in developing a procedure for commercial use, selection of the explant source should be carried out systematically and deliberately. Shoot tips have been the best suited for the propagation of many orchids, as well as *Asparagus* and *Gerbera,* root sections for the Convolvulaceae (15, 16, 39, 57), leaf sections for the begonias (208) and some members of the Solanaceae (58, 119, 255), inflorescence sections for *Haworthia* (90) and the sarcanthine orchids (81), and nucellus for the Rutaceae (41). Among seedling parts the cotyledon has been the most regenerative, e.g. *Biota orientalis* (104), *Curcurbita pepo* (85), *Ilex aquifolium* (79), *Lactuca sativa* (38), and *Vigna sinensis* (157). Anther explants have been used in a few cases to reproduce diploid plants (1, 56, 103). The behavior of *Nicotiana glauca* tissues in vitro illustrates the sometimes critical role of the explant. Paulet & Nitsch (174), as well as our own observations, have shown that stem section and callus cultures of *N. glauca* do not yield adventitious roots or shoots in response to cytokinin and auxin treatments. However, our experiments disclosed that cultures from stem tips produced adventitious organs profusely under the same conditions.[3] *Petunia* tissue cultures have also shown similar differences in behavior between stem segment and shoot tip cultures.[3] For *N. glauca* or *Petunia* then the choice is clearly one of using shoot tips and not stem sections as explants.

The variations in regenerative characteristics among explants are sometimes attributable to differences in their physiological age and the extent of differentiation among their constituent cells. Among *N. tabacum* stem section explants, for example, those from nearer the apical region produce adventitious roots and shoots more readily than those from the basal region.[3] A progressive decline in the organogenic characteristics has been observed down the length of the tobacco stem. Raju & Mann (179) reported that in *Echeveria elegans* leaf explants the young leaves regenerated only roots, whereas old leaves formed shoots; leaves of more median age produced both roots and shoots. In *Lunaria annua,* rooting occured readily in petiole sections of young leaves, but not of older leaves (175). Pierik (175) suggested that the poorer rooting in the older explants was due possibly to an age-related, increased production of root-inhibiting substances. The regeneration of bulbs in bulb scale explants of *Lilium* has also been reportedly polarized. Hackett (60) indicated that regeneration was highest among the older, outer scales and decreased progressively among the inner scales of bulbs. Robb (192) as well as Hackett (60) noted further that in a given bulb scale the regeneration occurred principally in the basal regions.

The season in which explants are obtained may also influence the regenerative characteristics in tissue culture, particularly with plant varieties adapted to the temperate climate. Robb (192) observed that in *Lilium speciosum,* bulb scale ex-

Table 3 Characteristics associated with the three major stages in tissue culture propagation of *Asparagus officinalis, Gerbera jamesonii,* and some bromeliads

Characteristic	*Asparagus officinalis*	*Gerbera jamesonii*	Bromeliads
	STAGE I		
Explant	0.15 mm shoot tip	2–3 mm shoot tip	Lateral bud
Medium specifications	Agar, MS salts, 0.3 mg/l NAA, 0.1 mg/l kinetin	Agar, MS salts, 0.5 mg/l IAA, 10 mg/l kinetin	Liquid, 1 rpm MS salts, 1.75 mg/l IBA, 1.75 mg/l NAA. 150 mg/l citric acid
Culture environment	27°C, 16 hr daily, 1000 lux, Gro lux	27°C, 16 hr daily, 1000 lux, Gro lux	27°C, 16 hr daily, 1000 lux, Gro lux
	STAGE II		
Method of multiplication	Axillary shoots, adventitious roots	Axillary shoots	Adventitious shoots
Medium changes from Stage I	None	None	Liquid, stationary, supplements replaced by 2 mg/l IAA, 2 mg/l kinetin, 80 mg/l adenine sulfate, 170 mg/l $NaH_2PO_4 \cdot H_2O$
Environmental differences from Stage I	None	None	None
	STAGE III		
Medium changes from Stage II	Remove NAA	Remove kinetin, increase IAA to 10 mg/l	Remove kinetin, adenine sulfate, and $NaH_2PO_4 \cdot H_2O$
Environmental differences	Increase light to 10,000 lux, white fluorescent	Increase light to 10,000 lux, white fluorescent	Increase light to 3000 lux

plants obtained during the spring and fall seasons regenerated freely, whereas those taken during summer or winter months hardly ever produced bulblets. Robb suggested that these seasonal variations in bulblet-forming characteristics were correlated with phases of development of the lily plant, the capacity for regeneration being limited to periods of vegetative growth. Organogenesis in *Solanum tuberosum* tissue cultures has been described as being seasonally influenced. According to Fellenberg (42), explants obtained in December and April were highly tuberogenic, whereas those of February and March or between May and November regenerated only poorly.

Among other characteristics associated with the explant, the frequency of survival in vitro as well as its rate of development into a reculturable structure has been related directly to its initial size. Meristem cultures are indeed impractical for achieving rapid asexual multiplication. The explant being extremely small, the rates of survival and development in vitro are distinctly poor. However, the probability of isolating a clean tissue, i.e. an explant free from microorganisms, is inversely related to its size.

The initial behavior of a cultured tissue may vary also with the overall physiological status of its original plant. A tissue isolated soon after heavy fertilization of its source plant may react in a different way to the nutrient medium compared with one isolated later or from an unfertilized plant. A difference of in vitro behavior may also result among tissues of healthy and diseased plants.

The Nutrient Medium

The nutrient medium during each of the three stages must be suitable in both chemical composition and physical qualities.

CHEMICAL COMPOSITION OF THE MEDIUM   Normally, it is possible to employ the same medium throughout Stages I and II. However, it should be recalled that the two stages have distinct objectives. It is usually only necessary that the Stage I medium enables survival in vitro and some enlargement of the explant. It is sometimes necessary to include antioxidants to retard browning and deterioration of the freshly excised tissue, or antibiotics to suppress microbial development. The Stage II medium is most critical, since it is intended for the multiplication of propagula. The medium is frequently enriched with substances that enhance organogenesis, especially shoot formation. When asexual embryogenesis is desired in callus cultures the auxin content of the nutrient medium should be reduced, particularly when 2,4-D is used. The medium of Stage III should contain rhizogenic substances if root initiation is desired; this medium has the simplest composition, especially when the only necessities in the stage are conditions that promote growth of fully differentiated but undersized plants.

The assessment of requirements in nutrient medium composition can be simplified substantially by considering the ingredients in these three categories: inorganic salt mixture, organic substances and natural complexes. The specific items within each of these categories are shown in Table 4. In most instances the inorganic salt requirement can be met very simply by comparing the salt mixtures of Table 4.

Table 4 Major constituents of nutrient media

Inorganic salts[a]

   White (239)
   Hildebrandt, Riker & Duggar (74)
   Heller (72)
   Murashige & Skoog (156)

Organic substances

   Carbohydrate: sucrose
   Vitamins: thiamin, inositol, nicotinic acid, pyridoxin
   Amino acids and amides: arginine, aspartic acid and asparagine, glutamic acid and
                           glutamine, tyrosine
   Nitrogen base: adenine
   Growth regulators:
      Auxin: IAA, IBA, NAA, CPA, 2,4-D
      Cytokinin: Ba, kinetin, 2iP
      Gibberellin: GA_3

Natural Complexes

   Hydrolyzed protein preparations: casein and lactalbumin hydrolysates, soy peptone
   Brewer's byproducts: malt and yeast extracts
   Endosperm fluids: coconut, corn
   Fruit pulp and juice: banana, orange juice, tomato juice
   Animal byproducts: fish emulsion

[a] Listed are major reference formulations of salts.

These mixtures have formed the basis of fulfilling salt requirements of most plant tissue and organ cultures. Their occasional modifications designed to meet specific needs have been reported (49, 50, 128, 138, 166, 201). Fortunately, despite variability in the plant genotype, the explant, and the purpose for which tissue cultures have been intended, there has been widespread consistency in inorganic salt requirements. The experiments in this laboratory with numerous plants and organs and in the pursuit of diverse objectives have been carried out successfully with the MS salt formula. The formula has been modified sometimes by raising its inorganic phosphate concentration with an addition of 170 mg/l of $NaH_2PO_4 \cdot H_2O$).

The carbohydrate requirement has been satisfied very easily, generally by incorporating sucrose at a concentration 2–3%. Glucose has been superior to sucrose only occasionally. Still other carbohydrates have been used, but none has shown superiority over sucrose or glucose.

The most commonly included vitamins are thiamin, inositol, nicotinic acid, and pyridoxin. Thiamin is critical, and it is usually provided in the range 0.1–0.4 mg/l. Inositol is not essential; nevertheless, it has been clearly beneficial and has been used at the rate of 100 mg/l. The need for numerous other vitamins remains equivocal, although many have been included in nutrient media. Biotin, choline, folic acid, pantothenic acid, and riboflavin are usually used chiefly for precautionary reasons. Ascorbic acid has been used, particularly in combination with citric acid, to retard browning of freshly excised tissues.

Amino acids or their amides have been beneficial to some tissue cultures. Arginine, aspartic acid, glutamic acid, and tyrosine may be advantageous in organ multiplication media. Sometimes amides may be more effective than the respective amino acids. Tests of amino acids should recognize two features. First, only the L isomers should be used. The D form is usually without effect, or even negates the L form when provided in a racemic mixture. Second, amino acids often antagonize one another, resulting in harmful effects rather than benefits. It is thus advisable to evaluate them in groups, especially when repressive effects are suspected.

In Stage II media the purine adenine may also be a desirable constituent. Other nitrogen bases have been used, particularly cytidylic and guanylic acids, but their effects appear confined to an enhancement of callus growth and not of organ multiplication.

The most critical organic components of plant propagation media are auxin and cytokinin. These two substances should be examined with respect to their kind and concentration. The auxins, for example, differ significantly in stability, effectiveness, and their influence on organogenesis. The preferred auxin is IAA. When effective, it shows minimum adversity on organ formation, but is perhaps the weakest auxin and is inactivated readily in some tissue cultures. In contrast, the auxin 2,4-D is the most potent, and whereas it stimulates callus cultures, it strongly antogonizes organized development. Those interested in promoting asexual embryogenesis have found it necessary to reduce substantially or completely exclude 2,4-D. Thus while 2,4-D may be necessary during Stage I of some cultures, it should be avoided or lowered in the supply in Stage II. The other auxins are more intermediate in effectiveness and in adverse morphogenetic activities.

Table 4 lists 3 cytokinins which are readily available on the commercial market. The cytokinin 2iP is the most active of the three; it is, however, the most expensive. Kinetin and BA are nearly equivalent in effectiveness, perhaps BA being slightly more. The concentration of cytokinin required in tissue culture media may be as high as 30 mg/l. The medium of *Gerbera* tissue culture, in which axillary shoot multiplication is desired, has an optimum kinetin concentration of 10 mg/l; that of *Gloxinia* has shown an optimum of 30 mg/l.[3]

Natural complexes should be used only when all attempts to use a chemically definable medium fail; or when benefits from additional stimulation are desired. Table 4 contains the more frequently used complexes. One disadvantage of natural complexes is their excessive variability from one source to another or from one batch to the next. Among users of coconut endosperm, some prefer the liquid contained in an immature fruit, whereas others are satisfied by utilizing the liquid or solid endosperm from mature fruits obtained readily in the local market.

The breakthrough which has made tissue cultures applicable to the propagation of diverse plants has been the discovery by Skoog & Miller (213) that root and shoot initiation is basically regulated by interactions between two hormonal substances, auxin and cytokinin. Their work with tobacco callus cultures showed that, whereas both substances are necessary for tissue growth, the pattern of organogenesis is determined by their relative concentrations in the nutrient medium. A relatively high concentration of auxin favors root initiation, while repressing shoot formation. In contrast, relatively high concentrations of cytokinin induce shoot initiation and suppress rooting. The control of root and shoot initiation by auxin-cytokinin balances appears to be a general phenomenon among plants. It can be see even in the mosses (125, 136, 140). Difficulty in observing its manifestation in a given plant is usually attributable to an inappropriate test tissue. Thus while stem or callus cultures of *Nicotiana glauca* do not produce adventitious organs in response to varying concentrations of IAA and kinetin, shoot tip explants will develop adventitious shoots or roots in media of the same composition.

Other substances appear to alter the effectiveness of auxin or cytokinin. Lee & Skoog (108) observed that certain phenolic substances enhanced shoot formation in tobacco callus cultures, and Rücker & Paupardin (194) reported that still other phenolic constituents stimulated root initiation. The phenolic constituents in the former case appeared to manifest their effects by stimulating auxin inactivation, consequently raising the physiologically effective level of cytokinin (109). The rhizogenic action in the latter instance, on the other hand, could be attributed to a sparing of auxin. Substances that appear to competitively inhibit auxin action, e.g. N-1-naphthylphthalamic acid (43), have also been shown to promote shoot initiation. Suppressive effects of an excessive supply of endogenous auxin can sometimes be overcome by the addition of auxin antagonists. For example, 2,4,6-trichlorophenoxyacetic acid enhances asexual embryogenesis in *Daucus carota,* presumably by depressing the effective auxin concentration (162).

Gibberellins, while stimulating growth of organs, generally repress organ initiation processes (14, 147–149, 202). According to Gautheret (53), however, gibberellin could substitute for light in stimulating root initiation in *Helianthus tuberosus* tuber sections. In the presence of light, gibberellin inhibits root formation; in darkness, however, especially in combination with an auxin, it markedly stimulates rooting. This stimulatory effect of gibberellin on rooting of *Helianthus* tissue, nevertheless, does not indicate desirability of its general inclusion in media intended for organ multiplication. The gibberellin might be used in Stage III, however, to hasten growth of already formed organs or asexually derived embryos.

The promotive effect of adenine on shoot initiation was first noted by Skoog & Tsui (214). Miller & Skoog (139) eventually showed that adenine sulfate reversed the anticaulogenic effect of auxin. They demonstrated a competition between adenine sulfate and IAA in shoot formation of tobacco stem sections. The adenine effect could not be duplicated by other purines, including guanine, hypoxanthine and xanthine. More recently, Nitsch et al (167) confirmed the stimulatory effect of adenine on shoot initiation in *Plumbago indica* internode cultures. They suggested that adenine favored the multiplication of diploid cells over endopolyploid cells, thereby enhancing organ initiation. They assumed that their *Plumbago* tissue was polysomatic, constituted by diploid as well as polyploid cells, and that the capacity for organized development was suppressed in the polyploid cells of the species. Jacquiot (83) reported an interesting observation regarding the relationship between adenine and inositol in shoot initiation of stem cambium cultures of *Ulmus campes-tris.* Adenine stimulated shoot formation among explants obtained during the winter, whereas inositol enhanced the process in summer-established cultures.

Some substances have been described as selectively enhancing shoot initiation in certain tissue cultures. Kochar, Bhalla & Sabharwal (95) reported of inducing shoots in haploid callus cultures of *Nicotiana tabacum* by the chelating agent 1,3-diamino-2-hydroxypropane-N,N,N',N',-tetraacetic acid. The optimum concentration of the substance was 10 mg/l. The same authors (96) also reported that certain tobacco smoke components, notably benzo(a)pyrene, benzo(e)pyrene, dibenz(a,h)anthracene, pyrene, and chrysene, caused shoots to develop in haploid tobacco callus. The substances were noted to be without the organogenic effects in diploid callus.

Sucrose also has been observed to elicit specific morphogenic responses. Menon & Lal (136) reported that apogamous sporophytes in the moss *Physcomitrium pyriforme* resulted only under a low sucrose concentration (0.5%) and low light intensity (50–100 lux). A high concentration of sucrose (6%) with a high light intensity (5000–6000 lux) produced gametophytic buds. These authors further indicated that the sucrose effect could not be reproduced with other sugars.

The NH^+_4 ion has been demonstrated to enhance asexual embyogenesis in callus cultures (63, 67, 87, 189, 190). This effect is apparently not very specific, since other nitrogenous compounds are somewhat effective. Skoog & Miller (213) reported from studies of tobacco callus cultures that casein hydrolysate was eventually replaceable by L-tyrosine, but not other amino acids.

PHYSICAL QUALITIES OF THE MEDIUM   In most instances the choice between a liquid or a gel medium is made rather arbitrarily, the decision resting on the available facilities and the accustomed practice of the investigator. This is an unwise and sometimes hazardous approach. With some plants, the success or failure of their tissue cultures may depend on whether a liquid or an agar nutrient is employed. For example, most bromeliads studied in this laboratory could be started in culture only in a liquid nutrient.[3] This has been true also with the orchid *Cattleya.*[3] In contrast, shoot tip cultures of *Asparagus* (155) and *Gerbera*[3] required initiation on an agar gel medium.

The same species may require a different physical form of medium during each of the three stages in vitro. Stage I might be accomplished in liquid and Stages II and III in agar, or Stages I and II may involve liquid while Stage III is carried out in agar, etc. This need to change the form of the nutrient medium in progressive stages of culture has been illustrated with *Asparagus officinalis* and *Daucus carota* by Steward and his associates (4, 216, 217): the initiation of callus from fresh explants in Stage I is accomplished on an agar medium; the cell and asexual embryo multiplication in Stage II is achieved in a liquid nutrient; and finally, the development of embryos into transplantable plants in Stage III is carried out on nutrient agar.

As early as 1939, White (238) observed that *Nicotiana* callus cultures differentiated shoots when transferred from an agar nutrient to a liquid medium. This observation was confirmed by Skoog (212) in a more detailed study. Wimber (243) noted that fresh explants of the *Cymbidium* orchid initiated development faster in an agitated liquid medium. However, further development in Stage II was reported to occur equally well in liquid or agar. The physical form of the nutrient medium apparently plays a significant role in determining the pattern of organ differentiation in excised *Cichorium intybus* roots (17, 128). Explants cultivated in a liquid nutrient and supported by a filter paper bridge produce vegetative buds. On the other hand, explants placed on agar medium regenerate flower buds. A relatively high concentration of agar, as much as 2.4%, is necessary to achieve maximum differentiation of flower buds.

White (238) suggested that oxygen gradients may be critical in regulating organ initiation. In his early studies with tobacco tissue, Skoog (212) discovered that the regeneration of shoots in liquid cultures occurred only when the cultures were left in darkness or under weak illumination, and not under high intensity light. Oxygen evolution was observed by Skoog in cultures placed under the high light intensity. In a more recent study, Kessel & Carr (92) showed that asexual embryogenesis and adventitious shoot formation in carrot callus were enhanced when the available oxygen in the culture was reduced, whereas root initiation was favored by increased oxygen. The data thus support White's early suggestion that oxygen gradients may be significant in regulating organogenesis.

Bouniols & Margara (18) observed differences in the amino acid composition of *Cichorium intybus* root section cultures obtained in liquid and agar media. Their observation implied a further important relationship between medium type and protein metabolism.

In using a gel medium it is important to consider both the gel concentration and the quality of the agar. Romberger & Tabor (193) have shown that the growth of excised *Picea abies* shoot apical meristems was influenced significantly by the quality of the agar. It is interesting to note that best growth occurred in a nutrient medium containing Difco "purified" agar, and the poorest in Difco "Noble" agar. Difco "Bacto" agar gave more intermediate results. Excessive concentrations of agar, resulting in hard gels, inhibit growth of plant tissues. The concentration of agar necessary to obtain a suitable gel will vary with the plant part being cultured, the quality of the agar, and the pH of the medium. Generally, the more acid the pH, the softer the gel.

Liquid nutrient can be provided variously. Successful cultures can be attained sometimes with the tissue submerged in nutrient solution in a stationary state. At other times a filter-paper bridge, glass-wool, or similar support may be used. Stationary liquid cultures involving large batches of tissue have also been carried out in phytostats, the higher plant counterparts of chaemostats or fermentors. More commonly, cultures in liquid nutrient are subjected to a degree of agitation. Rotating apparatus is used when gentle agitation is desired, the rate of rotation usually being about 1 rpm. Vigorous agitation requires reciprocating or gyrotory shakers. The latter enables agitation rates as high as 400 rpm. The high agitation rates have been used primarily with cell suspension cultures; cultures involving organized structures may do better with more gentle agitation.

The pH of nutrient media is also a critical factor; nevertheless, it has been much neglected in tissue culture studies. The usual practice is to set the pH of the medium at some value within the range 5.0–6.0 during preparation of the medium. Unfortunately pH drifts occur during the course of culture (52), and little is known of the influence of the actual pH values on the development of a culture.

The Culture Environment

The major factors of the tissue culture environment are light and temperature. Frequently, the literature also presents data on relative humidity. Information regarding the relative humidity of the culture facility is for the most part unimportant, inasmuch as the relative humidity of the microenvironment within a culture is usually about 100%. Such information may be valuable in extreme climates, however. In a normally very damp climate, there may be problems of mold development, while in dry areas moisture loss from the culture medium may occur more rapidly. The relative humidity may need to be regulated and maintained at more appropriate levels in extreme cases.

Light Requirements

The illumination of plant cultures must be considered in terms of intensity, length of the daily exposure period, and quality. At the outset, it should be clearly noted that the light requirements of tissue cultures are not the same as those of autotrophically developing whole plants. In tissue culture, photosynthesis is not a necessary activity, except perhaps during the latter part of Stage III, since carbohydrate is adequately provided. Nevertheless, light is needed to regulate certain morphogenetic processes. It has been reported to be important for the formation of shoots (153, 160), the initiation of roots (53, 111, 112, 230), the differentiation of cladophylls (69), and in asexual embryogenesis (59). Instances of failure of tissue cultures are sometimes caused by the use of plant growth chambers of similar facilities where the light provisions have been intended for autotrophic plant development. The difficulty most often encountered with such facilities is the excessively high light intensity; sometimes the quality of illumination is also unsuited for tissue culture.

LIGHT INTENSITY   In experiments with the moss *Physcomitrium turbinatum,* Nebel & Naylor (160) discovered that shoot-bud formation was related linearly to light intensity, at least in the range 300–700 lux. Nebel & Naylor used incandescent lamps and provided light continuously. Maximum root initiation in *Helianthus tuberosus* tuber section cultures has been reported to occur at an intensity of 5000 lux, using white light and a daily exposure period of 12 hr (53). Experiments in this laboratory with several plants, including *Asparagus* (69), *Gerbera,*[3] *Saxifraga,*[3] and bromeliads,[3] have disclosed an optimum light intensity of 1000 lux for Stage I and Stage II. A higher optimum, 3000–10,000 lux, has been observed for Stage III. These investigations employed Gro Lux or white fluorescent lamps and a daily exposure period of 16 hr. The higher optimum during Stage III of the *Asparagus* cultures has been correlated with the differentiation of cladophylls (69). With each of these plants, the higher intensities of light have been necessary in Stage III to achieve maximum rates of transfer of propagula from tissue culture to soil.

THE DAILY LIGHT PERIOD   With most of the plants for which data are available, the requirement of prescribed periods of exposure to light each day has not been equitable with photoperiod requirements in the traditional sense. Apparently the key is the total radiant energy of specified quality to which the culture is exposed. Hence, it involves the combined influence of both intensity and exposure period, and for a given species it is reasonable to expect varying optima in the length of the daily exposure period, depending on the light intensity used.

Gautheret (53) described a 12 hr daily light period as optimum for root initiation in *Helianthus* tuber sections. For the differentiation of roots and shoots in *Nicotiana* callus and in *Asparagus* shoot tip cultures (69, 153), the optimum light period each day has been 16 hr, using an intensity of 1000 lux. Margara (126) observed an optimum daily exposure period of 9 hr to 4000 lux light for shoot induction in cauliflower cultures. Experiments by Legrand (110) with *Cichorium* leaf sections showed that it was sufficient to provide only a single initial exposure to either darkness or 1600 lux light for adventitious shoots to form. The number of shoots produced per explant was, nevertheless, dependent upon the length of the initial exposure period to darkness or light. The highest rate of regeneration was obtained in a treatment in which the culture had been placed for three days continuously in darkness, followed by 37 days in constant light. The poorest regeneration resulted under an initial three-day period of continuous illumination, followed by 37 days of darkness.

Day length does influence the development of tissue cultures of plants which are normally responsive to photoperiod. For example, Alleweldt & Radler (3) observed that root initiation in stem sections of a short-day-sensitive grape variety occurred only on short days. In contrast, cultures of a day-length insensitive variety produced roots under any photoperiod. It is safe to assume that a plant that normally has a photoperiod requirement will somehow manifest this need in tissue culture.

LIGHT QUALITY The experiments of Weis & Jaffe (237) disclosed that the critical portion of the light spectrum for shoot induction was the blue region. Red light (660 nm) was without effect. These findings have been confirmed by Seibert (206), who reported that the most effective band was in the region of 467 nm. Seibert further reported that purple light (419 nm) also stimulated shoot initiation. Interestingly, root initiation, in contrast to shoot induction, is stimulated by red light but not by blue (112). In the moss *Pohlia nutans,* Mitra, Misra & Prabha (142) discovered that bud formation required a balanced exposure to both red and blue light. A combination of 11 hr of red and 6 hr of blue light daily gave the highest yields of shoots. Neither alone was effective, although a few shoot buds developed when exposed only to red light.

The above observations of light quality effects clearly indicate that key organogenetic processes in tissue cultures are photomorphogenic phenomena, most probably regulated by phytochrome.

Influence of Temperature

The general practice has been to maintain cultures in an environment in which the temperature is held constant, and the temperature usually employed has been in the neighborhood of 25° C. This practice fails to recognize the temperature fluctuations, diurnally and seasonally, under which plants normally develop. While constant temperatures may be adequate for the culture of many annual and tropical species, whose life cycles are completed during a period of relatively uniform temperature conditions, it may be desirable and perhaps necessary to explore the influence of periodically varied temperatures on the behavior of tissue cultures, especially plants adapted to the more temperate and even desert climates. Maximum benefits from tissue culture propagation may be attainable only by fulfilling the precise temperature needs of a plant.

An early study by Skoog (212) showed that shoot production in tobacco callus was highest with a culture temperature of 18°C. A temperature of 33°C was too high, and 12°C was too low. A more recent study with *Chondrilla juncea* root cultures by Kefford & Caso (91) showed that the temperature regime for maximum adventitious shoot formation ranged from 21 to 27°C during the daylight period and from 16 to 22°C at night. A constant temperature of 25°C also enabled maximum regeneration, but not other diurnal temperature combinations. Hasegawa et al (69) obtained no advantage by lowering the night temperature of shoot tip cultures of *Asparagus officinalis*. A constant 27°C was satisfactory for the multiplication of shoots and roots and for the development of transplantable plants.

In studies with *Helianthus tuberosus* tuber sections, Gautheret (53) discovered that rooting occurred best in an environment where the explants were exposed to alternating temperatures of 26°C during the day and 15°C at night. Gautheret suggested that the higher temperature was essential for the formation of cambia, and the lower nycototemperature for the differentiation of the cambia into root primordia.

Hildebrandt's (73) studies with *Gladiolus hortulans* disclosed that corms and plants obtained from tissue cultures could not develop into plants in soil unless the cultures in vitro had been exposed to a temperature of 2°C for a period of 4–6 weeks, just prior to the transfer to soil. A similar observation has been made in this laboratory with *Lilium longiflorum* cultures[3]. Bulbs and plants that developed from cultures of bulb scale or stem slices became dormant upon transfer to soil. The dormancy could be prevented, and vigorous plants were established in soil when the Stage III cultures were placed in darkness at 5°C for 4 weeks. The behavior of *Gladiolus* and *Lilium* cultures exemplify the significance of exploring and satisfying seasonal temperature requirements of some plants.

THE PLANTS FROM TISSUE CULTURE

Mere demonstration of the initiation of adventitious shoots, bulbs, corms, tubers, roots, asexual embryos, and other potential propagula is insufficient basis to claim applicability of the tissue culture method to the propagation of a given plant. A commercial method requires that data on certain economically related parameters, such as the rate of multiplication of propagulum and the incidence of propagula established in soil as plants, are available. Other equally significant information must be obtained. One of these is concerned with the consistency with which the desired plant is reproduced, and another with the probability of establishing a pathogen-free plant.

Reproduction of the Selected Plant

Genetically aberrant plants have been a sufficiently significant occurrence in tissue cultures. They have been reported with *Asparagus officinalis* (124, 241), *Brassica oleracea* (78), *Chrysanthemum morifolium* (12), *Crepis capillaris* (196), *Dianthus caryophyllus* (61), *Nicotiana tabacum* (151, 152, 197), *Oryza sativa* (164), and *Saccharum* sp. (70). In most cases the abnormality has been in the form of polyploid plants arising from diploid plants (70, 78, 124, 151, 152, 196, 197, 241). Other genetic variations, such as changes in flower pigmentation and branching pattern, have also occurred with substantial frequencies in some plants, e.g. *C. morifolium* (12), *D. caryophyllus* (61), and *O. sativa* (164). A cultivar desired for its chimera should be propagated with utmost caution, inasmuch as the chimera components are separated very easily in tissue culture and the desired traits of the cultivar are lost. This has happened in the White Sim carnation (61), the Indianapolis White chrysanthemum (12), and in many variegated plants in our laboratory (the It cryptanthus, the variegated pineapple, and the Pothos philodendron).[3]

Plants with chromosome numbers that deviate extensively from those of the original plant are not unexpected, especially when they are obtained in tissue culture by way of adventitious organogenesis. The data in Table 2 show that organized structures of most plants are obtained in vitro by the adventitious process. The frequency of genetically aberrant plants can be reduced considerably, even avoided entirely, if the plant multiplication can be achieved through an enhancement of axillary shoot formation, e.g. *Asparagus officinalis* (69, 155) and *Gerbera jamesoni.*[3] The occurrence of polyploids among adventitiously obtained plants is expected, in view of the polysomatic nature of most plants. Indeed, polysomatism has been observed in all examined plants (34, 35, 172, 173). Uniformly diploid cells can be found consistently only in the apical meristems and few other tissues, e.g. pericycle, of a diploid plant, and a mixture of diploid and polyploid cells is the typical makeup of other regions in which the cells have attained a degree of maturation and differentiation. Accordingly, tissue cultures arising from explants comprised of more than the apical meristem cells will very likely contain polyploid cells, and some of the plants resulting from such cultures will be polyploid. In fact, if desired, this feature can be utilized to obtain polyploid plants from the diploids (78, 151).

A decline in organ-forming tendencies during the course of successive subcultures has been observed in many plants, e.g. in *Allium cepa* (46), *Daucus carota* (137, 219), *Linaria vulgaris* (29), *Nicotiana tabacum* (150), *Pisum sativum* (227), and *Saccharum* sp. (11). In most of these the decline has been attributed to an attainment of predominance by polyploid cells, particularly aneuploids, e.g. *D. carota* (146), *N. tabacum* (152, 197), *P. sativum* (227), and *Saccharum* sp. (71). For reasons as yet unclear, the capacity for organized development in a species is repressed increasingly with progressive rise in the ploidy level of its cells.

There are abundant other data which show that maintenance of plant tissues, especially callus, for long periods in vitro results in greater variability and increase of the chromosome number among the constituent cells (88, 154, 196). A retention of the uniformly diploid status, or haploid status of a culture derived from a haploid explant, is more often the exception than the rule. The karyotypic change can occur extremely rapidly in tissue cultures of some plants. In callus cultures of *Citrus limon* (154), the frequency of diploid cells has been observed to decline from 100 to 71% within the first passage, and to 33% by the end of the third passage. The decrease of diploid cells in successive subcultures is compensated for by rises in tetraploid, octaploid, and ultimately aneuploid cells. In this study each passage was one month long; thus, the change occured quickly.

Disease-Free Plants through Tissue Culture

The plant obtained from tissue culture should not be assumed to be disease-free or pathogen-free. As Hollings (77) cautioned earlier, the term disease-free has been used very loosely and carelessly. The claim of a disease-free state must specify the pathogens which have been excluded, and the evidence must have been obtained through systematic tests, utilizing the most reliable detection methods. Unless this is done, the plant derived through tissue culture may not be labeled disease free, even though disease symptoms may not be immediately apparent.

FUTURE PROSPECTS

The information at hand does not allow routine clonal propagation of all plants. Nevertheless sufficient data have been accumulated and guidelines can be offered so that detailed steps for specific crops can be developed with a minimum of research. Routine employment of tissue cultures as an alternate method, in some cases the only method, of commercial propagation of diverse herbaceous plants will become a reality very soon. Table 2 contains an impressive list of plants whose multiplication through tissue cultures might be possible with a little additional research. However, this list should be interpreted with some caution. It is largely a compilation of plants with only the potential demonstrated, and not of plants actually propagated by in vitro methods. In only a few instances have the data been extracted from reports concerned specifically with plant propagation. A number of the plants of Table 2 may have no economic significance. Nevertheless, the critical step of initiating organs that can serve as propagula has been observed in each.

Hopefully, there will be major breakthroughs in investigations with the woody genera. The woody plants constitute a large group of economically important plants and many of them cannot be propagated asexually; no conventional methods have been applicable.

The tissue culture method of plant propagation owes its success to research directed at the elucidation of the physiology underlying organized development. The discovery by Skoog & Miller (213) of the fundamental role of auxin-cytokinin interactions in root and shoot formation has contributed most significantly. Other investigators have disclosed the participation of still further substances, and of light, temperature, and other factors. Nevertheless, much remains to be learned before tissue cultures can provide widespread benefits. Concepts of morphogenesis as they relate to the regulation of organized development need strengthening. A concept which I find helpful in understanding organ formation phenomena is the one proposed by Torrey (226). This concept states that the formation of an organized structure begins with a group of undifferentiated cells, or a meristemoid. The cells of the meristemoid, like those of an apical meristem, are typically very small and tightly grouped, relatively isodiametric and thin-walled, and contain dense cytoplasm and prominent nuclei. There is little evidence of vacuolation in these cells. The meristemoid is the structure that responds to organogenetic stimuli, and depending on the direction of stimulation, is capable of organizing into either root, shoot, or embryo. The absence of organized development in callus cultures of many species may be attributed to the inability of the callus cells to undergo transformation into meristemoids. Conversely, it is possible to attribute the success with shoot tip explants to the presence of the apical meristem cells, the original meristemoids. Observations of adventitious bud and lateral root initiation in *Convolvulus arvensis* root cultures suggested to Bonnett & Torrey (15, 16) that the pattern of organized development in meristemoids is undetermined. More direct experimentation with *Nasturtium officinale* by Ballade (9, 10) supports this suggestion. Organ primordia usually present in nodal segments of the *Nasturtium* can be stimulated to produce either adventitious roots or shoots by simply altering their supply of auxin or cytokinin. Champagnat (25) has observed that the apical meristem in root tips of the orchid *Neottia* can be redirected to differentiate into protocorms. The data thus indicate that meristemoid cells, whether of tissue culture or of apical meristems, are the cells capable of organized development. The pattern of their organization can be manipulated by chemical and physical stimuli.

The phenomenon of asexual embryogenesis in tissue cultures has been explored extensively and discussed at length (63–66, 115, 188, 217). A study of asexual embryogenesis in the Rutaceae, just completed by Esan (41), discloses some new and very significant information and deserves special discussion here. Esan's study revealed that the cells of the nucellus of all members of the Rutaceae possess the capacity to develop into embryos. However, the extent to which this capacity is manifested varies from one cultivar or species to another. The variation can be related to differences in concentration in the nucelli of a substance with potent antiembryogenic properties. This substance is transmitted through tissue grafts; it also diffuses through nutrient agar. Most interestingly, it appears to act at the level of gene expression. It causes an irreversible repression of embryo initiation among affected cells. The significance of Esan's observation in relation to other plants remains to be explored. A preliminary study shows that the Rutaceae factor also suppresses embryogenesis in callus culture of the wild carrot *Daucus carota* "Queen Anne's Lace."

Other exploratory approaches have been used to add to the understanding of the physiology of plant organ formation. Thorpe & Murashige (224, 225) observed that a significant accumulation of starch preceded shoot initiation in tobacco callus cultures. This observation has been confirmed by Brossard (20). Further studies by Thorpe & Meier (223) revealed that several sugars caused significant accumulation of starch during the critical period of development of the callus in culture and thereby enhanced shoot formation. In contrast, gibberellin prevented starch accumulation and concomitantly suppressed shoot formation. The accumulation of starch in tobacco callus was localized and quite orderly, and the cells that accumulated high concentrations of starch eventually differentiated into meristemoids and shoot primordia. During outgrowth of the primordia into readily recognizable shoots, the starch concentration diminished, indicating that the substance was being utilized in shoot formation.

The significance of nucleic acids in organogenesis has also been studied. For example, Vasseur (234) has been able to associate shoot initiation in *Cichorium intybus* leaf sections with alterations in the pattern of synthesis of RNA and certain nucleotides. An initial period of callus formation in explants was associated with a significantly high rate of RNA synthesis, and a subsequent period of shoot initiation was related with a rise in the UMP/CMP ratio. Kovacs (105) noted that shoot formation in *Nicotiana* tissue cultures followed increases in the RNA/DNA and histone/DNA ratios. The development of asexually arising embryos in *D. carota* callus has been correlated with DNA synthesis (248). DNA synthesis increased in readily identifiable patterns as embryo development progressed from the proembryonic mass to the torpedo stage.

Acknowledgments

The author expresses appreciation to his students and associates who have assisted in collecting and editing some of the data for this review. Special thanks go to Mrs. Heather Simko for help in compiling and organizing the bibliography.

Literature Cited

1. Abo El-Nil, M. M., Hildebrandt, A. C. 1971. *Plant Dis. Rep.* 55:1017–20
2. Ahuja, M. R., Hagen, G. L. 1966. *Develop. Biol.* 13:408–32
3. Alleweldt, G., Radler, F. 1961. *Plant Physiol.* 36:376–79
4. Ammirato, P. V., Steward, F. C. 1971. *Bot. Gaz.* 132:149–58
5. Andreasson, D. C., Ellison, J. H. 1967. *Proc. Am. Soc. Hort. Sci.* 90:158–62
6. Aneja, S., Atal, C. K. 1969. *Curr. Sci.* 38:69
7. Bajaj, Y. P. S., Bopp, M. 1972. *Z. Pflanzenphysiol.* 66:378–81
8. Ball, E. 1950. *Growth* 14:295–325
9. Ballade, P. 1971. *C. R. Acad. Sci.* 273:2079–82
10. Ibid 1972. 274:1282–85
11. Barba, R., Nickell, L. G. 1969. *Planta* 89:299–302
12. Ben-Jaacov, J., Langhans, R. W. 1972. *HortScience* 7:289–90
13. Bertsch, .W. 1967. *Am. Orchid Soc. Bull.* 36:32–37
14. Bigot, C., Nitsch, J. P. 1968. *C. R. Acad. Sci.* 267:619–21
15. Bonnett, H. T., Torrey, J. G. 1965. *Plant Physiol.* 40:1228–36
16. Bonnett, H. T., Torrey, J. G. 1966. *Am. J. Bot.* 53:496–508
17. Bouniols, A., Margara, J. 1968. *Ann. Physiol. Veg.* 10:69–81
18. Bouniols, A., Margara, J. 1971. *C. R. Acad. Sci.* 273:1104–7
19. Bristow, J. M. 1962. *Develop. Biol.* 4:361–75
20. Brossard, D. 1970. *C. R. Acad. Sci.* 271:56–59
21. Butenko, R. G., Atanasov, A. I., Urmantzeva, W. W. 1971. *Int. Symp. Morphogenesis in Plant Cell Tissue and Organ Cultures*, 54
22. Butenko, R. G., Grushvitskii, R. V., Slepyan, L. I. 1968. *Bot. Zh.* 53:906–11
23. Carter, O., Yamada, Y., Takahashi, E. 1967. *Nature* 214:1029–30
24. Caruso, J. L. 1971. *Am. J. Bot.* 58:429–31

25. Champagnat, M. 1971. *Ann. Sci. Nat. Bot.* 12:209–48
26. Champagnat, M., Morel, G. 1969. *Mem. Soc. Bot. Fr.* 111–32
27. Champagnat, M., Morel, G. 1972. *C. R. Acad. Sci.* 274:3379–80
28. Champagnat, M., Morel, G., Mounetou, B. 1970. *Ann. Sci. Nat. Bot. Biol. Veg.* 11:97–114
29. Charlton, W. A. 1965. *Nature* 207: 781–82
30. Chen, H. R., Galston, A. W. 1967. *Physiol. Plant.* 20:533–39
31. Churchill, M. E., Arditti, J., Ball, E. A. 1971. *Am. Orchid Soc. Bull.* 40:109–13
32. Churchill, M. E., Ball, E. A., Arditti, J. 1973. *New Phytol.* 72:161–66
33. Chylah, H. 1973. *Biol. Plant.* 15:80–87
34. D'Amato, F. 1952. *Caryologia* 4: 311–58
35. Ibid 1964. 17:41–52
36. Danckwardt-Lilliestrom, C. 1957. *Physiol. Plant.* 10:794–97
37. Desai, P., Narayanaswami, S. 1971. *Int. Symp. Morphogenesis in Plant Cell Tissue and Organ Cultures,* 70–71
38. Doerschug, M. R., Miller, C. O. 1967. *Am. J. Bot.* 54:410–13
39. Earle, E. D., Torrey, J. G. 1965. *Am. J. Bot.* 52:891–99
40. Engvild, K. C. 1973. *Physiol. Plant.* 28:155–59
41. Esan, E. B. 1973. *A detailed study of adventive embryogenesis in the Rutacea.* PhD thesis. Univ. California, Riverside. 233 pp.
42. Fellenberg, G. 1963. *Z. Bot.* 51:113–41
43. Feng, K. A., Linck, A. J. 1970. *Plant Cell Physiol.* 11:589–98
44. Fonnesbech, M. 1972. *Physiol. Plant.* 27:310–16
45. Ibid, 360–64
46. Fridborg, G. 1971. *Physiol. Plant.* 25: 436–40
47. Fujino, M., Fujimura, T., Hamada, K. 1972. *J. Jap. Soc. Hort. Sci.* 41:77–81
48. Gamborg, O. L., Constabel, F., Miller, R. A. 1970. *Planta* 95:355–58
49. Gamborg, O. L., Miller, R. A., Ojama, K. 1968. *Exp. Cell Res.* 50:151–58
50. Gautheret, R. J. 1939. *C. R. Acad. Sci.* 208:118
51. Ibid 1940. 210:632–34
52. Gautheret, R. J. 1947. *Rev. Gen. Bot.* 54:5–34
53. Gautheret, R. J. 1969. *Am. J. Bot.* 56:702–17
54. Gorter, C. J. 1965. *J. Hort. Sci.* 40:177–79
55. Grinblat, U. 1972. *J. Am. Soc. Hort. Sci.* 97:599–603
56. Guha, S., Maheshwari, S. C. 1964. *Nature* 204:497
57. Gunckel, J. E., Sharp, W. R., Williams, B. W., West, W. C., Drinkwater, W. O. 1972. *Bot. Gaz.* 133:254–62
58. Gupta, G. R., Guha, S., Maheshwari, S. C. 1966. *Phytomorphology* 16:175–82
59. Haccius, B., Lakshmanan, K. K. 1965. *Planta* 65:102–4
60. Hackett, W. P. 1969. *HortScience* 4:171
61. Hackett, W. P., Anderson, J. M. 1967. *Proc. Am. Soc. Hort. Sci.* 90:365–69
62. Hackett, W. P., Tse, A., Smith, R. J. 1973. *Univ. Calif. Flower and Nursery Rep.,* March 4–5
63. Halperin, W. 1966. *Am. J. Bot.* 53: 443–53
64. Halperin, W. 1966. *Science* 153: 1287–88
65. Halperin, W. 1966. *Ann. Rev. Plant Physiol.* 20:394–418
66. Halperin, W., Wetherell, D. F. 1964. *Am. J. Bot.* 51:274–83
67. Halperin, W., Wetherell, D. F. 1965. *Nature* 205:519–20
68. Handro, W., Rao, P. S., Harada, H. 1972. *C. R. Acad. Sci.* 275:2861–63
69. Hasegawa, P. M., Murashige, T., Takatori, F. H. 1973. *J. Am. Soc. Hort. Sci.* 98:143–48
70. Heinz, D. J., Mee, G. W. P. 1969. *Crop Sci.* 9:346–48
71. Heinz, D. J., Mee, G. W. P., Nickell, L. G. 1969. *Am. J. Bot.* 56:450–56
72. Heller, R. 1953. *Ann. Sci. Nat. Bot. Biol. Veg.* 14:1–223
73. Hildebrandt, A. C. 1971. In *Les cultures de tissus de plantes. Colloq. Int. CNRS* 193:71–93
74. Hildebrandt, A. C., Riker, A. J., Duggar, B. M. 1946. *Am. J. Bot.* 33:591–97
75. Hill, G. P. 1967. *Ann. Bot.* 31:437–46
76. Hill, G. P. 1968. *Physiol. Plant.* 21: 386–89
77. Hollings, M. 1965. *Ann. Rev. Phytopathol.* 3:367–96
78. Horak, J., Landa, Z., Lustinec, J. 1971. *Phyton* 28:7–10
79. Hu, C. Y., Sussex, I. M. 1972. *Phytomorphology* 21:103–7
80. Hughes, H., Lam, S., Janick, J. 1973. *HortScience* 8:335–36
81. Intuwong, O., Sagawa, Y. 1973. *Am. Orchid Soc. Bull.* 42:209–15
82. Jacobs, G., Bornman, C. H., Allen, P. 1968. *S. Afr. J. Agr. Sci.* 11:673–78
83. Jacquiot, C. 1951. *C. R. Acad. Sci.* 233:815–17
84. Jayakar, M. 1971. *Phytomorphology* 20:410–12
85. Jelaska, S. 1972. *Planta* 103:278–80

86. Johri, B. M., Bajaj, Y. P. S. 1962. *Nature* 193:194–95
87. Johri, B. M., Sehgal, C. B. 1963. *Naturwissenschaften* 50:47–48
88. Kao, K. N., Miller, R. A., Gamborg, O. L., Harvey, B. L. 1970. *Can. J. Genet. Cytol.* 12:297–301
89. Kato, H., Takeuchi, M. 1966. *Sci. Pap. Coll. Gen. Educ. Univ. Tokyo* 16:245–54
90. Kaul, K., Sabharwal, P. S. 1972. *Am. J. Bot.* 59:377–85
91. Kefford, N. P., Caso, O. H. 1972. *Aust. J. Biol. Sci.* 25:691–706
92. Kessel, R. J. H., Carr, A. H. 1972. *J. Exp. Bot.* 23:996–1007
93. Khanna, P., Staba, E. J. 1970. *Bot. Gaz.* 131:1–5
94. Kim, K. K., Kunisaki, J. T., Sagawa, Y. 1970. *Am. Orchid Soc. Bull.* 30:1077–80
95. Kochar, T. S., Bhalla, P. R., Sabharwal, P. S. 1970. *C. R. Acad. Sci.* 271:1619–22
96. Kochar, T. S., Bhalla, P. R., Sabharwal, P. S. 1971. *Plant Cell Physiol.* 12:603–8
97. Kochba, J., Spiegel-Roy, P., Safran, H. 1972. *Planta* 106:237–45
98. Kohlenbach, H. W. 1965. *Planta* 64:37–40
99. Kohlenbach, H. W. 1967. *Z. Pflanzenphysiol.* 57:305–9
100. Konar, R. N., Konar, A. 1966. *Phytomorphology* 16:379–82
101. Konar, R. N., Nataraja, K. 1965. *Phytomorphology* 15:132–37
102. Ibid, 206–11
103. Ibid, 245–48
104. Konar, R. N., Oberoi, Y. P. 1965. *Phytomorphology* 15:137–39
105. Kovacs, E. I. 1971. *Acta Bot.* 17:391–93
106. Kukulezanka, K., Suszynska, G. 1972. *Acta Soc. Bot. Pol.* 41:503–10
107. Kunisaki, J. T., Kim, K. K., Sagawa, Y. 1972. *Am. Orchid Soc. Bull.* 41:435–39
108. Lee, T. T., Skoog, F. 1965. *Physiol. Plant.* 18:386–402
109. Ibid, 577–85
110. Legrand, B. 1972. *C. R. Acad. Sci.* 275:31–32
111. Leroux, R. 1968. *C. R. Acad. Sci.* 266:106–8
112. Letouze, R., Beauchesne, G. 1969. *C. R. Acad. Sci.* 269:1528–31
113. Levine, M. 1947. *Bull. Torrey Bot. Club* 74:321–38
114. Lindemann, E. G. P., Gunckel, J. P., Davidson, O. W. 1970. *Am. Orchid Soc. Bull.* 39:1002–4
115. Linser, H., Neumann, K. H. 1968. *Physiol. Plant.* 21:487–99
116. Lustinec, J., Horak, J. 1970. *Experientia* 26:919–20
117. Ma, S., Shii, C. 1972. *J. Hort. Sci. China* 18:135–42
118. Maheshwari, P., Baldev, B. 1962. *Plant Embryology, A Symposium,* 129–38
119. Maheshwari, S. C., Gupta, G. R. P., Guha, S. 1965. *Naturwissenschaften* 52:623–24
120. Maheshwari, S. C., Gupta, G. R. P. 1965. *Planta* 67:384–86
121. Majumdar, S. K. 1970. *Planta* 90:212–14
122. Majumdar, S. K., Sabharwal, P. S. 1968. *Am. J. Bot.* 55:705
123. Majumdar, S. K., Schlosser, S. A. 1972. *Can. J. Bot.* 50:1013–16
124. Malnassy, P., Ellison, J. H. 1970. *HortScience* 5:444–45
125. Maltzahn, K. E. 1959. *Nature* 183:60–61
126. Margara, J. 1969. *Ann. Physiol. Veg.* 11:95–112
127. Margara, J. 1970. *C. R. Acad. Sci.* 270:698–701
128. Margara, J., Bouniols, A. 1967. *C. R. Acad. Sci.* 264:1166–68
129. Margara, J., Rancillac, M. 1966. *C. R. Acad. Sci.* 263:1455–58
130. Marston, M. E. 1967. *Sci. Hort. J. Hort. Educ.* 19:80–86
131. Marston, M. E., Voraurai, P. 1967. *Misc. Publ.* 17, Univ. Nottingham
132. Masteller, V. J., Holden, D. J. 1970. *Plant Physiol.* 45:362–64
133. Mayer, L. 1956. *Planta* 47:401–46
134. Mehra, P. N., Mehra, A. 1971. *Int. Symp. Morphogenesis in Plant Tissue and Organ Cultures,* 71–72
135. Mehra, R. N., Palta, H. K. 1971. *Phytomorphology* 21:367–76
136. Menon, M. K. C., Lal, M. 1972. *Naturwissenschaften* 59:514
137. Mestre, J., Ba, L.-T., Guignard, J. 1972. *C. R. Acad. Sci.* 274:54–57
138. Miller, C. 1965. *Proc. Nat. Acad. Sci. USA* 54:1052–58
139. Miller, C., Skoog, F. 1953. *Am. J. Bot.* 40:768–73
140. Mitra, G. C., Allsopp, A. 1959. *Nature* 183:974–75
141. Mitra, G. C., Chaturvedi, H. C. 1972. *Bull. Torrey Bot. Club* 99:184–89
142. Mitra, G. C., Misra, L. P., Prabha, C. 1965. *Planta* 65:42–48
143. Morel, G. M. 1960. *Am. Orchid Soc. Bull.* 29:495–97
144. Ibid 1964. 33:473–78

145. Morel, G. 1966. *Cymbidium Soc. News* 20:3–11
146. Muir, W. H. 1963. *Plant Tissue Culture*, ed. P. R. White, A. R. Grove, 485–92. Berkeley:McCutchan. 553 pp.
147. Murashige, T. 1961. *Science* 134:380
148. Murashige, T. 1963. See Ref. 146, 401–9
149. Murashige, T. 1964. *Physiol. Plant.* 17: 636–43
150. Murashige, T., Nakano, R. 1965. *Am. J. Bot.* 52:819–27
151. Murashige, T., Nakano, R. 1966. *J. Hered.* 57:115–18
152. Murashige, T., Nakano, R. 1967. *Am. J. Bot.* 54:963–70
153. Ibid 1968. 55:710
154. Murashige, T., Nakano, R., Tucker, D. P. H. 1968. *Phytomorphology* 17: 469–76
155. Murashige, T., Shabde, M. N., Hasegawa, P. M., Takatori, F. H., Jones, J. B. 1972. *J. Am. Soc. Hort. Sci.* 97:158–61
156. Murashige, T., Skoog, F. 1962. *Physiol. Plant.* 15:473–97
157. Murthy Reddy, K. B. S., Narayana, R. 1971. *Int. Symp. Morphogenesis in Plant Cell Tissue and Organ Cultures,* 31–32
158. Nakayama, F. 1966. *Rev. Fac. Agron. Univ. Nac. La Plata* 42:63–74
159. Nataraja, K. 1971. *Int. Symp. Morphogenesis in Plant Cell, Tissue and Organ Cultures,* 66
160. Nebel, B. J., Naylor, A. W. 1968. *Am. J. Bot.* 55:38–44
161. Netien, G., Raynaud, J. 1972. *Bull. Mens. Soc. Linn. Lyon* 41:49–51
162. Newcomb, W., Wetherell, D. F. 1970. *Bot. Gaz.* 131:242–45
163. Niizeki, M., Grant, F. W. 1971. *Can. J. Bot.* 49:2041–51
164. Nishi, T., Yamada, Y., Takahashi, E. 1968. *Nature* 219:508–9
165. Nitsch, C., Nitsch, J. P. 1967. *Planta* 72:355–70
166. Nitsch, J. P., Nitsch, C. 1956. *Am. J. Bot.* 43:831
167. Nitsch, J. P., Nitsch, C., Rossini, L. M. E., Ha, D. B. D. 1967. *Phytomorphology* 17:446–53
168. Norstog, K. 1965. *Am. J. Bot.* 52: 993–99
169. Norstog, K. 1970. *Develop. Biol.* 23: 665–70
170. Norstog, K., Rhamstine, E. 1967. *Phytomorphology* 17:374–81
171. Norton, J. P., Boll, W. G. 1954. *Science* 119:220–21
172. Partanen, C. R. 1959. *Developmental Cytology,* ed. D. Rudnick, 21–45. New York: Ronald
173. Partanen, C. R. 1963. *Int. Rev. Cytol.* 15:215–43
174. Paulet, P., Nitsch, J. P. 1963. *Bull. Soc. Bot. Fr.* 110:361–66
175. Pierik, R. L. M. 1967. *Regeneration, Vernalization and Flowering in Lunaria.* Wageningen: Veenman & Zonen. 71 pp.
176. Pillai, S. K., Hildebrandt, A. C. 1968. *Plant Dis. Rep.* 52:600–1
177. Pillai, S. K., Hildebrandt, A. C. 1968. *Phyton* 25:81–87
178. Pillai, S. K., Hildebrandt, A. C. 1969. *Am. J. Bot.* 56:52–58
179. Raju, M. V. S., Mann, H. E. 1970. *Can. J. Bot.* 48:1887–91
180. Rangan, T. S., Murashige, T., Bitters, W. P. 1968. *HortScience* 3:226–27
181. Rangaswamy, N. S. 1961. *Phytomorphology* 11:109–27
182. Rangaswamy, N. S., Promila. 1972. *Z. Pflanzenphysiol.* 20:367–74
183. Rao, P. S. 1965. *Phytomorphology* 15:175–79
184. Rao, P. S., Handro, W., Harada, H. 1973. *Physiol. Plant.* 28:458–63
185. Rao, P. S., Narayanaswami, S. 1968. *Planta* 81:372–75
186. Rao, P. S., Narayanaswami, S. 1972. *Physiol. Plant.* 27:271–76
187. Raste, A. P., Ganapathy, P. S. 1971. *Phytomorphology* 20:367–74
188. Reinert, J. 1959. *Planta* 53:318–33
189. Reinert, J., Backs, D., Krosing, M. 1966. *Planta* 68:375–78
190. Reinert, J., Tazawa, M., Semenoff, S. 1967. *Nature* 216:1215–16
191. Reinert, R. A., Mohr, H. C. 1967. *Proc. Am. Soc. Hort. Sci.* 91:664–71
192. Robb, S. M. 1957. *J. Exp. Bot.* 8:248–352
193. Romberger, J. A., Tabor, C. A. 1971. *Am. J. Bot.* 58:131–40
194. Rücker, W., Paupardin, C. 1969. *C. R. Acad. Sci.* 268:1279–81
195. Sabharwal, P. S. 1963. In *Plant Tissue and Organ—A Symposium,* ed. P. Maheshwari, N. S. Rangaswamy, 265–74. Delhi: Int. Soc. Plant Morphol.
196. Sacristan, M. D. 1971. *Chromosoma* 33:273–83
197. Sacristan, M. D., Melchers, G. 1969. *Mol. Gen. Genet.* 105:317–33
198. Sagawa, Y., Shoji, T. 1967. *Am. Orchid Soc. Bull.* 36:856–59
199. Sagawa, Y., Shoji, T., Shoji, T. 1966. *Am. Orchid Soc. Bull.* 35:118–22
200. Saka, H., Maeda, E. 1969. *Proc. Crop Sci. Soc. Jap.* 38:667–74

201. Schenk, R. U., Hildebrandt, A. C. 1972. *Can. J. Bot.* 50:199–204
202. Schraudolf, H., Reinert, J. 1959. *Nature* 184:465–66
203. Schroeder, C. A. 1968. *Bot. Gaz.* 129:374–76
204. Scully, R. M. Jr. 1967. *Am. Orchid Soc. Bull.* 36:103–8
205. Sehgal, C. B. 1972. *Curr. Sci.* 41:263–64
206. Seibert, M. 1973. *In Vitro* 8:435
207. Sheridan, W. F. 1968. *Planta* 82:189–92
208. Shigematsu, K., Matsubara, H. 1972. *J. Jap. Soc. Hort. Sci.* 41:196–200
209. Shimada, T., Sasakuma, T., Tsunewaki, K. 1969. *Can. J. Genet. Cytol.* 11:294–304
210. Simonsen, J., Hildebrandt, A. C. 1971. *Can. J. Bot.* 49:1817–19
211. Singh, U. P. 1963. *Plant Tissue and Organ Culture, A Symposium,* 275–77
212. Skoog, F. 1944. *Am. J. Bot.* 31:19–24
213. Skoog, F., Miller, C. O. 1957. *Symp. Soc. Exp. Biol.* 11:118–31
214. Skoog, F., Tsui, C. 1948. *Am. J. Bot.* 35:782–87
215. Staritsky, G. 1970. *Acta Bot. Neer.* 19:509–14
216. Steward, F. C., Mapes, M. O. 1971. *Bot. Gaz.* 132:70–79
217. Steward, F. C., Mapes, M. O., Mears, K. 1958. *Am. J. Bot.* 45:705–8
218. Stichel, E. 1959. *Planta* 53:293–317
219. Syono, K. 1965. *Plant Cell Physiol.* 6:403–19
220. Takatori, F., Murashige, T., Stillman, J. 1968. *Hort. Sci.* 3:20–22
221. Teo, C. K. H., Kunisaki, J. T., Sagawa, Y. 1973. *Am. Orchid Soc. Bull.* 42:402–5
222. Thomas, E., Street, H. E. 1972. *Ann. Bot.* 36:239–47
223. Thorpe, T. A., Meier, D. D. 1972. *Physiol. Plant.* 27:364–69
224. Thorpe, T. A., Murashige, T. 1968. *Am. J. Bot.* 55:710
225. Thorpe, T. A., Murashige, T. 1968. *Science* 160:421–22
226. Torrey, J. G. 1966. *Advan. Morphog.* 5:39–91
227. Torrey, J. G. 1967. *Physiol. Plant.* 20:265–75
228. Ueda, H., Torikata, H. 1968. *J. Jap. Soc. Hort. Sci.* 37:340–48
229. Ibid 1970. 39:202–5
230. Ueda, H., Torikata, H. 1972. *Am. Orchid Soc. Bull.* 41:322–27
231. Vasil, I. K., Hildebrandt, A. C. 1966. *Am. J. Bot.* 53:860–69
232. Ibid, 869–74
233. Vasil, I. K., Hildebrandt, A. C., Riker, A. J. 1964. *Science* 146:76–77
234. Vasseur, J. 1972. *C. R. Acad. Sci.* 275:2865–68
235. Walkey, D. G. A., Woolfitt, J. M. G. 1968. *Nature* 220:1346–47
236. Walkey, D. G. A., Woolfitt, J. M. G. 1970. *J. Hort. Sci.* 45:205–6
237. Weis, J. S., Jaffe, M. F. 1969. *Physiol. Plant.* 22:171–76
238. White, P. R. 1939. *Bull. Torrey Bot. Club* 66:507–13
239. White, P. R. 1943. *Growth* 7:53–65
240. Wilfret, G. J. 1971. *Proc. Fla. State Hort. Soc.* 84:9–11
241. Wilmar, C., Hellendoorn, M. 1968. *Nature* 217:369–70
242. Wimber, D. E. 1963. *Am. Orchid Soc. Bull.* 32:105–7
243. Wimber, D. E. 1965. *Cymbidium Soc. News* 20:7–20
244. Winton, L. L. 1968. *Science* 160:1234–35
245. Winton, L. L. 1968. *Am. J. Bot.* 55:159–67
246. Ibid 1970. 57:904–9
247. Winton, L. L. 1971. *Forest Sci.* 17:348–50
248. Wochok, Z. S. 1973. *Biol. Plant.* 15:107–11
249. Wolter, K. E. 1968. *Nature* 219:509–10
250. Wurm, G. 1960. *Flora* 149:43–76
251. Yakuwa, T., Harada, T., Saga, K., Shiga, Y. 1971. *J. Jap. Soc. Hort. Sci.* 40:347–53
252. Yamada, T., Nakagawa, H., Sinoto, Y. 1967. *Bot. Mag.* 80:68–74
253. Yoneda, Y. 1969. *Bot. Mag.* 82:204–9
254. Zenkteler, M. 1971. *Experientia* 27:101
255. Zenkteler, M. 1972. *Biochem. Physiol. Pflanz.* 163:509–12
256. Ziv, M., Halevy, A. H., Shilo, R. 1970. *Ann. Bot.* 34:671–76

Ann. Rev. Plant Physiol. 1974. 25:167–93

CONTROL OF SEED GERMINATION

❖7566

A. M. Mayer

Department of Botany, The Hebrew University of Jerusalem, Jerusalem, Israel

Y. Shain

Laboratory for Electron Microscopy, Tel-Aviv University, Tel-Aviv, Israel

CONTENTS

INTRODUCTION 167
SEED COATS AND OTHER PERMEABILITY BARRIERS 169
PROTEOLYTIC ENZYMES AND PROTEASE INHIBITORS 172
LIPID METABOLISM AND THE GLYOXYLATE CYCLE 173
CARBOHYDRATE METABOLISM 175
RESPIRATION 176
PHYTIN AND PHOSPHORUS METABOLISM 179
SYNTHESIS AND ACTIVATION OF PROTEINS AND ENZYMES 180
HORMONES AND GROWTH SUBSTANCES 183
ULTRASTRUCTURE 185
MEMBRANES 185
CONCLUSION 187

INTRODUCTION

The topic of seed germination was last reviewed in this series more than 10 years ago (173). A great deal of information has accumulated in the intervening period. Reviews of various kinds have provided partial coverage of this accumulated material (9, 29, 210, 341, 357). The subject of tree seed germination has been treated recently (178) and a multi-author series on seed biology has appeared (179). Two aspects of germination have been covered in very great detail in recent years—dormancy (172, 237, 278, 343) and viability (279). The proceedings of a symposium on seed germination, held in 1963, also appeared somewhat belatedly in 1967 (47), as well as the proceedings of a conference on seed proteins (263).

A further aspect of seed germination, that of light and phytochrome, has received attention in various reviews (42, 51, 115). Thus we feel justified in not covering these subjects in detail in the present review. We interpret the title of this review rather narrowly. We will regard seed germination as that series of steps normally occurring prior to the emergence of the radicle from the seedcoat. By this definition we exclude the very large number of papers describing the properties of enzymes or constituents in the seedling. Seedlings have been a very good source of enzymes and other plant constituents, but this type of study normally has not led to an understanding of germination. The many detailed and valuable studies on events occurring during seedling development after radicle protusion are also excluded. Lastly we do not discuss in detail the very large number of papers that describe the effect of various external conditions or exogenously applied compounds on seed germination and seedling development. Although these undoubtedly add greatly to our store of knowledge about seeds and possibly about germination, they do not help us greatly to understand what controls germination. Even given this very selective interpretation of the title of this review, we make no claim to cover all the remaining aspects of the subject. Hogan (personal communication) has estimated that in the period under review some 20,000 publications appeared in which seed germination is mentioned in some way.

Much of the work on the biochemistry of germination has been carried out on entire seeds, partly because of the practical difficulties involved in séparating the embryo or embryonic axis from the endosperm or the cotyledons. In some studies careful separations have been made and the behavior of each part followed separately. However, the separation of endosperm or cotyledons from the embryo or embryonic axis before germination is likely to lead to results not necessarily relevant to the germination of the entire seed, for example as in formation of peroxidases in lentil embryonic axis (167).

There is ample evidence (to be discussed later) that shows a very complex interaction between different parts of the seed. Separation into different parts obscures such interaction or even completely removes it. Interactions are probably an integral part of the control of germination. Another frequent comparison is made between the enzymology and biochemistry of cotyledons and endosperm tissue. Such a comparison can be highly misleading. It should be remembered that structurally and genetically cotyledons are entirely distinct from the endosperm. Undoubtedly both serve as a source of material for the seedling, but the embryonic axis-cotyledon interaction appears to differ from that of embryo with endosperm. The contribution of the cotyledons to seedling development differs greatly in different plants, depending partly on cotyledon size (4, 192).

The environment has a profound effect on germination behavior, which is brought about in two ways. The environment prevailing during seed formation as well as the location of the seeds on the parent plant affect subsequent germination behavior (20, 32, 80, 87, 88). However, in no case is information available about the mechanism by which germination behavior and dormancy are determined by conditions prevailing during seed formation and ripening. The same consideration also applies to the direct effect of the environment during germination on germination behavior. Such effects again have been profusely documented (80, 173, 210) and require no further citation. However, what is almost universally missing is an explanation of the mechanism of control. With what specific step or steps do such environmental factors as light, gas, temperature, etc interact to determine the germination behavior of the seed? At this level, ignorance is almost complete. Chen & Varner (67) concluded that the differences in degree of dormancy of *Avena fatua* cannot be due to a general shut-off of metabolism, but must be due to a specific metabolic block. This conclusion has much wider applications. Environmental factors also must act on specific sites of metabolic sequences in the seed. It is unlikely that an environmental factor controls germination by a general depression or activation of the entire metabolic apparatus of the seed.

A further consideration of the seed's relationship with its environment is the possible function of such control mechanisms. The possible significance of the control of germination by environmental factors has been discussed by a number of workers, but in most cases the function of the control mechanism, although intuitively understood, has never been experimentally established (80, 171, 210). In most cases, the survival value for the species is probably important but has not been proved. Cohen (75, 76), using mathematical models, has attempted to analyze the optimization of reproduction of a population in order to achieve survival of the species and long-term optimal growth. He shows that different strategies are required, depending on whether maximal seed production in the next generation or maximal number of established seedlings in any given year is desired. His conclusions lead to the view that germination behavior must be controled and that uniform germination in wild species of plants is not normally desirable for the species. It should be recalled that in cultivated species control mechanisms that would spread germination over time and space have deliberately been bred out by careful selection, since uniform rapid germination is desirable in a cultivated crop. Thus it is possible that cultivated species are the worst possible choice for studying germination control. However, this drawback of the nature of the cultivated species is counterbalanced by the convenience of their use in experimental work on the one hand and by the genetic uniformity of their seed population on the other hand.

SEED COATS AND OTHER PERMEABILITY BARRIERS

The seed coats have a profound influence on the ability of many seeds to germinate (80, 342, 343). Most of these seed coat effects have been attributed to the preservation of seed dormancy, but some effects may also influence early stages of germination. The coats may regulate germination by establishing a permeability barrier and interfering with these processes: uptake of water required for imbibition and subsequent radicle protrusion; gaseous exchange, particularly oxygen uptake, required for respiration and other oxidative processes; and the outward diffusion of endogenous germination inhibitors. Seed coats may also offer mechanical resistance to the growth of the embryo.

There is no doubt that seed coats may inhibit the germination of some seeds by preventing water uptake. This phenomenon is called "hard seededness" and is most prevalent in the Leguminosae. It is an inherited characteristic and in some cases may be determined by environmental effects on the mother plant (108). It appears to be an all or nothing effect rather than a control process for seed germination. Interestingly, the well-known opening of the strophiolar gap has been shown to be reversible (131).

Other seeds show a sensitivity to water. Their germination is arrested by the presence of excess water in the substrate. Studies with *Hirschfeldia incana* seeds show that small differences in the water potential of the substrate cause large differences in the amount of water held by the surrounding mucilage (236). However, in certain cultivated species, water tension has been shown to influence the rate of germination but not its final percentage (159), whereas Dasberg (85) claims that in the soil, water uptake by seeds is not affected by soil moisture content. He also relates germination to seed water content and claims that water movement in the soil to the seed is limited to not more than about 1 cm. Similar effects have been noted for the swelling of the integumentary mucilage of *Blepharis persica* seeds (352) and the ovary cap in the beet seed clusters (139). In seeds of *Hirschfeldia, Blepharis,* and beet, sensitivity to excess water was attributed to lengthening of the diffusion pathway for oxygen by these swollen integuments, although increasing the concentration of oxygen in the surroundings did not always relieve this effect (236). No significant difference was found in the rate of oxygen consumption of barley seeds sensitive to excess water as compared to the water-insensitive seeds. However, isolated embryos of the water-sensitive seeds germinate to a lesser degree at low oxygen tensions (83). Excess water may therefore interfere with oxygen diffusion. Such resistance to oxygen diffusion has never been measured directly. Those embryos requiring higher oxygen tensions for their development may be sensitive to excess water. This excess water might not merely establish a longer diffusion pathway in these seeds, it may also encourage the development of large mixed populations of microorganisms in and around the seed integuments. These microorganisms would then compete with the embryo for available oxygen (116, 138).

The complexity of interaction of water uptake with other factors is illustrated by recent work of Taylorson & Hendricks (313). They show that phytochrome is fully hydrated when 17–19% of water uptake in the seed has occurred. The lag in the light response in this case is not due to lack of hydration. In addition, once a phytochrome effect has been induced, it persists subsequently in the dry seed for at least a year (331).

The conditions under which water uptake occurs also seem to be critical in determining subsequent germination behavior. Water uptake at low temperatures, i.e. absence of a diffusion barrier, induces damage to seedling development and impairs germination (257), while the uptake of water vapor reduces this low temperature sensitivity (256). Villiers (334) suggests that fully imbibed lettuce seed held at 30°C can be stored for very long periods fully imbibed without damage. According to him, their subsequent germination is determined by the fact that repair mechanisms can operate under these conditions, thus maintaining the intactness of membranes. One would like to see this work extended to other species. It seems plausible that some of the contradictory results on seed coat effects may be related to the operation of repair mechanisms of this kind, although of course other explanations are possible.

Edwards (100–102) calculated that the seed coat of charlock seeds presents no resistance to water uptake yet offers a resistance to oxygen diffusion. Naked embryos could germinate at low oxygen tensions. The calculated partial pressure of oxygen at the surface of the embryo in intact seeds is low but apparently sufficient for germination. She attributed the effect of the seed coat to the establishment of low internal oxygen concentrations that lead to the production of growth inhibiting substances in the embryonic tissue. These substances accumulate within the testa, and when they reach a critical concentration, they prevent subsequent cell elongation. The seed coat therefore acts both as a diffusion barrier for oxygen and as a deposit for endogenous inhibitors. In later stages this oxygen diffusion barrier may also control germination by impeding the oxidation and subsequent destruction of the endogenous inhibitors (337, 341). The presence of endogenous growth inhibitors in seed integuments is quite common, and in many cases the inhibitory effects of seed coats on germination may be related to their prevention of the leaching out of these inhibitors from the embryo (10, 278). Integuments may also function as an oxygen barrier, due to oxygen consumption by the integuments themselves (79). In sugar beet the seed coat is said to contribute significantly to oxygen consumption by the seed (239).

Diffusion barriers, which may control exchange of gas and other compounds, need not be in the seed coat itself, but may be located in the endosperm. Thus the lettuce seed endosperm constitutes a barrier to externally applied leucine (170) and has also been shown to be a barrier to coumarin (11). The *Luzula* endosperm also appears to be a diffusion barrier (8). Diffusion barriers, however, are rather complex in their function. In a range of grasses, reduced O_2 concentration reduced germination (86). However, in dormant *Trifolium subterraneum* a period of decreased O_2 concentration resulted in subsequent increased germination (24). According to these authors, an intermediate of glycolysis is involved in controlling subsequent germination.

Lastly, the possibility remains that the seed coats offer a restraining force to the expansion of the embryo and radicle protrusion. Thus the seed coat effects on the light sensitivity of certain seeds are attributed to the exertion of a mechanical resistance by the seed coat to radicle growth. Light is thought to affect the ability of the radicle to overcome this resistance either by weakening this barrier or by increasing the expansive force of the embryo (62, 63, 65, 148). Actual measurements of the physical thrust developed by the entire seed and its separate components were made during the germination of *Xanthium* seeds (106). One third of the total thrust developed during the passive imbibitional phase. The remaining two thirds appeared during the active phases of enlargement, primarily because of the axial component, although the cotyledons also participated substantially. The force necessary to rupture the testa was also measured, and it was concluded that germinating seed embryos develop adequate physical thrust to overcome the restraint imposed by the testa and need not produce enzymes to soften this barrier.

PROTEOLYTIC ENZYMES AND PROTEASE INHIBITORS

Surprisingly little attention has been paid to the nature and function of proteolytic enzymes in germinating seeds.

The main reports on proteolytic enzymes and peptidases are those relating to the malting process of barley (38, 54, 55, 261). The protein bodies isolated from dry seeds contain an acid protease (243). Germinating barley has been shown to contain eight different peptidases and probably three different proteolytic systems, namely those localized in the aleurone layer, the starchy endosperm, and the scutellum (223). Various proteolytic enzymes have been reported present in germinating seeds, but the onset of proteolysis seems to be very different in so far as it has been studied. Thus in *Sorghum* an acid protease becomes active quite late in germination (117), whereas in *Sinapis alba* protein is broken down very early during germination (126). In *Cannabis* an acid proteinase is present in the aleurone grains of the dry, resting seed (15, 16). This proteinase acts on the native substrate, edestin. In peas a number of proteolytic enzymes as well as peptidases are present. Some of these are active in extracts of dry seeds while others become active only during germination, particularly peptidases (21, 31, 137, 141, 291). The exact characterization of these enzymes in peas is inadequate, but most seem to be located in the cotyledons and appear to be soluble enzymes. Interestingly, Matile (204) describes isolated vacuoles in the aleurone of peas and he designates them lysosomes, although proteolytic activity in them was not tested. However, they could give rise to the soluble proteolytic enzymes known to be present in peas. In *Phaseolus vulgaris* initial proteolytic activity in the dry seed also seems adequate for protein breakdown (266). The onset of proteolytic activity seems to be controlled in some cases by hormone action, by cytokinin in the embryo in the case of *Cucurbita maxima* (248, 348) and by gibberellic acid in the aleurone of barley (150). No such control by hormones exists in peas, where protein breakdown in the cotyledons does not depend on the embryo (22), although some factor in them may affect protein breakdown (70). In lettuce, at least three distinct, soluble, proteolytic enzymes occur, differing in nature, onset of activity, and pH optimum (284, 286). One of the proteolytic enzymes was shown to interact with an endogenous trypsin inhibitor, and it was suggested that this controls the onset of activity by autocatalysis of a trypsin-like enzyme which becomes active early in germination. This appears to be the first report ascribing a function to the widely reported presence of trypsin inhibitors in seeds (33, 162a, 162b, 289, 336, 345). Inhibition of proteolytic enzymes by endogenous inhibitors has also been described for barley (168) and *Vigna* (355). In these cases also the inhibitors may have a controlling function in proteolysis.

In contrast, the protease inhibitor in rice seeds does not seem to change in concentration during the early stages of germination, and therefore probably does not control proteolysis (144). Maize endopeptidase is located in a different part of the seedling than the endogenous trypsin inhibitor (219). In peas the endogenous inhibitor does not control the activity of the proteolytic enzyme, although the inhibitor is apparently destroyed during the early stages of germination (141). A family of inhibitors, whose relative concentrations change but which only disappear very late in germination, occurs in *Phaseolus* (265). Here also their function in germination is very doubtful. Endogenous inhibitors of proteolytic enzymes in germinating seeds could therefore be functioning in certain cases by controlling the onset of proteolysis during germination, although in other cases they may be a relict of seed formation, during which they protected the accumulating storage protein from decomposition (144).

Some of the contradictory findings about the function of the proteinase inhibitors are probably due to their location in different parts of the seed, embryo, endosperm, or cotyledons. Functional control, important in germination, can only be ascribed to inhibitors acting on enzymes in the embryonic axis. Proteolysis in the aleurone or the cotyledons is presumably a later event which supplies building blocks for the germinating seeds but does not control the onset of germination. However, the relevant experiments to investigate this point do not yet appear to have been made, except with the lettuce system. It seems to be characteristic of seeds that either in the dry seed or immediately upon germination certain proteolytic enzymes become active. Proteolytic enzymes could have a number of different roles in germination. The simplest function would be in the breakdown of storage proteins, which presumably does not constitute a control mechanism. However, the involvement of proteolytic enzymes in the formation and activation of amylolytic enzymes has been described in germinating peas (213, 285, 335). This would assign a much more important regulating function to the proteolytic enzymes. It would be important to find additional examples of this kind of function. Proteolytic enzymes could be releasing or activating bound, particulate, or masked enzymes during germination. This concept could be carried further; for example, proteolytic enzymes might function in releasing long-lived, possibly masked, RNA during the early stages of germination, as has been described in the case of sea urchin eggs (198).

The precise nature and function of proteolytic enzymes in germinating seeds still requires further elucidation, as does their interaction with endogenous inhibitors. Data presently available suggest that the proteolytic system may have a definite regulatory role in germination.

LIPID METABOLISM AND THE GLYOXYLATE CYCLE

Fat metabolism in seeds has continued to attract some attention (71, 287). The location of the storage lipids relative to the lipases causing their breakdown has been considered. It is not entirely clear whether the lipases arise in the fat bodies themselves (72) as appears to be the case in Douglas fir seeds, or whether they are separate from the spherosomes in which the lipids are located, as in peanut seedlings (149). The breakdown of lipids in germinating seeds is usually a fairly late event in the overall series of steps in germination (14, 287) and involves a variety of lipases (14, 72, 140).

The control of lipid breakdown has been ascribed to a variety of factors. Early reports of a function of light in controlling lipid breakdown seems to have been disproved, and light effects, if they exist at all, are indirect (130, 238a, 238b). The simplest control mechanism suggested is feedback control by availability of sugars in the case of the castor bean cotyledons (7). However, control is probably much more complex. Lipase from *Ricinus communis* requires a natural cofactor, a cyclic polymer of ricinoleic acid, for its activity (242). This could constitute a direct control of lipid breakdown by lipase. In wheat, triglycerate metabolism is under hormonal control from the embryo, and the hormonal control differs from that for the carbohydrates (310, 311). The control appears to be extremely complex, apparently involves lipase activity, and is regulated by cytokinins as well as by glutamine and possibly even by hydroxylamine. The function of glutamine is not entirely clear but would suggest an interaction between lipid metabolism and protein metabolism. Under normal conditions glutamine would not accumulate during germination.

The utilization of fatty acids during germination is presumably by the normal breakdown via β oxidation. β Oxidation has in fact been shown to occur in an extract of a number of seeds and seedlings, but does not appear in the early stages of germination (270–272). Interestingly, β oxidation activity in castor bean endosperm is restricted to the glyoxysomes (82) where this activity appears late during germination. This would appear to be very logical from a functional point of view. However, it should be recalled that malate synthetase is not located exclusively in the glyoxysomes (119) and that these organelles are also devoid of succinic dehydrogenase (81). This raises interesting questions of the possible role of transport of materials from one organelle to another in regulating seed metabolism, at least in its later stages.

Considerable effort has been devoted to investigating the occurrence of enzymes of the glyoxylate cycle in various seed tissues. It seems characteristic of isocitrate lyase that it is at an initial low level in the seed tissue, rises during germination, and decreases again in activity (111, 186, 208, 233, 262, 308, 309). The activity of this enzyme has been reported variously as being particulate or soluble. It is clear now that a considerable part of the activity is located in the glyoxysomes (81, 82, 119), although a certain and varying amount of the enzyme has been described as soluble (119, 208, 233, 260, 262). There is some controversy about whether the isocitrate lyase activity arises by de novo protein synthesis. Certainly a number of papers indicate such de novo synthesis (124, 142, 143, 181, 190), but some contrary evidence is also available (208, 262). More important perhaps is the question of the control of isocitrate lyase activity in germinating seeds. The dominant role of the glyoxylate cycle in *Ricinus* endosperm has been ascribed to the high level of isocitrate lyase activity and the limitation of ADP, which would restrict other pathways (308, 309). Others suggest that activity of isocitrate lyase in *Ricinus* is controlled by the level of glucose (181). The possible interaction between isocitrate lyase and isocitric dehydrogenase in controlling the activity of the glyoxylate cycle has also been discussed (208, 282). The interaction between different parts of the seed in controlling isocitrate lyase activity is not clear. Apparently, in castor bean endosperm the embryo has no control function (308), but in squash, cytokinin from the embryo controls the appearance of the lyase in the cotyledons (248). More recently, a role has been ascribed to gibberellin in the appearance of glyoxylate cycle enzymes in wheat aleurone (92).

Thus a considerable amount of confusion still remains regarding the control of isocitrate lyase activity in germinating seeds. However, it is reasonably clear that the glyoxylate cycle is not one of the early metabolic events of germination, although the conversion of fats to carbohydrate at some stages of germination will no doubt be of great importance. Thus in *Cucurbita pepo,* gluconeogenesis is slight for the first two days of germination (315) and leads to the formation of stachyose, sucrose, and a variety of other labeled compounds. One is left with a number of open questions regarding the exact regulatory role of the glyoxylate cycle in germinating seeds and the way the activity of the cycle is regulated.

The changes in ultrastructure related to the glyoxylate cycle also appear to occur rather late, especially in the glyoxysomes (283, 319), and they do not seem to control the initial stages of lipid breakdown.

A number of reports indicate the existence of lysosomes or lysosome-like organelles in dry and germinating seed, which are supposed to contain various hydrolytic enzymes (204, 205, 358). The special significance of these organelles in germination still remains obscure.

CARBOHYDRATE METABOLISM

Since the hormonal induction of amylase activity in barley aleurone was described (252, 327, 330), there has been a tendency to assume that carbohydrate breakdown is universally induced by gibberellic acid. However, there is good reason to believe that such is by no means the case, as in the cotyledons of peas (295, 328). Some indication of hormonal control does exist, however, even in pea cotyledons (118, 294). Interaction of gibberellic acid with boron has been reported (84). Unfortunately, little further insight is obtained from these findings since the breakdown of storage carbohydrates is quite a late event. In peas both phosphorolytic and amylolytic breakdown of starch occurs (302). Yet other work (213, 285, 335) indicates that amylopectin-1,6-glucosidase activity is formed very late and that its formation or release from a zymogen may control the overall rate of starch breakdown. An interesting illustration of the complexity in carbohydrate metabolism is provided by the work of Palmiano & Juliano (244). They indicate that amylases and amylopectin-1,6-glucosidase in normal rice varieties are formed by synthesis, presumably in the aleurone. In certain dwarf lines gibberellic acid induces enzyme formation in whole seeds, which is not the case for the normal varieties of rice, whose whole seeds do not respond to the hormone. The breakdown of starch in rice and other cereals is quite well understood, but we have insufficient knowledge about other plant species.

The breakdown of galactomannans in the endosperm of *Trigonella, Medicago, and Trifolium* is due to secretion of enzymes from the aleurone, but is not under control of the embryo (275). This breakdown is a rather late event in germination.

Some attention has been given to glucose metabolism in barley and wheat, particularly in relation to the question of viability and seed vigor (2, 13). The rates of metabolism of glucose differ considerably in wheat and barley endosperm as compared to embryo, and the endosperm loses its ability to utilize glucose more rapidly than the embryo (2, 13).

The loss of ability to utilize glucose precedes many other events such as a loss of ability to germinate (1). The great significance of glucose metabolism in seeds can also be deduced from the rapid respiratory rise in barley seed in the early stage of germination (1), which is due to glucose respiration. Seeds stored under unfavorable conditions rapidly lose the ability to utilize glucose (12). Glucose also seems to leach out readily from barley even in normally germinating seeds in the early stages of germination. In *Phaseolus* there is apparently no breakdown of cotyledon storage materials for the first 6 hr. of germination (77), and thus the substrates for respiration must be present in the embryo. It seems, therefore, that the production of respiratory substrate is a vital early event in germination. The source of respiratory substrate such as glucose is generally unknown, but it is probably not high molecular weight storage material such as starch, etc. Whether lack of respiratory substrate is ever a limiting factor in the early stages of germination seems doubtful, except in the case of those seeds which have deteriorated in some way.

It has also been claimed, using tritiated water, that amino acids are deaminated very early during germination both in *Sinapis* and *Phaseolus* (226, 293), thus forming respiratory substrate. However, the malic acid formed by transamination is partly compartmented and partly leached from the seed (227). It seems unlikely that it serves as a major respiratory substrate. The tritiated water technique apparently must be used with great care and may lead to seed damage (96).

RESPIRATION

The rise of respiration during germination of seeds is well known and has been repeatedly discussed (173). When the different parts of respiratory metabolism become active is still uncertain, nor has its control been satisfactorily identified. It has been proposed at various times that restriction of O_2 supply to the seed limits respiration and thereby directly or indirectly induces dormancy and reduces germination percentage or prevents germination. Roberts (278) has reviewed the extensive experimental evidence on which this view is based and proposed an alternative theory. He suggests that in the early stage of germination the pentose phosphate pathway in necessary and that in dormancy this pathway is somehow reduced or impaired. Some additional evidence exists to support the view that oxidation by the pentose phosphate pathway might be important. In lettuce there is a very high initial level of glucose phosphate dehydrogenase which does not alter during germination (212). NADPH is the only form of reduced pyridine nucleotide during the early stages of germination of rice and wheat seeds (232). Moreover, within the first 10 min. of peanut seed imbibition, or within the first 30 min. after the beginning of mung bean imbibition, there is a massive conversion of NAD to NADP. NADP is not present in the dry seed and its appearance during germination is preceded by the activation of the NAD kinase (273).

Lettuce seed respiration seems to show some unusual features. Respiration is only partially inhibited by cyanide. The initial level of cytochrome oxidase is more than adequate to account for O_2 uptake (134). Phenols and their oxidation products may interfere in the normal functioning of respiratory metabolism of lettuce at certain stages of development (206). The presence of ATP and the onset of its formation in lettuce are unclear, and contradictory results appear in the literature (46, 121, 258, 322). This question is not simply academic, for when ATP formation begins, the normal respiratory mechanism has become fully functional and thus can supply the germinating seed with its required energy. Furthermore, it has been shown that the ratios between ATP, ADP, and AMP, and hence the energy charge, might have a regulatory function in germinating seeds (46, 73, 258). The ATP level changes quite considerably in germination (52). In *Phaseolus* after the onset of imbibition, no Krebs cycle activity is noted in the axis for 30 min and for 1 hr in the cotyledons (77). Glycolysis in germinating peas can be inhibited by ATP (209, 230). In extracts of peas, phosphate seems to regulate glycolysis via its affect on phosphofructokinase (125). There does not seem to be a deficiency of glycolytic enzymes in dry seeds. Triose phosphate isomerase is present in dry pea seed (36), and the glycolytic system seems to function at all stages of germination in cotyledons of *Cucurbita pepo* (316).

The possible importance of the proper functioning of the redox system during germination is indicated by a number of authors. Cyanide can break dormancy (278) as well as stimulate germination (136), while uncouplers of respiration are capable of preventing the release from dormancy (23). Clearly, a correctly functioning redox system is highly important in seed germination. However, the question of when the redox system becomes fully functional is less clear. The fact that the effectiveness of mitochondria in oxidizing various substrates increases during germination has long been known (174). Various electron microscope observations indicate that mitochondria become increasingly orderly and normal appearing during germination (69, 191, 240, 241). The number of mitochondria increases during germination (48, 49, 133). Very rapid changes in the activity of mitochondria from pea cotyledons during imbibition have been described (234). These changes accompany the structural development of mitochondria from membrane-bound organelles with little or no internal structure to completely developed mitochondria with numerous cristae (21). The number of cristae in the mitochondria of rice seed has also been shown to increase markedly during germination (321). Essentially similar results have been obtained recently by Solomos et al (292), who also report the development of peroxisomes. They too find good correlation very early in germination between structural change and biochemical activity.

A very significant finding on the respiration of peanut embryos has been reported by Wilson & Bonner (351). They show that in the dry embryos the respiratory chain goes through a path deficient in cytochrome *c*, and that the mitochondria can phosphorylate but lack respiratory control. As growth of the embryo starts, normal mitochondria appear. Wilson & Bonner suggest that the special mitochondria in the dry embryo are required to control the initial stages of respiration. In pea cotyledons, the respiratory chain also appears to be deficient in some component which may control respiration (177).

The importance of the hydration step in bringing about changes in the activity of mitochondria is indicated by data on cytochrome *c* reductase in lettuce (104).

This enzyme increases rapidly during imbibition of water, and its initial level might be limiting O_2 uptake. The increase in activity of cytochrome c reductase was totally reversed by drying the seeds. The development of the enzyme did not parallel water uptake, whereas cytochrome c oxidase activity in the same organelle increased as expected. Crista formation in the mitochondria of rice also did not parallel water uptake (321). Early increases in cytochrome c NADH reductase and also glucose-6-phosphate dehydrogenase have also been shown in peanut cotyledons (68). The simple activation of alcohol dehydrogenase by imbibition has been reported for pea cotyledons (176), and the level of the enzyme is controlled by endogenous alcohol and acetaldehyde levels (175). Reversible activation of respiratory enzymes has also been shown to occur in castor beans (39), and has been suggested for alcohol dehydrogenase in peas (301). Alcohol formed early during germination of beans is readily utilized via the Krebs sycle (93). The rate of respiration during imbibition is reported as a good indicator of the subsequent growth and development of the seedling (353, 354).

It is unfortunate that the data on respiration are scattered in reports on different species, in some cases referring to different parts of the seed and in other cases to entire seeds.

Nevertheless, some degree of coherence seems to emerge from these observations. Mitochondria in dry seeds are not normal, active mitochondria, although they can probably maintain certain oxidative functions. They undergo rapid changes during imbibition and these changes increase their functionality. These changes are not simply dependent on water uptake, but probably involve structural changes, possibly in the membranes of the mitochondria. The activation of mitochondria during the early stages of imbibition of water may therefore be very significant in controlling the initial rate of seed respiration. Probably at some stage ATP, or the ratio between the adenosine nucleotides, assumes a regulatory function. It is not clear at what stage the pentose phosphate pathway is functional and how significant its role is in the control of respiration. It appears that some significant advances have been made in the area of respiration of germinating seeds. These may lead to a better insight into the precise control mechanism involved.

One further aspect of seed respiration should be considered—the initial substrates respired. It is clear that at some stage of germination one of the various reserve materials present in bulk is respired at the main substrate. However, the breakdown of these storage materials is quite a late event in germination and probably something else is respired in the early stages of germination. In lettuce it has been shown that sucrose seems to be respired in the initial stages of germination (251), although the main reserve material is lipid. Invertase in lettuce seems to be absent in the dry seed but is formed de novo, probably a little too late to account for sucrose respiration (105). In *Avena fatua* maltose is readily metabolized and converted to sucrose in non-dormant seeds but not in dormant ones (66). Particularly striking is the observation that in many species raffinose is metabolized very early in germination. This has been shown for barley (217) and cotton seed (288), in which the galactosidase activity rises during germination. In *Sinapis alba* and *Trigonella* small amounts of stachyose and raffinose are broken down early during germination (126, 274), while in barley, cabbage, radish, and beans, galactosidase activity rises early during germination (185). Enzymes of galactose metabolism are also among the first to change during germination (97). It would be premature to assign a special role in seed respiration to sugars containing galactose. The significance of the early metabolism of raffinose, and in some cases stachyose, may lie in the subsequent metabolism of galactose, for example, in the formation of wall materials. Possibly this triose is stored in seeds because it simultaneously provides galactose and a disaccharide which becomes available for respiration. This question should be followed more closely and may lead to interesting results.

PHYTIN AND PHOSPHORUS METABOLISM

The presence of phytin in seeds has long attracted attention. Phytin is formed from inositol and the phosphate donor is ATP (18, 189). Generally it has been assumed that phytin formation occurs only during seed formation, but it has recently been shown that the enzymes required for phytin formation are also present in the dry seed and synthesis occurs during seed germination (182, 195). At one time the suggestion that phytin serves as an energy store during germination seemed attractive. Morton & Raison (228) brought evidence that phytin could act as a donor for a transphosphorylation reaction, and this was further supported by Biswas & Biswas (41). However, later work has made this conclusion seem doubtful. Raison & Evans (269) question the possibility that phytin acts as an active phosphate donor on purely thermodynamic grounds. Mayer (207) describes extensive experiments trying to show the existence of the supposed transphosphorylation reaction in extracts of peas and lettuce, and he concludes that such a reaction does not exist. A similar conclusion was reached by Williams (350). However, there is additional evidence to throw doubt on the function of phytin as an active phosphate donor. The stage at which ATP formation starts in seeds is unclear, but it is probably quite late (121, 322), although Pradet et al (258) show a very rapid initial turnover of ATP as well as the presence of cyclic AMP (259). However, adenylic kinase is active very early in germinating lettuce (46), which may partially account for the rapid ATP turnover. If phytin breakdown were a controlling factor in seed germination, one would expect it to be a very early event. However, phytase rises in activity very late in germinating *Phaseolus* (123a, 123b), and in peas phytase activity lags behind germination itself (129). Similar effects have been noted by other workers (187). However, it is interesting to note that phytase activity or formation is repressed by inorganic phosphate (40, 197, 281). It seems likely, therefore, that available phosphate does in fact control directly or indirectly the breakdown of phytin. This in itself makes it extremely unlikely that its function is in ATP or GTP formation. Certain nitrogenous compounds are also involved in controlling phytase activity, but is not clear whether enzyme formation or activity is involved (98).

How phytase activity arises is in some dispute. Both in wheat and in mung bean, the enzyme is said to be formed by protein synthesis (40, 196), but it might arise in wheat seeds by activation caused simply by hydration (98). In lettuce (222) phytase might arise by activation, as its formation is only very partially inhibited by cycloheximide. Thus the mechanism of phytase formation is still in doubt and may differ in various tissues. However, it seems generally true that phytase forms rather late in the germination process and, therefore, presumably its importance is not in controlling germination as such. Rather it seems likely that the phytin-phytase system serves as a source for inorganic phosphorus during the later stages of germination when the phosphate supply may become limiting and the seedling cannot yet obtain its phosphate from other sources. This conclusion has been reached by Williams (350) and others. The need for a source of phosphate is obvious, and its formation as an insoluble salt during seed development has obvious advantages from purely osmotic considerations. Little is known of the fate of calcium and magnesium bound in phytin. Eastwood & Laidman (98) consider this question and regard phytin as a source for Ca and Mg of the germinating wheat grain. They discuss the interesting possibility that while phytin breakdown is not hormonally controlled, transfer of the Ca and Mg liberated by its breakdown from the aleurone to the embryo might be controlled by a hormone from the embryo. The inositol released by hydrolysis of phytin does not appear to have been the subject of any detailed study in germinating seed, although inositol is widely distributed in seedlings (123a). There seems to be little to indicate that inositol has any major importance in germination.

The phosphate release from phytin occurs rather late, but phosphatases seem to be abundant in dry seeds and increase rapidly during germination (222, 262). From this one may conclude that the initial need for phosphate during germination is supported by the rapid turnover of the various phosphates present and by the action of the numerous phosphatases. There seems to be little to indicate that phosphate supply limits or controls germination. The phytin-phytase-phosphate interaction is undoubtedly a very interesting adaptation of metabolism to the special needs of the seed, and represents interesting aspects of the reaction mechanism of hydrolysis, but it cannot be considered a control system at present.

SYNTHESIS AND ACTIVATION OF PROTEINS AND ENZYMES

A significant portion of research on the control of germination is devoted to elucidating the mechanisms of synthesis and activation of enzymes and proteins during the early hours of germination.

This problem has been approached in a conventional manner by feeding labeled precursors of proteins or nucleic acids to whole seeds or isolated seed portions and then determining the degree of incorporation of these precursors. Although this approach encounters some difficulties with the permeability and distribution of these precursors in intact seeds (170), the problem was partially overcome by using isolated seed embryos. It was found that protein synthesis in isolated wheat embryos commenced after 30 min of inbibition (201). In certain seeds or embryos all of the equipment required for protein synthesis was already present in the dry seeds. These dry seeds have been shown to contain ribosomes capable of protein synthesis (28, 103, 200, 299, 339) and a preformed mRNA (59, 60, 146, 193, 344, 346, 347). The activation of protein synthesis upon imbibition may be due to the formation of polysomes from preexisting ribosomes and mRNA, resulting from a series of reactions requiring ATP (200) or a ribosomal dissociation into subunits before the attachment of the mRNA (17). Although this is probably the sequence of events in wheat embryos, the general phenomenon of the existence of long-lived mRNAs in seeds has been questioned (26, 202, 203), and the de novo synthesis of ribosomes in germinating castor bean seeds was shown to precede polysome formation and protein synthesis (203). An increase in the number of membrane-bound ribosomes similar to that in germinating wheat embryos was also shown in the cotyledons of broad beans during germination (246). In this case, polysome formation was linked to de novo ribosome synthesis and not to the attachment of pre-existing free ribosomes. Numerous electron microscopical studies also show that polysomal structures appear during germination (34, 57, 95).

When whole wheat grains are fed labeled precursors of RNA, DNA, and proteins at subminimal germination temperatures and then placed to germinate at optimal temperatures, RNA synthesis preceeds the resumption of protein synthesis (276). The mature seed contains enzymes, including RNA polymerase, which permit the resumption of synthesis of RNA immediately after germination is initiated (215, 216, 245). There is general agreement that at least ribosomal RNA synthesis is resumed quite early after imbibition (56, 114, 156) and as early as 2 hr after the onset of imbibition in isolated wheat embryos (61). However, the earliest RNA shown to be synthesized in germinating corn embryos is a heterodisperse RNA, heavier than ribosomal RNA; this occurs 6–8 hr after germination begins (323). This RNA is seen in the chromatin region of autoradiographs and is considered to be similar to the nuclear heterodisperse RNA of animal cells (324). In these cells the majority of heterodisperse nuclear RNA with characteristics of mRNA is degraded within the nucleus (145) and its function is unknown.

A specific component of RNA, called the messenger fraction, was shown to be synthesized during the first 3 hr of germination of whole wheat grains (277). However, messenger-like RNAs were synthesized in isolated wheat embryos only after 12 hr of imbibition (59). These mRNAs were similar to the long-lived mRNAs present in the dry embryos and new mRNA was transcribed only after 48 hr of germination. Synthesis of RNA was preceded by increased RNA polymerase activity (152).

It has been shown that the increase in the protein synthesizing capacity of ribosomes during the first 3 hr of imbibition is not sufficient by itself to start a sequence of reactions leading to the germination of intact lettuce seeds (103). Even though the protein synthesis system is active quite early in germination, the possible products of the protein synthesis by the long-lived mRNA have been identified in only one case (147), and some caution should be exercised in interpreting such studies (26). Furthermore, no distinct proteins have been shown to be formed before radicle protrusion (200, 340).

The initiation of DNA synthesis occurs latest in this series of events and precedes cell division, which in many cases is the prerequisite for radicle protrusion (58, 151, 229, 264, 356). Thymidine was incorporated at a relatively early period exclusively into the cytoplasm of corn embryo root cells, but this is not definite proof of actual

DNA synthesis. Tritiated thymidine is catabolized to thymine by enzymes present in the seed coat of *Nigella* seeds (231), and the presence of these products in the cytoplasm can lead to erroneous conclusions regarding DNA synthesis. .

Another approach to the control of germination concerns the rapid activation of enzymes upon seed imbibition. The rationale behind this approach was originally suggested in 1963 (211). It is based on the fact that the maturing seed contains a full complement of all enzymes required for its metabolic activity. During germination there is an extremely rapid increase in the activities of some enzymes. Although the enzymatic requirements for seed formation and seed germination are not necessarily the same, at least some enzymes take part in both processes. It was envisioned that some of the enzymes present in the developing seed are converted into inactive forms which are activated during germination. Such activation would not necessarily involve de novo synthesis of protein. Evidence has appeared that germination can occur in the presence of inhibitors of protein synthesis such as chloramphenicol or azetidine-2-carboxylic acid (43, 113, 284, 359), even though these inhibitors effectively prevent protein synthesis in the germinating seed (44, 45). Activation of preexisting forms of enzymes has been implicated in the large increase in activities of glucose 6-phosphate dehydrogenase and aldolase in castor bean endosperms (39), in the early (3–4 hr) increase of cytochrome oxidase activity in isolated castor bean mitochondria (180), and in the initial rise in phosphatase, isocitritase ribonuclease, and proteolytic activities of various seeds (6, 27, 112, 122, 203, 222, 262, 281).

A trypsin-like proteolytic enzyme was shown to be blocked by an endogenous trypsin inhibitor in germinating lettuce seeds (284, 286). During germination this proteolytic enzyme increased in activity due to the inactivation of the endogenous inhibitor. This system was not dependent on de novo protein synthesis. The appearance of phosphoinositol kinase activity in germinating mung bean seeds was also shown to result from the removal of an endogenous inhibitor (194). An inactive form of amylopectin-1,6-glucosidase could be demonstrated in pea seed zymogen bodies (213, 285) after 4 hr of imbibition. This inactive form could be activated by limited proteolysis, either by exogenous tryspin or by endogenous proteolytic enzyme. Enzymes responsible for fatty acid synthesis in initial stages of germination are present in the dry seeds and may be activated during imbibition (135). The NADH-cytochrome *c* reductase of lettuce seed mitochondria rapidly increases in activity one-half hour after inhibition commences (104). This increase in activity does not parallel the rise in cytochrome oxidase activity or water uptake.

It is apparent, therefore, that protein synthesis and RNA synthesis occur quite early in germination and that DNA replication is rather late. It is possible that DNA replication has occurred during seed formation to a sufficient extent to permit the initial stages of germination. On the other hand, some proteins are activated during germination by mechanisms which are still insufficiently clear. Unfortunately, the accuracy of determining the time of development of protein activation as compared to protein synthesis is still quite inadequate. Consequently, it is impossible to decide which of the two processes controls and regulates germination. It seems quite possible that no general answer exists to this question and that in different tissues the control mechanism differs enormously.

HORMONES AND GROWTH SUBSTANCES

A large number of findings demonstrating the influence of a factor emanating from the embryo on the development of enzymatic activities in the cotyledons or endosperm, and vice versa, have led some workers to conclude that this control is hormonal in nature. Protein metabolism in pea seed cotyledons has been shown to be controlled by an axial component (70). The development of proteolytic activity in squash seed cotyledons is controlled by a substance which originates in axial tissue and is transported to the cotyledons (247, 348). The presence of the axis could be substituted for by the external application of cytokinins (249), and it was concluded that the axis possibly may secrete a cytokinin that regulates the formation of proteolytic enzymes in the cotyledon. The same type of axial regulation was also demonstrated for the synthesis of isocitrate lyase in these squash cotyledons (248). Cytokinins which may originate in the axis appeared to control amylase activity in *Phaseolus vulgaris* cotyledons (118). Physiologically active cytokinins are absent in dry lettuce seeds and appear during germination (30, 325).

The induction of lipase activity in the storage tissues of germinating wheat grains was found to be dependent on some factors originating from the embryo (311). The metabolism of triglycerides in this tissue is apparently under hormonal control (99, 183), although at least in one case the controlling factor may emanate from the starchy endosperm (310). Dipeptidase activity in squash cotyledons was shown to be under axial control. However, no such embryonic control could be demonstrated in one lot of squash seeds (305). This discrepancy was attributed to genetic differences. Thus the regulation of various enzymatic activities is under the influence of the embryonic axis, and in many cases the exogenous application of known plant hormones could substitute for the axis. Some workers consider that the control of seed germination by external application of hormones may reflect the natural control of germination (165). The rigorous proof that such a hormone exists and regulates metabolism in situ depends to a large extent on the isolation of that particular hormone from the embryo or other seed organs, and the demonstration that the endogenous hormone acts in a similar manner and at similar concentrations as the exogenously applied hormones. Such proof is usually unavailable.

The role of gibberellic acid in the formation and secretion of a great number of enzymes is the most thoroughly documented case of an endogenously produced hormone which controls seed metabolism. Gibberellins have been found in both immature and mature seeds. In many cases these gibberellins are present in bound or conjugated forms (184). During the germination of pea seeds, an increasing amount of the bound forms are converted into free forms which are then transported from the cotyledons to the embryo (25). Most of the research on the effects of gibberellins on the metabolism during germination has been concentrated on germinating barley seeds. Mature barley seeds predominantly contain GA_3, while GA_1 is secreted by the scutellum during germination (268). The initial synthesis of this gibberellin occurs in the scutellum, although the axis produces gibberellins starting from the third day of germination. Gibberellic acid-like substances formed in barley scutella during the first two days of germination move out of the embryo into the endosperm and aleurone layer (50, 267). However, the axis or some factor emanating from the axis is initially required for this scutellar gibberellin secretion (218, 268). The exact function of this endogenous plant hormone in the regulation of seed germination remains to be determined.

There is no doubt that gibberellins in some manner control the de novo synthesis of α-amylase in the endosperm (329, 330) even though this gibberellic acid requirement for the formation of α-amylase and other hydrolytic enzymes in other seeds is by no means universal (200, 235, 295). However, the production of α-amylase is not the primary response to gibberellic acid and occurs after a time lag in barley (128) and in wild oats even after postgerminative growth has commenced (64). Pollard and co-workers have determined the sequence of events occurring after the application of gibberellic acid to barley aleurone layers. A large number of hydrolytic and phosphorylytic enzymes were secreted well before the appearance of α-amylase (252). Some of these secretions could also be evoked by the application of cyclic AMP (94, 158, 253, 255). The primary response is probably the secretion of soluble carbohydrates with β-1,3 linkages. This secretion was not due to de novo protein synthesis (254). Gibberellic acid enhances the release of a β-1,3-glucanase, which may dissolve the β-1,3-linked polymer of the aleurone cells walls (306). The area nearest the endosperm was shown to be dissolved first. These findings may be of particular significance in understanding an additional effect of gibberellic acid. Gibberellic acid enables the embryo to germinate by overcoming the restraint imposed by the endosperm or other surrounding structures. This is thought to be achieved either by weakening these structures (225) or by increasing supplies of solutes from the endosperm to the embryo. The latter process allows the embryo to attain higher water uptake potentials and thus overcome mechanical restraints imposed by the surrounding tissues (63). Gibberellic acid may induce the production of hydrolytic enzymes in germinating barley seeds. However, the regulation of the rate of enzyme production may be due to the osmotic potentials exerted by the concentration of the products of enzymic hydrolysis which accumulate within the starchy endosperm (155).

The physiology and relation of endogenous abscisins to seed dormancy and germination have been reviewed extensively (5, 343). Abscisins exist in a large number of seeds and tissues surrounding seeds, and many seeds will not germinate in the presence of abscisins (19, 90, 91, 300, 312). Exogenously applied abscisins inhibit or interfere with the production of certain species of RNA in isolated pear and *Fraxinus* embryos (166, 332), although in isolated bean embryos this effect was shown to occur well after elongation commenced. Karssen (160) suggested that abscisic acid (ABA) prevents embryo elongation and hence prevents protrusion through the surrounding layers. However, as in other cases, the continuous presence of ABA appeared to be required. The reversal by ABA of gibberellic acid-induced polysome formation in barley aleurone has been described (110). This could be relevant in germination control by abscisic acid. Interactions between gibberellic acid and ABA have also been suggested in *Acer pseudoplantanus* (250). In a more general way promoter inhibitor ratios have been invoked in the control of germination and dormancy breaking in *Ambrosia* (349). Clearly, abscisins influence both dormancy and postgerminative growth. However, the effect of endogenous abscisins on the events occurring after the release from dormancy and up to radicle protrusion is still obscure.

Ethylene is another growth regulator produced by germinating seeds (298, 307). Ethylene production commences shortly after the start of imbibition and precedes radicle emergence (107). Some workers assign the main role of this endogenous ethylene production to the breaking of dormancy (107, 164), while others claim that it may play a role in the initial steps of germination (3, 298) or in enhancing the growth rate after germination (307). Gibberellic acid and ethylene are supposed to interact in the heat-induced, temporary dormancy of lettuce seeds, and this may be of some significance to the overall action of ethylene (53). The manner in which ethylene influences dormancy break or germination is still not clear. Its production in the later stages of germination may be a byproduct of germination and not a cause of germination.

Another compound which may be regarded as a hormonal regulator of germination is coumarin. Some of the recent work on the effect of coumarin on germination and its metabolism during the process has been reviewed by Van Sumere et al (326). Among other things they suggested that amino acid and protein synthesis may be effected by phenolics and coumarin. This would again focus attention on the same type of metabolism as effected by other of the regulators.

It is becoming more apparent that endogenous hormones and growth regulators do indeed play an important role in the control of some facets of germination. However, this role may not be due to the regulation of the de novo synthesis of hydrolytic enzymes, which occurs rather late in germination, but to the more general phenomenon of release or activation of prepackaged enzymes and other cellular components.

ULTRASTRUCTURE

Changes in ultrastructure are closely related to metabolism. In most cases changes in ultrastructure which can be detected are late events, occurring when germination is completed (318), or show few unusual features (169). Generally the subcellular organelles become better defined as germination proceeds (296, 297). Many of the changes seem to be correlated with water uptake (21, 240). Very early changes in ultrastructure as well as a rapid formation of starch grains (304) have been reported in the scutellum of wheat, the endoplasmic reticulum, and the dictyosomes (303). Changes in the nucleolus of *Fraxinus* embryos during dormancy breaking treatments have also been reported (333). The overall impression is that changes in ultrastructure of the various organelles reflect changes in the metabolism of the seed. As yet there is little to indicate that such changes control the early stages of germination.

MEMBRANES

From the discussion of the effect of seed coats on germination and the way in which coat effects come about, it is clear that the properties of membranes might have great importance in controlling germination. The question may therefore be asked: Is there any evidence for metabolic changes in membranes in the early stages of germination? Some such evidence has been accumulating lately. Experiments on the effect of saponins on the seed coat of lucerne show very convincingly that external factors can directly alter the properties and hence the permeability to oxygen of seed coats (199, 214). Saponins react directly with sterols, providing a partial theoretical basis for these findings (120). Initial leakiness of membrane which is rapidly repaired has been described for pea embryos (290). Taylorson & Hendricks (314) postulate that temperature potentiation of germination may be interpreted as a change in membrane permeability or enzyme conformation or removal of an inhibitor. This is an extension of the ideas of Cohen (74). Attempts to explain the very rapid actions of phytochrome in effecting germination of photoblastic seeds have also invoked changes in membrane permeability (37, 42). The damage to seeds induced by aging under conditions of high humidity or temperatures is partly repaired during subsequent imbibition of the seeds (35). The repair is ascribed to changes in the membranes of subcellular organelles, which are accompanied by their increased metabolic activity.

Extensive development of endoplasmic reticulum can also be observed during germination. This may be due to either a reorganization of preexisting elements (169) or a new synthesis of these elements (21). Large numbers of Golgi bodies are also formed (34) and mitochondria increase in both number and complexity. Thus both the data on the metabolic changes in membrance and the many observations on ultrastructural changes during germination implicate membranes or changes in them as one of the control mechanisms in germination. One of the early reports on metabolism of a membrane component is by Wagner et al (338), who showed that ^{32}P is incorporated into phosphorylcholine and ethanolamine early in the germination of soybeans. Similar results on incorporation of ^{32}P into seed lipids have been described for mung beans (163). The first and most strongly labeled compound was phosphatidic acid. The enzymes required for the synthesis of fatty acids were shown to be present in the dry pea seed and participated in the synthesis of membrane components, particularly phosphatidylinositol, phosphatidylethanolamine, and phosphatidylcholine. Activity was observed when a critical seed water content was achieved very early after the onset of imbibition (135). Early and rapid changes in nucleotides and nucleosides in the germinating seeds have been reported (52), and a loss in free nucleotides and nucleosides apparently occurs. What can be regarded as a stimulation of germination by purines has also been described (188). These reports are greatly strengthened by a number of recent papers. The enzymes involved in pyrimidine metabolism, orotidine phosphate pyrophosphatase, and orotidine phosphate carboxylase double in the first day of germination in peas (280), and their increase is not inhibited by cycloheximide. Other enzymes described are those concerned with metabolism of uridine and cytidine. Squalene metabolism in peas also rises very rapidly during germination, as indicated by ^{14}C incorporation into squalene (127). In *Calendula*, ^{14}C-labeled acetate is very rapidly incorporated into a variety of triterpenoid compounds, both in the embryo and in the cotyledons (161). The number of compounds present and labeled was more limited in the embryo.

Lecithin turnover and choline incorporation are early rapid events in castor bean endosperm (157). Finally, we should consider recent reports on the effect of gibberellic acid on membrane metabolism. Enzymes of the cytidine diphosphate-choline pathway, which is involved in lecithin synthesis, are rapidly and considerably induced by GA in barley aleurone (153). Within a few hours of its application, GA also induces rapid formation of rough endoplasmic reticulum in barley embryo (154), which is accompanied by membrane synthesis (109). Tocopherols may be involved in endoplasmic reticulum formation (132). GA may effect phospholipid synthesis in wheat aleurone. A very early effect of the hormone on ^{32}P incorporation into cytidine triphosphate was observed (78).

The membranes in the seed and the changes in them during germination are complex. We know very little about the nature and composition of these membranes. The fact that seed coat membranes have interesting properties is indicated by their selective permeability to gases and water. Whether special properties are shown by the membranes of the cell organelles cannot yet be determined. The present data are by no means adequate to ascribe a definite role to membrane transformation in germination. They are, however, sufficient to indicate that one of the important early events in germination is the formation or transformation of membranes by changing their permeability and that such changes occur prior to many other events in germination. The work of Dawson & Clarke (89) supports such an idea. They describe an early decrease in N-acylphosphatidyl ethanolamine in germinating peas and a number of other species. Removal of this compound from a membrane and its conversion to phosphatidylethanolamine in membranes would profoundly alter the properties of the membrane. Certainly this seems to us a promising line of research for the future. One of the ways of attacking this problem is to study the permeability of dry seeds to externally applied chemicals without the use of water. This nonaqueous solvent technique was first described by Millborrow (224) and further developed by Meyer & Mayer (220, 221) and has since been applied in hormone treatment of seeds (317). Some criticism of the method has been reported (11, 320).

CONCLUSION

Present knowledge of the control of seed germination is rather unsatisfactory. Information is very incomplete, scattered among work on a limited number of plant species, and relates in some cases to entire seeds and in others to isolated parts of the seed. The same is true, generally speaking, for seed dormancy. Future work should concentrate on the early stages of germination, which are probably physiologically and biochemically unique. More comparative work is called for, particularly comparisons between wild and closely related cultivated species. The number of species studied must be increased, taking into account the special ecological germination behavior of many plants. Lastly, a more careful study of the final stages of seed maturation may provide clues to the understanding of the control of seed germination.

Literature Cited

1. Abdul-Baki, A. 1969. *Crop Sci.* 9: 732–39
2. Abdul-Baki, A., Anderson, J. D. 1970. *Crop Sci.* 10:31–34
3. Abeles, F. B., Lonski, J. 1969. *Plant Physiol.* 44:277–80
4. Abrahamsen, M., Mayer, A. M. 1967. *Physiol. Plant.* 20:1–5
5. Addicott, F. T., Lyon, J. L. 1969. *Ann. Rev. Plant Physiol.* 20:139–64
6. Alberghina, F. 1964. *G. Bot. Ital.* 71:385–91
7. Alberghina, F., Marre. E. 1965. *Accad. Naz. Lincei* 38:237–42
8. Amen, R. D. 1965. *Ecology* 46:362–64
9. Amen, R. D. 1968. *Bot. Rev.* 34:1–31
10. Amen, R. D., Carter, G. E., Kelly, R. J. 1970. *New Phytol.* 69:1005–13
11. Anderson, J. D. 1973. *Science* 179: 94–95
12. Anderson, J. D. 1970. *Plant Physiol.* 46:605–8
13. Anderson, J. D., Abdul-Baki, A. A. 1971. *Plant Physiol.* 48:270–72
14. St. Angelo, A. J., Altschul, A. M. 1968. *Plant Physiol.* 39:880–83
15. St. Angelo, A. J., Ory, R. L. 1971. *Phytochemistry* 9:1933–38
16. St. Angelo, A. J., Ory, R. L., Hansen, H. J. 1969. *Phytochemistry* 8:1135–38
17. App, A. A., Bulis, M. G., McCarthy, W. J. 1971. *Plant Physiol.* 47:81–86
18. Asada, K., Tanaka, K., Kasai, Z. 1969. *Ann. N.Y. Acad. Sci.* 165:800–14
19. Aspinall, D., Paleg, L. G., Addicott, F. T. 1967. *Aust. J. Biol. Sci.* 20:869–82
20. Austin, R. B. 1972. *Viability of Seeds,* ed. E. H. Roberts, 114–49. London: Chapman & Hall
21. Bain, J. M., Mercer, F. V. 1966. *Aust. J. Biol. Sci.* 19:69–84
22. Ibid, 85–96
23. Ballard, L. A. T., Grant-Lipp, A. E. 1967. *Science* 156:398–99
24. Ballard, L. A. T., Grant-Lipp, A. E. 1969. *Aust. J. Biol. Sci.* 22:279–88
25. Barendse, G. W. M., Kende, H., Lang, A. 1968. *Plant Physiol.* 43:815–22
26. Barker, G. R., Bray, C. M., Detlefsen, M. A. 1971. *Biochem. J.* 124:5P–6P
27. Barker, G. R., Bray, C. M., Walter, T. J. 1971. *Biochem. J.* 124:11P
28. Barker, G. R., Rieber, M. 1967. *Biochem. J.* 105:1195–1202
29. Barton, L. V. 1967. *Bibliography of Seeds.* New York: Columbia Univ. Press
30. Barzilai, E., Mayer, A. M. 1964. *Aust. J. Biol. Sci.* 17:798–800

31. Beevers, L. 1968. *Phytochemistry* 7: 1837–44
32. Belderok, B. 1965. *Z. Acker Planzenbau* 122:297–313
33. Belitz, H. D., Wassner, H. P., Weder, J. 1968. *Z. Lebensm. Unters. Forsch.* 137:211–16
34. Berjak, P., Villiers, T. A. 1970. *New Phytol.* 69:929–38
35. Ibid 1972. 71:135–44
36. Bevilacqua, R. L., Valentily, S. 1970. *Att. Accad. Ligure Sci. Lett. Genoa* 27:126–30
37. Bewley, J. D., Black, M., Negbi, M. 1967. *Nature* 215:648–48
38. Bhatty, R. S. 1968. *J. Inst. Brew. London* 74:370–74
39. Bianchetti, R., Cornaggia, M. P. 1965. *G. Bot. Ital.* 72:370–82
40. Bianchetti, R., Sartirana, M. L. 1967. *Biochim. Biophys. Acta* 145:485–90
41. Biswas, S., Biswas, B. B. 1965. *Biochim. Biophys. Acta* 108:710–13
42. Black, M. 1969. *Symp. Soc. Exp. Biol.* 23:193–217
43. Black, M., Richardson, M. 1965. *Nature* 208:1114–15
44. Black, M., Richardson, M. 1967. *Planta* 73:344–56
45. Black, M., Richardson, M. 1968. *Bull. Soc. Fr. Physiol. Veg.* 14:73–81
46. Bomsel, J. L., Pradet, A. 1968. *Biochim. Biophys. Acta* 162:230–42
47. Borriss, H. 1967. *Physiologie, Okologie und Biochemie der Keimung.* Greifswald: Ernest Moritz Arndt Universitat
48. Breidenbach, R. W., Castelfranco, P., Criddle, R. S. 1967. *Plant Physiol.* 42:1035–41
49. Breidenbach, R. W., Castelfranco, P., Peterson, C. 1966. *Plant Physiol.* 41: 803–9
50. Briggs, D. E. 1972. *Planta* 108:351–58
51. Briggs, W. R., Rice, H. V. 1972. *Ann. Rev. Plant Physiol.* 23:293–334
52. Brown, E. G. 1965. *Biochem. J.* 95: 509–14
53. Burdett, A. N., Vidaver, W. E. 1971. *Plant Physiol.* 48:656–57
54. Burger, W. C., Prentice, N., Kastenschmidt, J., Huddle, J. D. 1966. *Cereal Chem.* 43:546–54
55. Burger, W. C., Prentice, N., Kastenschmidt, J., Moeller, M. 1968. *Phytochemistry* 7:1261–70
56. Chakravorty, A. K. 1969. *Biochim. Biophys. Acta* 179:67–82
57. Chapman, J. A., Rieber, M. 1967. *Biochem. J.* 105:1201–2

58. Chen, D., Osborne, D. J. 1970. *Nature* 225:336–40
59. Chen, D., Sarid, S., Katchalski, E. 1968. *Agrochimica* 12:389–97
60. Chen, D., Sarid, S., Katchalski, E. 1968. *Proc. Nat. Acad. Sci. USA* 60:902–9
61. Chen, D., Schultz, G., Katchalski, E. 1971. *Nature New Biol.* 231:69–72
62. Chen, S. S. C. 1968. *Am. J. Bot.* 55:1177–83
63. Chen, S. S. C. 1970. *Planta* 95:336–40
64. Chen, S. S. C., Chang, J. L. L. 1972. *Plant Physiol.* 49:441–42
65. Chen, S. S. C., Thimann, K. V. 1966. *Science* 153:1537–39
66. Chen, S. S. C., Varner, J. E. 1969. *Plant Physiol.* 44:770–74
67. Ibid 1970. 46:108–12
68. Cherry, J. H. 1963. *Plant Physiol.* 30:440–46
69. Cherry, J. H. 1963. *Proc. Seed Protein Conf. New Orleans,* 115–34
70. Chin, T. Y., Poulson, R., Beevers, L. 1972. *Plant Physiol.* 49:482–89
71. Ching, T. M. 1963. *Plant Physiol.* 38:722–28
72. Ching, T. M. 1968. *Lipids* 3:482–88
73. Ching, T. M., Ching, K. K. 1972. *Plant Physiol.* 50:536–40
74. Cohen, D. 1958. *Bull. Res. Counc. Isr. D* 6:111–17
75. Cohen, D. 1955. *J. Theor. Biol.* 12:119–29
76. Cohen, D. 1968. *J. Ecol.* 56:219–28
77. Collins, D. M., Wilson, A. T. 1972. *Phytochemistry* 11:1931–35
78. Collins, G. G., Jenner, C. F., Paleg, L. G. 1972. *Plant Physiol.* 49:404–10
79. Come, D. 1968. *Bull. Soc. Fr. Physiol. Veg.* 14:31–45
80. Come, D. 1970. In *Les Obstacle a la Germination.* Paris: Masson et cie
81. Cooper, T. G., Beevers, H. 1969. *J. Biol. Chem.* 244:3507–13
82. Ibid, 3514–20
83. Crabb, D., Kirsop, B. H. 1969. *J. Inst. Brew. London* 75:254–59
84. Cresswell, C., Nelson, H. 1973. *Ann. Bot.* 37:427–38
85. Dasberg, S. 1971. *J. Exp. Bot.* 22:999–1008
86. Dasberg, S., Enoch, H., Hillel, D. 1966. *Agron. J.* 58:206–8
87. Datta, S. C., Evenari, M., Gutterman, Y. 1970. *Isr. J. Bot.* 19:463–83
88. Datta, S. C., Gutterman, Y., Evenari, M. 1972. *Planta* 105:155–64
89. Dawson, B. M. C., Clarke, N., Quarles, R. H. 1969. *Biochem. J.* 114:265–70
90. Dey, B., Sircar, S. M. 1968. *Physiol. Plant.* 21:1054–59

91. Dorffling, K. 1970. *Planta* 93:243–56
92. Doig, R. I., Laidman, D. L. 1972. *Biochem. J.* 128:88p
93. Doireau, P. 1972. *C. R. Acad. Sci. B* 275:907–10
94. Duffus, C. M., Duffus, J. H.. 1969. *Experientia* 25:581
95. Durzan, D. J., Mia, A. J., Ramaiah, P. K. 1971. *Can. J. Bot.* 49:927–38
96. Durzan, D. J., Mia, A. J., Wang, B. S. P. 1972. *Can. J. Bot.* 49:2139–49
97. East, J. W., Nakayama, T. O. M., Parkman, S. B. 1972. *Crop Sci.* 12:7–9
98. Eastwood, D., Laidman, D. L. 1971. *Phytochemistry* 10:1275–84
99. Eastwood, D., Tavener, R. J. A., Laidman, D. L. 1969. *Biochem. J.* 113:32P–33P
100. Edwards, M. M. 1968. *J. Exp. Bot.* 19:583–600
101. Ibid, 601–10
102. Ibid 1969. 20:876–94
103. Efron, D., Evenari, M., De Groot, N. 1971. *Life Sci.* 10 (pt. 2):1015–19
104. Eldan, M., Mayer, A. M. 1972. *Physiol. Plant.* 26:67–72
105. Eldan, M., Mayer, A. M. 1974. *Phytochemistry* 13:1–7
106. Esashi, Y., Leopold, A. C. 1968. *Plant Physiol.* 43:871–76
107. Ibid 1969. 44:1470–72
108. Evenari, M., Koller, D., Gutterman, Y. 1966. *Aust. J. Biol. Sci.* 19:1007–16
109. Evins, W. H., Varner, J. E. 1971. *Proc. Nat. Acad. Sci. USA* 68:1631–33
110. Evins, W. H., Varner, J. E. 1972. *Plant Physiol.* 49:348–52
111. Firenzuoli, A. M., Vanni, P., Mastronuzzi, E., Zanobin, A., Baccari, V. 1968. *Life Sci.* 7:1251–58
112. Flinn, A. M., Smith, D. L. 1967. *Planta* 75:10–22
113. Fowden, L. 1963. *J. Exp. Bot.* 14:387–98
114. Frankland, B., Jarvis, B. C., Cherry, J. H. 1971. *Planta* 97:39–49
115. Furuya, M. 1968. *Progr. Phytochem.* 1:347–405
116. Gaber, S. D., Roberts, E. H. 1969. *J. Inst. Brew. London* 75:303–14
117. Garg, G. K., Virupaksha, T. K. 1970. *Eur. J. Biochem.* 17:4–12
118. Gepstain, S., Ilan, I. 1970. *Plant Cell Physiol.* 11:819–22
119. Gerhardt, B. P., Beevers, H. 1970. *J. Cell Biol.* 44:94–102
120. Gestetner, B. et al 1972. *Biochim. Biophys. Acta* 270:181–87
121. Gesundheit, Z., Poljakoff-Mayber, A. 1962. *Bull. Res. Counc. Isr. D* 11:25–30

122. Ghetie, V. 1966. *Rev. Roum. Biochim.* 3:353–61
123a. Gibbins, L. N., Norris, F. W. 1963. *Biochem. J.* 86:64–67
123b. Ibid, 67–71
124. Gientka-Rychter, A., Cherry, J. H. 1968. *Plant Physiol.* 43:653–59
125. Givan, C. V. 1972. *Planta* 108:29–38
126. Gould, S. E. B., Rees, D. A. 1964. *J. Sci. Food Agr.* 16:702–9
127. Green, T. R., Baisted, D. J. 1971. *Biochem. J.* 125:1145–47
128. Groat, J. I., Briggs, D. E. 1969. *Phytochemistry* 8:1615–27
129. Guardiola, J. L., Sutcliffe, J. F. 1971. *Ann. Bot.* 35:809–23
130. Hacker, M., Stohr, H. 1966. *Planta* 68:215–24
131. Hagen, C. E., Ballard, L. A. T. 1971. *Aust. J. Biol. Sci.* 23:519–28
132. Hall, G. S., Laidman, D. L. 1968. *Biochem. J.* 108:475–82
133. Hallam, N. D., Roberts, B. E., Osborne, D. J. 1972. *Planta* 105:293–309
134. Harel, E., Mayer, A. M. 1963. *Physiol. Plant.* 16:804–13
135. Harwood, J. L., Stumpf, P. K. 1970. *Plant Physiol.* 46:500–8
136. Hendricks, S. B., Taylorson, R. B. 1972. *Nature* 237:169–70
137. Henshall, J. D., Goodwin, T. W. 1964. *Phytochemistry* 3:677–91
138. Heydecker, W., Chetram, R. S. 1971. *Ann. Bot.* 35:17–29
139. Heydecker, W., Chetram R. S., Heydecker, J. C. 1971. *Ann. Bot.* 35:31–42
140. Hitchcock, C., Nichols, B. W. 1971. *Plant Lipid Biochemistry,* 241–45. London, New York: Academic
141. Hobday, S. M.1970. *A critical evaluation of proteolytic activity in seeds of Pisum sativum.* PhD thesis. Univ. Liverpool. 198 pp.
142. Hock, B. 1970. *Planta* 93:26–38
143. Hock, B., Beevers, H. 1966. *Z. Pflanzenphysiol.* 55:405–14
144. Horiguchi, T., Kitagishi, K. 1971. *Plant Cell Physiol.* 12:907–15
145. Houssais, J. F., Attardi, G. 1966. *Proc. Nat. Acad. Sci. USA* 56:616–23
146. Ihle, J. N., Dure, L. S. 1969. *Biochem. Biophys. Res. Commun.* 36:705–10
147. Ihle, J. N., Dure, L. S. 1972. *J. Biol. Chem.* 247:5048–55
148. Ikuma, H., Thimann, K. V. 1963. *Plant Cell Physiol.* 4:169–85
149. Jacks, T. J., Yatsu, L. Y., Altschul, A. M. 1967. *Plant Physiol.* 42:585–97
150. Jacobsen, J. V., Varner, J. E. 1967. *Plant Physiol.* 42:1596–1600
151. Jakob, K. M., Bovey, F. 1969. *Exp. Cell Res.* 54:118–26
152. Jarvis, B. C., Frankland, B., Cherry, J. H. 1968. *Plant Physiol.* 43:1734–36
153. Johnson, K. D., Kende, H. 1971. *Proc. Nat. Acad. Sci. USA* 68:2674–77
154. Jones, R. L. 1969. *Planta* 87:119–33
155. Jones, R. L., Armstrong, J. E. 1971. *Plant Physiol.* 48:137–42
156. Julien, R., Grellet, F., Guitton, Y. 1970. *Physiol. Plant.* 23:323–24
157. Kagawa, T., Lord, J. M., Beevers, H. 1973. *Plant Physiol.* 51:61–65
158. Kamisaka, S., Masuda, Y. 1971. *Plant Cell Physiol.* 12:1003–5
159. Kamra, S. K. 1969. *S. Bot. Tidskr.* 63:265–74
160. Karssen, C. M. 1968. *Acta Bot. Neer.* 17:293–308
161. Kasprzyk, Z., Sliwowski, J., Skwarku, B. 1972. *Phytochemistry* 11:1961–66
162a. Kassel, B. 1970. *Methods Enzymol.* 19:853–62
162b. Ibid, 862–71
163. Katayama, M., Funahashi, S. 1969. *J. Biochem. Tokyo* 66:479–85
164. Ketring, D. L., Morgan, P. W. 1969. *Plant Physiol.* 44:326–30
165. Khan, A. A. 1971. *Science* 171:853–59
166. Khan, A. A., Anojulu, C. C. 1970. *Biochem. Biophys. Res. Commun.* 38:1069–75
167. Khan, A. A., Gaspar, T., Roe, C. H., Bouchet, M., Dubucq, M. 1972. *Phytochemistry* 11:2963–69
168. Kirsi, M., Mikola, J. 1971. *Planta* 96:281–91
169. Klein, S., Ben-Shaul, Y. 1966. *Can. J. Bot.* 44:331–40
170. Klein, S., Negbi, M., Witztum, A., Rothberg, L. 1971. *New Phytol.* 70:143–47
171. Koller, D. 1964. *Herb. Abstr.* 34:1–7
172. Koller, D. 1969. *Symp. Soc. Exp. Biol.* 23:449–69
173. Koller, D., Mayer, A. M., Poljakoff-Mayber, A., Klein, S. 1962. *Ann. Rev. Plant Physiol.* 13:437–64
174. Kolloffel, C. 1967. *Acta Bot. Neer.* 16:111–22
175. Ibid 1968. 17:70–77
176. Ibid 1970. 19:539–45
177. Kolloffel, C., Sluys, J. V. 1970. *Acta Bot. Neer.* 19:503–8
178. Kozlowski, T. T. 1971. *Growth and Development of Trees,* Vol. I. New York: Academic
179. Kozlowski, T. T., Ed. 1972. *Seed Biology.* New York: Academic. 3 vols.
180. Lado, P. 1966. *G. Bot. Ital.* 73:37–40

181. Lado, P., Schwendimann, M., Marre, E., 1968. *Biochim. Biophys. Acta* 157:140–48
182. Lahiri Majumder, A. N., Mandal, N. C., Biswas, B. B. 1972. *Phytochemistry* 11:503–8
183. Laidman, D. L., Tavener, R. J. A. 1971. *Biochem. J.* 124:4P–5P
184. Lang, A. 1970. *Ann. Rev. Plant Physiol.* 21:537–70
185. Lechevallier, D. 1962. *C. R. Acad. Sci. Paris* 255:3211–13
186. Lee, H. J., Kim, S. J., Lee, K. B. 1963. *Arch. Biochem. Biophys.* 107:479–84
187. Lehmann, K., Garz, J. 1962. *Flora* 152:516–22
188. Libbert, E., Kentzer, T., Steyer, B. 1961. *Flora* 151:663–69
189. Loewus, F. 1969. *Ann. NY Acad. Sci.* 165:577–98
190. Longo, C. P. 1968. *Plant Physiol.* 43:660–64
191. Lott, J. N. A., Castelfranco, P. 1970. *Can. J. Bot.* 48:2233–40
192. Lovell, P. H., Moore, K. G. 1970. *J. Exp. Bot.* 21:1017–30
193. Maherchandani, N., Naylor, J. M. 1972. *Can. J. Bot.* 50:305–13
194. Majumder, A. L., Biswas, B. B. 1973. *Phytochemistry* 12:321–26
195. Mandal, N. C., Biswas, B. B. 1970. *Indian J. Biochem.* 7:63–67
196. Mandal, N. C., Biswas, B. B. 1970. *Plant Physiol.* 45:4–7
197. Mandal, N. C., Burman, S., Biswas, B. B. 1972. *Phytochemistry* 11:495–502
198. Mano, Y., Nagaro, H. 1970. *J. Biochem. Tokyo* 67:611–27
199. Marchaim, U., Birk, Y., Dovrat, A., Berman, T. 1972. *J. Exp. Bot.* 23:302–9
200. Marcus, A. 1969. *Symp. Soc. Exp. Biol.* 23:143–60
201. Marcus, A., Feely, J., Volcani, T. 1966. *Plant Physiol.* 41:1167–72
202. Marre, E. 1967. *Accad. Naz. Lincei* 104:157–61
203. Marre, E. 1967. *Curr. Top. Develop. Biol.* 2:75–105
204. Matile, P. 1968. *Z. Pflanzenphysiol.* 58:365–68
205. Matile, P., Spichiger, J. 1968. *Z. Pflanzenphysiol.* 58:277–80
206. Mayer, A. M. 1963. *Isr. J. Bot.* 12:55–63
207. Mayer, A. M. 1973. *Seed Sci. Technol.* 1:51–72
208. Mayer, A. M., Krishmaro, N., Poljakoff-Mayber, A. 1968. *Physiol. Plant.* 21:183–89
209. Mayer, A. M., Mapson, L. W. 1962. *J. Exp. Bot.* 13:201–12
210. Mayer, A. M., Poljakoff-Mayber, A. 1963. *Germination of Seeds.* London: Pergamon
211. Mayer, A. M., Poljakoff-Mayber, A. 1963. *Int. Symp. Physiol. Ecol. Biochem. Germin.* Greifswald
212. Mayer, A. M., Poljakoff-Mayber, A., Krishmaro, N. 1966. *Plant Cell Physiol.* 7:25–33
213. Mayer, A. M., Shain, Y. 1968. *Science* 162:1283–84
214. Mayevsky, A., Marchaim, U. 1972. *Plant Cell Physiol.* 13:927–30
215. Mazus, B., Buchowicz, J. 1972. *Phytochemistry* 11:77–82
216. Ibid, 2443–46
217. McLeod, A. M. 1957. *New Phytol.* 56:210–20
218. McLeod, A. M., Palmer, G. H. 1967. *Nature* 216:1342–43
219. Melville, J. C., Scandalios, J. G. 1972. *Biochem. Genet.* 7:15–31
220. Meyer, H., Mayer, A. M. 1971. *Science* 171:583–84
221. Ibid 1973. 179:96
222. Meyer, H., Mayer, A. M., Harel, E. 1971. *Physiol. Plant.* 24:95–101
223. Mikola, J., Kolehmainen, L. 1972. *Planta* 104:167–77
224. Millborrow, B. V. 1963. *Nature* 199:716–17
225. Monin, J. 1967. *C. R. Acad. Sci. Paris D* 264:300–2
226. Morohashi, Y., Shimokoriyama, M. 1972. *J. Exp. Bot.* 23:45–53
227. Ibid, 54–61
228. Morton, R. K., Raison, J. K. 1963. *Nature* 200:429–33
229. Mory, Y. Y., Chen, D., Sarid, S. 1972. *Plant Physiol.* 49:20–23
230. Mossberg, Y., Mayer, A. M., Mapson, L. W. 1964. *J. Exp. Bot.* 15:29–34
231. Moutschen, J., Lacks, S. 1968. *Exp. Cell Res.* 51:462–72
232. Mukherji, S., Dey, B., Sircar, S. M. 1968. *Physiol. Plant.* 21:360–68
233. Mulliken, J. A., Kust, C. A., Schrader, L. E. 1970. *Weed Sci.* 18:565–71
234. Nawa, Y., Asahi, T. 1971. *Plant Physiol.* 48:671–74
235. Naylor, J. M. 1966. *Can. J. Bot.* 44:19–32
236. Negbi, M., Rushkin, E., Koller, D. 1966. *Plant Cell Physiol.* 7:363–76
237. Nikolaeva, M. G. 1969. *Physiology of Deep Dormancy in Seeds.* Israel Program of Scientific Translations, Jerusalem
238a. Nyman, B. 1965. *Physiol. Plant.* 18:1085–94
238b. Ibid, 1095–1104

239. Ohmura, T., Howell, R. 1962. *Physiol. Plant.* 15:341–50
240. Opik, H. 1955. *J. Exp. Bot.* 16:667–82
241. Ibid 1968. 19:64–76
242. Ory, R. L., Baker, R. H., Boudreaux, G. J. 1964. *Biochemistry* 3:2013–16
243. Ory, R. L., Henningsen, K. W. 1969. *Plant Physiol.* 44:1488–98
244. Palmiano, E. P., Juliano, B. O. 1972. *Plant Physiol.* 49:751–56
245. Payne, J. F., Bal, A. K. 1972. *Phytochemistry* 11:3105–10
246. Payne, P. I., Boulter, D. 1968. *Biochem. J.* 108:44P
247. Penner, D., Ashton, F. M. 1966. *Nature* 212:935–36
248. Penner, D., Ashton, F. M. 1967. *Biochim. Biophys. Acta* 148:481–85
249. Penner, D., Ashton, F. M. 1967. *Plant Physiol.* 42:791–96
250. Pinfield, N. J., Stobart, A. K. 1972. *Planta* 104:134–45
251. Poljakoff-Mayber, A. 1952. *Palestine J. Bot. Jerusalem Ser.* 5:180–86
252. Pollard, C. J. 1969. *Plant Physiol.* 44:1227–32
253. Pollard, C. J. 1971. *Biochim. Biophys. Acta* 201:511–12
254. Pollard, C. J., Singh, B. N. 1968. *Biochem. Biophys. Res. Commun.* 33: 321–26
255. Pollard, C. J., Venere, R. J. 1970. *Fed. Proc.* 29:2386
256. Pollock, B. M. 1969. *Plant Physiol.* 43:907–11
257. Pollock, B. M., Toole, V. K. 1966. *Plant Physiol.* 41:221–29
258. Pradet, A., Narayanan, A., Vermeersch, J. 1968. *Bull. Soc. Fr. Physiol. Veg.* 14:107–14
259. Pradet, A., Raymond, P., Narayanan, A. 1972. *C. R. Acad. Sci. D* 275: 1987–88
260. Prathapasenan, G. R., Rao, D. 1972. *Biochem. J.* 128:54P
261. Prentice, N., Burger, W. C., Kastenschmidt, J., Huddle, J. P. 1967. *Physiol. Plant.* 20:361–67
262. Presley, H. J., Fowden, L. 1965. *Phytochemistry* 4:169–76
263. *Proc. Seed Protein Conf. 1963, New Orleans.* U.S.D.A., A.R.S.
264. Protopopova, E. M., Shevchenko, V. V., Generalova, M. V. 1967. *Genetika* 6:19–23
265. Pusztai, A. 1972. *Planta* 107:121–29
266. Pusztai, A., Duncan, I. 1971. *Planta* 96:317–25
267. Radley, M. 1967. *Planta* 75:164–71
268. Radley, M. 1968. *Soc. Chem. Ind. London Monogr.* 31:53–69
269. Raison, J. K., Evans, W. J. 1968. *Biochim. Biophys. Acta* 170:448–51
270. Rebeiz, C. A., Castelfranco, P. 1964. *Plant Physiol.* 39:932–38
271. Rebeiz, C. A., Castelfranco, P., Engelbrecht, A. H. 1965. *Plant Physiol.* 40:281–86
272. Rebeiz, C. A., Breidenbach, R. W., Castelfranco, P. 1965. *Plant Physiol.* 40: 286–89
273. Reed, J. 1970. PhD thesis, Univ. of Pennsylvania. See *Diss. Abstr. Int.* 31:6
274. Reid, J. S. G. 1971. *Planta* 100:131–42
275. Reid, J. S. G., Meier, H. 1972. *Planta* 106:44–60
276. Rejman, E., Buchowicz, J. 1971. *Phytochemistry* 10:2951–57
277. Ibid 1973. 12:271–76
278. Roberts, E. H. 1969. *Symp. Soc. Exp. Biol.* 23:161–92
279. Roberts, E. H., Ed. 1972. *Viability of Seeds.* London: Chapman & Hall. 448 pp.
280. Ross, C., Murray, M. G. 1971. *Plant Physiol.* 48:626–30
281. Sartirana, M. L., Bianchetti, R. 1967. *Physiol. Plant.* 20:1066–75
282. Satoh, Y. 1968. *Sci. Rep. Saitama Univ. Ser. B* 5:125–37
283. Schnarrenberger, C., Oeser, A., Tolbert, N. 1971. *Plant Physiol.* 48:566–74
284. Shain, Y., Mayer, A. M. 1965. *Physiol. Plant.* 18:853–59
285. Ibid 1968. 21:765–76
286. Shain, Y., Mayer, A. M. 1968. *Phytochemistry* 7:1491–98
287. Shewry, P. R., Pinfield, N. J., Stobart, A.K. 1972. *Phytochemistry* 11:2149–54
288. Shiroya, T. 1963. *Phytochemistry* 2: 33–46
289. Shyamala, G., Lyman, R. L. 1964. *Can. J. Biochem.* 42:1825–32
290. Simon, E. W., Raja Harun, R. M. 1972. *J. Exp. Bot.* 23:1076–85
291. Soedigo, R., Gruber, M. 1960. *Biochim. Biophys. Acta* 44:315–23
292. Solomos, T., Malhotra, S. S., Prasad, S., Malhotra, S. K., Spencer, M. 1972. *Can. J. Biochem.* 50:725–37
293. Spedding, D. J., Wilson, A. T. 1968. *Phytochemistry* 7:897–901
294. Sprent, J. I. 1968. *Planta* 81:80–87
295. Ibid. 82:299–301
296. Srivastava, L. M., Paulson, R. E. 1968. *Can. J. Bot.* 46:1437–45
297. Ibid, 1447–53
298. Stewart, E. R., Freebairn, H. T. 1969. *Plant Physiol.* 44:955–58
299. Sturani, E. 1968. *Life Sci.* 7:527–37
300. Sumner, D. C., Lyon, J. L. 1967. *Planta* 75:28–32

301. Suzuki, Y., Kyuwa, K. 1972. *Physiol. Plant.* 27:121–25
302. Swain, R. R., Dekker, E. E. 1966. *Biochim. Biophys. Acta* 122:87–100
303. Swift, J. G., O'Brien, T. P. 1972. *Aust. J. Biol. Sci.* 25:9–22
304. Ibid, 469–86
305. Sze, H., Ashton, F. M. 1971. *Phytochemistry* 10:2935–42
306. Taiz, L., Jones, R. L. 1970. *Planta* 92:73–84
307. Takayanagi, K., Harrington, J. F. 1971. *Plant Physiol.* 47:521–24
308. Tanner, W., Beevers, H. 1965. *Z. Pflanzenphysiol.* 53:72–85
309. Ibid, 126–39
310. Tavener, R. J. A., Laidman, D. L. 1972. *Phytochemistry* 11:981–87
311. Ibid, 989–97
312. Taylor, H. F., Smith, T. A. 1967. *Nature* 25:1513–14
313. Taylorson, R. B., Hendricks, S. B. 1971. *Plant Physiol.* 47:619–22
314. Ibid 1972. 49:127–30
315. Thomas, S. M., ApRees, T. 1972. *Phytochemistry* 11:2177–85
316. Ibid, 2187–94
317. Thomas, T. H., Palevitch, D., Austin, R. B. 1972. *Proc. 11th Brit. Weed Contr. Conf.*, 760–65
318. Treffry, T., Klein, S., Abrahamsen, M. 1967. *Aust. J. Biol. Sci.* 20:859–68
319. Trelease, R. N., Becker, W. M., Graber, P. J., Newcomb, E. H. 1971. *Plant Physiol.* 48:461–75
320. Triplett, L. L., Haber, A. H. 1973. *Science* 179:95–96
321. Ueda, K., Tsuji, H. 1971. *Protoplasma* 73:203–15
322. Ulitzur, S., Poljakoff-Mayber, A. 1963. *J. Exp. Bot.* 14:95–100
323. Van de Walle, C. 1971. *Arch. Int. Physiol. Biochem.* 79:852–53
324. Van de Walle, C. 1971. *FEBS Lett.* 16:219–22
325. Van Staden, J. 1973. *Physiol. Plant.* 28:222–24
326. Van Sumere, C. F., Cottenie, J., de Greef, J., Kint, J. 1972. *Recent. Advan. Phytochem.* 4:165–211
327. Varner, J. E. 1964. *Plant Physiol.* 39:413–15
328. Varner, J. E., Balce, L. V., Huang, R. C. 1963. *Plant Physiol.* 38:89–92
329. Varner, J. E., Chandra, G. R. 1964. *Proc. Nat. Acad. Sci. USA* 52:100–6
330. Varner, J. E., Chandra, G. R., Chrispeels, M. J. 1965. *J. Cell. Comp. Physiol.* 66 (Suppl. 1):55–68
331. Vidaver, W., Hsiao, A., Hsiung, I. 1972. *Can. J. Bot.* 50:687–89
332. Villiers, T. A. 1968. *Planta* 82:342–54
333. Villiers, T. A. 1972. *New Phytol.* 71:153–60
334. Villiers, T. A. 1973. *Seed Ecology,* ed. W. Heydecker, 265–88. London: Butterworths
335. Vlodawsky, L., Harel, E., Mayer, A. M. 1971. *Physiol. Plant.* 25:363–68
336. Vogel, R., Trautschold, I., Werle, E. 1968. *Proteinase Inhibitors.* New York: Academic
337. Vose, P. B. 1962. *Ann. Bot.* 26:197–206
338. Wagner, H., Hoelzl, J., Schmid, A., Hoerhammer, L. 1963. *Naturwissenschaften* 50:230
339. Walbot, V. 1971. *Develop. Biol.* 26:369–79
340. Walton, D. C., Soofi, G. S. 1969. *Plant Cell Physiol.* 10:307–15
341. Wareing, P. F. 1963. *Vistas Bot.* 3:195–227
342. Wareing, P. F. 1969. *The Physiology of Plant Growth and Development,* ed. M. B. Wilkins, 603–44. New York: McGraw
343. Wareing, P. F., Saunders, P. F. 1971. *Ann. Rev. Plant Physiol.* 22:261–88
344. Waters, L., Dure, L. S. 1966. *J. Mol. Biol.* 19:1–27
345. Weder, J., Belitz, H. D. 1969. *Deut. Lebensm. Rundsch.* 65:78–83
346. Weeks, D. P., Marcus, A. 1970. *Plant Physiol.* 46:Suppl. Abstr. No. 92
347. Weeks, D. P., Marcus, A. 1971. *Biochim. Biophys. Acta* 232:671–84
348. Wiley, L., Ashton, F. M. 1967. *Physiol. Plant.* 20:688–96
349. Willemsen, R. W., Rice, E. L. 1972. *Am. J. Bot.* 59:248–59
350. Williams, S. G. 1970. *Plant Physiol.* 45:376–81
351. Wilson, S. B., Bonner, W. D. 1971. *Plant Physiol.* 48:340–44
352. Witztum, A., Gutterman, Y., Evenari, M. 1969. *Bot. Gaz. Chicago* 130:238–41
353. Woodstock, L. W. 1969. *Proc. Int. Seed Test. Assoc.* 34:253–63
354. Woodstock, L. W., Grabe, D. F. 1967. *Plant Physiol.* 42:1071–76
355. Xavier Filho, J. 1973. *Physiol. Plant.* 28:149–54
356. Yamaguchi, H. 1969. *Radiat. Bot.* 9:341–48
357. Yamamato, Y. 1963. *Advan. Front. Plant Sci.* 6:163–85
358. Yatsu, L. Y., Jacks, T. J. 1968. *Arch. Biochem. Biophys.* 124:466–71
359. Young, J. L., Varner, J. E. 1959. *Arch. Biochem. Biophys.* 84:71–78

Ann. Rev. Plant Physiol. 1974. 25:195–223

RAPID RESPONSES TO PLANT HORMONES[1]

❖7567

Michael L. Evans[2]

Department of Botany, The Ohio State University, Columbus, Ohio 43210

CONTENTS

INTRODUCTION 195
TECHNIQUES FOR MEASURING RAPID RESPONSES 196
RAPID RESPONSES TO AUXIN... 197
    Relationship to Protein Synthesis 198
    Modification of Timing of the Growth Response 199
RAPID GROWTH PROMOTION BY NONHORMONAL FACTORS 202
    Promotion of Growth by Carbon Dioxide and Acid pH 203
    Relationship of the Acid Response to Auxin Action 204
    Auxin, Acid, and Cell Wall Chemistry 210
    Other Nonhormonal Factors 214
RAPID RESPONSES IN ROOTS 217
RAPID RESPONSES TO OTHER HORMONES.................................. 218

INTRODUCTION

That a review of rapid responses to plant hormones has been included in this volume attests to the widening recognition of the importance of kinetic studies to the elucidation of mechanisms of plant hormone action. Until recently the usual approach to the study of hormone action on a particular phenomenon such as growth had been to measure its rate or magnitude before and after treatment with hormone. While this approach provided a wealth of information on such matters as the concentration dependence of hormone action, sensitivity to inhibitors, etc, it largely ignored the most interesting phase of hormone action, i.e. that period during which hormone-induced changes in cellular processes are taking place, the latent period between application of the hormone and manifestation of the response. Information on the timing of responses to plant hormones is particularly useful in attempts to

[1]Paper 850 from the department of botany, The Ohio State University.

[2]Certain of the author's studies included in this paper were supported by a research grant (GB–37547) from the National Science Foundation.

establish cause-effect relationships in hormone responses. The stimulation of protein synthesis by a particular hormone, for instance, cannot be considered a possible cause of some other response to the hormone unless it can be shown that the stimulation of protein synthesis occurs earlier than the response in question.

This review deals with the nature and significance of recent information on rapid responses to plant hormones. A more general review containing information on rapid responses to auxin has appeared recently (44). Since the latent period in various responses to plant hormones varies from seconds (145, 147, 210) to days (62, 69, 200), let us arbitrarily consider as "rapid" those responses to plant hormones that are detectable within 1 hr. As described below, most of the recent advances in technique for studying rapid hormone action have been in the area of growth kinetics. This review therefore deals largely, but not exclusively, with rapid growth responses to plant hormones.

The recent availability of instruments for detecting short-term growth responses to plant hormones has led to a logarithmic phase in the accumulation of information and advancement of our understanding of initial hormone action. I offer this to explain the large number of citations given as abstracts or personal communication and the probability that much new information will have accumulated between the writing of this review and its appearance.

TECHNIQUES FOR MEASURING RAPID RESPONSES

One of the major reasons for the increased number of papers on rapid growth responses to plant hormones has been the development of a number of simple techniques for measuring such responses. This, in turn, has provided the incentive for more careful time-course measurements on biochemical (e.g. changes in nucleic acid synthesis, stimulation of enzyme synthesis or activity, etc) effects of hormone treatment.

Koningsberger (111) in 1922 was one of the first to use an automated technique for recording plant growth. He positioned an *Avena* seedling under a very light platinum strip. The growth of the coleoptile raised the strip, allowing it to make contact with a metal screw above. This completed an electrical circuit, which allowed a point to be recorded and caused the contact to be raised about 20 μ. A modified version of this auxanometer was later employed by Ranson & Harrison (162).

Lundegårdh (122) in 1947 used an automated technique for recording the growth of root hairs. He devised a contact clock-work mechanism that triggered a camera focused on the root hair every 3 min. Audus & Brownbridge (5) in 1957 used a similar technique to record changes in length of the upper and lower sides of pea roots during geotropic response.

Köhler (110) in 1956 used a compound microscope with an ocular micrometer to determine growth rates of isolated *Avena* coleoptile segments. He reported a lag of about 10 min in the response of such segments to auxin. Later, Ray (163) and Ray & Ruesink (169) used a modified version of this apparatus to examine the relationships between metabolism and auxin action. They also found a lag period of about 10 min in the response of *Avena* coleoptile segments to auxin. This method of measuring growth over short periods of time has since been used by several people in the study of short-term growth responses (25, 79, 147, 156, 182, 215).

A less tedious continuous recording technique was developed by Evans & Ray (59). They strung 10 or more *Avena* coleoptile segments on a thread in a vertical glass chamber with a glass weight resting on the uppermost segment. An arc lamp was used to cast a shadow of the weight onto a vertical slit in a baffle about a meter from the chamber. The vertical displacement of the shadow of the weight by the growing segments was continuously recorded on photographic paper on a kymograph drum behind the slit. This method has the advantage of averaging the growth of segments in the absence of the investigator. This device has since been used by several workers (8, 33, 37, 58, 60, 61, 172, 173).

Dela Fuente & Leopold (46) subsequently modified the Evans & Ray apparatus so that the elongation of a column of segments or a decapitated seedling could be measured using an angular position-sensing transducer attached to a millivolt recorder. This method has been used by many workers, in some cases with the more convenient linear position transducer (9, 145, 179, 180, 220). One of the most elegant growth recording devices is that used by Cummins & Green (40; personal communication). They record the elongation of a single coleoptile segment using a linear position transducer, the output of which is automatically differentiated and plotted as growth rate vs time (also see 1). This allows accurate detection of changes in growth rate. To facilitate the study of rapid responses, their system allows the pumping of growth medium along the outside of the coleoptile cylinder and through the central cavity (78). Solution changes are automatic so that complex experiments involving many solution changes can be done in the absence of the investigator. Descriptions of other types of rapid growth recording devices can be found in references 52, 77, 121, 138, and 223.

RAPID RESPONSES TO AUXIN

Table 1 lists reported latent periods in the effect of auxin on various processes. They vary from essentially zero (a few seconds) up to many hours or (not included in the table) days (62, 69, 200). Not all of these auxin effects or latent periods have been confirmed and for those where there are contradictory claims, the dissenting references are listed in parentheses following the original references.

There is a remarkable similarity in the latent periods of the growth response of seedling tissue to auxin. For nine types of tissue, the reported latent periods range from 6 to 15 min under normal conditions. In order for one of the auxin effects listed in the table to qualify as a possible mediator of the growth response to auxin, therefore, the effect in question should occur within about 10 to 15 min in auxin-responsive tissue. This includes the decreased ATP/ADP ratio (213), the claimed stimulation of RNA (53, 134) or nuclear protein (43) synthesis, synthesis of glycerophosphate (146), stimulation of glucan synthetase activity (166), increased permeability to water (102), increased wall extensibility (25, 215), stimulation of protoplasmic streaming (210), and stimulation of hydrogen ion leakage (34, 35, 171).

Of these possibilities, some seem less probable than others as mediators of the primary action of auxin on growth. An effect of auxin on the permeability of pea stem tissue to water, for example, is not likely to cause cell enlargement nor has it proved repeatable. Dowler et al (48) report a wide variability in the half time of tritiated water exchange in pea stem tissue grown in different laboratories but find no effect of auxin on the half time of exchange. Mild abrasion of the cuticle, however, causes the half time for ^{3}HHO exchange to decrease from about 40 min to about 2.5 min, suggesting that earlier reports of auxin effects on ^{3}HHO exchange may have resulted from the particular method of handling the tissue segments.

The data showing a rapid auxin effect on cell wall extensibility (25, 215) were obtained using the resonance frequency technique for measuring Young's modulus. Since resonance frequency measurements are highly dependent on turgor (144), the observed rapid decrease in Young's modulus may reflect turgor changes instead of physical changes in the wall. The observed decrease in Young's modulus does not correlate well with growth since it continues to decrease over a period of at least 100 min even though the growth rate reaches a maximum after 15 min. Using a stress-strain analyzer, Masuda (133) reported auxin-induced changes in wall elasticity and plasticity within 10 and 20 min, respectively. However, Cleland (29), using similar methods, could find no correlation between the timing of auxin-induced increases in cell wall extensibility and growth rate in *Avena* coleoptile tissue where growth rate is maximal after 15 min but extensibility begins to increase only after 20 min and reaches a maximun at 90–120 min.

The long known rapid stimulatory effect of auxin on protoplasmic streaming (210) also seems unlikely to be related to growth promotion by auxin. Cande & Ray (26) find that complete inhibition of streaming in *Avena* coleoptile segments by cytochalasin B has no effect on the promotion of elongation by auxin.

Relationship to Protein Synthesis

It is now clear that the sustained growth response to auxin of a variety of tissues depends on continual protein synthesis (44, 107, 149, 150). It is also known that auxin can stimulate RNA and protein synthesis in some tissues (107, 108, 155, 212). However, auxin-promoted incorporation of labeled precursors into RNA and protein has been detected mostly after a period of an hour or more, the work of Masuda & Kamisaka (134) and Esnault (53) standing as exceptions. While these slower effects of auxin on RNA and protein synthesis may well be important in long-term auxin responses, it is not likely that they are involved in initial (10–15 min latent period) responses to auxin (see review by Ray, 165). Evans & Ray (59) found that pretreatment of *Avena* coleoptile segments with inhibitors of RNA and protein synthesis does not extend the latent period in response to auxin, even though cyanide or low temperature does. Kinetic analysis of their data indicated that the results were consistent with the gene activation hypothesis of auxin action only under the improbable assumption that the half life of the auxin-induced RNA and protein was about 2 or 3 min. More recently the latent period in the response of other tissues to auxin has also been shown to be insensitive to antibiotics (8, 157).

Further evidence that the primary action of auxin is not at the level of protein synthesis has been provided by Pope & Black (160) and Penny (157), who report that auxin can cause a sizable promotion of elongation in antibiotic-treated tissue in which protein synthesis has been essentially eliminated.

Perhaps the most convincing evidence that the initial stimulation of elongation by auxin is not mediated by protein synthesis is the observation that, under certain conditions, the latent period in the response to auxin is reduced nearly to zero (145, 147, 159, 175). These data are discussed below.

Modification of Timing of the Growth Response

When auxin is added to coleoptile or stem segments there is a latent period usually of 9–15 min during which no increase in growth rate occurs (see Table 1). This is followed by a 3–15 min period during which the growth rate increases to a higher steady rate. In pea stem (8, 156), cucumber hypocotyl (8), lupin hypocotyl (156), and at lower concentrations in coleoptile tissue (8), the steady auxin-promoted rate lasts only about 20–25 min before dropping to a lower but still promoted rate. In some cases a second maximum growth rate occurs (158).

Some workers have reported that, during the latent period before auxin promotes growth, the hormone actually reduces the growth rate (8, 79, 175). Data in other reports show a similar transient inhibition phenomenon but it is either ignored or attributed to random fluctuations in growth rate (156, 170, 195). Durand & Zenk (50) report that they were unable to obtain such a transient inhibition in a variety of tissues. Since the initial reports of transient inhibition point out that it does not occur consistently, and since it seems never to occur using certain growth recording devices (50), the suggestion that transient inhibition is not a usual component of auxin action seems warranted.

A number of workers have reported that the promotion of growth by auxin (IAA) can occur with little or no latent period under certain conditions. Polevoy (159) reported that the methyl ester of IAA was capable of stimulating elongation in corn coleoptile segments in 3 min. Rayle et al (175) were able to repeat Polevoy's results but not in all trials and also found a dramatic but inconsistent rapid (latent period 2 min) promotion of short (4 mm) coleoptile segments by low concentrations of auxin. Durand & Zenk (50) reported that they were unable to obtain the rapid responses using either the methyl ester of IAA or short segments and low auxin concentration.

Barkley & Leopold (personal communication) have recently discovered another technique for obtaining an essentially immediate response to auxin in green pea stem segments. If at the time of auxin application the pH of the growth medium is reduced from 6.3 to 3.0, the response to auxin begins in about 1 min instead of after the usual 10–15 min delay. This is so even though green pea stem tissue is unresponsive to acid solutions alone (9). The step down in pH must be given simultaneously with auxin, and the magnitude of the reduction in the latent period has proved to be proportionate to the magnitude of the step down in pH. The significance of these observations is discussed in a later section.

Table 1 Latent periods in the effect of auxin on certain cellular processes

Phenomenon Affected	Material	Latent Period (min)	References[a]
Metabolism			
Stimulation of respiration	isolated mitochondria	"immediate"	189
	pea stem	120	128
	wheat coleoptile	120	182
Stimulation of CO_2 uptake	*Avena* coleoptile	"immediate"	223
Decreased ATP/ADP ratio	pea stem	5	213
	pea stem	30	128
Stimulation of RNA synthesis	*Avena* coleoptile	10	53, 134
		40	135
Increased RNA content	soybean hypocotyl	180	108
Stimulation of protein synthesis	pea stem	60	212
Increased specific activity of nuclear protein	pea stem	15	43(125, 212)
Stimulation of cell wall synthesis	pea stem	60	168
Stimulation of glycerophosphate synthesis	pea stem	5	146
Stimulation ^{32}P incorporation into phospholipid	*Avena* coleoptile	240	226
Stimulation of photosynthesis	bean leaf	30	15
Stimulation of photophosphorylation	isolated chloroplasts	2	203
Increased ratio of reduced/ oxidized glutathione	pea stem, *Avena* coleoptile	20	127
Stimulation of ethylene biosynthesis	pea stem	60	21
Increased enzyme activity level			
β-1, 3-Glucanase, β-1, 6-glucanase, hemicellulase	barley coleoptile, pea stem	180	207
β-1, 3-Glucanase	yeast	180	224
	Avena coleoptile	10	137
β-Galactosidase	*Avena* coleoptile	60	99
Cellulase	pea stem	360	62
Glucan synthetase	pea stem	15	166
Invertase	sugar cane internode	180	72
Benzoylaspartate synthetase	pea stem	10	218
Citrate synthetase	purified enzyme from castor bean	3	188
Acid phosphatase	Jerusalem artichoke	120	154
IAA oxidase (decrease)	cucumber seedling	30	103
Electrophysiology			
Change in membrane potential	bean root	1	96, 97
	Nitella internodal cell	60	197

Table 1 (Continued)

Phenomenon Affected	Material	Latent Period (min)	References[a]
Electrophysiology (Continued)			
Increased negative surface charge	mung bean root tip	2	204
Decreased negative surface charge	barley root tip	2	205
Permeability			
Increased permeability to water	pea stem	1	102(48)
Increased chloride uptake	*Avena* coleoptile	15	183
Decreased chloride uptake (increased efflux?)	*Petroselinum* root callus culture	20	14
Increased uptake ^{32}P	*Avena* coleoptile	240	226
Growth and wall extensibility			
Stimulation of growth	soybean hypocotyl	12	216
	gherkin hypocotyl	15	1
	pea stem segments (light grown)	10	8
	pea stem (etiolated, decapitated)	9	220
	lupin hypocotyl	14	156
	sunflower hypocotyl	6	215
	cucumber hypocotyl	10	8
	Avena coleoptile	12	59,169
	wheat coleoptile	12	61
	corn coleoptile	12–15	46,58
Stimulation of growth at elevated temperature	*Avena* coleoptile	"immediate"	147
	pea stem (green)	"immediate"	145
Stimulation of short segments or via auxin esters	corn coleoptile	3	159,175 (50)
Inhibition of growth	primary root of corn	5	18,121
Increased wall extensibility	*Avena* coleoptile	20	29
	pea stem	2–3	25
	sunflower hypocotyl	4	215
Miscellaneous			
Stimulation of cyclosis	*Avena* coleoptile	1	210
Bursting of isolated protoplasts	tobacco leaf	10	161
Increased intracellular solute effect	pea stem	20	225
Increased water uptake	bean leaf pulvinus	"immediate"	19
Hydrogen ion leakage	*Avena* coleoptile	15–20	34,35,171
Release of xyloglucan from wall	pea stem	10–15	113

[a]References in parentheses are those contradictory to the references reporting a given effect.

Nissl & Zenk (147) have also discovered a means of reducing the latent period in response to auxin essentially to zero. They found that increasing the temperature from 21 to 40° decreases the latent period in the establishment of a steady auxin-promoted growth rate in *Avena* coleoptile segments responding to 5 mM IAA from about 12 min to zero. Clearly, the induction of protein synthesis cannot be involved in such rapid responses. It should be pointed out, however, that at this temperature and auxin concentration, the growth conditions cannot be considered physiological. Under these conditions the segments stop growing after 3 min and begin to shrink after 6 min. The mechanism of this growth response, therefore, may not be similar to that under more physiological conditions. It is known that a variety of nonhormonal factors can strongly stimulate growth (see below). The experiments of Nissl & Zenk were conducted at pH 4.7 and it has been shown recently (35, 100, 171) that the pH optimum for acid-promoted cell elongation in peeled (epidermis removed) *Avena* coleoptile segments is near 5. Perhaps auxin rapidly modifies the cuticle to allow access of hydrogen ions which are responsible for the observed growth response.

In a later report however, Durand & Zenk (50) mention that these experiments can be repeated in solutions buffered at pH 6.3. Zenk (personal communication) has also found that the high temperature rapid response cannot be induced by benzoic acid or 3,5-D, indicating some specificity for auxin. If the immediate stimulation of elongation by mM IAA at 40° is in fact a rapidly occuring normal auxin response, it should also be possible to eliminate it using a high concentration of antiauxin or using various metabolic inhibitors. This does not seem to have been tested.

Murayama & Ueda (145) have repeated Nissl and Zenk's experiments using light-grown pea stem segments. At about 5.7×10^{-4} M IAA and 40°, they found a transient increase in elongation rate beginning within 1 min. These authors used media buffered at pH 5.4 at which, as mentioned earlier, a strong pH effect can be found in *Avena*. However, their experiments were done using light-grown pea stem segments which are reportedly insensitive to acid pH (9). They did not examine the effect of antiauxin or metabolic inhibitors on the rapid response.

In the absence of evidence that the rapid response at high temperature is mediated by the same events that occur in response to auxin under physiological conditions, and in view of the inconsistency in observing rapid responses to auxin esters or to low concentrations of auxin in short segments, it would seem that the normal latent period in the response of seedling tissue to auxin is about 10 min (see Table 1) and that this sets the time interval during which auxin-induced changes that might lead to growth promotion should be sought.

RAPID GROWTH PROMOTION BY NONHORMONAL FACTORS

The study of growth promotion by nonhormonal factors is of particular interest in attempts to elucidate the mechanism of action of auxin. If it can be shown that certain treatments promote growth more quickly than auxin itself and that the observed growth has features in common with auxin-promoted growth, valuable clues as to the nature of auxin action may be gained. A brief discussion of growth promotion by nonhormonal factors has recently appeared (57).

Promotion of Growth by Carbon Dioxide and Acid pH

It has been know for some time that carbon dioxide affects the growth rate of plants. Numerous workers have reported both inhibitory and stimulatory effects of various levels of CO_2 on the growth of intact coleoptiles (81, 140, 141, 223). Nitsch & Nitsch (148) found that CO_2 promotes the elongation of *Avena* coleoptile sections, and in 1962 Glinka & Reinhold (74, 75) showed that CO_2 rapidly increases or decreases (depending on the water potential of the tissue) the influx of water in sunflower hypocotyl tissue. The increased influx of water was attributed to rapid turgor pressure reduction by CO_2 (181).

That CO_2 strongly promotes elongation in coleoptile sections with a latent period of 1 min or less was shown by Evans (55) and Evans et al (60). Treatment with CO_2-saturated water (pH 3.8) induced a growth rate about twice that occuring in response to optimal levels of IAA, but the CO_2-stimulated increase in elongation rate lasted only about 25 min. Since no CO_2 response could be obtained at neutral pH and since acid pH (3 to 4) was also observed to promote growth within 1 min, they concluded that at least a major part of the action of CO_2 depends on its ability to reduce pH.

Their observation that acid pH stimulates elongation was not new. In 1934, Bonner (17) noted that hydrogen ions promote growth of the *Avena* coleoptile, and since then numerous workers have examined the relationship between pH and cell elongation (9, 23, 35, 49, 57, 60, 70, 79, 123, 129, 130, 171–174, 176, 178, 192). Rayle & Zenk (178) have reviewed some recent advances in this area (210). In a study by Rayle & Cleland (173, 174) of the relationship between CO_2 and acid promotion of cell elongation, they suggested that the action of CO_2 is not caused by its acidifying effect and that the CO_2 and acid effects are separate phenomena. This suggestion was based on the observations that (*a*) the growth response to CO_2-saturated water (pH 3.8) is about twice as great as the response to acidic buffers at that pH; (*b*) they were able to obtain a growth response to CO_2-saturated buffer at pH 5.9 but no growth response to buffer alone at pH 5.9, and (*c*) after terminating a pH response by changing the growth medium to buffer at pH 7.0, they were unable to obtain a second pH response by again lowering the pH but were able to obtain a response to CO_2.

These observations, however, do not rule out the possibility that the response to CO_2 is largely a pH effect. The magnitude of the growth response to acidic buffers has recently been shown to be equivalent to that induced by CO_2 under comparable osmotic conditions (57), so it seems there is no inherent difference in the extent to which CO_2-saturated solutions and acidic solutions can stimulate elongation. The observation that CO_2 can promote elongation at pH 5.9 also needs qualification. The response to CO_2 at this pH is considerably reduced relative to the response at pH 3.8. Furthermore, it has been shown that a pH of 5.5 is sufficient to "initiate massive cell extension" in *Avena* coleoptile segments from which the epidermis has been removed (35, 171, 177). Since Cleland (35 and personal communication) finds that the epidermis of *Avena* coleoptiles is quite impermeable to hydrogen ions, one would expect CO_2 to penetrate the cuticle and epidermis more readily than H^+ ions. Evans (unpublished results) has found that, during weak growth promotion by CO_2

in neutral buffered media, the pH of the external medium rises by 0.3 to 1.3 pH units depending on the buffer used. This strongly suggests a decrease in pH within the tissue or free space during the response to CO_2. Similarly, the ability of CO_2 to initiate a second growth response under conditions where acidic buffers cannot, may be attributed to the ability of CO_2 to penetrate the tissue. Barkley & Leopold (personal communication) have found that etiolated pea stem segments will respond to a second acid stimulus provided about a millimeter of tissue is cut off the end of each segment before the second treatment with acid. This suggests that the acid growth response in this tissue may normally be restricted to cells near the cut surface.

Kaufman and co-workers at the University of Michigan have found that internode segments of 45 day old *Avena* also exhibit a strong growth response at acid pH (personal communication). This response is particularly interesting since, unlike the situation in coleoptile tissue, the response can be turned on and off by repeated shifts in pH from 5 to 7, even though the tissue used is unresponsive to physiological levels of auxin (105).

Barkley & Leopold (9) have recently used another approach to distinguish between acid and CO_2 responses. They find that green pea stem tissue is completely insensitive to acid media even though the epidermis is removed to allow penetration of hydrogen ions. The same tissue does show a growth response to CO_2, indicating that the responses to acid pH and CO_2 are different phenomena. It should be noted, however, that the CO_2 response in etiolated, acid-sensitive tissue is about five times as great as the CO_2 response in green, acid-insensitive tissue. This, along with the evidence discussed above, indicates that the action of CO_2 on growth arises largely from its acidifying effect but that there is an additional smaller direct effect of CO_2.

In some very recent experiments on the acid growth response in green pea stem tissue, Rayle (personal communication) has found that green pea stem tissue does exhibit a growth response to acid solutions provided cuts are made through the cuticle to allow penetration of H^+ ions. This is in contrast to the report of Barkley & Leopold (9) that green pea stem tissue is insensitive to hydrogen ions even though cuts are made in the cuticle or the cuticle is removed. The issue is important since green pea stem tissue is very sensitive to auxin and insensitivity to H^+ ions would argue strongly against acid-mediated auxin action.

Relationship of the Acid Response to Auxin Action

When coleoptile or stem segments are treated with acidic buffers, there is a latent period of a minute or less and then the rate of elongation increases suddenly to a value comparable to that induced by optimal levels of auxin (9, 55, 60, 79, 171, 172, 174). This acid-promoted elongation continues for about an hour and then gradually declines during the next hour or so. The acid and auxin responses have been found to be similar in terms of Q_{10} (174), growth rate (172), and effects on wall extensibility (139, 172, 174), but dissimilar in that (*a*) various metabolic inhibitors prevent the auxin response but not the acid response (55, 60, 174); (*b*) acid solutions but not auxin will induce increased cell wall extensibility in frozen-thawed tissue segments (174, 176); and (*c*) the in vivo acid response is short lived.

Hager et al (79) performed a thorough study of the promotion of cell elongation and cell wall extensibility by acid solutions in sunflower hypocotyl and *Avena* coleoptile segments. They noted that basic solutions immediately and reversibly inhibit auxin-induced growth and that .01 mM carbonylcyanide m-chlorophenylhydrazone (CCCP), which increases membrane permeability to protons, inhibits auxin-promoted growth in 2 or 3 min with no effect on respiration. Exogenously supplied ATP was also found to stimulate elongation rapidly under anaerobic conditions in which auxin itself is ineffective. The effect of ATP was enhanced by K^+ and Mg^{2+} ions. Based on these and other data, they suggested that auxin acts to stimulate growth by activating a membrane-bound ATPase or proton pump driven by respiratory energy. Acidification of the wall resulting from the external pumping of hydrogen ions was viewed as activating or increasing the activity of one or more cell wall loosening enzymes with pH optima in the acid range.

There is corroborating evidence for an early auxin effect on the plasmalemma (14, 80, 87, 124, 175, 183). Hertel et al (87) have found auxin-specific receptor sites in particulate fractions from corn coleoptiles. The binding reaches equilibrium rapidly (less than 15 min) and exhibits an apparent K_m in agreement with physiologically effective concentrations of auxin. The authors suggest that the auxin receptor site is located on the plasmalemma, and it seems possible that the receptor could be a membrane-bound ATPase or could lead directly to stimulation of a membrane-bound ATPase. There is also evidence that plant cell membranes including the plasmalemma contain ATPases (91, 119), and that these play an important role in cation transport (65, 118). Auxin has been shown to stimulate the uptake of Rb^+ and K^+ in certain plant tissues (89, 90, 94, 190). In bean root tips, auxin treatment causes the development of a more negative surface charge in about 2 min (204) while having an equally rapid but opposite effect on the surface charge of barley root tips (205). In *Avena*, auxin treatment leads to the development of more negative membrane potentials, suggesting increased outward pumping of cations (54).

Thus there is good evidence that ion pumps exist in plant cell membranes and that auxin can influence their activity. The possibility of auxin-induced wall acidification either by direct auxin stimulation of an ATPase pumping H^+ ions outward or by a compensatory efflux of H^+ ions during auxin-stimulated cation uptake warrants further study.

Little attention has been paid to the problem of electrical balance that must accompany auxin-induced H^+ ion efflux. One would expect to be able to detect either a concurrent influx of cations or an efflux of anions. Perhaps auxin-induced Rb^+ or K^+ uptake (89, 90, 94, 190) compensates for H^+ ion efflux. Ilan (93) could detect auxin-induced H^+ efflux in sunflower hypocotyls only with concurrent K^+ influx. Rubinstein & Light (183), however, found that in *Avena* coleoptile segments which show auxin-induced H^+ ion efflux (34, 35, 171), IAA stimulated ^{36}Cl- uptake in about 15 min. In contrast, Bentrup et al (14) found auxin-induced inhibition of ^{36}Cl-uptake (probably via stimulation of efflux) in root callus tissue and suggested that this may play a role in charge balance during H^+ ion extrusion.

If the acid model of auxin action on growth is correct, it ought to be possible to show that (*a*) auxin causes increased hydrogen ion efflux in all auxin-responsive tissue within the latent period preceeding the stimulation of growth; (b) all tissues responsive to auxin are also responsive to acid solution; (c) there are glycosidases in the cell wall of auxin-responsive tissue which exhibit increased activity at reduced pH; and (d) the properties of acid-promoted and auxin-promoted growth are similar. It has been shown that auxin treatment of coleoptile segments in aqueous medium leads to acidification of the medium to about pH 5.0 during a subsequent 2 hr period, presumably via increased H^+ ion efflux from the tissue. In peeled coleoptile segments a pH of 5.0 has been found to be optimal for growth promotion (100, 171). Presumably, the pH optimum for growth of unpeeled segments is the same and the earlier reported optimum of 3.0 (172) was due to the resistance of the epidermis to penetration of hydrogen ions (35, 171). Although there was a 20 min latent period before the beginning of the pH drop, this does not rule out an earlier (i.e. within the 10 min latent period of auxin action on growth) acidification of the wall. The stimulation of H^+ ion efflux was found to be specific for auxins and inhibited by inhibitors of auxin-induced growth, such as abscisic acid, KCN, and cycloheximide (34, 35, 171, 177).

Similar results were reported by Marre and co-workers in an investigation of auxin-induced H^+ ion leakage in etiolated pea stem tissue (129, 130), while Ilan (93) was able to detect auxin-induced H^+ ion efflux in light-grown *Helianthus* hypocotyl tissue but only in the presence of potassium ions.

The common action of inhibitors such as ABA[3] and cycloheximide on growth and H^+ ion efflux is consistent with the acidification theory of auxin action. It may be noted, however, that reduction of the auxin-induced growth response in coleoptile segments by pretreatment with ABA (179) or cycloheximide (59) is not accompanied by an extension of the latent period as might be expected if reduction of wall pH to some critical point is a prerequisite to wall loosening. Inhibition of elongation by ABA is especially interesting since ABA has also been shown to inhibit acid-induced elongation whether given as a pretreatment or post-treatment (180). Thus the inhibition of auxin-induced growth by ABA may not be due to reduced H^+ ion efflux. The manner in which ABA might interfere directly with acid-stimulated elongation is unclear. If the hypotheses of Hager et al (79) is correct, it would seem that ABA must interfere directly with the wall loosening enzyme, although there is no evidence that this occurs.

Substantial H^+ ion efflux in the absence of exogenous auxin has been observed in a number of cell types (57, 66, 209). Albersheim and co-workers (66 and personal communication) have measured H^+ ion efflux in cultured cells of sycamore, rye, and red kidney bean, while Evans (57) has reported marked efflux of H^+ ions in etiolated corn coleoptile tissue without exogenous auxin. The efflux of H^+ ions in cultured sycamore and bean cells may be via a calcium-dependent ATPase, since the efflux is strongly dependent on Ca^{2+} and is inhibited by uncouplers of ATP synthesis. Unlike cultured sycamore or rye cells or excised *Helianthus* tissue, coleoptile tissue does not seem to exhibit a dependence on Ca^{2+} or K^+ for hydrogen ion secretion.

[3]Abscisic acid.

There is evidence, however, that the induction or maintenance of H^+ ion leakage by auxin is itself pH dependent. Cleland (35 and personal communication) has found that in peeled *Avena* coleoptile segments, auxin-induced H^+ ion leakage ceases when the pH of the medium has decreased to about 4.7. However, if H^+ ion efflux is measured at a constant pH of 7 by measuring the amount of base needed to maintain the pH of the medium at that value, auxin-stimulated H^+ ion leakage continues over a long period of time and total leakage exceeds that in experiments where the pH is allowed to drop. This suggests the existence of some type of feedback mechanism regulating the pH of the wall in the presence of auxin.

It is not yet known whether auxin-induced H^+ ion leakage occurs in all auxin-responsive tissue. Hydrogen ion efflux in light-grown *Helianthus* hypocotyl segments was detectable only after 2 hr and only in the presence of K^+, whereas the auxin response in this tissue occurs in less than 10 min (215) and shows no dependence on K^+. Cleland (personal communication) has been unable to detect auxin-induced proton efflux in either sunflower hypocotyl or pea epicotyl segments. Saftner & Evans (unpublished) do not observe as strong an auxin-induced proton leakage, as has been reported by others. Using the technique of Rayle (171) and Cleland (35), they found a reduction in pH of only 0.25 units (from 6.25 to 6.0) during a 2 hr period with most of the decline occuring during the second hour.

That the auxin-induced H^+ ion efflux in certain tissues is insufficient to account for growth stimulation suggests that even if the hydrogen ion pump hypothesis of auxin action is correct, it may not function in all auxin-responsive tissues. Perhaps some other auxin-induced wall loosening factor mediates growth in tissues such as sunflower hypocotyl or pea stem. Convincing evidence that acidification does not mediate auxin action in green pea stem tissue has been provided by Barkley & Leopold (9), who showed that green pea stem tissue which responds normally to auxin shows no growth response to solutions at pH 3 even if the cuticle is removed to allow access of H^+ ions. This is in contrast to *Avena* internode segments which respond to acid but not to auxin (Kaufman, personal communication).

The insensitivity of green tissue to acid seems to be an inherent developmental difference between etiolated and green tissue since etiolated tissue does respond to acidic solutions. A number of other striking differences in the growth properties of green and etiolated pea stem tissue are also known. The growth of green pea stem is known to be insensitive to ethylene, whereas etiolated tissue is highly sensitive (21, 22). Similarly, green pea stem tissue shows no sharp optimum concentration of auxin for stimulation of growth, while etiolated tissue shows the usual concentration dependence with an optimum concentration near 10^{-6} M IAA (68) and also responds better to lower concentrations of IAA and to certain derivatives of IAA (67). Stowe (198) has observed that certain lipids strongly enhance the action of auxin on the growth of green pea stem tissue with no effect on etiolated tissue, while Murayama & Ueda (145) have noted that the time course of the response of green pea stem tissue to auxin is not biphasic, although Barkley & Evans (8) report a consistent biphasic response in etiolated tissue. Similar differences in the growth properties of light-grown and dark-grown lupin hypocotyl segments (156) and *Avena* coleoptile segments (92) have also been observed.

The insensitivity of green pea stem tissue to acid makes it a useful tissue for studying the relationship between acid, auxin, CO_2, and growth. The fact that green pea stem tissue responds to CO_2 and auxin but not to acid suggests that auxin action in this tissue is not mediated by acidification but may have features in common with the direct (acid-independent) action of CO_2. Pope & Black (160) similarly concluded that the action of CO_2 and IAA is linked, since they apparently compete for the same growth-limiting protein.

Although the growth of green pea stem tissue is not affected by acid solutions, there is evidence that acidification may play at least a secondary role in the response of this tissue to auxin. As mentioned earlier, Barkley & Leopold have found that green pea stem segments will respond to auxin within 1 min, provided there is a simultaneous reduction in pH (e.g. from 6.3 to 3.0).

Ilan (93) has also questioned the validity of the H^+ ion pump hypothesis in sunflower hypocotyl tissue. He noted that when auxin is added to sunflower hypocotyl half segments in buffer at pH 6.8, growth is strongly promoted although the pH drops no lower than 6.5 over a 9 hr period. Half segments incubated at a lower pH (6.3) without auxin exhibited little growth. Since auxin at pH 6.5–6.8 induced much more growth than buffer at pH 6.3, Ilan concluded that acidification must not mediate auxin action. The crucial question, of course, is whether the pH of the cell wall in the vicinity of the cell membrane in auxin-treated tissue was the same (6.5–6.8) as that of the buffered medium. Ilan suggests that it must be although Rayle (171) points out that more than 50% of the tissue used was protected by cuticle which may retard pH equilibration somewhat.

There is another interesting feature of acid action on growth that may be useful in comparative analysis of auxin and acid effects. Rayle & Cleland (174) have found that acid pH is not effective in promoting growth or increasing wall extensibility (personal communication) unless the acid-treated tissue is under applied stress or turgor stress at the time of treatment. *Avena* coleoptile segments growing at pH 3 and transferred to a growth-inhibiting concentration of mannitol at pH 3 show no further increase in rate of elongation when returned to pH 3 in the absence of mannitol, i.e. they exhibit no "stored growth" at acid pH. If auxin action is pH-mediated, one would also expect no stored growth in auxin-treated tissue. Cleland & Bonner (36) as well as Carr & Ng (27) were able to demonstrate the development of auxin-induced growth potential (a residual effect of auxin similar to stored growth) in the presence of hypertonic mannitol, and Cleland (29) showed that auxin causes cell wall loosening even at reduced turgor. However, Ray (163), who coined the term "stored growth," did not observe stored growth in the presence of IAA, and Cleland & Rayle (37), in a recent re-evaluation of auxin-induced stored growth in *Avena* coleoptiles, stated that they found little or no stored growth in the presence of auxin. They presented evidence that the residual effect of auxin observed in previous work was an artifact resulting from incomplete inhibition of auxin action during the anaerobic expansion period that followed the treatment with IAA plus mannitol.

Nevertheless, stored growth in the presence of auxin has been observed by some workers under conditions where the artifacts noted by Cleland & Rayle do not exist. Cummins & Green (40), using a very sensitive growth-recording device, have consistently observed stored growth after a period at reduced turgor. The amount of stored growth increases directly with time spent at reduced turgor and the accumulation of growth potential is largely prevented by azide. Gillbank et al (73) have noted the development of stored growth in auxin-treated wheat coleoptile sections whose growth is temporarily reduced by cyanide. Upon removal of the cyanide there is a burst of growth so that the final length of the sections is the same with or without transient cyanide treatment. They also find that the amount of stored growth increases in proportion to the time spent in cyanide. Other instances of stored growth in coleoptiles have been noted by Wada (219) and Kobayashi et al (109).

If it turns out that auxin is in fact capable of increasing wall extensibility at reduced turgor or in the presence of cyanide, this would suggest that auxin action on the wall is not proton-mediated, since acid solutions are ineffective at reduced turgor and auxin-induced H^+ ion efflux is prevented by cyanide.

At present the evidence in favor of auxin action via cell wall acidification includes the following observations: 1. Acid solutions at pH 3 (or pH 5 for peeled coleoptile tissue) induce a growth rate equal to or greater than that elicited by optimal levels of auxin. 2. The response to acid occurs with a latent period shorter than the response to auxin. 3. Acid-promoted and auxin-promoted growth show a similar temperature dependence. 4. In coleoptile tissue, auxins, but not inactive auxin analogs or auxin antagonists, cause H^+ ion efflux with a latent period of about 20 min. 5. Inhibitors of auxin-induced growth also inhibit auxin-induced H^+ ion efflux. Evidence contrary to the wall acidification model of auxin action includes these observations: 1. Green pea stem tissue responds normally to auxin but is insensitive to acidic solutions. 2. Auxin action may continue at reduced turgor, whereas wall modification by acid solutions appears to be ineffective at low turgor. 3. Auxin-induced H^+ ion leakage is slight in dicot tissues such as pea stem or sunflower hypocotyl. 4. The time course of auxin-induced acidification of a small volume of growth medium containing coleoptile tissue does not fit well with the timing of growth promotion by auxin. In coleoptile segments, auxin-induced growth rate is maximal after about 15 min, while auxin-initiated acidification of the medium is detectable only after 20 min and reaches a maximum after 2 hr. While it is difficult to draw conclusions concerning the time course of the actual acidification of the cell wall from these data, a demonstration of rapid maximal acidification of the wall by auxin is needed. 5. The time course of acid-promoted growth differs considerably from that of auxin-promoted growth. Promotion of elongation at pH 5.0 in coleoptile segments with the cuticle partially removed is transient in nature. Green (personal communication) finds that solutions at pH 5.0 cause a sudden rise in elongation rate followed immediately by a gradual decline in rate back to the control rate during the next 1 ½ hr. Rayle (171) also finds a transient growth response to acid pH. Auxin-promoted growth, on the other hand, is steady for many hours. There is evidence that the brevity of the in vivo acid response may be attributable to turgor loss resulting from membrane damage at the high concentration of hydrogen ions. When turgor is replaced by mechanical tension, elongation in response to hydrogen ions continues for at least 9 hr (176). More recent evidence, however, suggests that this interpretation of the cause of the transient nature of the acid response may be too simplified. Rayle (171) has found that the duration and magnitude of elongation in the presence of auxin is as great at pH 4.8 as at pH 6.2. Since rapid growth is long-lived at acid pH in the presence of auxin, it seems necessary to conclude either that auxin affords some protection against pH damage or that auxin exerts some second effect necessary to sustained elongation but not provided by acid pH alone. The latter alternative seems more likely, especially in view of evidence that rapid growth induced by mild pH reductions not likely to be toxic (171) is also of shorter duration than auxin-induced growth stimulation, so that total growth in auxin is greater than total growth in acid media. This suggests the probability that if H^+ ions are secondary messengers for auxin action on growth, they may account for only part of the long-term auxin effect. 6. Although Hager et al (79) have reported that basic solutions inhibit auxin-promoted growth, Evans (57) has noted that they used sodium hydroxide at pH 12, a pH much higher than that required to inhibit acid-promoted growth. Evans found that 10 mM tris buffer at pH 8.0 had no effect on auxin-promoted elongation. It cannot be argued that the buffer at pH 8.00 failed to inhibit growth because of failure to penetrate the cuticle, since buffer at pH 7.0 inhibits acid-promoted growth almost immediately. It also seems unlikely that the failure of buffer at pH 8.0 to inhibit auxin-promoted growth is due to the continuous acidifying action of auxin in the medium. Growth has been shown to be very sensitive to changes in pH between 5.0 and 6.0 (171), and buffer at pH 8.0 would be expected to have some effect on cell wall pH, especially in view of the complete effectiveness of buffers at pH 7.0 in inhibiting acid-promoted growth.

Clearly, the cell wall acidification hypothesis demands further study. The demonstration that the stimulation of H^+ ion efflux is specific for auxins and is under feedback regulation is convincing evidence that the phenomenon is a real auxin effect. There is even some evidence that sensitivity to acid pH may play a role in geotropic responses. Ganot & Reinhold (70) have noted that negative geotropism in sunflower hypocotyl segments is enhanced at acid pH even in the absence of IAA. Their data suggest gravity-induced physiological asymmetry with respect to acid sensitivity.

In those tissues for which it has been shown that auxin does lead to a decrease in pH of the cell wall to a value sufficient to establish an acid growth response, it must be admitted that at least part of the response to auxin is acid-mediated. However, more research needs to be done before it can be concluded that auxin causes H^+ ion efflux in all tissues in which it promotes growth and that H^+ ion efflux is in fact the regulator of growth in various auxin-responsive tissues. Even if auxin-induced proton-efflux does prove to be universal in auxin-responsive tissues (and there is evidence that it is not), there still remain the questions of the mechanism of auxin regulation of proton efflux and the mechanism of H^+ ion action in wall loosening. In consideration of the latter, we turn to possible avenues of auxin or acid action on cell wall properties.

Auxin, Acid, and Cell Wall Chemistry

Two excellent reviews of cell wall chemistry and metabolism have appeared recently (116, 151), so here we are concerned with cell wall chemistry only from the standpoint of its possible rapid hormonal modification. For a more thorough discussion of the mechanical properties of primary cell walls and biochemical mechanisms of cell wall loosening, see the review by Cleland (32). There are a number of classes of possible biochemical modification of the cell wall that might be caused by auxin and lead to increased extensibility of the wall (32, 165). Auxin might cause either a splitting of polymer chains, a splitting of cross-linking bonds between polymer chains, or a stimulation of synthesis and incorporation of new wall material in a manner that loosens the existing wall.

Auxin has been shown to stimulate cell wall synthesis in tissues in which it promotes growth (7, 28), and a number of investigators have found an increase in β-glucan synthetase activity after auxin treatment (153, 166, 167, 194, 217). Ray found a latent period of 15 min in the onset of auxin stimulation of β-glucan synthetase activity in pea stem tissue, and noted that this corresponds closely with the timing of growth stimulation. He suggested that auxin-stimulated β-glucan synthetase activity does not occur early enough to be responsible for stimulation of growth but that both are triggered by some earlier action of auxin.

Information on the timing of cell wall biosynthesis stimulation by auxin indicates a latent period (7, 168) of about 1 hr, i.e. too slow to be considered the cause of growth stimulation. Furthermore, auxin can induce cell extension under conditions where there is little or no cell wall synthesis (11, 12, 163, 164), and there can be vigorous cell wall synthesis in tissue undergoing little growth (7, 164). This suggests that the primary action of auxin in the stimulation of growth is not a large stimulation of formation of new wall material. Attention has therefore shifted to auxin-induced degradative modification of the wall by stimulation either of the synthesis or activity of certain polysaccharidases.

A variety of polysaccharide hydrolase enzymes is known to exist in cell walls (see discussion in 32 and 165). These include β-1,3-glucanase, cellulase, β-1,6-glucanase, α-1,6-glucanase, and exogalactanase (32). But does auxin stimulate growth by increasing the amount or activity of one of these enzymes? There is little evidence to suggest that it does. There is evidence that auxin increases the activity of cell wall polysaccharide hydrolases in plant tissues (42, 62–64, 88, 104, 131, 134, 136) but with the exception of the claimed rapid stimulation of β-1,3-glucanase activity (137), these effects are either slight or occur long after growth has been maximally stimulated by auxin (42, 62, 63). There are also reports that treatment of coleoptile segments with β-1,3-glucanase causes a rapid increase in cell elongation and increased wall extensibility (132, 136), but there is evidence that this may have been caused by some contaminant of the enzyme preparation (165). Others (30, 184) have found no promotion of cell elongation by exogenous β-1,3-glucanase. Ray (165) has pointed out that the kinetics of the growth response to auxin do not fit well with the glucanase theory of cell elongation. Available evidence indicates that these glucanases are stable enzymes (99), yet the timing of growth stimulation by auxin shows that it cannot be due to the induction of synthesis of a stable enzyme (59). Furthermore, withdrawal of auxin is followed quickly by a reduction in growth rate (46, 58), indicating that the products of auxin action are short lived. Finally, there is no evidence that auxin increases the activity of glucanases in vitro, so a direct allosteric enhancement of glucanase activity by auxin seems unlikely.

One of the major difficulties inherent in investigations of auxin-induced modification of cell wall structure is the lack of knowledge of the exact arrangement of polymers within the wall and the lack of understanding of bonding patterns between polymers that play a role in determining the physical properties of wall material. In a recent series of papers, Albersheim and co-workers (10, 106, 202) have made great progress in the elucidation of wall structure in cultured sycamore cells. Using purified hydrolytic enzymes and methylation analysis, they have quantitatively characterized the macromolecular constituents of these walls. One of the interesting features of their model for wall structure is the existence of layers of xyloglucan (hemicellulose) attached by hydrogen bonds to the surfaces of cellulose microfibrils and attached covalently to the pectic fraction of the wall via galactan side chains from the rhamnogalacturonan backbone of pectin. This xyloglucan fraction of the wall is of particular interest from the standpoint of wall loosening during growth, since it occupies a strategic position between cellulose and pectin and the attachment to cellulose appears to be the only major noncovalent linkage among the polymers of the wall. Xyloglucan binds strongly but reversibly to purified cellulose or to cell wall cellulose (10, 16, 106), and it is conceivable that cell wall loosening by auxin (also reversible, see 30 and 31) is mediated by a reversible breaking and reformation of hydrogen bonds between xyloglucan and cellulose, allowing a slippage of cellulose microfibrils through the wall matrix. Albersheim and co-workers (106) have proposed that this might be initiated by auxin-induced acidification of the wall resulting in nonenzymatic weakening of hydrogen bond strength.

That the xyloglucan fraction of cell wall material may play an important role in the growth response to auxin is supported by observations of Labavitch & Ray (113 and personal communication). In an analysis of auxin-induced turnover of wall constituents in pea stem tissue, they found that the xyloglucan fraction was the only fraction to exhibit substantial turnover. Pulse-chase experiments showed that turnover was detectable within 15 min after adding IAA and the amount of turnover increased with time in IAA. The rapidity of this response and the fact that it appears to be a direct effect of auxin, i.e. turnover occurs in auxin-treated tissue in growth-inhibitory concentrations of mannitol, call for further investigation of the relationship between xyloglucan displacement and wall extension. It will be of particular interest to learn whether acid solutions mimic auxin in causing the turnover of wall xyloglucan and whether other xyloglucan-releasing treatments such as treatment with concentrated urea lead to increased wall extensibility.

Although there is much data to suggest that the primary action of auxin during rapid growth promotion is neither a stimulation of the synthesis of some cell wall degrading enzyme nor a direct enhancement of polysaccharide hydrolase activity, the data do not rule out the possibility of indirect enhancement of enzyme activity as proposed by the wall acidification model of auxin action. If auxin treatment leads to wall acidification and thus to enhanced activity of some polysaccharide hydrolase with a pH optimum in the acid range, the timing of the response to auxin should be independent of the stability of the enzyme involved. Similarly, withdrawal of auxin might be expected to lead quickly to a reduction in growth rate as H^+ ion efflux decreases and the pH of the cell wall rises.

Most plant polysaccharidases have pH optima in the acid range but not necessarily in close agreement with the reported pH optimum (5.0) for acid stimulation of growth. For example, the pH optima for β-galactosidase and α-mannosidase from germinating bean seeds is reported to be 4.0, with very much reduced activity at pH 5.0 (2). The pH optima for α-galactosidase, β-glucosidase, and β-acetyl-glucosaminidase in this same system are 6.5, 5.5, and 5.5, respectively, but in all cases the optimum is quite broad. In the case of β-glucosidase, for example, the activity at pH 6 or 4.5 is nearly as great as the activity at pH 5.5. Dey & Pridham (47) list the pH optima for α-galactosidases from a variety of plant and animal sources and in all cases the optimum is in the acid range. The pH optimum for increased cellulase activity induced by auxin (62) is 5.5–6.5, which is the same optimal range as that reported by Lee et al (117) for in vitro autolysis of corn coleoptile cell walls.

The obvious step now in testing the wall acidification model of auxin action is to search for a polysaccharidase present in plant cell walls that shows a strong pH optimum near 5 with little activity at pH 7.0, and demonstrate that auxin or acid treatment enhances the activity of this enzyme in vivo. Johnson et al (99, 100) have reported that β-galactosidase in *Avena* coleoptile cell walls may meet these criteria. They found that it has three to tenfold greater activity at its pH optimum between 4 and 5 than at pH 7 and that the enzyme is strongly inhibited by ABA, cycloheximide, *p*-chloromercuribenzoate (PCMB), and Cu^{2+}.

The evidence for a rapid substantial auxin effect on the in vivo activity of this enzyme is not as good. Over a 60–90 min period, 0.1 mM IAA was found to stimulate β-galactosidase activity in coleoptile segments by about 35% with only a slight (10% or less) effect during the first 30–60 min. Thus, neither the timing nor magnitude of auxin effects on the activity of this enzyme correlates well with auxin effects on growth. It is curious that even though in vivo β-galactosidase activity is greatly increased at pH 5.0, auxin treatment, which is known to cause wall acidification to pH 5.0 in this tissue, has only a slight effect on the activity of this enzyme. This suggests that β-galactosidase may not be involved in acid-mediated wall loosening. The report that PCMB strongly inhibits β-galactosidase activity (99) also indicates that this enzyme may not play an important role in acid-mediated wall loosening, since Hager (personal communication) has now found that inhibition of acid-induced straight growth by PCMB is poor and nonspecific.

Other glycosidases, such as β-glucosidase, which has a pH optimum between 5 and 6 (99), should also be examined. However, there is some evidence that wall loosening may not be mediated by a polysaccharidase at all. Cleland (30, 31) has found that auxin-induced wall loosening is readily reversible in the presence of metabolic inhibitors. This indicates that the loosening event might not be catalyzed by wall polysaccharidases since the activity of those that have been characterized is essentially irreversible (84, 222). Furthermore, a variety of enzyme inhibitors is reported to have little effect on acid-induced extension (55, 60, 173). Although Rehm & Cline (180) found inhibitory effects of KCN and $HgCl_2$, Hager (personal communication) has tested numerous other poisons and sulfhydryl inhibitors as well as trichloroacetic acid and found no significant inhibition of acid-induced straight growth. Furthermore, Rayle & Cleland (173) found that the acid growth effect occurs even after extensive pronase treatment and at pH values as low as 2 (172), suggesting a lack of enzyme involvement.

If wall loosening is enzyme mediated, it seems strange that it occurs only when the tissue is under turgor or applied stress. One does not usually consider turgor a requisite to enzyme activity, although Ray (167) has reported that auxin activation of β-glucan synthetase depends upon normal turgor pressure, and Cleland & Rayle (73) have discussed possible explanations for turgor-dependent enzyme action on cell walls. Perhaps acid-induced wall loosening occurs by direct acid hydrolysis when very low pH (less than 4.0) is used (123, 172) and is accomplished by disruption of hydrogen bonds at more mild pH (106).

There may be a simple means of determining whether or not glycosidases take part in auxin and acid responses and if so, which particular glycosidases are involved. The monomeric aldonolactone derivative of a sugar comprising a polysaccharide acted upon by a certain glycosidase is known to inhibit strongly and specifically the action of the glycosidase (38, 39, 120). Aldonolactones could therefore be useful tools in determining which glycosidases, if any, are important in plant growth regulation.

In unpublished experiments in this laboratory, aldonolactone inhibitors of glucosidase and galactosidase were found to inhibit strongly in vivo glucosidase and galactosidase activity in *Avena* coleoptile segments. However, these inhibitors were found to have no effect on either the acid growth response or the auxin response in peeled or unpeeled segments. This suggests that neither glucosidases nor galactosidases play an important role in the acid or auxin response in this tissue. The possible involvement of other glycosidases could also be tested using the appropriate glycosidase inhibitor.

Other Nonhormonal Factors

A key factor in the development of the hypothesis that auxin action is acid mediated was the observation that growth in response to acid treatment mimics in some respects growth in response to auxin. However, there are at least two other nonhormonal treatments capable of promoting cell elongation (57, 60, 114).

Fusicoccin, the toxin produced by the fungus *Fusicoccum amygdali* Del., has been shown to stimulate water uptake and cell elongation in etiolated pea stem segments (114, 115). At optimal concentrations (about 0.5 mM) the toxin is considerably more effective than auxin in the promotion of cell elongation, but at supraoptimal concentrations the toxin does not exhibit the growth-inhibitory effect characteristic of auxin. Since suboptimal concentrations of auxin and fusicoccin given together have an additive effect on elongation, the two substances may act at the same growth-limiting site. Marre and co-workers (129, 130) have investigated the relationship between H^+ ion efflux and the action of fusicoccin. In a paper appearing in 1973 (115), they reported that growth promotion by fusicoccin was accompanied by no significant decrease of the pH of the growth medium and concluded that H^+

efflux played no role in the action of the toxin. However, in later experiments in which the tissue volume to medium volume ratio was about four times greater, they were able to detect a substantial decrease in pH (from 6.5 to 4.6) during a 4 hr incubation in toxin. A smaller drop in pH (about 1 pH unit) was observed in the presence of various auxins but not in the presence of the auxin antagonist, p-chlorophenoxyisobutyric acid. Since toxin causes a greater stimulation of growth as well as a greater stimulation of H^+ efflux, the authors suggest that toxin action is acid-mediated. Fusicoccin has also been shown to cause stomatal closure in either light or dark in bean leaves. (214). Toxin-induced closure is accompanied by a rise in K^+ content in the guard cells. Perhaps fusicoccin-induced K^+ uptake and H^+ efflux are related phenomena coupled for charge balance.

Stimulation of elongation has also been observed in response to other pathotoxins. High concentrations of victorin, the host-specific pathotoxin of *Helminthosporium victoriae,* have been found to stimulate elongation in segments from coleoptiles of the sensitive variety of *Avena* (57, 185). The response occurs with a latent period of only 3 min but the magnitude of the response is only about half as great as the response to auxin and lasts only about 25 min. After 25 min the growth rate begins to decline and the segments eventually lose turgor and shrink. In resistant tissue, toxin treatment also stimulates growth, and although the magnitude of growth promotion is substantially less than in sensitive tissue, the response in resistant tissue continues for at least 20 hr. Since victorin is known to increase membrane permeability in sensitive tissue (185, 187), the possibility that victorin action on cell elongation is also mediated by H^+ efflux has been tested (Saftner & Evans, unpublished). Victorin had no significant effect on H^+ ion leakage from peeled segments of sensitive *Avena* coleoptiles, and neutral buffers influenced neither the timing nor the magnitude of the growth response to victorin. Low concentrations of victorin have been found to inhibit completely the auxin response in sensitive tissue while having no effect on the auxin response in resistant tissue.

The host-specific pathotoxin from *Helminthosporium maydis* race T (T-toxin) has also been observed to promote growth in segments from the susceptible variety of corn (185). The latent period is about 25 min and the promoted rate of elongation continues for 30–60 min and then very gradually declines over a period of 15 hr. T-toxin also promotes elongation in resistant tissue where the maximum rate of toxin-promoted elongation continues for 6–7 hr.

There are also reports that certain fungal toxins can strongly inhibit growth. The toxin of *Fusarium tricinctum* (T-2 toxin) has been shown to reduce the growth of pea seedlings (126) and to prevent the stimulation of soybean hypocotyl elongation by auxin (196).

A second nonhormonal treatment capable of mimicking the effect of auxin on elongation is transient exposure to heavy water (57, 60). When coleoptile segments are transferred from water to 100% heavy water, their growth is inhibited immediately and there is slight osmotic shrinkage due to the higher viscosity and lower diffusion coefficient of D_2O (211). Upon transfer back to water, even after only 5–10 min in D_2O, there is an immediate increase in elongation rate to a value comparable to that in response to IAA. The duration of this promoted rate of elongation varies from experiment to experiment over a range of about 25 min to 2.5 hr. When segments growing in auxin are transferred to D_2O containing auxin, their growth is inhibited immediately and resumes at the auxin-promoted rate immediately upon transfer back to auxin in water (41, 57).

The basis for these remarkable effects of heavy water on cell elongation is unknown. D_2O is known to inhibit the activity of a number of enzymes, including invertase, cholinesterase, urease, phosphatase, ATPase, and catalase, while its effect on glucosidases seems to depend on the particular enzyme and substrate involved (211).

One especially interesting property of D_2O is that the deuterium bond is considerably stronger than the hydrogen bond (86), so treatment with D_2O would be expected to have marked effects on surface phenomena, permeability, protein stability, etc. If the model for regulation of wall extensibility by hydrogen bonding put forward by Albersheim and co-workers (106) is correct, heavy water effects on growth may occur at the noncovalent xyloglucan-cellulose interface. The strength of bonding between xyloglucan and cellulose would be expected to increase in the presence of deuterium, thus rigidifying the wall and inhibiting growth. Replacement of D_2O with H_2O would result in reformation of weaker hydrogen bonds at the xyloglucan-cellulose interface, perhaps allowing a modification of wall extensibility or slippage during the transition.

In addition to fungal toxins and heavy water, there are reports of at least two nonhormonal substances capable of stimulating elongation. Acetylcholine has been reported to stimulate growth in isolated *Avena* coleoptile segments (56) and wheat seedlings (45). However, the suspected response of isolated coleoptile segments to acetylcholine has been found to be due to a spontaneous increase in growth rate at a precise time after excising the segments (57). Evans & Schmitt (unpublished) have found a close correlation between a rise in IAA synthetase activity and the rise in elongation rate in isolated segments. Thus, there appears to be no growth promoting activity of acetylcholine in isolated coleoptile segments, at least at the pH (6.8) used in these experiments. Dekhuijzen (45) qualifies his report of acetylcholine stimulation of wheat seedling elongation by noting that the response occurs only at somewhat acid pH (4.5–6.0). It is not certain whether this stimulation is related somehow to acetylcholine modification of a pH effect in wheat seedlings or whether the activity of acetylcholine depends strongly on the charge on the molecule.

There are also reports that cyclic AMP (cAMP) is capable of promoting cell elongation in *Avena* coleoptile segments (82, 186) and that auxin stimulates adenine incorporation into cAMP (6, 186). However, the reported response to cAMP is slight. Hartung (82) noted that a significant response to cAMP could be observed only in the presence of 25 mM glucose and exhibited a pH optimum of 5.2. It seems possible that the apparent growth response to cAMP is due to variation in the spontaneous increase in growth rate of isolated segments during long-term experiments (57). It might also be noted that the reported pH optimum (5.2) for growth promotion by cAMP is the pH at which maximal acid promotion of elongation occurs in peeled *Avena* coleoptile segments (35, 100, 171). In short-term growth experiments with *Avena* coleoptile segments, cAMP at neutral pH was found to have no growth-promoting activity (Evans, unpublished). Cline (unpublished) has also observed no increase in growth rate in response to cAMP or dibutyryl AMP. Hartung, in a more recent paper (83), reports that he does not observe growth stimulation by cAMP even in the presence of glucose. Instead he notes that cAMP can substitute for the effect of gibberellin in enhancing the promotion of elongation by auxin and suggests that cAMP lacks auxin activity but may function as a secondary messenger for gibberellin.

RAPID RESPONSES IN ROOTS

There are numerous reviews concerning the hormonal regulation of root growth (see 191 and references cited therein). It has become clear that low concentrations of auxin (ca $10^{-7}M$) can increase the rate of root cell elongation (20, 24, 199) but also reduce the period of time over which elongation occurs (24). The promotion of cell elongation in roots by auxin appears to have certain features in common with the promotion of stem tissue elongation by auxin. Morre & Bonner (143) found that IAA increases both cell wall synthesis and extensibility in corn roots during the first hour after auxin treatment. The enhancement of extensibility, however, was observed only at auxin concentrations inhibitory to growth. Growth-promoting concentrations of auxin did not increase root cell extensibility until 4 hr after the beginning of auxin treatment, even though growth rate as measured by fresh weight increased during the first hour of auxin treatment. After 4 hr in low concentrations of auxin, at a time when plasticity was found to increase, growth rate was observed to decrease.

Burstrom et al (25), using the resonance frequency method for measurement of extensibility, have detected an auxin-induced increase or, more accurately, an auxin-induced reduction in the normal time-dependent decrease in elastic extensibility of pea root sections. Although their data do not allow accurate determination of a time course, they say that the effect was significant within 15 min.

Reports of rapid stimulatory or inhibitory effects of auxin on the growth of stem cells also have their counterparts in root cells. Jackson (95) has found that IAA stimulates both cytoplasmic streaming and elongation in root hairs with a latent period of only a few minutes. Using a streak photography method, List (121) has found that treatment of intact corn roots with IAA (10^{-11} to $10^{-8}M$) results in a reduction in growth rate within 5 min followed by dampened oscillations of the reduced rate and then partial recovery. Treatment with higher levels of auxin also results in rapid inhibition of growth and, after 5 hr, complete recovery to a rate even greater than the initial rate. Similar rapid transitory inhibition of root cell elongation by auxin has been reported by others (71, 85, 193).

Auxin induction of changes in membrane potential has also been observed in root tissue. Jenkinson (97) and Jenkinson & Scott (98) have noted that oscillation of the external auxin concentration between zero and $10^{-7}M$ rapidly (latent period about 1 min) induces oscillations in bioelectric fields in bean roots. The oscillation is strongest in the growing region of the root and is occasionally accompanied by similar oscillations in growth rate. The rapid species-specific alteration of root tip surface charge reported by Tanada (204, 205) to be induced by low levels of auxin may be related to these auxin effects in intact roots.

It is interesting that the growth-inhibitory action of auxin in roots is greater in long-term experiments at somewhat acid pH (3, 4). Audus (4) has suggested that this is due to greater uptake of undissociated auxin, while Andreae (3), on the basis of evidence that the external concentration of auxin is the important factor in growth inhibition, suggests that acid activates auxin receptors on the cell surface. It seems possible that the inhibitory action of auxin at acid pH may be due in part to a direct long-term inhibitory effect of low pH on growth as has been found to occur in stem tissue after transient initial stimulation. Similarly, the masking of the growth-inhibitory action of auxin when given at pH 4.6 (3) may have been due to strong initial stimulation of elongation by hydrogen ions.

Edwards & Scott (51) have investigated the promotion of corn root segment elongation by acid pH. The sensitivity of these segments to H^+ ions was found to be about eightfold greater than the sensitivity of stem segments. Citric acid buffer at pH 4.0 caused an immediate increase in growth rate from about 1 μm/min per millimeter of tissue to about 30 μm/min per millimeter of tissue. Unlike coleoptile tissue (172) the acid response in root tissue can be turned on and off with some dampening by alternating between pH 4.0 and 7.0. IAA, which weakly promotes the elongation of these segments at pH 7.0, very strongly inhibits the promotion of growth at pH 4.0. The relationship between auxin action and H^+ ion action in the regulation of root growth in vivo is not clear. One would expect to find no auxin-induced efflux of H^+ ions in root tissue, since H^+ ions strongly promote root segment elongation whereas auxin is generally inhibitory. It would be interesting to determine whether auxin retards H^+ ion efflux in root tissue.

RAPID RESPONSES TO OTHER HORMONES

Warner & Leopold (220) surveyed the timing of the growth response of decapitated pea seedlings to a variety of plant hormones. They noted a latent period of about 24 min in the promotion of elongation by gibberellic acid. In internode segments of 40-day-old light growth *Avena* stem segments, Adams & Kaufman (personal communication) have found that GA_3 normally promotes elongation after a latent period of about 2 hr. However, treatment with IAA reduces the latent period in response to GA_3 to about 10 min even though IAA alone is somewhat inhibitory (105). The rapidity of the response to GA_3 suggests that the initial response to this hormone is not mediated by de novo protein synthesis.

Ben-Tal & Varner (13) have found that treatment of aleurone cells with gibberellic acid causes a two- to threefold increase in phosphorylcholine glyceride transferase activity within 4 hr. Results of experiments with various inhibitors of RNA and protein synthesis suggest that the increase in transferase activity is due to activation of existing enzyme rather than enzyme synthesis. Careful time-course studies of GA-stimulated incorporation of CDP-^{14}C-choline into lipid-soluble components in barley aleurone cells have revealed a 50% increase in incorporation within 30 min.

The action of abscisic acid has also proved to be quite rapid in a number of systems. ABA has been shown to induce stomatal closure within a few minutes of its application in a variety of plants (101, 112, 142). The rapidity of the ABA effect on stomatal closure has led to the suggestion (101, 112) that ABA alters ion pump activity in the cell membrane, an interesting suggestion in light of evidence that ABA can increase diffusional permeability to water within 30 min (76) and rapidly inhibit both auxin-induced H^+ ion secretion (177) and growth (179, 220).

ACKNOWLEDGMENTS

I would like to thank Drs. G. M. Barkley, K. D. Johnson, R. Cleland, P. Penny, D. Rayle, A. Hager, L. N. Vanderhoef, and M. Zenk for providing unpublished information to be included in this review.

Literature Cited

1. Addink, C. C. J., Meijer, G. 1972. In *Plant Growth Substances 1970*, ed. D. J. Carr, 69–75. Berlin: Springer
2. Agrawal, K. M. L., Bahl, O. P. 1968. *J. Biol. Chem.* 243:103–11
3. Andreae, W. A. 1967. *Can. J. Bot.* 45:737–53
4. Audus, L. J. 1949. *New Phytol.* 48:97–114
5. Audus, L. J., Brownbridge, M. E. 1957. *J. Exp. Bot.* 8:105–24
6. Azhar, S., Krishna Murti, C. R. 1971. *Biochem. Biophys. Res. Commun.* 43:58–64
7. Baker, D. B., Ray, P. M. 1965. *Plant Physiol.* 40:345–52
8. Barkley, G. M., Evans, M. L. 1970. *Plant Physiol.* 45:143–47
9. Barkley, G. M., Leopold, A. C. 1973. *Plant Physiol.* 52:76–78
10. Bauer, W. D., Talmadge, K. W., Keegstra, K., Albersheim, P. 1973. *Plant Physiol.* 51:174–87
11. Bayley, S. T., Setterfield, G. 1957. *Ann. Bot. London* 21:633–41
12. Bennet-Clark, T. A. 1956. In *The Chemistry and Mode of Action of Plant Growth substances*, ed. R. L. Wain, F. Wightman, 284–91. London: Butterworth
13. Ben-Tal, Y., Varner, J. E. 1973. *Plant Physiol.* 51 Suppl:5
14. Bentrup, F. W., Pfrue6ner, H., Wagner, G. 1973. *Planta* 110:369–72
15. Bidwell, R. G. S., Turner, W. B. 1966. *Plant Physiol.* 41:267–70
16. Blake, J. D., Richards, G. N. 1971. *Carbohyd. Res.* 17:253–68
17. Bonner, J. 1934. *Protoplasma* 21:406–23
18. Botrill, D. E., Hanson, J. B. 1968. *Aust. J. Biol. Sci.* 21:201–8
19. Brauner, L., Arslan, N. 1951. *Rev. Fac. Sci. Univ. Istanbul B* 16:257–300
20. Brauner, L., Diemer, R. 1967. *Planta* 77:1–31
21. Burg, S. P., Burg, E. A. 1966. *Proc. Nat. Acad. Sci. USA* 55:262–69
22. Burg, S. P., Burg, E. A. 1968. In *Biochemistry and Physiology of Plant Growth Substances*, ed. F. Wightman, G. Setterfield, 1275–94. Ottawa: Runge
23. Burstrom, H. G. 1961. *Encycl. Plant Physiol.* 14:258–310
24. Burstrom, H. G. 1969. *Am. J. Bot.* 56:679–84
25. Burstrom, H. G., Uhrstrom, I., Olausson, B. 1970. *Physiol. Plant.* 23:1223–33
26. Cande, W. Z., Ray, P. M. 1973. *Planta* 111:279–96
27. Carr, D. J., Ng, E. K. 1959. *Aust. J. Biol. Sci.* 12:373–87
28. Christiansen, G. S., Thimann, K. V. 1950. *Arch. Biochem.* 26:230–47
29. Cleland, R. 1967. *Planta* 74:197–209
30. Cleland, R. 1968. *Science* 160:192–94
31. Cleland, R. 1968. See Ref. 22, 613–24
32. Cleland, R. 1971. *Ann. Rev. Plant Physiol.* 22:197–222
33. Cleland, R. 1972. *Planta* 104:1–9
34. Cleland, R. 1973. *Plant Physiol.* 51 Suppl:2
35. Cleland, R. 1973. *Proc. Nat. Acad. Sci. USA* 70:3092–93
36. Cleland, R., Bonner, J. 1956. *Plant Physiol.* 31:350–54
37. Cleland, R., Rayle, D. L. 1972. *Planta* 106:61–71
38. Conchie, J., Gelman, A. L., Levvy, G. A. 1968. *Biochem. J.* 106:135–40

220   EVANS

39. Conchie, J., Levvy, G. A. 1957. *Biochem. J.* 65:389–95
40. Cummins, W. R., Green, P. B. 1973. *Plant Physiol.* 51 Suppl:1
41. Dahlhelm, H. 1969. *Planta* 86:224–34
42. Datko, A. H., Maclachlan, G. A. 1968. *Plant Physiol.* 43:735–42
43. Datta, A., Sen, S. P. 1965. *Biochim. Biophys. Acta* 107:352–57
44. Davies, P. J. 1973. *Bot. Rev.* 39:139–71
45. Dekhuijzen, H. M. 1973. *Planta* 111: 149–56
46. Dela Fuente, R. K., Leopold, A. C. 1970. *Plant Physiol.* 46:186–89
47. Dey, P. M., Pridham, J. B. 1972. *Advan. Enzymol.* 36:91–130
48. Dowler, M. J. et al 1974. *Plant. Physiol.* In press
49. Durand, H., Rayle, D. L. 1973. *Planta* 114:185–93
50. Durand, H., Zenk, M. H. 1972. See Ref. 1, 62–67
51. Edwards, K. L., Scott, T. K. 1973. *Plant Physiol.* 51 Suppl:2
52. Erickson, R. O., Sax, K. B. 1956. *Proc. Am. Phil. Soc.* 100:487–98
53. Esnault, R. 1965. *Bull. Soc. Fr. Physiol. Veg.* 11:55–67
54. Etherton, B. 1970. *Plant Physiol.* 45: 527–28
55. Evans, M. L. 1967. *Kinetic studies of the cell elongation phenomenon in Avena coleoptile segments.* PhD thesis. Univ. California, Santa Cruz. 215 pp.
56. Evans, M. L. 1972. *Plant Physiol.* 50:414–16
57. Evans, M. L. 1973. *Bioscience* 23: 711–18
58. Evans, M. L., Hokanson, R. *Planta* 85:85–95
59. Evans, M. L., Ray, P. M. 1969. *J. Gen. Physiol.* 53:1–20
60. Evans, M. L., Ray, P. M., Reinhold, L. 1971. *Plant Physiol* 47:335–41
61. Evans, M. L., Rayle, D. L. 1970. *Plant Physiol.* 45:240–43
62. Fan, D. F., Maclachlan, G. A. 1966. *Can. J. Bot.* 44:1025–34
63. Fan, D. F., Maclachlan, G. A. 1967. *Plant Physiol.* 42:1114–22
64. Fan, D. F., Maclachlan, G. A. 1967. *Can. J. Bot.* 45:1837–44
65. Fisher, J. D., Hansen, D., Hodges, T. K. 1970. *Plant Physiol.* 46:812–14
66. Fisher, M. L., Albersheim, P. 1973. *Plant Physiol.* 51 Suppl:2
67. Galston, A. W., Chen, H. R. 1965. *Plant Physiol.* 40:699–705
68. Galston, A. W., Kaur, R. 1961. In *Light and Life,* ed. W. D. McElroy, B. Glass, 687–705. Baltimore: Johns Hopkins
69. Galston, A. W., Lavee, S., Siegel, B. Z. 1968. See Ref. 22, 455–72
70. Ganot, D., Reinhold, L. 1970. *Planta* 95:62–71
71. Gast, A. 1942. *Ber. Schweiz. Bot. Ges.* 52:441–75
72. Gayler, K. R., Glasziou, K. T. 1969. *Planta* 84:185–94
73. Gillbank, L., Rowan, K. S., Spring, A. 1972. *Cytobios* 6:119–31
74. Glinka, Z., Reinhold, L. 1962. *Plant Physiol.* 37:481–86
75. Ibid 1964. 39:1043–50
76. Ibid 1971. 47:103–5
77. Gordon, S. A., Dobra, W. A. 1972. *Plant Physiol.* 50:738–42
78. Green, P. B. 1972. See Ref. 1, 9–16
79. Hager, A., Menzel, H., Krauss, A. 1971. *Planta* 100:47–75
80. Hardin, J. W., Cherry, J. H., Morre, D. J., Lembi, C. A. 1972. *Proc. Nat. Acad. Sci. USA* 69:3146–50
81. Harrison, A. 1965. *Physiol. Plant.* 18:321–28
82. Hartung, W. 1972. *Z. Pflanzenphysiol.* 67:380–82
83. Ibid 1973. 68:329–35
84. Hassid, W. Z. 1967. *Ann. Rev. Plant Physiol.* 18:253–80
85. Hejnowicz, Z., Erickson, R. O. 1968. *Physiol. Plant.* 21:302–13
86. Henderson, R. F., Henderson, T. R., Woodfin, B. M. 1970. *J. Biol. Chem.* 245:3733–37
87. Hertel, R., St. Thomson, K., Russo, V. E. A. 1972. *Planta* 107:325–40
88. Heyn, A. N. J. 1969. *Science* 167: 874–75
89. Higinbotham, N., Graves, J. S., Davis, R. F. 1953. *Science* 118:243–45
90. Higinbotham, N., Pratt, M. J., Foster, R. J. 1962. *Plant Physiol.* 37:203–14
91. Hodges, T. K., Leonard, R. T., Bracker, C. E., Keenan, T. W. 1972. *Proc. Nat. Acad. Sci. USA* 69:3307–11
92. Hopkins, W. G., Bonnell, K. F. 1969. *Plant Physiol.* 44:281–86
93. Ilan, I. 1973. *Physiol. Plant.* 38:146–48
94. Ilan, I., Reinhold, L. 1963. *Physiol. Plant.* 16:596–603
95. Jackson, W. T. 1960. *Physiol. Plant.* 13:36–45
96. Jenkinson, I. S. 1962. *Aust. J. Biol. Sci.* 15:101–14
97. Ibid, 115–25
98. Jenkinson, I. S., Scott, B. I. H. 1961. *Aust. J. Biol. Sci.* 14:231–43
99. Johnson, K. D., Daniels, D., Dowler,

M. J., Rayle, D. L. 1974. *Plant Physiol.* In press

100. Johnson, K. D., Daniels, D., Rayle, D. L. 1973. *Plant Physiol.* 51 Suppl:2
101. Jones, R. J., Mansfield, T. A. 1970. *J. Exp. Bot.* 21:714–19
102. Kang, B. G., Burg, S. P. 1971. *Proc. Nat. Acad. Sci. USA.* 68:1730–33
103. Katsumi, M., Sano, H. 1968. *Physiol. Plant.* 21:1348–55
104. Katz, M., Ordin, L. 1967. *Biochim. Biophys. Acta* 141:126–34
105. Kaufman, P. B., Petering, L., Adams, P. A. 1969. *Am. J. Bot.* 56:918–27
106. Keegstra, K., Talmadge, K., Bauer, W. D., Albersheim, P. 1973. *Plant Physiol.* 51:188–96
107. Key, J. 1969. *Ann. Rev. Plant Physiol.* 20:449–74
108. Key, J. L., Shannon, J. C. 1964. *Plant Physiol.* 39:360–64
109. Kobayashi, S., Hatakeyama, I., Ashida, J. 1956. *Bot. Mag.* 69:16–23
110. Köhler, D. 1956. *Planta* 47:159–64
111. Koningsberger, V. J. 1922. *Rec. Trav. Bot. Neer.* 19:1–136
112. Kriedemann, P. E., Loveys, B. R., Fuller, G. L., Leopold, A. C. 1972. *Plant Physiol.* 49:842–47
113. Labavitch, J., Ray, P. M. 1973. *Plant Physiol.* 51 Suppl.: 59
114. Lado, P., Pennachioni, A., Rasi Caldogno, F., Russi, S., Silano, V. 1972. *Physiol. Plant Pathol.* 2:75–85
115. Lado, P., Rasi Caldogno, F., Pennacchioni, A., Marre, E. 1973. *Planta* 110:311–20
116. Lamport, D. T. A. 1970. *Ann. Rev. Plant Physiol.* 21:235–70
117. Lee, S., Kivilaan, A., Bandurski, R. S. 1967. *Plant Physiol.* 42:968–72
118. Leonard, R. T., Hanson, J. B. 1972. *Plant Physiol.* 49:436–40
119. Leonard, R. T., Hansen, D., Hodges, T. K. 1973. *Plant Physiol.* 51:749–54
120. Levvy, G. A., Snaith, S. M. 1972. *Advan. Enzymol.* 36:151–81
121. List, A. L. Jr. 1969. *Planta* 87:1–19
122. Lundegårdh, H. 1947. *Ark. Bot. Ser. A* 33:1–19
123. Lundegårdh, H. 1949. *Ark. Bot. Ser. 2* 1:289–93
124. Lüttge, U., Higinbotham, N., Pallaghy, C. K. 1972. *Z. Naturforsch.* 27b:1239–42
125. Maclachlan, G. A., Davies, E., Fan, D. F. 1968. See Ref. 22, 443–53
126. Marasas, W. F., Smalley, E. B., Bamburg, J. R., Strong, F. M. 1971. *Phytopathology* 61:1488–91

127. Marre, E., Arrigoni, O. 1957. *Physiol. Plant.* 10:289–301
128. Marre, E., Forti, G. 1958. *Physiol. Plant.* 11:36–47
129. Marre, E., Lado, P., Rasi Caldogno, F., Colombo, R. 1973. *Plant Sci. Lett.*
130. Ibid, 185–92
131. Masuda, Y. 1968. See Ref. 22, 699–710
132. Masuda, Y. 1968. *Planta* 83:171–84
133. Masuda, Y. 1969. *Plant Cell Physiol.* 10:1–9
134. Masuda, Y., Kamisaka, S. 1969. *Plant Cell Physiol.* 10:79–86
135. Masuda, Y., Tanimoto, E., Wada, S. 1967. *Physiol. Plant.* 20:713–19
136. Masuda, Y., Wada, S. 1967. *Bot. Mag.* 80:100–2
137. Masuda, Y., Yamamoto, R. 1970. *Develop. Growth & Differentiation* 11:287–96
138. Meijer, G. 1968. *Acta Bot. Neer.* 17:9–14
139. Menzel, H. 1966. *Die pH-abhängige Veränderungen mechanischer und chemischer Eigenschaften der Zellwand und ihr Zusammenhang mit der Wuchsstoffwirkung.* PhD thesis. Ludwig-Maximilians-Univ., München. 76 pp.
140. Mer, C. L. 1959. *Ann. Bot.* 23:177–94
141. Mer, C. L. 1961. *Nature* 191:260–61
142. Mittelheuser, C. J., van Steveninck, R. F. M. 1971. *Planta* 97:83–86
143. Morre, D. J., Bonner, J. 1965. *Physiol. Plant.* 18:635–49
144. Morre, D. J., Eisinger, W. R. 1968. See Ref. 22, 625–45
145. Murayama, K., Ueda, K. 1973. *Plant Cell Physiol.* 14:973–79
146. Neumann, P. M. 1971. *Planta* 99:56–62
147. Nissl, D., Zenk, M. H. 1969. *Planta* 89:323–41
148. Nitsch, J. P., Nitsch, C. 1956. *Plant Physiol.* 31:94–111
149. Nooden, L. 1968. *Plant Physiol.* 43:140–50
150. Nooden, L. D., Thimann, K. V. 1966. *Plant Physiol.* 41:157–64
151. Northcote, D. H. 1972. *Ann. Rev. Plant Physiol.* 23:113–32
152. Ordin, L., Bonner, J. 1956. *Plant Physiol.* 31:53–57
153. Ordin, L., Garber, M. J., Kindinger, J. I. 1972. *Physiol. Plant.* 26:17–23
154. Palmer, J. M. 1968. See Ref. 22, 401–45
155. Patterson, B. D., Trewavas, A. J. 1967. *Plant Physiol.* 42:1081–86
156. Penny, P. 1969. *N. Z. J. Bot.* 7:290–301
157. Penny, P. 1971. *Plant Physiol.* 48:720–23
158. Penny, P., Penny, D., Marshall, D.,

Heyes, J. K. 1972. *J. Exp. Bot.* 23:23–36
159. Polevoy, V. V. 1967. *Wiss. Z. Univ. Rostock Math. Naturwiss. Reihe* 16:477–78
160. Pope, D., Black, M. 1972. *Planta* 102:26–36
161. Power, J. B., Cocking, E. C. 1970. *J. Exp. Bot.* 21:64–70
162. Ranson, S. L., Harrison, A. 1955. *J. Exp. Bot.* 6:75–79
163. Ray, P. M. 1961. In *Control Mechanisms in Cellular Processes,* ed. D. M. Bonner, 185–212. New York: Ronald
164. Ray, P. M. 1962. *Am. J. Bot.* 49:928–39
165. Ray, P. M. 1969. *Develop. Biol.* Suppl. 3:172–205
166. Ray, P. M. 1973. *Plant Physiol.* 51:601–8
167. Ibid, 609–14
168. Ray, P. M., Abdul-Baki, A. 1968. See Ref. 22, 647–58
169. Ray, P. M., Ruesink, A. W. 1962. *Develop. Biol.* 4:377–97
170. Ray, P. M., Ruesink, A. W. 1963. *J. Gen. Physiol.* 47:83–101
171. Rayle, D. L. 1973. *Planta* 114:63–73
172. Rayle, D. L., Cleland, R. 1970. *Plant Physiol.* 46:250–53
173. Rayle, D. L., Cleland, R. 1972. *Planta* 104:282–96
174. Rayle, D. L., Cleland, R. E. 1972. See Ref. 1, 44–51
175. Rayle, D. L., Evans, M. L., Hertel, R. 1970. *Proc. Nat. Acad. Sci. USA* 65:184–91
176. Rayle, D. L., Haughton, P. M., Cleland, R. 1970. *Proc. Nat. Acad. Sci. USA* 67:1814–17
177. Rayle, D. L., Johnson, K. D. 1973. *Plant Physiol.* 51 Suppl:2
178. Rayle, D., Zenk, M. H. 1974. *Biochem. J.* In press
179. Rehm, M. M., Cline, M. G. 1973. *Plant Physiol.* 51:93–96
180. Ibid, 946–48
181. Reinhold, L., Glinka, Z. 1966. *Plant Physiol.* 211:39–44
182. Rowan, K. S., Gillbank, L. R., Spring, A. 1972. See Ref. 1, 76–81
183. Rubinstein, B., Light, E. N. 1973. *Planta* 110:43–56
184. Ruesink, A. W. 1969. *Planta* 89:95–107
185. Saftner, R. A. 1972. *Promotion of cell elongation by host-specific fungal toxins.* MS thesis. Ohio State Univ., Columbus. 109 pp.
186. Salomon, D., Mascarenhas, J. P. 1971. *Life Sci.* 10:879–85
187. Samaddar, K. R., Scheffer, R. P. 1971. *Physiol. Plant Pathol.* 1:319–28

188. Sarkissian, I. V. 1966. *Physiol. Plant.* 19:328–34
189. Sarkissian, I. V., McDaniel, R. G. 1966. *Biochim. Biophys. Acta* 128:413–18
190. Satter, R., Marinoff, P., Galston, A. W. 1972. *Plant Physiol.* 50:235–41
191. Scott, T. K. 1972. *Ann. Rev. Plant Physiol.* 23:235–58
192. Segal, L. 1960. *Biol. Zentralbl.* 79:321–36
193. Seiler, L. 1951. *Ber. Schweiz. Bot. Ges.* 61:622–63
194. Spencer, F. S., Ziola, B., Maclachlan, G. A. 1971. *Can. J. Biochem.* 49:1326–32
195. Stahl, C., Vanderhoef, L. N., Siegel, N., Helgeson, J. P. 1973. *Plant Physiol.* 52:663–66
196. Stahl, C., Vanderhoef, L. N., Siegel, N., Helgeson, J. P. 1973. *Plant Physiol.* 52:663–66
197. Stolarek, J. 1968. *Acta Soc. Bot. Pol.* 27:473–82
198. Stowe, B. B. 1962. *Plant Physiol.* 37:158–64
199. Street, H. E. 1961. *Advan. Sci.* 18:13–18
200. Street, H. E., Collin, H. A., Short, K., Simpkins, I. 1968. See Ref. 22, 489–504
201. Sweeney, B. M., Thimann, K. V. 1937. *J. Gen. Physiol.* 21:439–61
202. Talmadge, K., Keegstra, K., Bauer, W. D., Albersheim, P. 1973. *Plant Physiol.* 51:158–73
203. Tamas, I. A., Atkins, B. D., Ware, S. M., Bidwell, R. G. S. 1972. *Can. J. Bot.* 50:1523–27
204. Tanada, T. 1973. *Plant Physiol.* 51:150–53
205. Ibid, 154–57
206. Tanimoto, E., Masuda, Y. 1968. *Physiol. Plant.* 21:820–26
207. Tanimoto, E., Masuda, Y. 1968. *Physiol. Plant.* 21:820–26
208. Tanimoto, E., Masuda, Y. 1971. *Plant Cell Physiol.* 12:663–73
209. Thimann, K. V. 1956. *Am. J. Bot.* 43:241–50
210. Thimann, K. V., Sweeney, B. M. 1937. *J. Gen. Physiol.* 21:123–35
211. Thomson, J. F. 1963. *Biological Effects of Deuterium.* New York: Macmillan
212. Trewavas, A. J. 1968. *Arch. Biochem. Biophys.* 123:324–35
213. Trewavas, A. J., Johnston, I. R., Crook, E. M. 1967. *Biochim. Biophys. Acta* 136:301–11
214. Turner, N. C. 1973. *Am. J. Bot.* 60:717–25
215. Uhrström, I. 1969. *Physiol. Plant.* 22:271–87

216. Vanderhoef, L. N., Stahl, C. P., Siegel, N., Zeigler, R. 1973. *Physiol. Plant.* 29:22–29
217. Vanderwoude, W. J., Lembi, C. A., Morre, D. J. 1972. *Biochem. Biophys. Res. Commun.* 46:245–53
218. Venis, M. A. 1964. *Nature* 202:900–1
219. Wada, S. 1969. *Kagaku Tokyo* 39: 86–94
220. Warner, H. L., Leopold, A. C. 1971. *Biochem. Biophys. Res. Commun.* 44:989–94
221. Wheeler, H., Black, H. S. 1963. *Am. J. Bot.* 50:686–93
222. Whitaker, D. R. 1963. In *Enzymatic Hydrolysis of Cellulose and Related materials,* ed. E. T. Reese, 51–70. New York: Pergamon
223. Yamaki, T. 1954. *Sci. Papers Coll. Gen. Educ. Univ. Tokyo* 4:127–54
224. Yanagishima, N., Shimoda, C. 1968. *Physiol. Plant.* 21:1122–28
225. Yoda, S., Ashida, J. 1961. *Nature* 192:577–78
226. Zimmerer, R. P., Hamilton, R. H. 1965. *Plant Cell Physiol.* 6:681–86

Ann. Rev. Plant Physiol. 1974. 25:225–58

ISOZYMES IN DEVELOPMENT AND DIFFERENTIATION[1]

❖7568

John G. Scandalios

Department of Biology, University of South Carolina, Columbia, South Carolina 29208

CONTENTS

INTRODUCTION 225
DEFINITION AND CLASSIFICATION. 226
OCCURRENCE OF ISOZYMES IN PLANTS 227
GENETICS AND DEVELOPMENT 235
SOME SPECIFIC ISOZYME SYSTEMS 235

   Alchohol Dehydrogenase 235

      Developmental expression of ADH isozymes 236
      Organ (tissue) distribution of ADH isozymes during development 237
      Effect of genetic background on ADH interactions and properties 237
      Effect of anaerobiosis 238
      Regulation of ADH expression during development 238

   Amylase 239
   Catalase 242

      Genetic control 242
      Developmental control of gene expression 242
      Differential turnover of the Ct_1 and Ct_2 catalases 243
      Subcellular localization of catalase isozymes 243
      Biochemical properties of the genetically and developmentally defined catalases 245
      Tissue (organ) specificity of catalase isozymes 246

   Malate Dehydrogenase 246
   Peptidases 248

      Aminopeptidase 248
      Endopeptidase 249

   Peroxidases 250

DISCUSSION AND PROSPECTS. 252

INTRODUCTION

A major concern of investigators interested in cellular differentiation is to discern the biochemical steps that accompany the development of cells, bringing about the diversification and specialization characteristic of multicellular organisms. It is now

[1]Dedicated to the memory of my teacher and friend Dr. Milislav Demerec.

225

well documented that as cellular differentiation progresses to bring about morphological development and functional specialization there is a continuous synthesis and/or degradation of specific enzymes and structural proteins. A common factor in cellular development and differentiation is the ability of cells to lose and acquire specific biochemical characteristics. Two principal alterations encountered in the life of most organisms are the quantitative and qualitative changes in protein (enzymatic) activity within their cells. The appearance of new or increased enzyme activity in a developing organism may result from either the de novo synthesis of the enzyme molecule or from the activation of a pre-existing enzyme precursor. The exact mechanisms by which cells of higher multicellular organisms can regulate differential expression of macromolecules during their developmental cycle are not known. It is certain, however, that the level of regulation would be either at the gene or in the pathway between the gene and its final product, the functional enzyme. Thus studies of differential gene action and/or gene expression during development are basic to our understanding of developmental processes. One approach to the problem is to study the ontogeny of enzymes characteristic of a particular system since this provides a sensitive index of the basic changes occuring during differentiation.

In recent years, there has been an increasing appreciation of the fact that enzymes commonly exist in multiple molecular forms (isozymes) within the cells of a single organism, and that this phenomenon presents the investigator with markers to study the sequential development of organisms. Isozymes are thus an expression of the differentiation of cells, and a detailed analysis of their changing patterns during development may lead to some understanding of basic mechanisms of cellular differentiation. Additionally, knowledge of the physicochemical nature and properties of individual isozymes is imperative in understanding their possible physiological function and their role(s) in regulation.

Various aspects of isozyme research have been reviewed in recent years by Markert & Whitt (106), Shannon (179), Scandalios (164), Shaw (183), Vessell & Fritz (210), and Masters & Holmes (108). This review is not intended as a comprehensive survey of the literature on isozymes; its purpose is an attempt to discuss and evaluate experiments that appear to be promising steps toward our understanding of the reasons why there are isozymes, what their biological function(s) may be, and why they may be a direct expression of gene function during cell differentiation in a developing system.

DEFINITION AND CLASSIFICATION

The term isozyme was first introduced by Markert & Moller (105), to refer to multiple molecular forms of an enzyme with similar or identical substrate specificity occurring within the same organism. Enzymes with very broad substrate specificity, sharing only a few of their numerous substrates, were not included in the above definition. However, in recent years investigations of multiple forms of enzymes have led to a need to more precisely define or categorize isozymes according to the level at which they have been investigated. Markert (104) proposed that one might modify isozyme by such adjectives as allelic, nonallelic, homomultimeric, hetero-multimeric, conformational, hybrid, conjugated, etc to more precisely reflect the knowledge we have of the particular isozyme system. In a more recent review, Shaw (183) classified isozymes into two major categories: (a) those that are distinctly different molecules and are presumably produced from different genetic sites; and (b) those which result from secondary alterations in the structure of a single poly-peptide species and may, in many cases, be in vitro artifacts.

One genetic mechanism by which isozymes might arise is gene duplication with subsequent mutations at daughter and parental loci. Thus more than one gene contributes to the structure of any enzyme composed of more than one kind of subunit. Furthermore, two genes are capable of generating a variety of isozymic forms if a number of multimers can be formed. In organisms which normally synthesize homomultimers from subunits encoded in a single gene, the presence of allelic variants of this gene may give rise to hybrid heteromultimeric isozymes [e.g. maize catalase (163)].

Multiple forms of enzymes may also arise by a variety of chemical or physical means. Isozymes may arise through the binding of a single polypeptide to varying numbers of coenzyme molecules (82, 203) or other prosthetic groups (e.g. divalent metals, sialic acid, AMP, etc); by conjugation or deletion of molecules with reactive groups such as amino, carboxyl, or hydroxyl groups of the amino acid residues of the polypeptide chain. Isozymes may result from variations in the tertiary or quater-nary structure of a given primary polypeptide structure; these have been termed "configurational isomers" by Hotchkiss (76) and "conformers" by Kitto et al (87). Multiple forms of some enzymes (e.g. LDH, peroxidase) may arise during prepara-tive procedures or during storage. It is particularly for the latter reasons that investigators employ genetically well-defined isozymes for developmental studies. That is, it would be most prudent for developmental biologists to follow the on-togeny of isozymes which are known to be regulated by specific genes in order to minimize the risk of introducing into their data unrecognized variation of unknown genetic origin.

In this review, it is my intention to stress, with examples, the usefulness of isozymes whose genetics is well understood as effective markers in studies of plant development and differentiation, developmental genetics, and in studies on the physiological role(s) of specific isozymes.

Toward these ends the literature survey is both selective and subjective.

OCCURRENCE OF ISOZYMES IN PLANTS

The occurrence of isozymes among plants and animals is widespread. Thus isozymes are the rule rather than the exception as previously believed. The number of enzymes known to occur in isozymic forms and the number of plant species examined has more than tripled in the last 5 years (see Tables 1 and 2). A number of isozyme systems in higher plants have been and are being investigated in depth with respect to genetic and biochemical regulation, physicochemical properties, ontogeny and specificity, and physiological role(s). It is these systems that will be discussed in some detail in the ensuing discussion.

Table 1 Compilation of isozyme systems studied since 1970 (See also Table 2)

ENZYME (No. isozymes)	PLANT (Tissue)	REF.	ENZYME (No. isozymes)	PLANT (Tissue)	REF.
Acetyl CoA synthetase			Esterase (cont.)		
(5)	Potato (tuber)	78	(2)	Tobacco (leaves)	139
Acid phosphatase			(14)	*Phaseolus*	202, 208
(3–4)	*Chlorella*	11	(7)	Pea (seeds)	207
(2)	*Neurospora*	140	(2–6)	*Polyporus*	182
(5)	Oats (leaves)	219	(2)	Sorghum (grain)	148
(1–4)	*Polyporus*	182	(4–13)	Wheat (seeds)	115, 121
(2)	Potato (tuber)	34	(7–14)	Barley (seedling)	107
(7)	Rice (lemma)	42	α–Galactosidase		
Alcohol dehydrogenase			(3)	*Aspergillus*	96
			β–Galactosidase		
(3)	Barley (leaves)	150	(3)	*Neurospora*	85
(5)	Wheat (seed)	115	Galactose dehydrogenase		
Aldolase					
(2)	*Chlamydomonas*	66	(1–5)	*Polyporus*	182
(2)	Pea (leaves)	2	Glutamate dehydrogenase		
Amylopectin debranching enzyme			(4–7)	*Chlorella*	150
(2)	Maize (kernel)	90	(2)	Wheat (seeds)	115
(2)	Rice (kernel)	6	Glucan synthetase		
Amylose branching enzyme			(3)	Spinach (leaves)	127
(2)	Algae (var.)	53, 54	Glucose–6–phosphate dehydrogenase		
Apyrase			(4–7)	*Chlorella*	11
(2)	Potato (tuber)	201	(3)	*Neurospora*	177
			Glucose–P–isomerase		
Catechol oxidase			(2)	Maize (endosperm)	202
(2)	*Polyporus*	182	(3)	Sweet potato (tuber)	152, 154
Chalcone-flavone isomerase			Glucosyl transferase		
(2)	*Phaseolus*	70	(2)	Algae (var.)	54
(3)	Bean (*Cicer*)	70	Glyceraldehyde–3–P dehydrogenase		
(5)	Parsley	70	(2)	Alfalfa	134
Chorismate mutase			(2)	*Euglena*	134
(2)	*Phaseolus* (seedling)	62	(2)	*Ochromonas*	134
DAHP Synthetase			Glycerate–3–P kinase		
(3)	*Neurospora*	36	(2)	Pea (leaves)	2
DNase			Hexokinase		
(2)	*Euglena*	16	(4)	Wheat (embryo)	111
Esterase			Invertase		
(10–13)	*Chlorella*	11	(5)	Potato (tuber)	153
(4–6)	Cotton	24			
(1–4)	*Neurospora*	141	Lactate dehydrogenase		
			(2–3)	*Neurospora*	141

Table 1 (Continued)

ENZYME (No. isozymes)	PLANT (Tissue)	REF.	ENZYME (No. isozymes)	PLANT (Tissue)	REF.
Lipoxygenase			Peroxidase (cont.)		
(4)	Alfalfa (leaves)	65	(6–14)	Wheat (var.)	178, 214
(2)	Pea (seed)	43	(5–8)	*Xanthium*	23
(1–2)	Soy bean	25, 26, 193	Phosphoenolpyruvate carboxylase		
			(2)	*Chlamydomonas*	22
Malate dehydrogenase			(3)	Cotton (leaves)	117
(2)	Cauliflower (head)	137	Phenolase		
(2)	*Chlorella*	194	(5)	*Schizophyllum*	212
(4)	*Neurospora*	10	Phosphoglucomutase		
(4)	Spinach (var.)	145, 146	(2)	Maize (endosperm)	202
(4–5)	Wheat (seeds)	115	(2)	*Neurospora*	114
			Phosphorylase		
Orotate dehydrogenase			(1–2)	Algae (var.)	54
(4–6)	*Schizophyllum*	212	(3)	Maize (var.)	18, 21
			(2)	*Oscillatoria*	55
Peroxidase			(1–5)	*Phaseolus* (var.)	61
(6)	Blueberry (fruit)	57	(1–4)	Onion (var.)	61
(2–4)	Cotton (var.)	216	(1–9)	Potato (var.)	61
(8–20)	Cucumber (var.)	142, 218	(3)	Rice (seeds)	61
(5)	*Cystoclonium*	119	(4–8)	*Vicia* (var.)	61
(3–7)	*Datura* (var.)	49, 67	Polyphenoloxidase		
(4–8)	*Dianthus* (callus)	109	(4)	Peach (fruit)	217
(2)	*Enteromorpha*	120	(3)	Sorghum (shoots)	191
(3–4)	Flax (stem)	50, 73	Ribonuclease		
(4–20)	Horseradish (var.)	32, 33, 98, 130, 185	(2)	Carrot	215
(7–12)	Lentil (var.)	86, 132	(3)	Maize (endosperm)	215
(3)	*Neurospora*	141	(4)	Tobacco (callus)	215
(3–5)	Pea (var.)	28, 151	(2)	Wheat (leaves)	188
(6–8)	Peanut (cotyledon)	209	Ribose–5–P isomerase		
(5)	Pear (fruit)	57	(2)	Pea (leaves)	1
(2)	*Phaseolus* (cultures)	113	Starch synthetase		
(1–3)	*Polyporus*	182	(2)	Maize (leaves)	199
(3)	Rice (lemma)	41	(2)	Rice (seed)	199
(2–7)	Sorghum (var.)	148, 172, 190	Thioglucosidase		
			(4–5)	*Brassica*	74
(8)	Soy bean	75	(3)	*Crambe*	74
(2)	Spinach	5	(4)	*Sinapis*	74
(3)	Sweet potato	181	Trehalase		
(6)	Tea (leaf)	197	(2)	*Neurospora*	225
(2–20)	Tobacco (var.)	17, 97, 139, 171, 218	Triose–P–isomerase		
			(2)	Pea (leaves)	2
(2–4)	Tomato	43, 57	Tyrosinase		
(several)	Water lily	15	(4)	Mushroom	99

Table 2 Compilation of isozyme systems in which the pattern of expression varies with the developmental or metabolic state of the organism

Plant	Tissue	No. Isozymes	No. Sub-units	Method[a]	Genetic Basis	Remarks	Ref.
Acetyl Esterase							
Barley	leaves	9-11	–	e	–	isozyme expression changes after infection	150
Acid Phosphatase (3.1.3.2)[b]							
Barley	leaves	4-5	–	e	–	isozyme expression changes after infection	150
Dianthus	callus	1-7	–	e	–	isozyme expression influenced by light and temperature	109
Lettuce	germ. seedling	9	–	e,gf	–	Isozyme expression linked to developmental state	112
Maize	scutellum	10	2	e	3 loci, 3 alleles at one of them		38
Schizophyllum	mycelia	7-12	–	e	–	isozyme expression linked to developmental state	212
Xanthium	leaves	2-7	–	e	–	isozyme expression linked to developmental state	23
Alcohol Dehydrogenase (1.1.1.1)							
Maize	immature endosperm	2	2	e,k	at least 2 loci with 2 alleles at each	subunits from one locus form hybrid enzyme; allelic subunits from the other locus do not	47 162 165 169
	scutellum	1-4	2	e,k,i			
	pericarp	1-3	2	e			
	mature endosperm	1	2	e		isozyme expression linked to developmental state	
	root	2	2	e,i			
	leaf	2	2	e			
Maize	scutellum	3	2	e	2 loci	claim evidence for regulator gene	39 40
Maize	kernel	3	2	e	2 loci	1 active and 1 inactive subunit can form active enzyme	56 174 175
Wheat	seed	3	2	e	1 locus with 3 alleles (on homeologous chromosomes)	subunits shared	71 72
Aldolase (4.1.2.7)							
Xanthium	leaves	9-10	–	e	–	isozyme expression linked to developmental state	23
Aminopeptidase (Leucine Aminopeptidase) (3.4.1.1)							
Barley	leaves	3	–	e	–	isozyme expression linked to developmental state	150

Table 2 (Continued)

Plant	Tissue	No. Isozymes	No. Sub-units	Method[a]	Genetic Basis	Remarks	Ref.
Pea	various	3	–	e,i	2 alleles at each of 2 or 3 loci	mitochondrial form under nuclear gene control	167, 168
Schizophyllum	mycelia	2	–	e	–	isozyme expression linked to developmental state	212
Amylase (uncharacterized)							
Xanthium	leaves	1–6	–	e	–	isozyme expression linked to developmental state	23
α–Amylase (3.2.1.1)							
Barley	aleurone layers	4	–	e,i	–	2 forms require Ca; all forms induced by gibberellin	80
Barley	GA-treated half seeds	5	–	e,ixc	–	–	198
Maize	endosp., scut., leaf, root, shoot	2–3	–	e,im	1 locus with 2 alleles	isozyme expression linked to developmental state	18–21
Rice	grains	9	–	e	–	–	123
Wheat	immature seeds	1	–	e,im	(2 loci)	de novo synthesis at imbibition; new isozymes immunologically distinct from immature forms	29, 30
Wheat	indosperm	16	–	e	2 loci, 3 alleles at each	–	123
β–Amylase (3.2.1.2)							
Barley	aleurone layers	4	–	e,k	–	zymogen activated by proteolysis in response to gibberellin	80
Maize	immature endosperm	4	–	e	1 locus with 2 alleles	isozyme expression linked to developmental state	18–21
Rice	seeds	2	–	e	–	–	6
Aspartate Aminotransferase (2.6.1.1)							
Pumpkin	cotyledon	7	–	e	–	4 sol. and 3 particulate forms; expression linked to developmental state	189
Catalase (1.11.1.6)							
Maize	immature endosperm	1	4	e,k,i	1 locus with 6 alleles; 2nd locus	isozymes have different rates of synthesis and degradation; isozyme expression linked to developmental state	8, 135, 163, 170
	scutellum	1–5	4	e,k,i	with 2 alleles		
Esterase							
Dianthus	callus culture	4–12	–	e	–	isozyme expression varies with light and temperature	109
Schizophyllum	mycelia	6–8	–	e	–	isozyme expression linked to developmental state	212

Table 2 (Continued)

Plant	Tissue	No. Isozymes	No. Sub-units	Method[a]	Genetic Basis	Remarks	Ref.
Xanthium	leaves	1–6	–	e	–	isozyme expression linked to developmental state	23
Maize	endosperm all tissues	4–13	2	e		isozyme expression is tissue and stage dependent	156
Glutamate Dehydrogenase (1.4.1.2)							
Barley	leaves	2	–	e	–	1 NAD specific; 1 NADP specific; isozyme expression linked to developmental state	150
Pea	leaves	4	–	e	–	isozyme expression varies with light treatment	88
Schizophyllum	mycelia	1–10	–	e	–	isozymes have different cofactor specificity; expression linked to developmental state	212
Glucokinase (2.7.1.2)							
Barley	leaves	6	–	e	–	isozyme pattern changes after infection	150
Glucose-6-P Dehydrogenase (1.1.1.49)							
Barley	leaves	7	–	e	–	isozyme pattern changes after infection	150
Schizophyllum	mycelia	6–13	–	e	–	isozyme expression linked to developmental state	212
Xanthium	leaves	6–9	–	e	–	isozyme expression linked to developmental state	23
Glucose-P-Isomerase (5.3.1.9)							
Barley	leaves	3–4	–	e	–	isozyme pattern changes after infection	150
Glyceraldehyde-3-P Dehydrogenase (1.2.1.12)							
Barley	seeds	2	–	k	–	isozymes have different cofactor specificity expression developmentally linked	37
Glycollate Oxidase (1.1.3.1)							
Barley	seeds	2	–	k	–	isozymes have different cofactor specificity expression linked to developmental state	37
Histidinol Dehydrogenase (1.1.1.23)							
Schizophyllum	mycelia	2–5	–	e	–	isozyme expression linked to developmental state	212
IAA Oxidase							
Pear	fruit	2	–	e	–	isozymes intensify during ripening	142

Table 2 (Continued)

Plant	Tissue	No. Isozymes	No. Sub-units	Method[a]	Genetic Basis	Remarks	Ref.
Tobacco	callus culture	7	–	e,i	–	isozymes differentially affected by hormones	91–94
Invertase (3.2.1.26)							
Carrot	root	2	–	e	–	isozyme expression linked to developmental state	143
Maize	endosperm	3	–	ixc,gf,k	–	2 sol. forms, 1 particulate; isozyme expression linked to developmental state	84
Isocitrate Dehydrogenase (1.1.1.41)							
Schizophyllum	mycelia	7–12	–	e	–	isozyme expression linked to developmental state	212
Lactate Dehydrogenase (1.1.1.27)							
Schizophyllum	mycelia	4–7	–	e	–	isozyme expression linked to developmental state	212
Malate Dehydrogenase (1.1.1.37)							
Barley	develop. grain	2	–	k	–	isozyme expression linked to developmental state	37
Barley	leaves	13	–	e	–	isozyme pattern changes after infection	150
Cotton	leaves	5	–	e	–	4 low MW forms, 1 high MW form; expression developmentally linked	125, 126
Maize	scutella		–	e,ixc,gf,k	–	mitochondrial forms are controlled by nuclear genes and are synthesized on cytoplasmic ribosomes	102, 166
Schizophyllum	mycelia	5–11	–	e	–	isozyme expression linked to developmental state	212
Tobacco	suspension culture	4	–	e,k	–	3 cyto. forms, 1 mito.; isozyme pattern influenced by temperature	31
Xanthium	leaves	5–7	–	e	–	isozyme expression linked to developmental state	23
Pectinesterase (3.1.1.11)							
Tomato	fruit	4	–	ixc	–	isozyme expression linked to developmental tate	133
Peroxidase (1.11.1.7)							
Apple	embryo	5	–	e,k	–	isozymes differentially stimulated by hormones	147

Table 2 (Continued)

Plant	Tissue	No. Isozymes	No. Sub-units	Method[a]	Genetic Basis	Remarks	Ref.
Banana	fruit	7		e	–	increase in enzyme activity during ripening due to particulate forms	68
Barley	leaves	5–6	–	e	–	isozyme pattern changes after infection	150
Datura	leaves	4–9	–	e	–	large interspecies polymorphism expression linked to developmental state	27
Jack Pine	germ. seed	10–18	–	e	–	isozyme expression linked to developmental state	138
Maize	immature endosperm	4–12	–	e	–	isozyme expression linked to developmental state	128
Pharbitis	various	4–7	–	e	–	isozyme expression linked to developmental state	223 224
Russian beans	embryos, cotyledons	4–11	–	e	–	isozyme expression linked to developmental state	14
Tobacco	various	7–14	–	e	–	isozymes differentially affected by hormones	95, 144 184
Tomato	fruit stem	9 6	–	e,heat stability	–	isozyme expression linked to developmental state	63, 89
6–Phosphogluconate Dehydrogenase (1.1.1.44)							
Barley	leaves	2	–	e	–	isozyme pattern changes after infection	150
Xanthium	leaves	1–5	–	e	–	isozyme pattern changes after infection	23
Phosphorylase (2.4.1.1)							
Xanthium	leaves	7–8	–	e	–	isozyme pattern linked to developmental state	23
Maize	immature endosperm	1–3	–	e	–	isozyme pattern linked to developmental state	18
Polyphenoloxidase							
Tea	leaves	6	–	e,ixc	–	isozyme expression linked to developmental state	196
Tobacco	pith	3–4	–	e,k	–	isozymes differentially affected by hormones	192
Barley	leaf	4–5	–	e	–	isozyme pattern changes after infection	150

[a]Key to method of determination: e = electrophoresis; gf = gel filtration; k = kinetics; i = differential inhibitor; ixc = ion exchange chromatography; im = immunological methods.

[b]Enzyme numbering system taken from "Report of the Commission on Enzymes of International Union of Biochemistry."

GENETICS AND DEVELOPMENT

Under the influence of Beadle's "one gene-one enzyme hypothesis" and the fact that there are now many examples of stage and tissue specific levels of enzyme activities during growth and differentiation of higher organisms, it has become fairly popular to interpret such enzyme fluctuations as the consequence of differential gene action. However, due to the fact that RNA has been shown to be the first and most direct product of gene function, the above assumption is not a priori valid, providing of course we interpret gene action to mean transcription. Until our methodology for directly measuring transcriptional events during development is perfected, we can at best speak of differential gene expression. But at whatever level of biological organization enzyme activity is regulated, the complement of enzymes in a cell constitutes a measure of its differentiated state and is a reflection of the genetic information contained in the cell (204). A variety of mechanisms could account for cell and stage specific levels of enzyme activity; among these are differential transcription, differential translation, differential activation, differential degradation, differential inhibition, differential accumulation, and differential organelle localization.

The enzyme activity of individual isozymes in a specific tissue is dependent, among other factors, on maturity and cellular environment. Changes in isozyme activity during development of a tissue can be detected most conveniently by pattern shifts on zymograms subsequent to electrophoresis. Some common isozyme fluctuations encountered by a number of investigators in a variety of organisms with respect to a given enzyme system are: (a) distinct isozymes in different tissues of a given organism; (b) some isozymes may be present in a tissue at a given developmental stage but absent at another; (c) genetically identical isozymes may be present in different tissues but in varying quantities. Relatively few investigators have gone beyond the descriptive aspects of such findings. Many reports on isozymes deal merely with the description of the behavior of the molecules in electrophoresis; though it is a powerful and convenient tool, electrophoresis by itself cannot answer the crucial questions regarding isozymes whether they be asked by the geneticist, biochemist, or physiologist. We must also utilize other techniques from protein chemistry. We must attempt to understand the genetic and physicochemical nature of isozymes in order to eliminate the possibility of artifacts. It is indeed difficult to comprehend encompassing statements or theories posed by some population biologists or those interested in regulation when in many instances the only data presented are the number and patterns of "bands" on a zymogram.

Research in this field has been very vigorous and cannot be covered in a single review, at least not if it is to be done critically. Consequently only a few isozyme systems will be discussed in this review.

SOME SPECIFIC ISOZYME SYSTEMS

Alcohol Dehydrogenase

Alcohol dehydrogenase (ADH; alchol: NAD oxidoreductase, EC 1.1.1.1) is distributed widely among animals, plants, and microorganisms, and catalyzes the following reaction: $RCH_2OH + NAD \rightleftharpoons RCHO + NADH_2$. The reaction is not highly specific with respect to substrate. The enzyme can react with a large number of substrates including normal and branched-chain aliphatic and aromatic alcohols (primary and secondary).

Among higher plants, isozymes of ADH have been reported for maize (160, 162, 176), wheat (71), *Chenopodium,* barley, peas, peanuts, sorghum and *Datura* (166). The most detailed investigations to date have been with the maize ADH isozyme system.

DEVELOPMENTAL EXPRESSION OF ADH ISOZYMES   During the early stages of kernel development in maize, two distinct forms of ADH are found; these have been designated as ADH-1 and ADH-2. These isozymes have been well defined genetically, being coded by two closely linked genes (162, 165). Each locus has two alleles (Adh_1^F and Adh_1^S; Adh_2^F and Adh_2^S) which code for either a slow or a fast electrophoretic form of the enzyme in a given inbred line. As kernel development progresses, two additional isozymes of ADH begin to emerge, becoming prominent in the scutellum of the dry caryopsis and during the first days of germination (Figure 1). One of these isozymes (ADH-3) has a slightly faster, and the other (ADH-4) a slower electrophoretic mobility than ADH-2. The specific activity of ADH in the scutellum at its maximum (i.e. 24 hr soaking of seed) is three- to fourfold higher than in the liquid endosperm of the same genetic strain. In the following days, the activity undergoes a rapid decline, and by the tenth day of germination, only one eighth of the peak activity remains in the scutellum. While ADH-2 remains during the first 10 days after germination, ADH-1, ADH-3, and ADH-4 are detectable zymographically only during the first days, disappearing usually by the fourth day; the timing varies slightly with some inbred strains, but the pattern is the same. There is sufficient evidence that mutations effecting the electrophoretic mobility of ADH-2

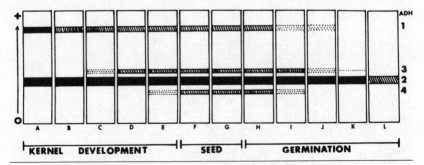

Figure 1 A composite schematic zymogram of the developmental pattern of the alcohol dehydrogenase isozymes in maize scutella. A = endosperm 16–30 days after pollination (for comparison); B = scutellum 16–33 days after pollination (pattern is same whether single or pooled scutella are assayed); C = scutellum 34–39 days after pollination; D = scutellum 45–49 days after pollination; E = scutellum 50–56 days after pollination; F = scutellum from dry dormant seed; G = scutellum from imbibed seed; H, I, J, K, L are respectively, scutella from 1, 2, 3, 4, and 10 days after germination (sporophytic development). 0 = point of sample insertion; migration is anodal.

do not simultaneously affect ADH-3 or ADH-4, suggesting separate structural genes for these isozymes (166, 169).

ORGAN (TISSUE) DISTRIBUTION OF ADH ISOZYMES DURING DEVELOPMENT   The isozymes ADH-1 and ADH-2 are the most common forms of the enzyme in all tissues examined at various developmental stages, but ADH-1 is not found in endosperm of mature kernels or during germination. Most differences between tissues are quantitative variations in ADH activity. The most apparent qualitative differences are those noted during scutellar development and the appearance of a fifth ADH isozyme (ADH-T) in the maternally derived pericarp tissue of developing kernels with an electrophoretic mobility greater than that of ADH-1. The existence of ADH-T is transient, being found only between days 19 and 40 of kernel development (169). None of the ADH isozymes have been found to be associated with any particular cellular component at any stage of development.

EFFECT OF GENETIC BACKGROUND ON ADH INTERACTIONS AND PROPERTIES   The isozymes ADH-1 and ADH-2 were isolated from both homozygous and heterozygous kernels and their biochemical properties examined (47). Both ADH-1F and ADH-2F have greater specific activity and are more heat stable than the alternative slow forms of both isozymes. In reciprocal heterozygotes, the ADH-1 activity patterns show genetic dosing due to the triploid nature of the endosperm, and the slow form is more active in S X F heterozygotes while the fast form is more active in F X S heterozygotes. For ADH-2, the hybrid molecule (F/S) generated in the F X S heterozygote is intermediate in activity between the F/F and S/S homodimers of ADH-2; however, in the reciprocal cross S X F, the S/F heterodimer of ADH-2 is catalytically more efficient than either the F/F or S/S homodimer. This is consistent with the possibility that the S subunit is a catalytically less efficient polypeptide than the F subunit. In the F X S heterozygote, the F/F:F/S:S/S forms should show enzyme activity on a 4:4:1 ratio, with gene dosing and identical enzymatic activity contributed by the F and S subunits. However, since the F/S heterodimer is intermediate in activity, one can presume the decrease to be due to the catalytically less efficient S polypeptide. With the dosing ratio being the same, but in the reverse for the S X F heterozygote, the S/F heterodimer is more active probably due to the greater efficiency of the F subunit. It is noteworthy that the F/F homodimer is almost as active as the S/S homodimer in the S X F heterozygote even though they should follow a 1:4 activity ratio. The hybrid enzymes have thermostability similar to the F/F homodimer; this could be due to possible stabilization of the S monomer by the F monomer following the dimerization process.

While the catalytic efficiency of the F/F homodimer of ADH-2 is considerably greater than that of the S/S homodimer, the K_m values for ethanol and other substrates (48) for the two forms of ADH-2 are not very different. This could mean that the S/S isozyme has a lower turnover number but binds the ethanol and other substrates as well as does the F/F isozymes.

The two variant forms of ADH-2 have been purified to homogeneity (48), and amino acid compositions of the acid hydrolysates of ADH-2S and ADH-2F were found to be similar. The similarity in amino acid compositions of these allelic isozymes provides evidence that the mutational event which differentiated these two forms of ADH-2 involved the substitution of only one or a few base sequences in the Adh_2 gene. These small alterations in the primary structure of ADH-2 exert a large influence on the biochemical properties of the molecule. The amino acid substitutions between ADH-2F and ADH-2S are probably not strategically located at the substrate binding sites of these molecules since the K_m values do not differ dramatically between the two isozymes. However, since the F form is much more thermostable than the S form and has a six fold greater specific activity than the S form, it is likely that the amino acid substitutions which differentiate the two isozymes are important in the tertiary and quaternary organization of ADH.

EFFECT OF ANAEROBIOSIS   Alcohol dehydrogenase is known to increase in activity under anaerobic conditions (69). However, it is not clear what the mechanism for the increase is, nor was it known whether the total increase reported was due to a specific isozyme. It is known that under anaerobic conditions the Krebs cycle is blocked, leading to accumulation of pyruvate. It is then possible that the excess pyruvate is decarboxylated to form acetaldehyde which acting as a substrate, induces ADH. If this be the case, anaerobiosis could possibly be used as a "tool" to study mechanisms involved in the regulation of the expression of the different ADH gene products in maize.

When various tissues (scutellum, root, shoot) taken from anaerobically grown seedlings were examined for ADH activity, significant increases (five- to eightfold) were apparent (122); however, no new isozymes were detected. Thus the apparent increase in ADH activity under anaerobiosis is not due to activation or "induction" of new isozymes. What becomes clear is that ADH-1 (specified by the Adh_1 gene) increases significantly under anaerobic conditions as compared to the other ADH isozymes. This is of interest since ADH-1 seems to favor the backward reaction (acetaldehyde $\longrightarrow$ ethanol).

REGULATION OF ADH EXPRESSION DURING DEVELOPMENT   Unlike most enzymes whose activity increases sharply after germination, alcohol dehydrogenase activity of maize scutella (169) and in germinating pea cotyledons (195) declines rapidly during this period.

These findings suggest two possibilities for the control of ADH: (a) faster degradation (or inactivation) than formation of active enzyme molecules; or·(b) only degradation (or inactivation) without further formation of active enzyme molecules.

Recent results from this laboratory have shown that the time course of ADH activity after germination remained unchanged in the presence of a protein synthesis inhibitor (cycloheximide, $10\mu g/ml$) or RNA synthesis inhibitor (actinomycin D, 50 $\mu g/ml$), suggesting that the control of ADH activity is independent of transcription and translation. Furthermore, by employing density labeling techniques (135), we found that ADH molecules from seeds germinated in 70% D_2O and 10 mM $^{15}NH_4Cl$ for 36 hours have exactly the same buoyant density as the ADH from seed germinated in H_2O and $^{14}NH_4Cl$, clearly showing that there is no turnover of ADH molecules during early sporophytic development. Having thus established the absence of de novo synthesis of ADH molecules, what then are the mechanisms for controlling the decrease in ADH activity? Is it due to degradation by a protease or to inactivation by a specific inhibitor? Reciprocal mixing experiments between scutellar extracts from early and late stages of germination resulted in a significant decrease in ADH activity of early scutellar development extracts; this suggested the presence of an inhibitory substance (or substances) generated in the later stages of germination. The inhibition can be prevented by including β-mercaptoethanol in the mixture. Since no maize protease is known to be inhibited by β-mercaptoethanol, the possibility that the inhibitor might be a protease was ruled out. The amount of inhibitor, assuming it is proportional to the extent of inhibition, rises steadily after 24 hours of germination; simultaneously, ADH activity begins to decline. This fact allows us to propose that the generation of this inhibitor(s) actually accounts for the decrease of ADH activity after germination. The inhibition is irreversible, and the inhibitor itself is heat labile and partially dialyzable.

Recently, alternative mechanisms, including a "regulator" gene, have been proposed (40, 56, 174) to explain regulation of ADH activity in maize. These alternatives are theoretically attractive, but they cannot account for our results, and we find no compelling elements in our data to postulate "regulatory" genes. It is apparent from our data that regulation is exerted at the gene product level primarily following termination of synthesis or translation.

Amylase

The enzymes of starch metabolism are of particular interest in biochemical studies of plant development due to their intrinsic involvement in seed maturation and in germination. Although carbohydrate metabolism has been studied in plants, critical genetic and developmental studies have been lacking until recently. The two enzymes which have been best characterized are α and β amylase. One obstacle in studying these enzymes is the lack of a quantitative assay which can distinguish between α and β amylase activities in a mixture of the two enzymes. After separation (by electrophoresis, for example), the enzymes may be characterized by endproduct analysis, ability to hydrolyze β-limit dextrin, and pH or heat sensitivity. The incorporation of ^{45}Ca into specific isozymes has been used to identify α-amylase (12), although the demonstration of two α-amylases which may not require Ca^{2+} (80) makes this an uncertain criterion.

Total amylolytic activity in several cereals typically rises during kernel development, decreases at maturation, and then increases dramatically during germination (6, 12, 21, 30). In maize, 80% of the amylolytic activity in germinating seeds is localized in the endosperm and scutellum, with the remaining 20% found in the shoot and root (21). This pattern is probably typical for other cereals as well. Analyses of the specific behavior of each amylase species during this period indicate some interesting contrasts in the developmental and regulatory patterns of the two enzymes.

In germinating barley seeds, α-amylase (alpha-1,4-glucan-4-glucanohydrolase, E.C. 3.2.1.1) is synthesized de novo in the aleurone layer in response to gibberellin (51, 206). Daussant & Corvazier (29) demonstrated ^{14}C incorporation into α-

amylase of germinating wheat, also indicating probable de novo synthesis in this system. It appears both in barley and in maize that the overall amylase increase during germination can be attributed largely to α-amylase (21, 80). During the first 4 days of germination in maize, β-amylase activity even decreases slightly (18).

Alpha-amylase has been shown to exist in isozymic forms in barley (21, 58), maize (159), rice (6), wheat (29), tobacco callus cultures (83), and peas (222). The pattern of amylase isozymes during early development in maize is shown in Figure 2. The electrophoretic patterns suggest that the majority of the amylase isozymes present during germination are also expressed in the immature kernel. Exceptions are the appearance of a third zone 1 amylase, and a zone 4 amylase during germination. This is in contrast to the observation of Daussant & Renard (30), who found no immunological relationship between the α-amylase of immature and germinating wheat kernels. Unfortunately, he did not publish zymograms comparing electrophoretic properties. Identical electrophoretic behavior of α-amylases from mature and immature barley seeds (12, 80) indicate that the wheat system may be unique in this regard. Immunological studies on barley and maize α-amylases will be necessary to fully resolve the question.

In contrast to α-amylase, β-amylase (α-1,4-glucan maltohydrolase, E.C. 3.2.1.2), does not appear to be newly synthesized during germination, but rather to be activated by limited proteolysis of a zymogen precursor present in the immature kernel. This appears to be the case for barley (12), maize (18), and wheat (29). In light of the complementary nature of the two enzymes, it is interesting that their regulation would involve such diverse mechanisms. This paradox is partially resolved by the demonstration (81), of a protease that is induced in the barley aleurone by gibberellin and secreted into the endosperm where it could presumably activate the β-amylase zymogen. Gene dosage studies in maize (19, 20) suggest that at least one species of β-amylase (or that of β-amylase zymogen) is synthesized in the scutellum rather than the endosperm. Since β-amylase activity is found in the endosperm, either the zymogen or the active enzyme must be secreted at some point in seed development.

Genetic characterization of the amylases has been carried out in barley (58, 164), wheat (123), and in maize (18–20). As in developmental studies, complete genetic characterization has been hindered by difficulties in distinguishing between α and β-amylase species. It seems clear that amylase is under nuclear gene control and follows Mendelian inheritance patterns (164). In maize, differential expression of the Amy-1 locus (which codes for an α-amylase) has been observed (20). Although differential gene expression has been observed in other systems, to our knowledge this is the first example of the phenomenon in plants.

To date, one locus controlling α-amylase and one controlling β-amylase have been reported in maize (18, 20). Two codominant alleles have been recovered at each locus. The sub-bands in each zone have not yet been genetically characterized and may involve additional loci. The two characterized loci are probably not linked (20).

Multiple α-amylase loci have been reported in wheat by Nishikawa & Nobuhara (123), although the evolutionary history of wheat makes it difficult to assess the true significance of this discovery.

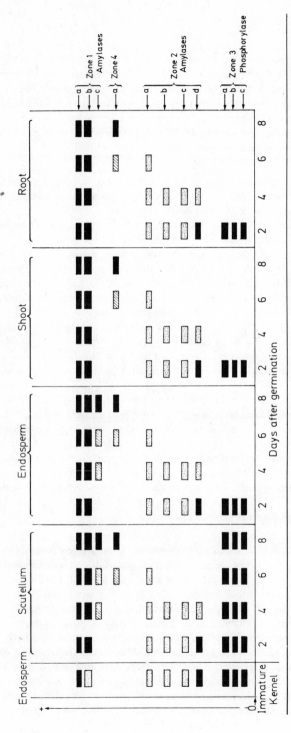

Figure 2 Composite schematic zymogram of amylase from gel assays of tissues of germinating maize seedlings. Zone 1, 2, and 4 are amylases. Bands 1a and 2d are the two genetically defined amylases (designated as Amy-1 alpha-amylase and Amy-2 beta-amylase). Zone 3 is phosphorylase and consists of either one or three bands depending on the strain used. The strains W64A and 38-11 have only one common phosphorylase isozyme, band 3c. The strain 58-3-6 has 3 phosphorylase isozymes as shown in the drawing.

Catalase

Catalase (H_2O_2:H_2O_2 oxidoreductase; E. C. 1.11.1.6) is the most thoroughly investigated isozyme system in higher plants. Although its biological role remains unknown, its presence seems to be important as an accessory to the consumption of oxygen by organisms. Catalases have four iron atoms per molecule attached to the protein and chelated to protoporphyrin IX. Catalase is widely distributed among microorganisms, plants, and animals.

GENETIC CONTROL   Catalase isozymes have been detected in peas, *Chenopodium*, sorghum, barley, peanuts, spinach, and maize (166); among these, maize catalases have thus far been examined in most detail.

In developing maize endosperm (16 days postpollination) there is one molecular form of catalase; six electrophoretic variants of this form have been found on screening endosperm of immature kernels from a large number of inbred maize strains (103, 163). It was further shown that the endosperm catalase variants are controlled by six allelic genes (Ct_1^F, Ct_1^K, Ct_1^M, Ct_1^S, Ct_1^V, $Ct_1^{V'}$) at the Ct_1 locus and that the frequency of occurrence of the six alleles in a given population size differed significantly, with the Ct_1^S allele being most common and $Ct_1^{V'}$ the least common (163, 164). In F_1 heterozygotes between any two variant strains (e.g. $Ct_1^F \times Ct_1^V$, catalase from milky endosperm is electrophoretically resolvable into five distinct forms—the two parental types and three new "hybrid molecules" (157). The hybrid catalases can also be generated in vitro by dissociation-reassociation experiments in 1 M NaCl (157); thus the genetic and chemical data reveal a tetrameric structure for catalase. In endosperm, we are dealing with a triploid tissue and consequently there are apparent gene dosage effects encountered in an obvious way with multimeric (functional enzyme composed of more than one polypeptide subunit) enzymes such as catalase. Thus in heterozygotes two kinds of individuals are observed, depending on the direction in which the genetic cross was made, since the maternal genomic contribution is twice the paternal; this offers an opportunity to examine the effects of gene dosing on enzyme structure and function. Gene dosing can also act as an internal marker to determine the time of expression of the maternal versus the paternal genome after fertilization.

DEVELOPMENTAL CONTROL OF GENE EXPRESSION   In any given inbred strain of maize homozygous for the Ct_1 gene, which is expressed during seed development, a second gene Ct_2 is also expressed, but at a different stage of development. The product of the Ct_2 gene, which is genetically and biochemically distinct from the product of any of the Ct_1 alleles, is first detected in the dry seed (primarily in the scutellum) and increases dramatically in the first 4 days of germination, while the Ct_1 gene product gradually disappears. At the developmental stage when both genes are simultaneously expressed and both classes of subunits are available, five species of active tetramers are detected, two homotetramers (multimer composed of identical subunits) and three heterotetramers [multimer composed of nonidentical subunits (Figure 3)]. Thus in the maize catalase system, hybrid isozymes are generated by both intragenic and intergenic complementation, a fact which renders it an excellent system for studying the possible functional advantages or disadvantages of heteromultimers over homomultimers.

DIFFERENTIAL TURNOVER OF THE CT_1 AND CT_2 CATALASES   The differential expression of the two catalase genes during maize sporophytic development raises the following questions: Is the slowly appearing product of the Ct_2 locus synthesized de novo and does it turn over as it accumulates? Does the disappearance of the Ct_1 locus represent degradation in the absence of further synthesis or are the subunits turning over as they disappear? Do the rates of synthesis and degradation of the two gene products differ from one another? These questions have been answered by employing the techniques of gel electrophoresis and density labeling techniques in conjunction with isopycnic equilibrium sedimentation (77, 135, 136). Thus de novo synthesis can be detected and quantified without recourse to enzyme isolation and purification. Results from such experiments showed that both catalase homotetramers V^4 (product of the Ct_1 gene) and Z^4 (product of the Ct_2 gene) turn over in the scutella of maize seeds during germination—Z^4 as it accumulates, V^4 as it disappears. Z^4 accumulates because the rate of synthesis exceeds the rate of degradation, whereas V^4 slowly disappears because the rate of degradation exceeds the rate of synthesis. These data clearly indicate that both classes of catalase subunits are synthesized de novo (Figure 4). In addition, pulse-chase density labeling experiments indicate that the rate of synthesis of Z^4 exceeds that of V^4, which suggests that this may be a major factor in the differential expression of the two catalase genes (135). These findings are consistent with the general pattern observed in higher organisms where protein turnover appears to be a general and continuous process and enzyme concentrations may be controlled by independent alterations in either the rate constants of degradation or synthesis (173).

SUBCELLULAR LOCALIZATION OF CATALASE ISOZYMES   During seed development, catalase is found almost exclusively in the soluble fraction and not associated with any distinct organelles. However, during early sporophytic development the situation is somewhat different. As development proceeds from dry seeds, glyoxysome

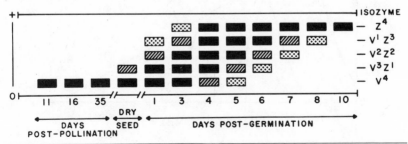

Figure 3   Zymogram changes in catalase isozyme patterns of maize kernels before and during seed germination. The V^4 isozyme is composed of subunits from the Ct_1^V locus. This isozyme is present in immature kernels as well as the developing seedling. The Z^4 isozyme is composed of subunits from the Ct_2 locus. This locus is expressed at the onset of germination. The intermediate isozymes V^1Z^3, V^2Z^2, and V^3Z^1 are hybrids composed of subunits from both genetic loci.

biogenesis in scutella also becomes apparent and reaches a peak at the fourth day of germination (100, 166). When glyoxysomes are isolated from 4-day-old scutella, approximately 25–30% of the total catalase present at this stage of development is associated with these organelles; none is associated with mitochondria, and the remainder remains associated with the soluble fraction. Thus all particulate catalase is exclusively associated with glyoxysomes, and the time course of catalase activity

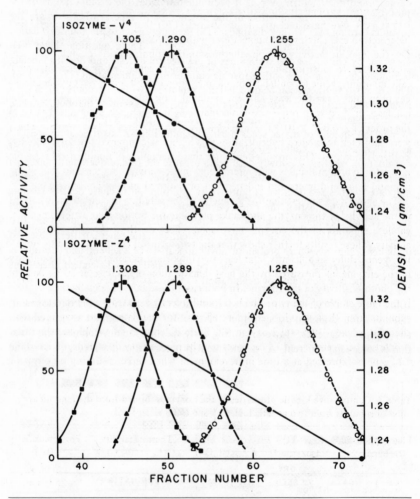

Figure 4   Equilibrium distribution in CsCl gradients of scutella catalase isozymes V^4 and Z^4 from seeds grown for 36 hr on either $K^{14}NO_3$ in H_2O (▲–▲) or $K^{15}NO_3$ in 70% D_2O (■–■). The activity of the LDH marker in the labeled (O–O) and unlabeled (△–△) gradients have been superimposed and drawn as one. Relative activity means that all points on these curves are expressed as a percentage of the highest point on each of the individual curves. Density of CsCl gradient (●–●).

closely parallels the development of these organelles. Furthermore, there is no particular catalase isozyme specific to glyozysomes; the isozyme complement of the organelles parallels that of scutellar development as a whole (See Figure 3) (166).

Recent investigations (101) by means of the diaminobenzidine histochemical reaction suggest that about 30% of the total catalase is localized in both membranes and matrix of glyoxysomes isolated from 4-day-old scutella.

BIOCHEMICAL PROPERTIES OF THE GENETICALLY AND DEVELOPMENTALLY DEFINED CATALASES   We have recently demonstrated (170) that the homotetrameric and heterotetrameric catalases of maize differ with respect to their biochemical properties (i.e. specific activity, Kapp, thermostability, photosensitivity, inhibitor sensitivity, etc). In most instances, the heterotetramers generated by either intragenic (allelic) or intergenic (nonallelic) complementation exhibit improved physicochemical properties over the least efficient parental molecules (Table 3). None of the catalases differed with respect to molecular weight which was determined to be in the order of 280,000 ± 10,000. Catalase activity in mixtures of two variants which were subjected to in vitro hybridization was higher as compared to simple (nonhybridized) mixtures. This provides evidence that interaction of nonidentical subunits generates hybrid molecules with altered enzymatic activity, higher than that of the parental homomultimers and independent of the total protein concentration.

The above data suggest that the geometry of the subunits in catalase is important in the activity of the enzyme and make plausible the notion that arrangements of catalase subunits in the enzyme have some effect on the expression of enzyme activity. These results further show that the two forms of catalase, coded by nonallelic genes, differ significantly in at least two important parameters: (a) the stability of the enzyme, as measured by the heat denaturation of catalase at 50°C; and (b) the photosensitivity of the enzyme. In both cases the catalase coded by the Ct_2 gene is the more stable of the two. The heteromultimers generated by the interaction of subunits from these two loci are more efficient for the parameters examined than the least efficient parental isozyme V^4. Such differences in the physicochemical properties between V^4 and Z^4 catalases may be physiologically significant, since the Ct_2 gene is expressed at a time in development when there is turning on of major

Table 3 Comparative kinetic properties of the isozymes formed from the random association of subunits from two genetic loci, Ct_1^V and Ct_2^Z

Electrophoretic Band	Isozyme	K_{app} (H$_2$O$_2$)	Thermostability ($t_{1/2}$ at 50° C)	Photosensitivity ($t_{1/2}$)
1	Z^4	0.057 M	141 min.	25.0 min.
2	Z^3V^1	0.051 M	46 min.	20.5 min.
3	Z^2V^2	0.038 M	20 min.	15.0 min.
4	Z^1V^3	0.083 M	10 min.	8.0 min.
5	V^4	0.143 M	6.5 min.	6.8 min.

metabolic processes essential for development and differentiation of the maize plant; it is at this stage in development that the root and shoot emerge.

TISSUE (ORGAN) SPECIFICITY OF CATALASE ISOZYMES   Catalase isozyme patterns undergo changes in development as in the case of the scutellum above. In addition, the complement of catalases is found to vary with some tissues at a given stage in development (e.g. scutellum, endosperm, pericarp, leaf at 4 days germination). Therefore, it is found that the same complement may be present in different tissues (e.g. stems, roots, husks, silks of adult plants), but comparatively the activity and relative concentrations of the catalase varies drastically among them. A third observation has been the appearance of new isozymes specific to a given tissue at a point in development. Such a situation exists in the case of pericarp development where a unique catalase isozyme appears at the twenty-fifth day of kernel development, and another at the seventh day of sporophytic development. Interestingly, the latter is present only on the seventh day and only if seeds are germinated and grown in light conditions. It is essential to point out that such variations appear to vary somewhat with the particular inbred strains used; thus the total genetic background apparently affects both the temporal and spatial specificity of isozyme expression, a point worth considering in studies of physiology and development in general.

The maize catalase system presents an opportunity to study differential gene expression in a higher plant, as controlled by different rates of synthesis and degradation of two distinct gene products. These two gene products are in the same cell with presumably similar physiological functions, though one may be more efficient than the other, and with apparently the same subcellular distribution and at the same stage of development, but differing in their rates of synthesis and/or degradation to the extent that one increases dramatically in activity while the other disappears. The differences in biochemical properties afford an opportunity to examine the effects of gene interaction and gene dosage on enzyme structure and function, and in the case of catalase its subcellular location and tissue specificity may shed some light on its biological role(s).

Malate Dehydrogenase

Malate dehydrogenase (MDH:E.C. 1.1.1.37) catalyzes the reaction:

$$\text{malate} + \text{NAD}^+ \rightleftharpoons \text{oxaloacetate} + \text{NADH}^+ + \text{H}^+$$

MDH has several important physiological functions within the cell. As one of the Krebs cycle enzymes, it plays a central role in most biochemical pathways within the cell. It is an integral part of the malate shuttle, the mechanisms for transferring reducing equivalents across the mitochondrial membranes, and it may participate in CO_2 fixation in higher plants.

Isozymes of malate dehydrogenase are known to occur in a variety of plant and animal tissues.

It appears that MDH isozymes exhibit few if any qualitative changes during the course of development (102, 125, 145). However, they are of developmental interest in that different isozymes are found in association with a wide array of subcellular organelles, and there appear to be dramatic differences in the regulation of MDH activities at these various subcellular sites. Organisms studied include maize (102), *Neurospora,* (10), barley (37, 64), cotton (125), cauliflower (137), *Euglena* (131), *Chlorella* (194), *Schizophyllum* (212), wheat (115), *Xanthium* (23), and tobacco suspension cultures (31).

MDH isozymes generally have molecular weights in the neighborhood of 60,000 (125, 146, 194), although the isozymes in maize seem to be somewhat larger (221). High molecular weight forms have been reported in cotton (126), but these may be simply aggregates of the native enzymes, or maybe enzyme still attached to membrane fragments. The latter possibility is supported by the finding of DeJong & Olson (31), that treatment with deoxycholate alters the electrophoretic mobility of the mitochondrial forms of the enzyme.

The total cellular MDH activity tends to increase during early maize development (102), and this increase has been shown to be due to de novo synthesis of the enzyme rather than to an activation mechanism (221).

The soluble forms make up a substantial portion of the MDH activity in the cell (102), and the occurrence of isozymes in this subcellular fraction appears to be a fairly general phenomenon (31, 102, 131, 146). The cytoplasmic forms are subject to glucose repression in *Neurospora* (10), and soluble MDH activity is approximately three times greater in dark grown *Euglena* than in light grown cells (131). Both effects are reversible, and the changes in activity during recovery are not reflected by corresponding changes in the activity of the particulate forms.

Mitochondrial MDH (mMDH) isozymes are the best characterized of the organelle-associated isozymes. Mendelian inheritance patterns, dosage effects in triploid tissues in maize (102), and the recovery of nuclear gene mutations affecting both catalytic efficiency and membrane binding ability of mMDH isozymes in *Neurospora* (118) demonstrate that the structural genes for the mitochondrial isozymes are located in the nuclear rather than the mitochondrial genome. Nuclear gene control is further supported by reports of different isozymes associated with different "mitochondrial populations" in heterotic barley hybrids (64). Antibiotic studies in both maize (221) and *Neurospora* (10) strongly suggest that the enzymes are synthesized on cytoplasmic ribosomes and subsequently incorporated into the mitochondrion. Earlier reports that mitochondrial isozymes were merely conformers of the soluble forms have been discredited by a wealth of somewhat circumstantial biochemical data (cf 10, 131, 146, 221), and more conclusively by immunological (194) and genetic analyses (102, 221). Mitochondrial isozymes are not subject to either glucose repression or light effects as are the cytoplasmic forms (10, 131).

Specific MDH isozymes have been found in association with glyoxysomes (gMDH) in maize (102, 221) and in spinach (146, 220). These forms have been best characterized from spinach (145, 146), although no genetic characterization has been done in any system.

Early reports of MDH activity associated with chloroplasts were discounted by Yamazaki & Tolbert (220) as being artifacts of inadequate organelle isolation procedures. Recent work, however, clearly demonstrates a chloroplast-associated MDH species which is specific for NADP as a cofactor rather than NAD (200). The physiological significance of this is not presently understood.

The MDH system offers good potential for answering a number of developmental questions. It is a potentially superior system for the study of enzyme compartmentation processes since physically similar proteins are highly specifically incorporated into varied membrane structures (i.e. mitochondria, glyoxysomes, chloroplasts). The MDH system offers interesting possibilities for regulatory studies, since both constitutive and repressible forms of the enzyme are available within the same cell. The fact that different and highly specific forms of the enzyme have been found in association with nearly every major subcellular site offers a unique system for studies of communication between organelles. Finally, the mMDH system may offer a fruitful approach to studying the interactions between the nuclear and mitochondrial genomes.

Peptidases

AMINOPEPTIDASE Aminopeptidases are exopeptidases which hydrolyze peptide linkages adjacent to the free α-amino groups of a peptide. The reaction results in a free amino acid and a smaller peptide, and the process may be repeated since the smaller peptide would also contain a free amino group (35). Aminopeptidase is often referred to by the more restrictive term "leucine aminopeptidase (LAP)," since it was originally believed to hydrolyze exclusively leucine N-terminals. However, in recent years there have been reports that these enzymes will readily hydrolyze amino acid residues other than leucine (164, 168). These enzymes have also been referred to as "naphthylamidases" and "arylamidases."

Aminopeptidases are widely distributed in microorganisms (9, 79), animals (7, 149, 161), and plants (156, 158, 164, 167, 168) for which isozymes have been reported.

Aminopeptidases are known to increase, both quantitatively and qualitatively, during active periods of development and differentiation in both animals (116, 149, 161) and plants (158, 164). Although the exact physiological role of aminopeptidases is not yet understood, it is likely that as exopeptidases they may have a regulatory function by playing a role in protein turnover during differentiation.

Isozymes of aminopeptidases (AmP) in higher plants have been reported in maize (156, 158, 164), *Phaseolus* (211, 213), and *Pisum* (167, 168).

The aminopeptidases of maize are controlled by four distinct, but linked, diallelic loci (164). The isozymes are distributed throughout the maize plant with some apparent tissue specificity (156). Temporally, the isozyme LAP-D, coded by the *LpD* gene, is interesting in that it is predominantly and transiently found in the liquid endosperm of developing kernels. In general, the specific activity of aminopeptidases is greatest in meristematic tissues or at developmental stages where there is rapid growth or differentiation (157). The latter is the case in all plant and animal species examined.

In peas, two forms of aminopeptidases (AmP) are found in all tissues and various stages of normal development and differentiation (168). One form (AmP-1) was found to be polymorphic with alternate forms controlled by allelic genes at the AmP_1 locus. The second isozyme (AmP_2) has thus far been found to be monomorphic and controlled by a second, presumably linked gene. The pea aminopeptidases, like those of maize, are not specific for leucine N-terminal residues. The AmP isozymes of peas are differentially inhibited by metal ions; however, Hg^{2+} proved to be the most effective inhibitor of all the aminopeptidases in both *Pisum* and maize.

The pattern of AmP in peas does not change spatially or temporally. However, significant quantitative fluctuations are apparent during the course of seedling development.

A third aminopeptidase isozyme (m-AmP) is found in peas and is exclusively associated with the mitochondria. Variants of m-AmP are known and formal genetic analysis indicates that it is encoded in chromosomal genes (167). Though it is difficult to assign a physiological function to the m-AmP isozymes in relation to their subcellular location, it is possible that they play a role in mitochondrial protein turnover.

Two major aminopeptidase isozymes are also found in a number of *Phaseolus* species. Genetic studies (211) have led to the conclusion that one form exhibits genetic variability based on codominant alleles at one locus.

ENDOPEPTIDASE   A trypsin-like endopeptidase was recently discovered in maize (110). In any single highly inbred strain examined only one electrophoretically distinct form of the enzyme is present. Variants of this endopeptidase (EP-1) were found among the inbreds tested, and genetic analyses show that it is controlled by codominant alleles at the Ep_1 locus. More recent data show the presence of five alleles of Ep_1, and the locus has been located on chromosome 6 (166).

No other isozymes appear in the course of development and differentiation of the maize plant; the single molecular form characteristic of the individual inbred line is the only form in every tissue and every stage examined. However, there are quantitative differences apparent during development, with the highest levels of endopeptidase activity in the 18-day-old liquid endosperm of immature kernels. The variant endopeptidases are similar with respect to molecular weight, K_m, thermostability, and pH optima; however, they were found to have distinct pI. None of the EP-1 variants were inhibited by the endogenous tryspin inhibitor as determined by quantitative spectrophotometric assay, but they were similarly affected by a number of metal ion inhibitors, being severely inhibited by Hg^{2+} and Cu^{2+}.

The fact that no detectable inhibition of maize endopeptidase by endogenous maize trypsin inhibitor was observed suggests that regulation of endogenous protease activity may not be an in vivo function of inhibitor proteins in *Zea mays*. However, it should be pointed out that other maize endopeptidases undetectable by these techniques may be regulated by such inhibitors. Since the endogenous maize trypsin-inhibitor was found to dramatically inhibit protease activity in extracts from two maize parasites, corn borer *(Ostrinia nubilalis)* and corn ear worm *(Heliothis zea)* (110), it is possible that this specific inhibitor has evolved to a point where it does not recognize and inhibit endogenous proteases but may function to inhibit and destroy protease of destructive parasites.

In contrast to animal proteases, plant proteases and particularly endopeptidases and exopeptidases are not well characterized. Very little is known about plant peptidases involved in metabolism and turnover of proteins, especially during development. Many of the better characterized proteases such as papain, chymopapain, ficin, and bromelain have low pH activity optima, are located in cell sap, and may not be involved in protein turnover (4). However, none of the aforementioned plant proteases has been defined genetically or developmentally.

As a group, the peptidases are likely involved in regulation and protein turnover during development and differentiation, and their study may uncover differential roles for the different peptidase isozymes during plant development.

Peroxidases

Peroxidases (donor: H_2O_2 oxidoreductase; E.C. 1.11.1.7) are enzymes which can utilize hydrogen peroxide to oxidize a wide range of hydrogen donors such as phenolic substances, cytochrome c, nitrite, leuco-dyes, ascorbic acid, indole, amines, and certain inorganic ions, especially the iodide ion (155). Like catalase, the peroxidases are hemoproteins, but while they are not particularly specific for the hydrogen donor, they are extremely specific for their requirement for hydrogen peroxide.

Peroxidases are widely distributed among higher plants, the richest known sources being the sap of the fig tree and the root of horseradish (155).

Isozymes of peroxidase are known to occur in a variety of tissues in a large number of plant species. In fact, peroxidase isozymes, because of their common occurrence and the ease of their detection, have been investigated more than any other plant isozyme to date. However, the majority of the earlier studies on peroxidases were purley descriptive, and the interpretation of results, in many instances were highly speculative. Perhaps the most serious drawback to the earlier studies on peroxidase isozymes was the lack of genetically defined peroxidases in studies of development and physiology (i.e. some of the isoperoxidases could be artifacts). In recent years, a few laboratories have invested their efforts in defining the genetic control of peroxidases as a requisite to developmental dissection of isoperoxidases and their possible physiological function(s). To my knowledge, the most thoroughly defined peroxidase systems from a genetic viewpoint are those of barley (46), maize (13, 164), and oats (107).

In barley the number of peroxidase isozymes detected ranges from 8 to 12, depending on the tissue and the developmental stage. Out of 44 inbred lines examined, the genetics of 4 variant isozymes was determined. Each of the variants was shown to be controlled by allelic genes at 4 distinct loci (46). In maize there are 10 electrophoretically detectable zones of peroxidase activity variably expressed in tissues throughout the life cycle of maize. Polymorphism at these 10 regions is determined by allelic variation at each of 10 distinct genetic loci (13). All the genetic studies to date confirm the notion that peroxidase exists functionally as a monomer with one mole of heme per mole of enzyme (164).

Peroxidases are known to be both temporally and spatially determined. It is well documented that peroxidase isozyme patterns undergo dramatic shifts in the course of development and differentiation in a large variety of plants (3, 44–46, 156, 186).

The expression of particular peroxidase isozymes in a developing plant was also shown to depend to some degree on the presence or absence of added indolacetic acid (IAA) in wheat (214) and in peas (124). Of course, enzymes other than peroxidase (i.e. some proteases) can be affected by levels of IAA.

Thus there is a multitude of peroxidase isozymes, and their number and relative concentration varies between different tissues and with the stage of plant development. Because there is so much peroxidase activity in a cell and because it is responsive to hormonal levels, this enzyme system has been used as a model to study hormonal control of growth processes in plants (59). As pointed out, however, the absence of genetics in some of the earlier studies left much to be desired as to the validity of the interpretations relating to hormonal effects and developmental pattern shifts in the peroxidase complement of differentiating plant systems. Often such studies lacked crucial controls to demonstrate that the enzymic activities measured truly represent the entire isoperoxidase complement of the particular cell or tissue being studied. In the case of peroxidase, crucial controls are more critical than with other enzymes because of the broad spectrum of artificial dyes used to assay peroxidase activity, and the observation that not all isozymes are equally reactive to any one substrate (98). Recently, however, new zymogram stains for peroxidase have been developed utilizing substrates of possible physiological significance; namely, eugenol (2-methoxy-4-allyl phenol), which is a lignin precursor, and tyrosine (98).

The most detailed biochemical analysis of peroxidases stem from work with horseradish peroxidase. The number of isozymes in horseradish root has been reported to range from 7 to 20, depending on the mode of extraction, storage, and age of tissue. Some of the "isozymes" have been shown to be artifacts resulting from secondary modification of the basic polypeptides (98, 180). The major drawback of the horseradish peroxidase system is that it lacks genetic definition which complicates rigorous characterization of the isozymes developmentally and physiologically.

Although genetically undefined, the temporal fluctuations in peroxidase activity in plant development have often been attributed to differential gene action (129, 187). The only case where a serious attempt was made to explain the differential expression of peroxidases in development is that of barley (3). Here the question posed was whether the appearance and/or disappearance of isozymes is due to new synthesis and/or degradation. Using a combination of gel electrophoresis, density labeling with deuterium oxide, and isopycnic equilibrium sedimentation, it was clearly shown that the C^2 isoperoxidase, which emerges during early barley germination and is genetically defined (46), is synthesized de novo (3). More recently, the technique has been perfected to the point where de novo synthesis can be determined simultaneously for the entire complement of isozymes from a given tissue (136). This technique further offers an opportunity to investigators concerned with hormonal effects on peroxidase activity to rigorously determine if new synthesis of peroxidase is involved in response to hormones.

The peroxidases as a group need to be further defined in terms of their genetics, physicochemical properties, and physiological significance. Like the esterases (which are not discussed in this review, but see 164), peroxidases are a complex and heterogeneous group of enzymes. Their broad substrate specificity may be indicative of diverse functional roles for the various forms of peroxidase; that is, they may be very distinct groups within a family of enzymes. It would indeed be prudent to methodically dissect this enzyme system from all viewpoints in order to fully begin to understand its role(s) and why it is present in such abundance.

DISCUSSION AND PROSPECTS

From the foregoing discussion of specific isozyme systems it may be readily deduced that the occurrence of isozymes is a general phenomenon in all organisms and that they provide a natural marker system for investigating a variety of problems in the genetics, biochemistry, and developmental biology of plants. However, it should be pointed out that the multiplicity of enzymes discovered to date probably represents only a small fraction of the immense potential that higher plant species hold for the investigator. Furthermore, only a small fraction of known isozyme systems in plants have thus far been studied in a reasonably detailed manner in relation to differentiation and development.

Enzyme heterogeneity has been resolved mainly by the popular and convenient methods of electrophoresis or chromatography. However powerful these methods, they resolve isozyme polymorphisms mainly on charge or size differences; this is not a sufficient stopping point for answering genetic, biochemical, or physiological questions. For example, mutations which insert or delete neutral amino acids from specific polypeptide chains are not likely to be detected by differences in mobility in an electric field. Yet such mutations may lead to altered physicochemical properties of the molecules which exert distinct controls on cellular metabolism. Thus it is imperative to investigate enzyme polymorphism, not only from a structural viewpoint, but to seek ways of detecting functional polymorphism of specific enzyme forms.

A precise definition of the bases for enzyme multiplicity is a necessary prerequisite to the understanding of the significance of spatial and temporal isozyme fluctuations encountered in development, yet this has been defined explicitly in only a few instances.

The appearance or disappearance of specific isozymes during development does not a priori reflect gene action in the sense of transcription. It does reflect the expression of genetic information, however, and the regulation of such differential gene activity can be at a number of control points. The first step in dissecting the mechanism of such regulation is to establish whether the new isozyme(s) or increased activity represents a concomitant synthesis of the enzyme or the activation of an enzyme precursor which was synthesized at some earlier time (205). Since protein turnover in higher organisms appears to be a general and continuous process, unlike microbial systems, enzyme concentrations or isozymic fluctuations may be controlled by independent alterations in either the rate constants of degradation or of synthesis (52, 135, 173). In spite of the fact, however, that alterations in the turnover rates of proteins are a critical factor in the changes of isozyme patterns during development, it should be emphasized that only in a few cases have the effects of activators or inhibitors or the relative rates of synthesis and degradation been explored in such studies.

A fruitful area for investigation provided by isozymes involves the subcellular distribution of specific forms of an enzyme. Knowledge of the factors determining the bases for association of a given isozyme(s) with a particular organelle during development together with a thorough investigation of the physicochemical properties of the isozyme may yield information as to the physiological role(s) that isozymes play during development; yet such investigations have been minimal to date. As more and more isozymes are investigated with respect to their specific kinetic properties, it is becoming obvious that although their catalytic functions may be similar, as the operational definition implies, there are enough kinetic differences to allow for flexibility in their biological role (48, 166, 168, 200). Such differences may allow for subtle though very important roles in the regulation of cellular metabolism during differentiation.

Another area where the use of isozymes may serve a critical function is in the developing area of somatic cell hybrids and genetic transfer. Isozymes provide a rapid means of distinguishing the hybrid cells from the parental types (60).

The origin of many isozyme systems may have resulted from attempts by organisms during the course of evolution to solve problems of regulating gene function in cellular differentiation; that is, organisms have exploited both genetic and epigenetic mechanisms for tailoring molecular properties of specific enzymes (isozymes) to fit special metabolic requirements (106). Gene duplication followed by subsequent mutations at the duplicated loci is a likely mechanism which can lead to the type of enzyme multiplicity we observe and to divergent physiological functions.

Perhaps the most important biological questions relating to the existence of multiple molecular forms of enzymes in the immediate future concern their role in cellular metabolism and differentation. The fact that many isozymes have been shown to have distinct kinetic properties that may enable them to function somewhat differently in fulfilling a specialized physiological role implicates them as factors in the regulation of orderly differentiation.

ACKNOWLEDGMENTS

The work from the author's laboratory reviewed here has been supported by U. S. Atomic Energy Commission Contracts AT(11-1)1338 and AT(38-1)-770. I wish to express my thanks to Dr. J. E. Varner for reading the manuscript carefully and critically. I am grateful to a number of colleagues who helped me gather some of the most recent information. I thank my associates J. C. Sorenson and M. A. Basset for help with the literature review.

Literature Cited

1. Anderson, L. E. 1971. *Biochim. Biophys. Acta* 235:245–49
2. Anderson, L. E., Advani, V. R. 1970. *Plant Physiol.* 45:583–85
3. Anstine, W., Jacobsen, J. V., Scandalios, J. G., Varner, J. E. 1970. *Plant Physiol* 45:148–52
4. Arnon, R. 1970. *Methods in Enzymology*, ed. G. Perlan, L. Lorand, 226–44. New York: Academic
5. Asada, K., Takahashi, M. 1971. *Plant Cell Physiol.* 12:361–75
6. Baun, L. C., Palmiano, E. P., Perez, C. M., Juliano, B. O. 1970. *Plant Physiol.* 46:429
7. Beckman, L., Bjorling, G., Christodoulou, C. 1966. *Acta Genet.* 15:218–23
8. Beckman, L., Scandalios, J. G., Brewbaker, J. 1964. *Science* 146:1174–75
9. Behal, F. J., Folds, J. D. 1967. *Arch. Biochem.* 121:364–71
10. Benveniste, K., Munkres, K. D. 1970. *Biochim. Biophys. Acta* 220:161–77
11. Bers, E. P., Pinevich, V. V. 1971. *Dokl. Akad. Nauk* 196:1463–66
12. Bilderback, D. E. 1971. *Plant Physiol.* 48:331–34
13. Brewbaker, J. L., Hamill, D. E. 1972. *Maize Genet. Newslett.* 44:48–49
14. Budilova, E. V., Rubin, B. A., Antonova, E. K. 1971. *Dokl. Akad. Nauk* 198:699–702
15. Budilova, E. V., Rubin, B. A., Ivanova, M. A., Semenova, M. A. 1971. *Dokl. Akad. Nauk USSR* 200:980–82
16. Carell, E. F., Egan, J. M., Pratt, E. A. 1970. *Arch. Biochem. Biophys.* 138:26–31
17. Chant, S. R., Bates, D. C. 1970. *Phytochemistry* 9:2323–26
18. Chao, S. E., Scandalios, J. G. 1969. *Biochem. Genet.* 3:537–47
19. Chao, S. E. 1970. *Biochemical genetics and developmental studies of starch-degrading enzymes in maize.* PhD dissertation. Michigan State Univ.
20. Chao, S. E., Scandalios, J. G. 1971. *Genetics* 69:47–61
21. Chao, S. E., Scandalios, J. G. 1972. *Mol. Gen. Genet.* 115:1–9
22. Chen, J. H., Jones, R. F. 1970. *Biochim. Biophys. Acta* 214:318–25
23. Chen, S. L., Towill, L. R., Loewenberg, J. R. 1970. *Physiol. Plant.* 23:434–43
24. Cherry, J. P., Katterman, F. R. H. 1971. *Phytochemistry* 10:141–45
25. Christopher, J., Axelrod, B. 1971. *Biochem. Biophys. Res. Commun.* 44:731–36

26. Christopher, J., Pistorius, E., Axelrod, B. 1970. *Biochim. Biophys. Acta* 198:12–19
27. Conklin, M. E., Smith, H. H. 1971. *Am. J. Bot.* 58:688–96
28. Czapski, J., Antoszewski, R. 1971. *Biochem. Biophys. Res. Commun.* 43:12–19
29. Daussant, J., Corvazier, P. 1970. *FEBS Lett.* 7:191–94
30. Daussant, J., Renard, M. 1972. *FEBS Lett.* 22:301–4
31. De Jong, D. W., Olson, A. C. 1972. *Biochim. Biophys. Acta* 276:53–62
32. Delincee, H., Radola, B. J. 1970. *Biochim. Biophys. Acta* 200:404–7
33. Delincee, H., Radola, B. J., Drawert, F. 1971. *Experientia* 27:1265–67
34. Desborough, S., Peloquin, S. J. 1971. *Phytochemistry* 10:571–72
35. Dixon, M., Webb, E. C. 1964. *Enzymes.* New York: Academic
36. Doy, C. H. 1970. *Biochim. Biophys. Acta* 198:364–75
37. Duffus, C. M. 1970. *Phytochemistry* 9:1415–21
38. Efron, Y. 1970. *Genetics* 65:575–83
39. Efron, Y. 1970. *Science* 170:751–53
40. Efron, Y. 1971. *Mol. Gen. Genet.* 11:97–102
41. Endo, T. 1971. *Jap. J. Genet.* 46:1–5
42. Endo, T., Shashi, B. B., Pai, C. 1971. *Jap. J. Genet.* 46:147–52
43. Erikson, C. E., Svensson, S. G. 1970. *Biochim. Biophys. Acta* 198:449–59
44. Evans, J. J. 1970. *Plant Physiol.* 45:66–69
45. Evans, J. L., Aldridge, N. A. 1965. *Phytochemistry* 4:499–503
46. Felder, M. R. 1970. *A comparative Genetic, Developmental and Biochemical Study of Peroxidases in Barley.* PhD thesis. Univ. California, Davis
47. Felder, M. R., Scandalios, J. G. 1971. *Mol. Gen. Genet.* 111:317–26
48. Felder, M. R., Scandalios, J. G., Liu, E. 1973. *Biochim. Biophys. Acta* 317:149–59
49. Ferri, M. V., Guzman, C. A. 1970. *Phyton* 27:137–40
50. Fields, M. A., Tyson, H. 1972. *Can. J. Genet. Cytol.* 14:625
51. Filner, P., Varner, J. E. 1967. *Proc. Nat. Acad. Sci. USA* 58:1520–26
52. Filner, P., Wray, J., Varner, J. E. 1969. *Science* 165:358–67
53. Fredrick, J. F. 1971. *Physiol. Plant.* 24:55–58

54. Fredrick, J. F. 1971. *Phytochemistry* 10:395–98
55. Fredrick, J. F. 1971. *Physiol. Plant.* 25:32–34
56. Freeling, M., Schwartz, D. 1973. *Biochem. Genet.* 8:27–36
57. Frenkel, C. 1972. *Plant Physiol.* 49:757–63
58. Frydenberg, O., Nielsen, G. 1965. *Hereditas* 54:123–29
59. Galston, A. W., Davies, P. J. 1969. *Science* 163:1288–97
60. Ganapathy, P. S., Scandalios, J. G. 1973. *J. Hered.* 64:186–88
61. Gerbrandy, S. J., Verleur, J. D. 1971. *Phytochemistry* 10:261–66
62. Gilchrist, D. G., Woodin, T. S., Johnson, M. L., Kosuge, T. 1972. *Plant Physiol.* 49:52–57
63. Gordon, A. R., Aldridge, N. A. 1971. *Can. J. Bot.* 49:1487–96
64. Grimwood, B. G., McDaniel, R. G. 1970. *Biochim. Biophys. Acta* 220:410–15
65. Grossman, S., Ben-Aziz, A., Ascarelli, I., Budowski, P. 1972. *Phytochemistry* 11:509–14
66. Guerrini, A. M., Gremona, T., Preddie, E. C. 1971. *Arch. Biochem. Biophys.* 146:249–55
67. Guzman, C. A., Ferri, M. V., Trippi, U. S. 1971. *Phytochemistry* 10:2389–91
68. Haard, N. F. 1973. *Phytochemistry* 12:555–60
69. Hageman, R. H., Flesher, D. 1960. *Arch. Biochem. Biophys.* 87:203–9
70. Hahlbrock, K., Wong, E., Schill, L., Grisebach, H. 1970. *Phytochemistry* 9:949–58
71. Hart, G. 1970. *Proc. Nat. Acad. Sci. USA* 66:1136–41
72. Hart, G. E. 1971. *Mol. Gen. Genet.* 111:61–65
73. Hart, M. A., Tyson, H., Bloomberg, R. 1971. *Can. J. Bot.* 49:2129–37
74. Henderson, H. M., McEwen, T. J. 1972. *Phytochemistry* 11:3127–33
75. Ho, H. H., Weaver, E. 1970. *Phyton* 27:163–67
76. Hotchkiss, R. D. 1964. *Brookhaven Symp. Biol.* 17:129–30
77. Hu, A. S. L., Bock, R. M., Halvorson, H. O. 1962. *Anal. Biochem.* 4:489–504
78. Huang, K. P., Stumpf, P. K. 1970. *Arch. Biochem. Biophys.* 140:158–73
79. Hunter, N. W. 1967. *Can. J. Microbiol.* 13:1133–38
80. Jacobsen, J. V., Scandalios, J. G., Varner, J. E. 1970. *Plant Physiol.* 45:367–71

81. Jacobsen, J. V., Varner, J. E. 1967. *Plant Physiol.* 42:1596–1600
82. Jacobson, K. B. 1968. *Science* 159:324–25
83. Jaspars, E. M. J., Veldstra, H. 1965. *Physiol. Plant.* 18:604–25
84. Jaynes, T. A., Nelson, O. E. 1971. *Plant Physiol.* 47:623–28
85. Johnson, H. N., DeBusk, A. G. 1970. *Arch. Biochem. Biophys.* 138:412–17
86. Khan, A. A., Gaspar, T., Roe, C. H., Bouchet, M., Dubucq, M. 1972. *Phytochemistry* 11:2963–69
87. Kitto, G. B., Wassarman, P. M., Kaplan, N. O. 1966. *Proc. Nat. Acad. Sci. USA* 56:578–85
88. Kretovich, V. L., Karyakina, T. I., Sidelnikova, L. I., Kaloshina, G. S. 1971. *Dokl. Akad. Nauk USSR* 201:1252–54
89. Ku, H. S., Yang, S. F., Pratt, H. K. 1970. *Plant Cell Physiol.* 11:241–46
90. Lee, E. Y. C., Marshall, J. J., Whelan, W. J. 1971. *Arch. Biochem. Biophys.* 143:365–74
91. Lee, T. T. 1971. *Plant Physiol.* 48:56–59
92. Lee, T. T. 1971. *Can. J. Bot.* 49:687–93
93. Lee, T. T. 1971. *Plant Physiol.* 47:181–85
94. Ibid 1972. 49:957–60
95. Lee, T. T. 1972. *Can. J. Bot.* 50:2471–77
96. Lee, Y. C., Wacek, V. 1970. *Arch. Biochem. Biophys.* 138:264–71
97. Leshem, Y., Galston, A. W. 1971. *Phytochemistry* 10:2869–78
98. Liu, E. 1971. *The isozymic forms of peroxidase found in the horseradish plant.* PhD dissertation. Michigan State Univ.
99. Long, T. J., Och, F. F., Alben, J. O. 1971. *Arch. Biochem. Biophys.* 146:64–70
100. Longo, C. P., Longo, G. P. 1970. *Plant Physiol.* 45:249–54
101. Longo, G. P., Dragonetti, C., Longo, C. P. 1972. *Plant Physiol.* 50:463–68
102. Longo, G. P., Scandalios, J. G. 1969. *Proc. Nat. Acad. Sci. USA* 62:104–11
103. Maletsky, S. I., Polyakova, E. V., Levites, E. V., Aksenovich, A. V. 1971. *Isozyme Bull.* 4:40
104. Markert, C. L. 1968. *Ann. NY Acad. Sci.* 151:14–40
105. Markert, C. L., Møller, F. 1959. *Proc. Nat. Acad. Sci. USA* 45:753–63
106. Markert, C. L., Whitt, G. S. 1968. *Experientia* 14:977–1088
107. Marshall, D. R., Allard, R. W. 1969. *J. Hered.* 60:17–19

108. Masters, C. J., Holmes, R. S. 1972. *Biol. Rev.* 47:309–61
109. McCown, B. H., McCown, D. D., Beck, G. E., Hall, T. C. 1970. *Am. J. Bot.* 57:148–52
110. Melville, J. C., Scandalios, J. G. 1972. *Biochem. Genet.* 7:15–31
111. Meunier, J. C., Buc, J., Ricard, J. 1971. *FEBS Lett.* 14:25–28
112. Meyer, H., Mayer, A. M., Harel, E. 1971. *Physiol. Plant.* 24:95–101
113. Misawa, M., Martin, S. M. 1972. *Can. J. Bot.* 50:1245–52
114. Mishra, N. C., Tatum, E. L. 1970. *Proc. Nat. Acad. Sci. USA* 66:638–45
115. Mitra, R., Bhatia, C. R. 1971. *Genet. Res.* 18:57–69
116. Mottet, M. K. 1967. *J. Exp. Zool.* 165:279–92
117. Mukerji, S. K., Ting, I. P. 1971. *Arch. Biochem. Biophys.* 143:297–317
118. Munkres, K. D., Benveniste, K., Gorski, J., Zuiches, C. A. 1970. *Proc. Nat. Acad. Sci. USA* 67:263–70
119. Murphy, M. J., O'hEocha, C. 1973. *Phytochemistry* 12:55–59
120. Ibid, 61–65
121. Nakai, Y., Tsunewaki, K. 1971. *Jap. J. Genet.* 46:321–36
122. Nielsen, G., Scandalios, J. G. 1971. *Plant Res.*, 97–98
123. Nishikawa, K., Nobuhara, M. 1971. *Jap. J. Genet.* 46:345–53
124. Ockerse, R., Siegel, B. Z., Galston, A. W. 1966. *Science* 151:452–53
125. O'Sullivan, S. A., Wedding, R. T. 1972. *Physiol. Plant.* 26:34–38
126. O'Sullivan, S. A., Wedding, R. T. 1972. *Plant Physiol.* 49:117–23
127. Ozbun, J. L., Hawker, J. S., Preiss, J. 1971. *Biochim. Biophys. Res. Commun.* 43:631–36
128. Padma, A., Reddy, G. M. 1971. *J. Hered.* 62:252–53
129. Pandey, K. K. 1967. *Nature* 213:669–72
130. Paul, K. G., Stigbrand, T. 1970. *Acta Chem. Scand.* 24:3607–17
131. Peak, M. J., Peak, J. G., Ting, I. P. 1972. *Biochim. Biophys. Acta* 284:1–15
132. Peron, P. et al 1970. *Phytochemistry* 9:73–86
133. Pressey, R., Avants, J. K. 1972. *Phytochemistry* 11:3139–42
134. Pupillo, P. 1972. *Phytochemistry* 11:153–61
135. Quail, P. H., Scandalios, J. G. 1971. *Proc. Nat. Acad. Sci. USA* 68:1402–6
136. Quail, P. H., Varner, J. E. 1971. *Anal. Biochem.* 39:344–55
137. Ragland, T. E., Carroll, E. W., Pitelka, L., Vandepeute, J., Sabar, Z. 1972. *Phytochemistry* 11:1303–9
138. Ramaiah, P. K., Durzan, D. J., Mia, A. J. 1971. *Can. J. Bot.* 49:2151–61
139. Reddy, M. M., Garber, E. D. 1971. *Bot. Gaz.* 132:158–66
140. Reddy, M. M., Threlkeld, S. F. H. 1971. *Can. J. Genet. Cytol.* 13:298–305
141. Ibid 1972. 14:527–31
142. Retig, N., Rudich, J. 1972. *Physiol. Plant.* 27:156–60
143. Ricardo, C. P., Ap Rees, T. 1970. *Phytochemistry* 9:239–47
144. Ritzert, R. W., Turin, B. A. 1970. *Phytochemistry* 9:1701–5
145. Rocha, V., Ting, I. P. 1970. *Plant Physiol.* 46:754–56
146. Rocha, V., Ting, I. P. 1971. *Arch. Biochem. Biophys.* 147:114–22
147. Rychter, A., Lewak, S. 1971. *Phytochemistry* 10:2609–13
148. Sae, S. W., Kadoum, A. M., Cunningham, B. A. 1971. *Phytochemistry* 10:1–8
149. Sakai, R. K., Tung, D. A., Scandalios, J. G. 1969. *Mol. Gen. Genet.* 105:24–29
150. Sako, N., Stahmann, M. A. 1972. *Physiol. Plant Pathol.* 2:217–26
151. Sano, H. 1970. *Plant Cell Physiol.* 11:747–56
152. Sasaki, T., Hosada, H., Tadokoro, K., Suzuki, S. 1972. *Phytochemistry* 11:2981–83
153. Sasaki, T., Tadokoro, K., Suzuki, S. 1971. *Phytochemistry* 10:2047–50
154. Sasaki, T., Tadokoro, K., Suzuki, S. 1972. *Biochem. J.* 129:789–91
155. Saunders, B. C., Seidle, A. G. H., Stark, B. P. 1964. *Peroxidase.* London: Butterworth
156. Scandalios, J. G. 1964. *J. Hered.* 55:281–85
157. Scandalios, J. G. 1965. *Proc. Nat. Acad. Sci. USA* 53:1035–40
158. Scandalios, J. G. 1965. *J. Hered.* 56:177–80
159. Scandalios, J. G. 1966. *Planta* 69:244–48
160. Scandalios, J. G. 1966. *Genetics* 54:359
161. Scandalios, J. G. 1967. *J. Hered.* 58:153–56
162. Scandalios, J. G. 1967. *Biochem. Genet.* 1:1–9
163. Scandalios, J. G. 1968. *Ann. NY Acad. Sci.* 151:274–93
164. Scandalios, J. G. 1969. *Biochem. Genet.* 3:37–79
165. Scandalios, J. G. 1969. *Science* 166:623–24

166. Scandalios, J. G. 1973. Unpublished results
167. Scandalios, J. G., Campeau, M. A. 1972. *Mutation Res.* 14:397–403
168. Scandalios, J. G., Espiritu, L. G. 1969. *Mol. Gen. Genet.* 105:101–12
169. Scandalios, J. G., Felder, M. R. 1971. *Develop. Biol.* 25:641–54
170. Scandalios, J. G., Liu, E., Campeau, M. A. 1972. *Arch. Biochem. Biophys.* 153:695–705
171. Schafer, P., Wender, S. H., Smith, E. C. 1971. *Plant Physiol.* 48:232–33
172. Schertz, K. F., Sumpter, N. A., Sarkissian, I. V., Hart, G. E. 1971. *J. Hered.* 62:235–38
173. Schimke, R. T., Doyle, D. 1970. *Ann. Rev. Biochem.* 39:929–73
174. Schwartz, D. 1971. *Genetics* 67:515–19
175. Schwartz, D. 1971. *Proc. Nat. Acad. Sci. USA* 68:145–46
176. Schwartz, D., Endo, T. 1966. *Genetics* 53:709–15
177. Scott, W. A., Tatum, E. L. 1970. *Proc. Nat. Acad. Sci. USA* 66:515–22
178. Seevers, P. M., Daly, J. M., Catedral, E. F. 1971. *Plant Physiol.* 48:353–60
179. Shannon, L. M. 1968. *Ann. Rev. Plant Physiol.* 19:187–210
180. Shannon, L. M., Kay, E., Lew, J. 1966. *J. Biol. Chem.* 241:2166–72
181. Shannon, L. M., Uritani, I., Imaseki, H. 1971. *Plant Physiol.* 47:493–98
182. Shannon, M. S., Ballal, S. K., Harris, J. W. 1973. *Am. J. Bot.* 60:96–100
183. Shaw, C. R. 1969. *Int. Res. Cytol.* 25:297–332
184. Sheen, S. J., Rebagay, G. R. 1970. *Bot. Gaz.* 131:297–304
185. Shih, J. H., Shannon, L. M., Kay, E., Lew, J. Y. 1971. *J. Biol. Chem.* 246:4546–51
186. Siegel, B., Galston, A. 1966. *Proc. Nat. Acad. Sci. USA* 56:1040–42
187. Siegel, B. Z., Galston, A. W. 1967. *Plant Physiol.* 42:221–26
188. Sodek, L., Wright, S. T. C., Wilson, C. M. 1970. *Plant Cell Physiol.* 11:167–71
189. Splittstoesser, W. E., Stewart, S. A. 1970. *Physiol. Plant.* 23:1119–26
190. Stafford, H. A., Bravinder-Bree, S. 1972. *Plant Physiol.* 49:950–56
191. Stafford, H. A., Dresler, S. 1972. *Plant Physiol.* 49:590–95
192. Stafford, H. A., Galston, A. W. 1970. *Plant Physiol.* 46:763–67
193. Stevens, F. C., Brown, D. M., Smith, E. L. 1970. *Arch. Biochem. Biophys.* 136:413–21
194. Stromeyer, C. T., Cole, F. E., Arquembourg, P. C. 1971. *Biochemistry* 10:729–35
195. Suzuki, Y., Kyuwa, K. 1972. *Physiol. Plant.* 27:121–25
196. Takeo, T., Baker, J. E. 1973. *Phytochemistry* 12:21–24
197. Takeo, T., Kato, Y. 1971. *Plant Cell Physiol.* 12:217–23
198. Tanaka, Y., Akazawa, T. 1970. *Plant Physiol.* 46:586–91
199. Tanaka, Y., Akazawa, T. 1971. *Plant Cell Physiol.* 12:493–505
200. Ting, I. P., Rocha, V. 1971. *Arch. Biochem. Biophys.* 147:156–64
201. Traverso-Cori, A., Traverso, S., Reyer, H. 1970. *Arch. Biochem. Biophys.* 137:133–42
202. Tsai, C. Y., Salamini, F., Nelson, O. E. 1970. *Plant Physiol.* 46:299–306
203. Ursprung, H., Carlin, L. 1968. *Ann. NY Acad. Sci.* 151:456–75
204. Ursprung, H., Dickinson, W. J., Murison, G., Sofer, W. H. 1969. In *Problems in Biology: RNA in Development,* ed. E. W. Hanley, 55–71. Univ. Utah Press
205. Varner, J. E. 1971. *Symp. Soc. Exp. Biol.* 25:197–205
206. Varner, J. E., Chandra, G. R. 1964. *Proc. Nat. Acad. Sci. USA* 52:100–6
207. Veerabhadrappa, P. S., Montgomery, M. W. 1971. *Phytochemistry* 10:1171–74
208. Ibid, 1175–82
209. Verma, D. P. S., van Huystee, R. B. 1970. *Can. J. Bot.* 48:429–31
210. Vesell, E. S., Fritz, P. 1971. In *Enzyme Synthesis and Degradation in Mammalian Systems,* ed. M. Recheigl, 339–74. Univ. Park Press
211. Wall, J. R. 1968. *Biochem. Genet.* 2:109–18
212. Wang, C. S., Raper, J. R. 1970. *Proc. Nat. Acad. Sci. USA* 66:882–89
213. West, N. B., Garber, E. D. 1967. *Can. J. Genet. Cytol.* 9:646–49
214. Whitmore, F. W. 1971. *Plant Physiol.* 47:169–71
215. Wilson, C. M. 1971. *Plant Physiol.* 48:64–68
216. Wise, B., Morrison, M. 1971. *Phytochemistry* 10:2355–59
217. Wong, T. C., Luh, B. S., Whitaker, J. R. 1971. *Plant Physiol.* 48:19–23
218. Wood, K. R. 1971. *Phytochemistry* 10:2383–84
219. Wyen, N. V., Udvardy, J., Farkas, G. L. 1971. *Phytochemistry* 10:765–70
220. Yamazaki, R. K., Tolbert, N. E. 1969. *Biochim. Biophys. Acta* 178:11–20
221. Yang, N. S., Scandalios, J. G. 1974. *Arch. Biochem. Biophys.* In press

222. Yomo, H., Varner, J. E. 1973. *Plant Physiol.* 51:708–13
223. Yoneda, Y. 1970. *Jap. J. Genet.* 45:183–88
224. Yoneda, Y., Endo, T. 1970. *Plant Cell Physiol.* 11:503–6
225. Yu, S. A., Garrett, K., Sussman, A. S. 1971. *Genetics* 68:473–81

Ann. Rev. Plant Physiol. 1974. 25:259–307

THE CHEMISTRY AND PHYSIOLOGY OF ABSCISIC ACID

❖7569

B. V. Milborrow

Shell Research Limited, Milstead Laboratory of Chemical Enzymology
Sittingbourne Laboratories, Sittingbourne, Kent, England

CONTENTS

INTRODUCTION AND SPECIFICATION 260
CHEMISTRY OF ABSCISIC ACID 261
    Physical Properties 261
        Ultraviolet absorption.. 262
        Optical rotatory dispersion 262
        Circular dichroism 262
        Infrared... 262
        Nuclear magnetic resonance 262
    Properties of the Optical Isomers 262
    Chemical Reactions.. 263
    Analogs and Structural Requirements for Activity.......................... 264
    Naturally Occurring Compounds Related to Abscisic Acid................... 272
    Quantitative Determination 274
METABOLISM OF ABSCISIC ACID 275
    Degradation of Abscisic Acid 275
    Biosynthesis.. 277
    Biosynthesis in a Cell-Free System 280
    Occurrence in Cellular Compartments 281
THE PHYSIOLOGICAL ROLE OF ABSCISIC ACID............................ 281
    Methods of Analysis... 281
    Dormancy 282
    Abscission 285
    Effect of Wilting on Abscisic Acid Content and Stomata..................... 287
    Inhibition of Growth... 290
    Stimulation of Growth 291
    Fruit Set and Development 291
    Flowering.. 292
    Senescence 293
    Effects on Permeability... 295
OTHER PROPERTIES OF ABSCISIC ACID.................................... 295
    Transport in Plants.. 295
    Rapid Responses in Growth Rate 297
    Tissue Culture 297

259

Effects on Nucleic Acids, Protein Synthesis, and Isolated Enzymes   297
Interaction with Growth-Promoting Compounds   299
Other Effects   299
    Ultrastructural changes   299
    Effects on fungi and animals   300
CONCLUDING REMARKS   300

INTRODUCTION AND SPECIFICATION

When Addicott & Lyon (8) reviewed this compound in 1969, they used its newly acquired name, abscisic acid (ABA),[1] which had just been agreed upon by the workers involved with its isolation as "abscisin II" from cotton (217) and "dormin" from sycamore (7).

This review starts with a further overhaul of the nomenclature in accordance with the recent revision of the absolute configuration by a number of independent groups. The original determination was carried out by the application of Mills' rule to the isomeric diols (57); it gave the stereochemistry of the tertiary hydroxyl group to be the opposite of that shown in I and was described as (S) according to the Cahn, Ingold & Prelog rules of 1956 (40). The chemical conversion of natural violaxanthin into (+)-ABA (38) related two compounds with opposite stereochemistry at the analogous site and demonstrated, therefore, that the configuration of one was wrong (124, 125). Neither compound had been determined by an unequivocable method, so the direct chemical comparison of (+)-ABA with malic acid by Ryback (276) not only revised the absolute configuration of (+)-ABA but confirmed that of the epoxy group of violaxanthin (23). The Cahn, Ingold & Prelog notation for (+)-ABA also would have required revision if the three authors had not introduced a small change into the definitive version of their rules published in 1966 (41). This change reversed the notation for ABA (356) so that, according to the accepted 1966 version of the rules, (+)-ABA of the revised absolute configuration shown in I is (S). Four other papers have confirmed the revised configuration by independent methods (103, 147, 198. 223). Unhappily, the definitive rules have already been misapplied to the revised structure (119, 223).

In preparing this review from the 600 or more papers dealing with ABA, we found a number of papers which report the activity of externally applied ABA but neglect to state whether natural (+) or synthetic (±) material was used.

Since its first appearance in the 1969 volume of this series (8), abscisic acid has been the subject of several review articles (100, 179, 182, 183, 197, 352); it has lent itself to some aspects of research and defied others. In some ways the knowledge of ABA is more advanced than that of other plant hormones (isolation and measurement, metabolism, optical isomerism) but less advanced than others (biosynthetic precursors, transport, chemistry). It is hoped that this review will highlight some of these topics so that they will be thoroughly investigated in the years ahead.

[1]There is still further imprecision regarding the nomenclature of the geometrical isomers in the side chain. The 2-cis-4-trans structure is implicit in the name abscisic acid, and the 2-trans-4-trans isomer should be referred to as 2-trans-abscisic acid (t-ABA).

CHEMISTRY OF ABSCISIC ACID

Physical Properties

The physical properties of ABA have been reported on many occasions, and values of some diagnostic characteristics are shown in Table 1. Mass (201), IR (217), UV (176), NMR (182), and ORD (176, 277) spectra have been published. The optical properties (and of course the optical inactivity of synthetic racemic material) have been exploited for measurement of (+)-ABA concentrations (60, 61, 176, 177), but the difference between the melting points of the synthetic and natural forms has not been stressed. Crystalline natural (+)-ABA melts at 160–161°C (217), whereas the synthetic racemate melts at about 191°C (59, 112, 301). The apparently identical

Table 1 Structure of (+) – (S)–abscisic acid and some derivatives

I   (+) –Abscisic acid
     (Revised absolute configuration)

II   Phaseic acid

III   Dihydrophaseic acid

IV

V   1′, 4′ –*cis*-diol of (+) –absisic acid

VI   1′, 4′ –*trans*-diol of (+) –absisic acid

160° melting points of natural (+)-ABA isolated from *Vernonia,* synthetic ABA, and a mixture of these two (282) presumably must be attributed to inadvertent contamination of the racemate.

ULTRAVIOLET ABSORPTION The wavelength and intensity of the absorption maximum change in response to pH; in acidic conditions the absorption maximum ($\epsilon = 21, 400$) occurs at 262 nm (60) with a shoulder at 240 nm. In basic conditions the maximum occurs at 245 nm and is about 20% more intense. The methyl ester is easier to measure because its spectrum is unaffected by pH (λ_{max} 264–265 nm, $\epsilon = 20, 900$) (62, 190); this spectrum is illustrated in (176).

OPTICAL ROTATORY DISPERSION The ORD spectrum also is affected by pH, and so it is usually measured in 0.005 N H_2SO_4 (60, 176, 182, 277) or the spectrum of the methyl ester, which is unaffected by pH, is measured. The spectrum in acidic ethanolic solution is illustrated in (176). $[\alpha]D$ (589 nm) = +430°; $[\alpha]$269 and 225 nm = 0°; $[\alpha]$289 nm = +24000°; $[\alpha]$246 nm = –69000°

CIRCULAR DICHROISM The data of Cornforth and Ryback are reported in (176). Methanolic 0.005 N H_2SO_4: $\Delta\epsilon$ 262 nm = +39.5; $\Delta\epsilon$ 230 nm = –34; $\Delta\epsilon$ 318 nm = –2.5.

INFRARED The IR spectrum of abscisic acid is illustrated in (4) and discussed in (216) and (165). The methyl ester shows, in addition, two strong bands at 1160 and 1235 cm^{-1}.

NUCLEAR MAGNETIC RESONANCE The original 60-MHz spectral data were given by Ohkuma et al (216). A 100-MHz spectrum is illustrated in (182) and (184) and data for D_6-acetone and CCl_4 (60-MHz) spectra are given by MacMillan & Pryce (165).

Properties of the Optical Isomers

Abscisic acid was the first optically active plant hormone to be synthesized chemically and resolved into its natural and unnatural antipodes (57). The resolved (+) and (–) materials have the same growth inhibitory activity in a dissected wheat embryo assay (177) and quite similar activities in a number of tests with growing plant tissues. The dissimilar metabolism of the two forms by growing tissues would be expected to distort the apparent activity of the two forms in such assays whereas the ungerminated embryo test measures ability to prevent the development of metabolic activity. Sondheimer et al (301) report that in a stomatal closure assay, a barley half-seed amylase assay, and a cotton explant abscission assay the (+)-and (–)-enantiomers were equally effective, whereas the natural (+) was up to 3 times more effective than the unnatural in bean embryo and barley embryo assay. Nevertheless, the concentrations of the (–)-enantiomer in the bean axes was 4 to 5 times that of the (+). (+)-ABA penetrated into the axes more rapidly than (–)-ABA, but whether this was brought about by selective uptake or by faster passive diffusion, because of the rapid conversion of the (+) into M-1 [now identified as phaseic acid, II Table 1 (178, 301)] and M-2 [dihydrophaseic acid, III, (324, 347)] could not be determined. The differential metabolism of the (+)- and (–)-enantiomers when racemic [2-^{14}C] ABA was fed to tomato (181) and bean (346) plants has been described, and Sondheimer et al have separated (+)-[2-^{14}C] and (–)-[2-^{14}C] ABA and confirmed these results. The striking feature of all the tests of biological activity is the potency of the unnatural form. Although ABA has an extremely intense optical rotatory dispersion, the molecule itself is surprisingly symmetrical—the two sides of a plane through the optical center differ only in that C-6' carries two methyl groups whereas C-2' carries one and a double bond. Consequently, it is possible for the hydroxyl group of the (–) enantiomer to occupy the same position in an active site as that of the (+), if the cyclohexene ring lies on its other face and C-6' and C-2' are interchangeable (183). The alternative explanation is that the tertiary hydroxyl group does not interact with the active site but is present to adjust the solubility and stability of the molecule. The similar inhibitory activity of 1'-desoxy ABA methyl ester (177, 218) (XLIV), in comparison with methyl abscisate, favors the latter hypothesis, but its hydroxylation within the plant to ABA has not been excluded.

Chemical Reactions

The study of the chemistry of abscisic acid has been hampered by the difficulty of synthesis and, although some kilograms have been prepared, most material has been used for biological experiments. The trivial chemistry is exploited by the formation of derivatives as an aid to isolation and identification; most papers on the chemistry of ABA deal with its synthesis (58, 59, 87, 112, 139, 259, 303, 357). A complete chemical degradation of the carbon skeleton still awaits development, although Ryback (276) has recently described a procedure for isolating part of the ring by ozonolysis followed by performate oxidation.

Antoszewski & Rudnicki (13) reported that ABA gives a yellow-green fluorescent compound after heating with sulphuric acid on silica gel, but they did not characterize the product. Mallaby & Ryback (166) have found a color test whereby first acid and then alkali treatments give an intense violet-red color. Several products are formed on acidification, but (IV) is the only one of these that gives the purple color. The proportion of ABA converted into the colored derivative varies widely and is affected by contaminants; moreover, the color fades rapidly and therefore cannot be used to determine ABA quantitatively although it is a sensitive and specific qualitative test. Amounts of ABA as small as 100 ng can be detected. The major acid rearrangement product, lactone (IV), has also been used to dissect out the C-4 hydrogen of ABA (185).

The following data are given in (185): methods for the formation of methyl esters by diazomethane (57, 210); hydrolysis by alcoholic alkali (211); the reduction of the ketone by borohydride (211) to give a mixture of the 1', 4'-cis and 1',4'-trans diols (V and VII), and their reoxidation to ABA by MnO_2 in chloroform. The remaining feature of the chemistry of ABA to be discussed is the base-catalyzed exchange of six carbon-borne hydrogen atoms with water at pH 11 and above (178). The technique has been used to prepare deuterated ABA as a precursor of phaseic acid (178), to prepare a heavy-isotope labeled standard (182), and to remove the tritium at C-3' and C-5' of ABA derived from stereospecifically tritiated mevalonate (185, 261).

The lactone (IV) is believed to hydrolyze to a 4-keto acid on treatment with base (166) and, just as the hydrogens adjacent to the 4'-ketone of ABA exchange with the medium, so does the C-5 hydrogen of the 4-keto acid (185). The 4-keto acid collapses to a spirolactone on acidification, and the hydrogen on C-2 thereby comes to be adjacent to an enolisable carbonyl group, and so it is now potentially removable by exchange with the medium. All the other nonmethyl hydrogens have been dissected out, but the degradative rearrangement of ABA was not known at the time the origin of the C-2 hydrogen (261) was investigated, and therefore this step is hypothetical.

Analogs and Structural Requirements for Activity

The most frequently cited analogs of ABA are its isomeric reduction products, the 1',4'-cis (V) and 1',4'-trans diols (VI). They are formed in approximately equal amounts on treatment of the free acid, and more readily the methyl ester with aqueous methanolic sodium borohydride at 0°C (57). They have almost the same ORD spectrum as ABA and are readily separated from it and each other by TLC; consequently the division of radioactive label, or material with the requisite optical activity, between these two diols at the expected Rf is an extremely good proof of identification of ABA (210).

The diols are rapidly reoxidized to ABA with MnO_2 in dry chloroform, but they are also autoxidized to ABA in aqueous solution in air—particularly the 1',4'-cis diol (188). This may account for the residue of the diols recovered from wheat plants by Noddle (211) being racemic and for their growth-inhibitory effects (348). Robinson & Wareing (263) noted that borohydride deactivated the inhibitor (ABA) from sycamore leaves, but Noddle found that ABA was reduced to a 2',3'-dihydro diol in ethanolic solution at room temperature [this material cannot be formed from the 1',4'-diols by borohydride and is biologically inactive (187)].

Methyl abscisate is prepared by treatment of the free acid with cold ethereal diazomethane, and this procedure is used during the standard isolation to change the properties of the molecule so that it can be separated from the impurities remaining after chromatography as free acid. Although the tertiary hydroxyl group can be trimethylsilylated with extreme difficulty (66), the methyl ester is the preferred form of ABA for gas chromatography (201). The methyl ester is not, or only slightly, inhibitory to growth in experiments lasting 12–24 hr (89, 134, 153, 175), so if a bioassay is to be carried out, the methyl ester has to be hydrolyzed. This is done with facility at room temperature in 10 N NaOH (1 vol) absolute ethanol (2 vol) for half an hour (185). Bean plants can hydrolyze the methyl ester slowly (89).

As has been stressed before, the validity of structure/activity relationships depends on the assumptions that the compound added to the plant is solely responsible for the biological activity throughout the period of the experiment, that all compounds can penetrate equally to the site of action, and that all the analogs compared act by affecting the same reaction. Without a considerably experimental analysis of each compound, penetration can be certain to have occurred only with active compounds. The catabolism of an active molecule to an inactive derivative, or the conversion of an inactive analog into an active one, may be responsible for the results observed. The metabolism of [^{14}C] ABA shows that it can penetrate into the cells quite rapidly (347), and the structural similarity of the analogs suggests that their rate of penetration would be similar. Indeed, many are less polar than ABA and could be expected to pass into the cells even more readily.

The only compound related to ABA whose activity has been examined in detail is (LIII) (188, 189). It is one of the very few analogs found to be more active than ABA itself in a bioassay, and yet its activity is probably attributable to ABA formed from its (R)-enantiomer only. This paradoxical result could have arisen because the less oxygenated and less polar precursor is able to penetrate into the cells so much faster than ABA that its metabolism to ABA can produce higher internal concentrations than when ABA itself is supplied. The continuous release of ABA from the precursor, rather than a high initial level which is then depleted by metabolism may also affect the compound's potency. One compound has already been shown to be converted into ABA by nonbiological processes (302). These examples highlight the need for caution in interpreting the factors determining activity.

Data on the activity of a number of analogs of ABA are collected together as Table 2; the overriding impression is that any change in the molecule of ABA decreases the growth-inhibitory activity.

One of the most dramatic changes occurs on isomerization of the 2-*cis* bond of ABA to give 2-*trans*-ABA. Not only is the latter compound almost inactive (175), but this bond cannot be isomerized enzymatically, and its presence in the *cis* configuration is required to influence the conversion of (XLIII) into ABA. The 2-*trans* isomers of a number of related compounds are less inhibitory than the 2-*cis*. As the 2-double bond is formed in the *trans* configuration, it is probably isomerized at an early stage of the biosynthesis. Some experiments (259) have shown 2-*trans*-ABA to be as active as ABA, but they were carried out in light which would be expected to isomerize the 2-*trans* isomer to a 1:1 mixture with ABA (157, 202, 204, 208, 209).

The length of the side chain is important and the upper and lower vinylogs are much less active. Whether the slight inhibitory activities are caused by action at the ABA site or by nonspecific poisoning is uncertain for these and the other very weak inhibitors. The growth inhibitory activity of many analogs may be the result of narcosis; a more specific test of abscisic acid-type activity than growth inhibition would be extremely valuable in deciding this question. A stomatal closure assay or competition with gibberellic acid in a barley aleurone α-amylase assay would be suitable.

The carboxyl group, or a group that can be converted into it, is required and the 4-double bond must be *trans.* The 1-cyano group is probably resistant to hydrolysis because (XLCIII) is inactive; the hydrolysis product would be expected to be inhibitory by conversion to ABA. However, the presence of the cyano group may prevent the hydroxylation of (XLVIII) at C-4' or the other steps required to form ABA. When two structural differences from ABA occur in the same molecule it is uncertain whether one, which is itself of little effect, can eradicate activity in the presence of the other.

Table 2 Structures of analogs of abscisic acid and their biological activity in a number of different tests

Structure	Biological activity is usually recorded or calculated as a % of that of (±)-ABA
	Cress seed germination assay (320) μg/ml required to inhibit growth 50% after 40 hr; (±)-ABA = 0.20 μg/ml

VII

(+)-Xanthoxin (2-<u>cis</u>)

0.013

VIII

(+)-Xanthoxin (2-<u>trans</u>)

0.6

IX

(+)-Xanthoxin acid (2-<u>cis</u>)

0.5

X

Xanthoxin acid methyl ester (2-<u>cis</u>-isomer)

0.04

XI

(±)-Abscisic alcohol

0.009

XII

(±)-Abscisic aldehyde

0.011

	Phaseolus vulgaris embryonic axis assay (305) % activity in relation to (±)–ABA	*Wheat coleoptile assay* (139) 50% inhibition of growth by (±)–ABA at 0.2 μg/ml	*Rice seedling assay* calculated values in relation to (±)–ABA
XIII	18		
XIV	1.5		
XV	2	12	1
XVI		2	0.01
XVII	2		

Wheat coleoptile assay (203)
% activity in relation to (±) –ABA [growth
reduced by 50% at 0.01 μg/ml (±) –ABA]

XVIII	0.08 (see also XLVIII)
XIX	1.4
XX	1
XXI	0.08
XXII	0.025

Cotton explant abscission assay (214)
(±)–ABA 50% effective at 2½ days 0.01
μg/ abscission zone; % activity in relation to (±) –ABA

	(266)

XXIII   ca 2   10

XXIV   ca 3

XXV   inactive

XXVI   inactive

Cotton explant abscission assay (154) 0.005 μg (±)–ABA/zone 50% effective at 2½ days; % activity in relation to (±) –ABA	*Rice seedling assay* (218) calculated data relative to (±)–ABA at 2.5 μg/ml
XXVII 12	ca 10
XXVIII moderately active	ca 0.05
XXIX inactive	

Rice seedling assay (219)
50% effective dose [(±)–ABA in other rice seedling
assays completely inhibited growth at 2.5 μg/ml]

XXX   2.6 μg/ml

XXXI   2.6 μg/ml

XXXII   inactive

XXXIII   inactive

Rice seedling assay (220)
(±)-ABA completely inhibited 2nd leaf sheath growth at 2.6 µg/ml; % activity in relation to (±) -ABA

XXXIV	CO_2H	inactive
XXXV	CO_2H	inactive
XXXVI	OH CN	inactive
XXXVII	H CO_2H	inactive
XXXVIII	OH CH (cis & trans) CHO	10
XXXIX	OH CH_2OH	1
XL	OH CH_2OH	1

	Rice seedling assay (218) approximate calculated value relative to ABA [(±)-ABA completely inhibited leaf sheath growth at 2.5 µg/ml] ; % activity in relation to (±) -ABA	*Oat mesocotyl assay* (175) (±)-ABA inhibited growth 50% of 0.2 µg/ml	*Wheat embryo assay* (177) (±)-ABA methyl ester
XLI CO_2H	ca 1		
XLII CO_2H	ca 0.01		
XLIII OH CO_2H	ca 1	ca 2	
XLIV H CO_2Me	ca 1		50
XLV CO_2Me H	ca 1		
XLVI CO_2Me	inactive		

	Rice seedling assay (313)	*Rice seedling assay* (314)

Rice seedling assay (313)
($\pm$)-ABA caused a 50%
growth reduction of
the 2nd leaf sheath
at 2.3 μg/ml; % activity
in relation to ($\pm$)-ABA

Compound	Activity	Note
XLVII	135	
XLVIII	42 (see also XVIII)	
XLIV	4.7	
XLV	9.6	
XLVI	153	This compound was 4 times as potent as ABA
XLVII		
XLVIII	0.3	
XLIX	5.8	

L	*Bean axis bioassay* (302) activity probably caused by nonenzymatic formation of ABA

Rice seedling assay (314)
($\pm$)-ABA inhibited growth of 2nd leaf sheath 50%
at 2.5 μg/ml; % activity in relation to ($\pm$)-ABA

Compound	Activity
LI	ca 2
LII	1
LIII	4.4
LIV	0.5

LV

Cotton explant abscission assay (213)
1% of (±)-ABA

Rice seedling assay (222)
ABA completely inhibited growth at 2.5 µg/ml;
% activity in relation to (±)-ABA

LVI   10

LVII   0.1

LVIII   0.5

LIX   0.5

Rice seedling assay (221)
(±)-ABA completely inhibited growth of
2nd leaf sheath at 2.5 µg/ml; % activity
in relation to (±)-ABA

LX   1
(in a mixture with 2-*trans*)

LXI   ca 1
(in a mixture with 2-*trans*)

LXII   ca 1

LXIII   0.01
(in a mixture with 2-*trans*)

Wheat coleoptile assay (39)

LXIV

(±)-1', 2'-4'-*cis*, 0-methyl xanthoxin
(a mixture of 2-*cis* and 2-*trans* isomers)   20% of activity of xanthoxin

LXV   (±)-1', 2'-4'-*trans*, 0-methyl
       xanthoxin (a mixture of   inactive
       2-*cis*- and 2-*trans* isomers)

The essential features of the ring are less clearly defined. The conversion of (LIII) into ABA shows that the 4'-ketone can be generated very easily and so the activity of analogs lacking this function is dubious. The 2'-double bond seems to be necessary but the strong inhibitory activity of desoxy abscisic acid methyl ester (XLIV), which would depend on metabolic hydrolysis to form the free acid, may be attributable to hydroxylation of C-1' to form ABA.

Naturally Occurring Compounds Related to Abscisic Acid

Abscisic acid seems to be the sole member of its class if xanthoxin (88) is considered to be a precursor and the breakdown products and conjugates of ABA are discounted. ABA has been isolated and identified by a satisfactory range of physical methods from a wide variety of angiosperms, gymnosperms (33, 160, 179), a fern (179), a horsetail (260), and a moss (251). However, no attempts to find abscisic acid in liverworts have succeeded; the potent growth inhibitor (LXVI), lunularic acid, has been found in the eight liverwort species investigated (250) and also in algae (251). It appears that in lower plants lunularic acid concentrations are correlated with the physiological state of the organism and the compound may function in the same role as ABA (286). Several other groups of inhibitors have been characterized recently, but their role in the plant is less well known and they will not be discussed here. The similarity of other compounds considered to be related to ABA is based on the resemblance of their structures, but they could be derived either from carotenoids or from ABA. Their structures have been defined unambiguously, but whether they occur within the living plant or are artefacts formed by fermentation [e.g. during the processing of tea (120)] or by adventitious physical processes during extraction is not known. Little or nothing is known of their effects on plants [Vomifoliol (249), Blumenol (91), Theaspirone (120)].

At this juncture a note of warning is necessary. The relative ease with which ABA can be isolated and identified by TLC and spectropolarimetry or GLC and mass spectrometry may focus attention on the (+)-ABA present in a plant extract so that other related compounds are discarded. The total biological activity of an extract

Table 3 Structures of some naturally occurring compounds related to abscisic acid

LXVI   Lunularic acid

LXVII   Metabolite C.

LXVIII   Theaspirone

LXIX   Vomifoliol
(Blumenol A)

LXX   Blumenol B

LXXI   Blumenol C

LXXII   2-*trans*-Dehydrofarnesol

should be measured quantitatively by comparing its activity in serial dilution with a standard dilution series of natural (+)-ABA and then comparing the (+)-ABA content with the amount equivalent to the biological activity in the extract (201). Other compounds in an extract that contributes to the inhibitory activity may be discovered by this means.

Quantitative Determination

Pure synthetic ABA can be measured conveniently by its UV absorption, but the absorbance is pH-dependent and is usually determined at acid pH or on the methyl ester. The acidic solution cannot be evaporated without neutralization because ABA is destroyed by strong acids (166). Measurement of the ABA present in extracts almost invariably depends on some preliminary purification which is usually done by partitioning between solvents followed by paper or silica gel chromatography. The ABA-rich fraction can then be further purified by electrophoresis (53), gas-liquid (66, 156), thin layer (185), silica-gel dry-column (16), or Sephadex (306) chromatography.

Further cleanup is facilitated by making derivatives (methyl ester, reduction to diols, trimethylsilyl esters, etc) and rechromatography. All these processes cause losses of ABA, and the proportion isolated can be monitored by the "racemate dilution" method (176), by adding labeled material (190), or by adding a known amount of the 2-*trans* isomer (158) and assuming that the extraction efficiency and rate of destruction of ABA and 2-*trans*-ABA are identical. More important, all the manipulations have to be carried out in very dull light to prevent interconversion of the two isomers. The ABA can be tentatively identified by its retention times or Rfs, but spectropolarimetry (60, 176) provides a more satisfactory identification, and mass spectrometry of the separated compound in the effluent gas from a gas-liquid chromatographic column is the most conclusive method (76, 93, 201). The ABA derivatives are detected by flame ionization (66) or electron capture (288–290).

Spectrofluorimetry (13) of an acid derivative of ABA is quite sensitive but destructive of material. The color reaction is specific and sensitive but destructive and nonquantitative (166).

Immunological assays for ABA have been attempted (90, 172), but the method does not appear to be specific enough at present; it is possible that the oxygenated rings of xanthophylls can react with the hapten.

Bioassay of the inhibitory effect of ABA has been widely used although most assays require the addition of a growth promoter; otherwise the increments are too small for accurate measurement. The most important criticism is that growth inhibition is a common effect of most compounds at some concentration or other. Paleg's (17, 295) α-amylase assay and inhibition of growth of *Spirodela* (337) have the advantage that they can be carried out under aseptic conditions. The stomatal closure assay (330) promises to be a specific and sensitive method, and it may be possible to quantitate the effect on the surface potential of roots to make it the most sensitive and specific bioassay for ABA (317).

METABOLISM OF ABSCISIC ACID

Degradation of Abscisic Acid

The inactive 2-*trans* isomer of ABA (XLIII) has been isolated from several plants and was believed to occur naturally because it was detectable by GLC when precautions were taken to prevent its formation by photoisomerization during the isolation procedure (93). Its presence in field rose (*R. arvensis*) before extraction was demonstrated by dropping leaves, which had been harvested from a plant subjected to bright sunlight, into methanol-containing racemic [2-^{14}C] ABA and unlabeled (±)-2-*trans*-ABA (181). Any ABA isomerized to the 2-*trans* isomer during the workup would carry label. Consequently, when the purified natural (+)-2-*trans*-ABA was measured spectropolarimetrically, the contribution of the (+)-ABA isomerized during isolation could be monitored by its [^{14}C] content. The experiment showed that approximately 4% of the total (+)-ABA was present in insolated leaves as the 2-*trans* isomer. In a similar experiment with avocado seeds, which are shielded from sunlight by pigmented skin, no 2-*trans* isomer was found (181). In solvents ABA isomerizes to a 50:50 equilibrium mixture with the 2-*trans* isomer (58, 157, 202).

The metabolism of the 2-*trans* isomer into a glucose ester by tomato shoots is more rapid than that of ABA; no isomerization of the (±)-[2-^{14}C]-2-*trans* isomer into ABA by the tomato plants was found (181). This is in accord with the lack of inhibitory activity observed with the 2-*trans* isomers of several analogs of ABA and suggests that this bond is isomerized to the *cis* configuration at an early stage of the biosynthesis. The early experiments on the metabolism of ABA were carried out with racemic [2-^{14}C] material supplied as a 1 µg/ml solution. Three labeled derivatives were found (177); the major one "B," a polar, water soluble, hydrolyzable glucose ester, was identified (181) and compared with the same material isolated by Koshimizu et al (149) from yellow lupin (*Lupinus luteus*). The only difference was that the natural glucose ester gave (+)-ABA on hydrolysis whereas the glucose ester biosynthesized from racemic ABA gave a mixture of (+)- and (–)-ABA with a preponderance of the latter. Hence the unnatural (–)-enantiomer can be conjugated as easily as the natural (+)-enantiomer.

The glucose ester of ABA, and particularly its tetra acetate, transesterifies in acidic methanol to give abscisic acid methyl ester and glucose. Methyl abscisate cochromatographed with the minor component "metabolite A" so this material was probably an extraction artefact.

The glucose ester of [^{14}C] ABA can be isolated from tomato plants for several days after supplying [^{14}C] ABA and it appears to be stable (although recycling has not been excluded). When it was tested in a rice seedling bioassay by Koshimizu et al, it had approximately half the activity of ABA, presumably on a weight basis, and so it was virtually identical with ABA on a molar basis. The ester is hydrolyzed rapidly by expressed sap from tomato shoots (181); consequently its inhibitory activity may be accounted for by the hydrolytic release of ABA. The apparent stability of the ester within the tomato plant in contrast to its hydrolysis by cell sap suggests that the conjugate and the esterase molecules are held in different cellular compartments.

The glucose ester has been identified in two species, but free ABA is released by alkaline hydrolysis of the methanolic extracts of several other plants [bean (229), sycamore (177), and wheat leaves; avocado (187), rose, citrus (97), and strawberry (273) fruits] and this could be bound in a glucose ester or similar form. The amount of ABA released by this treatment is usually between one tenth and one third of the amount existing as free acid (187, 273), but in the peel of oranges matured on the tree "bound-ABA" content exceeded free acid content tenfold (97).

The glucose ester appears to be a rapid-storage product for extra ABA when this is added to plant tissues. No data are available at present to show whether the ABA can be destroyed while conjugated or whether this bound ABA can be released.

The third metabolite "C," was isolated in crystalline form from tomatoes supplied with racemic ABA. The free acid had an intense ORD spectrum, similar to that of (+)-ABA, but for its other physical properties to be investigated it was methylated with diazomethane whereupon it rearranged to a compound with a weak ORD spectrum. Mass, IR, UV, and MNR spectrometry of the rearrangement product showed us that it was identical to the methyl ester of phaseic acid, which was isolated previously from beans (*Phaseolus vulgaris*) by MacMillan & Pryce (164). The formation of phaseic acid by the rearrangement of a metabolite of ABA indicated that the formula that had been proposed for phaseic acid when isolated from beans (164) was incorrect. An experimental verification of a new structure for phaseic acid was obtained (178) by labeling the 2'-ring methyl of ABA with deuterium and feeding this to tomato shoots. The phaseic acid formed was isolated and subjected to NMR spectrometry; the absence of a methyl signal in the NMR spectrum of phaseic acid (182) excluded the earlier structure (164) and was as expected for the new one (II) (178). The new structure of phaseic acid is now accepted as correct (88, 249) and is as shown in II.

Metabolite C was deduced to be the 6'-hydroxymethyl derivative (178) of ABA (LXII), and the rearrangement to phaseic acid was the nucleophilic attack of the 6'-hydroxyl group on C-2' to form a tetrahydrofuran ring. Five further attempts to reisolate metabolite C have given phaseic acid (184), indicating that the former compound is extremely unstable and may rearrange spontaneously in the plant. Quantitative measurements of (+)-[^{14}C], (−)-[^{14}C], and endogenous (+)-[^{12}C] ABA present in tomatoes as free acid, glucose ester, phaseic acid/metabolite C after (±)-[2-^{14}C] ABA had been fed suggested that only the (+)-ABA is hydroxylated to give phaseic acid; this has also been confirmed by Sondheimer et al (301), who supplied resolved (+)-[^{14}C] ABA and (−)-[^{14}C] ABA to bean seedlings and found that the (+)-enantiomer only was metabolized in this this way.

Phaseic acid appears to be a natural metabolite ("M-1") in bean embryos (347) and seedlings because not only is it extractable after feeding [^{14}C] ABA but its reduction product "M-2" accumulates; M-2 has now been identified as dihydrophaseic acid (III) (324). If the 4'-ketone group of ABA or metabolite C were reduced to a hydroxyl group, then the molecule would be much less likely to undergo the internal nucleophilic rearrangement. Consequently, the presence of dihydrophaseic acid suggests the occurrence of phaseic acid within the cells. However, when tomato plants were fed with [^{14}C] phaseic acid prepared biogenetically from ABA, only one metabolite was detected and this was less polar than phaseic acid, whereas dihydrophaseic acid is much more polar. In addition, this new material was absent from plants fed with [^{14}C] ABA (184). It appears that in this tissue either the formation of dihydrophaseic acid is less important than in bean axes [as suggested by the data of Taylor & Burden (321)] or phaseic acid supplied to cut shoots is metabolized differently from that made endogenously.

Biosynthesis

Label from mevalonate has been shown to be incorporated into ABA on several occasions (185, 189, 190, 210, 261), but in the absence of a degradation method for ABA, proof of the direction incorporation of mevalonate molecules (rather than incorporation after dissection into acetate) has been based on the amount and position of tritium in the ABA. The origin of the hydrogens at 5 positions in ABA has been deduced from the ^{3}H/^{14}C ratios of ABA made from stereospecifically tritiated mevalonates by avocado fruit, and the validity of this technique depends on a number of assumptions. First, the three residues of mevalonate must be derived equally from the labeled precursor. Second, the nominally [2-R-^{3}H$_1$] and [4-R-^{3}H$_1$] mevalonates carry a tritium in the R positions and a protium in the S position, but they exist in a mixture with the mirror image (3-S) forms which carry tritium in the 2-S and 4-S positions respectively. Consequently, the mevalonate is a stereospecifically labeled precursor if, as in animal systems, the natural 3-R enantiomer only is incorporated and the unnatural 3-S enantiomer remains unused. The ^{3}H/^{14}C ratio of 1.93:3 (2:3) of ABA formed from [2-^{14}C, 4-R-^{3}H$_1$] mevalonate and 0.05:3 from [2-^{14}C, 4-S-^{3}H$_1$] material (261) confirm both assumptions because if the three residues had not been equally derived from one pool, the expected ratio would not have been obtained, and if the 3-S had been incorporated, a significant amount of tritium from the 3-S[4-R-^{3}H$_1$] would have been incorporated into ABA when the nominally [4-S-^{3}H$_1$] was fed (Figure 1). Methods for locating the tritium are described by Milborrow (185) and have shown that the *pro*-4-R hydrogen of mevalonate is retained on C-2 and C-5' of ABA (261), the 5-S on C-5 of ABA (185), and a preponderance of the *pro*-2-R hydrogen of mevalonate at C-4 and C-3'. Under the action of isopentenyl pyrophosphate isomerase the *pro*-2-R and *pro*-2-S hydrogens originally of mevalonate are racemized to a considerable extent, and the ratios in ABA obtained when 2-R and 2-S tritiated mevalonates are fed are somewhat imprecise. Both 2-S and 2-R tritiums are retained in one of the 6'-methyl groups.

These results have significance beyond their intrinsic interest; the hydrogens retained at C-4 and C-5 are the same as those in the analogous positions of carotenoids and indicate that the 4-double bond was formed by a *trans* elimination. The presence of the *pro*-2-R hydrogen of mevalonate at C-3' is the same as the tentative result cited by Goodwin (99) for the analogous position in α-carotene, and the retention of the *pro*-4-R hydrogen of mevalonate at C-2 suggests that the 2-*cis*-double bond of ABA is formed in the *trans* configuration and is isomerized at a

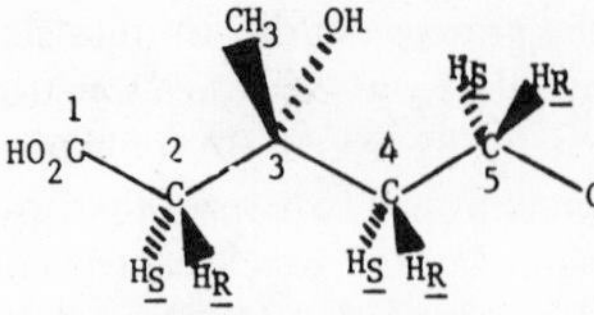

CH₃ OH ... (structure)

(+)-(3R)-Mevalonic acid.
This is the natural enantiomer and
is incorporated into ABA; the
stereochemistry of the hydrogens on
C-2, C-4, and C-5 is shown. C-2, C-3,
C-4, C-5, and the methyl group become
an isoprene unit; C-1 is lost by
decarboxylation.

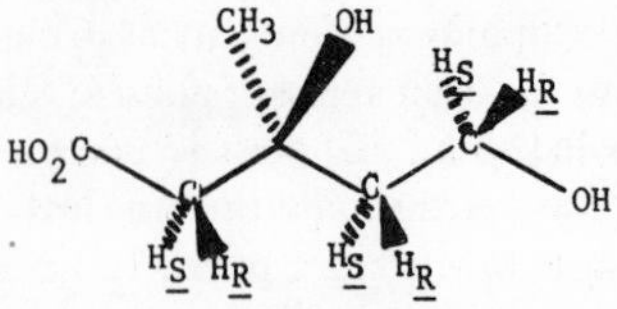

(-)-(3S)-Mevalonic acid.
This is the unnatural enantiomer and is
not incorporated into ABA.

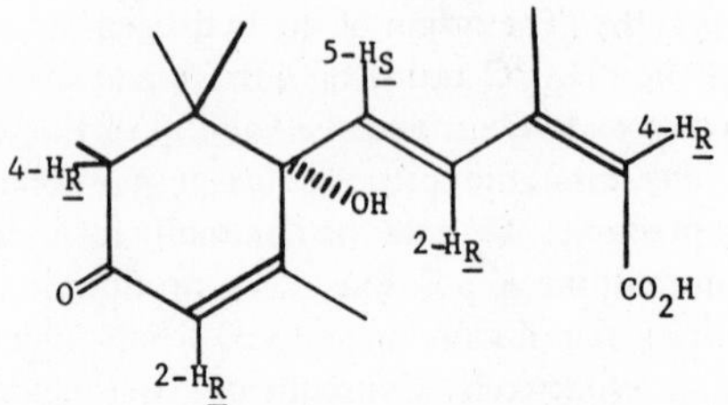

(+)-Abscisic acid (revised absolute configuration).
The hydrogen atoms are labeled with
their position in mevalonic acid.

Figure 1   The stereochemistry of mevalonic acid and the origin of the hydrogen atoms of
(+)-abscisic acid.

later stage of the biosynthesis. If the *pro*-4-*S* hydrogen of mevalonate had been
retained in ABA, this, by showing that the 2-double bond of ABA was formed in
the *cis* configuration, would have excluded carotenoids as precursors of ABA
because the analogous double bond in carotenoids is formed by a *trans*-elimination
with retention of the *pro*-4-*R* hydrogen of mevalonate (247). Similarly, if the
retention of other tritiums from mevalonate (185) in ABA had been different from
those in the analogous positions in carotenoids, this also would have differentiated
between ABA and carotenoid biosynthesis.

The stereochemistry of the hydrogens at C-5' of ABA has yet to be defined; one
comes from the *pro*-4-*R* of mevalonate, the other (presumably) from the medium
during cyclization. The direction of cyclization and hence the stereochemistry of the
6'-methyl group derived from C-2 of mevalonate also await investigation.

When the structure of abscisic acid was proposed by Ohkuma et al (216), its
similarity to the end parts of many carotenoids was noted. Circumstantial evidence

leading to the hypothesis that carotenoids might be the natural precursors of abscisic acid (322) included: the occurrence of carotenoids in phototropic organs of fungi and the similarity of their action spectrum to the absorption spectrum of carotenoids; the occurrence of more inhibitory material in light-grown plants than in etiolated ones (170, 361); the identification of the major active constituent of this inhibitor-β as abscisic acid (176); and the work of Simpson & Wain (293) suggesting that an inhibitor is formed in plants in the light.

Taylor and Smith exposed a number of carotenoid pigments on damp filter paper to bright light and found that violaxanthin gave rise to a strongly inhibitory neutral material although other xanthophylls with a 3-hydroxy-5,6-epoxy cyclohexyl terminal group also produced inhibitory products. The active constituent was isolated and characterized as xanthoxin by Taylor & Burden (318–320). The active compound is the 2-*cis* isomer (VII) in a mixture of this and approximately equal amounts of the less active 2-*trans* isomer (VIII). Both have now been found in extracts of dwarf bean (*Phaseolus vulgaris*) and wheat (*Triticum vulgare*). However, in the leaf extracts the ratio of 2-*cis*- to 2-*trans*-xanthoxin is similar to that present in the products of violaxanthin photolysis, and the lesser activity of the 2-*trans* isomer suggests that, like the 2-*trans*-ABA, it is not readily isomerized enzymatically to the active form. It is unlikely, therefore, that the 2-*trans*-xanthoxin is a precursor of the 2-*cis* isomer of abscisic acid; its presence in the leaf may indicate that it is an adventitious product formed by light.

The yield of ca 2% xanthoxin from violaxanthin is so low and such high light intensities are required for photolysis in vitro that it seems unlikely that the extremely sensitive phototropic responses of some higher plant organs, which require the order of a few dozen quanta for activation, could be mediated by this means.

Recently Firn & Friend (89) have reported that soybean lipoxygenase is capable of cleaving violaxanthin oxidatively to form a similar range of products, in similar yield, to that formed during photolysis; whether the enzyme functions in vivo is unknown. The possibility that xanthoxin is produced by the action of lipoxygenase removes the requirement of light for its production, but the system then requires a photosensitive mechanism if the production of inhibitor is responsible for light-induced growth inhibition and phototropism.

The enzymatic production of xanthoxin from carotenoids could, if it is a normal precursor of ABA, account for the synthesis of ABA by avocado fruit and wheat leaves which occurs equally rapidly in darkness. The possibility has not been excluded that xanthoxin is a normal intermediate in ABA biosynthesis formed from a C-15 precursor and that it does not come from a carotenoid in vivo. 2-*cis*-[^{14}C]-Labeled xanthoxin has been shown to be converted into abscisic acid in high yield (10% in 8 hr) (321).

Two experiments (183) have been carried out which suggest that ABA in avocado fruit is made from C-15 precursors and is not derived from a carotenoid. In the first the uncyclized carotenoid phytoene was made with [^{14}C] label and supplied to avocado fruit, mixed with [^{3}H] mevalonate. [^{14}C] From phytoene and [^{3}H] from mevalonate were incorporated into carotenoids, showing that both had entered the sites of synthesis within the cells. In contrast the ABA was heavily labeled with tritium but contained no [^{14}C], which strongly suggests that carotenoids are not involved in ABA biosynthesis. In the second experiment, unlabeled (LXXII) 2-*trans*-dehydrofarnesol and its 2-*cis* isomer (both synthesized by R. Mallaby) were added as "cold traps" to avocado fruit synthesizing abscisic acid from [2-^{14}C] mevalonate. In three experiments approximately 0.1% of the label added was recovered in 2-*trans*-dehydrofarnesol when this was reextracted. The 2-*cis*-dehydrofarnesol contained less than one twentieth of the amount. Both experiments can be criticized; the former because different cellular compartments could be involved, the latter because neither the [^{14}C]-2-*trans*-dehydrofarnesol incorporated into ABA nor the labeled trap have been degraded to ensure that the label is in the expected positions, so the result still has to be verified. The evidence in favor of the direct synthesis pathway via a C-15 precursor is good but does not exclude the possibility that, for instance in brightly illuminated leaves, xanthoxin is formed from violaxanthin and metabolized to ABA.

No other precursors between dehydrofarnesol and ABA have been identified. (±)-1',2'-[^{18}O, 2-^{14}C] Epoxyionylidene acetic acid (LIII) (189) and [2-^{14}C] xanthoxin acid (IX) have been shown to be converted into (+)-ABA (191) by highly stereospecific reactions which exclude the (−)-diastereoisomers (188), but several attempts to find traces of these acids in nature have been unsuccessful. The epoxide oxygen of [1',2'-^{18}O, 2-^{14}C] compound LIII became the oxygen of the tertiary hydroxyl group of (+)-ABA, but this reaction might have been brought about by enzymes other than those of the ABA pathway.

Like gibberellins and auxins, ABA is synthesized in several different parts of plants. Leaves, stems, fruit, and seed tissues (cotyledons, endosperm, and embryos) have been shown to incorporate labeled mevalonate into ABA (190).

Biosynthesis in a Cell-Free System

The difficulty of penetration of mevalonate into the site of ABA biosynthesis in leaves was reminiscent of the impermeability to mevalonate of intact chloroplasts synthesizing carotenoids, reported by Goodwin (98); moreover, the similarity of the structures of ABA and carotenoids suggested that both could be synthesized in chloroplasts. Avocado fruit slices synthesize ABA rapidly whether they are wilted or not (190), so intact chloroplasts were isolated from ripening fruit, lysed in dilute phosphate buffer, and supplied with labeled mevalonate. The cell-free system was able to synthesize ABA when supplied with a range of cofactors, and the chloroplast membrane was shown to be the major barrier to the penetration of mevalonate because intact chloroplasts were about one eighth as effective (188). The lysed chloroplasts were centrifuged and synthetic capacity was divided between the supernatant and the pellet; diphenylamine and a number of other inhibitors of carotenoid biosynthesis were ineffective and etioplasts from the white inner parts were as effective as those from the outer green parts of the fruit. ABA has been shown to be synthesized within chloroplasts from fruit and also from bean and avocado leaves, but the possibility that it is also synthesized outside chloroplasts cannot be excluded. Rogers et al have demonstrated that there are two pools of terpenoid biosynthesis: chloroplastic and extrachloroplastic (264), and the presence of (+)-ABA in nectar

(179) demonstrates that some must also be present outside the chloroplasts. No plastid-free plant tissue culture lines have been reported, (308) so whether ABA can be made outside chloroplasts cannot be tested at present.

Occurrence in Cellular Compartments

The first indication that ABA could occur in different cellular compartments came from work on the glucose ester and its metabolism; whereas the ester was apparently stable for several days in tomato shoots in which it had been formed (181) from exogenously applied ABA, it inhibited growth to the extent expected of its ABA content (149) and was rapidly hydrolyzed by the expressed sap of tomato leaves. Thus glucosyl abscisate was apparently stable in cells but was hydrolyzed when fed to the seedlings.

A more direct proof of the existence of two pools of ABA comes from the work of Milborrow et al (183, 191). When avocado fruits synthesize [^{14}C] ABA from [2-^{14}C] mevalonate in the presence of a "cold trap" of the isomeric diols (IV and V), the diols can be reisol ed and do not contain label. On the other hand, when (±)-[2-^{14}C] ABA is added to the fruit, mixed with a similar "cold trap," the 1',4'-trans diol becomes heavily labeled (97%) and the 1',4'-cis diol becomes weakly labeled (3%). Thus the newly biosynthesized ABA is separated from the diols or the enzyme responsible; in contrast, the [^{14}C]ABA added to the cell, or formed from added [^{14}C] xanthoxin acid, is reduced (in spite of a net oxidation of diols to ABA) and exchanges into the 1',4'-trans diol. Synthesis of ABA from mevalonate has been shown to occur with chloroplasts and this is probably the site of the "nontrapping" ABA. The rapidity with which ABA exerts its effect on growth suggests that it can penetrate rapidly to its site of action, which is probably in the cytoplasm. The conversion of [^{14}C] xanthoxin acid [apparently not a normal intermediate in ABA biosynthesis (188)] into [^{14}C] ABA in a different part of the cell from that in which ABA is normally biosynthesized emphasizes the care necessary in interpreting such data.

Walton & Sondheimer (347) have found indications that the content of free ABA within bean axes transferred from a 4.5-μg/ml solution to fresh buffer is not directly related to the growth rate—possibly some of the ABA absorbed by the axes is stored in a cellular compartment where it cannot exert an effect.

THE PHYSIOLOGICAL ROLE OF ABSCISIC ACID

Methods of Analysis

There is no unique method for determining the role of a regulatory compound in vivo; its controlling influence on a given process gradually comes to be accepted as different kinds of evidence which confirm the possible role are amassed. Jacobs (129) proposed six rules to help decide whether a given compound regulated a process in vivo, and while these rules are a valuable aid to formulating experiments, no single one of them is absolute. Even the parallelism of hormone concentration and effect could be validly expected to follow an inverse relationship.

The highly integrated nature of many growth processes and the involvement of negative feedback loops and metabolic interlock of different pathways make a simple logical analysis of such processes a hazardous exercise. How much more difficult is it to ensure making valid interpretations when experimenting with the control mechanisms of growth which act in unknown ways at unknown sites?

Against this background of uncertainty we have to review the physiological role of abscisic acid and bear in mind that when abscisic acid is supplied to a plant the supernormal concentrations, possibly in parts of the cell into which it does not normally penetrate, may be able to induce observable changes, but that these responses may not be natural functions.

Dormancy

One of the lines of research that led to the isolation of (+)-ABA as "dormin" in sycamore leaves was the change in growth-inhibitory activity in extracts of tree seedlings grown under long or short days (263) and the increase in content of the growth-inhibitory material in leaves during the spring, summer, and early autumn (236–238, 262). Furthermore, the idea that bud dormancy in potato tubers may be caused by growth-inhibiting substances had been suggested by Hemberg in 1949 (108).

Eagles & Wareing (77) had been able to induce the formation of buds with many of the features of resting buds on birch (*Betula pubescens*) seedlings grown under long-day conditions by treating the plants with an extract of plants growing under short days. El-Antably et al were able to repeat the experiment with pure synthetic abscisic acid when this became available (83) and to induce formation of dormant winter buds in black currant (*Ribes nigrum*) and sycamore (*Acer pseudoplatanus*) as well.

The original correlations of inhibitory material in leaves grown under short and long days and the induction of dormancy were based on measurements obtained by bioassay. Kaska has investigated apple leaves (138) and found no change during the season. Recently Lenton, Perry & Saunders (158) have attempted to repeat these determinations using gas chromatography to compare the amounts of ABA present. They found that the transfer to short days had no effect on ABA content of birch, red maple (*Acer rubrum*), or sycamore plants. They discuss the reasons for the discrepancy and cite the possibilities that another compound is responsible (they consider this unlikely because of the ability of (±)-ABA to induce the formation of winter buds) or that the low titer of inhibitor in young leaves and long-day leaves could be the result of high concentrations of gibberellins interfering with the bioassay. Still another possibility is that the young leaves and leaves of plants grown under long days are more resistant to wilting and synthesize less ABA during conditions of incipient water stress. The ca fortyfold increase in ABA content that occurs on wilting (see section on stomata) makes direct correlations of dormancy with leaf ABA contents somewhat suspect; indeed Zeevaart found an increase in ABA content when spinach (*Spinacea oleracea*) plants were transferred from short to long days (366, 367). The importance of a balance between growth promoters and growth inhibitors has been stressed frequently (110–112, 141, 242, 333, 353), and the possibility that transport of ABA out of a photoperiodically induced leaf and into the apex is important has been noted (83). Tinklin & Schwabe (325) found considerably more inhibitor (probably ABA) in bud scales than in the bud axis of black currant, and the ABA concentrations were correlated with the degree of dormancy and reduced by treatments that encouraged bud break. Seeley & Powell (290), however, found more ABA in the apical part of apple buds than in the bud scales. Tsukamoto et al (329) investigated the activity of growth-promoting substances and a growth inhibitor that they were able to identify as (+)-ABA in onions and found that the ABA content increased as the plants became dormant and formed bulbs. In onions this occurs in long-day conditions and under short days less ABA was present. Similar changes in ABA contents of potato tubers were found by Bielinska-Czarnecka & Domanska (31).

A further complication attending the investigation of the roles of regulatory compounds that has received virtually no attention is the possible alteration of the responsiveness of the target system by day-length or other inductive treatments. Hashimoto & Tamura (106) found that ABA had very little effect on vernalized *Dioscorea* tubers, and metabolism of the added ABA did not occur because it could be recovered unchanged. While competition from growth-promoting compounds can be invoked, a possible change in the responsiveness of a receptor system by vernalization cannot be discounted.

Little change in the ABA content of peach flower buds occurred during winter until they were given their cold requirement, whereupon the concentrations fell (56). Seasonal changes of ABA contents in vegetative apple buds have been found by Seeley & Powell (290). These observations, and the fall in the ABA content of rose achenes (126) on stratification, pose an awkward question of order—does stratification cause a fall in ABA which then permits germination, or does stratification stimulate germination which then leads to the destruction of the ABA? In support of the role of ABA maintaining bud dormancy in woody species and resting organs are the observations of a number of authors who find that applications of ABA maintain or prolong dormancy (69, 102, 132, 163, 174, 212, 242, 329). El-Antably et al (83) were able to promote tuber formation with (±)-ABA, but Claver (50) was unable to repeat this using plants in test tubes. The question of potato tuber dormancy is discussed by Rappaport & Wolf (253).

Perhaps the most convincing evidence suggesting that ABA induces dormancy is the production of turions (specialized overwintering organs) in the Lemnaceae. When (±)-ABA is added to the medium under conditions that allow continuous growth, it not only inhibits growth [growth of the Lemnaceae is extremely susceptible to inhibition by ABA (334–337)] but causes the production of the dense perennating buds. This action of ABA has been found with *Lemna* (307) (frond to turion ratio 1:1 at 0.05 µg/ml) and *Spirodela* (at 0.01 µg/ml).

(±)-ABA is a potent inhibitor of seed germination, and its presence as the major growth inhibitor in dormant seeds of many species (159, 240, 275) has cast it in the role of the maintainer of seed dormancy. ABA has been isolated from seeds of many genera of higher plants, and seeds of an equally large number of species have been prevented from germinating by soaking in ABA solutions. When seeds and fruit parts are separated it is usually found that the concentration of (+)-ABA in the fruit is about five to ten times greater than in the seed (179, 271). The role of the ABA contained in the fruit in relation to seed dormancy has been investigated only by Sondheimer et al (304). They found a decrease in ABA content during cold stratification of intact seeds of ash (*Fraxinus americana*, a species with dormant seeds), and the concentration fell to the level characteristic of *F. ornus* seeds (a species which does not require stratification). These authors studied the effect of ABA on the germination of isolated embryos of both of these species and found no effect of ABA on the germination of *F. ornus* embryos isolated from seeds previously soaked in a solution of the compound. The ABA strongly inhibited the germination of isolated embryos of *F. ornus* which were soaked in ABA after removal from the seed. It was concluded that only ABA present in the embryo inhibits germination, while any present in the fruit wall does not affect the seed and is probably associated with regulation of ripening or abscission of the fruit. An inhibitor of seed germination, present in fruit, has been reported (29). A recent investigation (190) of the parts of the plants able to incorporate labeled mevalonate into ABA has shown that the embryo, and the endosperm to a lesser extent, of wheat and the cotyledons of avocado seeds are able to synthesize ABA, so the increases in concentration of ABA could arise from synthesis in situ rather than by importation from elsewhere.

Seeds of a number of species have been analyzed during stratification; in some the ABA content falls [*Ambrosia* (359); *Juglans* (169); apple (267); and rose (126)] while in peach (360) stratification had no effect. Dissected yew (*Taxus baccata*) embryos contain ABA and did not germinate until at least some of the ABA had leaked out into the medium in which they were cultured (159). Lipe & Crane (162) found that ABA in peach seeds decreased during stratification. Obviously, the part played by endogenous growth-promoting compounds and the balance between them and ABA during the breaking of dormancy needs to be explored in more detail. Certainly the balance between the two kinds of regulator is important (269). ABA is not an irreversible inhibitor—one of its most striking features is the facility with which it can be leached out of treated tissues to permit the resumption of growth (320, 335).

A number of investigators have found that (±)-ABA can prevent or inhibit germination of seeds (17, 113, 136, 137, 142, 240, 267, 294, 300, 359). In several papers it has been reported that ABA inhibits coleoptile growth more than root growth (12, 142) of seedlings and this is not unexpected in view of its stimulatory effect on lateral root initiation. In *Chenopodium album* seeds (137), (±)-ABA had no effect on the splitting of the testa (this reaction is normally stimulated by light) but it inhibited the next observable phase of germination: extrusion of the radicle. At 10–20 μg,(±)-ABA/ml seedlings were prevented from germinating and even after 2 weeks the inhibition could be relieved by transfer to water. An interesting feature of these experiments was that the ABA was less effective in the light than in darkness, but before its action on light-controlled processes can be certain it is necessary to demonstrate that light-catalyzed isomerization of ABA to inactive 2-*trans*-ABA is not responsible.

Seed germination is accelerated by both gibberellins and cytokinins, growth-promoting compounds that counteract the inhibitory action of ABA. There is a considerable variation in the susceptibility of the seeds of different plants to cytokinins and gibberellins, ranging from cereals which respond almost solely to gibberellins, to lettuce where gibberellin alone is unable to reverse inhibition by ABA and benzyladenine and kinetin are active (26). Dörffling & Böttger (73) found that sugars enhance the inhibitory activity of ABA to lettuce seeds.

Davis & Addicott (65) have shown that (+)-ABA contents of entire cotton fruit rise sharply during middevelopment and again before ripening, the increase occurring both in the fruit and in the seed. Ihle & Dure (118) were able to dissect out the immature embryos of cotton seeds and cause them to germinate precociously. These embryos were susceptible to ABA, as were dissected embryos of dormant hybrid oats (*Avena sativa* X *A. fatua*), although the untreated embryos of dormant seeds germinated spontaneously. Dry storage of hazel nuts causes the development of a deeper state of dormancy (secondary dormancy) and this has been attributed by Bradbeer (37) to a block to gibberellin biosynthesis; a similar after-ripening of apple seeds is prevented by ABA (241).

The essential effect of chilling intact hazel nuts, which is the natural means of breaking their dormancy, may then be to activate a mechanism for gibberellin synthesis; the subsequent synthesis of gibberellin is believed to occur at the germination temperature (20°C) and not at the chilling temperature (5°C).

Abscission

During the last few years several hundred experiments have been carried out in which plants and parts of plants of many genera have been treated in a variety of ways with (±)-ABA. It is quite unusual for any report of the results to record that abscission of leaves occurred, so we may conclude that exogenously applied (±)-ABA has little effect on leaf abscission. Furthermore, the increase in (+)-ABA content of leaves suffering a water deficit is so great that it is difficult to believe that the observed tendency of wilting plants to shed a few of their older leaves can be attributed directly to a change in ABA concentration of this magnitude. It is perhaps significant that it is the mature and premortal leaves that are shed in such situations, and one may ponder whether the large amount of wilt-induced ABA is not accelerating senescence and exerting its effect sequentially through, or together with, other regulatory compounds. Nevertheless, abscisic acid was first isolated by following its abscission-accelerating activity in the petiolar stumps of cotton explants, and the growth-inhibitory activity of the factor believed to be responsible for the premature abscission of immature yellow lupin (*Lupinus luteus*) fruits led to the isolation of a material by Rothwell and Wain that was later identified as (+)-ABA (61, 148). Consequently, the abscission-accelerating effect of ABA is well documented and has been extensively discussed (3, 5, 6, 9, 42, 202, 215, 228, 269, 298, 326).

Rather than repeat the analyses made in these reviews it may be helpful to look for patterns in the data presently available. Stimulation of abscission by ABA has been reported in excised leaf explants of apple (239), citrus (10, 11), bean (63, 128, 228), *Cassia* (2), *Coleus* (2, 26, 72), and cotton (30, 34, 63, 301).

Dörffling & Böttger (72) measured the ABA diffusing out of *Coleus* leaves towards the abscission zones and found that more ABA and less IAA came out of old leaves; thus the hormonal flux would prepare the abscission zone for dehiscence. Supporting evidence implicating ABA in abscission comes from analyses of cotton leaves treated with ethrel (46), a synthetic abscission-accelerating substance. The data for an "abscisic acid-like substance" are only relatively quantitative but show a considerable increase after ethrel treatment. Similarly, two strains of a pathogenic fungus (*Verticillium albo-atrum*) of cotton were used by Wiese & DeVay (358) to monitor the concentrations of endogenous growth regulators during defoliation. The effects of a defoliating (T9) and a nondefoliating (SS4) strain were compared; the former caused a doubling in the ABA content of leaves while the latter was without effect. The infection was accompanied by a rise in ethylene production (fivefold with T9; twofold with SS4), and the possibility that the ethylene was the effective agent is suggested by the fact that treatment of uninfected plants with ethylene duplicated some of the symptoms of the fungal attack and stimulated abscission without affecting the ABA content. The relatively small change in ABA content could be the indirect result of slight loss of turgor caused by some other fungal toxins. Several experiments can be marshaled against this view. Commercial defoliants cause a marked rise in endogenous ABA contents of peach fruits, and the chemical thinners 3-chlorophenoxy propionamide, ethephon, and ethrel caused the content of abscisic acid-like material in cotton leaves to rise (46, 168).

Many of the experiments reporting leaf abscission have been carried out on tree crops using extremely high (1000 μg/ml) concentrations, often towards the end of the growing season, in attempts to cause the abscission of fruit. The observed stimulation of leaf abscission, (22, 55, 79, 155, 230) therefore, may be an indirect effect of unphysiologically high concentrations stimulating ethylene production. For example, Cooper & Henny (55) treated orange with sprays of 500 μg/ml ($\pm$)-ABA in summer and winter. The summer treatments caused coloring to develop and leaves to fall but the winter treatments had no such effect. Olive trees have been found to suffer some leaf abscission (22) in one experiment and no effect in another (105).

It appears that ABA is not closely involved in the regulation of leaf abscission; the test systems in which it has a stimulatory action consist of isolated petiole explants containing presumptive abscission zones and mature leaves nearing the end of their life, and even these require applications of abnormally high concentrations to manifest an effect. The breakdown product of ABA, phaseic acid (178), has approximately 10% of the activity of ABA on cotton explants (67).

Turning now to consider fruit abscission, the role of ABA is more certain. The early papers of Van Steveninck showed that an inhibitor now known to be (+)-ABA (61, 148, 266, 338-341) was intimately involved in the abortion of the younger immature fruitlets of yellow lupin. Applications of ABA to mature peach, olive, citrus, and apple fruits (79, 168, 230, 368) accelerated abscission, and the effect of ABA was also marked on young grape flowers and berries (355).

Davis & Addicott (65) have painstakingly measured the ABA content of developing intact cotton fruit from anthesis to ripening by GLC. Their graph shows a sudden rise in weight/fruit at day 8 from 0.5–3 μg/fruit followed by as sudden a fall to almost undetectable levels (0.2 μg/fruit) by day 20. At day 30 a second and final increase occurs and reaches 4.5 μg/fruit when the fruits dehisce at day 50.

The first increase coincides with the period of self-thinning or "June drop," and they find that aborted fruitlets at this time contain 4 μg ABA whereas the attached, developing ones contain much less. Two strains with a slight tendency (c.v. Acala SJ-1) and a strong tendancy (c.v. Acala 4-42) to drop immature fruit were also analyzed, and again low ABA content paralleled the plants' ability to retain the fruit. These results corroborate those of Van Steveninck and leave little doubt that ABA regulates the loss of a proportion of the young fruit, the "June drop," and is involved in the final stages of fruit development. Dissected embryos from cotton seeds germinate prematurely almost up to the time of fruit ripening (118), and as the growth is inhibited by ABA (24), one may suggest that at least some part of the final rise in ABA content is associated with the maturation of the embryo. Davis & Addicott (65) determined the ABA content of the seeds dissected from fruits during the last 20 days of growth and found a fall in ABA content; this, and the earlier period of low ABA content from day 20 to 30, was associated with two periods during which seed could be prematurely germinated (1).

Effect of Wilting on Abscisic Acid Content and Stomata

Wright (362, 363) found that when cut shoots were wilted there was an increase in the titer of β-inhibitor. He went on to identify the major inhibitor as (+)-abscisic acid and defined the conditions under which the increase occurred. A water loss of about 10% of the total fresh weight causes an approximately 40-fold increase in ABA content while further water loss has negligible effect. Wright & Hiron (364) have reported that other stress conditions such as waterlogging cause a similar rise in ABA, but they point out that such treatments cause incipient wilting by reducing the efficiency of water uptake (194, 195).

The surprising feature of the increase in ABA is the rapidity with which it occurs. The content of turgid drawf bean leaves can be calculated from Wright & Hiron's histograms as 6 μg/kg, rising to 9 μg/kg within 7 min of the application of a draught of warm air, 33 μg/kg by 25 min, and 68 μg/kg within 45 min; wheat leaves increased from 23 to 171 μg/kg within 4 hr of wilting. The content of ABA in bean leaves remained at 67 μg/kg while they were kept waterlogged for 5 days. The graphs of ABA contents after the rewatering of severely wilted Brussels sprout plants (364) show a much slower rate of decrease; a half-life of 12 hr can be calculated, with 2 or 3 days required to restore the normal level. The implications of this have yet to be explored in detail, but the observations offer a feasible explanation of the growth check observed after crops suffer drought. The foregoing ABA contents are lower than those of wilted wheat leaves reported by Milborrow & Noddle (189), who used the "racemate dilution" method to calculate the amounts of ABA present in leaves excluding losses during extraction.

The "extra" ABA is probably formed by synthesis rather than by release from a precursor or conjugate because much more labeled mevalonate was incorporated into ABA by a sample of leaves that had been fed and then wilted, in comparison with another half of the same batch that was kept moist during the same time. Furthermore, the presence of 40 times the amount of a precursor or conjugate able to release ABA probably would have been detected by extraction and bioassay. The glucose ester, the most probable candidate for this role, seldom exceeds one third of the amount of free ABA. A similar dramatic rise in ABA content on wilting has been found in french bean, Brussels sprouts (364), sugar cane (200), wheat (189), avocado (190), spinach (367), cotton and pea (363), and tomato (187), but leaves or leafy shoots were used in all experiments.

Similar contents of ABA occur in wilted leaves whether the wilt is slight or severe and remain constant until turgor is regained, so there are probably three switch mechanisms operating: (a) rapid synthesis triggered by wilting; (b) a "stop" message when sufficient ABA has been formed; and (c) the commencement of destruction which occurs when turgor is regained (this may be merely the cessation of rapid synthesis). Milborrow and Noddle fed turgid wheat leaves with the racemic [2-^{14}C] diols (V and VI) of ABA and then caused the plants to wilt. The diols are rapidly oxidized to ABA and from the optical activity, UV absorption, and radioactivity of the ABA they were able to calculate that there had been no biosynthesis of (+)-ABA in the wilted plants. From this they deduced that the excess ABA formed from the diols operated a negative feedback loop and stopped its own biosynthesis. Almost all of the (+)-ABA was degraded and therefore the unnatural (−)-enantiomer must be able to act at the feedback site as well as at the site for growth inhibition.

Milborrow & Robinson (190) investigated the sites of synthesis of ABA and its regulation by measuring both the incorporation of labeled mevalonate and the increase in ABA content. The leaves of avocado seedlings increased their ABA content on wilting whereas roots and stems showed a very slight response. The incorporation of mevalonate into ABA and the usual rise in ABA content during fruit ripening were unaffected by the loss of water from avocado fruit slices which not only contain very large amounts of ABA but continue synthesizing it rapidly. Thus ABA biosynthesis is regulated differently in roots, stems, and fruit.

The ability of exogenously applied ABA to close stomata was known, and the rise in concentration of ABA in wilted leaves had been correlated with stomatal closure by Wright and Hiron, so a water plant (hornwort, *Ceratophyllum demersum*) lacking stomata was investigated. Wilting caused a slight rise in ABA content (1.7-fold increase). Another water plant (water starwort, *Callitriche stagnalis*) was dissected into submerged parts and floating aerial rosettes (190); the former increased their ABA content 2-fold on wilting whereas the wilting rosettes increased theirs 6.5-fold. Furthermore, the ABA content of the submerged parts resembled that of *Ceratophyllum* whereas the content of the rosettes approximated that usually found in land plants. The differences in content and the magnitude of the alterations on wilting were considered to reflect an environmentally controlled change in ABA regulation, although the experiment can be criticized because the flowering rosettes and submerged shoots differ morphologically and physiologically. The difference in spectral composition of the light received by the two parts of the plant may also be responsible for the differences in ABA contents (21, 331).

The closure of stomata by ABA is an important and unexpected observation first reported by Mittelheuser & Van Steveninck in 1969 (192). When supplied to cut leaves of wheat and barley, (±)-ABA as a 1-μg/ml solution caused the stomata to close and reduced transpiration by one half. Kinetin stimulated transpiration of wheat (54) and slightly antagonized the effect of the ABA. Jones & Mansfield, (134, 135) and Cummins et al (64) have investigated the interaction of CO_2 and (±)-ABA on stomata of *Xanthium* and barley and conclude that in both plants CO_2 and ABA exert their effects independently. The methyl and phenyl esters were also active but the minimum of 12 hr that elapsed between treatment and observation might have allowed some hydrolysis to occur. Similarly a "slow-release" of the free acid could account for persistence of the effect for 9 days (134). Adding 0.26 μg (±)-ABA/ml to the water supplied to barley leaves caused a detectable increase in stomatal resistance within 5 min (193) and, unlike the effect of wilting, replacement of the solution by water caused a rapid fall in resistance (64). In addition to inducing closure of the stomata, ABA prevents their opening (116). Milborrow (179) speculated that stomatal closure could be brought about by ABAs known ability to prevent the synthesis of α-amylase, invoking an old explanation of stomatal operation.

In an elegant series of experiments, Mansfield & Jones (133, 167) showed that starch accumulated in the chloroplasts of guard cells treated with ABA and also that there was a fall in the osmotic pressure of guard cells from 14.1 to 9.8 bars. There was also a flux of potassium ions out of the guard cells on treatment with ABA which would accentuate the reduction of osmotic pressure. The synthesis of extra ABA in guard cells on wilting (thereby preventing α-amylase synthesis, permitting the synthesis of starch, and lowering the osmotic pressure) would seem to be too slow to account for the rapid closure of stomata, but the fast potassium fluxes could cause rapid movement which could then be "locked" by an osmotic adjustment involving starch hydrolysis. The ubiquitous presence of chloroplasts [the site of ABA synthesis (186) and of starch synthesis] in guard cells may be significant, and the ability of ABA to inhibit the influx of potassium ions into stomatal guard cells (117) agrees with this hypothesis.

Perhaps the best evidence for the direct involvement of ABA in stomatal closure is afforded by a wilty tomato mutant (*flacca*) (119, 309–312) produced by X-irradiation of cultivar Rheinlands Ruhm. *Flacca* shoots contained one tenth of the amount of inhibitor (ABA) (309, 310) present in the normal variety and their stomata were permanently open. Applications of 0.1–10 μg (±)-ABA caused a rapid and progressive reduction in transpiration rate of *flacca* leaves and leaf discs; in 10 μg ABA/ml the stomata closed in darkness (119). The exudate from decapitated *flacca* plants had less volume and higher osmotic pressure than that from RR plants (121); whether the differences reflect an effect of low ABA content or another facet of the mutant syndrome is uncertain. Fusicoccin has been shown to partially reverse the effect of ABA on stomata (45).

Inhibition of Growth

The inhibition of the growth of whole plants, excised organs, or seeds is the most easily measured response to ABA. Several hundred papers report the effect of natural (+) or racemic (±) ABA, either alone or in combination with other growth-promoting compounds, on the growth of the test objects. With the exception of the few examples cited in the next section, ABA inhibits growth of all parts of plants and counteracts the stimulatory effects of the natural growth-promoting compounds when applied with them. The growth inhibition is remarkable in three ways: (a) it is extremely potent, being of the same order as the other natural regulators (0.05–0.5 μg/ml gives a 50% response in most tests) (4, 17, 49, 131, 175, 266, 295, 364); (b) it can be reversed by removal of the source or leaching the tissues (320); (c) ABA counteracts the toxicity of supraoptimal concentrations of the growth-promoting compounds (20, 175).

The question of whether endogenous ABA inhibits normal growth is more difficult to answer because there is no specific inhibitor of ABA biosynthesis known at present and ABA can be biosynthesized in several different parts of the plant. It is not easy, therefore, to remove or inhibit the source. The only physiological tool available at present is the *flacca* (wilty) tomato mutant (119, 309–312), which makes much less ABA than the cultivar from which it was derived. The mutant plants are unable to make as much ABA as the normal, but nevertheless the genetic lesion is not absolute and the mutants still contain some 10% of the normal content. The growth form of the *flacca* plants suggests supraoptimal IAA levels, but whether this is the result of low ABA concentrations or another manifestation of the mutation is unknown.

The *flacca* plants certainly do not adopt a spindly growth form and are smaller than the controls; they are frequently in a semiwilted condition, a factor that may be responsible for their smaller size.

Simpson & Saunders (292) have made a comprehensive analysis of the ABA contents of tall (Alaska) and dwarf (Meteor) pea seedlings. They make allowance for fresh and dry weights and find no difference in ABA content between the tall and dwarf plants either when turgid or when wilted. The large increases in ABA observed on wilting are considered by these authors to negate the possibility that ABA acts as a correlative inhibitor, as proposed by Arney & Mitchell (15). The results of these experiments (292) are in conflict with those reported by Barnes & Light (21), who report that red-light grown dwarf peas contain ten times more inhibitor than dark grown dwarf or tall (Alaska) peas. The effect of water loss in causing increased ABA biosynthesis was not known at the time Barnes and Light did their experiments. Incipient wilting might have affected the results somewhat, but Tucker & Mansfield (331) found that red/far red light caused *Xanthium* plants to increase the content of abscisic acid-like material in lateral buds and these buds did not grow, whereas plants grown without red/far red illumination branched profusely and contained between 50 and 250 times less inhibitor than those given red/far red light. Another interesting feature of the ABA contents of tall and dwarf pea plants grown by Simpson and Saunders is that in darkness they contained 6.6

and 10.7 μg/kg fresh weight and these values rose to 34.0 and 69.2 μg/kg on wilting. The plants grown with a daily photoperiod contained 61.1 and 51.1 μg/kg respectively and 359 and 434 μg/kg on wilting. In these experiments ABA is associated with changes in growth form resulting from the light quality received, but ABA contents cannot be correlated with the dwarf/tall habit.

Other evidence involving endogenous ABA in the control of growth of nondormant plants can be deduced from the slight promotive effects that applications of gibberellin have on the growth of normal plants. It is possible that the stimulation is attributable to the raising of suboptimal concentrations of gibberellin to the optimum; on the other hand, the stimulation may reflect the disturbance of a balance between gibberellins in growth promotion and the retarding effects of the small endogenous concentrations of ABA that have been found even in actively growing tissues (176).

Finally, there is the slight growth check that is observed when plants wilt severely. The high concentrations of ABA (see section on the response of stomata to ABA) produced in wilted leaves may have some effect on the growth of the rest of the plant (364).

Stimulation of Growth

There are very few exceptions to the general rule that ABA inhibits growth; two were noted by Addicott in the previous review (8), namely that ABA stimulates parthenocarpic seed development in rose (127) and hypocotyl elongation in cucumber (17). Further work has added the stimulation of rooting of stem cuttings of mung beans and ivy (48) and *Poinsettia* (256) [in which ($\pm$)-ABA competes against the inhibitory effect of gibberellic acid] and bean [in which ($\pm$)-ABA counters the inhibitory activity of gibberellic acid (152)] and the stimulation of lateral roots in tomato (51). The most pronounced effect is the tenfold stimulation of rice mesocotyl growth in darkness by 2 μg ABA/ml (gibberellic acid increased growth still more); while ($\pm$)-ABA promotes the formation of buds on *Begonia* leaves (107), this action may be related to its ability to accelerate senescence.

In addition to these observations, ABA has been found to initiate (10, 11, 239) and promote the growth and development of callus tissue at the abscission zone of apple and orange petiole explants. Also, ($\pm$)-ABA has been found to increase the stimulatory effect of kinetin on soybean callus growth (32).

Nagl (205) treated *Allium cepa* root tips with 0.1–26 μg ($\pm$)-ABA/ml. Growth was inhibited but resumed after a recovery period when it was noted that the ABA had stimulated polyploid nuclei in mature tissues to divide. This is an interesting and unexpected observation, but while the ABA was used as a tool to dissect the regulatory mechanisms of mitosis, it also highlights the dangers inherent in experiments in which natural growth regulators are applied to tissues, i.e. that some of the effects produced may be anomalous.

Fruit Set and Development

No further observations of pathenocarpic development induced by ABA have been reported since Jackson and Blundell's initial observations on *Rosa* (126, 127).

Arditti et al (14) have found that orchid flowers *(Cymbidium)* treated with ABA (1–0.001 μg/flower) underwent several of the postpollination changes, but their stigmata did not close nor did their columns swell, so ABA was unable to complete the initiation of fruit development.

Young fruits were the source of two of the earliest isolates of ABA (217, 266). The highest concentrations measured in 1967 were found in fruit (176). Fruit tissues were shown to incorporate labeled mevalonate into ABA. The concentration of ABA rises during ripening (70, 71, 270–272, 356, 368) and yet no role for ABA in fruit maturation other than abscission has been proposed until recently (53, 190).

Wang et al (350) found that cooling pears on the trees caused premature ripening. There was a close parallelism between softening and ABA content in chilled and normal fruit, but applications of ABA to fruit have had little or no effect even when 500 μg/ml sprays were used on oranges by Cooper & Henry (55); the treatment caused coloring in winter but not in summer. Smock reports that 250 μg ABA/ml dips had no effect on apples, yet a 100 μg/ml spray stimulated respiration (299). The treatment presumably must swamp the endogenous concentration to be effective and this is difficult with bulky fruit. Furthermore, Rudnicki & Pieniazek (273, 274) with strawberry and Dörffling with tomatoes (70, 71) have found that ABA contents increase until the fruit is ripe and then decrease. The ABA present in the hard endocarp of plum (278) can be leached as it can from a fleshy fruit. Dörffling (71) finds that even at maturity the ABA concentration in tomato fruit is insufficient to inhibit germination of the seeds.

Coombe et al (53) have investigated the changes in grape berries that occur during the second rapid phase of enlargement, which depends solely on enlargement of the pericarp cells and is not correlated with any changes in ethylene production. They found that both 2-chloroethyl phosphonic acid (CEPA) and benzothiazole-2-oxyacetic acid (BTOA) increased the levels of endogenous ethylene although they had different effects on ripening. The authors suggest that ABA plays an important regulatory role in fruit development because the changes in endogenous ABA levels are closely connected with ripening and enlargement, the rises in ABA concentrations were correlated with the effects of CEPA in hastening—and BTOA in delaying —ripening, and application of ABA to the young fruit accelerated ripening. There is now a considerable amount of evidence to suggest that ABA regulates fruit ripening, a role that is unrelated to its effect on seed dormancy.

Flowering

Abscisic acid treatments have a weak but consistent promoting effect on flower growth in short-day plants and can stimulate the induction of partially induced *Chenopodium rubrum* (150, 151) and *Pharbitis nil* (35, 104), acting as an inducer of flowering under some conditions (82). ABA has no inductive capacity in *Plumbago indica* but promotes flower development (209) even on internodal explants (208).

High concentrations of ABA inhibit or delay flowering of *Kalanchoe blossfeldiana* (285), coffee (332), *Dianthus caryophyllus* (43), olive (19), *Lemna paucicostata* (101), and *Wolffia microscopica* (344). ABA inhibited flower initiation in the long-day plant *Lolium tementulum* (84).

Gibberellins have been found to induce the formation of male flowers on female *Cannabis sativus* plants; this change was reversed by (±)-ABA but no feminizing effect of ABA alone was observed (196).

Senescence

Senescence has been afforded its own section in this review because publications discuss its advent, course, and the effect of treatments on its amelioration. Senescence is a little understood phenomenon, and the justification for treating it separately from growth inhibition and dormancy (which themselves overlap) is rather tenuous. The maturation of fruit, the death of outer parts of bark, the processes prior to the abscission of tree leaves, and the death of an annual plant can all be considered as senescence and yet be regulated in different ways. The convenient terms "ripening" and "aging" may reflect a real physiological difference between controlled induced senescence and senescence brought about by unfavorable influences. Only 4 of the 18 papers that cite the action of ABA on senescence record the effect of treatments applied to whole plants, while 16 deal with ca 10-mm leaf discs, section, or explants. It is not surprising, therefore, that these pieces, having been subjected to major surgery, cannot survive for more than a few days unless battered with nutrients and growth regulators which distort their physiology and delay their death. With such ailing experimental material, any effects have to be observable rapidly; consequently the effects of ABA recorded in such assays are usually those most readily observed (color), and much larger doses of ABA have to be applied to obtain a noticeable effect on senescence (ca 20 μg/ml) in comparison with those used in assays of growth inhibition or stomatal closure. This is not to say that leaf discs, explants, or sections should not be used; they certainly should, but in conjunction and comparison with the same tissues in other and less damaged forms if valid information on the normal role of the compound is to be obtained. The paucity of reports of ABA inducing senescence is silent testimony to its lack of this effect on young and undamaged parts of plants.

The promotion of senescence by ABA is closely linked with the same effect of ethylene, but a logical analysis of the situation and the relationship between these compounds is rendered impossible by the complex interaction between the various factors, the variety of plants on which they have been tested, and the apparent contradiction between results obtained with different tissues. This is shown well by Gertman & Fuchs (94), who treated orange peel discs and pea seedlings with ABA. The ethylene production of the former was increased 56% while that of the latter was decreased 40%. Similar observations abound. Ethylene treatments cause changes in ABA concentrations; consequently the action of ABA on processes which are also affected by ethylene is extremely difficult to unravel (171, 172). Furthermore, Osborne (228) has written: "It is evident that the extent to which protein and nucleic acid synthesis is disturbed by abscisic acid depends upon the state of maturity of the material under study." It also appears to be dependent on the species of the plant selected and the part of the plant used.

Most measurements of the effect of ABA on senescence have been carried out on leaf discs or sections (17, 18, 25, 52, 68, 83, 145, 224, 231, 279, 281, 351). Chlorophyll is gradually destroyed, a process that is accelerated by ABA and inhibited by additions of kinetin or bunzyl adenine (17, 18, 224, 234, 281) and by potassium ions (279). Gibberellin alone promotes senescence of *Rumex* leaf discs and this action is inhibited by ABA, whereas ABA alone also promotes the loss of chlorophyll. During the first 24 hr after excision, ABA promoted senescence (measured as pigment loss) of radish leaf discs (52), but when applied after a 6-day incubation period, ABA retarded the decline in pigment content although it promoted the decline in protein content. The high concentration applied (26.4 μg/ml) may have prevented the synthesis of some degradative enzymes as was found in bean petioles with 500 μg/ml applications (228). Evidence that the net synthesis of degradative enzymes occurs in senescing leaf discs was provided by Knypl & Mazurczyk (145) using kale leaf discs; cycloheximide and vanillin decreased the loss of protein and retarded the loss of chlorphyll while ($\pm$)-ABA increased both. The changes induced by ABA affect a variety of cell constituents in different ways. De Leo & Sacher (68) found that acid phosphatase and RNase activities increase in *Rhoeo* leaf sections after ABA treatment, and Paranjothy & Wareing (231) found that ABA promoted the senescence of radish leaf discs but had no effect on the incorporation of [^{3}H] cytidine.

Sloger & Caldwell (296) compared the effect of sprays of 100 μg ($\pm$)-ABA/ml on a number of soybean varieties and found a wide variation in their susceptibilities, which was maintained when cut leaves were supplied with solution, although the isolated organs were more susceptible.

Trewavas (327, 328) has carried out an elegant and detailed kinetic analysis of the protein contents of *Lemna minor* plants and reports that 1.3 μg ($\pm$)-ABA/ml reduces the protein content by both reducing the rate of synthesis and accelerating the rate of degradation. The rate of protein degradation is not as fast as occurs when the plantlets are transferred to water, and this may result from the inhibition of synthesis of degradative enzymes by the ABA. The synthetic cytokinin benzyladenine apparently antagonized the action of ABA, but analysis of the turnover rates shows that it decreased the rate of degradation while leaving the rate of synthesis unaffected.

When synthetic abscisic acid became available it was tested by Osborne to discover whether it was responsible for the abscission and senescence accelerating activity of leachates from yellowing leaves that she had been investigating (130, 225–227). Although ABA was active in the tests it was not as active as impure preparations of the senescence factor. Consequently an attempt was made to separate the two. Not only were the (+)-ABA contents of leachates or methanolic extracts of yellow and green *Euonymus* and bean leaves more active than their (+)-ABA content warranted, but whereas the senescence factor increased in yellowing leaves, the (+)-ABA content remained constant or fell slightly (229). Furthermore, the senescence factor activity was separable from ABA by thin layer chromatography, as had also been found by Smith (297). The senescence factor activity in eluates of the chromatograms paralleled their capacity to stimulate ethylene production; ($\pm$)-ABA did not have this effect. Thus the action of ABA on senescence and abscission does not seem to be direct, and it may exert its effect on mature and aged organs by inducing the production of a senescence factor which in turn controls ethylene production.

Effects on Permeability

The permeability of carrot root cells to water is increased by 20 μg ($\pm$)-ABA/ml when measured as THO flux half-time (96) or by the loss and gain of weight (95). In the former experiments the effect of ABA is antagonized by metabolic inhibitors which alone have no effect at the concentrations used. In the latter experiments Glinka & Reinhold found that ABA increases the hydraulic conductivity and the diffusional permeability of the carrot discs and also stem discs of *Pelargonium*. The effect of kinetin was antagonistic.

Effects of ion permeability are discussed in the section on stomata, but wheat aleurone cells also undergo changes which affect the leakage of K, PO_4, Mg, and Ca ions during germination. Gibberellin stimulates leakage and ABA inhibits it, but this inhibition is dependent on protein synthesis (78). The release of hydrolytic enzyme molecules from the aleurone cells is unaffected by ABA (343).

One of the most exciting recent discoveries in plant physiology was that made by Tanada (316)—the ability of red light to change the electrical charge on cell surfaces, causing them to attach to glass charged with phosphates and become detached in far red light. Addition of 0.00053 μg ($\pm$)-ABA/ml to the solution quickly enhances root tip attachment in red light but in far red the tips gradually detach with time (240). When 0.0013 μg ($\pm$)-ABA/ml is used the tips remain attached under both light conditions. The ABA effect is reversed by 0.0035 μg IAA/ml. Thus it seems that phytochrome acts in conjunction with IAA and ABA to effect fast changes in surface potential and that these hormones have opposing effects—ABA induces a positive and IAA a negative surface potential.

Tanada considers that the rapidity of the changes (detachment or attachment of most tips was observed within 2 min of adding IAA or ABA respectively) indicates that the initial sites of action are probably on the plasmalemma. This is in accord with the effectiveness of ABA at the lowest concentrations ever reported (2 $\times$ 10^{-10} M). It should be possible to develop the technique into an extremely sensitive bioassay.

OTHER PROPERTIES OF ABSCISIC ACID

Transport in Plants

The first direct observations of the transport of ABA through plant parts were reported in 1968 by Milborrow (177) using ($\pm$)-[2-^{14}C] ABA and by Dörffling & Böttger (72). The latter authors measured the ABA passing out of stem and petiole segments of *Coleus* by an oat coleoptile assay and confirmed that young explants (but not old ones) transport ABA basipetally faster than acropetally; Milborrow reported a 3:1 differential in bean petiole explants. Dörffling and Böttger calculated the rate of transport of ABA through their explants at between 24 and 35 mm/hr by the same extrapolation procedure that McCready & Jacobs (173) used for IAA in bean petioles. The data from these two sets of experiments indicate that ABA is transported 4–6 times faster than IAA and the higher temperature (27°) used for the *Coleus* experiments in comparison with 25° for bean is unlikely to produce a change of this magnitude.

McCready & Jacobs used [^{14}C] IAA which passed *through* the explants, whereas a rapid "shunting" of endogenous ABA by the applied ABA could have caused a more rapid apparent movement when the ABA in the receiver block was bioassayed. Ingersoll & Smith (121) obtained a rapid rate of transport of (±)-[2-^{14}C] ABA (20–30 mm/hr) through cotton explants, but their experiments were carried out at 30°. In a later paper they give a more refined estimate of 22.4 mm/hr at 30°, showing that transport is reduced by DNP, anaerobiosis, and low temperature (2°). They also gave a pulse of (±)-[2-^{14}C] ABA followed by unlabeled material and found that 60% of the [^{14}C] ABA passed through the section within 6 hr; this far exceeds the proportion of IAA transported. The continuous destruction of [1-^{14}C] IAA by decarboxylation and other catabolic reactions as it passed through the sections would give a low apparent velocity even in "pulse and chase" experiments, and the calculation of a "true" rate of movement will require further detailed investigation. The apparent higher velocity of ABA transport in comparison with IAA has not been confirmed in one tissue at one temperature and so the validity of the comparison has not been established; ideally the experiment could be carried out for the two compounds (^{3}H- and ^{14}C-labeled) simultaneously.

The transport of ABA and other materials through explants is considered to be a metabolically controlled cell to cell transfer rather than phleom transport because the sections are too short for sieve tubes to function. However, the rates observed are considerably slower than those calculated for intact phleom (100–1500 mm/hr) and some residual phloem activity may be responsible. Identification of (+)-ABA has been made in phloem and in small amounts in xylem sap of willow (36, 156), in the honeydew of aphids feeding in willow phloem (110), and in honey made from honeydew of aphids feeding on silver fir (179), so in the intact plant it is probably translocated in sieve tubes.

In sycamore and bean petiole section (±)-[2-^{14}C] ABA was metabolized to glucose ester and metabolite C/phaseic acid. Although the receiver blocks contained ABA only (177, 311), it is not known whether the ABA is transported as free acid or glucose ester. The passage of glucose ester through damaged cells adjacent to the agar blocks, or through aphids, could be expected to hydrolyze any glucose ester so that only the free acid would be detected. The trapping of transported glucose [^{14}C] abscisate in agar might be accomplished by incorporating unlabeled glucose ester in the agar receiver blocks, and esterase activity leaking from cut cells could be detected by incorporating glucose [^{14}C] abscisate in the blocks placed against the petiole segments.

Hocking and co-workers (111) measured the uptake of (±)-[2-^{14}C] ABA by primary leaves of intact bean seedlings and transport into the rest of the plant. Radioactivity was widely distributed throughout the plant except for the opposite primary leaf, and accumulation was most marked below the point of application, but even so some label was found in the apical bud. Some radioactivity passed upwards past a steam girdle but none passed downwards past a girdle, suggesting that the radioactive material is transported principally in the phloem. Some metabolism of the [^{14}C] ABA was observed, but no information on the form in which ABA was transported was given.

It has been noted that (±)-ABA inhibited its own transport in cotton petioles and also reduced the velocity of IAA transport through lentil hypocotyls by between 9 and 11% (122, 244). There was no effect on the rate of [^{14}C] IAA transport through maize coleoptile sections (206) by (±)-ABA, but it caused the retention of more label within the tissue.

Rapid Responses in Growth Rate

The means by which the rapid changes in growth rate are brought about by plant growth regulators is still unknown (85, 207, 254, 255) as are the lengths of the lag phases (75). Warner & Leopold (354) have shown that 2.6 μg/ml ABA inhibits the growth rate of decapitated pea seedlings detectably within 5 min at 24°, which is faster than IAA (9.3 min), Ga$_3$ (23.7 min), ethylene (6.4 min), or benzyladenine (11.7 min). The inhibitory effect may be easier to detect than a promotive one; nevertheless it is similar to the lag time for dinitrophenol inhibition and much quicker than that of actinomycin D (110 min). Mittelheuser & Van Steveninck (193) have detected an increase in stomatal resistance after application of 1.0 μg (±)-ABA/ml to wheat leaves within 5–10 min, so the time course of this effect is very similar to that of the growth response.

Rehm & Cline (257) have repeated and confirmed the results of Nissl & Zenk (207) where (±)-ABA inhibited the IAA-induced elongation of oat coleoptiles within 4 to 5 min. An inhibitor of ribosomal RNA synthesis, 5-fluorouracil, had no effect on coleoptile elongation. Cycloheximide (an inhibitor of protein synthesis) inhibited elongation with a lag time similar to that of ABA but the kinetics of the two inhibitors were different, and ABA also inhibits the low pH induced elongation which is insensitive to cycloheximide. Nevertheless the major part of the effect of ABA could be on translational control.

Tissue Culture

ABA is a weak inhibitor of callus growth, and the data of Li et al (161) show that tobacco callus was inhibited 50% by 5 μg (±)-ABA/ml, while Taylor & Burden (320) obtained 50% inhibition with ca. 50 μg ABA and xanthoxin per milliliter on the same tissue. Gamborg & Larue (92) obtained 50% inhibition with 5 μg ABA/ml for rose cell suspensions. Ipomea cotyledon callus was strongly inhibited by 1 μg/ml (280). Soybean callus, which requires a cytokinin for growth, was stimulated by ABA in the presence of kinetin.

Pieniazek (239) and Altman & Goren (10) noted that (±)-ABA at 1 μg/ml caused a proliferation of cells of the abscission zones of apple and Citrus petiole explants.

Effects on Nucleic Acids, Protein Synthesis, and Isolated Enzymes

The first observations of the effects of abscisic acid on nucleic acids were made by Van Overbeek et al (335) using Lemna. The incorporation of [^{32}P] phosphate into nucleic acid fractions during inhibition by ABA and its reversal by benzyladenine caused changes in the amount of label in all fractions, but the primary site of action of ABA cannot be deduced with certainty because of the time scale and the complexity of the responses. Subsequent work has indicated that DNA synthesis is almost certainly not the primary target of ABA (342, 345, 349). This has been clearly shown in dry wheat embryos by Chen & Osborne (47), who found that protein synthesis commenced from imbibition and was inhibited at 6 hr by ABA whereas RNA synthesis (incorporation of [³H] uridine) was not measurable until 12 hr, and DNA ([³H] thymidine incorporation) until 24 hr.

Investigations of the barley aleurone α-amylase system have shown that gibberellic acid initiates the synthesis of new enzymes (142, 246, 342, 365) and this is inhibited by ABA. Actinomycin has little effect on amylase production in short-term experiments whereas the inhibitors of protein synthesis and ABA have a potent action. Consequently the evidence points to ABA's having an effect on translation (47, 246, 342).

Zwar & Jacobsen (369) found gibberellin stimulated RNA synthesis in barley aleurone and most of the labeled uridine went into a small fraction which comprised 1% of the total RNA—this fraction showed properties typical of mRNA. Using pear embryos and lentil roots, Khan & Anojulu (144) and Khan et al (143) were able to measure a change in base composition of a rapidly labeled RNA species which was inhibited by ABA, so the effect of the hormone appears to be on a specific fraction of the RNA. Changes in overall RNA levels have been detected (27, 231, 243, 258).

Attempts to obtain inhibition of various steps in isolated systems capable of protein synthesis have been unsuccessful. Pearson & Wareing (232) prepared a chromatin DNA-dependent RNA polymerase which was slightly (28%) inhibited when 0.26 μg (±)-ABA/ml was present in the grinding medium but not when it was added to the pure preparation. Bex (28) found that the isolated RNA polymerase of maize coleoptiles was inhibited when they had been preincubated in ABA but ABA had no effect when added to the grinding medium. Bex also reports that ABA has no effect on the binding between nucleohistones and DNA as measured by their melting point measurements. Schwartz (287) has shown that ABA can alter the balance of alcohol dehydrogenase in maize but the inhibitor was added during the growth of the cells.

Ihle & Dure (118), working with prematurely germinated cotton embryos, obtained evidence that the translation of mRNA was inhibited by ABA, but the system is probably more complex than a direct inhibitory effect because actinomycin D inhibited the ABA-induced inhibition; possibly a suppressor molecule has to be formed to bring about these effects.

The ability of plant hormones to affect directly the activity of enzymes has not been extensively investigated, and when an effect has been reported it is very much smaller than would be intuitively expected if their functions were operated by this means (283). Hemberg (109) and Mousseron-Canet (203) report that ABA can inhibit α-amylase but as the enzyme used was extracted from fungi and the significance of the observations to higher plants requires further investigation. (±)-ABA, but not its 2-*trans* isomer, complexed with fungal α-amylase and changed its physical (44) properties. Saunders & Poulson (284) found a slight (15%) stimulatory action of ($\pm$)-ABA on invertase at $10^{-7} M$, followed by slight inhibition at 5×10^{-7} M and above; again, the significance is difficult to assess as a fungal enzyme was used, and the change brought about by ($\pm$)-ABA in invertase activity found in carrot discs (284), the decrease in hot transaminase in lentil (245), and the effects on gibberellin biosynthesis in spinach plants (351) can be attributed to changes in amount of enzyme.

Interaction with Growth-Promoting Compounds

The effects of abscisic acid on a wide range of growth processes are antagonized by one or mixtures of the auxin, gibberellin, or cytokinin growth regulators. Occasionally when two growth promoters have antagonistic effects, ABA is found to accentuate the action of one or the other (146, 331). There is some evidence that ABA acts at the same site (317) as IAA in very short term experiments, but Rothwell and Wain's method is still the most detailed that has been applied to the investigation of interaction between ABA and a growth-promoting substance in experiments lasting between 12 and 24 hr (61, 148, 266). They took IAA as the substrate and the induced growth increment divided by the initial length as the product of the reaction and applied the methods of enzyme kinetics to the data of wheat coleoptiles grown in varying concentrations of (+)-ABA and IAA. If an allowance for endogenous IAA were made (0.178 μg/g), the regression lines intercepted the x axis at one point indicating noncompetitive inhibition. However, Taylor & Burden (320) have repeated the experiments and found that the sets of lines for ($\pm$)-ABA and for (+)-xanthoxin do not intercept at any one position on their respective x axes, so IAA and the inhibitors are not interacting competitively and the kinetic analysis may not be valid.

A recent controversy on the interaction of ABA and gibberellic acid can be found in *Science* (74, 180).

Other Effects

Other effects that have been observed as a result of ABA treatments are inhibition of nodulation in pea (235), runner formation in strawberry (140), and an increase in cold hardiness (114, 115, 123).

ULTRASTRUCTURAL CHANGES   The direct effects of ABA in preventing germination of seeds, growth of young tissues, and the senescence of mature organs are obviously accompanied by the induction of gross morphological differences between the experimental samples and controls. Few investigations have been made of the detailed changes that occur at the inception of treatment and those that have are somewhat contradictory. Pearson & Wareing (233) found that while ABA inhibited the unrolling and greening of young wheat leaf segments, it did not cause a preferential decrease or inhibition of polysome formation. Poulson & Beevers (248) report that etiolated barley leaves contained more polysomes after gibberellic acid treatment and fewer after ABA treatment. Evins & Varner (86) found the same was true in barley aleurone and that ABA inhibited endoplasmic reticulum formation.

The ultrastructural changes induced in excised buds of resting potato (*Solanum tuberosum*) tubers when treated with ABA or GA_3 were investigated by Shih & Rappaport (291). Little difference was seen between cells of the buds in water and those treated with gibberellin, but ABA caused considerable vacuolation which was detectable after 1 hr. Roland & Pilet have reported changes in the cell walls of blackberry apices (265).

EFFECTS ON FUNGI AND ANIMALS   As described earlier, ABA has not been identified in liverworts, algae, or fungi; the ABA in *Penicillium* cultured from oranges was lost after six transfers of the fungus in synthetic medium (268). ABA was reported to have slight juvenile hormone activity when injected into mealworms but no effect when supplied in the diet to spruce bud worm (80, 81).

In *Fusarium moniliforme* ($\pm$)-ABA does not inhibit gibberellin synthesis, and the reduction in gibberellin levels reported by Wareing et al (351) may be an indirect effect, as indeed may be the ($\pm$)-ABA increased gibberellin biosynthesis in *Solanum andigena* leaves observed by Railton & Wareing (252) and the changes in both IAA and ABA in response to other hormones measured in pea seedlings by Tietz & Dörffling (323).

CONCLUDING REMARKS

At the close of his review, Addicott (8) predicted that abscisic acid would be applied to innumerable plants and pieces of plants over the next few years; this has occurred and some of the effects produced have been recorded. Attempts to identify the one or several primary sites of action have not yet succeeded. The burden of the evidence suggests that there may be two kinds of response to ABA and to other plant hormones: a direct, rapid response possibly operating on membranes or some other existing structure, and a slower effect involving the synthesis of new enzyme protein. Only when these problems have been solved will it be possible to give a meaningful definition of plant hormones. The old definitions are becoming increasingly irrelevant, and the criterion of "action away from the site of synthesis" is much less appropriate to plant hormones than to the animal hormones for which the criteria were developed. Indole acetic acid, gibberellins, cytokinins, abscisic acid, and ethylene have powerful, specific, and interacting roles in plant growth and development, and it is obvious that they have similar roles in the grand design of metabolism. Attempts to force them into the rigid mold of "hormones" could turn out to be as unsuitable as Procrustes' adjustment of tall and short men to fit his bed.

Literature Cited

1. Abdel-Al, M. S. M. 1964. *Some Aspects of Seed and Boll Maturation in Cotton.* Master's thesis. Mississippi State Univ.
2. Abeles, F. B. 1967. *Physiol. Plant.* 20:442–54
3. Abeles, F. B., Leather, G. R., Forrence, L. E., Cracker, L. E. 1971. *HortScience* 6:371–76
4. Addicott, F. T., Carns, H. R., Lyon, J. L., Smith, O. E., McMeans, J. L. 1964. *Proc. 5th Int. Conf. Natural Plant Growth Regulators,* 687–703
5. Addicott, F. T. 1965. *Encycl. Plant Physiol.* 15(2):1094–1126
6. Addicott, F. T., Ohkuma, K., Smith, O. E., Thiessen, W. E. 1966. *Advan. Chem. Ser.* 53:97–105
7. Addicott, F. T. et al 1968. *Science* 159:1493
8. Addicott, F. T., Lyon, J. L. 1969. *Ann. Rev. Plant Physiol.* 20:139–64
9. Addicott, F. T. 1970. *Biol. Rev.* 45:485–525
10. Altman, A., Goren, R. 1971. *Plant Physiol.* 47:844–46
11. Ibid. 47 (Suppl.) :23
12. Amen, R. D., Carter, G. E., Kelly, R. J. 1970. *New Phytol.* 69:1005–13
13. Antoszewski, R., Rudnicki, R. 1969. *Anal. Biochem.* 32:233–37
14. Arditti, J., Flick, B., Jeffrey, D. 1971. *New Phytol.* 70:333–41.
15. Arney, S. E., Mitchell, D. L. 1969. *New Phytol.* 68:1001–5
16. Asmundson, C. M., Kumamoto, J., Smith, O. E. 1969. *J. Chromatogr.* 39:2228–29
17. Aspinall, D., Paleg. L. G., Addicott, F. T. 1967. *Aust. J. Biol. Sci.* 20:869–82
18. Back, A., Richmond, A. E. 1971. *Physiol. Plant.* 24:76–79
19. Badr, S. A. M., Hartmann, H. T., Martin, G. C. 1969. *Plant Physiol.* 44 (Suppl):25
20. Barlow, H. W. B., Hancock, C. R., Lacy, H. J. 1961. *Proc. 4th Int. Conf. Plant Growth Regulators,* 127–40. Ames: Iowa Univ. Press
21. Barnes, M. F., Light, E. N. 1969. *Planta* 89:303–8
22. Barnsley, G. E., Gabbott, P. A., Milborrow, B. V. 1968. *British Patent No. 1 101 844*
23. Bartlett, L. et al 1969. *J. Chem. Soc.* 18:2527
24. Beasley, C. A., Ting, I. P. 1971. *Plant Physiol.* 47(Suppl.):19
25. Beevers, L. 1968. *Biochemistry and Physiology of Plant Growth Substances,* ed. F. Wightman, G. Setterfield, 1417–35. Ottawa: Runge
26. Bewley, J. D., Fountain, D. W. 1972. *Planta* 102:368–71
27. Bex, J. H. M. 1972. *Planta* 103:1–10
28. Ibid, 11–17
29. Bhandari, M. C., Sen, D. N. 1972. *Z. Naturforsch. B* 27:72–75
30. Bhardwaj, S. N., Abrol, Y. P. 1967. *Indian J. Exp. Biol.* 5:264–65
31. Bielinska-Czarnecka, M., Domanska, J. 1969. *Bull. Acad. Pol. Sci.* 17:635–39
32. Blumenfeld, A., Gazit, S. 1970. *Plant Physiol.* 45:535–36
33. Bonnet-Masimbert, M. 1969. *Ann. Sci. Forest.* 26:511–17
34. Bornman, C. H., Spurr, A. R., Addicott, F. T. 1967. *Am. J. Bot.* 54:125–35
35. Bose, T. K., Harada, H. 1970. *Bot. Mag. (Tokyo)* 83:281–84
36. Bowen, M. R., Hoad, G. V. 1968. *Planta* 81:64–70
37. Bradbeer, J. W. 1968. *Planta* 78:266–76
38. Burden, R. S., Taylor, H. F. 1970. *Tetrahedron Lett.* 47:4071–74
39. Burden, R. S., Dawson, G. W., Taylor, H. F. 1972. *Phytochemistry* 11:2295–99
40. Cahn, R. S., Ingold, C. K., Prelog, V. 1956. *Experientia* 12:81
41. Cahn, R. S., Ingold, C. K., Prelog, V. 1966. *Angew. Chem. Int. Ed. Engl.* 5:385
42. Carns, H. R. 1966. *Ann. Rev. Plant Physiol.* 17:295–314
43. Cathey, H. M. 1968. *Proc. Am. Soc. Hort. Sci.* 93:560–68
44. Chabaud, J. P., Mousseron-Canet, M., Durand, B. 1969. *C. R. Acad. Sci. Ser. C.* 269:865–68
45. Chain, E. B., Mantle, P. G., Milborrow, B. V. 1971. *Physiol. Plant. Pathol.* 1:495–514
46. Chatterjee, S., Chatterjee, S. K. 1972. *Sci. Cult.* 38:32–34
47. Chen, D., Osborne, D. J. 1970. *Nature* 226:1157–60
48. Chin, T. Y., Meyer, M. M., Beevers, L. 1969. *Planta* 88:192–96
49. Chrispeels, M. J., Varner, J. E. 1966. *Nature* 212:1066–67
50. Claver, F. K. 1970. *Phyton* 27:25–29
51. Collet, G. F. 1970. *C. R. Acad. Sci. Ser. D* 271:667–70
52. Colquhoun, A. J., Hillman, J. R. 1972. *Planta* 105:213–24
53. Coombe, B. G., Hale, C. R. 1973. *Plant Physiol.* 51:6629–34

54. Cooper, M. J., Digby, J., Cooper, P. J. 1972. *Planta* 105:43–49
55. Cooper, W. C., Henry, W. H. 1968. *Isr. J. Agr. Res.* 18:161–74
56. Corgan, J. N., Martin, G. C. 1971. *HortScience* 6:405–6
57. Cornforth, J. W., Draber, W., Milborrow, B. V., Ryback, G. 1967. *Chem. Commun.* No. 3, 114–16
58. Cornforth, J. W., Mallaby, R., Ryback, G. 1968. *J. Chem. Soc. C* 1565–68
59. Cornforth, J. W., Milborrow, B. V., Ryback, G. 1965. *Nature* 206:715
60. Ibid 1966. 210:627–28
61. Cornforth, J. W., Milborrow, B. V., Ryback, G., Rothwell, K., Wain, R. L. 1966. *Nature* 211:742–43
62. Cornforth, J. W., Milborrow, B. V., Ryback, G., Wareing, P. F. 1965. *Nature* 205:1269–70
63. Cracker, L. E., Abeles, F. B. 1969. *Plant Physiol.* 44:1144–49
64. Cummins, W. R., Kende, H., Raschke, K. 1971. *Planta* 99:347–51
65. Davis, L. A., Addicott, F. T. 1972. *Plant Physiol.* 49:644–48
66. Davis, L. A., Heinz, D. E., Addicott, F. T. 1968. *Plant Physiol.* 43:1389–94
67. Davis, L. A., Lyon, J. L., Addicott, F. T. 1972. *Planta* 102:294–301
68. De Leo, P., Sacher, J. A. 1970. *Plant Physiol.* 46:806–11
69. DeMaggio, A. E., Freeberg, J. A. 1969. *Can. J. Bot.* 47:1165–69
70. Dörffling, K. 1970. *Planta* 93:233–42
71. Ibid, 243–56
72. Dörffling, K., Böttger, M. 1968. *Planta* 80:299–308
73. Ibid 1972. 103:340–47
74. Drury, R. E. 1969. *Science* 164:564–65
75. Durand, H., Zenk, M. H. 1972. *Plant Growth Substances 1970*, ed. D. J. Carr, 62–67. Berlin: Springer
76. Durley, R. C., MacMillan, J., Pryce, R. J. 1971. *Phytochemistry* 10:1891–1908
77. Eagles, C. F., Wareing, P. F. 1964. *Physiol. Plant.* 17:697–709
78. Eastwood, D., Laidman, D. L. 1971. *Phytochemistry* 10:1459–67
79. Edgerton, L. J. 1971. *Hortscience* 6:378–82
80. Eidt, D. C., Little, C. H. A. 1968. *Can. Entomol.* 100:1278–79
81. Eidt, D. C., Little, C. H. A. 1970. *J. Econ. Entomol.* 63:1966–68
82. El-Antably, H. M. M., Wareing, P. F. 1966. *Nature* 210:328–29
83. El-Antably, H. M. M., Wareing, P. F., Hillman, J. 1967. *Planta* 73:74–90
84. Evans, L. T. 1966. *Science* 151:107–8
85. Evans, M. L., Ray, P. M. 1969. *J. Gen. Physiol.* 53:1
86. Evins, W. H., Varner, J. E. 1972. *Plant Physiol.* 49:348–52
87. Findlay, J. A., Mackay, W. D. 1971. *Can. J. Chem.* 49:2369
88. Firn, R. D., Burden, R. S., Taylor, H. F. 1972. *Planta* 102:115–26
89. Firn, R. D., Friend, J. 1972. *Planta* 103:263–66
90. Fuchs, Y., Mayak, S., Fuchs, S. 1972. *Planta* 103:117–25
91. Galbraith, M. N., Horn, D. H. S. 1972. *Chem. Commun.* 113–14
92. Gamborg, O. L., LaRue, T. A. G. 1971. *Plant Physiol.* 48:399–401
93. Gaskin, P., MacMillan, J. 1968. *Phytochemistry* 7:1699–1701
94. Gertman, E., Fuchs, Y. 1972. *Plant Physiol.* 50:194–95
95. Glinka, Z., Reinhold, L. 1971. *Plant Physiol.* 48:103–5
96. Ibid 1972. 49:602–6
97. Goldschmidt, E. E., Goren, R. R., Even-Chen, Z., Bittner, S. 1973. *Plant Physiol.* 51:870–82
98. Goodwin, T. W. 1958. *Biochem. J.* 70:612
99. Ibid 1971. 123:293
100. Gross, D. 1972. *Pharmazie* 27:619–30
101. Gupta, S., Maheshwari, S. C. 1970. *Plant Cell Physiol.* 11:97–106
102. Haissig, B. E., King, J. P. 1970. *Forest Sci.* 16:210–11
103. Harada, N. 1973. *J. Am. Chem. Soc.* 95:240–42
104. Harada, H., Bose, T. K., Cheruel, J. 1971. *Z. Pflanzenphysiol.* 64:267–69
105. Hartmann, H. T., Heslop, A. J., Whisler, J. 1968. *Calif. Agr.* 22:14–16
106. Hashimoto, T., Tamura, S. 1969. *Bot. Mag. (Tokyo)* 82:69–75
107. Heide, O. M. 1968. *Nature* 219:960–61
108. Hemberg, T. 1949. *Physiol. Plant.* 2:24–36
109. Hemberg, T. 1967. *Acta Chem. Scand.* 21:1665–66
110. Hoad, G. V. 1967. *Life Sci.* 6:1113–18
111. Hocking, T. J., Hillman, J. R., Wilkins, M. B. 1972. *Nature* 235:124–25
112. Hoffman-La Roche, F. & Co. 1968. *Dutch Patent No. NE 68 01967*
113. Holm, R. E., Miller, M. R. 1972. *Weed Sci.* 20:150–53
114. Holubowicz, T., Boe, A. A. 1969. *J. Am. Soc. Hort. Sci.* 94:661–64
115. Ibid 1970. 95:85–88
116. Horton, R. F. 1971. *Can. J. Bot.* 49:583–85
117. Horton, R. F., Morran, L. 1972. *Z. Pflanzenphysiol.* 66:193–96

118. Ihle, J. N., Dure, L. S. 1972. See Ref. 75, 216–21
119. Imber, D., Tal, M. 1970. *Science* 169:592–93
120. Ina, K., Sakato, Y., Fukami, H. 1968. *Tetrahedron Lett.* 23:2777–80
121. Ingersoll, R. B., Smith, O. E. 1970. *Plant Physiol.* 45:576–78
122. Ingersoll, R. B., Smith, O. E. 1971. *Plant Cell Physiol.* 12:301–9
123. Irving, R. M. 1969. *Plant Physiol.* 44:801–5
124. Isoe, S., Hyeon, S. B., Katsumura, S., Sakan, T. 1972. *Tetrahedron Lett.* No. 25, 2517–20
125. Isoe, S., Hyeon, S. B., Sakan, T. 1969. *Tetrahedron Lett.* 4:279
126. Jackson, G. A. D. 1968. *Soc. Chem. Ind. London Monogr.* No. 31, 127–56
127. Jackson, G. A. D., Blundell, J. B. 1966. *Nature* 212:1470–71
128. Jackson, M. B., Osborne, D. J. 1972. *J. Exp. Bot.* 23:849–62
129. Jacobs, W. P. 1959. *Develop. Biol.* 1:527–33
130. Jacobs, W. P., Shield, J. A., 1962. *Plant Physiol.* 37:104–6
131. Jacobsen, J. V. 1972. See Ref. 75, 336–43
132. Jangaard, N. O., Sckerl, M. M., Schieferstein, R. H. 1971. *Weed Sci.* 19:17–20
133. Jones, R. J., Mansfield, T. A. 1970. *J. Exp. Bot.* 21:714–19
134. Jones, R. J., Mansfield, T. A. 1971. *Nature* 231:331–32
135. Jones, R. J., Mansfield, T. A. 1972. *Physiol. Plant.* 26:321–21
136. Kaminski, W., Rudnicki, R., Pieniazek, J. 1971. *Biol. Plant* 13:128–32
137. Karssen, C. M. 1968. *Acta Bot. Neer.* 17:293–308
138. Kaska, N. 1970. *University of Ankara Year Book of the Faculty of Agriculture.* 17 pp.
139. Kefeli, V. I., Kadyrov, Ch. Sh., Turetskaya, R. Kh., Yakovleva, L. V., Livshits, N. D. 1970. *Fiziol. Rast.* 17:1047–51
140. Kender, W. J., Carpenter, S., Braun, J. W. 1971. *Ann. Bot.* 35:1045–52
141. Ketring, D. L., Morgan, P. W. 1971. *Plant Physiol.* 47:488–92
142. Khan, A. A. 1969. *Physiol. Plant.* 22:94–013
143. Khan, A. A., Andersen, L., Gaspar, T. 1970. *Plant Physiol.* 46:494–95
144. Khan, A. A., Anojulu, C. C. 1970. *Biochem. Biophys. Res. Commun.* 38:1069–75
145. Knypl, J. S., Mazurczyk, W. 1971. *Curr. Sci.* 40:294–95
146. Kollmann, G. E., Stanforth, D. W. 1972. *Weed Sci.* 20:472–77
147. Koreeda, M., Weiss, G., Nakanishi, K. 1973. *J. Am. Chem. Soc.* 95:239–40
148. Koshimizu, K., Fukui, H., Mitsui, T., Ogawa, Y. 1966. *Agr. Biol. Chem.* 30:941–43
149. Koshimizu, K., Inui, M., Fukui, H., Mitsui, T. 1968. *Agr. Biol. Chem.* 32:789–91
150. Krekule, J., Horavka, B. 1972. *Biol. Plant.* 14:254–59
151. Krekule, J., Ullmann, J. 1971. *Biol. Plant.* 13:60–63
152. Krelle, E., Libbert, E. 1969. *Flora (Jena) Abt. A* 160:299–300
153. Kriedemann, P. E., Loveys, B. R., Fuller, G. L., Leopold, A. C. 1972. *Plant Physiol.* 49:842–47
154. Kumamoto, J., Smith, O. E., Asmundson, C. M., Ingersoll, R. B., Sadri, H. A. 1970. *J. Agr. Food Chem.* 18:531–33
155. Larsen, F. E. 1969. *HortScience* 4:216–18
156. Lenton, J. R., Bowen, M. R., Saunders, P. F. 1968. *Nature* 220:86–87
157. Lenton, J. R., Perry, V. M., Saunders, P. F. 1971. *Planta* 96:271–80
158. Ibid 1972. 106:13–22
159. Le Page-Digivry, M. T. 1970. *C. R. Acad. Sci. Ser. D* 271:482–84
160. Le Page-Digivry, M. T., Bulard, C., Milborrow, B. V. 1969. *C. R. Acad. Sci. Ser. D* 269:2534–36
161. Li, H. C., Rice, E. L., Rohrbaugh, L. M., Wender, S. H. 1970. *Physiol. Plant.* 23:928–36
162. Lipe, W. N., Crane, J. C. 1966. *Science* 153:541–42
163. Little, C. H. A., Eidt, D. C. 1968. *Nature* 220:498–99
164. MacMillan, J., Pryce, R. J. 1968. *Chem. Commun.* 124–26
165. MacMillan, J., Pryce, R. J. 1969. *Tetrahedron* 25:5893–5901
166. Mallaby, R., Ryback, G. 1972. *J. Chem. Soc. Perkin Trans. II* 8:919
167. Mansfield, T. A., Jones, R. J. 1971. *Planta* 101:147–58
168. Martin, G. C., Nishijima, C. 1972. *HortScience* 7:209
169. Martin, G. C., Mason, M. I. R., Forde, H. I. 1969. *J. Am. Soc. Hort. Sci.* 94:13–17
170. Masuda, Y. 1962. *Plant Physiol.* 31:780
171. Mayak, S., Halevy, A. H., Katz, M. 1972. *Physiol. Plant.* 27:1–4
172. Mayak, S., Halevy, A. H. 1972. *Plant Physiol.* 50:341–46

173. McCready, C. C., Jacobs, W. P. 1963. *New Phytol.* 62:19–34
174. Meyer, M. M., Binnie, S. W., Gartner, J. B. 1969. *J. Am. Soc. Hort. Sci.* 94:658–60
175. Milborrow, B. V. 1966. *Planta* 70: 155–71
176. Ibid 1967. 76:93–113
177. Milborrow, B. V. 1968. See Ref. 25, 1531–45
178. Milborrow, B. V. 1969. *Chem. Commun.* 966–67
179. Milborrow, B. V. 1969. *Sci. Progr. London* 57:533–58
180. Milborrow, B. V. 1970. *Science* 168:875–77
181. Milborrow, B. V. 1970. *J. Exp. Bot.* 21:17–29
182. Milborrow, B. V. 1971. *Aspects of Terpenoid Chemistry and Biochemistry*, ed. T. W. Goodwin, 137–51. New York: Academic
183. Milborrow, B. V. 1972. *Proc. Symp. Chem. Biochem. Plant Growth Regulators*, Syracuse, N.Y.
184. Milborrow, B. V. 1972. See Ref. 75, 281–90
185. Milborrow, B. V. 1972. *Biochem. J.* 128:1135–46.
186. Milborrow, B. V. *Phytochemistry.* In press
187. Milborrow, B. V. Unpublished
188. Milborrow, B. V., Garmston, M. 1973. *Phytochemistry* 12:1597–1608
189. Milborrow, B. V., Noddle, R. C. 1970. *Biochem. J.* 119:727–34
190. Milborrow, B. V., Robinson, D. R. 1973. *J. Exp. Bot.* 24:537–48
191. Milborrow, B. V., Taylor, H. F., Burden, R. S. In preparation
192. Mittelheuser, C. J., Van Steveninck, R. F. M. 1969. *Nature* 221:281–82
193. Mittelheuser, C. J., Van Steveninck, R. F. M. 1971. *Planta* 97:83–86
194. Mizrahi, Y., Blumenfeld, A., Richmond, A. E. 1970. *Plant Physiol.* 46:169–71
195. Mizrahi, Y., Blumenfeld, A., Richmond, A. E. 1972. *Plant Cell Physiol.* 13:15–21
196. Mohan Ram, H. Y., Jaiswal, V. S. 1972. *Planta* 105:263–66
197. Morgan, C. M., Morgan, D. *N. T. P. International Review of Science.* In press
198. Mori, K. 1973. *Tetrahedron. Lett.* 2635–38
199. Moss, G. P. 1971. *Terpenoids and Steroids.* Chem. Soc. Spec. Period. Rep. 1:214
200. Most, B. H. 1971. *Planta* 101:67–75
201. Most, B. H., Gaskin, P., MacMillan, J. 1970. *Planta* 92:41–49
202. Mousseron-Canet, M., Mani, J. C., Dalle, J. P., Olive, J. L. 1966. *Bull. Soc. Chim. Fr.* 12, 3874–78
203. Mousseron-Canet, M. et al 1970. *C. R. Acad. Sci. Ser. D* 270:1936–39
204. Mousseron-Canet, M., Mani, J. C., Olive, J. L., Dalle, J. P. 1966. *C. R. Acad. Sci. Ser. C* 262:1397–1400
205. Nagl, W. 1972. *Am. J. Bot.* 54:346–51
206. Naqvi, S. M. 1972. *Z. Pflanzenphysiol.* 67:454–56
207. Nissl, D., Zenk, M. H. 1969. *Planta* 80:323
208. Nitsch, C. 1968. See Ref. 25, 1385–98
209. Nitsch, C. 1968. *Ann. Sci. Nat. Bot. Paris Ser.12* 9:1–92
210. Noddle, R. C., Robinson, D. R. 1969. *Biochem. J.* 112:547–48
211. Noddle, R. C. 1972. *The Biosynthesis of Abscisic Acid.* PhD thesis. University of Warwick
212. Novais, M.C. 1970. *Port. Acta Biol.* 11:301–9
213. Ohkuma, K. 1965. *Agr. Biol. Chem.* 29:962–64
214. Ibid 1966. 30:434–37
215. Ohkuma, K. 1970. *Kagau (Tokyo)* 40:64–73
216. Ohkuma, K., Addicott, F. T., Smith, O. E., Thiessen, W. E. 1965. *Tetrahedron Lett.* 29:2529–35
217. Ohkuma, K., Lyon, J. L., Addicott, F. T., Smith, O. E. 1963. *Science* 142: 1592–93
218. Oritani, T., Yamashita, K. 1970. *Agr. Biol. Chem.* 34:108–114
219. Ibid, 830–37
220. Ibid, 1184–90
221. Ibid, 1821–25
222. Ibid 1972. 36:362–69
223. Oritani, T., Yamashita, K., Meguro, H. 1972. *Agr. Biol. Chem.* 36:885–88
224. Oritani, T., Yoshida, R., Oritani, T. 1969. *Nippon Sakumotsu Gakkai Kiji* 38:587–92
225. Osborne, D. J. 1955. *Nature* 176: 1161–63
226. Osborne, D. J. 1958. *Trop. Agr.* 35:145–58
227. Osborne, D. J. 1959. *Nature* 183:1593
228. Osborne, D. J. 1968. See Ref. 25, 815–40
229. Osborne, D. J., Jackson, M., Milborrow, B. V. 1972. *Nature* 240:98–101
230. Palmer, R. L., Hield, H. Z., Lewis, L. N. 1969. *Proc. 1st Int. Citrus Symp.* Univ. Calif. Riverside, 1135–43
231. Paranjothy, K., Wareing, P. F. 1971. *Planta* 99:112–19

232. Pearson, J. A., Wareing, P. F. 1969. *Nature* 221:672–73
233. Pearson, J. A., Wareing, P. F. 1970. *Planta* 93:309–13
234. Perry, T. O., Byrne, O. R. 1969. *Plant Physiol.* 44:784–85
235. Phillips, D. A. 1971. *Planta* 100:181–90
236. Phillips, I. D. J., Wareing, P. F. 1958. *Naturwissenschaften.* 13:317
237. Phillips, I. D. J., Wareing, P. F. 1958. *J. Exp. Bot.* 9:350–64
238. Ibid 1959. 10:504–14
239. Pieniazek, J. 1971. *Bull. Acad. Pol. Sci.* 19:125–29
240. Pieniazek, J., Grochowska, M. J. 1967. *Acta Soc. Bot. Pol.* 36:579–87
241. Pieniazek, J., Rudnicki, R. 1969. *Bull. Acad. Pol. Sci.* 17:707–11
242. Ibid 1971. 19:201–4
243. Pilet, P. E. 1970. *J. Exp. Bot.* 21:446–51
244. Pilet, P. E. 1971. *Physiol. Plant.* 25:28–31
245. Pilet, P. E. 1971. *Experientia* 27:880–81
246. Pollard, C. J. 1970. *Biochim. Biophys. Acta* 222:501–7
247. Popjak, G., Cornforth, J. W. 1966. *Biochem. J.* 101:553
248. Poulson, R., Beevers, L. 1970. *Plant Physiol.* 46:782–85
249. Poussat, J. L., Poisson, J. 1969. *Tetrahedron Lett.* 1173–74
250. Pryce, R. J. 1971. *Planta* 97:354–57
251. Pryce, R. J. 1972. *Phytochemistry* 11:1759–61
252. Railton, I. D., Wareing, P. F. 1973. *Planta* 112:65–69
253. Rappaport, L., Wolf, N. 1969. *Symp. Soc. Exp. Biol.* 219–40
254. Ray, P. M. 1973. *Plant Physiol.* 51:601–8
255. Ibid, 609–14
256. Read, P. E., Hoysler, V. 1971. *HortScience* 6:350–51
257. Rehm, M., Cline, M. G. 1973. *Plant Physiol.* 51:93–96
258. Rijven, A. H. G. C., Parkash, V. 1971. *Plant Physiol.* 47:59–64
259. Roberts, D. L., Heckman, R. A., Hege, B. P., Bellin, S. A. 1968. *J. Org. Chem.* 33:3566–69
260. Robinson, D. R. Unpublished
261. Robinson, D. R., Ryback, G. 1969. *Biochem. J.* 113:895–97
262. Robinson, P. M. 1962. *The Nature and Physiological Action of Growth Inhibitors.* PhD thesis. Univ. Wales
263. Robinson, P. M., Wareing, P. F. 1964. *Physiol. Plant.* 17:314–23
264. Rogers, L. J., Shah, S. P. J., Goodwin, T. W. 1966. *Biochem. J.* 99:381

265. Roland, J. C., Pilet, P. E. 1971. *C. R. Acad. Sci. Ser. D* 272:72–75
266. Rothwell, K., Wain, R. L. 1954. *Proc. 5th Int. Conf. Plant Growth Regulators,* edition of CNRS, 363–75
267. Rudnicki, R., Borecka, H., Pieniazek, J. 1969. *Planta* 86:63–68
268. Ibid, 195–96
269. Rudnicki, R., Kaminski, W., Pieniazek, J. 1971. *Biol. Plant.* 13:122–26
270. Rudnicki, R., Machnik, J., Pieniazek, J. 1968. *Bull. Acad. Pol. Sci.* 16:509–12
271. Rudnicki, R., Machnik, J., Pieniazek, J. 1970. *Sci. Lett. Copernicus Univ. Torun (Poland)* 23:43–44
272. Rudnicki, R., Pieniazek, J. 1970. *Bull. Acad. Pol. Sci.* 18:577–80
273. Ibid 1971. 19:421–23
274. Rudnicki, R., Pieniazek, J., Pieniazek, N. 1968. *Bull. Acad. Pol. Sci.* 16:127–30
275. Rudnicki, R., Suszka, B. 1969. *Bull. Acad. Pol. Sci.* 17:325–31
276. Ryback, G. 1972. *Chem. Commun.* 1190
277. Ryback, G., Robinson, D. R. 1970. *Bull. Photoelect. Spect. Group* No. 19, 587–94
278. Ryugo, K. 1969. *J. Am. Soc. Hort. Sci.* 94:5–8
279. Sankhla, N. 1971. *Curr. Sci.* 40:302–3
280. Sankhla, N., Sankhla, D. 1968. *Naturwissenschaften* 55:91–92
281. Sankhla, N., Sankhla, D. 1968. *Experientia* 24:294–95
282. Sanyal, T., Ganguly, S. N., Sircar, P. K., Sircar, S. M. 1970. *Planta* 92:282–84
283. Sarkissian, I. V. 1972. See Ref. 75, 265–71
284. Saunders, P. F., Poulson, R. H. 1968. See Ref. 25, 1581–91
285. Schwabe, W. W. 1972. *Planta* 103:18–23
286. Schwabe, W. W., Valio, R. F. M. 1970. *J. Exp. Bot.* 21:122–37
287. Schwartz, D. 1971. *Genetics* 67:411–25
288. Seeley, S. D., Powell, L. E. 1970. *Anal. Biochem.* 35:530–33
289. Seeley, S. D., Powell, L. E. 1970. *HortScience* 5:340
290. Ibid 1971. 6:26
291. Shih, C. Y., Rappaport, L. 1971. *Plant Physiol.* 48:31–35
292. Simpson, G. M., Saunders, P. F. 1972. *Planta* 102:272–76
293. Simpson, G. M., Wain, R. L. 1961. *J. Exp. Bot.* 12:207
294. Sinska, I., Lewak, S. 1970. *Sci. Lett. Copernicus Univ. Torun (Poland)* 23:283–87

295. Sivori, E. M., Sonvico, V., Fernandez, N. O. 1971. *Plant Cell Physiol.* 12:993–96
296. Sloger, C., Caldwell, B. E. 1970. *Plant Physiol.* 45:634–35
297. Smith, O. E. 1969. *New Phytol.* 68:313–32
298. Smith, O. E., Lyon, J. L., Addicott, F. T., Johnson, R. E. 1968. See Ref. 25, 1547–60
299. Smock, R. M. 1972. *J. Am. Soc. Hort. Sci.* 97:509–11
300. Sondheimer, E., Galson, E. C. 1966. *Plant Physiol.* 41:1397–98
301. Sondheimer, E., Galson, E. C., Chang, Y. P., Walton, D. C. 1971. *Science* 174:829–31
302. Sondheimer, E., Michniewicz, B. M., Powell, L. E. 1969. *Plant Physiol.* 44:205–9
303. Sondheimer, E., Tinelli, E. T. 1971. *Phytochemistry* 10:1663–64
304. Sondheimer, E., Tzou, D. S., Galson, E. C. 1968. *Plant Physiol.* 43:1443–47
305. Sondheimer, E., Walton, D. C. 1970. *Plant Physiol.* 45:244–48
306. Steen, I., Eliasson, L. 1969. *J. Chromatogr.* 43:558–60
307. Stewart, G. R. 1969. *Nature* 221:61–62
308. Street, H. E. Personal communication
309. Tal, M., Imber, D. 1970. *Plant Physiol.* 46:373–76
310. Ibid, 367–72
311. Ibid 1971. 47:849–50
312. Tal, M., Imber, D. 1972. *New Phytol.* 71:81–84
313. Tamura, S., Nagao, M. 1969. *Agr. Biol. Chem.* 33:1357–60
314. Tamura, S., Nagao, M. 1969. *Planta* 85:209–12
315. Tamura, S., Nagao, M. 1970. *Agr. Biol. Chem.* 34:1393–1401
316. Tanada, T. 1968. *Proc. Nat. Acad. Sci. USA* 59:376–80
317. Tanada, T. 1972. *Nature* 236:460–61
318. Taylor, H. F., Burden, R. S. 1970. *Nature* 227:302
319. Taylor, H. F., Burden, R. S. 1970. *Phytochemistry* 9:2217
320. Taylor, H. F., Burden, R. S. 1972. *Proc. Roy. Soc. London B* 180:317–46
321. Taylor, H. F., Burden, R. S. 1973. *J. Exp. Bot.* 24. In press
322. Taylor, H. F., Smith, T. A. 1967. *Nature* 215:1513–14
323. Tietz, A., Dörffling, K. 1969. *Planta* 85:118–25
324. Tinelli, E. T., Sondheimer, E., Walton, D. C. 1973. *Tetrahedron Lett.* 139–40
325. Tinklin, I. G., Schwabe, W. W. 1970. *Ann. Bot.* 34:691–706

326. Tomaszewska, E. 1968. *Arboretum Kornickie* 13:177–219
327. Trewavas, A. 1970. *Plant Physiol.* 45:742–51
328. Ibid 1972. 49:47–51
329. Tsukamoto, Y., Fujita, M., Inaba, T., Asahira, T. 1969. *Mem. Res. Inst. Food Sci. Kyoto Univ,* 24–37
330. Tucker, D. J., Mansfield, T. A. 1971. *Planta* 98:157–63
331. Ibid 1972. 102:140–51
332. Van der Veen, R. 1968. *Acta Bot. Neer.* 17:373–76
333. Vanes, A., Hartmans, K. J. 1969. *Eur. Potato J.* 12:59–63
334. Van Overbeek, J. 1968. *Soc. Chem. Ind. London Monogr.* No. 31, 181–87
335. Van Overbeek, J., Loeffler, J. E., Mason, M. I. R. 1967. *Science* 156:1497–99
336. Van Overbeek, J., Mason, M. I. R. 1968. *Acta. Bot. Neer.* 17:441–44
337. Van Staden, J., Bornman, C. H. 1970. *J. S. Afr. Bot.* 36:9–12
338. Van Steveninck, R. F. M. 1957. *Bot. Gaz.* 119:63–70
339. Van Steveninck, R. F. M. 1958. *J. Exp. Bot.* 9:372–83
340. Van Steveninck, R. F. M. 1959. *Nature* 183:1246–48
341. Van Steveninck, R. F. M. 1959. *J. Exp. Bot.* 10:367–76
342. Varner, J. E., Johri, M. M. 1968. See Ref. 25, 793–814
343. Varner, J. E., Mense, R. 1971. *Plant Physiol.* 47(Suppl):24
344. Venkataraman, R., Seth, P. N., Maheshwari, S. C. 1970. *Z. Pflanzenphysiol.* 62:316–27
345. Villiers, T. A. 1968. *Planta* 82:342–54
346. Walton, D. C., Sondheimer, E. 1971. *Plant Physiol.* 47:22
347. Ibid 1972. 49:285–89
348. Ibid, 290–92
349. Walton, D. C., Soofi, G. S., Sondheimer, E. 1970. *Plant Physiol.* 45:37–40
350. Wang, C. Y., Wang, S. Y., Mellenthin, W. M. 1972. *J. Agr. Food Chem.* 20:451–53
351. Wareing, P. F., Good, J., Manuel, J. 1968. See Ref. 25, 1561–79
352. Wareing, P. F., Ryback, G. 1970. *Endeavour* 19:84–88
353. Wareing, P. F., Saunders, P. F. 1971. *Ann. Rev. Plant Physiol.* 22:261–88
354. Warner, H. L., Leopold, A. C. 1971. *Biochem. Biophys. Res. Commun.* 44:989–94
355. Weaver, R. J., Pool, R. M. 1969. *J. Am. Soc. Hort. Sci.* 94:974–78

356. Weedon, B. C. L. 1971. *Carotenoids,* ed.
     O. Isler, 267–323. Basel: Birkaeuser
357. Weedon, B. C. L., Hoffman-La Roche,
     F. & Co. 1968. *British Patent 7094/67*
358. Wiese, M. V., DeVay, J. E. 1970. *Plant
     Physiol.* 45:304–9
359. Willemsen, R. W., Rice, E. L. 1972.
     Am. J. Bot. 59:248–57
360. Wong, M. K., Dennis, F. G. 1970.
     HortScience 5:305
361. Wright, S. T. C. 1954. *A Chromato-
     graphic Study of Auxins in Relation to
     Fruit Morphogenesis and Fruit Drop in
     Blackcurrant (Ribes nigrum).* PhD the-
     sis. Univ. Bristol

362. Wright, S. T. C. 1969. *Planta* 86:10–20
363. Wright, S. T. C., Hiron, R. W. P. 1969.
     Nature: 224:719–20
364. Wright, S. T. C., Hiron, R. W. P. 1972.
     See Ref. 75, 291–98
365. Yomo, H. 1971. *Plant Physiol.*
     47(Suppl): 23
366. Zeevaart, J. A. D. 1971. *Plant Physiol.*
     47:821–27
367. Ibid. 48:86–90
368. Zucconi, F., Stösser, R., Bukovac, M. J.
     1969. *BioScience* 19:815–17
369. Zwar, J. A., Jacobsen, J. V. 1972. *Plant
     Physiol.* 49:1000–6

Ann. Rev. Plant Physiol. 1974. 25:309–62

MICROTUBULES AND MICROFILAMENTS

♦7570

Peter K. Hepler and Barry A. Palevitz

Department of Biological Sciences, Stanford University, Stanford, California 94305

CONTENTS

INTRODUCTION 309
MICROTUBULES 310
    Morphology 310
    Biochemistry 312
    Control of Assembly 315
    Assembly within the Cell 317
        Microtubule organizing centers (MTOC) 317
    Cell Polarity 324
    Cell Wall Formation 328
    Cell Shape 335
    Mechanism of Action 336
MICROFILAMENTS 337
    General 337
    Biochemistry 338
    Morphology 340
    Cytochalasin B (CB) 342
    P-Protein 346
    Mechanisms of Motility 347
MICROTUBULE-MICROFILAMENT COOPERATION 351
CONCLUSIONS 352

INTRODUCTION

Microtubules and microfilaments are recognized as ubiquitous components of virtually all eukaryotic cells. With the increasing realization that they are intimately associated with processes of motility and morphogenesis our interest is further intensified in elucidating their structure, composition, organization, and function. Microtubules, in particular, have received considerable attention following the discovery more than 10 years ago that they could be preserved for electron microscopy with glutaraldehyde (234). Structural and biochemical studies have advanced quickly in the last few years and have characterized the basic protein subunit, tubulin, and have most recently established the critical conditions required for their assembly in vitro (43, 491). The investigations have benefited immeasurably from the use of certain drugs, notably colchicine, which have specific inhibitory effects on microtubules and which have permitted us to correlate them with many diverse activities from chromosome motion to cellulose microfibril orientation.

Microfilaments, until recently, have received less attention than microtubules, although they are also recognized as common cellular components in both plants and animals. Our appreciation for their importance to cellular functions, especially in plants, stems in large measure from observations which suggest that microfilaments, rather than microtubules, are responsible for generating cytoplasmic streaming (296). Significant support for this view is derived from investigations in several systems, including a recent study in the green alga *Nitella* (314), which indicate that microfilaments consist of actin, one of the contractile proteins of muscle. With the knowledge of the widespread occurrence of actin, considerable excitement has arisen recently over the identification and characterization of related motile proteins, in particular myosin, in an effort to elucidate the basic processes of motility.

Each of these subjects would be sufficient for an entire review, and therefore we have tried to limit and direct our coverage to recent developments, especially those in plants. Since the general and prophetic account of microtubules by Porter (364) and the authoritative treatment of plant microtubules by Newcomb (299) there have been several more recent reviews covering microtubule structure and biochemistry (309, 446, 508), their role in mitosis (23, 26, 27, 123, 169, 249, 301) in animal cells (466), in plant cells (169, 343), and in plant cell wall formation (169, 304, 386). Therefore, we will be brief on some of the above subjects; for example, the function of microtubules in mitosis, which has received so much attention, will not be covered in this chapter. Instead we will attempt to focus our attention on other aspects of microtubules in plant cell function and development.

Microfilaments and the motility phenomena for which they may be important have also been reviewed in many recent articles (2, 12, 15, 16, 192, 199, 211, 228, 354, 367, 377, 415, 495, 496, 512, 514). Because microfilaments are similar to muscle actin, reviews on this and related contractile proteins and their function in muscle are pertinent (37, 105, 106, 190, 192, 462). Much of the material discussed here has been derived from findings made on animal systems because of the limited information on microfilaments in plants. However, an attempt will be made to correlate these findings with what is known about microfilaments in plants and particularly of their role in cytoplasmic streaming.

MICROTUBULES

Morphology

Microtubules are commonly recognized in electron micrographs as long structures having a rather straight, rigid profile; in cross section they appear as a circle 240 Å in outside diameter with a densely stained cortex and lightly stained core (234, 346). The basic subunits which make up the cortex are about 40–50 Å wide (235) and are organized along the long axis of the microtubules into protofilaments (31, 32, 152, 323, 484). Approximately 13 laterally associated protofilaments comprise the cortex of the microtubule (235, 484). Because of an axial displacement of the subunits between adjacent protofilaments, the subunits also exhibit a pitch relative to the axis of the tubule (364, 422). While the earlier studies on dried, negatively stained preparations indicated that the pitch of subunits relative to the axis of the tubule was about 10°, more recent investigations of wet preparations using X-ray diffraction suggest that the axial displacement is much greater and that subunits exhibit a "half-stagger" in their lateral associations (84). A recent theoretical discussion of the structure of cylindrical macromolecular aggregates utilizes the possibility that the subunits may be hexagonally packed and develops a system for analyzing tubules based on the helical ranks of monomers (parastichies) which are evident (108).

In addition to the well-described structure of the microtubule itself, it is now recognized that there are structures often referred to as cross-bridges or cross-arms which are associated with the outer wall of the microtubule. In highly organized microtubule systems such as the pharyngeal basket of the ciliate *Nassula* (474, 475), the axopodia of the protozoan *Echinosphaerium* (396, 466, 467) or the axostyle of the flagellated protozoan *Saccinobaculus* (151, 269, 271, 286), cross-bridges are very well delineated. In less highly organized microtubule systems, for example, in the spindle apparatus, the cross-arms or cross-bridges can be recognized (132, 173, 504) but they are much less clearly defined.

Depending on the system being studied, the cross-bridges generally are about 20–50 Å thick and from 100–400 Å long. Commonly these lateral projections are observed between closely adjacent tubules (61, 132, 151, 173, 269, 271, 272, 286, 390, 395, 396, 465–467, 474, 475, 504), but they may occur between a microtubule and a closely adjacent vesicle (173, 396, 476) or between a microtubule and other membranous components like the nuclear envelope (127), the endoplasmic reticulum (ER) (128), or the plasma membrane (89, 216, 219, 383). It is especially noteworthy that cross-bridges have been observed between microtubules and the plasmalemma where the membrane overlies the developing bands of secondary wall in xylem elements (89), and that even when subjected to severe washing sufficient to remove much of the cytoplasm, the microtubule-membrane association retains its structural integrity (D. Brower, P. K. Hepler, unpublished results). In view of the generally accepted lability of microtubules, it would seem that its cross-bridged association with the plasmalemma serves as an important stabilizing factor. The role of microtubule cross-bridge associations in wall development will be discussed later in this chapter.

The application of alternative techniques such as lanthanum staining (71) and whole mount preparation (68) has provided additional evidence on the structure of cross-bridges and has done much to dispel the skepticism often raised about the existence of these structures in less highly ordered arrays of microtubules. Using the whole mount technique to visualize chromosomes and their attached microtubules, Burkholder et al (68) revealed numerous arms or "stalks" projecting from the surface of the tubules. When two tubules are seen close together, they are cross-bridged by numerous such structures. Comparisons made from tissue prepared in the conventional way for thin sectioning has revealed "stalks" and bridges of a similar morphology and spacing along the microtubule. In the whole mount preparations, if microtubules are cross-bridged together, they appear more rigid than single unbridged microtubules, thus providing further support for the contention that the bridges at least serve as a structural or stabilizing element.

The possible active role of the cross-bridge in microtubule mediated motility has received considerable attention recently in studies of the axostyle of the protozoan *Saccinobaculus* (269, 271, 286). The axostyle consists of a nearly crystalline array of microtubules. Microtubules are disposed in rows, within which they are cross-bridged together, and in addition, there are cross-links between the rows. Mooseker & Tilney (286) have shown that the axostyle can be isolated in relatively pure form and that under the proper conditions, with exogeneously applied ATP, it can continue to beat. They also show that the organelle has ATPase activity. Biochemical fractionation and identification of some of the macromolecular components of the isolated axostyle reveal that in addition to the usual tubulin components, there is a high molecular weight component which is similar in size and electrophoretic mobilities to the dynein ATPase which had been obtained earlier by Gibbons (138) from cilia. The presence of an ATPase in the axostyle leads to the speculation that it might correspond in structural terms to the cross-bridge and might be a mechanochemical unit which generates the force for motion.

Isolated spindle apparatuses from sea urchin eggs have also been shown to contain an ATPase. Using an improved technique, Mazia et al (264) found that the ATPase, which is Ca^{2+} activated, is present in the isolated spindle in a concentration three times that in the cytoplasm. Studies throughout different stages of division reveal that the ATPase activity fluctuates during the cell cycle, showing peaks at late interphase and again at metaphase (327). Unfortunately, we have even less idea in this system than we do in the axostyle of *Saccinobaculus* as to what the ATPase is structurally and how it is associated with the microtubule, if at all, although the suggestion has been made that it might correspond to the bridges and might be similar in activity to the Ca^{2+}-activated ATPase of myosin (264).

In summary, it seems quite certain that cross-bridges have a structural role, that they can serve to stabilize tubules to one another, and possibly even stabilize tubules to membranes. It has also been suggested that cross-bridges play a major role in defining the pattern in which tubules will associate, for example, as postulated by Tilney & Byers (467) in the formation of the twelvefold symmetry observed in the axopodial tubules of *Echinosphaerium*. Finally, it is tempting to speculate that the cross-bridge, like the dynein arms of ciliary outer doublet microtubules (138, 242) contain an ATPase and that through the utilization of energy derived from ATP they can generate motion relative to the tubule surface (270, 286).

Biochemistry

Microtubule protein has been studied from a wide variety of different sources, although mostly animal in origin (309, 446, 508). The results show that there is a remarkable uniformity in the character of the protein subunit; it is a dimer with a sedimentation of 6S, molecular weight of about 120,000, and upon denaturation, yields two monomers of 55,000 to 60,000 mol wt. Each dimer binds two moles of guanidine nucleotide (450); one mole (GDP) is tightly bound, while the other mole

(GTP) is loosely bound and exchangeable (39,418). Current studies show that the tightly bound mole of GDP may become transphosphorylated by GTP (418). Drug binding studies reveal that each tubule dimer binds one mole of colchicine (44, 45, 309, 507, 508) and one mole of vinblastine at separate sites (55, 508). The binding site for colchicine, however, can also be occupied by yet another plant alkaloid, podophyllotoxin (55, 508).

The widely used plant alkaloid colchicine has played an immensely important role in the studies of microtubule biochemistry. The discovery by Taylor and co-workers (44, 45, 421, 461, 493) that microtubule proteins specifically bind colchicine has assisted biochemists greatly in their attempts to isolate pure microtubule protein. To date, many investigations reveal a great similarity between the microtubule proteins from a variety of sources, not only in their molecular weight and colchicine binding activity, but in their cross-reactivity in serological gels (94, 134, 456). Furthermore, amino acid sequencing of α tubulin from sea urchin sperm tail and chick brain reveals that there are no differences in the sequence of the first 24 amino acid residues (248). These preliminary studies on amino acid sequencing reveal that tubulin, like actin, may be a highly conserved protein.

Although most biochemical studies support a similarity in the protein subunit from tubules of different sources, it is nevertheless important to emphasize that microtubules in different organelles such as the spindle apparatus or the cilium exhibit quite different sensitivities following treatment with low temperature, colchicine, or proteolytic enzymes (34, 469). These studies have been used to support the idea that the proteins of the various microtubule organelles are different. While slight differences may exist (see below) it may be more reasonable to account for variations in tubule stability from its relative degree of cross-bridging (396, 469). Generally speaking, those tubules that are more tightly cross-linked like ciliary outer doublets are more stable than those that are not like spindle elements.

In the last few years it has become apparent that tubulin is composed of two slightly different monomers with molecular weights of 53,000 and 56,000 respectively (56, 114, 117, 119, 276, 310, 445, 510). This heterogeneity was recognized first by Stephens (445), who thought that the two subunits were related to the A and B subfiber of the outer doublets of ciliary microtubules. More recent work indicates that the two different subunits, referred to hereafter as tubulins α and β, are found within the same microtubule (276, 510), and that they occur in almost exactly equal proportions. It has not been possible, however, to unequivocally distinguish between several models which may account for the association of tubulins α and β in the formation of dimers, protofilaments, and tubules. Microtubule protein may be composed of homodimers (α:α), (β:β), or heterodimers (α:β). If the dimers are homodimers, then protofilaments may consist of homofilaments (α:α)$_n$ or heterofilaments (α:α - β:β)$_n$. Consequently, an intact tubule might be composed of (a) either entirely homofilaments (α:α)$_n$ or (β:β)$_n$; (b) a mixture of homofilaments (α:α)$_n$ with (β:β)$_n$; or (c) entirely heterofilaments (α:α - β:β)$_n$. If the dimers are heterodimers(α:β), then a protofilament and hence a tubule would consist of (d)(α:β)$_n$.

The results to date strongly argue against model a since, as mentioned above, both kinds of monomers are present in the A and B outer doublet tubules of flagella (276,

510). Witman et al (509, 510), in their studies of *Chlamydomonas* flagellar tubulins, support model *b*, since they find upon selective isolation and analysis of the common partition protofilaments between the A and B tubule that only one kind of monomer is present (510). The protofilaments, they argue, must be homofilaments and the dimers homodimers.

Contrary evidence has been obtained by Meza et al (276), who, using similar techniques of Witman and co-workers (509), find that the partition elements from the outer fibers of sea urchin sperm tail contain both tubulins α and β. Meza et al (276) argue more strongly in favor of a tubule composed of heterodimer (model *d*). It is difficult at this point to reconcile the differences between Witman et al (510) and Meza et al (276); they may lie in the fact that two widely different organisms have been studied, the green alga *Chlamydomonas* (510) on the one hand, and the sea urchin *Strongylocentrotis* (276) on the other. The heterodimer microtubule model is more attractive to most workers in the field (56, 117, 119) since on theoretical grounds it would seem to more readily account for the unique drug and nucleotide binding properties of the dimers. Furthermore, if a tubule, like a cytoplasmic tubule, has 13 protofilaments, then it would be difficult if not impossible to construct it out of homofilaments and still yield equal portions of tubulins α and β.

There are suggestions in the literature that yet additional chemical differences between the microtubule subunits exist. Witman et al (510), for example, report from studies using isoelectric focusing that there may be as many as five slightly different kinds of microtubule protein. Further studies along these lines coupled with a more detailed amino acid sequencing of the microtubule protein should help clarify problems of biochemical properties and differences between the protein subunits.

The initial findings showing the presence of bound nucleotide on the microtubule dimer (450) raised the possibility that tubulin might be similar to the contractile protein actin (2, 378, 443, 450). However, more recent studies indicate that actin and tubulin differ significantly in molecular weight, peptide composition, and drug binding (2, 444, 446). They also fail to cross-react in immunological tests (134).

With the notable exception of the investigations on the green alga *Chlamydomonas* (310, 509, 510) very few studies have been made on the biochemistry of plant tubulin. Hart & Sabnis (158) isolated a colchicine binding protein from vascular tissue of *Heracleum* and found, in agreement with others, a protein with a molecular weight of about 120,000. Phloem contains more "tubulin" than xylem, which they reason is due to companion cells and others which are relatively nonvacuolated. They note that the colchicine binding activity in vitro is much less stable than that for tubulin from more conventional animal sources (158). It is well known that a much greater concentration of colchicine is required to block cell division in most plants than in animals (222). For example, 10^{-4} *M* colchicine is required to block division in cultured *Haemanthus* endosperm cells (172), whereas 10^{-7} *M* is sufficient to block mitosis in HeLa cells (461). Based on this and the lower stability of the colchicine binding activity, there may be significant biochemical differences between plant and animal microtubule protein. In studies of yeasts it is found that colchicine is much less effective in blocking growth than its derivative colcemid (155, 236, 452). Biochemical fractionation of *Saccharomyces cerevisiae* reveals a protein of 110,000 molecular weight, thought to be tubulin, which binds colcemid ten times more effectively than colchicine (155). The aquatic phycomycete *Allomyces,* however, is sensitive to colchicine, although its spindle microtubules apparently do not depolymerize in the presence of the drug (311). In view of the fact that plants are the natural producers of most of the well-known microtubule inhibitors like colchicine, vinblastine, vincristine, podophyllotoxin, and griseofulvin, it might be important and informative to give more attention to the biochemical characterization and properties of plant tubulins. It might be especially interesting to investigate tubulins from the same species which produce the alkaloids.

Control of Assembly

It is now widely appreciated that the assembly of microtubules from monomers to polymers is controlled by an equilibrium process (195, 197, 394, 446, 447, 449, 466). Cells possess a pool of microtubule subunits, and under the proper conditions, the subunits polymerize to form the intact microtubules. A number of agents are capable of shifting the equilibrium and thus may play an important role in the control of the formation of microtubule polymers. For example, low temperature and high hydrostatic pressure (466) lead to the dissolution of the tubules, while D_2O (67, 197, 466) enhances their formation. These findings support the theory developed by Inoué & Sato (197) that the microtubule polymer results from hydrophobic bonding of the subunits. In the process of polymerization a shell of ordered water which is thought to be present around the subunits is removed, allowing hydrophobic interaction. In addition to the agents mentioned above, some of the antimicrotubule drugs like colchicine and vinblastine are thought to interfere with the normal equilibrium process, presumably by binding to the subunits and preventing their assembly into a microtubule (44, 45, 309, 393, 394, 507, 508).

In vitro polymerization of microtubules from monomer to polymer, which has long perplexed researchers in this field, has recently been achieved in a study that marks a significant breakthrough in understanding microtubule formation. Weisenberg (491) discovered that lowered levels of calcium ($<1 \times 10^{-6}$ *M*) were essential for tubule formation in vitro. The microtubules obtained had a normal morphology when viewed in the electron microscope, and in addition, their polymerization could be inhibited by low temperature and colchicine. The initial finding by Weisenberg (491) has been confirmed by Borisy & Olmsted (43), who also provide evidence suggesting that an initiating factor is required for microtubule assembly. The initiating factor is thought to be a disk about 290 Å in diameter with a 170 Å core. Centrifugation of extracts at a speed sufficient to remove aggregates down to 35S, including the disks but not the 6S, tubulin dimer, prevents the subsequent assembly of tubules. Furthermore, during the polymerization process the disks are removed from the extract as the tubules form, but reappear upon depolymerization of the tubule with added calcium or low temperature. It is suggested that the disks serve as a template or initiating site upon which the microtubule polymer grows (43). These studies have been confirmed by Shelanski et al (420), who have prepared a precipitate at 230,000 g which when added back to the supernatant allows microtubule assembly.

The presence of two moles of nucleotide on the microtubule dimer has led to the idea that they may be essential for polymerization (107, 145, 290). Recent studies suggest that polymerization is dependent upon the addition of nucleotide; GTP enhances the rate of polymerization but it may not be involved in the direct linkage of the subunit (420). The role of the nucleotide in polymerization, however, still continues to be one of considerable interest since the studies of Eipper (107) show that only the faster moving tubulin monomer (β tubulin) on electrophoretic gels is the one which is phosphorylated.

An emerging line of inquiry concerns the role of cyclic AMP in the control of microtubule function and/or assembly (107, 145, 290, 374, 391, 397, 498). The effects of cyclic AMP, especially in animal systems, are numerous and well established. The studies of Goodman et al (145) show that microtubule proteins can serve as a substrate for the cyclic AMP-stimulated protein kinase. The idea has been put forth that cyclic AMP through activation of the protein kinase would control the phosphorylation of microtubules, whereupon microtubules might be activated for assembly or for some functional role (145, 374). Cyclic AMP is also known to be intimately related to the calcium levels within the cell (374), and since we know that calcium plays a key role in the polymerization of microtubules (491), the hormonal effects on microtubule activity might instead be controlled at this level, especially in view of the lack of compelling evidence showing a requirement for phosphorylation in tubule assembly or function.

Although not as well documented as in the numerous animal systems, it is now becoming established that cyclic AMP exists in different plant systems. In particular, the evidence seems clear that it is present in *Chlamydomonas* and that it can be equated with the protein kinase stimulating activity which is found there (20, 397). Using the methylxanthines caffeine and aminophylline, Amrhein & Filner (20) find a tenfold increase in cyclic AMP levels, presumably due to the inhibition of phosphodiesterase activity by the drug. Under these conditions, flagellar function as well as growth are inhibited. Rubin & Filner (397) argue that cyclic AMP is affecting microtubules, but the action is unknown. They do not, however, support the view that cyclic AMP is affecting phosphorylation, since they fail to detect any incorporation of P^{32}-O_4 into microtubular protein.

The effects of methylxanthines on plants are of long-standing interest since it is well known that they can block cell plate formation and give rise to binucleate cells (222, 322, 337). It is also known that caffeine at least does not destroy microtubules, nor does it appear to inhibit their actions since cell plate vesicles continue to migrate to the central region of the phragmoplast (322, 337). It does seem apparent from the electron micrographs that caffeine blocks the fusion of phragmoplast vesicles (322, 337). If in the dividing cell the methylxanthines lead to increased levels of cyclic AMP, which in turn causes the abnormalities, then it would seem that the hormone affects neither microtubule formation nor function since it is apparent in these dividing cells that the spindle apparatus forms and continues to function. Again, in view of the importance of the levels of calcium to microtubule polymerization, it becomes necessary to understand how the varying levels of cyclic AMP are affecting calcium. It has been suggested by Paul & Goff (322) that caffeine might be disturbing calcium-membrane interaction which results in inhibition of vesicle fusion in cytokinesis. In the flagellum of *Chlamydomonas* the methylxanthines and cyclic AMP might also be intimately associated with the levels of calcium and thus possibly affect microtubule formation and function.

Assembly within the Cell

Microtubule proteins are probably continually synthesized throughout the cell cycle except during "M" (385, 457). In sea urchin embryos substantial evidence has accumulated supporting the presence of maternal mRNA for tubulin and thus explaining the continued synthesis of microtubular protein even in the absence of new RNA systhesis (370, 371). Only a portion of the total microtubular protein required for cell division need be synthesized at each cycle; the remainder can be derived from microtubular protein which was previously used and subsequently disassembled and added to the subunit pool (429). Although tubulin itself may be synthesized continuously, some of the nontubulin proteins which are associated with the intact microtubule may only be formed immediately prior to the formation of the microtubule containing organelle. Stephens (448) has evidence suggesting that some of the linking proteins in the ciliary axoneme are formed in developing sea urchin embryos just before the scheduled appearance of the cilia, and thus are possibly intimately involved in regulating microtubule assembly.

Recent studies suggest that the size of the pool available for polymer formation can be varied experimentally (447, 449) and that in some cells a significant amount of tubulin may be present in a rapidly sedimenting and largely nonmicrotubular aggregate (372, 492). Investigating changes in spindle birefringence as a function of temperature in sea urchin embryos, Stephens (447) finds that there is a series of events just prior to the breakdown of the nuclear envelope which controls the actual size of the pool. The amount of microtubule protein has not changed and yet the pool size can be increased by increasing the temperature, suggesting that more monomers have become available for polymerization. Tubulin appears to exist in three separate and identifiable forms: 1. the monomeric subunits; 2. the "matrix" or large particulate aggregates which contain only few tubules; and 3. the assembled microtubule. Weisenberg (492) suggests that in the formation of the tubule within the cell there are two possible schemes: (*a*) the conversion from matrix to monomer to the tubule; or alternatively (*b*) the conversion from monomer to matrix to the tubule. If the matrix corresponds to the storage form of tubulin observed in the studies of spindle birefringence of sea urchin embryos (447), then it seems more likely, as in scheme *a*, that the matrix is first converted to the monomer which is subsequently available for polymerization.

MICROTUBULE ORGANIZING CENTERS (MTOC) The formation of microtubules within the cell in both plants and animals appears in many instances to occur at recognizable structures or zones called microtubule nucleating regions (466, 470) or organizing centers (MTOC) (338). These centers, which have widely differing morphologies, are often characterized by the aggregation of amorphous or fibrous material into which microtubules are inserted.

In plants some of the most clearly delimited MTOCs are those associated with the spindle apparatus in dividing cells. The kinetochore, for example, where the spindle tubules attach to the chromosome, occurs in higher and lower plants and usually consists of an amorphous ball of finely fibrous or flocculent material which is more lightly stained than the neighboring chromatin (25, 33, 49, 157, 172; Figure 1). In some algae the kinetochore may be a more differentiated structure possessing discretely stained layers (268, 349). Kinetochores of endosperm of the African blood lily *Haemanthus katherinae* may contain over 150 microtubules which fan outward from the chromosome (P. K. Hepler, unpublished observations; Figure 1).

Another MTOC in higher plants probably resides in the central region of the phragmoplast where the cell plate vesicles aggregate and fuse and where the microtubules appear to overlap (171). Although much less defined than the kinetochore, the phragmoplast MTOC is also characterized by the presence of an amorphous, lightly stained, flocculent material into which the ends of microtubules appear to be embedded.

That the kinetochore and phragmoplast are MTOCs is supported by studies with the polarizing microscope which reveal that they are regions from which the birefringent fibers (microtubules) grow (196). Furthermore, destruction of the kinetochore or the midzone of the phragmoplast with a UV microbeam not only destroys the birefringence of the associated fibers, but prevents the material from reforming (195). The phragmoplast MTOC, however, may have a more stable configuration than those of the spindle apparatus since digitonin, while inhibiting tubules during prophase through anaphase, does not block the formation of segments of the phragmoplast (307).

A microtubule nucleating region that has received considerable attention in the last few years, especially in lower plants such as fungi and algae, is that associated with the spindle pole. With the development of improved fixation techniques, it has become possible to preserve greater cellular detail, including in particular the spindle microtubules. Spindle pole structures with their associated tubules have now been widely observed, and while their individual structures vary markedly from organism to organism, they are all in part characterized by the presence of an amorphous, flocculent material. Fungi usually possess discrete structures at the poles of the spindle apparatus which have been referred to in the literature as spindle plaques, centrosomal plaques, centriolar plaques, kinetochore equivalents, and spindle pole bodies (9, 343, 344). In view of the confusion surrounding current terminology and our lack of understanding of the function of these structures in all examples, we prefer the term spindle pole body (9) and will use it in the following discussion. In basidiomycetes spindle pole bodies consist of a dumbbell-shaped structure, densely stained, which resides close to but outside of the nucleus (82, 140, 141, 239, 246, 266, 267, 273, 289, 373). During division, for example, in the heterobasidiomycete *Leucosporidium* (266), this densely stained organelle invades the nuclear regions through a temporary break in the nuclear envelope, splits into two parts,

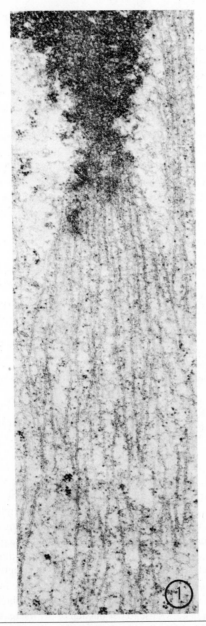

Figure 1 A kinetochore on a chromosome of an endosperm cell of *Haemanthus katherinae*. Microtubules fan outward from a region containing an amorphous, flocculent material. X 34,000. From Hepler, McIntosh & Cleland (173).

and generates a spindle apparatus. Ascomycetes (8, 9, 86, 100, 245, 265, 281, 282, 326, 388, 424, 426, 494, 497, 531) and at least one phycomycete (130) possess spindle pole bodies that appear to be an integral part of the nuclear envelope. Their structure may be highly differentiated, as evidenced by the electron microscopic observations on *Saccharomyces* (326) and *Ascobolus* (531). In *Saccharomyces* Peterson et al (326) reveal a complex layered structure fused to the nuclear envelope into which microtubules insert. A recent investigation has uncovered meiotic spindle mutants in *Podospora* in which the spindle pole bodies may fail to split and may be associated with disordered microtubules (424). In *Phycomyces blakesleeanus* (130) the pole structure is part of the inner layer of the nuclear envelope, but it is not structured as it is in *Saccharomyces*. Microtubules emanate from the pole and appear to provice a rigid framework for growth and spindle pole separation. Although the spindle pole bodies of these groups differ somewhat in their organization and the details of their fine structure, they nevertheless seem to be closely related in form, function, and evolution. Most of them behave similarly during division and appear to control the organization of spindle as well as astral microtubules, and thus they may participate in both karyokinesis and nuclear migration (9).

In addition to the spindle pole bodies, several species of fungi possess centrioles at their poles (10, 182, 186, 193, 240, 324, 363, 454). The centriole in *Caternaria* resides in an indentation in the nuclear envelope but outside of the nucleus (193). The microtubules, being intranuclear, radiate from the nuclear envelope near the centrioles. The myxomycete *Physarum* deserves special attention since widely differing spindle morphologies may be exhibited depending on the species and life cycle stages being examined. In the plasmodial stage of *Physarum polycephalum* (154, 403, 459), a MTOC appears inside the nucleus associated with the nucleolus. Microtubules radiate in all directions in an aster-like array. As division progresses and the nucleolus disappears, the MTOC disperses and the spindle becomes bipolar with no apparent structure at the spindle pole (459). The microtubules in *Physarum,* as well as in another myxomycete *Arcyria* (277), focus to an ill-defined region inside an intact nuclear envelope. The myxamoeba stage in *P. flaviconum* (10) possesses an entirely different spindle, being composed of centrioles located at the poles and a completely dispersed nuclear envelope.

Some dividing algal cells also possess discrete structures at the poles of the spindle apparatus. A layered spindle precursor, similar to the spindle pole bodies of fungi, is observed in the diatom *Lithodesmium* (254–257). During meiotic prophase it splits and generates a spindle apparatus between the separating halves (254, 255). In the red alga *Membranoptera* (268), a densely stained circle of material called a polar ring is observed at the spindle pole. Except for fenestrations at the poles, the nuclear envelope is intact; spindle microtubules occur within the nucleus while a perinuclear sheath of microtubules, observed in other species (258, 345), surrounds the outside of the nucleus and is separated from the cytoplasm by a closely appressed layer of endoplasmic reticulum (ER). A defined layer of material, or rhizoplast, from which microtubules emanate, resides at the poles of the spindle apparatus in *Ochromonas* (46). It appears to have a dual function and may control microtubule initiation both in the generation of cell shape and mitosis (46, 54).

Finally, centrioles or basal bodies have been observed in numerous species (50, 121, 206, 230, 233, 237, 244, 253, 258, 333, 339, 341, 345, 348, 506). In some they are present in all divisions, while in others, notably *Chara* and *Oedogonium* (341), they arise only in those cells about to produce or become motile gametes. Even though a centriole or basal body may be present, it may not always reside at the spindle pole during division, and several examples are known where it remains at the cell periphery associated with the flagellum or within the cell but to one side of the spindle apparatus (50, 206, 230, 233, 346).

Nonflowering vascular plants possess discrete spindle pole structures in those cells giving rise to motile gametes (168, 238, 280, 288, 416, 417). In the water fern *Marsilea*, for example, a blepharoplast, which is a densely stained, spherical organelle (0.5-1.0 μ diameter) (Figure 2) interpenetrated by numerous lightly stained channels, arises in the spermatogenous tissues and participates as a spindle pole body for the final two or three divisions (168, 417). Although the blepharoplast is structurally quite different from a centriole, during the course of development it transforms into numerous basal bodies (centrioles) and these subsequently become involved in flagellar formation (280). In spite of its primary function in the formation of the motile apparatus, during divisions electron micrographs reveal that the blepharoplast acts as the focus and presumably assembly region for spindle microtubules (P. K. Hepler, unpublished observations; Figure 2).

Finally, the structureless or anastral spindle pole observed throughout the plant kingdom, especially in the higher vascular plants, deserves attention because it stands in marked contrast to the amphiastral spindles observed throughout the animal kingdom and, as noted above, in many of the lower plants (503). That no spindle pole structure is present has been clearly demonstrated in dividing endosperm cells of *Haemanthus*, which have been analyzed in detail in the living state with phase contrast, polarized light (195, 196), or Nomarski interference microscopy (24), and in fixed preparations with electron microscopy (25, 27, 172). While the structureless condition is common, an increasing number of reports suggest that elements of the ER may be preferentially aggregated at the poles of the spindle apparatus and that they may serve as, or indicate, an MTOC capability (66, 93, 111, 156, 401, 402, 505). ER aggregations are especially prominent in dividing pollen mother cells where extensive membrane lamellae, interspersed with microtubules, radiate outward from the pole (402). Although an aggregation of an amorphous material thought to be the spindle pole has been reported for the massulate orchid (177), generally the material which characterizes the discrete MTOC is not found at the poles of higher plant spindles.

In the absence of a spindle pole structure, the major question is how the typical plant cell defines its poles and organizes its microtubules. Studies on spindle formation in *Haemanthus* indicate that the pole may be multiple in early prophase but that it subsequently becomes defined into two broad regions as division progresses (25). The fact that long structures like microtubules tend to align mutually with one another might account in part for the bipolar configuration. The normal bipolar arrangement, however, is sensitive to disruption with drugs. Isopropyl N-phenylcarbamate (IPC), for example, without destroying the microtubules in dividing *Hae-*

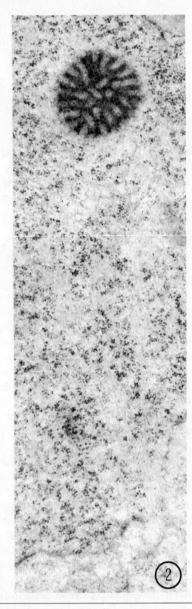

Figure 2 A blepharoplast during prophase of the final spermatogenous cell division of the water fern *Marsilea vestita*. A shaft of microtubules appears to emerge from the blepharoplast and terminate in a deep indentation in the nuclear envelope. During or immediately following the final division, the blepharoplast enlarges and gives rise to more than 100 basal bodies. X 28,000. P. K. Hepler, unpublished micrograph.

manthus cells, leads to the formation of a multipolar condition in which the microtubules aggregate into focal arrays (172). Over short distances it can be noted that microtubules still tend to mutually align but that the overall control of the spindle structure has been disturbed. Other drugs may also induce aster-like spindles or multipolar conditions in plants without destroying the microtubules (27, 284, 479), suggesting that the position of the loosely organized spindle MTOC is relatively unstable and sensitive to disruption.

The lack of a discrete structure at the spindle pole in many plant cells provides compelling evidence against the theory that organelles, like centrioles, are essential for spindle formation. Further evidence against the necessity of a centriole is provided by investigations on lower plants which show in some instances that even when a centriole or basal body is present, it is not located at the spindle pole or associated with the spindle microtubules (50, 206, 230, 233, 346). The example in the fungus *Basidiobolus* (454) is especially instructive since the centriole, which ostensibly arises at the spindle pole, does not move with the spindle when the latter rotates during metaphase, revealing that even when the centriole appears to be structurally associated with the spindle in reality it may not be. Even in animal cells, where the centriole has long been considered a necessary and integral part of the spindle apparatus, its removal by micromanipulation away from the spindle destroys neither the subsequent formation nor function of the spindle (98, 99).

However, centrioles are clearly associated with basal body production and with the formation of cilia and flagella of motile cells (133). The observation that centrioles or their equivalents arose de novo specifically in those cells which were destined to become motile gametes led Sharp (416), in a classic study on spermatogenesis in the horsetail *Equisetum,* to conclude that the blepharoplast (the organelle that produces centrioles or basal bodies) was primarily required for the subsequent elaboration of the flagellar apparatus. These views have been more recently amplified by Pickett-Heaps, based on his extensive studies on cell division in several species of algae (338, 340, 343, 344).

It may be an oversimplification, however, to consider the centriole as nonfunctional in spindle organization. IPC, which severely disrupts the spindle pole structure in *Haemanthus* endosperm (172) and other higher plants, is virtually without effect on HeLa cells and other dividing animal cells even at highly elevated concentrations (P. K. Hepler & J. R. McIntosh, unpublished results). Further investigation with this herbicide on dividing spermatogenous cells of *Marsilea,* where there is a transition in the spindle apparatus from anastral to astral concomitant with the appearance of the blepharoplast, reveals that only the anastral divisions are inhibited by IPC (168). These observations support the idea that the centriole or its equivalent when present may impart to the spindle pole a resistance to disruption by drugs like IPC, perhaps by serving as a template or aggregation point to which the previously loosely organized MTOC can bind.

Aside from the spindle pole and other regions within the mitotic apparatus, plant cells may possess still other MTOCs. The presence in many species of cortical microtubules (see 299 for review) suggests that microtubule initiating factors, or at least stabilizing elements, probably are present in the cortical cytoplasm conceivably associated with the plasma membrane. The preprophase band (351, 352) may indicate a cortical MTOC that has become localized in response to factors controlling cell polarity. The specific predisposition of tubules in cells which differentiate into xylem elements (174) or into guard cells (213, 425; Figure 6) also suggests the presence of cortical factors responsible for controlling microtubule formation and position. Unfortunately, except for the presence of microtubules, no indicators such as the amorphous, finely fibrous material are observed within the cortical cytoplasm which might provide clues about the structural basis of tubule formation.

As our understanding of the in vitro polymerization of microtubule protein increases, we can begin to anticipate the properties and requirements of a microtubule organizing center and how it functions. The highly variable outward morphology of these areas, from distinct centrioles to virtually no structure at all, suggests that the structure itself may not be important and may even be misleading. Low levels of calcium are now recognized to be essential for polymerization (43, 491), and thus we would suspect that MTOCs have the ability to remove this ion. In this regard it is tempting to mention the sacroplasmic reticulum of muscle cells which is involved in the control of calcium release and sequestration during muscle contraction and relaxation. It seems reasonable, therefore, that MTOCs might consist of macromolecular aggregates or membraneous elements which are capable of extracting calcium at least from local areas of the cytoplasm and thus allow for microtubule polymerization. For example, even in the anastral pole of the higher plant spindle apparatus, elements of the endoplasmic reticulum which have been observed there may play an important role, like the sacroplasmic reticulum of muscle, in calcium sequestration. Similarly, the formation of specific patterns of microtubules in the cortex of the plant may in part be regulated by local levels of calcium as defined and controlled by the plasma membrane. It is anticipated that further clarification of the factors involved in controlling in vitro microtubule polymerization will greatly assist us in delineating the composition and function of the cellular MTOC.

Even when we understand what microtubule organizing centers are and possibly how they work, we may still be some distance from understanding how they are positioned within the cell and activated specifically at one place or another at certain times during cell division or differentiation. Some MTOCs, notably the kinetochore, have a defined place on the chromosomes which can be permanently structured. Others, like the phragmoplast, may be derived from spindle pole MTOCs which became repositioned during anaphase to the midzone of the cell as a result of microtubule sliding, as proposed by McIntosh et al (270). However, in general we do not know how microtubule organizing sites are positioned nor how they are controlled temporally. Elucidation of these events is essential for a complete understanding of several aspects of cell division, differentiation, and their control.

Cell Polarity

The mechanism by which dividing cells define and control the plane of the cell plate has long intrigued botanists and is a problem deserving special attention since plant cells, which are surrounded by wall, are unable to move and change their position with respect to neighboring cells as do animal cells, except through differential growth. Formation of a new cross wall at cytokinesis establishes the fundamental spatial relationship between daughter cells and thus contributes significantly to morphogenesis of the tissue. There are many examples throughout plant development where the plane of division appears to be intimately coupled with subsequent cellular differentiation. One of the best is that of stomatal differentiation in leaves of higher plants. In grass epidermal cells a coordinated sequence of events including nuclear migrations and asymmetric divisions delimit the cells which form the stomatal complex (442). Both spindle orientation and the lateral growth of the cell plate, especially in the subsidiary cells where the plate is highly curved, appear to participate in creating the basic morphological relationships. Since microtubules are the dominant aligned components of the spindle and phragmoplast (23, 25–27, 171, 175), it is reasonable to suspect that the control of their position and/or orientation will play an important role in determining the plane of the plate.

The discovery by Pickett-Heaps & Northcote (351, 352) of a band of cortical microtubules at preprophase which is positioned exactly in the plane of the future cell plate shifted our attention away from the spindle apparatus and introduced the possibility that cortical factors, including microtubules, might participate in defining the plane of division. The close positional association of the preprophase band with the future plane of the cell plate was made even more apparent from studies of asymmetrically dividing cells of the stomatal complex in which highly curved cell plates are formed (352). While the preprophase band has been observed in several different species (60, 64–66, 92, 96, 299), it does not occur in all dividing cells (26, 62, 93, 115, 177). Nevertheless, its occurrence and its position in the cell raises the interesting question as to how, if at all, it may function in determining the plane of division and in controlling cell polarity. From their studies, Burgess (64) and Burgess & Northcote (65) conclude that the preprophase band is more closely associated with the equatorial plane of the spindle apparatus and that it might be involved in the positioning of the nucleus—for example, in controlling the migration of the nucleus in those cells which undergo an unequal division. This view has been challenged by Pickett-Heaps (335), who finds that the preprophase band does not appear until after nuclear migrations have taken place, although it may help maintain the nucleus in its asymmetric position (336). Pickett-Heaps (343) currently favors the view that the preprophase band may be the result rather than the cause of a polarizing event in the cell.

Although cortical microtubules are common in a number of plant cells, we think it is unlikely that the preprophase band simply forms by chance specifically in the plane of the future cell plate. We propose, therefore, that the band may indicate the position of a microtubule organizing center possibly associated with the plasma membrane or residing in the cortical cytoplasm. The microtubules themselves may have no function; they simply appear at preprophase at the time when the tubulin monomer has reached its highest concentration, but when spindle initiating sites have not yet become active. Thus tubulin polymerization, which is governed by the equilibrium, would be initiated by the MTOC; the resulting microtubules might be aligned by association with remaining cortical tubules. During prophase-prometaphase as the mitotic apparatus forms, the spindle MTOCs compete successfully for tubulin subunits and the preprophase band breaks down. However, a cortical MTOC may remain and may assist later in division in controlling the axis of the spindle or the direction of the growing edges of the centrifugally expanding phragmoplast by influencing tubule formation and/or placement.

While orientation of the spindle apparatus prior to or during metaphase may be a key event for controlling the plane of division in some cells (103, 178), it cannot explain the phenomena in others since studies show that the spindle apparatus can move during later stages of division and that its initial orientation may be different from its final orientation and from the orientation of the resulting cell plate (315, 427, 428). In *Allium,* guard mother cells divide in a longitudinal direction, and thus one might expect the spindle apparatus to be oriented transversely and hence the metaphase plate to be in the longitudinal axis of the cell. Our results show in almost all cases that it is not and that the metaphase plate may be almost at right angles to the final plane of division (315). This skewed orientation is maintained often through anaphase. During late anaphase or telophase, however, a reorientation of the entire spindle apparatus, including associated nuclei and phragmoplast, occurs (see Figures 3–5). The control of the plane of the cell plate thus takes place at the very end of division almost at the last possible moment. Certainly it does not occur at prophase in spite of the fact that there is a very clear preprophase band in these cells (315).

In trying to understand the mechanism of spindle reorientation, we think it is not unreasonable to look to the plasmalemma or some associated area as the site for the controlling element. As we argued above, we think it is possible that the preprophase band which occurred earlier in these cells may indicate the presence of some specialized membrane site possibly possessing a microtubule organizing center or the capacity to interact with elements of the forming cell plate (315). Furthermore, it seems possible that during late anaphase-telophase, this site or the microtubules assembled there could interact directly with the spindle or the phragomoplast tubules, or quite possible it could initiate a short inwardly growing stub of the cell plate which then could interact with the bulk of the normal cell plate that is growing outward. In either case forces might be generated between elements of the spindle or phragmoplast and the site at the plasmalemma and cause the rotational movement observed (315). Although the mechanism of spindle reorientation is unknown, the occurrence of spindle rotations in many different plants (427), including fungi (8, 86, 100, 273, 426, 454) and algae (206), suggests that the phenomenon may be relatively widespread.

Nuclear migrations which occur in many different plants (58, 93, 428) from the algae and fungi to the higher plants may also play an important role in determination of cell polarity, or at least are an important result of the factors governing cell polarity. The epidermal cells which give rise to the root hair (21) or the stomatal complex (59, 441, 442) are good examples where nuclear migration occurs in a polarized fashion. At present, however, there seems to be no mechanism that universally accounts for these movements. The fact that the nuclear migration associated with the formation of guard mother cells of onion seems insensitive to colchicine and other antimicrotubule agents (B. A. Palevitz & P. K. Hepler, unpublished observations) argues against the involvement of microtubules, although Zeiger (530) reports that colchicine inhibits nuclear migration during subsidiary cell formation in barley. Microfilaments have also been considered as likely candidates for causing nuclear migration, and evidence showing microfilaments near the nucleus (73), coupled with the observation that cytochalasin B (CB) inhibits migration of nuclei in *Tradescantia* leaves, supports this view (409). Further work is needed to confirm and extend these studies, especially in light of recent reports that question the specificity of CB for microfilaments.

In contrast to the situation in higher plants, compelling evidence supports a role for microtubules in nuclear migration in some algae and fungi. Perinuclear clusters of microtubules are observed in the desmids *Micrasterias* (216, 218, 219), *Cosmarium* (347), and *Closterium* (350), in the diatom *Melosira* (88), and in the marine green alga *Acetabularia* (517). In *Closterium* (350) a shaft of microtubules appears

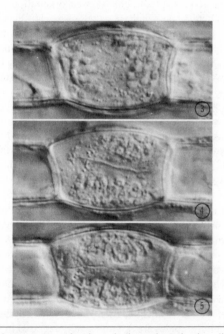

Figures 3-5 A time lapse sequence showing spindle reorientation in a dividing guard mother cell of *Allium cepa*. *Figure 3* During late anaphase-telophase, the daughter chromosomes are situated near the end walls and the spindle is oriented close to the longitudinal axis of the cell. *Figure 4* The spindle soon begins to reorient as an oblique cell plate forms. The nucleus on the right moves along the top side of the cell while the one on the left moves along the bottom side. *Figure 5* Reorientation movement ceases when the nuclei reach the center of cell and the young cell plate becomes longitudinally oriented. Micrographs made with Reichert Nomarski Interference Contrast optics. X 2,000. From Palevitz & Hepler (315).

to lead the way for the migrating nucleus and to participate in the cleaving of the chloroplast. Furthermore, inhibition of post telophase nuclear migration from the growing half cell back to the isthmus region in *Micrasterias* with several antimicrotubule agents such as colchicine, vinblastine, IPC, and trifluoralin (217, 220, 221) provides strong support for tubule participation in these directed movements. Antimicrotubule agents also block nuclear spacing in *Acetabularia* (517). In fungi, microtubules have also been seen associated with the moving nuclei, where they have been observed in the cytoplasm but attached to the centrosomal region or spindle pole body on the surface of the nucleus (9, 140, 141, 273, 376, 494, 531). Observations on living cells further show that the spindle pole regions are mobile and appear to lead or pull the nucleus (8, 9, 140, 141, 426, 502). Unfortunately, there have been no experimental tests with the antimicrotubule drugs which might give additional support to a microtubule motile hypothesis.

Cell Wall Formation

Ever since the discovery by Ledbetter & Porter (234) of microtubules in the cortical cytoplasm of plant cells which were oriented parallel to the underlying cellulose microfibrils of the wall, there has been a long-standing interest in their possible role in the control of cell wall formation (169, 299, 304, 343, 386). Subsequent investigations have confirmed these initial observations and have established that the mutual alignment between microtubules and cellulose microfibrils occurs widely, especially in higher plants (169, 299) but also in some algae (331, 343, 348), and that it is found in cells undergoing both primary (51, 302, 303, 511) and secondary wall formation (89, 90, 110, 170, 174, 251, 329, 330, 384, 386, 439, 520). These observations, together with the experimental findings showing that removal of microtubules with colchicine (51, 170, 330) leads to disruption of the cellulose microfibril pattern (170), provide support for the theory that microtubules in some cells are the cytoplasmic element that controls the orientation of cellulose in the extra-cytoplasmic wall (174, 234, 299).

Microtubules do not appear to be involved in cellulose synthesis, however, since they are conspicuously absent in certain cells, notable the tips of tip growing cells (148) like root hairs (300), pollen tubes (392), fern protonema (451), and fungal hyphae (153), where active wall synthesis and deposition occurs. In addition, the removal of microtubules with colchicine, while having a pronounced effect on wall structure, does not appear to affect the synthesis of the wall components in general (170, 330) or of cellulose in particular (261). These results suggest that cellulose synthesis and orientation are controlled by separate cellular systems (169, 170, 299). It is also clear that microtubules are not universally required in order to achieve an ordered alignment of cellulose microfibrils, since electron microscopic investigations of certain algae, in particular *Hydrodictyon* (259, 260), *Pediastrum* (137, 278), and *Cladophora* (366, 389), reveal that microtubules are absent when wall formation begins. However, the lack of microtubules in these examples does not disprove their possible role in wall organization in those cells in which they are present.

A few reports have questioned the role of microtubules in cellulose microfibril orientation since observations reveal that the two elements are not always mutually aligned (76, 179, 300, 304, 332, 382, 436–438). Unfortunately, while it is possible to detect microtubule orientation with accuracy at least over small regions, the individual orientation of cellulose microfibrils may not be so well known. Therefore, in those examples where a microtubule is skewed with respect to the predominant direction of cellulose, it cannot be established with certainty whether the two elements are actually misaligned or whether possibly a small and uneasily detected number of cellulose microfibrils are also skewed. In two examples a general discrepancy between microtubules and cellulose microfibril orientation has been observed. Newcomb & Bonnett (300) find in root hairs that microtubules aligned in the axial direction are localized within 3–4 microns from the tip of the cell, whereas the longitudinally oriented cellulose microfibrils are not found until 25 microns from the tip. A zone of 20 microns exists wherein the microtubules are axially aligned and the cellulose microfibrils appear random. In analyzing this result, it must be pointed out, as Newcomb & Bonnett (300) have done, that the root hair is growing very rapidly (100 μ/hr) and the distance of 20 microns where the microtubules are not aligned with the cellulose microfibrils would be replaced every 12–15 minutes, and therefore it seems reasonable that the microtubules might be aligned in anticipation of their subsequent role in the longitudinal orientation of cellulose microfibrils. In addition, since the techniques for detecting fine layers of cellulose are not extremely sensitive, it is quite possible that a very thin but as yet undetectable layer of longitudinally oriented cellulose microfibrils already exists closer than 25 microns from the tip. A lack of parallel orientation has also been reported by Chafe & Wardrop (76) in their studies of collenchyma cells of *Apium*. Microtubules are found either parallel or at marked angles to the underlying cellulose microfibrils. However, since the wall is composed of successive layers of cellulose microfibrils of alternating orientation, the authors (76) argue that a lack of mutual alignment between the tubules and fibrils may indicate that the tubules have become repositioned in anticipation of their future role in controlling the orientation of cellulose microfibrils of the next wall layer. Because of particular properties of these two systems in which cellulose microfibril orientation is changing either as a result of rapid growth or the addition of new wall layers, it cannot be concluded that microtubules do not participate in cellulose orientation.

Among the investigations that show a strong correlation between the microtubules and the underlying cellulose microfibrils, those dealing with the formation of the thickened wall surrounding the stoma in guard cells (Figures 6, 7), the nacreous wall of sieve elements (Figure 8), and the secondary wall bands of tracheary elements (Figure 9) are especially convincing. Several reports have confirmed the initial finding that microtubules in xylem cells are specifically grouped over the bands of secondary walls and are invariably oriented parallel to the cellulose microfibrils (89, 90, 110, 170, 174, 251, 329, 330, 439, 520; for review 169, 299, 386). A similar situation exists in guard cells (213, 425; Figures 6, 7). During the course of differentiation a thickening develops on both sides of the primary wall shared by the paired guard cells. Cellulose microfibrils within the thickening are parallel to one another, and as the wall spreads to the far sides of the guard cells, electron microscope (425; Figure 7) and polarized light studies (532; B. A. Palevitz & P. K. Hepler,

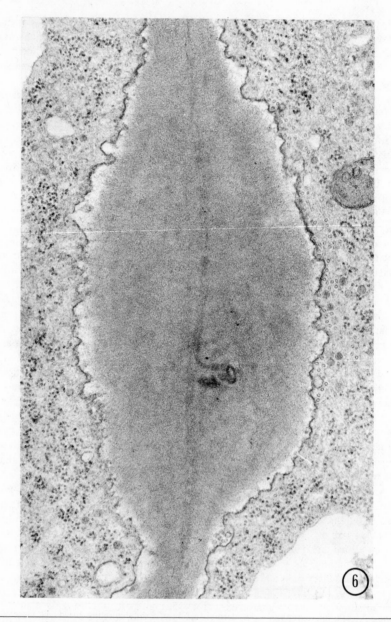

Figure 6 An electron micrograph of a paradermal section through the middle of a developing wall thickening in a differentiating guard cell of *Allium cepa*. Microtubules are specifically clustered adjacent to the thickening. X 43,000. B. A. Palevitz & P. K. Hepler, unpublished micrograph.

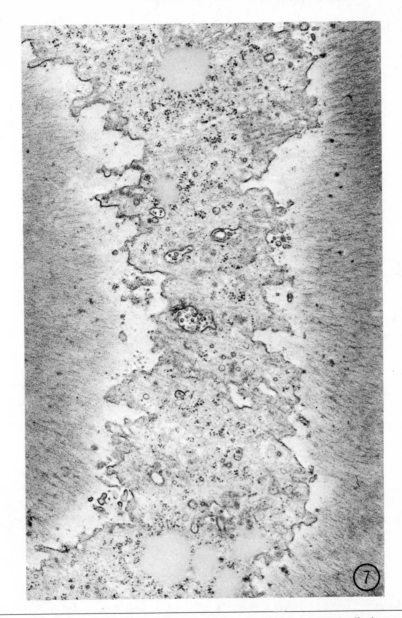

Figure 7 In a micrograph of a paradermal section of a differentiating guard cell, closer to the outer epidermal surface than in Figure 6, the microfibrils of the wall radiate outward from the pore thickening (on the left) to the upper and far sides of the cell (on the right). The microtubules in the subjacent cytoplasm also radiate outward in a pattern which mirrors that of the wall microfibrils. X 30,000. B. A. Palevitz & P. K. Hepler, unpublished micrograph.

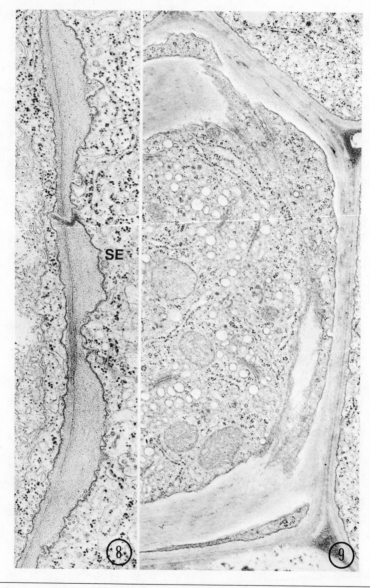

Figure 8   Longitudinal section through a differentiating sieve element (SE) of *Phaseolus vulgaris*. Microtubules are arrayed hooplike around the cell in association with the developing nacreous wall. X 35,000. B. A. Palevitz & E. H. Newcomb, unpublished micrograph.

Figure 9   Microtubules in a xylem element of *Phaseolus aureus* reflect the pattern and microfibril orientation of the adjacent secondary wall band. X 18,000. B. A. Palevitz & E. H. Newcomb, unpublished micrograph.

unpublished observations) reveal that the microfibrils fan outward. Observations of the cortical cytoplasm show that the microtubules fan out in an identical pattern (425; Figure 7). Furthermore, during the inception of differentiation, microtubules become clustered along the primary wall in the region where the thickening will subsequently occur (213, 425), supporting the view that they anticipate and control the formation of the wall.

The strongest support for the role of microtubules in the control of cell wall pattern and cellulose microfibril orientation comes from the studies using the drug colchicine (30, 51, 146, 147, 170, 330, 387). Prior to our knowledge of the existence of microtubules in the cortical cytoplasm, Green (146, 147) found that colchicine led to a disordered array of cellulose microfibrils in *Nitella*. These observations led him to hypothesize that there might be a filamentous component in the cortical cytoplasm which was involved in the control of cellulose microfibril orientation and which might be similar to the colchicine-sensitive filaments comprising the spindle and phragmoplast of dividing cells. These ideas have been supported by numerous studies which show the similarity between cortical and spindle microtubules (169, 299). More recent studies have sought to characterize better the relationship between microtubules and the underlying cellulose microfibrils. At the ultrastructural level, it has been shown that microtubules are removed by colchicine (51, 170, 330). In differentiating xylem elements the drug leads to the formation of aberrantly shaped secondary wall thickenings; instead of being deposited in discrete ridges, new wall material is smeared unevenly over the surface of the primary wall (170, 330; Figures 10, 11). Studies with polarized light and electron microscopy reveal that the microfibrilar order within the wall has been severely disturbed (170). Interestingly, though, the drug does not lead to a random array of cellulose microfibrils, but to a condition in which small groups or bundles of microfibrils occur in swirls and may

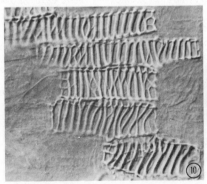

Figure 10 A wound xylem element of *Coleus blumei*. Note the discrete, reticulate pattern of the secondary wall bands. X 700.

Figure 11 A wound xylem element cultured in the presence of colchicine. The secondary wall has become smeared over the primary wall and the characteristic banded, reticulate pattern of untreated cells is not present. Figures 10 and 11 are Nomarski Interference Contrast images of cells which have been cleared with NaOH. X 700. From Hepler & Fosket (170).

be deposited at marked angles to other groups of microfibrils (170). In view of the well-known specific binding of colchicine to the microtubule subunit and the resultant depolymerization of the tubules, these results provide convincing support for the idea that microtubules in some cells are the primary controlling element in determining the orientation of cellulose microfibrils.

Not only do microtubules define the orientation of cellulose microfibrils, but they determine the pattern of cell wall thickening in xylem elements (170, 330). If a *Coleus* wound vessel element is treated with colchicine in an early stage of secondary wall formation, the thickenings will be smeared out over the surface of the primary wall and the characteristic reticulate pattern will be entirely lost (170; Compare Figures 10, 11). However, if a young xylem element is adjacent to one that has already differentiated, the new thickenings will be deposited in ridges across the primary wall from the thickenings of the mature element even in the presence of colchicine. These observations confirm earlier studies which show that neighboring xylem elements usually form their secondary thickenings at the same place along their shared primary wall and further suggest that this influence over pattern formation is independent of microtubules. Nevertheless, in cells that have no neighboring elements, microtubules seem to be the crucial cytoplasmic factor involved in controlling both secondary wall pattern and cellulose microfibril orientation (170).

How do microtubules, which are in the cytoplasm and separated from the nearest wall layer by a plasma membrane, control cellulose microfibril orientation? Initially, it was thought that microtubules might be directing cytoplasmic streaming and that the moving stream would orient the cellulose microfibrils (234, 262). This mechanism is not considered likely since (*a*) the direction of cytoplasmic streaming normally does not correspond either to the direction of microtubules or cellulose microfibrils (331); (*b*) streaming is not sensitive to colchicine (495) and thus seems not to be controlled by microtubules; and finally (*c*) studies of *Nitella* (296) show that the cytoplasmic stream occurs in the endoplasm and is separated from the wall by a layer of stationary ectoplasm. Although bulk streaming probably does not provide the orienting force, it has been suggested that microtubules might cause an oriented flow specifically of the Golgi vesicles (251, 302, 334) presumed to contain either the cell wall precursors or the cell wall synthesizing enzymes. As the vesicles move along parallel to the microtubules, they might fuse with the plasma membrane and impart a flow-directed shear which orients either the synthesizing molecules in the membrane or possibly the cellulose microfibrils themselves (302).

More recently the idea of a microtubule cross-bridge generated shear acting on the plasmalemma has been put forth by Hepler & Fosket (170). Several studies (89, 216, 220, 235, 382, 383) have reported that microtubules in the cortical cytoplasm are linked by cross-bridges to the plasma membrane and in addition, these microtubules may be linked to one another (216). It seems possible, therefore, that the cross-bridges might be active mechanochemical units capable of generating movement parallel to the tubule surface. These ideas find their genesis in the theoretical paper on mitosis by McIntosh et al (270), in which it is suggested that the cross-bridges between adjacent tubules of the spindle apparatus may be capable of generating an active sliding between adjacent tubules and thus cause the movement of chromosomes during division. In plant cells forming wall, it also seems possible that the tubules in the cortical cytoplasm could slip past one another and create a shear which might orient nearby cellulose microfibrils. This hypothesis presupposes that cellulose microfibrils are synthesized in the cortical cytoplasm and not in or outside of the membrane, and it would also require that the cell have a mechanism whereby it could extrude an oriented cellulose microfibril through the plasma membrane without any loss of orientation. A more attractive theory suggests that microtubules interact directly with the plasmalemma through cross-bridges and generate an oriented flow of fluid components within the membrane (169, 170). As a result of a directed flow, macromolecular components in or on the membrane, including possibly the cellulose synthesizing enzymes or the cellulose microfibrils themselves, might become aligned. In generating motion within the membrane, it seems possible that either the microtubule-membrane cross-bridge actively causes the flow or that adjacent tubules actively slide relative to one another and simply transmit the resultant directed movement to the membrane through a cross-bridge.

Although it is possible to suggest ways in which microtubules may influence the oriented deposition of wall microfibrils, the mechanism by which the microtubules themselves become aligned is much less clear. Based on their observations showing an initial increase in girth in young apical cells of *Nitella,* Green and co-workers (149, 150) suggest that the transverse strain might align the microtubules of the cortical cytoplasm. Once aligned they would remain transversely oriented in spite of extensive subsequent strain in the longitudinal axis. It is difficult, however, to apply this mechanism to cells like wound xylem elements where there is an ordered alignment of microtubule but no appreciable growth or strain (170, 174). As we mentioned earlier, the hypothetical membrane sites or MTOCs may play an important role in organizing or stabilizing the position of microtubules, although we recognize that such an explanation is unsatisfactory since it fails to account for localization of the initiating sites. New thought and experimentation on this important question awaits further elucidation on the character and function of MTOCs.

Cell Shape

Microtubules, because of their influence over the orientation of the deposited cellulose microfibrils, play an important role in controlling the formation of shape in plant cells. Even in the construction of a cylinder like the internode cells of *Nitella,* it is essential that the cellulose microfibrils be traversely oriented in order that they might effectively withstand the stress imposed by turgor pressure. The loss of transverse alignment, which has been achieved experimentally with the application of colchicine and the resultant depolymerization of the cortical microtubules, causes cylindrical cells to swell and become spherical (51, 146, 147). The development of irregular shapes also may be related to a specific wall pattern which is controlled by microtubules. In stomatal differentiation the formation of the characteristic kidney shape of the guard cells appears to be determined by the radial pattern of the cellulose microfibrils of the thickened wall (Figure 7). In addition, the radially oriented microfibrils are thought to control the aperture opening of the pore during gas exchange by regulating the direction of swelling in the mature guard cells (22,

425). Physical models verify the efficacy of the radial pattern of reinforcement in establishing a functional guard cell (22).

In some plant cells where no wall is present (46, 54, 137, 259, 260, 278, 366, 389) or where a wall may be forming (274, 342, 408), microtubules may act directly as structural cytoskeletal elements in the formation and maintenance of cell shape analogous to a role frequently assigned to them in animal cell morphogenesis (364, 466). Recently Bouck & Brown (46), in an investigation of *Ochromonas*, revealed two sets of microtubules involved in shape generation and indicated that these microtubules are controlled in their formation by distinct nucleating centers within the cell. Destruction of the microtubules with either high hydrostatic pressure or with colchicine destroyed the shape of the cell (54). If the hydrostatic pressure is removed, the normal shape regenerates even in the absence of new protein synthesis (54). Furthermore, the process of reassembly of microtubules seems to be closely controlled both temporally and spatially by the initiating sites (46, 54).

Microtubules also appear to be the important cytoskeletal elements in determing the shape of the generative nuclei in pollen grains of higher plants (63, 404). Sanger & Jackson (404) have shown that the elongated generative cell in *Haemanthus* pollen is surrounded by a sheath of microtubules and that the shape can be destroyed by colchicine and IPC. Microtubules may be important elements in controlling the shape of sperm nuclei in the lower vascular plants and in some of the algae (88, 104, 165, 283, 317, 318, 477, 485). The suggestion has been made that microtubules not only maintain the shape of highly asymmetric and elongated nuclei, but they may participate in directing nuclear growth during differentiation. Studies with colchicine on sperm nuclei in *Nitella* reveal that while the drug does not block chromatin condensation, it does inhibit normal shape formation (477), thus indicating the probable involvement of microtubules.

Mechanism of Action

Microtubules are associated with many diverse cellular events ranging from chromosome motion to cellulose microfibril orientation, and yet it seems likely that their mechanism of action is the result of two processes: (*a*) microtubule assembly and growth which is controlled by an equilibrium between monomer and polymer and which is directed at MTOCs; and (*b*) the possible movement of cellular structures, including an adjacent tubule, vesicle, or membrane component, relative to the microtubule surface as a result of forces generated by cross-bridges. Microtubule growth is a well-established process that seems sufficient to account, for example, for shape generation and spindle elongation in dividing cells. With regard to motility relative to a tubule surface, it has now been shown in different systems, including flagellar axonemes (407, 453), the KM fibers of *Stentor* (29, 187), and the axostyle of *Saccinobaculus* (269), that adjacent microtubules can slide past one another, presumably through activity of the bridges or arms on the tubule surface. It seems possible that structures other than adjacent tubules to which binding can occur might also be moved relative to the tubule surface because of cross-bridge function, and therefore it may be possible to account for several diverse activities including chromosome to pole movement in anaphase, aggregation of phragmoplast vesicles during cytokinesis, particle saltations, and conceivably microtubule control of cellulose orientation.

Extensive studies on microtubule function in a number of systems, especially those which possess highly ordered arrays of microtubules, are moving rapidly. With the combined application of biochemical and biophysical technique our understanding of microtubule formation and function will increase greatly. It will be especially important to decipher the mechanism of microtubule organization and how the cell controls the position and activation of initiating centers.

MICROFILAMENTS

General

The hypothesis that all eukaryotic cells contain a "primitive" apparatus responsible for a variety of movements such as cytoplasmic streaming and amoeboid movement has intrigued biologists for over 100 years (199 for review). Following the isolation of actin, myosin, and associated proteins from muscle, efforts were made to establish whether similar proteins might constitute this general system causing movement in other cell types. In recent years, following the identification by Loewy (243) and T'so and co-workers (473) of an actomyosin from *Physarum,* an extraordinary volume of research involving diverse techniques has succeeded in showing that many eukaryotic cells contain these proteins. Observations with the electron microscope have correlated this system with filamentous structures in the cytoplasm. Particular attention has been focused on arrays of 50–80 Å microfilaments similar to the thin, actin-containing filaments of muscle. The general distribution of actomyosin proteins and microfilaments, and the variety of motile phenomena for which they may be responsible, cast doubt on the usefulness of the term "primitive" in describing this system (16).

In order to establish whether an actomyosin-like system is present and responsible for movement in a given cell, it is important to establish certain criteria for identification. First, actin and myosin have been isolated in pure form and characterized with standard procedures. It is noteworthy that actin from many different sources consists of globular subunits (G-actin) of approximately 46,000 molecular weight, which under conditions of high ionic strength plus ATP polymerize to fibrillar F-actin. In the latter form, each monomer contains one mole of ADP. Presumptive actins from cells such as plants should be analyzed for similar biochemical properties. Second, F-actin has a distinctive morphology, being composed of two helically wound chains organized into microfilaments approximately 50 Å in diameter. Similar microfilaments can be seen in situ in many eukaryotic cells at sites indicative of their role in cell movements, and thus they serve as a morphological criterion for the presence of actin. Myosin may also appear as filaments in situ, but are thicker in diameter (130–250 Å). Third, actins specifically bind heavy meromyosin (HMM) (Figures 12, 15) and thus can be identified electron microscopically in isolated cell fractions or within cells which have been glycerinated (190, 198). HMM is the globular ATPase portion which can be separated from the rest of the myosin molecule by trypsin or papain digestion. As a result of several factors including the beaded, double helical nature of actin, its native polarity, and the particular shape of the HMM moiety (190, 192, 285), when HMM is incubated with F-actin, it binds and yields a distinctive herringbone or arrowhead pattern in which all the arrowheads on a filament point in the same direction (190, 285; Figures 12, 15). Pyrophosphate and ATP inhibit or reverse binding and are used as controls (Figure 16). Since actin is conservative and the HMM reaction is so specific, actin-containing microfilaments can be realibly identified in nonmuscle cells although the arrowhead pattern is often not as discrete as with muscle actin (198). In spite of the diagnostic quality of the HMM reaction, recent studies inject a note of caution since it has been reported that glycerination and HMM may induce the formation of microfilaments not normally visible with standard electron microscopic procedures (124, 125). Finally, and ideally, actin microfilaments should be disrupted by drugs which at the same time inhibit the streaming movements presumed to be generated by them in much the same way colchicine affects microtubule structure and function. In recent years the fungal metabolite cytochalasin B (74, 75) has been used extensively to inhibit a variety of morphogenetic processes and cell movements (495), possibly by disrupting 50–80 Å microfilaments. It clearly inhibits streaming in higher plants and algae. Whether its effects are due to a specific action on microfilaments or reflect some general, nonspecific, or indirect action remains the subject of heated debate as will be discussed below. Many studies have now appeared which utilize any or several of the above procedures. Together they constitute a massive body of evidence implicating actin-like microfilaments in a variety of cell movements.

Biochemistry

Actin has now been isolated and characterized in a variety of animal cells (5, 52, 120, 354, 368, 471, 472, 526), and it has also been identified in other organisms such as *Physarum* (3, 4, 160, 181, 295), *Acanthamoeba* (358, 362, 488–490), *Amoeba* (287), and *Dictyostelium* (522; K. Lord & J. A. Spudich, in preparation). It has not been isolated from higher plants. Actin often constitutes a significant portion of the total cell protein—for example, 10 to 20% in *Acanthamoeba* and neurons (120, 358). The results establish that actins from a wide variety of cell types and species are remarkably similar to each other and to muscle actin in structure, molecular weight, and ability to self-assemble into double helical filaments (354). They often co-migrate on gels with muscle actin and have similar amino acid composition and peptide finger prints (52, 490). For example, like muscle actin they contain the rare amino acid 3-methylhistidine (5, 488, 489, 522). They can also activate the Mg-dependent ATPase of muscle myosin and bind HMM in typical arrowhead configurations (5, 192, 295, 354, 362, 471, 472, 522, 526). Thus actin, like tubulin, is conservative in composition and behavior in the cell types in which it has been found.

Far fewer results have been reported concerning the presence of myosin in various cells, possibly reflecting lower quantities of this protein or difficulties in detecting it. Yet enough have been characterized to make certain general statements. Myosin-like molecules from several animal tissues (e.g. 6, 7) and different organisms including *Physarum* (3, 4, 159, 162, 292–294) and *Dictyostelium* (M. Clarke & J. A.

Spudich, in preparation; Figure 13) show similarities to muscle myosin (354) in molecular weight ($\sim$ 460,000), EDTA or Ca^{2+}-dependent ATPase activity, the ability to decorate muscle actin (7,292), and the capacity to self-assemble into thick, filamentous, bipolar aggregates (6, 7, 292, 293; M. Clarke & J. A. Spudich, in preparation; Figure 13).

In general, the results indicate that nonmuscle myosins are much more variable than their actin counterparts (52, 192, 354). For example, *Acanthamoeba* myosin

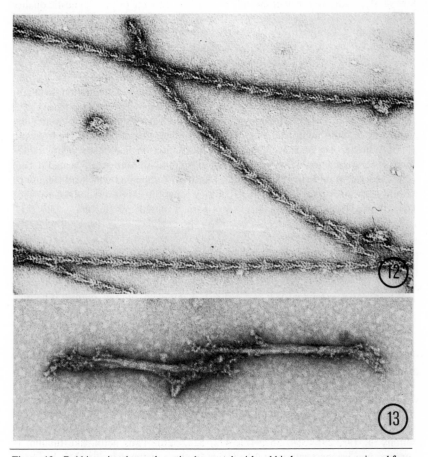

Figure 12   Rabbit striated-muscle actin decorated with rabbit heavy meromyosin subfragment 1 (HMM–S1) obtained by papain digestion. Note the distinctive, polar arrowhead pattern. X 149,000. From Spudich, Huxley & Finch (434).

Figure 13   Reaggregated myosin filaments prepared from a homogeneous solution of *Dictyostelium* myosin by lowering the ionic strength to 0.1 *M* KCl in the presence of 10 m*M* MgCl$_2$. The aggregated filaments exhibit the bipolar configuration characteristic of muscle myosin. X 82,000. From M. Clarke & J. A. Spudich, in preparation.

has a molecular weight of only 180,000 (358, 360). The myosins differ in their solubility properties and the conditions under which they polymerize. Unlike other myosins, *Physarum* myosin is soluble at low ionic strength (4, 159, 292) and specifically requires divalent cations, especially Ca^{2+}, in order to self-assemble (293, 294). Myosins also vary in the degree in which their Mg^{2+}ATPase is activated by actin (192, 354). Thus the properties of myosin, unlike actin, vary considerably, a characteristic which may be important in determining its organization in the cell and the type of movement produced.

Thick filaments suggestive of myosin have been observed in a limited number of cells including *Chaos* (87, 291), *Dictyostelium* (M. Clarke, & J. A. Spudich, in preparation), and under certain conditions in platelets (36) and *Physarum* (18, 180, 215). They have also been seen in motile cytoplasmic extracts (356, 516). The thick filaments bear some resemblence to bipolar aggregates of myosin assembled in vitro, although their arrangement in living cells and their interaction with microfilaments remain obscure. The failure to visualize thick filaments in many cells is not surprising, since the presence of thick myosin filaments in smooth muscle was in question until only recently (380, 381). Myosin has not been purified from plants, although actomyosin-like fractions with ATPase activity have been obtained from *Nitella* (480) and vascular tissue of *Cucurbita* and *Nicotiana* (528).

These data establish the ubiquity of actin and myosin and complement the results of other experiments which indicate that a "contractile" system is present in many cells. It has been shown that cells can exhibit movement when treated with ATP following glycerination (183, 211, 423, 455), and cytoplasmic preparations obtained from a variety of cells can stream in the presence of ATP (15, 356, 516). Such preparations contain bundles of thick and thin filaments. Actomyosin gels similar in behavior to those obtained from muscle have also been prepared from various cells (41, 297, 521).

Morphology

Numerous morphological and electron microscope observations have identified microfilaments in regions of cells, suggesting that they function in a variety of morphogenetic processes and cell movements (495). Microfilaments appear to be involved in changes in shape of epithelial cells leading to gland formation (431, 523), ascidian tail resorbtion (80), and neurulation (28, 69). Similar microfilaments constitute the "contractile" ring present in the cleavage furrow of certain animal cells (411, 412, 414). Microfilaments are present in cells undergoing gross locomotion, amoeboid movement, and cytoplasmic streaming. They are present, for example, in migrating fibroblasts and glial cells (57, 142, 144, 247, 432), the advancing growth cones of axons (247, 524), sperm tails (35, 124), various amoebae (87, 291, 356, 362), the acrosomal process of sperm (204, 471), and intestinal microvilli (468). Similar microfilaments are located in the ectodermal tube of *Physarum*. Their location and primarily radial or circumferential orientation favor their role in providing the motive force for shuttle streaming (211, 228, 379, 478, 512). The microfilament bundles in *Physarum* also exhibit dense areas (228) similar to the dense bodies present along filaments in smooth muscle and other cells (185, 232, 432). In several papers, it has been argued that HMM binding microfilaments present in meiotic and mitotic spindles provide the motive force for chromosome movement (35, 122, 123, 125, 136). Microfilaments have been seen in dividing plant cells as well (25).

Most of the microfilaments in these diverse cells are similar in appearance and behavior. They measure 50–80 Å in diameter and usually occur in parallel bundles and sheaths, or as a loose network, just below the plasmalemma. Many can be decorated with HMM, yielding typical arrowhead arrays (17, 19, 72, 77, 87, 124, 125, 144, 198, 204, 325, 357, 413, 430, 472). Many of them appear sensitive to cytochalasin B, which both disrupts the microfilaments, leaving patches of amorphous material (81, 252, 412, 431, 432, 523, 524), and inhibits many of the movements involved (72, 495). Removal of the drug allows resumption of movement and reappearance of the microfilaments even in the presence of protein synthesis inhibitors, indicating reformation from a pool of monomers. Recent experiments show that microfilaments can be induced experimentally from such a pool (70).

Our understanding of the structure and function of microfilaments is complicated somewhat by the presence in animal cells of several classes of filamentous structures. For example, microfilaments of various diameters have been reported (356, 413). In migrating fibroblasts and glial cells, two microfilament systems are present (143, 247, 496); one consists of parallel microfilaments, organized as a sheath or coarse fibers located toward the cell posterior, which bind HMM and are not disrupted by CB, while the other system consists of a loose network of microfilaments just below the plasmalemma in the anterior of the cell. The latter may not bind HMM but are sensitive to CB. Both sets of microfilaments may have separate functions in cell locomotion (1, 194, 496), but appear to be interconnected and may represent alternative forms of the same basic unit (247, 496). In addition, many animal cells contain intermediate size filaments (tonofilaments, neurofilaments) approximately 100 Å in diameter (2, 142, 144, 185, 380). They do not appear to be related to microfilaments or microtubule protofilaments and their function is unknown (142, 380, 419).

Plant microfilaments, similar in size and structure to the 50–80 Å structures found in animal cells, have been observed in many different species, and results from different investigations implicate them in streaming. For example, the green alga *Nitella* has provided excellent material for experiments on the relation between microfilaments and streaming (101, 102, 164, 200, 202, 203, 207–210, 212, 231), and recent investigations indicate that its microfilaments consist of actin (314; Figures 14–16). Bundles of microfilaments occur at the interface of the mobile endoplasm and the stationary ectoplasm (the sol-gel interface) oriented in the direction of the stream (296, 331). Fibrils, which are probably identical to the bundles of microfilaments, are observed in light microscopic investigations to be in close association with rapidly moving particles (207, 208). In addition, these fibrils form closed motile loops either in isolated droplets or in centrifuged cells (200, 202, 203, 207, 209, 210, 231). Finally the electron microscope examination of extruded *Nitella* cytoplasm in negatively stained preparations reveals bundles of 50 Å microfilaments having a periodic, beaded structure similar to actin (Figure 14), which bind HMM in a reaction that is reversed by ATP (Figure 16) to yield the characteristic arrowhead pattern (Figure 15). The axial repeat on the bare microfilaments and the arrowhead repeat are approximately the same (350–375 Å) and conform to the known half-pitch of actin (around 355 Å). Taken together these observations support the contention that the *Nitella* microfilaments are closely similar to muscle actin and that they constitute one of the essential components required for streaming.

Microfilaments of higher plants, which were first observed in the peripheral cytoplasm and transvacuolar strands of epidermal, parenchyma, and vascular cells of the oat coleoptile (306), have been reported by several other workers (reviewed in 321) and appear correlated with the intensity and direction of cytoplasmic streaming (305). They seem to be relatively common in vascular, cambial, and procambial cells (321); for example, they have been observed in companion cells, phloem parenchyma, and in developing and mature sieve elements (91, 109, 312, 321; Figure 17, 18). Franke et al (129) have also observed microfilaments in streaming pollen tubes.

Microfilaments of higher plants are similar to those in characean cells. They measure 50–70 Å in diameter, occur in bundles a few tenths of a micron wide and at least several microns long, and they often appear hexagonally packed (Figures 17, 18). The number of filaments per bundle varies from only a few to a score or more. At least several bundles may be present per cell, usually oriented parallel to the longitudinal axis or the direction of streaming.

O'Brien & Thimann (306) postulated that plant microfilaments actually may be microtubule protofilaments. This possibility seems unlikely, especially if microfilaments consist of actin, since actin is not similar to microtubule protein. Some reports have claimed that microtubules and microfilaments may be evolutionarily related (214, 328).

In the fungi, microfilaments are present in amoeboid forms, as would be expected (188), and seem to be present in at least one filamentous species (375). Filaments of larger diameter (200 Å) have also been seen in the hyphae of certain species (85).

Cytochalasin B (CB)

Cytochalasin B inhibits cytoplasmic streaming in many plant cells, including the algae *Nitella* (48, 78, 499), *Caulerpa,* and *Acetabularia* (176), and in higher plants, the root hairs of *Lepidium* and *Raphanus* (176), the epidermal cells of *Zea, Avena, Pisum* (73), and *Allium* (B. A. Palevitz & P. K. Hepler, unpublished observations), and the pollen tubes of *Tradescantia* (263), *Lilium,* and *Clivia* (129, 176). The effective concentrations vary widely, from as low as 0.1 μ/ml for pollen tubes (176, 263) to 20–50 μ/ml for coleoptiles (73). The differences in concentration may reflect actual variations in susceptibility or may indicate differences in uptake. In epidermal cells (73; B. A. Palevitz & P. K. Hepler, unpublished observations) several minutes after the application of CB, streaming begins to slow down, but only at certain places, usually at the ends of the cell and near the nucleus. Cytoplasm continues to stream into these areas creating several large, rotating clumps that are stringy or reticulate in appearance (Figure 19). The cells also develop small vacuoles that may contain particles undergoing Brownian movement, a characteristic of CB treatment also observed in *Nitella* (78, 499). Ultimately all streaming ceases. If the drug is replaced with distilled water, even after treatment of whole seedlings for as long as 48 hours, the masses quickly begin to rotate and flatten as cytoplasm begins to

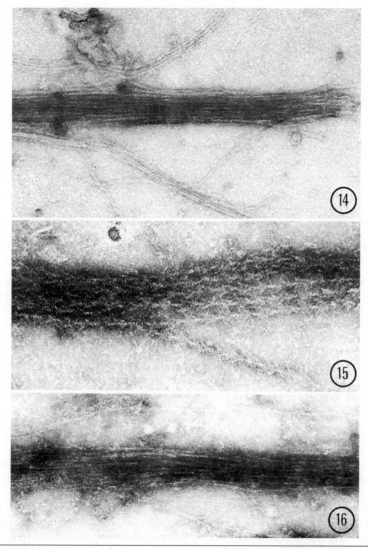

Figure 14   A bundle of 50 Å beaded filaments in a cytoplasmic suspension obtained from streaming internode cells of *Nitella flexilis* and observed after negative straining with uranyl acetate. X 170,000.

Figure 15   A similar bundle of filaments which were decorated with rabbit HMM prior to negative straining. Note the arrowheads and the fact that all the filaments within this bundle appear to have the same polarity. X 170,000.

Figure 16   A bundle of filaments treated with 1 m*M* ATP following HMM. The arrowheads have been removed. X 162,000. Figures 14–16 from Palevitz, Ash & Hepler (314).

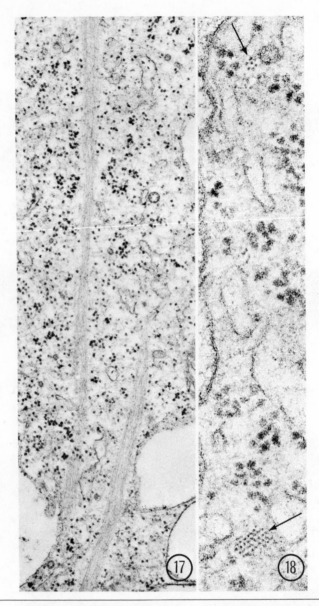

Figure 17 Microfilament bundles in longitudinal section in a phloem parenchyma cell of *Phaseolus vulgaris.* X 45,000. B. A. Palevitz & E. H. Newcomb, unpublished micrograph.

Figure 18 Microfilament bundles in transverse section (arrows) in a phloem parenchyma cell of *Pisum sativum.* Note the hexagonal packing of the 50 Å microfilaments within the bundles. X 100,000. B. A. Palevitz & E. H. Newcomb, unpublished micrograph.

stream out. Microscopic examination of CB-treated *Nitella* and higher plant cells reveals that the drug does not break down the microfilaments but may actually induce a greater degree of aggregation (48, 73, 78). Similarly, CB inhibits motility of fibrillar bundles in isolated cytoplasmic droplets of *Chara,* but does not cause their breakdown (499).

Cytochalasin B has a variety of effects in plant cells including inhibition of nuclear migration in *Tradescantia* leaves (409), inhibition of light-induced chloroplast movement in *Mougeotia* (481), and interference with sucrose transport in *Heracleum* phloem (464), although Williamson reports that CB has no effect on phloem transport in *Lepidium* (500). Quatrano (369) and Nelson & Jaffe (298) report that CB disrupts photopolarization and germination in fucoid eggs, and since these eggs do not exhibit cytoplasmic streaming, it can be argued that the drug is not affecting microfilaments (298).

Although the effects of CB at first seemed directly related to disruption of actin-like microfilaments, considerable controversy has arisen concerning its mode of action (75, 113, 126, 143, 144, 184, 185). The controversy has been fueled by a variety of conflicting data. For example, some workers report no direct effect on isolated actin (126), whereas others report a clear disruption of F-actin (433, 435). Spudich maintains that this discrepancy may reflect differences in the purity of preparations, since the presence of tropomyosin-troponin in isolated actin prevents the CB effect (433). Several reports indicate the drug inhibits sugar and nucleotide transport and assimilation (112, 226, 279, 353, 405). However, Wessells' group maintains that the morphological effects of CB are not due to the inhibition of transport (460, 525). Debate surrounds conflicting data on whether CB affects cleavage and associated microfilaments (42, 75, 95, 229, 412), contraction and structure of muscle (241, 252, 406), secretion of various substances (97, 319, 410, 463, 529), and phagocytosis or pinocytosis (113, 223, 501). Chrispeels (79) has reported that the drug does not affect α-amylase secretion or wall glycoprotein deposition in aleurone cells. The cytochalasins have been reported to affect growth in prokaryotes and certain filamentous fungi (40, 308). CB does not inhibit chromosome or sperm movement (75), although microfilaments seem to be present in spindles and sperm tails. In a recent paper, Cande et al (73) found that the effects

Figure 19 Epidermal cells of *Allium cepa* treated with cytochalasin B (5 μg/ml). The cytoplasm has aggregated in large clumps which have a reticulate appearance. N = nucleus. X 1,850. B. A. Palevitz & P. K. Hepler, unpublished micrograph.

of CB treatment on streaming and growth were not due to a breakdown of microfilaments, nor were they related to an effect on metabolite uptake or transport. The drug only partially inhibits auxin transport. Palevitz (313) reported that CB affects cytokinesis in dividing guard mother cells by inducing misaligned cell plates: however, no trace of microfilaments has been found in these cells. To complicate matters, the effects of the drug varied widely; those seen one week were not observed the next.

Cytochalasin B thus may produce a variety of detrimental effects. The drug may bind to actin, but the amount of binding may be affected by conditions in each cell. It may have a general effect on the cell; it may affect other structures besides actin, or alternatively, CB might bind to membranes or membrane-microfilament attachment sites and thus affect microfilament structure indirectly. The mode of action of CB is therefore still obscure, and interpretations based on the drug's effects should be treated with caution. Resolution of this problem awaits more analytical studies, including work on the binding of radioactive CB and CB analogs (J. A. Spudich, personal communication).

P-Protein

Considerable speculation has surrounded the relation of P-protein to actin and microfilaments. P-proteins are aggregations of tubular, crystalline, fibrous, and amorphous materials found in the phloem of higher plants (e.g. 91, 316, 320). All forms probably consist of the same subunits since they are interconvertible depending on factors controlling self-assembly. Kollmann and co-workers have isolated and partially characterized P-protein-like material from *Cucurbita* (224, 225, 227, 487). They find that the material exhibits several molecular weights in multiples of approximately 15,000, is soluble with dithiothreitol and low temperature, and polymerizes into filaments with 0.1 M KCl. Other proteinanceous fractions have also been obtained from phloem, but their relation to P-protein is uncertain (482, 483, 527).

There has been speculation that P-protein may be similar to microfilaments and may therefore provide the motive force for assimilate movement in the sieve elements (118, 205, 250, 486, 518). Thompson & Thompson (464) found that CB inhibits sucrose transport in *Heracleum,* and they interpret these results as support for a "contractile" role of P-protein in phloem. Although these hypotheses are attractive in light of all our new findings on microfilaments in eukaryotes, the data now available do not prove any structural or functional similarity betweem P-protein and microfilaments. Neither microtubules nor microfilaments normally undergo the assembly-disassembly reactions typical of P-protein in vivo. Microfilaments are present in sieve elements, often with P-protein bodies, but have no discernable ontogenetic or spatial relation to them (91, 109, 312, 321). P-protein and actin paracrystals also show different axial periodicities [100–150 Å for P-protein (91, 316) vs 350–360 Å for actin (181, 434)]. Although P-protein and actin share some similarities, including a fibrous structure and polymerization with KCl, the molecular weights observed are not characteristic of actin (225, 487). Furthermore, isolated P-protein fractions do not contain bound nucleotide nor do they have any associated ATPase (225). Williamson (500) and Palevitz (unpublished observation) have found that fibrillar and crystalline P-protein respectively do not bind HMM whereas microfilaments in *Nitella* do (314). Williamson found no effect of CB on ^{14}C transport in *Lepidium* phloem (500). Nor does P-protein appear related to microtubule protein, as several studies report that P-protein aggregation in vivo is not affected by a variety of treatments known to affect microtubules including cold, IPC, colchicine, and vinblastine sulfate (312, 399, 519). The colchicine binding protein in phloem mentioned earlier is probably tubulin and not P-protein (158). Finally, the fractions obtained by Kleinig et al (225) revealed no colchicine binding activity. It is possible that P-protein can be broadly categorized with actin and microtubule protein as structural proteins, since they all can be precipitated with vinblastine sulfate and calcium (225, 487, 508). Until new data are obtained, however, it seems unwarranted to confuse P-protein with microfilaments, microtubules, or actin, as has been done recently (118, 205, 464).

Mechanisms of Motility

Microfilaments occur commonly throughout eukaryotes including plants. They are usually associated with movements related to streaming, and evidence suggests they are composed of actin. However, we are as yet unable to say how they function. Actin by itself is incapable of generating motion and needs other components, notably myosin. In striated muscle, actin-myosin interactions have been analyzed extensively, and it is well- known that the two kinds of filaments function by sliding past one another as a result of forces driven by the myosin ATPase cross-bridges (37, 191, 192, 367). Although we suspect a similar shear-generated force in the nonmuscle systems, the evidence supporting this contention is limited, due to lack of a regular structural packing of actin and myosin and the difficulty in unequivocally identifying myosin in these cells. Nevertheless, a mechanism involving a sliding interaction between an actin and an associated myosin-like molecule seems most reasonable (192, 367, 514). Thus microfilaments may operate in the same basic way in all systems. The gross movement produced, however, will depend on the organization of the filaments in each cell (228, 354, 398, 496), for example, as a random network or discrete linear bundles. In the migrating fibroblast or glial cell, the anterior, loose meshwork is thought to be involved in the extension of the leading lamella or ruffle, whereas the linear sheath or fibers that extend back towards the posterior of the cell is believed to act by pulling the cell body up as new cell-substrate contact points are made (1, 194, 496). Thus the two microfilament systems are organized differently and may produce different types of movement, yet both may consist of the same subunits.

In *Physarum* the network microfilaments in the cortical cytoplasm could slide past one another (228, 294), causing a constriction which would give rise to a pressure increase and thus drive the cytoplasmic stream. In *Nitella* it seems reasonable that the long microfilament bundles could produce shear at the sol-gel interface (101, 102, 200, 202, 209, 210, 212, 514) through the same sliding mechanism utilizing an as yet unidentified myosin-like component (192). The microfilament bundles in *Nitella* appear to be attached to the chloroplasts or ER of the ectoplasm and may use them as an anchor to generate motion. Waves have been observed along fibril bundles and these may move adjacent particles (11, 203, 231). Bulk flow in *Nitella* may result from an interaction between bundles of microfilaments and cytoplasmic structures like the ER (48), mitochondria, dictyosomes, etc, which might effectively carry along the rest of the endoplasm in a hydrodynamic flow (102). In this system the actin filaments appear fixed in position while the myosin either occurs as monomers or oligomers attached to them or to moving particles or to membranes of mobile elements. The attachment of myosin to vesicles has been postulated for nerve cells (38, 53), and observations from intact cells (129, 305) and isolated cytoplasmic droplets (200, 202, 210, 231) also indicate a direct interaction between organelles and microfilaments in streaming in plants.

That microfilaments may be attached or anchored to membranes is supported by several investigations. Evidence showing microfilament-membrane linkages suggests that the plasmalemma may play a critical role in movement in many cells ranging from smooth muscle to the *Acanthamoeba*. Based on studies using a variety of techniques, microfilaments appear to be linked to the plasmalemma of several animal cells (e.g. 57, 412, 432, 440, 496, 524) and amoebae (87, 359) and to the plasmalemma and tonoplast of *Physarum* (211, 228, 478, 512). In glial cells and fibroblasts, both sheath and network microfilaments are inserted in the plasma membrane, often at discrete dense regions (166). Similar dense attachment sites are present in testacean amoebae (513) and in microvilli, where Tilney & Cardell (468) have shown that microfilament formation is initiated at these dense areas. HMM binding indicates that all the microfilaments may have the same polarity (198, 472), which is probably determined by the membrane attachment. Recently, Pollard & Korn (359) isolated plasma membranes from *Acanthamoeba* and found microfilaments attached. The microfilaments bind HMM and can be removed by procedures which solubilize actin.

It has been suggested that antiparallel microfilaments attached to the plasmalemma may affect movement of the cytoplasm in *Acanthamoeba* by sliding relative to each other under the influence of bridging monomeric myosin molecules (358). Presumably the sliding produces a deformation of the plasmalemma. A similar mechanism has been invoked for *Physarum* utilizing antiparallel microfilaments bridged by bipolar or oligomeric myosins (228, 292, 294). Supporting evidence indicates that the myosins involved can cross-link isolated actin (292, 294, 361). Wolpert & Gingell (515) have found that although the plasmalemma does not itself produce the force for amoeboid movement, it can be deformed in response to forces within the cytoplasm (perhaps produced by microfilaments?). Other evidence indicates that microfilaments can induce cell shape changes during microvillus formation (468), contact withdrawal (166), and possibly during cell transformation (275).

It is thus possible that microfilament-membrane interactions are also important for bulk cytoplasmic streaming in plants. Attachment to cell membranes would enable coordinated or sequential microfilament action via myosin-like molecules allowing flow of the ground plasm. The viscoelastic nature of the cytoplasm would also contribute to mass flow (13–15, 102). Individual organelles or particles could also interact with the filaments and undergo saltation or rapid linear movement. The coordinated action produced by anchorage at the cell membranes could consist of movement or deformation of the plasmalemma, tonoplast, or ER, the generation of coherent wave forms, or the uniform beating of attached myosins (4). Waves conceivably could be generated by the mechanisms outlined by Jarosch (203) and Hejnowicz (167), or by the sliding of antiparallel microfilaments within a given bundle, in much the same way microtubule sliding generates wave forms in flagella. However, recent evidence suggests all microfilaments in a bundle in *Nitella* have the same polarity (314). Evidence exists showing that waves can be propagated along microfilament bundles in *Nitella* (11, 200, 202, 203, 209), but similar evidence in higher plants is extremely limited (321).

When epidermal cells are excised, streaming usually ceases for a short time (approximately 10 minutes) because of some shock effect (201, 209). Streaming restarts in sequence from saltations, to more directed movement of particles, and finally to bulk flow in addition to directed particle movement (201; B. A. Palevitz & P. K. Hepler, unpublished observation). It has been postulated that this sequence of events reflects a progressive increase in the degree of aggregation of microfilaments into coarser fibrils (201, 203), and the increased aggregation would enable progressively greater screw-like waves to be propagated along the fibrils by changes in state of individual α-helices (203). However, this fascinating sequence in the resumption of streaming can be explained in a different way. During injury, microfilaments become detached from fragile attachment sites on the plasmalemma, tonoplast, or ER. Particles would still interact with these free microfilaments and saltations would result. Gradually, the microfilaments or microfilament bundles become reattached or resynthesized at the membranes, producing more directed movement. Eventually a sufficient number become attached to enable coordinated action and bulk flow.

Intrinsic in these arguments is the determination of the polarity of microfilaments by attachment to the membranes. Bulk streaming could occur if most filaments in a cytoplasmic strand were of the same polarity, whereas changes in direction would be possible when particles encountered filaments of different polarity or orientation (305). Actin filaments are polar structures (190), and a consequence of their association with or assembly at a membrane might be the establishment of this polarity relative to the membrane. Polarity would be visualized by HMM arrowheads all pointing in one direction, for example, away from the cell surface membrane (294, 358). The polarity of actin filaments in striated muscle is constant with reference to the Z bands in which they are embedded. Just as this polarity is essential for sliding and contraction in muscle, it may also be important for sliding during cytoplasmic streaming and amoeboid movement in other cells.

The presence of microfilament-membrane attachment sites could explain certain diverse phenomena. The disruption of microfilaments by various treatments such as CB and glycerination might be due to their effect on sensitive attachment sites. Recent findings that CB dislodges microfilament bundles from the sol-gel interface in *Nitella* also supports this hypothesis (78). Similarly, the wounding of plant tissue might also disrupt these attachments and cause the cessation of streaming.

This hypothetical mechanism is presented to stimulate discussion in light of new findings concerning the interaction of microfilaments and membranes in other cell types. Of importance is the polarity of various microfilaments within a cell and whether the microfilaments in higher plants are attached to the plasmalemma, tonoplast, or ER. Conclusive evidence of such connections have not yet been reported and might be difficult to find, considering the diameter of the microfilaments and the inability to locate them consistently in thin sections with precision. However, Esau recently reported that microfilaments may be linked to ER cisternae in phloem parenchyma of *Mimosa* (109). In *Nitella,* the microfilaments clearly are not connected to the plasmalemma, but appear to be anchored to the sol-gel interface where they may be linked to other membranes such as the chloroplast envelope or the ER (48,296). Bradley (48) has postulated that streaming in *Nitella* may be produced by mechanochemical coupling between microfilaments and ER cisternae.

Cell membranes could control microfilament function in another way, possibly by regulating levels of ions such as calcium which might stimulate microfilament activity. Increasing evidence indicates that calcium exerts control over movement in many nonmuscle cells (228, 354) as it does it striated muscle (105, 106, 434). The level of calcium ions is important for fibroblast and amoeboid movement (135, 163), shuttle streaming (161), and cortical "contractions" in eggs and embryo cells (139, 496). In striated muscle, the complex of tropomyosin plus troponins (TM-TP) arranged along the actin filaments is involved in the binding of calcium released by the sarcoplasmic reticulum and the regulation of actin-myosin interaction (105, 106, 434). Tropomyosin-like proteins have now been reported in other cells such as *Physarum* (458), platelets (83), and fibroblasts (526). In these and other cells, membranes may serve to pump and sequester calcium ions in a manner analogous to that of the sarcoplasmic reticulum. Such activity has been localized at the plasmalemma or ER in smooth muscle (189) and fibroblasts (see 526) and in membranous vesicles in *Physarum* (47) and *Spirostomum* (116). Thus calcium appears to control movement in these cells, although the exact mechanism remains unclear. Calcium may interact with components like TM-TP along the actin microfilaments and directly regulate interaction with myosin, or it could influence the aggregation state of myosin. In *Physarum,* the self-assembly of bipolar myosin aggregates capable of cross-linking actin is sensitive to Ca^{2+} (293,294), suggesting that the ion may regulate myosin polymerization and thus control movement. A similar regulation may occur in platelets (36, 83). Cyclic AMP, which as we mentioned earlier is related to calcium levels and microtubule function, might also affect microfilaments indirectly through an effect on membranes and calcium transport, or directly through phosphorylation of actin and associated proteins (365).

A similar role for calcium ions and membranes might be found in plants. In this respect, the presence of ER cisternae close to microfilament bundles in *Nitella* (48, 296) and phloem parenchyma (109) may be important. Any speculation on the nature of calcium control must be made with caution, however, since information on this subject is quite incomplete. Finally, Pollard et al have isolated a "cofactor" from *Acanthamoeba* which controls actin-myosin interaction, but the material is not similar to TM-TP, nor is the system sensitive to calcium (355, 358, 361).

It is apparent from these discussions that a critical consideration for the control of streaming in plants is the nature of the myosin-like component that seems to be required. Pringle (367) has emphasized that in addition to microfilaments, the minimum further requirement for a relative force to develop between actin microfilaments of opposite polarity is some kind of myosin. The myosin need not be organized as visible thick filaments and might only consist of a monomeric globular ATPase capable of cross-linking actin. Such a myosin appears to be present in *Acanthamoeba*. Variations in the properties of these myosins might provide for differences in the form and control of movement between species, just as it may help explain differences in behavior between muscle types (52). In some systems myosin has been shown to be present as discrete thick filaments (87; M. Clarke, & J. A. Spudich, in preparation). In others, myosin is probably functional as monomers or oligomers (18, 292–294, 358, 360, 361). In *Physarum,* a cyclic aggregation and disaggregation of myosin may be important for the control of movement (293). Both microfilaments and thick filaments have been reported to aggregate during "contraction" in *Physarum* (18, 228, 292), and myosin may only form thick filaments in smooth muscle prior to or during contraction (381). Since the interaction with actin is probably governed by the nature of myosin, its properties may be crucial in consideration of the type of movement being considered. The nature of the myosin-like molecules in plants is therefore of extreme interest, especially since thick filaments have never been reported in the cells of green plants.

MICROTUBULE-MICROFILAMENT COOPERATION

In attempting to decipher the role of microtubules and microfilaments, we must not overlook the possibility that these two elements in some circumstances might function cooperatively. Microtubules could provide the intracellular framework upon which microfilaments and/or associated motile molecules could bind and generate force. Because of the long rigid structure of the microtubule, directionality and relatively long range working distances might be achieved for forces which otherwise might be loosely organized and effective only for short distances. Buckley & Porter (57) have discussed an active role of a microtubule-microfilament complex in moving fibroblasts and suggest that microfilaments may slide along microtubules via ATPase cross-bridges in much the same way actin interacts with myosin filaments in muscle. With the finding that actin-like microfilaments are present in the spindle apparatus Forer & Behnke (125) suggested that they may provide the motive force and that microtubules serve as structural elements that orient the microfilaments.

The association of a cellular process with microtubules or microfilaments has often been based upon the sensitivity of the particular process either to colchicine and related antimicrotubule agents on the one hand or to cytochalasin B on the other hand. Caution, however, must be exercised in trying to draw specific conclusions about microfilament and microtubule function as a result of drug inhibition of a particular process. We have already discussed the many and varied effects of CB and again urge restraint in equating its action to a specific effect on microfilaments. Colchicine, in contrast to CB, has a rather specific and well-documented effect on microtubules, and thus the inhibition of a cellular process, for example chromosome motion, with the drug indicates that microtubules are involved. However, stopping motion with colchicine does not prove that microtubules provide the motive force; inhibition could result from the destruction of a structural scaffolding of microtubules upon which force-producing macromolecules might be organized. Experiments with colchicine have already demonstrated an apparent structural and functional association between microtubule and the intermediary 100 Å filaments in cultured fibroblast cells (142, 144). In addition to disrupting microtubules, the drug causes the intermediary filaments to aggregate in a perinuclear region and blocks normal cell locomotion. In a recent review Rebhun (377) argues that inhibition of long particle saltations (4 μ) with colchicine, which has been reported by Freed & Lebowitz (131), does not by itself indicate that microtubules provide the motive force. Microfilaments which could be organized or aligned by microtubules might in reality provide the driving force (377).

The possibility of a role for a microtubule-microfilament complex in cytoplasmic streaming in plants seems remote, since cytoplasmic microtubules are usually located close to the plasmalemma and away from the microfilaments. Moreover, the two are usually aligned perpendicular to each other (109, 299, 331). A microtubule-microfilament complex could be present in *Caulerpa,* however, where the tubules are located within the streaming cytoplasm (400).

Similarly, there is no evidence linking microtubules and microfilaments in mitosis in plant cells. This may be due in part to our inability to visualize microfilaments possibly as a result of improper fixation procedures. The studies of Forer & Behnke (125) suggest that microfilaments in the spindle apparatus of crane fly spermatocytes may become apparent only after treatment with glycerin and HMM, raising the possibility that they are a preparation artifact. Nevertheless, if microfilaments are loosely organized, there is reason to suspect that they might be destroyed or washed out during fixation and embedment for electron microscopy. In plants it may be especially troublesome to preserve microfilaments in all instances where they might exist, and therefore the delineation of their structural relationship with microtubules may depend upon the development of new and improved techniques of tissue preservation.

In view of the ubiquity of microtubules and microfilaments and of the likelihood that microfilaments consist of actin and have a motile function, it becomes important to give serious consideration to a cooperative interaction between these elements in different processes, especially when movement is involved.

CONCLUSIONS

Considerable progress has been made in our understanding of microtubules and microfilaments, although many large gaps in our knowledge remain. Information is especially needed on the factors within the cell which control their organization and activation. We have already emphasized the importance of identifying the details of the spatial and temporal control of microtubule assembly. Of equal importance is an understanding of the control of microfilament assembly. While certain sites in the cell can be designated as microtubule nucleating centers, we know much less about where and how microfilaments are organized. The application of HMM to glycerinated plant cells may make it possible to localize actin filaments in situ and to decipher their polarity especially in relation to the direction of streaming and to points of attachment to other structures such as membranes. It seems likely that the correlation of these findings with our present knowledge of cytoplasmic streaming will help clarify the mechanism of force generation.

Another important area of inquiry which needs elucidation is that of the role of calcium. A variety of interrelationships are evident between microtubules, actomyosin, and calcium, including the low levels of calcium needed for microtubule assembly, the calcium regulation of dynein and actomyosin ATPase, the possible role of calcium in myosin assembly, and the relationship between calcium and cyclic AMP and the mechanism by which this hormone may control microtubule and microfilament activity. Together with its involvement in plant cell wall formation, it is evident that calcium may participate in many cellular processes, and therefore it is important to understand both the way it functions and factors regulating its intracellular concentration.

Finally, the discovery that microfilaments consist of actin immediately focuses our attention on the nature of myosin-like proteins and other associated molecules which must be present to regulate microfilament function. With the current interest in the isolation and characterization of myosins from nonmuscle cells and similar concern over the interaction of dynein-like molecules with microtubules, investigations during the next few years should bring us much closer to an understanding of the basic mechanisms of motility.

ACKNOWLEDGMENTS

We thank Dr. James A. Spudich, University of California Medical Center, San Francisco, for providing Figures 12 and 13. The preparation of this review was supported by funds from the National Science Foundation, grant number GB 25152, and a postdoctoral fellowship (to B. A. P.) from the National Institutes of Health.

Literature Cited

1. Abercrombie, M. J., Heaysman, J. E. M., Pegrum, S. M. 1971. *Exp. Cell Res.* 67:359–67
2. Adelman, M., Borisy, G., Shelanski, M., Weisenberg, R., Taylor, E. 1968. *Fed. Proc.* 27:1186–93
3. Adelman, M. R., Taylor, E. W. 1969. *Biochemistry* 8:4964–75
4. Ibid, 4976–88
5. Adelstein, R. S., Conti, M. A. 1972. *Cold Spring Harbor Symp. Quant. Biol.* 37:599–605
6. Adelstein, R. S., Conti, M. A., Johnson, G. S., Pastan, I., Pollard, T. D. 1972. *Proc. Nat. Acad. Sci. USA* 69:3693–97
7. Adelstein, R. S., Pollard, T. D., Kuehl, W. M. 1971. *Proc. Nat. Acad. Sci. USA* 68:2703–7
8. Aist, J. R. 1969. *J. Cell Biol.* 40:120–35

9. Aist, J. R., Williams, P. H. 1972. *J. Cell Biol.* 55:368–89
10. Aldrich, H. C. 1969. *Am. J. Bot.* 56:290–99
11. Allen, N. S., Allen, R. D. 1972. *J. Cell Biol.* 55:2a
12. Allen, R. D. 1968. *Symp. Soc. Exp. Biol.* 22:151–68
13. Allen, R. D. 1971. *Science* 174:1237–40
14. Allen, R. D. 1972. *Exp. Cell Res.* 72:34–45
15. Allen, R. D. 1973. *The Biology of Amoeba,* ed. K. W. Jeon, 201–47. New York: Academic. 628 pp.
16. Allen, R. D., Kamiya, N., Eds. 1964. *Primitive Motile Systems in Cell Biology.* New York: Academic. 642 pp.
17. Alléra, A., Beck, R., Wohlfarth-Bot-

terman, K.-E. 1971. *Cytobiologie* 4: 437–49
18. Alléra, A., Wohlfarth-Botterman, K.-E. 1972. *Cytobiologie* 6:261–86
19. Allison, A. C., Davies, P., De Petris, S. 1971. *Nature New Biol.* 232:154–55
20. Amrhein, N., Filner, P. 1973. *Proc. Nat. Acad. Sci. USA* 70:1099–1103
21. Avers, C. J. 1963. *Am. J. Bot.* 50:140–48
22. Aylor, D. E., Parlange, J.-Y., Krikorian, A. D. 1973. *Am. J. Bot.* 60:163–71
23. Bajer, A. 1968. *Symp. Soc. Exp. Biol.* 22:287–310
24. Bajer, A., Allen, R. D. 1966. *Science* 151:572–74
25. Bajer, A., Molè-Bajer, J. 1969. *Chromosoma* 27:448–84
26. Bajer, A., Molé-Bajer, J. 1971. *Advan. Cell Mol. Biol.* 1:213–66
27. Bajer, A. S., Molé-Bajer, J. 1972. *Int. Rev. Cytol. Suppl.* 3
28. Baker, P. C., Schroeder, T. E. 1967. *Develop. Biol.* 15:432–50
29. Bannister, L. H., Tatchell, E. C. 1968. *J. Cell Sci.* 3:295–308
30. Barlow, P. W. 1969. *Protoplasma* 68:79–83
31. Barton, R. 1967. *J. Ultrastruct. Res.* 20:6–19
32. Barton, R. 1969. *J. Cell Biol.* 41:637–41
33. Bech-Hansen, C. W., Fowke, L. C. 1972. *Can. J. Bot.* 50:1811–16
34. Behnke, O., Forer, A. 1967. *J. Cell Sci.* 2:169–92
35. Behnke, O., Forer, A., Emmerson, J. 1971. *Nature* 234:408–10
36. Behnke, O., Kristensen, B. I., Nielsen, L. E. 1971. *J. Ultrastruct. Res.* 37:351–69
37. Bendall, J. R. 1969. *Muscles, Molecules, and Movement.* London: Heinemann. 219 pp.
38. Berl, S., Puszkin, S., Nicklas, W. J. 1973. *Science* 179:441–46
39. Berry, R. W., Shelanski, M. L. 1972. *J. Mol. Biol.* 71:71–80
40. Betina, V., Mičekova, D., Nemec, P. 1972. *J. Gen. Microbiol.* 71:343–49
41. Bettex-Galland, M., Lüscher, E. F. 1961. *Biochim. Biophys. Acta* 49: 536–47
42. Bluemink, J. G. 1971. *Z. Zellforsch. Mikrosk. Anat.* 121:102–26
43. Borisy, G. G., Olmsted, J. B. 1972. *Science* 177:1196–97
44. Borisy, G. G., Taylor, E. W. 1967. *J. Cell Biol.* 34:525–34
45. Ibid, 535–48

46. Bouck, G. B., Brown, D. L. 1973. *J. Cell Biol.* 56:340–59
47. Braatz, R., Komnick, H. 1970. *Cytobiologie* 2:457–63
48. Bradley, M. O. 1973. *J. Cell Sci.* 12:327–43
49. Braselton, J. P., Bowen, C. C. 1971. *Caryologia* 24:49–58
50. Braten, T., Nordby, O. 1973. *J. Cell Sci.* 13:69–81
51. Brennan, J. R. 1971. *Phytomorphology* 20:309–15
52. Bray, D. 1972. *Cold Spring Harbor Symp. Quant. Biol.* 37:567–71
53. Bray, D. 1973. *Nature* 244:93–96
54. Brown, D. L., Bouck, G. B. 1973. *J. Cell Biol.* 56:360–78
55. Bryan, J. 1972. *Biochemistry* 11: 2611–16
56. Bryan, J., Wilson, L. 1971. *Proc. Nat. Acad. Sci. USA* 68:1762–66
57. Buckley, I. K., Porter, K. R. 1967. *Protoplasma* 64:349–80
58. Bünning, E. 1958. *Protoplasmatologia* VIII(9a)
59. Bünning, E., Biegert, F. 1953. *Z. Bot.* 41:17–39
60. Burgess, J. 1969. *Planta* 87:259–70
61. Ibid 1970. 92:25–28
62. Burgess, J. 1970. *Protoplasma* 69: 253–64
63. Burgess, J. 1970. *Planta* 95:72–85
64. Burgess, J. 1970. *Protoplasma* 71:77–89
65. Burgess, J., Northcote, D. H. 1967. *Planta* 75:319–26
66. Ibid 1968. 80:1–14
67. Burgess, J., Northcote, D. H. 1969. *J. Cell Sci.* 5:433–51
68. Burkholder, G. O., Okada, T. A., Comings, D. E. 1972. *Exp. Cell Res.* 75:497–511
69. Burnside, B. 1971. *Develop. Biol.* 26:416–41
70. Burnside, B. 1972. *J. Cell Biol.* 55:33a
71. Burton, P. R., Fernandez, H. L. 1973. *J. Cell Sci.* 12:567–83
72. Burton, P. R., Kirkland, W. L. 1972. *Nature New Biol.* 239:244–46
73. Cande, W. Z., Goldsmith, M. H. M., Ray, P. M. 1973. *Planta* 111:279–96
74. Carter, S. B. 1967. *Nature* 213:261–64
75. Carter, S. B. 1972. *Endeavour* 31:77–82
76. Chafe, S. C., Wardrop, A. B. 1970. *Planta* 92:13–24
77. Chang, C-M., Goldman, R. D. 1973. *J. Cell Biol.* 57:867–74
78. Chen, J. C. W. 1973. *Protoplasma* 77:427–35
79. Chrispeels, M. J. 1972. *Planta* 108: 283–87

80. Cloney, R. A. 1966. *J. Ultrastruct. Res.* 14:300–28
81. Cloney, R. A. 1972. *Z. Zellforsch. Mikrosk. Anat.* 132:167–92
82. Coffey, M. D., Palevitz, B. A., Allen, P. J. 1972. *Can. J. Bot.* 50:231–40
83. Cohen, I., Cohen, C. 1972. *J. Mol. Biol.* 68:383–87
84. Cohen, C., Harrison, S. C., Stephens, R. E. 1971. *J. Mol. Biol.* 59:375–80
85. Cole, G. T. 1972. *J. Ultrastruct. Res.* 41:463–71
86. Colson, B. 1934. *Ann. Bot.* 58:211–24
87. Comly, L. T. 1973. *J. Cell Biol.* 58:230–37
88. Crawford, R. M. 1973. *J. Phycol.* 9:50–61
89. Cronshaw, J. 1967. *Planta* 72:78–90
90. Cronshaw, J., Bouck, G. B. 1965. *J. Cell Biol.* 24:415–31
91. Cronshaw, J., Esau, K. 1967. *J. Cell Biol.* 34:801–15
92. Cronshaw, J., Esau, K. 1968. *Protoplasma* 65:1–24
93. Cutter, E. G., Hung, C-Y. 1972. *J. Cell Sci.* 11:723–37
94. Dales, S. 1972. *J. Cell Biol.* 52:748–54
95. DeLaat, S. W., Luchtel, D., Bluemink, J. G. 1973. *Develop. Biol.* 31:163–77
96. Deysson, G., Benbadis, M. 1968. *C. R. Soc. Biol.* 162:601–4
97. Diegelmann, R. F., Peterkofsky, B. 1972. *Proc. Nat. Acad. Sci. USA* 69:892–96
98. Dietz, R. 1959. *Z. Naturforsch.* 14b:749–52
99. Dietz, R. 1966. *Chromosomes Today* 1:161–66
100. Dodge, B. O., Singleton, J. R., Rolnick, A. 1950. *Proc. Am. Phil. Soc.* 94:38–52
101. Donaldson, I. G. 1972. *Protoplasma* 74:329–44
102. Donaldson, I. G. 1972. *J. Theor. Biol.* 37:75–91
103. Dover, G. A. 1972. *J. Cell Sci.* 11:699–711
104. Duckett, J. G. 1973. *J. Cell Sci.* 12:95–129
105. Ebashi, S. 1972. *Nature* 240:217–18
106. Ebashi, S., Endo, M. 1968. *Progr. Biophys. Mol. Biol.* 18:123–83
107. Eipper, B. A. 1972. *Proc. Nat. Acad. Sci. USA* 69:2283–87
108. Erickson, R. O. 1973. *Science* 181:705–16
109. Esau, K. 1973. *Ann. Bot.* 37:625–32
110. Esau, K., Cheadle, V. I., Gill, R. H. 1966. *Am. J. Bot.* 53:765–71
111. Esau, K., Gill, R. H. 1969. *Can. J. Bot.* 47:581–91
112. Estensen, R. D., Plagemann, P. G. 1972. *Proc. Nat. Acad. Sci. USA* 69:1430–34
113. Estensen, R. D., Rosenberg, M., Sheridan, J. D. 1971. *Science* 173:356–58
114. Everhart, L. P. Jr. 1971. *J. Mol. Biol.* 61:745–48
115. Evert, R. F., Deshpande, B. P. 1970. *Am. J. Bot.* 57:942–61
116. Etiènne, E. M. 1970. *J. Gen. Physiol.* 56:168–79
117. Feit, H., Slusarek, L., Shelanski, M. L. 1971. *Proc. Nat. Acad. Sci. USA* 68:2028–31
118. Fensom, D. S. 1972. *Can. J. Bot.* 50:479–97
119. Fine, R. E. 1971. *Nature New Biol.* 233:283–84
120. Fine, R. E., Bray, D. 1971. *Nature New Biol.* 234:115–18
121. Floyd, G. L., Stewart, K. D., Mattox, K. R. 1972. *J. Phycol.* 8:68–81
122. Forer, A. 1966. *Chromosoma* 19:44–98
123. Forer, A. *Handbook of Molecular Cytology*, ed. A. Lima-de-Faria, 553–601. Amsterdam: North Holland. 1508 pp.
124. Forer, A., Behnke, O. 1972. *J. Cell Sci.* 11:491–519
125. Forer, A., Behnke, O. 1972. *Chromosoma* 39:145–73
126. Forer, A., Emmerson, J., Behnke, O. 1972. *Science* 175:774–76
127. Franke, W. W. 1971. *Z. Naturforsch.* 26b:626–27
128. Franke, W. W. 1971. *Exp. Cell Res.* 66:486–89
129. Franke, W. W., Herth, W., Vanderwoude, J., Morrè, D. J. 1972. *Planta* 105:317–41
130. Franke, W. W., Reau, P. 1973. *Arch. Mikrobiol.* 90:121–29
131. Freed, J. J., Lebowitz, M. M. 1970. *J. Cell Biol.* 45:334–54
132. Fuge, H., Müller, W. 1972. *Exp. Cell Res.* 71:241–45
133. Fulton, C. 1971. *Origin and Continuity of Cell Organelles*, ed. J. Reinert, H. Ursprung, 170–221. New York: Springer-Verlag. 342 pp.
134. Fulton, C., Kane, R. E., Stephens, R. E. 1971. *J. Cell Biol.* 50:762–73
135. Gail, M. H., Boone, C. W., Thompson, C. S. 1973 *Exp. Cell Res.* 79:386–90
136. Gawadi, N. 1971. *Nature* 234:410
137. Gawlik, S. R., Millington, W. F. 1969. *Am. J. Bot.* 56:1084–93
138. Gibbons, I. R. 1963. *Proc. Nat. Acad. Sci. USA* 50:1002–10
139. Gingell, D. 1970. *J. Embryol. Exp. Morphol.* 23:583–609

140. Girbardt, M. 1968. *Symp. Soc. Exp. Biol.* 22:249–59
141. Girbardt, M. 1971. *J. Cell Sci.* 9:453–66
142. Goldman, R. D. 1971. *J. Cell Biol.* 51:752–62
143. Ibid 1972. 52:246–54
144. Goldman, R. D., Knipe, D. M. 1972. *Cold Spring Harbor Symp. Quant. Biol.* 37:523–34
145. Goodman, D. B. P., Rasmussen, H., DiBella, F., Guthrow, C. E. Jr. 1970. *Proc. Nat. Acad. Sci. USA* 67:652–59
146. Green, P. B. 1962. *Science* 138:1404–5
147. Green, P. B. 1963. *Cytodifferentiation and Macromolecular Synthesis,* ed. M. Locke, 203–34. New York: Academic. 247 pp.
148. Green, P. B. 1969. *Ann. Rev. Plant Physiol.* 20:365–94
149. Green, P. B., Erickson, R. O., Richmond, P. A. 1970. *Ann. N. Y. Acad. Sci.* 175:712–31
150. Green, P. B., King, A. 1966. *Aust. J. Biol. Sci.* 19:421–37
151. Grimstone, A. V., Cleveland, L. R. 1965. *J. Cell Biol.* 24:387–400
152. Grimstone, A. V., Klug, A. 1966. *J. Cell Sci.* 1:351–62
153. Grove, S. N., Bracker, C. E. 1970. *J. Bacteriol.* 104:989–1009
154. Guttes, S., Guttes, E., Ellis, R. A. 1968. *J. Ultrastruct. Res.* 22:508–29
155. Haber, J. E., Peloquin, J. G., Halvorson, H. O., Borisy, G. G. 1972. *J. Cell Biol.* 55:355–67
156. Hanzely, L., Schjeide, O. A. 1973. *Cytobios* 7:147–62
157. Harris, P., Bajer, A. 1965. *Chromosoma* 16:624–36
158. Hart, J. W., Sabnis, D. D. 1973. *Planta* 109:147–52
159. Hatano, S., Ohnuma, J. 1970. *Biochim. Biophys. Acta* 205:110–19
160. Hatano, S., Oosawa, F. 1968. *Biochim. Biophys. Acta* 127:488–98
161. Hatano, S., Oosawa, F. 1971. *J. Physiol. Soc. Japan* 33:589–90
162. Hatano, S., Tazawa, M. 1968. *Biochim. Biophys. Acta* 154:507–19
163. Hawkes, R. B., Holberton, D. V. 1973. *J. Cell. Physiol.* 81:365–70
164. Hayashi, T. 1964. See Ref. 16, 19–29
165. Heath, I. B., Darley, W. M. 1972. *J. Phycol.* 8:51–59
166. Heaysman, J. E. M., Pegrum, S. M. 1973. *Exp. Cell Res.* 78:71–78
167. Hejnowicz, Z. 1970. *Protoplasma* 71:343–364
168. Hepler, P. K. 1972. *J. Cell Biol.* 55:112a
169. Hepler, P. K. 1974. *Plant Biochemistry,* ed. J. Bonner, J. Varner. New York: Academic. 3rd ed. In press
170. Hepler, P. K., Fosket, D. E. 1971. *Protoplasma* 72:213–36
171. Hepler, P. K., Jackson, W. T. 1968. *J. Cell Biol.* 38:437–46
172. Hepler, P. K., Jackson, W. T. 1969. *J. Cell Sci.* 5:727–43
173. Hepler, P. K., McIntosh, J. R., Cleland, S. 1970. *J. Cell Biol.* 45:438–44
174. Hepler, P. K., Newcomb, E. H. 1964. *J. Cell Biol.* 20:529–33
175. Hepler, P. K., Newcomb, E. H. 1967. *J. Ultrastruct. Res.* 19:498–513
176. Herth, W., Franke, W. W., Vanderwoude, W. J. 1972. *Naturwissenschaften* 59:38–39
177. Heslop-Harrison, J. 1968. *J. Cell Sci.* 3:457–66
178. Heslop-Harrison, J. 1971. *Symp. Soc. Exp. Biol.* 25:277–300
179. Heyn, A. N. J. 1972. *J. Ultrastruct. Res.* 40:433–57
180. Hinssen, H. 1970. *Cytobiologie* 2:326–31
181. Ibid 1972. 5:146–64
182. Hoch, H. C., Mitchell, J. E. 1972. *Protoplasma* 75:113–38
183. Hoffmann-Berling, H. 1964. See Ref. 16, 365–75
184. Holtzer, H., Sanger, J. W. 1972. *Develop. Biol.* 27:443–46
185. Holtzer, H., Sanger, J. W., Ishikawa, H., Strahs, K. 1972. *Cold Spring Harbor Symp. Quant. Biol.* 37:549–66
186. Howard, K. L., Moore, R. T. 1970. *Bot. Gaz.* 131:311–36
187. Huang, B., Pitelka, D. R. 1973. *J. Cell Biol.* 57:704–28
188. Hung, C-Y., Olive, L. S. 1972. *Mycologia* 64:1312–27
189. Hurwitz, L., Fitzpatrick, D. F., Debbas, G., Landon, E. J. 1973. *Science* 179:384–86
190. Huxley, H. E. 1963. *J. Mol. Biol.* 7:281–308
191. Huxley, H. E. 1969. *Science* 164:1356–66
192. Huxley, H. E. 1973. *Nature* 243:445–49
193. Ichida, A. A., Fuller, M. S. 1968. *Mycologia* 60:141–55
194. Ingram, V. M. 1969. *Nature* 222:641–44
195. Inoué, S. 1964. See Ref. 16, 549–98
196. Inoué, S., Bajer, A. 1961. *Chromosoma* 12:48–63
197. Inoué, S., Sato, H. 1967. *J. Gen. Physiol.* 50 (suppl.):259–92
198. Ishikawa, H., Bishoff, R., Holtzer, H. 1969. *J. Cell Biol.* 43:312–28

199. Jahn, T. L., Bovee, E. C. 1969. *Physiol. Rev.* 49:793–862
200. Jarosch, R. 1956. *Phyton* 6:87–108
201. Jarosch, R. 1956. *Protoplasma* 47: 478–86
202. Ibid 1958. 50:93–108
203. Jarosch, R. 1964. See Ref. 16, 599–622
204. Jessen, H., Behnke, O., Wingstrand, K. G., Rostgaard, J. 1973. *Exp. Cell. Res.* 80:47–54
205. Johnson, R.P.C. 1968. *Planta* 81: 314–32
206. Johnson, U. G., Porter, K. R. 1968. *J. Cell Biol.* 38:403–25
207. Kamitsubo, E. 1972. *Protoplasma* 74:53–70
208. Kamitsubo, E. 1972. *Exp. Cell Res.* 74:613–16
209. Kamiya, N. 1959. *Protoplasmatologia* 8(3a)
210. Kamiya, N. 1960. *Ann. Rev. Plant Physiol.* 11:323–40
211. Kamiya, N. 1968. *Symp. Soc. Exp. Biol.* 22:199–214
212. Kamiya, N., Kuroda, K. 1956. *Bot. Mag.* 69:544
213. Kaufman, P. B., Petering, L. B., Yocum, C. S., Baic, D. 1970. *Am. J. Bot.* 57:33–49
214. Kavanau, J. L. 1965. *Structure and Function of Biological Membranes*, 2:323–760. San Francisco: Holden-Day
215. Kessler, D., Nachmias, V. T. 1970. *J. Cell Biol.* 47:105a
216. Kiermayer, O. 1968. *Planta* 83:223–36
217. Kiermayer, O. 1968. *Naturwissenschaften* 55:299–300
218. Kiermayer, O. 1970. *Protoplasma* 69: 97–132
219. Kiermayer, O. 1970. *Ann. N. Y. Acad. Sci.* 175:686–701
220. Kiermayer, O. 1972. *Protoplasma* 75: 421–26
221. Kiermayer, O., Hepler, P. K. 1970. *Naturwissenschaften* 57:252
222. Kihlman, B. A. 1966. *Actions of Chemicals on Dividing Cells.* Englewood Cliffs: Prentice-Hall. 260 pp.
223. Klaus, G. G. 1973. *Exp. Cell Res.* 79:73–78
224. Kleinig, H., Dörr, I., Kollmann, R. 1971. *Protoplasma* 73:293–302
225. Kleinig, H., Dörr, I., Weber, C., Kollmann, R. 1971. *Nature New Biol.* 229:152–53
226. Kletzien, R. F., Perdue, J. F., Springer, A. 1972. *J. Biol. Chem.* 247:2964–66
227. Kollmann, R., Dörr, I., Kleinig, H. 1970. *Planta* 95:86–94
228. Komnick, H., Stockem, W., Wohlfarth-Botterman, K-E. 1973. *Int. Rev. Cytol.* 34:169–249
229. Krishan, A. 1972. *J. Cell Biol.* 54:657–64
230. Kubai, D. F., Ris, H. 1969. *J. Cell Biol.* 40:508–28
231. Kuroda, K. 1964. See Ref. 16, 31–41
232. Langford, G. A., Heller, C. G. 1973. *Science* 179:573–75
233. Leadbeater, B., Dodge, J. D. 1967. *Arch. Mikrobiol.* 57:239–54
234. Ledbetter, M. C., Porter, K. R. 1963. *J. Cell Biol.* 19:239–50
235. Ledbetter, M. C., Porter, K. R. 1964. *Science* 144:872–74
236. Lederberg, S., Stetten, G. 1970. *Science* 168:485–87
237. Leedale, G. F. 1970. *Ann. N. Y. Acad. Sci.* 175:429–53
238. Lepper, R. J. 1956. *Bot. Rev.* 22:375–417
239. Lerbs, V., Thielke, Ch. 1969. *Arch. Mikrobiol.* 68:95–98
240. Lessie, P. E., Lovett, J. S. 1968. *Am. J. Bot.* 55:220–36
241. Lieberman, M., Manasek, F. J., Sawanobori, T., Johnson, E. A. 1973. *Develop. Biol.* 31:380–403
242. Linck, R. W. 1973. *J. Cell Sci.* 12: 951–81
243. Loewy, A. G. 1952. *J. Cell. Physiol.* 40:127–56
244. Lovlie, A., Braten, T. 1970. *J. Cell Sci.* 6:109–29
245. Lu, B. C. 1967. *Chromosoma* 22: 210–26
246. Lu, B. C. 1967. *J. Cell Sci.* 2:529–36
247. Ludueña, M. A., Wessells, N. K. 1973. *Develop. Biol.* 30:427–40
248. Ludueña, R. F. 1973. *Partial Characterization of Microtubular Protein.* PhD thesis. Stanford Univ., Stanford, Calif.
249. Luykx, P. 1970. *Int. Rev. Cytol. Suppl.* 2.
250. MacRobbie, E. A. C. 1971. *Biol. Rev.* 46:429–81
251. Maitra, S. C., De, D. N. 1971. *J. Ultrastruct. Res.* 34:15–22
252. Manasek, F. J., Burnside, B., Stroman, J. 1972. *Proc. Nat. Acad. Sci. USA* 69:308–12
253. Manton, I. 1964. *J. Roy. Microsc. Soc.* 83:317–25
254. Manton, I., Kowallik, K., von Stosch, H. A. 1969. *J. Microsc.* 89:295–320
255. Manton, I., Kowallik, K., von Stosch, H. A. 1969. *J. Cell Sci.* 5:271–98
256. Ibid 1970. 6:131–57
257. Ibid. 7:407–43
258. Marchant, H. J., Pickett-Heaps, J. D. 1970. *Aust. J. Biol. Sci.* 23:1173–86

259. Ibid 1972. 25:265–78
260. Ibid, 1199–1213
261. Marx-Figini, M. 1971. *Biochim. Biophys. Acta* 237:75–77
262. Marx-Figini, M., Schulz, G. V. 1966. *Biochim. Biophys. Acta* 112:81–101
263. Mascarenhas, J. P., LaFountain, J. 1972. *Tissue Cell* 4:11–14
264. Mazia, D., Petzelt, C., Williams, R. O., Meza, I. 1972. *Exp. Cell Res.* 70:325–32
265. McCully, E. K., Robinow, C. F. 1971. *J. Cell Sci.* 9:475–507
266. Ibid 1972. 10:857–81
267. Ibid. 11:1–31
268. McDonald, K. 1972. *J. Phycol.* 8:156–66
269. McIntosh, J. R. 1973 *J. Cell Biol.* 56:324–39
270. McIntosh, J. R., Hepler, P. K., Van Wie, D. G. 1969. *Nature* 224:659–63
271. McIntosh, J. R., Ogata, E. S., Landis, S. C. 1973. *J. Cell Biol.* 56:304–23
272. McIntosh, J. R., Porter, K. R. 1967. *J. Cell Biol.* 35:153–73
273. McLaughlin, D. J. 1971. *J. Cell Biol.* 50:737–45
274. McLaughlin, D. J. 1973. *Can. J. Bot.* 51:145–50
275. McNutt, N. S., Culp, L. A., Black, P. H. 1973. *J. Cell Biol.* 56:412–28
276. Meza, I., Huang, B., Bryan, J. 1972. *Exp. Cell Res.* 74:535–40
277. Mims, C. W. 1972. *J. Gen. Microbiol.* 71:53–62
278. Millington, W. F., Gawlik, S. R. 1970. *Am. J. Bot.* 57:552–61
279. Mizel, S. B., Wilson, L. 1972. *J. Biol. Chem.* 247:4102–5
280. Mizukami, I., Gall, J. 1966. *J. Cell Biol.* 29:97–111
281. Moens, P. B. 1971. *Can. J. Microbiol.* 17:507–10
282. Moens, P. B., Rapport, E. 1971. *J. Cell Biol.* 50:344–61
283. Moestrup, O. 1970. *J. Mar. Biol. Assoc. U. K.* 50:513–23
284. Molè-Bajer, J. 1969. *Chromosoma* 26:427–48
285. Moore, P. B., Huxley, H. E., DeRosier, D. J. 1970. *J. Mol. Biol.* 50:279–95
286. Mooseker, M. S., Tilney, L. G. 1973. *J. Cell Biol.* 56:13–26
287. Morgan, J. M. 1971. *Exp. Cell Res.* 65:7–16
288. Moser, J. W., Kreitner, G. L. 1970. *J. Cell Biol.* 44:454–58
289. Motta, J. J. 1969. *Mycologia* 61:873–86
290. Murray, A. W., Froscio, M. 1971. *Biochem. Biophys. Res. Commun.* 44:1089–95

291. Nachmias, V. T. 1968. *J. Cell Biol.* 38:40–50
292. Ibid 1972. 52:648–63
293. Nachmias, V. T. 1972. *Proc. Nat. Acad. Sci. USA* 69:2011–14
294. Nachmias, V. T. 1972. *Cold Spring Harbor Symp. Quant. Biol.* 37:607–12
295. Nachmias, V. T., Huxley, H. E., Kessler, D. 1970. *J. Mol. Biol.* 50:83–90
296. Nagai, R., Rebhun, L. I. 1966. *J. Ultrastruct. Res.* 14:571–89
297. Nakajima, H. 1964. See Ref. 16, 111–23
298. Nelson, D. R., Jaffe, L. F. 1973. *Develop. Biol.* 30:206–8
299. Newcomb, E. H. 1969. *Ann. Rev. Plant Physiol.* 20:253–88
300. Newcomb, E. H., Bonnett, H. T. 1965. *J. Cell Biol.* 27:575–89
301. Nicklas, R. B. 1971. *Advan. Cell Biol.* 2:225–97
302. Northcote, D. H. 1969. *Proc. Roy. Soc. B* 173:21–30
303. Northcote, D. H., Lewis, D. R. 1968. *J. Cell Sci.* 3:199–206
304. O'Brien, T. P. 1972. *Bot. Rev.* 38:87–118
305. O'Brien, T. P., McCully, M. E. 1970. *Planta* 94:91–94
306. O'Brien, T. P., Thimann, K. V. 1966. *Proc. Nat. Acad. Sci. USA* 56:888–94
307. Olah, L. V., Hanzely, L. 1973. *Cytologia* 38:55–72
308. Oliver, P. T. P. 1973. *Protoplasma* 76:279–81
309. Olmsted, J. B., Borisy, G. G. 1973. *Ann. Rev. Biochem.* 42:507–40
310. Olmsted, J. B., Witman, G. B., Carlson, K., Rosenbaum, J. L. 1971. *Proc. Nat. Acad. Sci. USA* 68:2273–77
311. Olson, L. W. 1972. *Arch. Mikrobiol.* 84:327–38
312. Palevitz, B. A. 1971. *Ultrastructural Studies on Sieve Element Plastids and P-Proteins in the Primary Phloem of Legumes.* PhD Thesis. Univ. Wisconsin, Madison. 244 pp.
313. Palevitz, B. A. 1972. *J. Cell Biol.* 55:198a
314. Palevitz, B. A., Ash, J. F., Hepler, P. K. *Proc. Nat. Acad. Sci. USA.* In press
315. Palevitz, B. A., Hepler, P. K. 1974. *Chromosoma.* In press
316. Palevitz, B. A., Newcomb, E. H. 1971. *Protoplasma* 72:399–426
317. Paolillo, D. J., Kreitner, G. L., Reighard, J. A. 1968. *Planta* 78:226–47
318. Ibid, 248–61
319. Parkhouse, R. M. E., Allison, A. C. 1972. *Nature New Biol.* 235:220–22
320. Parthasarathy, M. V., Muhlethaler, K. 1969. *Cytobiologie* 1:17–36

321. Parthasarathy, M. V., Muhlethaler, K. 1972. *J. Ultrastruct. Res.* 38:46–62
322. Paul, D. C., Goff, C. W. 1973. *Exp. Cell Res.* 78:399–413
323. Pease, D. C. 1963. *J. Cell Biol.* 18:313–26
324. Perkins, F. O. 1970. *J. Cell Sci.* 6:629–54
325. Perry, M. M., John, H. A., Thomas, N. S. T. 1971. *Exp. Cell Res.* 65:249–53
326. Peterson, J. B., Gray, R. H., Ris, H. 1972. *J. Cell Biol.* 53:837–41
327. Petzelt, C. 1972. *Exp. Cell Res.* 70:333–39
328. Pichichero, M. E., Avers, C. J. 1973. *Subcell. Biochem.* 2:97–105
329. Pickett-Heaps, J. D. 1966. *Planta* 71:1–14
330. Pickett-Heaps, J. D. 1967. *Develop. Biol.* 15:206–36
331. Pickett-Heaps, J. D. 1967. *Aust. J. Biol. Sci.* 20:539–51
332. Ibid 1968. 21:255–74
333. Ibid, 665–90
334. Pickett-Heaps, J. D. 1968. *Protoplasma* 65:181–205
335. Pickett-Heaps, J. D. 1969. *Aust. J. Biol. Sci.* 22:375–91
336. Pickett-Heaps, J. D. 1969. *J. Ultrastruct. Res.* 27:24–44
337. Pickett-Heaps, J. D. 1969. *J. Cell Sci.* 4:397–420
338. Pickett-Heaps, J. D. 1969. *Cytobios* 3:257–80
339. Pickett-Heaps, J. D. 1970. *Protoplasma* 70:325–47
340. Pickett-Heaps, J. D. 1971. *Cytobios* 3:205–14
341. Pickett-Heaps, J. D. 1971. *Protoplasma* 72:275–314
342. Ibid 1972. 74:169–93
343. Pickett-Heaps, J. D. 1974. *Plant Microtubules.* In press
344. Pickett-Heaps, J. D. 1972. *Cytobios* 5:59–77
345. Pickett-Heaps, J. D. 1972. *Ann. Bot.* 36:693–701
346. Pickett-Heaps, J. D. 1972. *New Phytol.* 71:561–67
347. Pickett-Heaps, J. D. 1972. *J. Phycol.* 8:343–60
348. Pickett-Heaps, J. D. 1972. *Cytobios* 6:167–83
349. Pickett-Heaps, J. D., Fowke, L. C. 1970. *Aust. J. Biol. Sci.* 23:71–92
350. Pickett-Heaps, J. D., Fowke, L. C. 1970. *J. Phycol.* 6:189–215
351. Pickett-Heaps, J. D., Northcote, D. H. 1966. *J. Cell Sci.* 1:109–20
352. Ibid, 121–28

353. Plagemann, P. G., Estensen, R. D. 1972. *J. Cell Biol.* 55:179–85
354. Pollard, T. D. 1973. See Ref. 15, 291–317
355. Pollard, T. D., Eisenberg, E., Korn, E. D., Kielley, W. W. 1973. *Biochem. Biophys. Res. Commun.* 51:693–98
356. Pollard, T. D., Ito, S. 1970. *J. Cell Biol.* 46:267–89
357. Pollard, T. D., Korn, E. D. 1971. *J. Cell Biol.* 48:216–19
358. Pollard, T. D., Korn, E. D. 1972. *Cold Spring Harbor Symp. Quant. Biol.* 37:573–84
359. Pollard, T. D., Korn, E. D. 1973. *J. Biol. Chem.* 248:448–50
360. Ibid, 4682–90
361. Ibid, 4691–97
362. Pollard, T. D., Shelton, E., Weihing, R. R., Korn, E. D. 1970. *J. Mol. Biol.* 50:91–97
363. Porter, D. 1972. *Protoplasma* 74:427–48
364. Porter, K. R. 1966. *Principles of Biomolecular Organization. CIBA Foundation Symposium,* ed. G. E. W. Wolstenholme, M. O'Connor, 308–34. London:Churchill. 491 pp.
365. Pratje, E., Heilmeyer, L. M. G. 1972. *FEBS Lett.* 27:89–93
366. Preston, R. D., Goodman, R. N. 1968. *J. Roy. Microsc. Soc.* 88:513–27
367. Pringle, J. W. S. 1968. *Symp. Soc. Exp. Biol.* 22:67–86
368. Probst, E., Lüscher, F. 1972. *Biochim. Biophys. Acta* 278:577–84
369. Quatrano, R. S. 1973. *Develop. Biol.* 30:209–13
370. Raff, R. A., Colot, H. V., Selvig, S. E., Gross, P. R. 1972. *Nature* 235:211–14
371. Raff, R. A., Greenhouse, G., Gross, K. W., Gross, P. R. 1971. *J. Cell Biol.* 50:516–27
372. Raff, R. A., Kaumeyer, J. F. 1973. *Develop. Biol.* 32:309–20
373. Raju, N. B., Lu, B. C. 1973. *J. Cell Sci.* 12:131–41
374. Rasmussen, H. 1970. *Science* 170:404–12
375. Raudaskoski, M. 1970. *Protoplasma* 70:415–22
376. Raudaskoski, M. 1972. *Arch. Mikrobiol.* 86:91–100
377. Rebhun, L. I. 1972. *Int. Rev. Cytol.* 32:93–137
378. Renaud, F. L., Rowe, A. J., Gibbons, I. R. 1968. *J. Cell Biol.* 36:79–90
379. Rhea, R. P. 1966. *J. Ultrastruct. Res.* 15:349–79
380. Rice, R. V., Brady, A. C. 1972. *Cold*

Spring Harbor Symp. Quant. Biol. 37:429–36

381. Rice, R. V., Moses, J. A., McManus, G. M., Brady, A. C., Blasik, L. M. 1970. *J. Cell Biol.* 47:183–96

382. Robards, A. W. 1968. *Protoplasma* 65:449–64

383. Robards, A. W. 1969. *Planta* 88:376–79

384. Robards, A. W., Humpherson, P. G. 1967. *Planta* 77:233–38

385. Robbins, E., Shelanski, M. 1969. *J. Cell Biol.* 43:371–73

386. Roberts, L. W. 1969. *Bot. Rev.* 35:201–50

387. Roberts, L. W., Baba, S. 1968. *Plant Cell Physiol.* 9:315–21

388. Robinow, C. F., Marak, J. 1966. *J. Cell Biol.* 29:129–51

389. Robinson, D. G., White, R. K., Preston, R. D. 1972. *Planta* 107:131–44

390. Robison, W. G. 1966. *J. Cell Biol.* 29:251–65

391. Roisen, F. J., Murphy, R. A., Braden, W. G. 1972. *Science* 177:809–11

392. Rosen, W. G. 1968. *Ann. Rev. Plant Physiol.* 19:435–62

393. Rosenbaum, J. L., Carlson, K. 1969. *J. Cell Biol.* 40:415–25

394. Rosenbaum, J. L., Moulder, J. E., Ringo, D. L. 1969. *J. Cell Biol.* 41:600–19

395. Ross, J. 1971. *Tissue and Cell* 3:35–56

396. Roth, L. E., Pihlaja, D. J., Shigenaka, Y. 1970. *J. Ultrastruct. Res.* 30:7–37

397. Rubin, R. W., Filner, P. 1973. *J. Cell Biol.* 56:628–35

398. Rüegg, J. C. 1968. *Symp. Soc. Exp. Biol.* 22:45–66

399. Sabnis, D. D., Hart, J. W. 1973. *Planta* 109:123–33

400. Sabnis, D. D., Jacobs, W. P. 1967. *J. Cell Sci.* 2:465–72

401. Sakai, A. 1969. *Cytologia* 34:57–70

402. Ibid, 593–604

403. Sakai, A., Shigenaga, M. 1972. *Chromosoma* 37:101–16

404. Sanger, J. W., Jackson, W. T. 1971. *J. Cell Sci.* 8:303–15

405. Sanger, J. W., Holtzer, H. 1972. *Proc. Nat. Acad. Sci. USA* 69:253–57

406. Sanger, J. W., Holtzer, S., Holtzer, H. 1971. *Nature New Biol.* 229:121–23

407. Satir, P. 1967. *J. Gen. Physiol.* 50(Suppl.): 241–58

408. Schnepf, E. 1972. *Naturwissenschaften* 59:471

409. Schnepf, E., Von Traitteur, R. 1973. *Z. Pflanzenphysiol.* 69:181–84

410. Schofield, J. G. 1971. *Nature New Biol.* 234:215–16

411. Schroeder, T. E. 1969. *Biol. Bull.* 137:413–14

412. Schroeder, T. E. 1970. *Z. Zellforsch. Mikrosk. Anat.* 109:431–49

413. Schroeder, T. E. 1973. *Proc. Nat. Acad. Sci. USA* 70:1688–92

414. Selman, G. G., Perry M. M. 1970. *J. Cell Sci.* 6:207–27

415. Seravin, L. N. 1971. *Advan. Comp. Physiol. Biochem.* 4:37–111

416. Sharp, L. W. 1912. *Bot. Gaz.* 54:89–119

417. Ibid 1914. 58:419–31

418. Shelanski, M. L. 1973. *J. Histochem. Cytochem.* 21:529–39

419. Shelanski, M. L., Albert, S., DeVries, G. H., Norton, W. T. 1971. *Science* 174:1242–45

420. Shelanski, M. L., Gaskin, F., Cantor, C. R. 1973. *Proc. Nat. Acad. Sci. USA* 70:765–68

421. Shelanski, M. L., Taylor, E. W. 1967. *J. Cell Biol.* 34:549–54

422. Ibid 1968. 38:304–15

423. Simard-Duquesne, N., Couillard, P. 1962. *Exp. Cell Res.* 28:85–91

424. Simonet, J. M., Zickler, D. 1972. *Chromosoma* 37:327–51

425. Singh, A. P., Srivastava, L. M. 1973. *Protoplasma* 76:61–82

426. Singleton, J. R. 1953. *Am. J. Bot.* 40:124–44

427. Sinnott, E. W. 1944. *Am. J. Bot.* 31:388–91

428. Sinnott, E. W. 1960. *Plant Morphogenesis.* New York: McGraw Hill. 550 pp.

429. Sisken, J. E., Wilkes, E. 1967. *J. Cell Biol.* 34:97–110

430. Spooner, B. S., Ash, J. F., Wrenn, J. T., Frater, R. B., Wessells, N. K. 1973. *Tissue and Cell* 5:37–46

431. Spooner, B. S., Wessells, N. K. 1972. *Develop. Biol.* 27:38–54

432. Spooner, B. S., Yamada, K. M., Wessells, N. K. 1971. *J. Cell Biol.* 49:595–613

433. Spudich, J. A. 1972. *Cold Spring Harbor Symp. Quant. Biol.* 37:585–93

434. Spudich, J. A., Huxley, H. E., Finch, J. T. 1972. *J. Mol. Biol.* 72:619–32

435. Spudich, J. A., Lin, S. 1972. *Proc. Nat. Acad. Sci. USA* 69:442–46

436. Srivastava, L. M. 1966. *J. Cell Biol.* 31:79–93

437. Srivastava, L. M., O'Brien, T. P. 1966. *Protoplasma* 61:257–76

438. Ibid, 277–93

439. Srivastava, L. M., Singh, A. P. 1972. *Can. J. Bot.* 50:1795–1804

440. Staehelin, L. A., Chlapowski, F. J.,

Bonneville, M. A. 1972. *J. Cell Biol.* 53:73–91

441. Stebbins, G. L., Jain, S. K. 1960. *Develop. Biol.* 2:409–26
442. Stebbins, G. L., Shah, S. S. 1960. *Develop. Biol.* 2:477–500
443. Stephens, R. E. 1968. *J. Mol. Biol.* 32:277–83
444. Stephens, R. E. 1970. *Science* 168:845–47
445. Stephens, R. E. 1970. *J. Mol. Biol.* 47:353–63
446. Stephens, R. E. 1971. *Biological Macromolecules*, ed. S. N. Timasheff, G. D. Fasman, 4:355–91. New York: Dekker
447. Stephens, R. E. 1972. *Biol. Bull.* 142:145–59
448. Ibid, 489–504
449. Stephens, R. E. 1973. *J. Cell Biol.* 57:133–47
450. Stephens, R. E., Renaud, F. L., Gibbons, I. R. 1967. *Science* 156:1606–8
451. Stetler, D. A., DeMaggio, A. E. 1972. *Am. J. Bot.* 59:1011–17
452. Stetten, G., Lederberg, S. 1973. *J. Cell Biol.* 56:259–62
453. Summers, K. E., Gibbons, I. R. 1971. *Proc. Nat. Acad. Sci. USA* 68:3092–96
454. Sun, N. C., Bowen, C. C. 1972. *Caryologia* 25:471–94
455. Takata, M. 1958. *Kagaku* 28:142
456. Tamura, S. 1971. *Exp. Cell Res.* 68:169–79
457. Ibid, 180–85
458. Tanaka, H., Hatano, S. 1972. *Biochim. Biophys. Acta* 257:445–51
459. Tanaka, K. 1973. *J. Cell Biol.* 57:220–24
460. Taylor, E. L., Wessells, N. K. 1973. *Develop. Biol.* 31:421–25
461. Taylor, E. W. 1965. *J. Cell Biol.* 25:145–60
462. Taylor, E. W. 1972. *Ann. Rev. Biochem.* 41:577–611
463. Thoa, N. B., Wooten, G. F., Axelrod, J., Kopin, I. J. 1972. *Proc. Nat. Acad. Sci. USA* 69:520–22
464. Thompson, R. G., Thompson, A. D. 1973. *Can. J. Bot.* 51:933–36
465. Tilney, L. G. 1971. *J. Cell Biol.* 51:837–54
466. Tilney, L. G. 1971. See Ref. 133, 222–60
467. Tilney, L. G., Byers, B. 1969. *J. Cell Biol.* 43:148–65
468. Tilney, L. G., Cardell, R. R. 1970. *J. Cell Biol.* 47:408–22
469. Tilney, L. G., Gibbins, J. R. 1968. *Protoplasma* 65:167–79
470. Tilney, L. G., Goddard, J. 1970. *J. Cell Biol.* 46:564–75

471. Tilney, L. G., Hatano, S., Mooseker, M. S. 1972. *J. Cell Biol.* 55:261a
472. Tilney, L. G., Mooseker, M. 1971. *Proc. Nat. Acad. Sci. USA* 68:2611–15
473. T'so, P. O., Bonner, R. J., Eggman, L., Vinograd, J. 1956. *J. Gen. Physiol.* 39:325–47
474. Tucker, J. B. 1968. *J. Cell Sci.* 3:493–514
475. Ibid 1970. 7:793–821
476. Ibid 1972. 10:883–903
477. Turner, F. R. 1970. *J. Cell Biol.* 46:220–34
478. Usui, N. 1971. *Develop. Growth & Differentiation* 13:241–55
479. Vannereau, A., Deysson, G., Benbadis, M-C, Brulfert, A., Pareyri, C. 1972. *C. R. Acad. Sci. Paris* 275:2477–79
480. Vorob'eva, I. A., Poglazov, B. F. 1963. *Biofizika* 8:427–29
481. Wagner, G., Haupt, W., Laux, A. 1972. *Science* 176:808–9
482. Walker, T. S. 1972. *Biochim. Biophys. Acta* 257:433–34
483. Walker, T. S., Thaine, R. 1971. *Ann. Bot.* 35:773–90
484. Warner, F. D., Satir, P. 1973. *J. Cell Sci.* 12:313–26
485. Watson, M. W., Arnott, H. J. 1973. *J. Phycol.* 9:15–29
486. Weatherley, P. E., Johnson, R. P. C. 1968. *Int. Rev. Cytol.* 24:149–92
487. Weber, C., Kleinig, H. 1971. *Planta* 99:179–82
488. Weihing, R. R., Korn, E. D. 1969. *Biochem. Biophys. Res. Commun.* 35:906–12
489. Weihing, R. R., Korn, E. D. 1971. *Biochemistry* 10:590–600
490. Ibid 1972. 11:1538–43
491. Weisenberg, R. C. 1972. *Science* 177:1104–5
492. Weisenberg, R. C. 1972. *J. Cell Biol.* 54:266–78
493. Weisenberg, R. C., Borisy, G. G., Taylor, E. W. 1968. *Biochemistry* 7:4466–79
494. Wells, K. 1970. *Mycologia* 62:761–90
495. Wessells, N. K. et al 1971. *Science* 171:135–43
496. Wessells, N. K., Spooner, B. S., Ludueña, M. A. 1973. *Locomotion of Tissue Cells. CIBA Foundation Symposium* 14: 53–82. New York: Elsevier. 381 pp.
497. Westergaard, M., Von Wettstein, D. 1970. *C. R. Trav. Lab. Carlsberg* 37:195–237
498. Williams, J. A., Wolf, J. 1972. *J. Cell Biol.* 54:157–65

499. Williamson, R. E. 1972. *J. Cell Sci.* 10:811–19
500. Williamson, R. E. 1972. *Planta* 106:149–57
501. Wills, E. J., Davies, P., Allison, A. C., Haswell, A. D. 1972. *Nature New Biol.* 240:58–60
502. Wilson, C. L., Aist, J. R. 1967. *Phytopathology* 57:769–71
503. Wilson, E. B. 1928. *The Cell in Development and Heredity.* New York: Macmillan. 1232 pp. 3rd ed.
504. Wilson, H. J. 1969. *J. Cell Biol.* 40:854–59
505. Wilson, H. J. 1970. *Planta* 94:184–90
506. Wilson, H. J., Wanka, F., Linskens, H. F. 1973. *Planta* 109:259–67
507. Wilson, L. 1970. *Biochemistry* 9:4999–5007
508. Wilson, L., Bryan, J. 1973. *Advan. Cell Mol. Biol.* In press
509. Witman, G. B., Carlson, K., Berliner, J., Rosenbaum, J. L. 1972. *J. Cell Biol.* 54:507–39
510. Witman, G. B., Carlson, K., Rosenbaum, J. L. 1972. *J. Cell Biol.* 54:540–55
511. Wochok, Z. S. 1973. *Cytobios* 7:87–95
512. Wohlfarth-Botterman, K.-E. 1964. See Ref 16, 79–109
513. Wohlman, A., Allen, R. D. 1968. *J. Cell Sci.* 3:105–14
514. Wolpert, L. 1965. *Symp. Soc. Gen. Microbiol.* 15:270–93
515. Wolpert, L., Gingell, D. 1968. *Symp. Soc. Exp. Biol.* 22:169–98
516. Wolpert, L., Thomson, C. M., O'Neil, C. H. 1964. See Ref. 16, 143–71
517. Woodcock, C. L. F. 1971. *J. Cell Sci.* 8:611–21
518. Wooding, F. B. P. 1967. *Protoplasma* 64:315–24
519. Wooding, F. B. P. 1969. *Planta* 85:284–98
520. Wooding, F. B. P., Northcote, D. H. 1964. *J. Cell Biol.* 23:327–37
521. Woolley, D. E. 1970. *J. Cell. Physiol.* 76:185–90
522. Woolley, D. E. 1972. *Arch. Biochem. Biophys.* 150:519–30
523. Wrenn, J. T. 1971. *Develop. Biol.* 26:400–15
524. Yamada, K. M., Spooner, B. S., Wessells, N. K. 1971. *J. Cell Biol.* 49:614–35
525. Yamada, K. M., Wessells, N. K. 1973. *Develop. Biol.* 31:413–20
526. Yang, Y.-Z., Perdue, J. F. 1972. *J. Biol. Chem.* 247:4503–9
527. Yapa, P. A. J., Spanner, D. C. 1972. *Planta* 106:369–73
528. Yen, L.-F., Shih, T.-C. 1965. *Sci. Sinica* 14:601–8
529. Yoshinaga, M., Waksman, B. H., Malawista, S. E. 1972. *Science* 176:1147–49
530. Zeiger, E. 1971. *Planta* 99:89–111
531. Zickler, D. 1970. *Chromosoma* 30:287–304
532. Ziegenspeck, H. 1944. *Protoplasma* 38:197–224

Ann. Rev. Plant Physiol. 1974. 25:363–92

PROTEIN TURNOVER IN PLANTS AND POSSIBLE MEANS OF ITS REGULATION

❖7571

R. C. Huffaker and L. W. Peterson[1]

Department of Agronomy and Range Science, University of California
Davis, California 95616

CONTENTS

INTRODUCTION 364
PROBLEMS OF METHODOLOGY 365
METHODS FOR STUDYING PROTEIN TURNOVER 368
    Single Administration or Pulse 368
    Kinetic Analysis of Uptake 369
    Constant Infusion or Continuous Labeling 369
    Inhibitors of Protein Synthesis 370
    Dual Labeling 370
    Density Labeling 370
    Kinetic Analysis of Changes in Enzyme Activities 371
TURNOVER OF TOTAL PROTEIN 371
TURNOVER OF SPECIFIC ENZYMES AND PROTEINS 374
    Nitrate Reductase 374
    Phenylalanine Ammonia Lyase 375
    Invertase 377
    Ribulose 1,5-Diphosphate Carboxylase 377
    Enzymes for Chlorophyll Synthesis 379
    Sulfate Permease 379
    Other Evidence of Turnover 379
REGULATION OF PROTEIN BREAKDOWN 381
    Proteolytic Enzymes 382
    Structural Considerations of the Protein Molecule as a Substrate 384
    Proteolytic Control Through Zymogen Activation 385
    Lysosomes 385
    Membranes 386
    Proteolytic Control Through Endogenous Inhibitors 386
CONCLUSIONS 387

[1]We express our gratitude to Doctors R. S. Criddle and R. W. Breidenbach, and Mr. B. L. Miller for helpful discussion and for their careful reading of the manuscript.

INTRODUCTION

Protein turnover is now recognized as an important component in the regulation of biological systems. It provides a way of altering the general protein constituents as well as varying the enzymatic complement during differentiation, growth, and response to environmental conditions. The ability to alter protein and enzymatic complement is important to a plant's ability to compete both under optimum and unfavorable environmental conditions. When nutrients are limiting, for example, turnover of existing protein is probably the only mechanism available for providing amino acids to allow changes in the protein complement. The importance of the ability to inactivate induced enzymes has been pointed out by other investigators (52, 62, 132, 198). In bacteria, during exponential growth, the concentrations of particular proteins are altered mainly by changes in synthetic rates. Unlike bacteria, plants do not divide rapidly and outgrow their induced enzyme complements, but must regulate enzymes in other fashions, e.g. degradation, inactivation, or inhibition. In both plants and mammals, protein levels change with changes in the rate of synthesis or degradation of the protein.

Since Vickery et al (242) obtained evidence for turnover of protein in plants, most investigations for many years dealt with the turnover of total protein. Studies of total protein turnover, however, yield very little information on the intricate interaction of synthesis and degradation or activation and inactivation in controlling the specific biochemical sequences which are in turn reflected by physiological response. Analysis of these processes requires information on turnover of specific enzymes and proteins. Studies of the turnover of total protein are valuable, however, as they show that protein turnover is a common phenomenon, and provide information on turnover rates during different developmental stages of various plants. Also, information about cellular protein turnover in the whole organism might be informative in studies involving plant modeling or energy budgets. Because of experimental and conceptual difficulties, however, few of the reported rates of protein turnover have been accurate. Such studies have elucidated many of the problems involved and have shown how these affect the accuracy of determinations of turnover.

Turnover can now be considered on a molecular, organelle, cellular, or whole-organism level if one is conscious of the limitations that exist at each level and adapts the methodology accordingly.

The number of studies of turnover of individual proteins in animals and bacteria has increased greatly during the past ten years. Much circumstantial evidence has begun to appear for the turnover of specific plant proteins, though unequivocal evidence showing turnover or lack of turnover of individual proteins during specific phases of their induction is limited. Such information, although difficult to obtain, is vital to understanding internal regulation of the plant.

Terminology in this field has been somewhat confusing as turnover has been defined in many ways (188, 258). We shall define turnover as the *flux of amino acids through protein.* With this definition, protein will be in turnover even if both synthesis and degradation are occurring simultaneously so that no net change in protein concentration is observed. As discussed below, control in such situations differs from that present when proteins are not simultaneously synthesized and degraded but change concentrations in response to germination, senescence, or environmental changes. In these cases, synthesis and degradation seem to occur independently. Sometimes it may be difficult to prove the occurrence of simultaneous synthesis and degradation if one of the two processes occurs at a much greater rate than the other (119).

Problems in terminology also arise with the level at which turnover is applied. Some studies involve the flux of amino acids through total cellular protein. Others involve the flux of amino acids through an enzyme or particular protein. The former often leads to a loose definition of turnover, e.g. in experiments involving either pulse incorporation of labeled amino acids into protein or loss of radioactivity after a pulse, heterogeneous mixtures of protein cannot be considered as a single protein having a turnover rate equal to the mean of the mixture (59, 119, 131, 226). The proteins turning over more rapidly receive more of the pulse dose, and the slope of the resulting decay curve is too steep. As a result, the apparent rate decreases with time.

Accurate measurements of turnover of protein are difficult when synthesis and degradation are occurring simultaneously. To obtain accurate rates of turnover, both the rate constant for synthesis (k_s) and the rate constant for degradation (k_d) must be determined. Various equations have been developed to describe the relationship between synthesis and degradation of protein (188, 258). A change in concentration per g of tissue can be described by:

$$\frac{dP}{dt} = k_s - k_d P$$

where P is the content of protein [g(g tissue)$^{-1}$]; k_s is the rate constant of synthesis, usually zero-order [g(g tissue)$^{-1}$ time $^{-1}$] (198), but first-order (time^{-1}) in exponentially growing tissue (236); and k_d is the rate constant for degradation, which, with the known exception of hemoglobin of red blood cells, is a first-order process (time^{-1}) (198). At steady state, when $dP/dt = 0$, $k_s = k_d P$, and $P = k_s/k_d$, then the turnover rate can be estimated by determining either k_s or k_d.

PROBLEMS OF METHODOLOGY

Because of the difficulties involved in accurately determining turnover, a description of the problems involved becomes important. Estimates of protein turnover rely strongly on isotopic methods. Determining the rate of turnover requires accurate measurements of the change in radioactivity in the protein and the precursor pool per unit time, as well as the loss of radioactivity from the product. Measurement of the precursor pools of amino acids represents the largest error and the major difficulty involved in studies of protein turnover. A great deal of evidence has accumulated to show a compartmentation of metabolites into active and relatively inactive pools within plant cells. Immediate precursor pools of amino acids may not be in rapid equilibrium with pools of stored amino acids; however, some amino acids —for example, alanine (19) and asparagine (219)—may bridge the separated compartments. Evidence for this concept is well documented in an excellent review by Oaks & Bidwell (163). These authors point out that the linear increase of ^{14}C-amino acid incorporation into protein product often precedes the saturation of the total extractable precursor (162, 220). In addition, the specific activity of the product may be greater than that of the total extractable precursor (23, 86, 130). This suggests the existence of separate pools of precursor (161, 220).

The lag time required before the increase of labeled precursor into protein becomes linear depends on the size of the precursor pool (23, 162). With this approach Oaks identified two leucine pools in maize roots, one metabolically active and the other an apparent storage pool. Holleman & Key (86) found evidence of two pools each for leucine and valine: a precursor pool closely related to protein synthesis; and a storage pool only remotely connected to protein synthesis. They also observed that the immediate leucine precursor pool turned over 20 times as fast as did the valine pool. The immediate precursor pools of valine in soybean hypocotyl (86) and leucine in maize root tips (161) are expandable to a degree, enlarging in response to increasing concentration of either amino acid.

Feeding experiments with labeled acetate or glucose (130) show that large amounts of individual amino acids are physically remote from the respiratory centers of the cell and that the amounts of amino acids and organic acids in turnover pools vary from tissue to tissue. Experiments with *Neurospora crassa* indicate that there are two ornithine pools which do not readily mix. One pool is supplied by exogenous sources, or by the catabolism of arginine, and serves as a protein precursor. The second pool is supplied by an endogenous source, i.e. N-acetylglutamate, and serves as an arginine precursor (163).

Hellebust & Bidwell (82) determined the proportions of carbon coming either from soluble amino acid pools or by direct route from photosynthate in wheat leaves. More than half of the serine and glycine incorporated into protein was derived from newly assimilated CO_2, while glutamic acid, aspartic acid, and alanine incorporated into protein came more from the soluble pools.

Using carrot explants, Bidwell et al (19) and Steward & Bidwell (219) found further evidence of multiple pools. Exogenous sugar and glutamine were more direct sources of amino acids for protein synthesis than other exogenously supplied amino acids or internal pools of stored amino acids. Amino acids preferentially used in protein synthesis were derived from sugar and mixed but little with the stored amino acid pools. Alanine was the only amino acid investigated that was in fairly rapid equilibrium with stored pools. Asparagine accumulated in soluble pools that were metabolically inactive and contributed only slightly to metabolism, respiration, and protein synthesis, whereas exogenous glutamine was freely utilized in those processes. In contrast, Kemp & Sutton (112) reported that the total soluble leucine pool may also be the precursor pool for leucine incorporation into protein in cultured tobacco cells. The specific activity of the soluble leucine pool remained constant during the labeling period, whereas incorporation of labeled leucine was linear.

Since different amino acids apparently can come through different precursor pools with differing turnover rates, the determination made of protein turnover may vary with the labeled amino acid chosen for the study. Poole et al (174) have shown how important those considerations are. They used three different substrates to determine the half-life of rat liver catalase: ^{3}H-leucine, $t_{1/2} = 3.7$ days; guanidino-^{14}C-arginine, $t_{1/2} = 2.5$ days; and ^{14}C-S-amino levulinic acid, $t_{1/2} = 1.8$ days.

Oaks (161) also reported that the uptake of an amino acid precursor can be decreased by other amino acids in the medium. Autoradiographic experiments showed that different plant cells accumulate amino acids at different rates (36, 169). These factors could well influence the specific activity of the precursor pool, especially in short-term experiments. Problems might also arise from any changes in the pool size that feeds protein synthesis during the experiment (193).

Reutilization of amino acids released from protein is another problem to be considered in studies involving protein turnover. This could be as important in plants as in animal systems, where up to 50% of the free amino acids in rat liver may be derived from protein catabolism (56). Reutilization of amino acids released from protein causes estimated rates of degradation to be less than the actual rates, the degree of error being greater with proteins that have high rates of degradation. Zielke & Filner (257) observed this problem in studies with tobacco cells, as did Zucker (260) with *Xanthium* discs. The error resulting from utilization of amino acids released from proteins can be decreased if a portion of the amino acid is removed from the site of protein synthesis. Bidwell et al (19) have shown that such removal may occur to a degree in some plant systems. They have evidence that part of the released amino acids can be removed by respiration in carrot explants, and estimate that amino acids released from protein can account for up to 25% of the total CO_2 released. In wheat leaves, however, they noted that protein accounted for very little of the respired CO_2 during the experiment (81). They also observed that amino acids released in carrot explants enter pools separate from those closely associated with protein synthesis (19, 219). The amount of reutilization apparently depends on the amino acid used as the label.

End-product repression must also be recognized as being partially responsible for competition among exogenously supplied sugars, amino acids, and endogenous amino acids as carbon sources for proteins (103, 163). Oaks (161, 162) presents evidence for both end-product repression and discrete pools of amino acids in maize roots.

When labeled amino acids are used in a turnover study, it is important to consider the various metabolic reactions that might be involved, including interconversions to other amino acids and nonamino-acid metabolites, which could affect the measured turnover rates. It therefore becomes important to consider where the labeled amino acid is located in the metabolic "family" sequence (79). Glutamic acid as the head of a family is readily metabolized (55, 190) and can label protein glutamate, arginine, ornithine, proline, and hydroxyproline. In contrast, proline and arginine, situated at the end of the family sequence, do not contribute carbon to other protein amino acids (1, 2). Bidwell (18), using wheat leaves, found that glutamate-1-^{14}C can also label aspartic acid. Aspartate, in turn, can donate carbon to the members of its family: Threonine, isoleucine, lysine, and methionine (55). To further complicate matters, Nair & Vining (157) observed direct conversion of phenylalanine to tyrosine in spinach leaves. It has also been found that fungi have a phenylalanine ammonia lyase that converts phenylalanine-^{14}C to $^{14}CO_2$, thus resulting in loss of the label if phenylalanine is ring labeled. Catalysis of this reaction has been suggested as another possible role of phenylalanine ammonia lyase in plants (42, 152, 153). Joy & Folkes (103) observed that aspartate and glutamine in barley embryos yielded significantly more respiratory CO_2 than did other amino acids. In carrot explants, glutamic acid-1-^{14}C lost more $^{14}CO_2$ to respiration than did glutamic acid-3, 4-^{14}C. The latter labeled compound resulted in greater distribution of label into other amino acids than the former (19). Amino acids closely related to Krebs cycle intermediates are those most likely to be labeled from sucrose or glutamine and to rapidly lose their radioactivity (219). Hence it becomes important to know which carbon is labeled and how much of the radioactive carbon is reworked to other amino acids.

Another important facet to consider is that plants can readily refix some of the CO_2 released through respiration (8, 73, 98). With wheat leaves, $^{14}CO_2$ labeled all the protein amino acids that were studied by Bidwell (18). Since photosynthesis appears to furnish substrates directly for synthesis of amino acids in some plants (19, 219), refixation of labeled CO_2 lost from amino acids could also affect the specific activity of the precursor pool.

In addition to the problems discussed above, other factors must also be considered in a turnover study. An important consideration is the method of getting the label into the plant. If labeled amino acids or sugars are to be used, it may be necessary to utilize detached leaves because application to roots results in dilution, slow uptake, and translocation. Since detaching leaves may alter the turnover rates of proteins, labeling intact plants with $^{14}CO_2$ may be more desirable. However, $^{14}CO_2$ incorporation, as mentioned above, results in wide distribution of labeled products. In some cases, labeled substrate could be injected directly into the stem, allowing for rapid uptake in intact plants (87). Age and growth conditions of the plant and other factors could also affect the turnover rates observed. Even slight environmental changes at the beginning of or during the experiment could affect the turnover enzymes sensitive to such changes.

In summary, amino acid uptake, pool size, pool accessibility to protein synthesis, end-product repression, metabolic interconversions, and reutilization must all be carefully considered in turnover studies.

METHODS FOR STUDYING PROTEIN TURNOVER

Single Administration or Pulse

The method used most commonly in estimating degradation rates has been the single administration of a precursor, i.e. a pulse procedure. Interpretation is based on the loss of the radioactivity from the protein after removal of the exogenous labeled precursor. At a steady-state level of protein, when $k_s = k_dP$, the loss of radioactivity from the protein is an apparent first-order reaction and allows an estimation of the degradation rate. A major limitation of this method is that the released amino acids may be reutilized, resulting in an erroneous estimate of degradation rate (198). This is especially important if the turnover rate of the protein in relation to the turnover rate of the precursor pools is great enough to supply significant amounts of labeled amino acids to the precursor pools.

As mentioned above, another problem with this method is that the half-life obtained can vary with the length of the exposure to labeled amino acid. The proteins of a plant organ are a mixture, having different half-lives. During short exposure to a labeled amino acid, protein having a high turnover rate will be highly labeled. More stable proteins will be less labeled during short exposure, and their turnover rates will not be revealed. A longer exposure allows labeling of the more stable proteins and results in an apparent increase in the half-life (131, 225, 236). Swick (225) found that the half-life of rat liver protein varied from 1.8 to 3.8 days depending on the length of exposure to labeled CO_2.

Kinetic Analysis of Uptake

This approach can and should be incorporated into many of the presently used methods. Oaks (161) has shown that much useful information can be obtained concerning estimation of equilibration times and relative sizes of precursor pools by following a time course for amino-acid incorporation into protein. Her results showed that when incorporation of labeled presursor into protein was linear, the precursor pool was saturated and the newly labeled protein had the same specific activity as that of the precursor pool. In addition, the use of several concentrations of labeled precursor allows determination of the concentration at which swamping of the precursor pool is approached, since in this limit the specific activity of the pool approaches that of the added label. Several investigators have shown that the incorporation of labeled precursor under these conditions is quite constant at several concentrations of the exogenous label (86, 161, 193). Nevertheless, the researcher must beware since, as pointed out (103, 163), there are dangers to swamping. When a tissue is supplied with a large amount of amino acid, inhibition of enzymes, amino acid antagonisms, and disruption of metabolic pathways can occur.

Constant Infusion or Continuous Labeling

This method involves continuous administration of a labeled amino acid (or other precursor) of constant specific activity. The degradative rate constant can be determined from the time course of the approach of the labeled protein's specific activity to that of the specific activity of the administered isotope (198). This eliminates the problem of major changes in the specific activity of the precursor pool early in the experiment; however, problems of reutilization become increasingly important as the specific activity of the protein increases. The difficulty with reutilization has been minimized by the interesting approach of Swick et al (226). By constant administration of ^{14}C-carbonate to rats they achieved uniform labeling of the guanidine carbon of arginine. In rat liver ^{14}C-carbonate went predominantly to the guanidine carbon of arginine, and because of the close relationship of cellular arginine to urea, the prevailing specific activity of the free liver arginine could be measured by determining radioactivity in the excreted urine (225). The turnover rate could then be calculated by measuring the specific activity of the guanidine-^{14}C-arginine from the protein and the average specific activity of the urea during the exposure period (144, 226). The same theoretical approach was utilized in following ^{35}S-cystine labeling of protein while monitoring the appearance of labeled inorganic sulfate in the urine as a measure of the specific activity of the endogenous pool (9).

Hellebust & Bidwell (83) used a method similar to constant infusion by supplying $^{14}CO_2$ in light for 11½ hr each day for 6 days to primary and secondary leaves of wheat while concurrently measuring the specific activities of the precursor amino acids and the protein (described below). Trewavas (236) used a constant-labeling procedure with *Lemna* (described below), in which rate constants for synthesis and degradation were determined at times when the specific activity of methionyl-acyl-tRNA was constant and incorporation of label into protein and protein content were increasing linearly. The method of constant infusion may also suffer from the limitation that rate constants depend on the period of exposure to isotope. The seriousness of this problem can be reduced, however, by determining rate constants at various times during the experiment.

Inhibitors of Protein Synthesis

Theoretically, rate of degradation could be based on the decay of a protein after its synthesis has been halted by an inhibitor. A cautious approach is required, however, since inhibitors of protein synthesis have also been shown to alter the rates of loss of nitrate reductase (233), pheynlalanine ammonia lyase (47), thymidine kinase (89, 90), UDP galactose polysaccharide transferase (223), and fatty acid synthetase enzymes (250). Glasziou et al (63) successfully used protein syntheses inhibitors to determine the turnover rate of invertase in sugar cane (described below). Price et al (183) and Rechcigl (186) went a step further and used allylisopropylacetamide, a compound which specifically blocks the synthesis of catalase without affecting total protein synthesis, to measure the degradation rate of rat liver and kidney catalase.

Dual Labeling

Recently developed dual labeling techniques show great promise both in ease of analysis and reliability. Arias et al (5) used a simple double isotope method for estimating rates of protein degradation in rat liver. The technique involved the incorporation of ^{14}C-amino acid; then, after a given period for decay, a second injection was made of the same amino acid, this time labeled with ^3H. A short time later, the animals were killed, the various protein fractions isolated, and the $^3H:^{14}C$ ratios determined. The proteins with high $^3H:^{14}C$ ratios were degraded faster than the proteins with low $^3H:^{14}C$ ratios. [For a discussion on the assumptions and limitations of the procedure, see Arias et al (5).] Glass & Doyle (61) modified the dual-labeling method to give rate constants of degradation and half-lives of liver proteins comparable to those obtained by constant infusion of guanidino ^{14}C-arginine (197).

Density Labeling

Since its introduction by Hu et al (92) density labeling has been used by many researchers to prove de novo synthesis of various enzymes (52). The organism is allowed to metabolize D_2O, $H_2^{18}O$, or ^{15}N-nitrate under conditions which result in enzyme induction, i.e. germination, hormonal treatments, or substrate changes.

The density of the isolated protein is compared both before and after induction by isopycnic equilibrium centrifugation in CsCl. Even though density labeling has been frequently used in proving de novo synthesis, it has very seldom been applied to protein-turnover studies. Zielke & Filner (257) used ^{15}N-density labeling successfully in conjunction with labeled amino acids to demonstrate both de novo synthesis and turnover of nitrate reductase (discussed further below).

Kinetic Analysis of Changes in Enzyme Activities

This procedure is less rigorous than those which require isolation of specific proteins but can give an indication of the relative rates of turnover. In this procedure, an increase of the enzyme level is induced by changes in diet (226, 228), hormones (200, 205, 228), etc. Measurements of k_s, k_d, and the half-life can then be made by following changes in enzymatic activity as the stimulus is given and later removed. This procedure has been useful in determining the turnover rates of several enzymes in animals (198). Even though significant changes can be induced in a wide variety of plant enzymes by such factors as light, temperature, hormones, and substrates, as well as by changes that occur during germination, aging, and senescence (52, 62, 132, 175, 261), kinetic means have not yet been applied to any of these enzymes to measure rate constants and turnover. One of the major problems involved in such studies is the need to rely solely on enzymatic activity to determine changes in enzymatic protein level.

Studies involving only changes in enzymatic activity are fraught with problems. Thus Joy (102) has shown that what was thought to be induction of glutamate dehydrogenase (101) was merely a change of enzyme from EDTA-sensitive to EDTA-insensitive state. Enzymatic specific activity of ribulose 1,5-di-P carboxylase increases with time as barley plants are left in darkness (171). Turnover estimates based on activity would then be partially masked. Loss of ornithine transcarbamylase activity was the result of the binding of an inhibitor protein and not loss of enzymatic protein (14). Loss of activity of both phenylalanine ammonia lyase in gherkin (261) and invertase in maize (100) may be due to the binding of inhibitor protein rather than degradation.

Because of these problems, it is almost imperative to purify or otherwise isolate the enzyme under investigation rather than relying on enzymatic activities or inhibitor studies to unequivocally prove turnover. In many cases enzyme purification procedures are laborious, time consuming, insufficiently quantitative, and often result in poor yields. To overcome these problems, many researchers have begun to use immunological methods which offer specific advantages: (a) they are highly specific and permit rapid analysis of a constituent in a mixture without chemical fractionation; (b) very small amounts of antigen are required for protein analysis by the Folin-Ciocalteau method; and (c) precipitates of antigen and antibody can be washed, dissolved, and analyzed for radioactive label in the antigen.

TURNOVER OF TOTAL PROTEIN

Most methods used in the past to estimate protein turnover suffered from inaccurate estimates of the precursor amino acid pool. Where the specific activity of the total extractable pool was considered to be the specific activity of the precursor, inaccurate estimates of protein turnover were the likely results. As Oaks & Bidwell (163) pointed out, the general presence of multiple pools of metabolites has led many unwary workers astray. For this reason this presentation covers only studies that recognized the presence of precursor pools and attempted to deal with the problem.

Hellebust & Bidwell (83) used a method similar to constant infusion to help solve the problem of determining the specific activity of the precursor pool. Wheat seedlings were supplied with $^{14}CO_2$ in light for 11½ hr each day for 6 days, during which time the specific activities of various amino acids and protein were determined. The object was to label all the possible precursors of protein carbon to the same extent and measure turnover rates as proteins accumulate radioactivity. The free amino acids and sugars attained about the same specific activity after the first day and the specific activities remained quite constant during the experiment. Incorporation of ^{14}C into protein was approximately linear during the experiment, strongly indicating that the precursor pools had early reached a constant specific activity which remained almost constant throughout the six day experimental period. If the specific activity based on the total content of each amino acid is representative of the specific activities of the precursor pools, the turnover values obtained in this study seem fairly accurate. Turnover rates of about 0.4 to 0.5% per hour were obtained in rapidly growing secondary wheat leaves and 0.2 to 0.3% per hour in nongrowing primary wheat leaves. An important observation was that turnover was greatest during growth and decreased when growth stopped. Hence, turnover appears to be important in changing enzyme levels during biochemical differentiation.

The above authors (83) also applied the pulse-chase method using $^{14}CO_2$ to label tobacco leaf protein. After waiting until the soluble compounds had decreased to a low level of radioactivity, determinations of turnover were begun. The estimates of turnover were made difficult because the loss of label from soluble compounds was slow. The turnover rates calculated were 0.15 to 0.2% per hour for expanding tobacco leaves and little or none for fully expanded leaves.

Holleman & Key (86) used methods similar to those of Oaks (161) to estimate turnover in soybean hypocotyl. By following incorporation of labeled leucine and valine at increasing concentrations, they detected both concentrations and time at which swamping of the precursor pool was assumed to approach that of the exogenous amino acid (86). They calculated turnover rates of 2.5% per hour by determining the rate of incorporation of leucine and valine, their contents in the protein, and the steady-state amount of protein. They estimated the sizes of the precursor pools for leucine and valine by multiplying the output rate (in umoles/min) of the precursor pools by the lag time required before linear incorporation of ^{14}C into protein occurred. This allowed calculation of the relative turnover rates of leucine and valine precursor pools, the former having 20 times the turnover rate of the latter.

Kemp & Sutton (112) used techniques involving constant infusion, a kinetic analysis of absorption of labeled precursor into the precursor pools, and incorporation of precursor into protein in tobacco callus. During the experiment the specific activity of the free amino acid pool remained constant between 0.5 and 7 hr while incorporation into protein was linear during the same time course. The results were interpreted to mean that the soluble leucine pool was the precursor pool. However, leucine in the immediate precursor pool might also have been in rapid isotopic equilibrium with the other amino acid pools present in the tissue.

In contrast to other investigations, they found that the rate of incorporation of precursor into protein was independent of the exogenously supplied precursor. As long as the specific activity of leucine was followed in both the free amino acid pool and in the protein, the rate of incorporation was similar whether the source of label was sucrose or leucine. As mentioned above, other investigators, working with carrot explants, found that sucrose was a much better source of precursor for protein synthesis than were exogenously added amino acids.

Kemp & Sutton (112) estimated the turnover rate by determining the difference between the measured rate of protein synthesis and the measured rate of protein accumulation. A turnover rate of 1.1% per hour for protein was determined.

Trewavas (236), in an excellent study, overcame the problems listed above by using a combination of procedures including constant infusion, pulse labeling, dual-labeling techniques, and kinetic analysis. In both the constant-infusion and pulse-chase method, he used an amino-acyl-tRNA fraction for analysis of the specific activity of the immediate precursor pools. He solved the problems of determining low levels of the amino acid attached to tRNA by growing *Lemna* to isotopic equilibrium on $^{35}SO_4$. The plants were then transferred to ^3H-methylmethionine. Isolation of the protein methionine from the exponentially growing plants and determination of the $^3H:^{35}S$ ratio gave a direct measurement of the specific radioactivity of the proteins. The specific radioactivity of the methionine pool contributing to protein synthesis was determined by isolating methionyl-acyl-tRNA (methionyl-tRNA).

In the constant-labeling experiment, the specific radioactivity of methionyl-tRNA, the specific radioactivity of protein, and the concentration of protein were followed as a function of time. The rates of synthesis and degradation were determined at a time when the specific radioactivity of methionyl-tRNA had reached a constant value, the incorporation of label into protein was exponential, and the protein content was exponentially increasing.

In the second method, the protein was pulse-labeled, then chased with unlabeled precursor until the specific activity of the methionyl-tRNA was effectively zero. Estimates of the rates of synthesis, degradation, and turnover were in very good agreement with those obtained by constant labeling. A problem with both methods is that the methionyl-tRNA complex is relatively unstable (overnight storage at $-15°$ resulted in some loss). Trewavas noted that, since losses may occur during extraction, the results probably do not represent in vivo rates of turnover.

From these methods the rate constants in cultures grown under good nutritional conditions were about 0.02 hr^{-1} for protein synthesis and about 0.087 $days^{-1}$ for degradation. Under limiting nutritional conditions, i.e. H_2O instead of sucrose and salts, the rate of synthesis was decreased while the rate of degradation was increased. This same result occurred when nutritional elements were withheld one at a time (236, 237). Benzyl adenine (BA) increased the rate of sythesis without affecting the rate of degradation under growth conditions of sufficient nutrition (236, 237). Under growth-limiting conditions, BA did not affect the rate of synthesis but decreased the rate of degradation. On the other hand, abscisic acid reduced k_s while increasing k_d.

TURNOVER OF SPECIFIC ENZYMES AND PROTEINS

To our knowledge, nitrate reductase is the only specific plant protein for which incontrovertible evidence of turnover has been obtained. A great deal of circumstantial evidence, however, now indicates that quite a large number of specific enzymes are turned over in plants. As purification procedures are developed for these, the interaction of synthesis and degradation in their regulation will be worked out.

Nitrate Reductase

The synthesis of this enzyme is induced by its substrate nitrate. After induction, it reaches a steady-state level which is modulated by environmental conditions such as nitrate concentration (15, 71), temperature (15), light (33, 71, 233, 234), and moisture (95). When induced plants are placed under adverse or noninducing conditions, the enzyme is rapidly lost (15, 71, 104, 233, 234). The loss can be greatly decreased when induced plants are treated with inhibitors of protein synthesis or maintained at low temperatures (233). Such evidence strongly indicates the presence of a turnover system of nitrate reductase (NR) in several plants.

Zielke & Filner (257) provided unequivocal evidence for the turnover of NR in tobacco cells by using a procedure which involved triple labeling. Preexisting proteins were labeled with ^{14}C-arginine and with ^{15}N to increase the buoyant density. Cells were subsequently transferred to a medium containing ^{14}N and ^{3}H-arginine. The degradation of ^{15}N-labeled proteins was followed after transfer of cells to the new medium. The effect of the preexisting pools of ^{15}N-amino acids on the density of newly synthesized protein was determined by the ^{3}H label. The labels were followed during induction of NR, during steady-state activity, and after a shift to noninducing conditions. During these times protein was extracted and isopycnic equilibrium centrifugation was carried out. The results showed that while the enzyme level remained constant, the buoyant density of NR decreased from that of ^{15}N-NR toward that of ^{14}N-NR, showing that both synthesis and degradation were occurring. Preexisting protein labeled with ^{14}C and newly synthesized protein labeled with ^{3}H both turned over.

These workers (257) showed that the enzyme was under constant turnover, being continuously synthesized and degraded during the induction phase, during the steady-state phase, and during the decay phase of noninducing conditions.

The turnover rate of NR in the tobacco cells was difficult to measure because released ^{15}N-amino acids were apparently reused. The rapid turnover rate of proteins furnished a large amount of ^{15}N-amino acids to the protein precursor pools. Taking into account the problem of reutilization of released amino acids, Zielke & Filner estimated the lower limit of turnover for NR to be 4.3 hr. On the basis of rate of loss of NR activity under noninducing conditions, half-lives have been reported of 4 hr for corn leaves (204), 2 to 3 hr for corn roots (164), and 9 to 12 hr for barley leaves (233).

The mechanism of induction of NR is still unknown; however, it is obvious that both synthesis and degradation are important during induction. Changes in either or both rates could result in net induction or net degradation. Zielke & Filner's (257) data show that the rate of turnover of NR is close enough to the turnover rate of the precursor amino acid pool in tobacco cells to make the estimates of k_s and k_d inaccurate. Hence, both the rate of turnover of the precursor pool and reutilization of released amino acids have been shown experimentally to confound the estimates of synthetic and degradative rates. Therefore, accurate rates of synthesis and degradation for NR are going to be difficult to obtain.

The rate of turnover of NR, as measured by loss of activity during noninducing conditions, can differ according to the treatment of induced plants. When nitrate was removed from the growth medium of tobacco cells, the turnover rate was about 6.5 hr (80). When casein hydrolysate was added to a growth medium containing nitrate, the half-life was 3.7 hr. Glucose in the incubation medium greatly retarded the loss of NR activity in darkness in barley leaves, giving a half-life of 30 hr, compared with 14.5 for the control lacking glucose (8). This study showed that respiration was required for a net induction and maintenance of NR activity. In darkness with glucose, respiration probably maintained the synthetic phase of the turnover system of NR at a higher level than in the control. Turnover during darkness can be greatly slowed by placing induced plants at a low temperature (233). An increase in temperature is accompanied by a more rapid loss of activity. As will be discussed below, the degrading system of NR itself appears to be turning over.

Inhibitors of protein synthesis such as cycloheximide and actinomycin D greatly retard the loss of NR in induced barley plants placed in darkness (233). One explanation for this is that both the synthesis of NR and of its degrading system are stopped. The degrading system itself may then be turned over, accounting for decreased rate of loss of NR. This postulated degrading system in corn appears more stable since cycloheximide has been reported to have no effect on the rate of loss of NR during noninducing conditions (164, 204).

Nitrate reductase activity is rapidly lost during heat stress (142, 166). Treatment with cycloheximide just prior to heat stress halved the rate at which NR activity is lost (166). Both the apparent rate constant for loss and the inhibitory effect of cycloheximide on loss of NR activity indicated that NR was being degraded under the unfavorable conditions of heat stress. Chloramphenicol has no effect on either induction (203) or loss (233) of NR activity. This indicates that both NR and its degrading system are not dependent on chloroplast protein synthesis but probably are synthesized on 80S cytoplasmic ribosomes.

Phenylalanine Ammonia Lyase

Evidence is being accumulated to support the possibility that phenylalanine ammonia lyase (PAL) is also controlled by a turnover system, in some plants at least. In contrast to proteins under constant turnover, the induction of PAL synthesis and the induction of PAL inactivation may be sequential, the induction of the inactivating system occurring after that of the synthesis (260). After induction of the inactivation system, the enzyme is still apparently synthesized during a time when its activity is rapidly disappearing (259). Regulation of the inactivation phase is becoming recognized as an important means of controlling the amount of PAL in the tissue (261). Zucker presented evidence for the turnover of PAL, and his results show the difficult problems which must be surmounted to identify the controls of this enzyme.

Zucker (260) induced PAL in *Xanthium* leaf discs for 48 hr, pulse-labeled with ^{14}C-leucine for 4 hr, then chased with ^{12}C-leucine for 16 hr in both light and dark. The enzyme was then isolated by sucrose density-gradient centrifugation. In light, the specific radioactivity (cpm/milliunit of enzymatic activity) remained quite constant. If turnover were occurring, dilution of the ^{14}C-labeled amino acids with the chase ^{12}C-amino acids would be expected to result in a lower specific activity. In darkness both total radioactivity and enzymatic activity greatly decreased. The apparent lack of turnover in light indicates that the loss in darkness is due to a sequential rapid synthesis of a protein inactivator. Synthesis of the enzyme continued during inactivation as evidenced by the incorporation of ^{14}C-labeled amino acids into PAL in darkness.

The mechanism of inactivation of PAL is not yet known. The kinetics for the disappearance of activity fit either degradation (turnover) (261) or combination with a protein inhibitor (46, 48, 261). Zucker's work (260) showed that although PAL activity and total amount of radioactivity were decreasing in darkness, the specific activity of the enzyme increased twofold. It was suggested that this might be due to extensive reutilization of released amino acids from PAL during turnover, which increased the proportion of radioactive amino acids in the precursor pools. Reutilization of released amino acids from a pool not equilibrated with ^{12}C-amino acids might also have masked turnover of PAL in light under steady-state conditions. Since the specific radioactivity was based on enzymatic activity instead of enzyme protein, a decreased enzymatic activity per unit protein could also result in increased specific radioactivity. Hence, a combination of PAL protein with an inhibitor protein resulting in decreased PAL activity could also explain the twofold increase in specific radioactivity. Engelsma (48) reported results with gherkin seedlings which can be explained by the complexing of a protein inhibitor with PAL which is dependent upon temperature. The complex can be weakened by treatment at low temperature, and the active enzyme can appear again after return to normal temperature.

Similar to nitrate reductase, the inactivation of PAL can be largely prevented by cycloheximide in some plants (46, 261). At least two possible explanations exist: (a) that induction of the inactivating system of PAL is sequential to that of the synthesis of PAL; or (b) that synthesis of the degrading system is stopped and the degrading system itself disappears through turnover. Zucker (261) interpreted the available evidence in favor of the former on the basis that inactivation may be low or absent in light but increases greatly in darkness.

The pattern of PAL development and the inducing agents can vary depending upon the plant and whether excised or intact tissue (245) was used. The increase in PAL activity in excised bean axes (245), coleus and soybean callus (191), and asparagus discs (65) does not require light. Other differences in the manner of inactivation of PAL have also been reported. After induction, cycloheximide did not prevent the loss of PAL activity in asparagus discs (65).

Elucidation of the interaction of synthesis and inactivation in the control of the level of PAL and the type of inactivation await a purification of the enzyme protein. Indications are that if the enzyme is degraded, accurate rates of synthesis and inactivation will be difficult to obtain. The apparent rapid rate of inactivation of PAL in relation to the rate of turnover of the precursor pool and the possible extensive reutilization of released amino acids for the synthesis of PAL are complications difficult to surmount. These are the same problems encountered in studies of nitrate reductase, as mentioned above.

Invertase

Regulation of the enzyme invertase appears to vary in different plants. Available evidence indicates that regulation of its content in sugar cane may be by continuous synthesis and degradation (63). In a number of other plants, including corn (100), beets and sweet potatoes (181), and potato tuber (182), the activity seems, at least partially, controlled by a protein inhibitor.

Glasziou et al (63) used inhibitors of protein synthesis to determine the turnover rate of invertase in sugar cane. The addition of chloramphenicol, puromycin, or actinomycin D markedly decreased the activity of internodal invertase, presumably by inhibition of synthesis of invertase. Exogenous glucose also caused the same rate of loss of invertase activity, presumably by inhibiting the synthesis and allowing degradation of the enzyme. The rapid loss of activity indicated the presence of a degrading system. The like effect of glucose indicated that the presence of the inhibitors of protein synthesis did not alter the rate of degradation of invertase. No evidence was found in that study for the presence of low or high molecular-weight inhibitors of invertase activity. The apparent half-life was about 2 hr.

Seitz & Lang (206) observed a similar loss of invertase activity from lentil epicotyls in the presence of cycloheximide, and concluded that invertase was under continuous turnover. The estimated half-life of invertase in lentil epicotyl was 14 hr.

From Pressey & Shaw's work (182) it appears that both total invertase activity and an invertase inhibitor protein vary in concentrations in potato tubers according to their storage temperature. The changes in each are reversible when tubers are subjected to alternating temperatures. These results indicate that both invertase and the invertase inhibitor protein are turned over. Hence, two protein turnover systems seem involved in controlling invertase, one controlling its content and the other controlling its activity by regulating the content of inhibitor protein.

Future work on the interaction of these possible turnover systems in the control of invertase level and activity should be particularly rewarding. The protein inhibitor has been purified (180) and invertase at least partially purified (63). The time seems ripe for determination of the specific types of turnover and rates of turnover for these two proteins for further elucidation of the interaction of these two controls.

Ribulose 1,5-Diphosphate Carboxylase

The interaction of synthesis and degradation of ribulose 1,5-diphosphate carboxylase (RuDPCase) in the regulation of steady-state levels represents a different type of control. This protein is quite unique in that it comprises a large percentage of the total soluble protein of many plant leaves and therefore is probably a major storage protein (43, 118, 184, 185) as well as a major catalyst for photosynthetic CO_2 fixation (168, 247). Its abundance and great solubility make it a major source of protein for animal life. Life ultimately depends on this protein since it catalyzes the net fixation of CO_2 during photosynthesis. The C4 pathway appears to be an adjunct of the Calvin cycle rather than a separate pathway (43); hence, RuDPCase and the Calvin cycle are required for the net reductive fixation of CO_2. The enzyme is located in chloroplasts, and its appearance is closely correlated with leaf (215) and chloroplast development (93, 94). Light is required for development of both the chloroplast and RuDPCase (94, 133). Several investigators have evidence that induction of RuDPCase may be related to a phytochrome response (51, 67). It has been shown unequivocally that de novo synthesis of the enzyme occurs during greening of barley seedlings (118). The enzyme is also rapidly degraded during aging of tobacco (39, 108, 110) and *Perilla* leaves (253) and in barley during extended periods of darkness (171). During aging of tobacco (111) and *Perilla* (105) leaves and extended dark treatment of barley leaves (171), 90% of the protein decrease is accounted for by RuDPCase. When barley plants were returned to light the synthesis of RuDPCase accounted for about 90% of the increase in soluble protein (171).

To determine whether the enzyme was being turned over in barley leaves while its concentration remained quite constant (in light), RuDPCase was labeled with ^{14}C by introducing $^{14}CO_2$ when the leaves were rapidly synthesizing the enzyme. After removal of $^{14}CO_2$ the plants were put into $^{12}CO_2$, and the ^{14}C content of RuDPCase and other soluble protein was followed with time. Analyses were begun after a steady-state level of RuDPCase had been achieved. The concentration of RuDPCase was determined by precipitation with a RuDPCase-specific rabbit antibody (117).

The specific radioactivity of RuDPCase remained constant during the 120 hr of the experiment, showing no turnover (neither synthesis nor degradation), while there was little change in its concentration. In contrast, dilution of label did occur with other soluble proteins. Their specific activity decreased significantly during the first 50 hr of the experiment, showing the occurrence of turnover of non-RuDPCase protein.

In barley leaves, RuDPCase was remarkably stable after its synthesis. Although it can be both degraded and synthesized, these processes seem not to occur simultaneously, but rather are induced independently by changing environmental conditions. Zucker (260) also observed the stability of RuDPCase in green *Xanthium* leaf discs. While significant amounts of radioactivity were incorporated into phenylalanine ammonia lyase, little was detected in fraction I protein. Abundant evidence shows that fraction I protein is crude RuDPCase (111, 118, 238, 241).

In tobacco leaves the ratio of fraction I protein to total protein reaches a maximum as leaf elongation is completed and then steadily declines (111). It has been proposed that the enzyme in tobacco leaves is under constant turnover and that the changing concentration of fraction I protein is due to changes in either the rates of synthesis or degradation. Since simultaneous synthesis and degradation of this protein have not yet been detected, a slow degradation after the synthetic phase has ceased would also explain the observed results. The appearance and disappearance of fraction I protein in *Perilla* leaves follows a pattern similar to that in tobacco leaves (105, 253). Woolhouse interpreted these results in like manner, i.e. that synthesis is switched off and a slow degradation ensues.

Enzymes for Chlorophyll Synthesis

Chlorophyll synthesis in most plants is under light control. Placing plants in darkness or adding cycloheximide or chloramphenicol (13, 60, 156, 224, 261) will inhibit further accumulation of chlorophyll or protochlorophyllide. The phytochrome-induced response appears to be at the level of δ-aminolevulinic acid (δ-ALA) synthesis, probably δ-ALA synthetase (156, 224), although sites further on in the path of porphyrin biosynthesis have also been suggested (70). These phytochrome-controlled enzymes seem to be turned over very rapidly. In barley, half-life estimates range from 10 min (224) to about 1-½ hr (156). The lifetime of the enzymes in a light-requiring mutant of *Chlorella* is estimated at 30 min (13). Since these estimates are arrived at from kinetic studies (time to stop protochlorophyllide synthesis or loss of enzymatic activities) they are subject to the limitations and considerations already discussed.

Sulfate Permease

Results from investigations of the sulfate permease and reduction system of *Neurospora* are particularly interesting for several reasons. *Neurospora* possesses many of the attributes of higher organisms, including chromosomes and nuclei. Because of ease of manipulation of this organism, types of control can be revealed which emulate the organization of higher systems. The permease in *Neurospora* develops by de novo synthesis (137). The turnover system of the permease is not present in dormant conidia but seems to develop soon after germination begins, the half-life of sulfate permease being about 2 hr. The turnover of sulfate permease is inhibited by cycloheximide, similar to nitrate reductase and phenylalanine ammonia lyase. The manner of the inhibition is not yet known.

The location of the permease in membranes is a strategic point for regulation of entire pathways by modulating the influx of substrates into intracellular pools. Rapid turnover of permeases then represents an effective means of cellular control. Permeases have not yet been proved to be present in roots of higher plants. Jackson et al (97) recently presented evidence for the possible induction of a nitrate permease system in corn seedlings. Such controls may yet be found in uptake of specific ions by higher plants.

Other Evidence of Turnover

Studies involving acrylamide gel electrophoresis of plant proteins from aging or metabolically changing organs indicate that significant reworking of the protein complement does occur during these processes. Major changes in protein banding have been observed during the transition of vegetative apices to floral shoots in *Xanthium* (159), violets (136), and tulips (11). There is a decrease in the number of protein bands with the aging of roots (187, 221), leaves (30, 34, 128), and coleoptiles (187). One exception is cinnamon fern leaves, where there was an increase in the number of bands in the oldest leaves (30). Similar results on aging have been obtained with immunochemical procedures. Kawashima et al (109) have shown that seven antigenic components from tobacco leaves change significantly with age. Both seed germination (12, 129) and fruit ripening (21) result in significant changes in electrophoretic patterns. It has also been observed that the isoenzyme patterns of several enzymes not only vary from tissue to tissue (129) but also vary with changes in development or age (17, 34, 35, 113, 129, 189, 210, 256). Even though these observations are not solid proof of turnover per se, they do show that the plant's protein complement is not static but is in a dynamic state of fluctuation. Changes in age, environment, or development can effectively change not only the quality but the quantity of the plant's protein complement. For such changes to occur, it is necessary that proteins be turned over.

The circumstances surrounding the appearance and disappearance of a number of other enzymes have prompted various groups to suggest that protein turnover might be active in these systems. A common occurrence, already discussed in relation to NR and PAL, is inhibition of the loss of enzymatic activity by inhibitors of protein synthesis. In addition, there are other cases in which an enzyme is induced by environmental changes, its substrate, or as a consequence of the normal developmental cycle of the plant. Both the synthesis and subsequent loss of activity are delayed by inhibitors of protein synthesis. Such results have been documented in the case of the appearance and disappearance of thymidine kinase during DNA synthesis in the microspores of *Lilium* (89, 90) and wheat embryo (91), the accumulation and disappearnce of UDP galactose polysaccharide transferase during cytodifferentiation of *Dictyostelium discoideum* (222, 223), the loss of netural phosphatase in *Euglena* after induction (125), and the developmental time course of fatty acid synthetase enzymes in aging potato tuber slices (250).

Cytokinins are well known for maintaining protein and retarding senescence in many plants (194, 195, 213). Controversy exists as to whether cytokinins increase the rate of protein synthesis (213) or decrease the rate of degradation (121, 148, 229, 239). Trewavas' work with *Lemna* is probably the most rigorous study showing the effect of benzyl adenine (BA) on turnover of protein (237). As mentioned above, the BA effect on turnover of protein can differ with the growth conditions. Under optimum growing conditions BA increased the rate of synthesis without affecting the rate of breakdown, while under growth-limiting conditions, BA did not influence the rate of synthesis but decreased the rate of degradation. Rigorous studies like the above are required to delineate the effects of cytokinins on protein content of the many plants studied. Particular attention should be paid to defining the effect of growth conditions and detachment of plant parts since it now appears that cytokinins can influence the rate of either protein synthesis or degradation.

Protein turnover has also been implicated as explaining various hormonal effects in plants. Hormonal treatments often result in increased protein synthesis, which is believed to mediate the response. Once the hormone is removed, the response generally stops. One explanation is that the enzymes or proteins synthesized in response to the hormonal treatment are rapidly turned over. Once the inducer is removed, synthesis decreases and the induced enzymes rapidly disappear, ending the mediated response. Such mechanisms have been suggested to explain the auxin-induced growth response in Jerusalem artichokes (160, 231), stem elongation and deformability in pea stems (154, 160) and *Avena* coleoptiles (20, 160), and auxin control of cellulase activity in Alaska pea seedlings (49).

Rapidly turned over mRNA (127) also implicates the involvement of protein turnover. In detached soybean hypocotyl the mRNA has a mean life of 2 hr, and continued synthesis is required for growth of the excised tissue (114). The necessity for RNA synthesis in maintenance of growth may not be attributed directly to RNA synthesis, but rather to RNA-directed protein synthesis. If that is true, then the protein fractions limiting cell expansion in soybean hypocotyls may also be characterized by rapid turnover with a half-life of a few hours.

REGULATION OF PROTEIN BREAKDOWN

Although information on protein synthesis has increased greatly, little is known about the regulation of protein degradation systems. Even less is known about how synthesis and degradation are integrated to control turnover rates. The removal of unneeded proteins from the cell may occur on a very specific basis, with single enzymes disappearing independently of all others. In some cases the degradative systems responsible for the hydrolysis of certain enzymes might themselves be rapidly turned over. Coupled with this, the heterogeneity of degradation rate constants and the fact that those rate constants can be changed on an individual basis indicate that the plant's proteolytic system is very complex. Understanding the degradative system undoubtedly will be difficult, and future work probably will show the existence of many types of control.

A major difficulty in studies of this type is the selection of an appropriate substrate. Ideally, the protease's natural protein substrate should be used. In some cases specific proteins may be required to assay certain proteolytic enzymes. Thus assays using casein or hemoglobin as substrates are not expected to represent the in vivo activity, and therefore are not a good measure of the total activity. Some researchers have attempted to minimize this problem by using natural protein substrates (98, 214, 217), generally the seed's storage protein. Even then the results may not be clear. Skupin & Warchalewski (214) characterized a protease from wheat seed that has twice the activity toward casein as toward gluten, a storage protein isolated from the same wheat seeds. There are several possibilities for such a response (some discussed in succeeding sections). Since in the majority of proteolytic studies synthetic substrates and proteins have been utilized that are not natural substrates, it is difficult to assess the role the various enzymes play in protein degradation.

This assessment is further complicated when the proteolytic enzymes are removed from their natural cellular environment. Such factors as compartmentation, location, and microenvironment interactions could markedly alter the degradative system. Once removed from the cell some proteases may rapidly lose their activity, or changes in specificity may occur. These effects are not at all uncommon. During the curing of tobacco leaves, chloroplast protein was lost more rapidly than cytoplasmic protein. However, the in vitro proteolytic activity of the cytoplasm was many times greater than that of the chloroplast (108). Results of Schimke et al (201) indicate that the rapid in vivo loss of rat liver tryptophan pyrrolase, as determined by immunological and enzymatic activity, cannot be duplicated in liver homogenates. Studies in both mammals (22, 84, 170) and bacteria (64, 131, 172, 202, 218, 251) have revealed the necessity of respiratory energy for active protein turnover to occur. It appears the energy is required to maintain a structural component of the protein catabolic system which is either important in the initiation or regulation or in the site of degradation. However, the protease involved in the catabolic process does not require respiratory energy in order to cleave the peptide bonds (22). Elucidation of these interactions may hold an important key to understanding the regulation of protein breakdown. This section presents some of the possibilities for modulation and control of the plant's protein content. Many of the examples are taken from fields other than plant research and should be considered in that light. Siekevitz (211) has presented an interesting theoretical discussion probing the apparent necessity for protein turnover.

Proteolytic Enzymes

In a recent review, Ryan (192) documented the known proteolytic enzymes of higher plants. As yet there is no complete documentation of the numbers and types of proteolytic enzymes in any given plant tissue; in fact, the heterogeneity of isolation procedures and substrates used for assay makes difficult any definitive comparisons between results of two different groups working with the same tissue. The most extensive studies of proteases have been done with germinated barley seeds, mainly because of their importance in the malting industry. Accurate count of the number of different enzymes described is difficult because the information has come from a number of different laboratories. However, there appear to be at least five endopeptidase enzymes which hydrolyze gelatin, casein, and hemoglobin (24, 25, 44, 45), three carboxypeptidases (126, 147, 150, 243), and three aminopeptidases (120, 146, 178) with varying pH optima and substrate specificities. There are also several peptidases which hydrolyze various synthetic substrates (25–28, 176, 177). Several of these enzymes have been purified to homogeneity and characterized as to substrate specificity, pH optimum, active groups, and physical qualities.

A number of other plant proteases have also been purified and studied in detail (192). Some of these enzymes possess unusual substrate specificities. For example: an acid protease isolated from germinated sorghum seeds (58) specifically cleaves the peptide linkages involving the α-carboxyl group of either aspartic acid or glutamic acid, with release of the acyl portion of these acidic amino acids. It is necessary that the side-chain carboxyl groups of the two amino acids be unsubstituted. An acid protease from the insectivorous plant *Drosera peltata* preferentially splits peptide bonds on the carboxyl side of aspartic acid, alanine, and perhaps lysine. It also has limited ability to hydrolyze the peptide bond on the amino side of asparatic acid (3). Some of the carboxypeptidases (243), aminopeptidases (120), and peptidases (7, 146, 149) also have narrow substrate specificities. The proteases of soybean have been separated into six different proteolytic fractions by column chromatography (246). All fractions can hydrolyze casein, but differ in specificity toward synthetic substrates. The interesting observation was also made that there was no self-digestion in the purified fractions, nor did one fraction hydrolyze another (173). Thus within a given tissue there are a number of different types of proteolytic enzymes with various types of bond specificities and probably protein specificities.

The basic classification of proteolytic enzymes into serine proteinases, thiol proteinases, acid proteinases, and metallo proteinases (72) suggests basic methods by which the activity of the various groups might be controlled. Serine and thiol groups are highly reactive and will interact both reversibly and irreversibly with a large number of compounds (145). Acid proteinases require low pHs (from 3 to 4) for maximum activity. Thus compartmentation coupled with changes in pH could partially regulate their activity. The removal of metal ions from animal carboxypeptidase A (240) and B (54), aminopeptidase (85), and neutral proteases (50) results in an apoenzyme with no enzymatic activity. In most cases full activity can be restored with the addition of the metal ion. It is interesting that most of the carboxypeptidases and aminopeptidases of plants are not metallo proteases. Even so, some di and tripeptidases (6, 7, 26, 32), as well as endopeptidases (99, 176), have been isolated which require metals for activity. Several plant proteases have been sufficiently characterized to be classified as serine proteases (96, 135, 248, 249), sulfhydryl proteases (4, 45, 99, 120, 143, 212), or acidic proteases (3, 45, 57, 143, 216). Most others, however, have not yet been characterized sufficiently for classification.

The probability that the degradation of individual proteins might be carried out by specific proteases seems more likely today than it did a short time ago (198). There is good evidence that in at least three cases specific proteases react only with specific proteins or types of proteins. A single enzyme that proteolytically degrades insulin has been purified 1000-fold from rat skeletal muscle (41). The enzyme appears not to degrade insulin to its amino acid components, but it does cleave approximately nine peptide bonds, leading to loss in TCA or antibody-precipitable insulin. The enzyme is very specific for insulin and does not attack proinsulin. An enzyme that is specific toward the apoprotein of pyridoxal enzymes has been found in rat skeletal muscles and small intestines (107). This enzyme specifically degrades ornithine transaminase and tyrosine transaminase to smaller oligopeptides and is completely inhibited by the binding of pyridoxal phosphate to the apoprotein. A similar enzyme with activity toward the apoprotein of the NAD-dependent enzymes lactic dehydrogenase and glutamic dehydrogenase has been located in rat small intestines (106). Like the pyridoxal enzyme protease, this protease splits the apo-NAD-dependent enzymes to lower molecular weight compounds and the hydrolysis is prevented by NAD. Undoubtedly, more enzymes will be added to this list in time, perhaps some from the plant kingdom.

Circumstantial evidence for protein-specific proteases in plants which may bring about the breakdown of nitrate reductase, phenylalanine ammonia lyase, UDP-gal-polysaccharide transferase, and fatty acid synthetase enzymes has been alluded to in previous sections. The almost specific loss of RuDPCase protein when barley seedlings are placed in the dark (171) also suggests some degree of specificity.

Structural Considerations of the Protein Molecule as a Substrate

There are substantial differences in the rates at which proteins undergo inactivation by proteolytic enzymes (124). Proteolytic cleavage of a particular bond of a native protein is not likely if the bond is buried inside the molecule (232) or is included in a rigid region of the peptide chain. It is only in exposed regions characterized by a high degree of local flexibility that peptide bonds will be able to assume the position in the active center of the protease that allows them to be hydrolyzed (158). Such bonds in the native protein might be considered hypersensitive to proteolytic attack. This has been confirmed by findings that a series of proteolytic enzymes of different specificities can cleave methionyl-tRNA synthetase into very similar fragments (31) and that both the "hinge" region of immunoglobulin (196) and the peptide links between globular units of plasma albumin (252) are particularly susceptible to proteolysis. Therefore, only certain regions of the protein are attacked even though the peptide bonds of proper specificity are probably distributed along the entire polypeptide chain. In many instances proteins are much more susceptible to hydrolysis if they are denatured (165) or if certain peptide bonds are broken (167). Both cases generally result in destruction of the molecule's inherent stability, causing the peptide chain to unfold and expose more sites to proteolytic attack. Since protein molecules can exist in a number of different thermodynamic states resulting from conformational changes, it is not surprising that the degree to which a protein can be hydrolyzed varies under differing conditions. Thus the oxidized forms of cytochrome a (254) and cytochrome c (165) are much more sensitive to proteolysis than the reduced form. Studies with *E. coli* suggest that at least bacteria have the ability to recognize abnormal proteins and specifically degrade them (64). In those experiments unfinished polypeptides containing puromycin and abnormal proteins containing amino acid analogs were degraded more rapidly than normal cell proteins. It was suggested that normal proteins of *E. coli* share certain general conformational features that prevent their rapid hydrolysis. Deviations from these common morphological characteristics might then result in proteins that are more sensitive to the degradative system.

Decreased digestibility of proteins in the presence of various ligands and changes in pH, ionic strength, and temperature have been frequently reported. In most cases the protective effect is considered to result from conformational changes that are less susceptible to attack; however, other models are possible. Several hypersensitive sites have been identified in cytochrome b_2 which are sensitive to endogenous proteases as well as trypsin. The sensitivity of the various sites to hydrolysis is modulated by changes in ionic strength or the binding of ligands (heme and flavin). Such treatments resulted only in changes of the relative rates of hydrolysis of certain bonds and had no effect on the fragments being formed (158). The treatment of serum albumin with various ligands which will bind to the protein significantly reduced hydrolysis of the protein by several proteolytic enzymes. The binding of one mole of ligand per mole of protein was sometimes enough to slow digestion significantly (134). Similar effects were observed with Ca^{+2} and Mn^{+2} ions (66). Conalbumin was less susceptible to trypsin hydrolysis in the presence of iron (10) or substrate cofactors (235). Homologous haptens significantly reduced the digestibility of rabbit antibody (134). The presence of substrate molecules also stabilizes enzyme proteins (69). Both in vivo and in vitro degradation of tryptophan oxygenase is decreased by tryptophan (199, 201), thymidine prevents degradation of thymidine kinase (116, 126), and the administration of iron stabilizes rat liver ferritin (40). When appropriate experimental controls were done it was shown that ligands, cofactors, activators, or substrates act on the protein substrate, not on the protease enzyme. However, it is possible that such factors may concurrently act on both the degraded and the degrading system to modulate the cell's protein components.

Proteolytic Control Through Zymogen Activation

The proteolytic enzymes produced by the mammalian pancreatic tissue are present as inactive zymogens. Limited proteolysis of these precursors results in the active protease. The activation of a steptococcal protease, of mucous membrane prorennin, and the cascading series of proenzyme-enzyme transformation leading to the clotting of blood all involve limited proteolysis for activation (167). No plant protease has yet been shown unequivocally to be activated in a similar manner. However, the rapid increase in proteolytic activity during the germination of many seeds (192) might suggest such an origin for some enzymes. Some suggestive evidence has accumulated in favor of zymogen-type proenzymes in plants (53, 68, 179, 207). Shain & Mayer (207) have invoked an autocatalytic process involving a kind of trypsinogen-like form coupled with the removal of proteolytic inhibitors to account for the activation of a trypsin-like enzyme in germinating lettuce seeds. Ample evidence exists that a protease in yeast, protease-c, exists first as a proprotease which is later activated by limited hydrolysis or conformational changes (74–78). Another possible example of a proenzyme comes from germinating pea seeds. The enzyme amylopectin 1,6-glucosidase is associated with a particulate fraction, and its release from that fraction requires proteolysis (208, 244) and results in activation of the enzyme.

Lysosomes

The catabolic nature of lysosomes has been implicated with a variety of the cell's processes (38) including intracellular digestion of food, autolysis of mitochondria and microsomes, and turnover of various cell components. The classical lysomsomal organelle of animal cells is yet to be discovered in plants. It has been argued, however, that turnover of protein, cytoplasmic nucleic acids, and other plant cell constituents indicates that the lysosomes or lysosomal apparatus must be present in higher plant cells (140). Whether lysosomes have or will be discovered in plants probably depends on the definition of the organelle. Plant spherosomes (141), microsomes (37), vacuoles (16, 138), and aleurone grains (139, 255) have been implicated as lysosomes because of the presence of the various acid hydrolases. Important to our discussion here is the existence of proteolytic enzymes in these organelles. These have acid protease with a pH optimum between 3 and 4. Interestingly enough, most of the plant proteases have pH optima higher than this (192) and do not appear to be particulate-bound. In understanding the degradative process, it is not enough to endow lysosomes with the sole responsibility, but it must somehow be determined how nonparticulate, nonacid proteases are involved. As Schimke & Doyle (198) pointed out, it is difficult to understand how the lysosome could function in the process, since protein degradation involves randomness, heterogeneity of degradation rate constants, and the rate constants that can be altered by various experimental treatments. Implication of the lysosome does not alter the problem of specificity but simply moves the problem to the lysosomes. Thus, some mechanism must be invoked for the recognition of protein molecules that are to be degraded and then specifically transported into the lysosome. It might be more reasonable to propose that the plant's lysosomal systems are important at a time when gross changes in the rates of protein degradation occur. However, the possibility of some role in protein turnover cannot be completely dismissed.

Membranes

A discussion of lysosomes logically leads to a consideration of the importance of membranes and how they might function in giving specificity to the turnover system. Practically no information is available in this area, even though it may be of major importance. A growing number of enzymes are suggested to be associated with membranes. It is possible that membrane binding, besides endowing activity, might also eliminate or reduce the chances of proteolysis. A possible example of this comes from work with NADPH-cytochrome c reductase in rats. Injecting rats with phenobarbitol speeds synthesis and slows degradation of the microsomal membrane-bound enzyme. The slower degradation appears to be the result of the enzyme becoming more tightly bound to microsomal membranes in treated animals (211). Furthermore, studies indicate that newly synthesized NADPH-cytochrome c reductase is more susceptible to degradation than old membrane-bound enzyme (122, 123). It is suggested that newly synthesized enzyme molecules are first released from the ribosome into the cytoplasmic pool and then incorporated into a proper site on the membrane. While in the cytoplasmic pool, the enzyme is more unstable and thus more easily hydrolyzed than its membrane-bound counterpart.

The mechanism of membrane binding might also be applied as a method of activating, inactivating, or changing the specificity of proteolytic enzymes as well. Not much is known about the interaction of proteases and membranes; even in cases where proteases are associated with lysosomal-like particles, the interaction, if any, with the membrane has not been investigated. However, there is at least one example of a membrane protease in animals. A protease with some chymotrypsin-like activity has been isolated from human erthrocyte membranes (151, 155). It has a pH optimum of 7.4, and experiments indicate that the activity is a part of, or at least is bound to, the lipoprotein of the membrane.

Proteolytic Control Through Endogenous Inhibitors

Protein inhibitors from plants with activity against trypsin and chymotrypsin have been well documented (192). These trypsin inhibitors are widely distributed in higher plants but apparently have very little if any function in controlling the bulk of endogenous proteolytic activity. Yet controlling certain of the plant's proteolytic enzymes by inhibitors could represent not only a simple but rapid and effective means of control. To date very little definitive information is available concerning endogenous inhibitors. Knowledge about this very interesting and important area of physiological control in plants is mostly circumstantial. Generally, evidence has come merely as sidelight observations during studies of proteolytic enzymes. The proteolytic activity of crude extracts frequently can be significantly enhanced by dialysis (29, 45, 115, 227) or chromatography (7, 44, 230, 246), suggesting the presence of endogenous inhibitors in the extracts.

Extracts of barley seeds (45) and seedlings (29) contain endogenous inhibitors of barley endopeptidase activity. The embryo of rice (88) and barley seeds (29, 115) contains the highest concentration of the inhibitors. There is a rapid decline in inhibitor activity during germination of barley (45, 115), rice (88), lettuce (209), and sorghum (57). Correlated with this loss is an increase in proteolytic activity. Haynes & Feeney (79) suggested that inhibitors in seeds may function by inhibiting proteolytic enzymes while storage proteins are being laid down. At the onset of germination the inhibitors may be removed, allowing proteolytic enzymes to hydrolyze the stored proteins. In this case, inhibitors may express control over the breakdown of storage proteins. In the same sense, inhibitors might influence not only the turnover rate but also the concentration of other plant enzymes.

CONCLUSIONS

Development of information on protein turnover in plants has lagged well behind that of animals and microorganisms. At present turnover or lack of turnover under specific conditions has been demonstrated for only two plant enzymes, nitrate reductase and ribulose-diP carboxylase. However, much recent circumstantial evidence indicates that a large number of plant enzymes might be turned over. Techniques are now more generally available to either minimize or overcome many of the procedural problems involved in proving the occurrence of turnover of plant proteins and in estimating turnover rates. The future will see more research efforts directed toward such studies.

A most intriguing aspect of turnover is the control of its occurrence and rate. What modulates the rates of synthesis and degradation during induction, during steady state levels, and during losses of specific enzymes? Relevant information is largely lacking on these subjects for living organisms. The study of such regulation is vastly complicated by the possibilities that the proteolytic enzyme(s) itself is rapidly turning over or is sequentially released, activated, or synthesized, and then degraded or inactivated when no longer required. Ellucidation of these complex controls will be a major achievement.

Literature Cited

1. Abelson, P. H. 1954. *J. Biol. Chem.* 206:335–43
2. Abelson, P. H., Vogel, H. J. 1955. *J. Biol. Chem.* 213:355–64
3. Amagase, S. 1972. *J. Biochem.* 72:73–81
4. Anderson, J. W., Rowan, K. S. 1965. *Biochem. J.* 97:741–46
5. Arias, I. M., Doyle, D., Schimke, R. T. 1969. *J. Biol. Chem.* 244:3303–15
6. Ashton, F. M., Dahmen, W. J. 1967. *Phytochemistry* 6:641–53
7. Ibid, 1215–25
8. Aslam, M., Huffaker, R. C., Travis, R. L. 1973. *Plant Physiol.* 52:137–41
9. Awwad, H. K., El Sheraky, A. S., Helmi, S. A., Shetaiwy, S. K., Potchen, E. J. 1970. *J. Biol. Chem.* 245:469–76
10. Azari, P. R., Fenney, R. E. 1961. *Arch. Biochem. Biophys.* 92:44–52
11. Barber, J. T., Steward, F. C. 1968. *Develop. Biol.* 17:326–49
12. Barber, J. T., Wood, H. L., Steward, F. C. 1967. *Can. J. Bot.* 45:5–19
13. Beale, S. 1971. *Plant Physiol.* 48: 316–19
14. Bechet, J., Wiame, J. M. 1965. *Biochem. Biophys. Res. Commun.* 21: 226–34
15. Beevers, L., Schrader, L. E., Flesher, D., Hageman, R. H. 1965. *Plant Physiol.* 40:691–98
16. Belitser, N. V. 1972. *Dokl. Akad. Nauk SSSR Ser. Biol.* 203:211
17. Bhatia, C. R., Nilson, J. P. 1969. *Biochem. Genet.* 3:207–14
18. Bidwell, R. G. S. 1963. *Can. J. Bot.* 41:1623–38
19. Bidwell, R. G. S., Barr, R., Steward, F. C. 1964. *Nature* 203:367–73
20. Boroughs, H., Bonner, J. 1953. *Arch. Biochem. Biophys.* 46:279–90
21. Brady, C. J., Palmer, J. K., O'Connell, P. B. H., Smillie, R. M. 1970. *Phytochemistry* 9:1037–47
22. Brostrom, C. O., Jeffay, H. 1970. *J. Biol. Chem.* 245:4001–8
23. Britten, R. J., McClure, F. T. 1962. *Bacteriol. Rev.* 26:292–335
24. Burger, W. C. 1966. *Cereal Sci. Today* 11:19–23, 31, 32
25. Burger, W. C., Prentice, N., Kastenschmidt, J., Huddle, J. D. 1966. *Cereal Chem.* 43:546–54
26. Burger, W. C., Prentice, N., Kastenschmidt, J., Moeller, M. 1968. *Phytochemistry* 7:1261–70
27. Burger, W. C., Prentice, N., Moeller, M. 1970. *Plant Physiol.* 46:860–61
28. Burger, W. C., Prentice, N., Moeller, M., Kastenschmidt, J. 1970. *Phytochemistry* 9:33–40
29. Burger, W. C., Siegelman, H. W. 1966. *Physiol. Plant.* 19:1089–93
30. Caponetti, J. D., Harvey, W. H., De Maggio, A. E. 1972. *Can. J. Bot.* 50:1479–83
31. Cassio, D., Waller, J. P. 1971. *Eur. J. Biochem.* 20:283–300
32. Catsimpoolas, N., Funk, S. K., Wang, J., Kenney, J. 1970. *J. Sci. Food Agr.* 22:79–82
33. Chen, T. M., Ries, S. K. 1969. *Can. J. Bot.* 47:341–43
34. Chen, S. L., Towill, L. R., Loewenberg, J. R. 1970. *Physiol. Plant.* 23:434–43
35. Clements, R. L. 1970. *The Biochemistry of Fruits and Their Products,* ed. A. C. Hulme, 159–77. New York: Academic. 620 pp.
36. Clowes, F. A. L. 1958. *J. Exp. Bot.* 9:229–38
37. Coulomb, P. 1969. *J. Microsc.* 8:123–38
38. Dingle, J. T., Fell, H. B. 1969. *Lysosomes in Biology and Pathology.* London: North-Holland. Three vols. 1788 pp.
39. Dorner, R. W., Kahn, A., Wildman, S. G. 1957. *J. Biol. Chem.* 229:945–52
40. Drysdale, J. W., Munro, H. N. 1966. *J. Biol. Chem.* 241:3630–37
41. Duckworth, W. C., Heinemann, M. A., Kitabchi, A. E. 1972. *Proc. Nat. Acad. Sci. USA* 69:3698–3702
42. El-Basyouni, S. Z., Chen, D., Ibrahim, R. K., Neish, A. C., Towers, G. H. N. 1964. *Phytochemistry* 3:485–92
43. Ellis, R. J. 1973. *Comment. Plant Sci.* 4:29–38
44. Enari, T. M., Puputti, E., Mikola, J. 1963. *Eur. Brew. Conv. Proc. 9th Congr.,* 37–44
45. Enari, T. M., Mikola, J. 1967. *Eur. Brew. Conv. Proc. 11th Congr.,* 9–16
46. Engelsma, G. 1967. *Naturwissenschaften* 54:319–20
47. Engelsma, G. 1968. *Planta* 82:355–68
48. Engelsma, G. 1969. *Naturwissenschaften* 56:563
49. Fan, D. F., Maclachlan, G. A. 1966. *Can. J. Bot.* 44:1025–34
50. Feder, J., Garrett, L. R. 1971. *Biochem. Biophys. Res. Commun.* 43:943–48
51. Filner, B., Klein, A. O. 1968. *Plant Physiol.* 43:1587–96
52. Filner, P., Wray, J. L., Varner, J. E. 1969. *Science* 165:358–67

53. Flinn, A. M., Smith, D. L. 1967. *Planta* 75:10–22
54. Folk, J. E., Gladner, J. A. 1961. *Biochim. Biophys. Acta* 48:139–47
55. Fowden, L. 1965. *Plant Biochemistry*, ed. J. Bonner, J. E. Varner, 361–88. New York: Academic. 1054 pp.
56. Gan, J. C., Jeffay, H. 1967. *Biochim. Biophys. Acta* 148:448–59
57. Garg, G. K., Virupaksha, T. K. 1970. *Eur. J. Biochem.* 17:4–12
58. Ibid, 13–18
59. Garlick, P. J., Millward, D. J. 1972. *Biochem. J. (Proc.)* 129:1P–2P
60. Gassman, M., Bogorad, L. 1967. *Plant Physiol.* 42:774–80
61. Glass, R. D., Doyle, D. 1972. *J. Biol. Chem.* 247:5234–42
62. Glasziou, K. T. 1969. *Ann. Rev. Plant Physiol.* 20:63–88
63. Glasziou, K. T., Waldron, J. C., Bull, T. A. 1966. *Plant Physiol.* 41:282–88
64. Goldberg, A. L. 1972. *Proc. Nat. Acad. Sci. USA* 69:422–26
65. Goldstein, L. D., Jennings, P. H., Marsh, H. V. Jr. 1972. *Plant Cell Physiol.* 13:783–93
66. Gorini, L., Audrain, L. 1952. *Biochim. Biophys. Acta* 9:180–92
67. Graham, D., Grieve, A. M., Smillie, R. M. 1968. *Nature* 218:89–90
68. Greenwood, C. T., MacGregor, A. W. 1965. *J. Inst. Brew.* 71:405–17
69. Grisolia, S. 1964. *Physiol. Rev.* 44:657–712
70. Grossman, A., Mavrides, C. 1967. *J. Biol. Chem.* 242:1398–1405
71. Hageman, R. H., Flesher, D. 1960. *Plant Physiol.* 35:700–8
72. Hartley, B. S. 1960. *Ann. Rev. Biochem.* 29:45–72
73. Hatch, M. D., Slack, C. R. 1970. *Ann. Rev. Plant Physiol.* 21:141–62
74. Hayashi, R., Hata, T. 1972. *Agr. Biol. Chem.* 36:630–38
75. Hayashi, R., Minami, Y., Hata, T. 1972. *Agr. Biol. Chem.* 36:621–29
76. Hayashi, R., Oka, Y., Doi, E., Hata, T. 1968. *Agr. Biol. Chem.* 32:359–66
77. Ibid, 367–73
78. Hayashi, R., Oka, Y., Hata, T. 1969. *Agr. Biol. Chem.* 33:196–206
79. Haynes, R., Feeney, R. E. 1967. *J. Biol. Chem.* 242:5378–85
80. Heimer, Y. M., Filner, P. 1971. *Biochim. Biophys. Acta* 230:362–72
81. Hellebust, J. A., Bidwell, R. G. S. 1963. *Can. J. Bot.* 41:969–83
82. Ibid., 985–94
83. Ibid 1964. 42:1–12
84. Hershko, A., Tomkins, G. M. 1971. *J. Biol. Chem.* 246:710–14
85. Himmelhoch, S. R. 1969. *Arch. Biochem. Biophys.* 134:597–602
86. Holleman, J. M., Key, J. L. 1967. *Plant Physiol.* 42:29–36
87. Holmsen, T. W., Koch, A. L. 1964. *Phytochemistry* 3:165–72
88. Horiguchi, T., Kitagishi, K. 1971. *Plant Cell Physiol.* 12:907–15
89. Hotta, Y., Stern, H. 1963. *Proc. Nat. Acad. Sci. USA* 49:648–54
90. Ibid, 861–65
91. Hotta, Y., Stern, H. 1965. *J. Cell Biol.* 25:99–108
92. Hu, A. S. L., Bock, R. M., Halvorson, H. O. 1962. *Anal. Biochem.* 4:489–504
93. Hudock, G. A., McLeod, G. C., Moravkova-Kiely, J., Levine, R. P. 1964. *Plant Physiol.* 39:898–903
94. Huffaker, R. C., Obendorf, R. L., Keller, C. J., Kleinkopf, G. E. 1966. *Plant Physiol.* 41:913–18
95. Huffaker, R. C., Radin, T., Kleinkopf, G. E., Cox, E. L. 1970. *Crop Sci.* 10:471–74
96. Ihle, J. N., Dure, L. S. III 1972. *J. Biol. Chem.* 247:5041–47
97. Jackson, W. A., Flesher, D., Hageman, R. H. 1973. *Plant Physiol.* 51:120–27
98. Jackson, W. A., Volk, R. J. 1970. *Ann. Rev. Plant Physiol.* 21:385–432
99. Jacobsen, J. V., Varner, J. E. 1967. *Plant Physiol.* 42:1596–1600
100. Jaynes, T. A., Nelson, O. E. 1971. *Plant Physiol.* 47:629–34
101. Joy, K. W. 1969. *Plant Physiol.* 44:849–53
102. Ibid 1971. 47:445–46
103. Joy, K. W., Folkes, B. F. 1965. *J. Exp. Bot.* 16:646–66
104. Kannangara, C. G., Woolhouse, H. W. 1967. *New Phytol.* 66:553–61
105. Ibid 1968. 67:533–42
106. Katunuma, N., Kito, K., Kominami, E. 1971. *Biochem. Biophys. Res. Commun.* 45:76–81
107. Katunuma, N., Kominami, E., Kominami, S. 1971. *Biochem. Biophys. Res. Commun.* 45:70–75
108. Kawashima, N., Fukushima, H., Tamaki, E. 1967. *Phytochemistry* 6:339–45
109. Kawashima, N., Imai, A., Tamaki, E. 1967. *Plant Cell Physiol.* 8:447–58
110. Kawashima, N., Mitaki, T. 1969. *Agr. Biol. Chem.* 33:539–43
111. Kawashima, N., Wildman, S. G. 1970. *Ann. Rev. Plant Physiol.* 21:325–58
112. Kemp, J. D., Sutton, D. W. 1971. *Biochemistry* 10:81–88

113. Keswani, C. L., Upadhya, M. D. 1969. *Physiol. Plant.* 22:386–91
114. Key, J. L., Ingle, J. 1964. *Proc. Nat. Acad. Sci. USA* 52:1382–88
115. Kirsi, M., Mikola, J. 1971. *Planta* 96:281–91
116. Kit, S., Dubbs, D. R., Frearson, P. M. 1965. *J. Biol. Chem.* 240:2565–73
117. Kleinkopf, G. E., Huffaker, R. C., Matheson, A. 1970. *Plant Physiol.* 46:204–7
118. Ibid 1970. 46:416–18
119. Koch, A. L. 1962. *J. Theor. Biol.* 3:283–303
120. Kolehmainen, L., Mikola, J. 1971. *Arch. Biochem. Biophys.* 145:633–42
121. Kuraishi, S. 1968. *Physiol. Plant.* 21:78–83
122. Kuriyama, Y., Omura, T. 1971. *J. Biochem.* 69:659–69
123. Kuriyama, Y., Omura, T., Siekevitz, P., Palade, G. E. 1969. *J. Biol. Chem.* 244:2017–26
124. Linderstrom-Lang, K. 1949. *Cold Spring Harbor Symp. Quant. Biol.* 14:117–26
125. Liedtke, M. P., Ohmann, E. 1969. *Eur. J. Biochem.* 10:539–48
126. Littlefield, J. W. 1965. *Biochim. Biophys. Acta* 95:14–22
127. Loening, U. E. 1968. *Ann. Rev. Plant Physiol.* 19:37–70
128. Loewenberg, J. R. 1970. *Plant Cell Physiol.* 11:361–65
129. Macko, V., Honold, G. R., Stahmann, M. A. 1967. *Phytochemistry* 6:465–71
130. MacLennan, D. H., Beevers, H., Harley, J. L. 1963. *Biochem. J.* 89:316–27
131. Mandelstam, J. 1960. *Bacteriol. Rev.* 24:289–308
132. Marcus, A. 1971. *Ann. Rev. Plant Physiol.* 22:313–36
133. Margulies, M. M. 1964. *Plant Physiol.* 39:579–85
134. Markus, G. 1965. *Proc. Nat. Acad. Sci. USA* 54:253–58
135. Martin, C., Thimann, K. V. 1972. *Plant Physiol.* 49:64–71
136. Marushige, K., Marushige, Y. 1962. *Plant Cell Physiol.* 3:319–22
137. Marzluf, G. A. 1972. *Arch. Biochem. Biophys.* 150:714–24
138. Matile, P. 1966. *Z. Naturforsch.* 21b:871–78
139. Matile, P. 1968. *Z. Pflanzenphysiol.* 58:365–68
140. Matile, P. See Ref. 38, 1:406–28
141. Matile, P., Balz, J. P., Semadeni, E., Jost, M. 1965. *Z. Naturforsch.* 20B:693–98

142. Mattas, R. E., Pauli, A. W. 1964. *Crop Sci.* 5:181–84
143. McDonald, C. E., Chen, L. L. 1969. *Cereal Chem.* 41:443–55
144. McFarlane, A. S. 1963. *Biochem. J.* 89:277–90
145. Means, G. E., Feeney, R. E. 1971. *Chemical Modification of Proteins.* San Francisco: Holden-Day. 254 pp.
146. Mikola, J., Kolehmainen, L. 1972. *Planta* 104:167–77
147. Mikola, J., Pietila, K., Enari, T. M. 1971. *Eur. Brew. Conv. Proc. 13th Congr.,* 21–18
148. Mizrahi, Y., Amir, J., Richmond, A. 1970. *New Phytol.* 69:355–61
149. Moeller, M., Burger, W. C., Prentice, N. 1969. *Phytochemistry* 8:2153–56
150. Moeller, M., Robbins, G. S., Burger, W. C., Prentice, N. 1970. *J. Agr. Food Chem.* 18:886–90
151. Moore, G. L., Kocholaty, W. F., Cooper, D. A., Gray, J. L., Robinson, S. L. 1970. *Biochim. Biophys. Acta* 212:126–33
152. Moore, K., Rao, P. V. S., Towers, G. H. N. 1968. *Biochem. J.* 106:507–14
153. Moore, K., Towers, G. H. N. 1967. *Can. J. Biochem.* 45:1659–65
154. Morré, D. J. 1965. *Plant Physiol.* 40:615–19
155. Morrison, W. L., Neurath, H. 1953. *J. Biol. Chem.* 200:39–51
156. Nadler, K., Granick, S. 1970. *Plant Physiol.* 46:240–46
157. Nair, P. M., Vining, L. C. 1965. *Phytochemistry* 4:401–11
158. Naslin, L., Spyridakis, A., Labeyrie, F. 1973. *Eur. J. Biochem.* 34:268–83
159. Nitsan, J. 1962. *Plant Physiol.* 37:291–95
160. Nooden, L. D., Thimann, K. V. 1963. *Proc. Nat. Acad. Sci. USA* 50:194–200
161. Oaks, A. 1965. *Plant Physiol.* 40: 142–49
162. Ibid, 149–55
163. Oaks, A., Bidwell, R. G. S. 1970. *Ann. Rev. Plant Physiol.* 21:43–66
164. Oaks, A., Wallace, W., Stevens, D. 1972. *Plant Physiol.* 50:649–54
165. Okunuki, K. 1961. *Advan. Enzymol.* 23:29–82
166. Onwueme, I. C., Laude, H. M., Huffaker, R. C. 1971. *Crop Sci.* 11:195–200
167. Ottesen, M. 1967. *Ann. Rev. Biochem.* 36:55–76
168. Park, R. B., Pon, N. G. 1961. *J. Mol. Biol.* 3:1–10
169. Pate, J. S., O'Brien, T. P. 1968. *Planta* 78:60–71

170. Penn, N. W. 1960. *Biochim. Biophys. Acta* 37:55–63
171. Peterson, L. W., Kleinkopf, G. E., Huffaker, R. C. 1973. *Plant Physiol.* 51:1042–45
172. Pine, M. J. 1966. *J. Bacteriol.* 92:847–50
173. Pinsky, A., Grossman, S. 1969. *J. Sci. Food Agr.* 20:374–75
174. Poole, B., Leighton, F., de Duve, C. 1969. *J. Cell Biol.* 41:536–46
175. Preiss, J., Kosuge, T. 1970. *Ann. Rev. Plant Physiol.* 21:433–66
176. Prentice, N., Burger, W. C., Kastenschmidt, J., Moeller, M. 1970. *Phytochemistry* 9:41–47
177. Prentice, N., Burger, W. C., Moeller, M. 1971. *Phytochemistry* 10:1497–99
178. Prentice, N., Burger, W. C., Moeller, M., Kastenschmidt, J. 1970. *Cereal Chem.* 47:282–87
179. Presley, H. J., Fowden, L. 1965. *Phytochemistry* 4:169–76
180. Pressey, R. 1967. *Plant Physiol.* 42:1780–86
181. Ibid 1968. 43:1430–34
182. Pressey, R., Shaw, R. 1966. *Plant Physiol.* 41:1657–61
183. Price, V. E., Sterling, W. R., Tarantola, V. A., Hartley, R. W. Jr., Rechcigl, M. Jr. 1962. *J. Biol. Chem.* 237:3468–75
184. Racusen, D., Foote, M. 1962. *Plant Physiol.* 37:640–42
185. Racusen, D., Foote, M. 1965. *Can. J. Bot.* 43:817–24
186. Rechcigl, M. Jr. 1967. *Enzymologia* 34:23–39
187. Reimers, F. É., Khavkin, É. E. 1970. *Sov. Plant Physiol.* 17:279–87
188. Reiner, J. M. 1953. *Arch. Biochem. Biophys.* 46:53–79
189. Roberts, D. W. A. 1969. *Can. J. Bot.* 47:263–65
190. Roberts, R. B., Abelson, P. H., Cowie, D. B., Bolton, E. T., Britten, R. J. 1957. *Carnegie Inst. Washington Publ. 607*
191. Rubery, P. H., Fosket, D. E. 1969. *Planta* 87:54–62
192. Ryan, C. A. 1973. *Ann. Rev. Plant Physiol.* 24:173–96
193. Sacher, J. A. 1966. *Plant Physiol.* 41:701–8
194. Sacher, J. A. 1967. *Aspects of the Biology of Ageing*, 269–303. New York: Academic. 634 pp.
195. Sacher, J. A. 1973. *Ann. Rev. Plant Physiol.* 24:197–224
196. Sarma, V. R., Silverton, E. W., Davies, D. R., Terry, W. D. 1971. *J. Biol. Chem.* 246:3753–59
197. Schimke, R. T. 1964. *J. Biol. Chem.* 239:3808–17
198. Schimke, R. T., Doyle, D. 1970. *Ann. Rev. Biochem.* 39:929–76
199. Schimke, R. T., Sweeney, E. W., Berlin, C. M. 1964. *Biochem. Biophys. Res. Commun.* 15:214–19
200. Schimke, R. T., Sweeney, E. W., Berlin, C. M. 1965. *J. Biol. Chem.* 240:322–31
201. Ibid, 4609–20
202. Schlessinger, D., Ben-Hamida, F. 1966. *Biochim. Biophys. Acta* 119:171–82
203. Schrader, L. E., Beevers, L., Hageman, R. H. 1967. *Biochem. Biophys. Res. Commun.* 26:14–17
204. Schrader, L. E., Ritenour, G. L., Eilrich, G. L., Hageman, R. H. 1968. *Plant Physiol.* 43:930–40
205. Segal, H. L., Kim, Y. S. 1963. *Proc. Nat. Acad. Sci. USA* 50:912–18
206. Seitz, K., Lang, A. 1968. *Plant Physiol.* 43:1075–82
207. Shain, Y., Mayer, A. M. 1965. *Physiol. Plant.* 18:853–59
208. Ibid 1968. 21:765–76
209. Shain, Y., Mayer, A. M. 1968. *Phytochemistry* 7:1491–98
210. Shannon, L. M. 1968. *Ann. Rev. Plant Physiol.* 19:187–210
211. Siekevitz, P. 1972. *J. Theor. Biol.* 37:321–34
212. Singh, N. 1962. *J. Sci. Food Agr.* 13:325–32
213. Skoog, F., Armstrong, D. J. 1970. *Ann. Rev. Plant Physiol.* 21:359–84
214. Skupin, J., Warchalewski, J. 1971. *J. Sci. Food Agr.* 22:11–15
215. Smillie, R. M. 1962. *Plant Physiol.* 37:716–21
216. St. Angelo, A. J., Ory, R. L. 1970. *Phytochemistry* 9:1933–38
217. St. Angelo, A. J., Ory, R. L., Hansen, H. J. 1969. *Phytochemistry* 8:1135–38
218. Steinberg, D., Vaughan, M. 1956. *Arch. Biochem. Biophys.* 54:93–105
219. Steward, F. C., Bidwell, R. G. S. 1966. *J. Exp. Bot.* 17:726–41
220. Steward, F. C., Bidwell, R. G. S., Yemm, E. W. 1958. *J. Exp. Bot.* 9:11–49
221. Steward, F. C., Lyndon, R. F., Barber, J. T. 1965. *Am. J. Bot.* 52:155–64
222. Sussman, M. 1965. *Biochem. Biophys. Res. Commun.* 18:763–67
223. Sussman, M., Sussman, R. R. 1965. *Biochim. Biophys. Acta* 108:463–73
224. Suzer, S., Sauer, K. 1971. *Plant Physiol.* 48:60–63
225. Swick, R. W. 1958. *J. Biol. Chem.* 231:751–64

226. Swick, R. W., Rexroth, A. K., Strange, J. L. 1968. *J. Biol. Chem.* 243:3581–87
227. Sze, H., Ashton, F. M. 1971. *Phytochemistry* 10:2935–42
228. Szepesi, B., Freedland, R. A. 1969. *Arch. Biochem. Biophys.* 133:60–69
229. Tavares, J., Kende, H. 1970. *Phytochemistry* 9:1763–70
230. ten Hoopen, H. J. G. 1968. *Cereal Chem.* 45:19–27
231. Thimann, K. V., Loos, G. M. 1957. *Plant Physiol.* 32:274–79
232. Timasheff, S. N., Gorbunoff, M. J. 1967. *Ann. Rev. Biochem.* 36:13–54
233. Travis, R. L., Jordan, W. R., Huffaker, R. C. 1969. *Plant Physiol.* 44:1150–56
234. Travis, R. L., Jordan, W. R., Huffaker, R. C. 1970. *Physiol. Plant.* 23:678–85
235. Trayser, K. A., Colowick, S. P. 1961. *Arch. Biochem. Biophys.* 94:169–76
236. Trewavas, A. 1972. *Plant Physiol.* 49:40–46
237. Ibid, 47–51
238. Trown, P. W. 1965. *Biochemistry* 4:908–18
239. Tung, H. F., Brady, C. J. 1972. *Plant Growth Substances, 1970,* ed. D. J. Carr, 589–97. New York: Springer. 837 pp.
240. Vallee, B. L., Rupley, J. A., Coombs, T. L., Neurath, H. 1960. *J. Biol. Chem.* 235:64–69
241. Von Noort, G., Wildman, S. G. 1964. *Biochim. Biophys. Acta* 90:309–17
242. Vickery, H. B., Pucher, G. W., Schoenheimer, R., Rittenberg, D. 1940. *J. Biol. Chem.* 135:531–39
243. Visuri, K., Mikola, J., Enari, T. M. 1969. *Eur. J. Biochem.* 7:193–99
244. Vlodawsky, L., Harel, E., Mayer, A. M. 1971. *Physiol. Plant.* 25:363–68
245. Walton. D. C. 1968. *Plant Physiol.* 43:1120–24
246. Weil, J., Pinsky, A., Grossman, S. 1966. *Cereal Chem.* 43:392–99
247. Weissbach, A., Horecker, B. L., Hurwitz, J. 1956. *J. Biol. Chem.* 218:795–810
248. Wells, J. R. E. 1965. *Biochem. J.* 97:228–35
249. Wells, J. R. E. 1968. *Biochim. Biophys. Acta* 167:388–98
250. Willemot, C., Stumpf, P. K. 1967. *Plant Physiol.* 42:391–97
251. Willetts, N. S. 1967. *Biochem. J.* 103:453–61
252. Wilson, W. D., Foster, J. F. 1971. *Biochemistry* 10:1772–80
253. Woolhouse, H. W. See Ref. 194, 179–214
254. Yamamoto, T., Okukuki, K. 1970. *J. Biochem.* 67:505–6
255. Yatsu, L. Y., Jacks, T. J. 1968. *Arch. Biochem. Biophys.* 124:466–71
256. Yue, S. B. 1969. *Plant Physiol.* 44:453–57
257. Zielke, H. R., Filner, P. 1971. *J. Biol. Chem.* 246:1772–79
258. Zilversmit, D. B., Entenman, C., Fishler, M. C. 1943. *J. Gen. Physiol.* 26:325–31
259. Zucker, M. 1970. *Biochim. Biophys. Acta* 208:331–33
260. Zucker, M. 1971. *Plant Physiol.* 47:442–44
261. Zucker, M. 1972. *Ann. Rev. Plant Physiol.* 23:133–56

Ann. Rev. Plant Physiol. 1974. 25:393–421

METABOLITE EXCHANGE
BETWEEN CHLOROPLASTS AND
CYTOPLASM[1]

♦7572

Ulrich Heber
Botanisches Institut der Universität Düsseldorf, Germany

CONTENTS

INTRODUCTION 394
METHODS TO STUDY METABOLITE TRANSFER 395
    Metabolite Flow in vivo 395
    Metabolite Flow in vitro 397
TRANSPORT OF METABOLITES DURING PHOTOSYNTHESIS OF C$_3$ PLANTS 398
METABOLITE TRANSFER DURING PHOTOSYNTHESIS IN C$_4$ PLANTS 405
EXPORT OF ENERGY FROM THE CHLOROPLASTS 407
    Permeability of the Envelope Towards Adenylates 407
    Permeability of the Envelope Towards Pyridine Nucleotides 409
    The PGA/DHAP Shuttle 410
    The Malate/OAA Shuttle 410
    Metabolic Control by Transfer Reactions 412
THE PROTON GRADIENT 414
CARRIERS 415
    The Phosphate Translocator 415
    The Dicarboxylate Translocator 416
    The Adenine Nucleotide Translocator 417
    Carriers Mediating Transfer of Sugars and Amino Acids 417
RELATIONSHIPS BETWEEN CHLOROPLASTS AND MITOCHONDRIA 418
CONCLUDING REMARKS 418

[1]Abbreviations used: A$^-$ (anion); AH (undissociated acid); ADP, AMP, ATP (respectively, adenosine di-, mono-, triphosphate); chl (chlorophyll); DHAP (dihydroxyacetone phosphate); FDP (fructose-1,6-diphosphate); GAP (glyceraldehyde-3-phosphate); NAD, NADH (nicotinamide adenine dinucleotide and its reduced form); NADPH (nicotinamide adenine dinucleotide phosphate, reduced form); OAA (oxaloacetate); PEP (phosphoenolpyruvate); PGA (3-phosphoglycerate); P$_i$ (phosphate, inorganic); RuDP (ribulose-1,5-diphosphate); SuDP (sedoheptulose-1,7-diphosphate); UDPG (uridine diphosphoglucose).

INTRODUCTION

After discovery of photophosphorylation (4) made the postulate of a participation of respiratory ATP (122) in photosynthesis unnecessary, an attractively simple view of chloroplast function was that a substrate, CO_2, moved into the chloroplast and was converted into an end product of photosynthesis, perhaps sucrose, which then left the scene of its formation. Deviations from this idea were made difficult by the knowledge that photosynthesis and respiration share a good number of intermediates. An orderly coexistence of both processes obviously could be envisaged only if a strict separation prevented intermediates of photosynthesis from meddling into the affairs of respiration and vice versa. As a matter of fact, chloroplasts can be seen in good electronmicrographs to be separated from the cytoplasmic compartment by two adjoining membranes.

However, there are numerous obstacles against maintaining a simple view of exchange processes between chloroplasts and surroundings. It has been known for a long time that intact chloroplasts can be isolated in a medium made isotonic by sucrose. If sucrose were easily permeable, it would not provide the required osmotic support and chloroplasts would rupture. The conclusion, which is confirmed by recent findings (57, 88, 129), is that chloroplasts are practically impermeable to a compound which is known to be a major product of photosynthesis. How then is carbon exported from the chloroplasts? In the presence of added PGA, intact chloroplasts evolve oxygen on illumination and DHAP accumulates in the medium (9, 13, 22, 103, 121). The enzymic system capable of reducing PGA to DHAP resides in the stroma inside the limiting chloroplast envelope (45, 107, 110). Obviously the highly hydrophilic anionic species PGA^{3-} and $DHAP^{2-}$ can, in contrast to sucrose, pass the lipid-containing membranes of the envelope even though lipid bilayers, which are believed to form the backbone of biological membranes, are practically impermeable to ions (8). The situation is aggravated by the observed rates of penetration. Maximum rates of transfer of PGA and DHAP are higher than 1800 μatoms carbon per milligram chlorophyll per hour at 20°C (41), one order of magnitude higher than maximum rates of photosynthesis. Thus intermediates of both photosynthesis and respiration can, in contrast to a presumed end product of photosynthesis, practically freely exchange between chloroplastic and cytoplasmic compartments (38). This fact shatters all simplicity in the relation between photosynthesis and respiration.

This can be illustrated easily by an example. Respiration is controlled at different levels. Enzymic control can be identified by a large deviation of an enzyme reaction from the equilibrium state. Phosphofructokinase is one of the enzymes controlling glycolysis and, consequently, respiration (94). In the dark, high levels of fructose-6-phosphate ($\sim 2.10^{-4} M$, calculated from 48) and ATP ($\sim 5.10^{-4} M$, calculated from 47) exist in the cytoplasm side by side with a very low level of FDP ($\sim 10^{-5} M$). On illumination, DHAP and FDP levels rise dramatically by a factor of more than 20, first in the chloroplasts of leaf cells (48). From there the cytoplasm is flooded with photosynthetically produced triosephosphate and FDP. The controlling step of the phosphofructokinase reaction is bypassed, and glycolysis would be expected to be stimulated as well as respiratory reactions. In fact, a number of studies provide evidence that the opposite is true (18, 62, 69, 101). Obviously other interactions between chloroplasts and cytoplasm counteract the effect of flooding sites of respiration with respiratory substrate. A relevant mechanism will be considered later.

These relations illustrate the difficulties arising from the available data on substrate flow across the chloroplast envelope. Research in the field of metabolite exchange between chloroplasts and their surroundings is, mainly for methodological reasons, of recent origin. A first survey of results was published in 1970 (3). As an excellent and penetrating account of the present situation (125) will shortly appear, this article can concentrate on selected aspects of the problem.

METHODS TO STUDY METABOLITE TRANSFER

Several techniques are available to study retention by or flow across the chloroplast envelope, all requiring kinetic studies. They are listed in Table 1. As a brief evaluation has been given before (39, 125), discussion will be limited to a few critical points.

Metabolite Flow in vivo

Fixation of the intracellular distribution of watersoluble metabolites is achieved by fast freezing and subsequent freeze-drying of tissue. Nonaqueous fractionation of the dry tissue prevents secondary spread of metabolites. Success of the nonaqueous

Table 1 Methods to study transfer across the chloroplast envelope

A. Information on distribution and flow of compounds in vivo

    I. Nonaqueous cell fractionation

        (a) Kinetic measurements of substrate levels and substrate distribution (46–48)

        (b) Kinetic measurements of tracer distribution (48, 50, 115)

    II. Aqueous cell fractionation

        Measurements of chloroplast contents in intact chloroplasts after "fast" isolation (88)

B. Information on metabolite distribution and flow in vitro

    I. Direct methods using aqueously isolated chloroplasts

        (a) Distribution of metabolites or tracer between chloroplasts and medium (13, 51)

        (b) Measurements of substrate concentration after centrifugation of chloroplasts through silicone oil (55, 57)

    II. Indirect methods using aqueously isolated chloroplasts

        (a) Response of chloroplast metabolism to the addition of metabolites (9, 29, 124, 127)

        (b) Measurement of the activity of "cryptic" enzymes (42, 84)

        (c) Osmotic response of chloroplasts to additives (90, 129) chloroplast isolation depends on the strict control of experimental parameters and the careful execution of individual steps from the fast freezing of the leaves to the final chloroplast isolation. It appears from the successful application of the method in different laboratories (47, 70, 104, 109, 112, 114) that excessive contamination of chloroplast fractions by nonchloroplast material is avoidable. In a recent paper, Bird et al (14) emphasize that even careful isolation does not yield chloroplast preparations with less than 10% cytoplasmic contamination. However, most workers still perform only density fractionation. This does not remove materials that differ from chloroplasts in size (50) but not in density.

A combination of density and size fractionation minimizes chloroplast contamination. It is the author's experience that preparations which can be obtained routinely from shoots of *Elodea densa* are contaminated by not more than 5% cytoplasm as indicated by the pyruvate kinase assay (42, 49), while 30 to 50% of all chloroplasts in the tissue can be collected in the purified chloroplast fraction. Since the chloroplasts of *Elodea* contain only about 30% of the total protein of the cells (average of stem and leaf tissue), determination of metabolite levels or radioactivity and of chlorophyll in the chloroplast fraction and in the material remaining behind after the indicated percentage of the chloroplasts has been removed can give a fairly accurate account of the metabolite or tracer distribution between chloroplasts and the rest of the cells. Data on the predominant or exclusive occurrence of a compound in the chloroplasts can be viewed with a high degree of confidence. If only a small percentage of a compound is found in the chloroplasts, doubts concerning the significance of the data may be justified. Obviously the method is not well suited to establish a low activity of a particular enzyme—for instance, phosphogluconate dehydrogenase—in the chloroplasts in the face of a high activity in the cytoplasm (42).

Nobel tried to circumvent the technical difficulties of the nonaqueous method by devising a fast procedure for isolating intact chloroplasts in a conventional isotonic medium (88). However, there is the danger that even brief contact with an aqueous medium provides moderately permeable solutes with sufficient opportunity to escape into the surroundings. An additional complication is the difficulty in obtaining chloroplasts uncontaminated by stripped ones that have lost their content of water-soluble materials together with their envelope. The problem of handling the method may be exemplified by contradictory results on the movement of Mg^{2+} between chloroplasts and cytoplasm. Earlier work suggested an outflow of Mg^{2+} in the light (88), while a recent publication gives evidence of a light-dependent accumulation inside the chloroplasts (81).

While there can be no question of their relevance to the problem, an important disadvantage of in vivo observations on intracellular flow processes consists in the complexity of the system under study. If a labeled compound changes its distribution between chloroplasts and cytoplasm with time, does it really move from one compartment to another? There are different possibilities to explain the appearance of compound A in a compartment where it did not previously occur. If it originated outside, it may have traversed the membrane enclosing the compartment directly. If the latter is impermeable to A, it may alternatively have been converted outside into the permeable transport metabolite B, which after its import is converted back into A. The reaction B $\longrightarrow$ A may or may not be a simple reversal of A $\longrightarrow$ B. The net result of direct and indirect transfer is the same, but the mechanisms are different and so are the possibilities of control.

Metabolite Flow in vitro

A simpler experimental system than the intact cell is the isolated chloroplast. The question of the relevance for the situation in vivo of work with aqueously isolated chloroplasts has lost some, though not all, of its impact since chloroplasts became available which reduced CO_2 at rates comparable to those observed in leaves (21, 65, 123). These chloroplasts evidently are not only microscopically but also functionally intact. Photosynthesizing chloroplasts take up CO_2 and excrete products into the medium (12, 13). At first sight, compounds found in the supernatant after chloroplasts were sedimented must have traversed the chloroplast envelope and hence are permeable. However, this is not necessarily so. Often intact chloroplasts have not been washed for fear of losing activity. These chloroplast preparations are contaminated by cytoplasmic enzymes and enzymes from stripped chloroplasts. Metabolites found in the supernatant may have been formed there secondarily and not in the chloroplasts. There is evidence that this is true for FDP (39, 56) which repeatedly has been assumed to be a transport metabolite (12, 13, 22, 24, 42).

Another possible source of misinterpretation is the often observed instability of intact chloroplasts. Chloroplasts stripped during the experiment lose their content which will be found in the supernatant together with "true" transport metabolites. Even good chloroplast preparations are not homogenous and contain a population of different plastids. In addition to photosynthetically active chloroplasts there are others which do not or only sluggishly respond to CO_2 but readily evolve oxygen on addition of PGA. Still others are stripped. In contrast to "intact" chloroplasts they reduce ferricyanide in the light (20, 47). It is conceivable that there are more intermediate types of chloroplasts between the photosynthetically active and the stripped ones (99). Chloroplast preparations rarely have been defined in other than qualitative terms regarding contamination with envelope-free or otherwise damaged chloroplasts. It appears that biochemical criteria are much better suited than simple microscopical observation to judge the quality of preparations (32, 47). A very useful classification of chloroplast types which hopefully clarifies confusion in the field has been published by Hall (32).

When isolated chloroplasts are illuminated in the presence of bicarbonate, a lag phase in photosynthetic oxygen evolution is observed. The shortening of this lag phase (126, 127) by added intermediates of photosynthesis such as fructose-6-phosphate may be interpreted in different ways. In the usual interpretation it is assumed that isolated chloroplasts correspond to chloroplasts in vivo, and that the added compound penetrates the envelope of all chloroplasts and speeds up the formation of intermediates to a level sufficient to sustain rapid CO_2 reduction. However, it is also possible that the compound penetrates only the envelope of chloroplasts with changed permeability characteristics and causes them to respond while fully intact chloroplasts (chloroplasts in the in vivo state) are not influenced.

Penetration would then be a nonphysiological process. The distinction between these possibilities may in favorable cases be easy (penetration of PGA, DHAP, and inorganic phosphate), but in others is difficult. This is especially true when the shortening of the lag phase is very slight or not always reproducible.

The danger of artifacts may be illustrated by still another example. The appearance of the product of an enzyme reaction in the medium after addition of substrate can be used as a criterion of permeability of both the substrate and the product if the enzyme is localized in the stroma of intact chloroplasts. As adenylate kinase is a soluble enzyme of the stroma, the formation of ADP from added ATP and AMP by a washed preparation of chloroplasts was used to answer the question of whether adenylates penetrate the chloroplast envelope (41). Positive but variable results finally led to the conclusion that the broken chloroplasts which contaminated the preparation but were not expected to interfere because of the release of soluble adenylate kinase, in fact retained some of the enzyme and were responsible for the reaction rate observed.

A particularly useful direct method and, in fact, the only one that has led to information on the mode of transfer of metabolites across the chloroplast envelope (55–57) is to measure the amount of an added metabolite which is sedimented with chloroplasts through an inert layer of silicone oil. Different extrachloroplast and chloroplast spaces can be defined by measuring the amounts of (tritiated) water and of nonpenetrating solutes such as (^{14}C-labeled) dextrane and sucrose sedimenting with the chloroplasts. Experimental data must be corrected accordingly, and the necessary correction is often large.

Based on the Boyle/van't Hoff-relationship, Nobel measured reflection coefficients comparing the osmotic response of chloroplasts to the addition of different compounds (89, 90, 129). It remains unclear to what extent obtained values must be corrected for exposure times as the osmotic response is time-dependent in the case of permeable compounds. Also, nonosmotic volume changes may have to be taken into account as complicating factors.

These relations illustrate the difficulties of interpretation encountered in the field. While none of the methods listed in Table 1 is free of handicaps, agreement of the conclusions drawn from their combined application in different laboratories leads to a picture of the interrelationship between chloroplasts and cytoplasm which, though incomplete, can be considered to be reliable in its main aspects.

TRANSPORT OF METABOLITES DURING PHOTOSYNTHESIS OF C$_3$ PLANTS

Attempts to trace movements of metabolites during photosynthesis have been made both in vivo and in vitro only with so-called C$_3$ plants (35) whose primary product of photosynthesis is the 3-carbon compound PGA (10). If $^{14}CO_2$ is fed to photosynthesizing leaves of such plants, acid-stable labeled material appears first in the chloroplasts (48, 50, 115, 134). However, the distribution of radioactivity between chloroplasts and the remainder of the cells changes rapidly during photosynthesis indicating fast export of labeled compounds from the chloroplasts (Figure 1). After about 3 min a steady state in the distribution is reached in which the portion of total fixation residing in the chloroplasts is 45% in spinach or broad bean, 30% in the water plant *Elodea,* and 15% in the brown alga *Fucus serratus.* Appreciable amounts of labeled PGA, fructose-and glucose-6-phosphate, FDP, and uridine diphosphoglucose have appeared in the cytoplasm after as little as 10 sec photosynthesis in the presence of $^{14}CO_2$. Interestingly, labeled RuDP and SuDP remain confined to the chloroplast and do not enter the cytoplasm. Sedoheptulose-7-phosphate appears only very slowly in the cytoplasm. Sucrose becomes significantly labeled only after a lag phase of about 30 sec, and there is always more labeled sucrose in the cytoplasm than in the chloroplasts. A high percentage (60 to 70%) of labeled malate, aspartate, glycine, serine, and alanine is also found in the nonchloroplastic part of leaf cells after short times (30 sec to 4 min) of photosynthesis in the presence of $^{14}CO_2$(50).

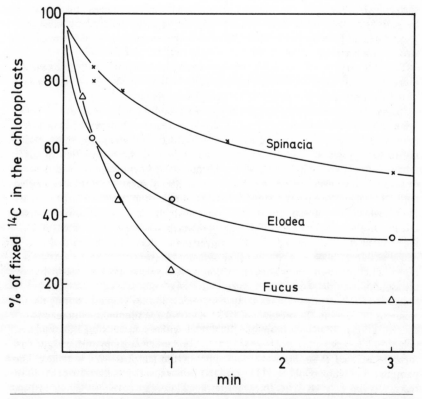

Figure 1   Distribution of acid-stable labeled carbon between plastids and the nonplastid part of intact cells from leaves of *Spinacia oleracea* and *Elodea densa* or thalli from *Fucus serratus* during steady state photosynthesis. Data from (48) and (134) with kind permission of *Zeitschrift für Naturforschung* and of *Planta.*

If taken at face value, these findings suggest the undiscriminating transfer of phosphorylated and nonphosphorylated intermediates from the chloroplast to the cytoplasm. However, feeding experiments with both $^{14}CO_2$ and $H^{32}PO_4^{2-}$ indicate that the situation is more complex (49). The intracellular distribution of ^{14}C- and ^{32}P-labeled sugar monophosphates remains markedly different even after the steady state distribution is reached, indicating that exchange of chloroplastic and cytoplasmic sugar monophosphates is at least not rapid. In fact, isolated chloroplasts largely retain glucose-6-phosphate and fructose-6-phosphate which have been formed during photosynthetic CO_2 reduction (12, 13). Chloroplastic hexosephosphate isomerase is a cryptic enzyme that reacts very slowly or not at all with added fructose-6-phosphate except when the chloroplast envelope is destroyed, which stimulates the reaction (42). The lag phase in photosynthetic oxygen production of isolated chloroplasts which presumably is caused by lack of intermediates is not shortened by the addition of glucose-6-phosphate as it is by permeable intermediates such as PGA (22). Also, the phosphate inhibition of photosynthesis that is relieved by permeable intermediates is not, or only very slowly, relieved by glucose-6-phosphate and fructose-6-phosphate. Obviously these compounds do not reach the stroma compartment or penetrate only slowly (39, 56, 125).

Thus it is very doubtful whether the fast spread of photosynthetically fixed carbon into cytoplasmic sugar monophosphates in vivo can be explained by a direct transfer of these phosphate esters across the chloroplast envelope.

In the case of sugar diphosphates it appears established that RuDP and SuDP are unable to penetrate the chloroplast envelope. During photosynthesis of leaves in the presence of $^{14}CO_2$, labeled RuDP and SuDP appear only in the chloroplasts, not in the cytoplasm (48, 50). In agreement with this, the distribution of sugar diphosphates labeled with ^{32}P between chloroplasts and cytoplasm is, as in the case of sugar monophosphates, very different from that of sugar diphosphates labeled with ^{14}C even in the steady state (48, 49). On illumination there is a large increase in the level of chloroplastic sugar diphosphates which is not paralleled by a similar increase in the cytoplasm. RuDP is largely retained inside actively photosynthesizing isolated chloroplasts (12, 13). No conversion of PGA is observed if RuDP is added with bicarbonate to a suspension of intact chloroplasts. The carboxydismutase reaction proceeds only after the chloroplast envelope has been destroyed by ultrasound, osmotic shock, or detergent (42, 124).

Labeled FDP, on the other hand, appears rapidly in the cytoplasm during photosynthesis of leaves in the presence of $^{14}CO_2$ (48, 50). On illumination of leaves, the concentration of FDP rises dramatically, though with remarkably different kinetics, in both chloroplasts and cytoplasm (48). It is found in the medium during photosynthesis of isolated chloroplast (12) and shortens the lag phase (7) or relieves the phosphate inhibition of photosynthesis (22). It is not surprising, therefore, that FDP repeatedly has been reported to permeate the chloroplast envelope. Closer inspection, however, shows that the situation is not unequivocal and that, in fact, negative evidence may in this case be more significant than positive evidence. A direct penetration of FDP has not been observed by Heldt & Rapley (56), and the shortening of the lag phase of photosynthesis by FDP (7) is not nearly as dramatic as that caused by DHAP or GAP (22, 108, 126). It appears possible that FDP, like RuDP and SuDP, cannot traverse the chloroplast envelope. The action of triosephosphate isomerase and aldolase may be responsible for reported cases of direct penetration. These two enzymes, which convert triosephosphates into one another and into FDP and vice versa, occur in high activities in both chloroplasts and cytoplasm of leaf cells, or, in the absence of careful washing of the chloroplasts, in the medium used for suspending isolated chloroplasts. It has already been mentioned that DHAP is a transport metabolite. Export into the cytoplasm of chloroplastic DHAP, which together with GAP is close to equilibrium with chloroplastic FDP, will result in FDP formation in the cytoplasm even if there is no direct transfer of FDP. Similar relations may hold also for in vitro observations.

Both DHAP and 3-PGA are rapidly transferred across the chloroplast envelope (20, 40, 50, 55–57, 65, 103, 108, 121, 124, 128). The carbon of cytoplasmic PGA reaches the specific activity of $^{14}CO_2$ fed to the leaves as fast as chloroplastic PGA (48). Both PGA and DHAP are major products of excretion during photosynthesis of isolated chloroplasts (12, 13). Both abolish the lag phase in photosynthetic CO_2 reduction and relieve the phosphate inhibition of photosynthesis (22, 126). This inhibition is presumably due to a counter exchange between external phosphate and internal intermediates of photosynthesis which depletes the chloroplasts of substrates necessary for the operation of the carbon reduction cycle (125). While early observations indicated the reduction of not more than 7 μmoles PGA mg^{-1} chl hr^{-1} by intact chloroplasts in vitro (121), the best chloroplast preparations now available reduce as much as 450 μmoles added PGA mg^{-1} chl hr^{-1} to DHAP at 20°C and more at higher temperatures without addition of cofactors (41). The easy penetration of the chloroplast envelope, which contains a high proportion of phospholipids (83), by PGA and DHAP is very surprising and raises the question of the mechanism of transfer. Heldt and co-workers (55–58, 130) have shown in very elegant experiments that transfer is mediated by a special transport system, the so-called phosphate translocator, in the inner membrane of the envelope.

Of considerable interest is the capability of the carrier to transfer inorganic phosphate (58, 130). If sucrose were an important end product of chloroplast metabolism, a high capacity for the transfer of phosphate across the chloroplast envelope clearly would be unnecessary. On the other hand, if assimilated carbon leaves the chloroplasts in the form of phosphate esters such as PGA or DHAP, then import of phosphate corresponding in amount to the export of esters becomes an absolute necessity.

From the experimental findings outlined above, a picture of intracellular transfer processes during photosynthesis emerges as depicted in Figure 2. On illumination the light-dependent increase in the levels of chloroplastic ATP, NADH, and NADPH causes the chloroplastic triosephosphate dehydrogenase system to reverse direction towards reduction (39). At the expense of both chloroplastic and cytoplasmic PGA, the levels of DHAP, GAP, and FDP increase dramatically although at first only in the chloroplasts (48). Besides FDP accumulation, light activation of fructose diphosphatase and of other enzymes of the carbon reduction cycle opens the way for an increase in the level of RuDP (11, 29, 98). This in turn reacts with

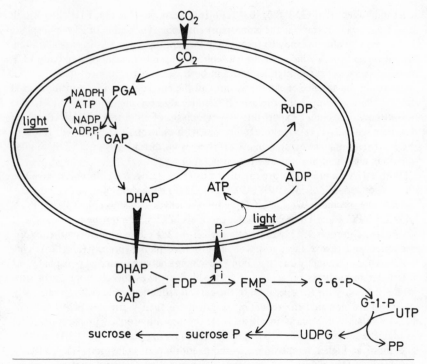

Figure 2 Possible pathway of sucrose synthesis from CO_2 in the light. The enclosed space represents the chloroplast compartment (FMP, G-6-P, G-1-P, UDPG are fructose-6-phosphate, glucose-6-phosphate, glucose-1-phosphate, and uridine diphosphoglucose, respectively).

CO_2 which appears to enter the chloroplasts as such and not as bicarbonate anion. This has been concluded by Heldt et al (59, 131) from the observed accumulation of bicarbonate inside the chloroplasts which follows the pH gradient across the chloroplast envelope as predicted by the Henderson-Hasselbach equation, if equal concentrations of CO_2 inside and outside the envelope are assumed. The maintenance of equal concentrations of CO_2 inside and outside the envelope of "resting" chloroplasts in the presence of different concentration of bicarbonate is most easily explained by the unhindered diffusion of CO_2 across the membrane barrier separating chloroplasts from the surroundings.

As substrate levels of carbon cycle intermediates increase and finally stabilize, sometimes showing "overshoot" phenomena (48, 105), carbon fixation accelerates until the steady state is reached. In the steady state the principal pathway for the transfer of carbon into the cytoplasm appears to consist in the export of DHAP. It must be admitted that this view rests primarily on the present lack of evidence for the existence of other transferable compounds which either are end products of photosynthesis or can easily be converted into them in the cytoplasm. Sucrose has repeatedly been shown not to permeate the osmotic space of intact chloroplasts (57, 88, 90) which is assumed to incorporate the stroma and thylakoid compartments. There is also considerable uncertainty concerning the conditions of sucrose formation in the chloroplasts (26, 125). In leaves, which are illuminated in the presence of $^{14}CO_2$, labeled sucrose accumulates slowly in the chloroplasts, but a higher proportion is found in the cytoplasm (31, 50). Glucose and fructose appear to penetrate the chloroplast envelope only at a very low rate, as indicated by a high reflection coefficient (129), and a shortening or even absence of the induction period of photosynthesis of isolated chloroplasts (17). In addition, they do not become significantly labeled during photosynthesis in the presence of $^{14}CO_2$ and cannot, therefore, be considered to be immediate end products of photosynthesis. Some free pentoses such as ribose (17, 129) encounter fewer difficulties in traversing the chloroplast envelope than the hexoses, and a special carrier has been suggested for their transfer (129). As no metabolic route of sufficient capacity is known that would lead from pentoses to recognized end products of photosynthesis, the significance of these findings is not yet entirely clear. There is also considerable evidence on the possible transfer of pentosephosphates across the chloroplast envelope (9, 12, 13, 17, 20, 22, 108, 124, 126), although the phosphate translocator does not seem to be involved in their transport (56, 58). However, enzyme distribution studies and labeling data suggest that the conversion of pentose phosphates into triose phosphates, a necessary prerequisite for sucrose formation, is only slowly possible in the cytoplasm (48, 50).

Under conditions where no significant storage of photosynthetic products inside the chloroplasts takes place, hexosephosphates would have to be transferred across the chloroplast envelope at a rate of ca 15 μmoles mg^{-1} chl hr^{-1} or more to account for the flow of carbon from the chloroplasts to the cytoplasm of leaf cells and from there to the vascular tissue. Observed transfer rates are two orders of magnitude lower (125). Thus hexose phosphates seem to be ruled out as important transport metabolites.

Of the intermediates of photosynthesis in C_3 plants, only PGA is capable of flow rates comparable to those of DHAP and exceeding, in fact, maximum transfer requirements by a large factor. However, there appears to be good reason to believe that export of PGA does not contribute to sugar synthesis in the cytoplasm of leaf cells. This would require massive export of ATP and of reducing equivalents from the chloroplasts. Both are possible, as will be discussed later, but the known pathways (43, 44, 47, 113) imply that PGA cannot be reduced to the sugar level outside the chloroplasts and is actually produced there from GAP during energy export from the chloroplasts into the cytoplasm (39). Irrespective of whether net export or import of PGA takes place, there is no doubt that chloroplastic and cytoplasmic PGA pools exchange rapidly and that fluctuations in one compartment are immediately communicated to the other (38, 39, 121).

Glycine and serine have been proposed to function as transport metabolites in photosynthesis, transferring newly assimilated carbon into the cytoplasm instead of phosphate esters (102). However, their conversion into sucrose would involve phosphorylation and reductive steps which may be very difficult to achieve in the cytoplasm (120).

The available evidence thus forces one to the conclusion that carbon is transferred during photosynthesis from the chloroplasts to the cytoplasm mainly in the form of DHAP. To explain cytoplasmic sucrose formation, a cytoplasmic fructose diphosphatase should exist which dephosphorylates cytoplasmic FDP which is derived from DHAP. This enzyme should have special properties. It must be inactive in the dark in order not to interfere with glycolytic FDP formation by phosphofructokinase. Conditions which inhibit phosphofructokinase—such as an increase in the phosphorylation potential—should activate the diphosphatase to permit formation of cytoplasmic hexose monophosphate from photosynthetically produced FDP. This could explain the fast appearance of labeled hexose monophosphates in the cytoplasm of leaf cells during $^{14}CO_2$ photosynthesis (48, 50). Indeed, a cytoplasmic fructose diphosphatase has been found (78). Recent work shows that it differs from the chloroplastic enzyme in the pH profile. Inhibition of the fructose diphosphatase by AMP suggests that its activity is regulated by the cytoplasmic phosphorylation potential which is high in the light and low in the dark (77). Formation of uridine diphosphoglucose from hexose monophosphate is a further necessary intermediate step in sucrose formation. In view of the impermeability of the chloroplast envelope towards uridine diphosphoglucose (53), the rapid appearance of labeled uridine diphosphoglucose in the cytoplasm during $^{14}CO_2$ photosynthesis and its high level (70) may be considered as evidence that this reaction can take place in the cytoplasm. In contrast to this view, Bird et al (15) found UDPG pyrophosphorylase only in the chloroplasts of tobacco leaves.

During $^{14}CO_2$ photosynthesis of leaves, label enters fairly rapidly also into the amino acids, aspartate, alanine, glycine, and serine, while labeling of some organic acids involved in the citric acid cycle is remarkably slow (1, 18, 28, 50). Alanine and aspartate arise by transamination from labeled pyruvate and OAA in both the chloroplasts and the cytoplasm. The involved transaminases are located in both compartments (37, 71, 107), and substrates and products of the reactions can traverse the chloroplast envelope (42, 43, 56, 58). Evidence has been presented by Nobel & Wang (90) that some amino acids such as glycine can almost freely cross the chloroplast envelope. Two carriers are thought to be involved in the transport of neutral amino acids (89). Dicarboxylates such as aspartate and OAA are transferred by another carrier system which has been characterized by Heldt et al (56, 58, 79). It may be interesting to note that pyruvate kinase is lacking in the chloroplasts of some plant species (14, 42, 78). The pyruvate needed for chloroplastic alanine formation must therefore be provided by the cytoplasm.

Labeled glycine is believed to be formed outside the chloroplasts in the peroxisomes via glyoxylate from labeled glycolate which originates in the chloroplasts during photosynthesis in the presence of $^{14}CO_2$ (72, 120), although glycine formation inside the chloroplasts has also been proposed (102). Like other salts of monocarboxylic acids possessing pK values around 4, glycolate appears to experience little difficulty in penetrating the chloroplast envelope. It is probable that the transport form is the free acid, which is in equilibrium with the anion and as a small molecule can diffuse without the aid of a special carrier across the chloroplast envelope. Such a mechanism has first been postulated for the transfer of acetate across thylakoid membranes (93). Glycine is supposed to leave the peroxisomes to be converted in the mitochondria into serine. There is a fast metabolic route in leaves from serine to sugars (92). Oxygen uptake during glycolate formation and CO_2 evolution during serine formation are assumed to be the gas exchange reactions of photorespiration. A discussion of this problem is beyond the scope of this article.

METABOLITE TRANSFER DURING PHOTOSYNTHESIS IN C_4 PLANTS

In a number of plant species including the important crop plants maize and sugar cane, the 4-carbon compound malate has been shown to be the primary product of CO_2 fixation in photosynthesis rather than the 3-carbon compound PGA (35). Photosynthesis of these so-called C_4 plants, in contrast to the situation for C_3 plants, is not inhibited by oxygen and proceeds until CO_2 is exhausted, irrespective of the oxygen concentration (16). At present, direct information on the intracellular transfer of intermediates of photosynthesis is unavailable for this group of plants, and judgment is possible only in the light of our knowledge on transfer in spinach and related plants. This is all the more regrettable as transfer processes suggested to occur in C_4 photosynthesis are extraordinarily complicated (3, 27, 35, 85). Primary CO_2 fixation occurs by PEP-carboxylase in the mesophyll cells and not by carboxydismutase as in C_3 plants. The resulting OAA is assumed to be reduced to malate by NADP-dependent malic dehydrogenase (68), which resides in the chloroplasts of mesophyll cells or is transaminated to aspartate (3). Kinetic studies provide clear evidence that carbon from C_4 of malate or aspartate is then transferred into the C_1 position of PGA (35). In the absence of evidence on a direct transcarboxylation reaction, the transfer of carbon is envisaged to occur in two steps, one involving decarboxylation, in the case of malate by malic enzyme, and the other one refixation of the released CO_2 by carboxydismutase. Both enzymes are located in the chloroplasts of the adjoining bundle sheath cells (25, 110). Therefore, malate (or aspartate) is assumed to leave the mesophyll chloroplasts and move through the cytoplasm of both mesophyll and bundle sheath cells into bundle sheath chloroplasts, where the complete reaction sequence of the reductive pentose phosphate cycle is supposed to operate. The CO_2 acceptor molecule of the mesophyll cells, PEP, is regenerated inside the mesophyll chloroplasts by pyruvate P_i dikinase from pyruvate (34), which is proposed to be formed during malate decarboxylation in the bundle sheath chloroplasts. Obviously pyruvate must be transferred back into the mesophyll. The rate of the cyclic transfer of malate (or aspartate) and pyruvate (or alanine, which is assumed to be formed during decarboxylation of aspartate), required to satisfy observed photosynthesis rates is high, i.e. in the order of 200 μmoles mg^{-1} chl hr^{-1}. High activities of the triosephosphate dehydrogenase system in both the mesophyll and bundle sheath chloroplasts (110, 111) and low photosystem II activity in the latter organelles (2, 85, 97) have led to the additional postulate that mesophyll chloroplasts, though unable to perform a number of the reactions of the reductive pentosephosphate cycle and, therefore, of complete photosynthesis, contribute to carbon reduction either by transferring reducing equivalents into the bundle sheath chloroplasts or by reducing PGA imported from bundle sheath chloroplasts. Since pyridine nucleotides cannot cross the membrane barriers (20, 42, 46, 84), the former contribution would involve a cyclic transfer between the two chloroplast types of a system capable of carrying hydrogen such as the couples OAA/malate or aspartate/malate (43, 44), the latter a cyclic transfer of PGA/DHAP (47, 113).

The complicated proposal of a necessary cooperation between two types of chloroplasts and of the involvement of a rapid shuttle transfer of different metabolites rests almost entirely on enzyme distribution studies. Measurements showing that mesophyll cells are deficient in some enzymes of the carbon reduction cycle have been reported by several laboratories (25, 63, 96, 110). However, it should be remembered that it has taken more than 10 years to remove lingering doubts concerning a role of carboxydismutase and of other enzymes of the reductive pentose phosphate cycle whose measured activities were not high enough to account for observed rates of photosynthesis in C_3 plants. In addition, many C_4 plants contain phenolic compounds such as tannins and high activities of polyphenoloxidase, which make quantitative enzyme measurements difficult and can interfere with enzyme distribution studies (6). Interfering materials have prevented, for instance, the isolation of functionally active chloroplasts from mature leaves of C_4 plants. The only study of in vitro photosynthesis available for C_4 plants has been performed with chloroplasts isolated from very young maize leaves. Photosynthesis by these plastids was not fundamentally different from that observed in spinach chloroplasts (91). In fact, carboxydismutase has been found also in mesophyll cells of C_4 plants (6, 96), and the view has been expressed that these chloroplasts are capable of complete photosynthesis (23).

In the absence of direct measurements of metabolite transfer in C_4 plants, it may be useful to consider the known transfer capacity of spinach chloroplasts in the context of C_4 photosynthesis. Problems posed by the necessary transfer between different cells will be disregarded. On addition of OAA, uncoupled spinach chloroplasts may evolve oxygen at rates well above 200 μmoles mg^{-1} chl hr^{-1}, indicating transfer of 200 μmoles OAA into and of 200 μmoles malate out of the chloroplasts (40, 43). If these rates are limited by the enzymic equipment of the chloroplasts rather than by transport, then the transfer capacity of the envelope may be even higher than indicated by reduction rates. In other words, even spinach chloroplasts can transfer malate at least as fast across the chloroplast envelope as is required for C_4 plants. Transfer of aspartate is also very rapid (58). Maximum transfer of PGA and DHAP in spinach is again much higher than needed to account for proposed transfer routes during cooperative photosynthesis in C_4 plants. However, release of pyruvate or of alanine formed in bundle sheath chloroplasts by decarboxylation of malate or aspartate and transfer into mesophyll chloroplasts may be a problem. Pyruvate has a pK of 2.25 and, therefore, cannot be transferred very rapidly as the free acid. While there is no doubt that pyruvate and alanine can cross the envelope of spinach chloroplasts (43, 90), data of Heldt (53) indicate that their transfer rate is two orders of magnitude below that of malate or aspartate (see 90 for reflection coefficient of alanine). If there is no special carrier in chloroplasts of C_4 plants, supplying mesophyll chloroplasts with pyruvate (and alanine) from bundle sheath chloroplasts appears to be difficult at the level of transfer across the chloroplast envelope, not to mention transfer from one cell to the next. If PEP-carboxylase is not contained with pyruvate phosphodikinase (34) in the chloroplasts of mesophyll cells, as a number of data suggest (23, 71, 82, 111, 119), transfer of PEP may also be required. In the position of phosphate group PEP differs from the easily transferable phosphate esters DHAP and 3-PGA. It appears to be transported only slowly by the phosphate translocator (56, 58). Clearly, measurements of pyruvate, glycine, and PEP transfer in chloroplasts of C_4 plants are desirable for further judgment of current proposals concerning cooperation of different cell types in photosynthesis.

EXPORT OF ENERGY FROM THE CHLOROPLASTS

Permeability of the Envelope Towards Adenylates

Light is known to stimulate a number of energy-dependent processes in green cells (86), which are believed to be localized outside the chloroplasts. Among them are anion uptake of aquatic plants (67) and glucose uptake of *Chlorella* (118). The latter may reach respectable rates well above 10 μmoles mg^{-1} chl hr^{-1}. The inference from these observations is that chloroplasts can export energy to other parts of the cell, perhaps in the form of ATP. Such an export could also help to satisfy the energy requirement of sucrose synthesis in the cytoplasm, which may need around 10 μmoles UTP mg^{-1} chl hr^{-1}. Indeed, analysis of adenylate levels in chloroplasts and cytoplasm after nonaqueous fractionation of leaves has revealed that not only chloroplastic but also cytoplasmic ATP increases in the light, while ADP and AMP decrease (47, 105). Radioactive phosphate fed to leaves of *Elodea* in the dark rapidly labeled not only cytoplasmic but also chloroplastic ATP (106). This and other evidence (66, 103) was first interpreted as indicating rapid transport of adenylates across the chloroplast envelope. However, the kinetics of AMP changes were found by Keys & Whittingham to be different in chloroplasts and cytoplasm (70). Markedly different concentrations of ATP and ADP are maintained in chloroplasts and cytoplasm even though concomitant fluctuations are induced by light or by darkening (47). ATP levels are higher in the cytoplasm than in the chloroplasts by a factor of about 2. These differences are also reflected in the ratio of ATP/ADP, which under the simplified (and probably wrong) assumption of equal phosphate concentrations in chloroplasts and cytoplasm is a measure of the phosphorylation potential (ATP)/(ADP) $\cdot$ (P$_i$). In *Elodea* the chloroplastic ratio has been observed to rise from about 1 in the dark to 5 in the light (Figure 3). The cytoplasmic ratio was already higher than 2 in the dark and rose up to 10 in the light. Similar relations have also been reported for tobacco (70).

Work with isolated chloroplasts also indicated that the chloroplast envelope is not freely permeable for adenylates. Stokes & Walker (116) reported that intact chloroplasts, which after uncoupling of phosphorylation from electron transport could no longer photoreduce added PGA, did not respond to the addition of ATP by resumption of oxygen evolution, while a reconstituted system containing envelope-free

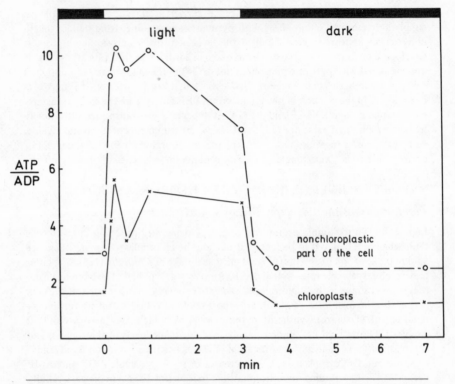

Figure 3 The ratio ATP/ADP in chloroplasts and cytoplasm of leaf cells of *Elodea densa* in the light and in the dark. From (47) with kind permission of *Zeitschrift für Naturforschung.*

chloroplasts did. Reports claiming photosynthetic control of electron transport by added adenylates in intact chloroplasts (75, 132), i.e. stimulation of electron transport by added ADP and phosphate and inhibition by ATP, were probably based on wrong assumptions concerning the quality of the chloroplast preparations used. Intact chloroplasts capable of photoreducing CO_2, PGA, or OAA neither reduce ferricyanide, which has been used as electron acceptor but cannot traverse the chloroplast envelope (30, 47), nor do they exhibit photosynthetic control by external adenylates. In contrast, control of electron flow by the internal phosphorylation potential has indeed been observed in functionally active chloroplasts (43).

In contrast to broken chloroplasts, intact chloroplasts phosphorylate added ADP in the light only very slowly, at a rate of less than 4 μmoles mg^{-1} chl hr^{-1} (47). Direct measurements of adenylate transfer were made by Heldt (51) and Strotmann & Heldt (117). They concluded that in analogy to mitochondria chloroplasts contain a specific translocator which facilitates exchange transfer of adenylates. As the translocator had a higher affinity for external ATP than for ADP, and as its capacity was too low to account for the observed light-dependent fluctuations of adenylate levels in the cytoplasm in vivo, its main function was seen in supplying the chloroplasts with ATP in the dark (51). However, as will be discussed later (p. 414), chloroplasts do not depend on a slow direct import of cytoplasmic ATP in the dark since they are, contrary to earlier assumptions, able to produce their own ATP. The possibility must remain open, therefore, that the adenylate carrier can under as yet unknown conditions function differently and more efficiently than presumed today. However, as long as this possibility is not experimentally verified, attempts are necessary to understand the observed fast communication of chloroplastic and cytoplasmic adenylate pools in vivo in the face of slow or even absent transfer of adenylates across the chloroplast envelope in vitro.

Permeability of the Envelope Towards Pyridine Nucleotides

To answer the question whether known transfer reactions can bridge the gap between the observations and link adenylate pools in chloroplasts and cytoplasm, it is necessary to consider first the permeability of the chloroplast towards pyridine nucleotides. Intact chloroplasts, in contrast to broken chloroplasts, do not photoreduce added NADP (20, 42, 46, 84, 103). Only after osmotic shock or other treatment has ruptured the chloroplast envelope does rapid reduction take place. Contrary reports (33) may, as in the case of photosynthetic control in intact chloroplasts by added adenylates, be traced back to the use of damaged chloroplasts which had lost the barrier preventing entry of NADP. The redox state of NADP is very different in chloroplasts and cytoplasm of intact cells (46). In the dark, only about 20% of chloroplastic NADP is in the reduced state, while NADPH accounts for 70 to 100% of the total cytoplasmic NADP system. No large changes in the cytoplasmic redox state of NADP have been observed on illumination, while the proportion of NADPH in the chloroplasts increased as should be expected. Chloroplastic enzymes requiring pyridine nucleotides as cofactors are "cryptic" and do not react at steady rates with externally supplied substrates unless the chloroplast envelope is ruptured (42). Osmotic shock of intact chloroplasts uncovers high activities of NAD-dependent malic dehydrogenase which did not oxidize external NADH in the presence of OAA before the shock, although OAA and malate can rapidly traverse the chloroplast envelope. According to Ting (119) and Tolbert (120), this effect would have to be ascribed to malic dehydrogenase residing in peroxisomes which contaminate chloroplast preparations. However, oxaloacetate added to intact chloroplasts in the dark completely oxidizes internal NADH and keeps it oxidized in the light while OAA is reduced to malate (44). In the absence of OAA the chloroplastic NADH level increases in the light, though less than the NADPH level. In the dark internal NADPH is not influenced by OAA, and in the light it is much less influenced by OAA than NADH (133).

These observations are clear evidence of the presence in chloroplasts of NAD-dependent malic dehydrogenase and also, more important, of the low permeability of the chloroplast evelope towards NADH. This low permeability has also been confirmed by direct measurements of NAD and NADP penetration (53).

The PGA/DHAP Shuttle

In spite of the low permeability of the envelope for pyridine nucleotides, Stocking and Larson (113) observed reduction of external NAD by intact chloroplasts during photoreduction of PGA in the presence of glyceraldehydephosphate dehydrogenase and phosphoglycerate kinase. Since reduction did not occur in the absence of these enzymes, it was concluded that a shuttle transfer of triosephosphate and of PGA was responsible for export of reducing equivalents. Added PGA was assumed to be reduced in the chloroplasts to transferable triosephosphate, which was enzymatically oxidized outside the chloroplasts to PGA, yielding NADH in the process. ATP is a second product of external oxidation of triosephosphate and could indeed be shown to be produced from ADP and P_i during reduction of PGA or CO_2 by intact chloroplasts in the presence of an external system for triosephosphate oxidation in the expected stoichiometric relationship to NADH (76). Interestingly, in washed chloroplasts addition of triosephosphate isomerase was necessary for reduction of NAD to occur (47). This proves that the phosphate translocator of the envelope, which has been shown by Heldt & Rapley (56) and Walker et al (22, 126) to be capable of GAP transfer, can effectively exclude GAP in the presence of DHAP, which has a higher affinity for the carrier and occurs in higher concentration. The transferred molecular species is thus DHAP. Indirect export of ATP and of reducing equivalents was under mass action control (47, 76). Its rate was decreased by high external ratios of ATP/ADP and NADH/NAD. Observed indirect ATP export, which was obviously not maximal in view of the known transport capacity for PGA and DHAP, was about 50 μmoles mg^{-1} chl hr^{-1}. Such a rate is certainly more than sufficient to explain the observed light-dependent adenylate fluctuations in the cytoplasm in vivo. In addition, it could satisfy cytoplasmic ATP requirements even under conditions where respiratory reactions would not contribute to the ATP supply.

However, the stoichiometric coupling of ATP to NADH is a complicating factor. In vivo no cytoplasmic NADH increase corresponding in amount to the light-dependent rise of the cytoplasmic ATP level has been observed. If the PGA/DHAP shuttle operates as proposed, supplying the cytoplasm with ATP, the NADH generated in the cytoplasm during indirect ATP export must in some way be removed. Before respiratory NADH oxidation as a possible means is discussed, another reaction capable of controlling the cytoplasmic NADH level will be considered.

The Malate / OAA Shuttle

If isolated chloroplasts are supplied with malate dehydrogenase and its substrates OAA, malate, NAD, and NADH in such a way that a high ratio of NAD to NADH results at equilibrium, illumination of the system brings about reduction of external NAD (Figure 4). This process proceeds in the light until about 30% of the external pyridine nucleotide is in the reduced state (43, 44). However, if PGA is added to the medium, which keeps internal pyridine nucleotides oxidized under appropriate illumination, little export of reducing equivalents is observed. In fact, if the external ratio of NADH to NAD is high to start with, illumination in the presence of PGA

light

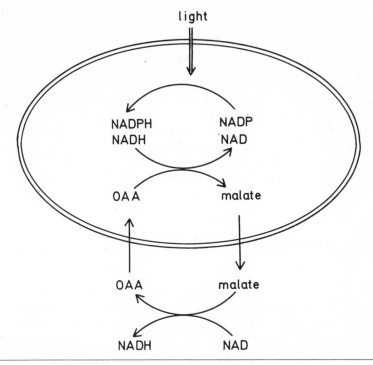

Figure 4 Export of reducing equivalents from the chloroplasts of leaf cells in the light via a cyclic shuttle transfer of malate and OAA. The chloroplast envelope has a low permeability to pyridine nucleotides.

even results in the oxidation of external NADH. Obviously under these conditions the cyclic transfer system reverses direction and transfers reducing equivalents into the chloroplasts, where consumption takes place during PGA reduction. These experimental findings demonstrate the existence in leaf cells of a reversible system capable of linking the cytoplasmic NAD system with the chloroplastic pyridine nucleotide systems. NAD-dependent malate dehydrogenase occurs not only in the chloroplasts but also in the cytoplasm (37), while NADP-dependent malate dehydrogenase resides in the chloroplasts only and needs light for activation (68).

Though no experimental evidence is presently available, the shuttle may operate in vivo also via a cyclic transfer of malate and aspartate. In this case ketoglutarate and glutamate would also need to be transferred, because OAA reacts with glutamate to form ketoglutarate and aspartate. Glutamate oxaloacetate transaminase, the enzyme catalyzing this reaction, occurs in the chloroplasts and in the cytoplasm (37, 71, 107). As a transferable substrate aspartate may be better suited than OAA to support the cycle as its concentration in the leaf is much higher. It is as readily transferred across the chloroplast envelope as malate (58). Transfer of glutamate and ketoglutarate, however, may be limiting.

Metabolic Control by Transfer Reactions

All considered shuttles operate under an overall ΔG_0 of zero. At first sight they should therefore be expected to equalize the external and internal redox states of pyridine nucleotides, at least during slow metabolic turnover. However, even though dicarboxylates and PGA or DHAP are efficiently transferred by special carrier systems across the chloroplast envelope, this transfer does not necessarily equalize concentrations of transferable substrates on both sides of the chloroplast envelope. There is evidence from in vitro and in vivo studies that concentration gradients are maintained by the carriers (48, 55, 57). In addition, a proton gradient is set up in the light across the chloroplast envelope (43, 44, 59, 131). Since protons take part in redox reactions involving pyridine nucleotides, a proton gradient must necessarily result in stable differences in the redox state of pyridine nucleotides at both sides of the chloroplast envelope. This may be exemplified by the equilibrium condition for the malate/OAA shuttle (net flux = 0)

$$\left[\frac{(OAA)\,(NADH)\,(H^+)}{(malate)\,(NAD^+)} \right]_{inside} = \left[\frac{(OAA)\,(NADH)\,(H^+)}{(malate)\,(NAD^+)} \right]_{outside}$$

Since OAA and malate are exchangeable, a decrease in the hydrogen ion concentration inside the chloroplasts relative to that outside must lead to a corresponding increase in the reduction of internal pyridine nucleotide. As the equation also shows, differences in the redox state of external and internal pyridine nucleotides also can be supported by concentration gradients of OAA and malate.

Depending on source/sink relationships, fluxes of reducing equivalents created when the equilibrium is disturbed may occur uphill as well as downhill. It is not difficult, therefore, to construct a model involving both the malate / OAA shuttle and the PGA/DHAP shuttle, in which a low ATP/ADP ratio inside the chlorplasts exists side by side with a high ATP/ADP ratio outside, while the reverse situation holds true for the ratio of reduced to oxidized NAD. Indeed this is the situation in the leaf cell in the light (46, 47, 70). In other words, NADH formed in the cytoplasm during indirect ATP export from the chloroplasts by the PGA/DHAP shuttle can be transferred back into the chloroplasts by the malate/OAA shuttle (or a shuttle involving malate and aspartate) to be oxidized in photosynthetic reactions (Figure 5) (cf 36). An oxidation by respiratory reactions is therefore not necessary. In fact, it is questionable whether a significant oxidation via established pathways of dark respiration is possible in the light (18, 28, 39, 62, 69, 100, 101, 105). Mitochondrial oxidation is known to be controlled by the phosphorylation potential. High ATP/ADP ratios decrease and low ratios stimulate substrate oxidation (19). In addition, regulatory enzymes of catabolic pathways such as phosphofructokinase, pyruvate dehydrogenase, and isocitrate dehydrogenase are subject to control by AMP, ADP, or ATP (5). The light-dependent increase in the cytoplasmic ratio of ATP/ADP, which is transmitted to the mitochondria via the mitochondrial adenylate translocator (95), and the concomitant decrease in AMP brought about by adenylate kinase

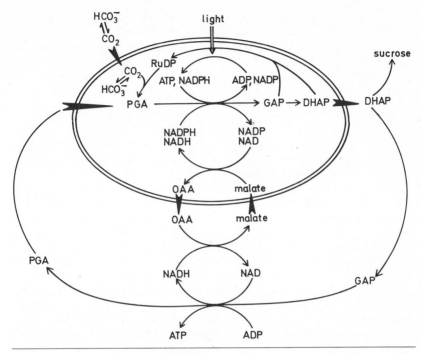

Figure 5   Export of carbon and of phosphate energy from the chloroplasts of photosynthesizing leaf cells. Sucrose is formed outside the chloroplasts from DHAP. Formation of ATP outside the chloroplasts is brought about by shuttle transfers of DHAP and PGA and of OAA and malate. The chloroplast envelope has a low permeability to sucrose and ATP.

cannot, under these circumstances, remain without effect on respiration. There is considerable evidence that the dark respiration of leaves is partially inhibited in the light. When leaves or algae are supplied with $^{14}CO_2$ in the dark, citric acid is labeled much faster than during photosynthesis in the light (18, 50). As it is now known that in the light the cytoplasm is flooded with respiratory substrates such as FDP, triosephosphate, or PGA, which originate in the chloroplasts, fast labeling of intermediates of the citric acid cycle would be expected if respiration were left undisturbed. The inhibition of labeling suggests a decrease of citric acid cycle activity in the light. Control of glycolytic activity is indicated by the onset of rapid oxidation of triosephosphate on darkening (61, 69). The inhibition of "dark" respiration in the light may not become apparent in gas exchange measurements as it can be masked by photorespiratory reactions (64). Present evidence suggests that it is brought about by adenylate control which is facilitated by exchange translocation shuttles in the membranes of chloroplasts and mitochondria.

In the dark the shuttle systems responsible for energy export in the light can reverse direction (43, 44) and may supply the chloroplasts with ATP. An excess of reducing equivalents can be removed by the OAA/malate shuttle or the aspartate/ malate shuttle (Figure 6). Accordingly, chloroplasts in vivo have a much higher ATP content in the dark than isolated chloroplasts which are disconnected from their supply of ATP (47).

THE PROTON GRADIENT

In contrast to broken chloroplasts, which take up protons from the medium on illumination, intact chloroplasts actually excrete protons as mitochondria do (43, 44, 59) if they are illuminated in the absence of electron acceptors such as HCO_3^- or PGA [whose reduction would result in stoichiometric proton consumption (44)]. From the accumulation of bicarbonate or dimethyloxazolidinedione and methylamine, Heldt et al have shown the pH in the stroma of intact chloroplasts to rise up to 0.8 pH units on illumination, while that in the thylakoids is drastically decreased as should be expected from the behavior of broken chloroplasts (59, 60, 131). The failure of the chloroplast envelope to transmit the pH rise in the stroma to the external medium indicates that it has a low permeability to protons. However, from the pH dependence of CO_2 or PGA-dependent oxygen evolution, it must be concluded that there is a link between external and internal pH. Also, carbonylcyanide p-trifluorophenylhydrazone, which is known to increase the proton permeability of membranes, fails to abolish the pH difference across the chloroplast envelope seen in the dark (and also that across the thylakoid membrane), indicating that this pH difference, in contrast to the light-dependent one which is sensitive to carbonylcyanide p-trifluorophenylhydrazone, is caused by Donnan distribution and not by

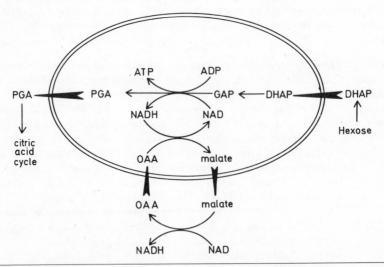

Figure 6   ATP synthesis in chloroplasts in the dark by triosephosphate oxidation and export of excess reducing equivalents by a cyclic transfer of malate and OAA.

proton impermeability (59). The internal and external pH may be linked in the dark by proton leakage or buffer transfer or both. In view of this communication the observed light-dependent pH difference across the envelope must be maintained by an appropriate mechanism. Possibilities are a light-dependent proton pumping by the envelope, which so far has been attributed only to the thylakoid membranes, or a direct connection of the thylakoid space via the intermembrane space of the envelope with the outside medium which compensates proton movement from the medium into the stroma. The pH gradient across the chloroplast envelope has important consequences. It is indicative of cation gradients in the same direction and of anion gradients in the opposite direction. In simple cases (salts of weak acids or bases, flux zero with no carrier involved, membrane permeable for the undissociated but not for the charged molecule) the size of the gradient can be predicted from the equation

$$\Delta pH = \lg \frac{(A^-)\ \text{inside}}{(A^-)\ \text{outside}} = \lg \frac{(\text{cation})\ \text{outside}}{(\text{cation})\ \text{inside}}$$

which is a consequence of the equilibrium relation

$$\left[\frac{(A^-)\ (H^+)}{(AH)}\right]_{\text{inside}} = \left[\frac{(A^-)\ (H^+)}{(AH)}\right]_{\text{outside}}$$

and a corresponding equation for cation/base couples. The involvement of asymmetric carriers would complicate the situation. Obviously, a light-dependent change in ΔpH must be accompanied by fluxes of transferable charged metabolites until a stable redistribution is reached. A shift in the stroma pH has also been recognized to regulate chloroplast metabolism (cf 11, 59).

CARRIERS

The Phosphate Translocator

Useful criteria for the existence of specific carriers involved in the transfer of a metabolite across a membrane are saturation of transfer, competition by suitable substrates, and sensitivity to poisoning. Based on the latter two criteria, Heldt et al (55, 56–58, 130) postulated a special translocator in the inner membrane of the chloroplast envelope which facilitates, in a competitive fashion, transfer of PGA, DHAP, GAP, and P_i, but not of some other phosphate esters such as FDP or fructose-6-phosphate or of carboxylic acids. Transfer is initiated by p-chloromercuriphenylsulfonic acid (130). Light was reported to stimulate only PGA transfer into the chloroplasts. The suggested mechanism of activation involved cotransport of a proton with PGA^{3-} which should be stimulated in the light by the decreased proton concentration in the stoma. Alternatively, transfer of PGA^{2-} instead of $PGA^{3-} + H^+$ may be envisaged in view of the probability that other substrates such as DHAP, GAP, or P_i are transferred as divalent anions. Light activation of transfer can then be understood by trapping PGA^{3-} in the alkaline stroma or simply by removal of PGA by reduction. In fact, the apparent K_m of chloroplasts for added PGA as measured by PGA-dependent oxygen evolution increased with pH (41) (K_m 0.09 mM at pH 7, 0.17 mM at pH 7.5, and 0.6 mM at pH 8) which would be consistent with a transport of PGA^{2-} (K_m for PGA^{2-} ca 5 μM at all 3 pH values). Interestingly, the K_m of the chloroplastic triosephosphate dehydrogenase system for PGA as measured after osmotic shock was somewhat higher, not lower, than that of intact chloroplasts (41). At first sight, this interesting phenomenon appears to be inconsistent with the capability of chloroplasts to reduce CO_2 to the sugar level, since PGA formed during carboxylation of RuDP should prefer escape rather than reduction. However, PGA appears to be accumulated inside the chloroplasts (55). The high affinity of the carrier for PGA shows at any rate that the chloroplast envelope is no significant barrier for the supply of the chloroplastic triosephosphate dehydrogenase system with external PGA. The affinity for P_i was lower than that for PGA or DHAP (130).

The liberation of substrates from preloaded chloroplasts by the addition of competitive metabolites suggested that transfer catalyzed by the carrier is an anion exchange process and probably does not involve significant cotransport of cations (56). Ribose-5-phosphate which can penetrate the chloroplast envelope does not seem to be transferred by the phosphate translocator. 3-carbon compounds with phosphate esterified in the 3-carbon position and inorganic phosphate are preferred substrates as indicated by the drastically decreased liberation of 3-PGA or phosphate from preloaded chloroplasts on addition of 2-phosphoglycerate or PEP, which are probably only slowly transferred. Even a "preferred" substrate such as GAP can be practically excluded from transfer in the presence of a higher concentration of another transferable substrate such as DHAP (cf 47). Similar relations may explain contradictory findings on the rate of phosphate transfer in vitro (20, 56, 57) and in vivo (105).

To obtain an impression of the amount of carrier needed to account for measured transfer rates, in the absence of relevant data it may be useful to base a calculation on an assumed turnover number of the translocator of 10^5 per minute, a molecular weight of 10^5 daltons and a protein content of the inner membrane of the envelope approaching 1% of the total chloroplast protein. Under these conditions around 10% of the protein of the inner membrane may be attributed to the phosphate translocator. In spite of the high transfer capacity in relation to photosynthesis, maximum transfer of the carrier per unit membrane area is only around 0.5 μmole cm^{-2} per hour as can be calculated from the number of chloroplasts per milligram of chlorophyll (ca 4.10^8) and their surface.

The Dicarboxylate Translocator

As in the case of substrates of the phosphate translocator, anion exchange translocation was also shown to occur when chloroplasts preloaded with malate were supplied with other transferable dicarboxylates such as succinate, OAA, aspartate, or glutamate (56, 58, 79). No release of malate was observed on addition of malonate, citrate, monocarboxylates, or PGA. Likewise, transfer of malate into the chloroplasts was competitively inhibited by OAA, aspartate, and some other dicarboxylates, but not by malonate, monocarboxylates, and PGA. As the outer membrane of the chloroplast envelope is unspecifically permeable to metabolites (57), the translocator responsible for the specific transfer of dicarboxylates was concluded to be situated in the inner membrane of the chloroplast envelope. Measurements of substrate uptake versus substrate concentration reveal a high affinity of the translocator for OAA. The apparent K_m of intact chloroplasts for OAA (K_m 0.05 mM) was not much higher than that of NAD-dependent malic dehydrogenase residing in the chloroplasts (41). Other Michaelis constants were 0.27 mM for succinate, 0.41 mM for malate, 0.62 mM for aspartate, and 1.3 mM for glutamate (79).

The Adenine Nucleotide Translocator

The adenine nucleotide translocator defined by Strotmann & Heldt (51, 117) on the basis of back exchange measurements is characterized by surprisingly low exchange rates, especially for ADP and AMP, which are below 0.5 μmoles mg^{-1} chl hr^{-1} at 20° C. The back exchange observed on addition of ATP is higher, but, as has been discussed, its capacity is still insufficient to account for light-dependent adenylate fluctuations in the cytoplasm in vivo. Unexplained is the sensitivity of adenine nucleotide transfer to uncoupling reagents. Also, there is some question concerning the specificity of translocation in relation to observed ATP/ADP ratios in vivo, which are higher in the cytoplasm than in the chloroplasts (39, 47, 70). Exactly the opposite should be expected, at least in the dark, from the results of Heldt's back exchange experiments if the translocator would play a significant physiological role in correlating chloroplastic and cytoplasmic energy levels. In fact, the preference of the mitochondrial adenine nucleotide translocator for external ADP (95) has been used to explain the lower ATP/ADP ratio inside the mitochondria as compared with the external medium or the cytoplasm (54). No analogous explanation is possible for the different ATP/ADP ratios in chloroplasts and cytoplasm.

Carriers Mediating Transfer of Sugars and Amino Acids

Nobel concluded from osmotic measurements that chloroplasts contain a carrier responsible for transport of aldopentoses and two carriers involved in amino acid uptake (89, 90, 129). His conclusions are based on the observation that intact chloroplasts behave as perfect osmometers in the presence of sucrose, but not when aldopentoses such as ribose or amino acids such as glycine or serine are added. In the latter cases, concentrations up to 50 mM produced virtually no osmotic water efflux. Surprisingly, at higher concentrations the osmotic response observed on addition of these compounds approached that seen in the presence of sucrose. This behavior was interpreted as reflecting carrier-mediated uptake. The carrier was assumed to be saturated at those concentrations which became osmotically effective. Nonadditivity of osmotic effects caused by the addition of different pentoses or amino acids was interpreted as indicating competition for the same carrier. It appears that these interesting osmotic measurements should be complemented by direct measurements of penetration. The few available data on direct penetration appear to be inconsistent with the osmotic effects. Very low reflection coefficients observed for the amino acids glycine and alanine indicate rapid transfer of these amino acids. High reflection coefficients for leucine and isoleucine suggest slower uptake. In contrast, direct penetration as measured by Heldt (53) was faster by a factor of 10 for leucine and isoleucine than for glycine and alanine. The rate of uptake in the latter case was below 1 μmole mg^{-1} chl hr^{-1}.

RELATIONSHIPS BETWEEN CHLOROPLASTS AND MITOCHONDRIA

For purposes of comparative biochemistry it may be useful to list a few properties pertaining to transport which chloroplasts and mitochondria have in common. Both are surrounded by two membranes, the outer of which is unspecifically permeable to small solutes (57, 73). The inner membrane of the envelope of both organelles contains different carriers engaged in specific transfer of metabolites (52, 73, 125). It is impermeable to sucrose (57, 73) and to pyridine nucleotides (46, 80). However, internal pyridine nucleotides are linked with the external NAD system via suitable shuttle mechanisms (43, 73, 113). Reducing equivalents of the external NAD system can under appropriate conditions be transferred "uphill" into both organelles. Both have a low permeability for protons and can excrete protons into the external medium (43, 59, 87). Finally, both organelles are engaged in energy conservation, but maintain an internal ratio of ATP/ADP which is lower than that in the outside medium (cytoplasm) (47, 52, 54, 74).

CONCLUDING REMARKS

In view of the well-documented rapid export of photosynthetic intermediates, which are lost for the regeneration of the CO_2 acceptor, the observation of efficient photosynthesis of isolated chloroplasts is surprising. Export obviously must be under control. Carriers mediating anion exchange instead of net export appear to be the controlling factors. During photosynthesis, DHAP leaving the chloroplasts will have to be exchanged against inorganic phosphate, and under some conditions perhaps against PGA. When PGA is exported, phosphate or (in the dark) DHAP may have to enter. Compounds exported in the light are further metabolized in the cytoplasm. From PGA well-known metabolic pathways lead to the formation of amino acids and fatty acids, from DHAP to sugars and other compounds. We may conclude that compounds formed from transport metabolites in the cytoplasm can in turn become available to the chloroplasts for synthetic reactions. This may be true not only for precursors of amino acid biosynthesis (99), but also for amino acids themselves and for other compounds. Thus chloroplastic and cytoplasmic reactions, even though separated by a membrane barrier, are linked through a few bridges which lead to a highly integrated metabolic network throughout the leaf cell.

Acknowledgments

I am most grateful to D. A. Walker, H. W. Heldt, E. Latzko, and R. M. Leech for making unpublished manuscripts and data available to me. Discussions with several colleagues, especially with H. W. Heldt, G. Krause, J. A. Bassham, and D. A. Walker, widened my horizon. My colleagues at the Institute of Botany in Düsseldorf by their criticism helped to improve the manuscript. Work performed in my laboratory was supported by the Deutsche Forschungsgemeinschaft.

Literature Cited

1. Aach, H. J., Heber, U. 1967. *Z. Pflanzenphysiol.* 57:317–28
2. Anderson, J. M., Woo, K. C., Boardman, N. K. 1971. *Biochim. Biophys. Acta* 245:398–408
3. Andrews, D. J., Johnson, H. W., Slack, C. R., Hatch, M. D. 1971. *Phytochemistry* 10:2005–13
4. Arnon, D. I., Allen, M. B., Whatley, F. R. 1954. *Nature* 174:394–96
5. Atkinson, D. E. 1966. *Ann. Rev. Biochem.* 35:85–124
6. Baldry, C. W., Bucke, C., Coombs, J. 1971. *Planta* 97:310–19
7. Baldry, C. W., Walker, D. A., Bucke, C. 1966. *Biochem. J.* 101:642–46
8. Bangham, A. D. 1972. *Ann. Rev. Biochem.* 41:753–75
9. Bamberger, E. S., Gibbs, M. 1965. *Plant Physiol.* 40:919–26
10. Bassham, J. A. 1964. *Ann. Rev. Plant Physiol.* 15:101–20
11. Bassham, J. A. 1971. *Science* 172:526–34
12. Bassham, J. A., Jensen, R. G. 1967. In *Harvesting the Sun,* ed. A. S. Pietro, F. A. Greer, T. J. Army, 79–110. New York: Academic
13. Bassham, J. A., Kirk, M., Jensen, R. G. 1968. *Biochim. Biophys. Acta* 153: 211–18
14. Bird, I. F., Cornelius, M. J., Dyer, T. A., Keys, A. J. 1973. *J. Exp. Bot.* 24:211–15
15. Bird, I. F., Porter, H. K., Stocking, C. R. 1965. *Biochim. Biophys. Acta* 100:366–75
16. Björkman, O. 1971. In *Photosynthesis and Photorespiration,* ed. M. D. Hatch, C. B. Osmond, R. O. Slatyer, 18–32. New York: Wiley Interscience
17. Bucke, C., Walker, D. A., Baldry, C. W. 1966. *Biochem. J.* 101:636–41
18. Calvin, M., Massini, P. 1952. *Experientia* 8:445–57
19. Chance, B., Williams, G. R. 1956. *Advan. Enzymol.* 17:65–98
20. Cockburn, W., Baldry, C. W., Walker, D. A. 1967. *Biochim. Biophys. Acta* 143:614–24
21. Cockburn, W., Walker, D. A., Baldry, C. W. 1968. *Plant Physiol.* 43:1415–18

22. Cockburn, W., Walker, D. A., Baldry, C. W. 1968. *Biochem. J.* 107:89–95
23. Coombs, J. 1973. *Commentaries in Plant Science* 1:1–10
24. Coombs, J., Baldry, C. W. 1971. *Plant Physiol.* 48:379–81
25. Edwards, G. E., Guttierrez, M. 1972. *Plant Physiol.* 50:728–34
26. Everson, R. G., Cockburn, W., Gibbs, M. 1967. *Plant Physiol.* 42:840–44
27. Farineau, J. 1971. See Ref. 16, 202–10
28. Gibbs, M. 1953. *Arch. Biochem. Biophys.* 45:156–60
29. Gibbs, M., Ed. 1971. In *Structure and Function of Chloroplasts,* 169–214. Berlin-Heidelberg-New York: Springer Verlag
30. Gimmler, H. In press
31. Grant, B. R., Canvin, D. T., Fock, H. 1972. *Proc. 2nd Int. Conf. Photosyn. Res.,* ed. G. Forti, M. Avron, A. Melandri, 1917–25. The Hague: W. Junk
32. Hall, D. O. 1972. *Nature New Biol.* 235:125–26
33. Harvey, M. J., Brown, A. P. 1969. *Biochim. Biophys. Acta* 172:116–25
34. Hatch, M. D., Slack, C. R. 1968. *Biochem. J.* 106:141–46
35. Hatch, M. D., Slack, C. R. 1970. *Ann. Rev. Plant Physiol.* 21:141–62
36. Healey, F. P., Myers, J. 1971. *Plant Physiol.* 47:373–79
37. Heber, U. 1960. *Z. Naturforsch.* 15b:100–9
38. Heber, U. 1967. In *Biochemistry of Chloroplasts,* ed. T. W. Goodwin, 2:71–78. London, New York: Academic
39. Heber, U. 1970. *Int. Symp. "Transport and Distribution of Matter in Cells of Higher Plants,"* ed. K. Mothes, E. Müller, A. Nelles, D. Neumann, 151–84. Berlin: Akademie
40. Heber, U. 1973. *Biochim. Biophys. Acta* 305:140–52
41. Heber, U. Unpublished
42. Heber, U., Hallier, U. W., Hudson, M. A. 1967. *Z. Naturforsch.* 22b:1200–15
43. Heber, U., Krause, G. 1971. See Ref. 16, 218–25
44. Heber, U., Krause, G. 1972. See Ref. 31, 1023–33
45. Heber, U., Pon, N. G., Heber, M. 1963. *Plant Physiol.* 38:355–60

46. Heber, U., Santarius, K. A. 1965. *Biochim. Biophys. Acta* 109:390–408
47. Heber, U., Santarius, K. A. 1970. *Z. Naturforsch.* 25b:718–28
48. Heber, U., Santarius, K. A., Hudson, M. A., Hallier, U. W. 1967. *Z. Naturforsch.* 22b:1189–99
49. Heber, U., Santarius, K. A., Urbach, W., Ullrich, W. 1964. *Z. Naturforsch.* 19b:576–87
50. Heber, U., Willenbrink, J. 1964. *Biochim. Biophys. Acta* 82:313–24
51. Heldt, H. W. 1969. *FEBS Lett.* 5:11–14
52. Heldt, H. W. 1972. *Angew. Chem.* 84:792–98
53. Heldt, H. W. Unpublished
54. Heldt, H. W., Klingenberg, M., Milovancev, M. 1973. *Eur. J. Biochem.* In press
55. Heldt, H. W., Rapley, L. 1970. *FEBS Lett.* 7:139–42
56. Ibid. 10:143–48
57. Heldt, H. W., Sauer, F. 1970. *Biochim. Biophys. Acta* 234:83–91
58. Heldt, H. W., Sauer, F., Rapley, L. 1972. See Ref. 31, 1345–55
59. Heldt, H. W., Werdan, K., Milovancev, M., Geller, G. 1973. *Biochim. Biophys. Acta* 314:224–41
60. Heldt, H. W., Werdan, K. 1973. *Ber. Deut. Bot. Ges.* 86:203–8
61. Hirt, G., Tanner, W., Kandler, O. 1971. *Plant Physiol.* 47:841–43
62. Hoch, G., Owens, O. v. H., Kok, B. 1963. *Arch. Biochem. Biophys.* 101:171–80
63. Huang, A. H. C., Beevers, H. 1972. *Plant Physiol.* 50:242–48
64. Jackson, W. A., Volk, R. J. 1970. *Ann. Rev. Plant Physiol.* 21:385–432
65. Jensen, R. G., Bassham, J. A. 1965. *Proc. Nat. Acad. Sci. USA* 56:1095–1101
66. Jensen, R. G., Bassham, J. A. 1968. *Biochim. Biophys. Acta* 153:227–34
67. Jeschke, W. D. 1967. *Planta* 73:161–74
68. Johnson, H. W., Hatch, M. D. 1970. *Biochem. J.* 119:273–80
69. Kandler, O., Haberer-Liesenkötter, I. 1963. *Z. Naturforsch.* 18b:718–30
70. Keys, A. J., Whittingham, C. P. 1969. In *Progress in Photosynthesis Research*, ed. H. Metzner, 1:352–58. Tübingen: Laupp Jr.
71. Kirk, P. R., Leech, R. M. 1972. *Plant Physiol.* 50:228–34
72. Kisaki, T., Tolbert, N. E. 1969. *Plant Physiol.* 44:242–50
73. Klingenberg, M. 1970. *FEBS Lett.* 6:145–54
74. Klingenberg, M., Heldt, H. W., Pfaff, E. 1969. *The Energy Level and Metabolic Control in Mitochondria*, ed. S. Papa, J. M. Tager, E. Quagliariello, E. C. Slater, 237–53. Bari: Adriatica Editriche
75. Kraayenhof, R. 1969. *Biochim. Biophys. Acta* 180:213–15
76. Krause, G. 1971. *Z. Pflanzenphysiol.* 65:13–23
77. Latzko, E. In press
78. Latzko, E., Gibbs, M. 1968. *Z. Pflanzenphysiol.* 59:184–94
79. Lehner, K., Heldt, H. W. 1973. *Hoppe Seyler's Z. Physiol. Chem.* In press
80. Lehninger, A. L. 1951. *J. Biol. Chem.* 190:345–52
81. Lin, D. C., Nobel, P. S. 1971. *Arch. Biochem. Biophys.* 145:622–32
82. Lyttleton, J. W. 1971. See Ref. 16, 232–39
83. Mackender, R. O., Leech, R. M. 1972. See Ref. 31, 1431–40
84. Mathieu, Y. 1967. *Photosynthetica* 1:57–63
85. Mayne, B. C., Edwards, G. E., Black, C. C. 1971. *Plant Physiol.* 47:600–5
86. MacRobbie, E. A. C. 1970. *Quart. Rev. Biophys.* 3:251–94
87. Mitchell, P. 1966. *Biol. Rev.* 41:445–502
88. Nobel, P. S. 1969. *Biochim. Biophys. Acta* 172:134–43
89. Nobel, P. S., Cheung, Y. S. 1972. *Nature New Biol.* 237:207–8
90. Nobel, P. S., Wang, C. -T. 1970. *Biochim. Biophys. Acta* 211:79–87
91. O'Neal, D., Hew, C. S., Latzko, E., Gibbs, M. 1972. *Plant Physiol.* 49:607–14
92. Ongun, A., Stocking, C. R. 1965. *Plant Physiol.* 40:819–24, 825–31
93. Packer, L., Crofts, A. R. 1967. In *Current Topics in Bioenergetics*, ed. D. R. Sanadi, 2:24–64. New York: Academic
94. Passoneau, J. V., Lowry, O. H. 1963. *Biochem. Biophys. Res. Commun.* 13:372–79
95. Pfaff, E., Klingenberg, M. 1968. *Eur. J. Biochem.* 6:66–79
96. Poincelot, R. P. 1972. *Plant Physiol.* 50:336–40
97. Polya, G. M., Osmond, C. B. 1972. *Plant Physiol.* 50:728–34
98. Preiss, J., Kosuge, T. 1970. *Ann. Rev. Plant Physiol.* 21:433–66
99. Ridley, S. M., Leech, R. M. 1968. *Planta* 84:20–34
100. Ried, A. 1968. *Biochim. Biophys. Acta* 153:653–63
101. Ried, A., Setlik, I. 1972. See Ref. 31, 2077–87

102. Roberts, G. R., Keys, A. J., Whittingham, C. P. 1970. *J. Exp. Bot.* 21:683–92
103. Robinson, J. M., Stocking, C. R. 1968. *Plant Physiol.* 42:1597–1604
104. Ruppel, H. G., van Wyk, D. 1965. *Z. Pflanzenphysiol.* 53:32–38
105. Santarius, K. A., Heber, U. 1965. *Biochim. Biophys. Acta* 102:39–54
106. Santarius, K. A., Heber, U., Ullrich, W., Urbach, W. 1964. *Biochem. Biophys. Res. Commun.* 15:139–46
107. Santarius, K. A., Stocking, C. R. 1969. *Z. Naturforsch.* 24b:1170–79
108. Schacter, B., Eleg, J. H., Gibbs, M. 1971. *Plant Physiol.* 48:707–11
109. Slack, C. R. 1969. *Phytochemistry* 8:1387–91
110. Slack, C. R., Hatch, M. D. 1967. *Biochem. J.* 103:660–65
111. Slack, C. R., Hatch, M. D., Goodchild, D. J. 1969. *Biochem. J.* 114:489–98
112. Stocking, C. R. 1971. *Methods Enzymol.* 23:221–28
113. Stocking, C. R., Larson, S. 1969. *Biochem. Biophys. Res. Commun.* 37:278–82
114. Stocking, C. R., Shumway, L. K., Weier, T. E., Greenwood, D. 1968. *J. Cell Biol.* 36:270–75
115. Stocking, C. R., Williams, G. R., Ongun, A. 1963. *Biochem. Biophys. Res. Commun.* 10:416–21
116. Stokes, D. M., Walker, D. A. 1971. See Ref. 16, 226–31
117. Strotmann, H., Heldt, H. W. 1969. See Ref. 70, 1131–40
118. Tanner, W., Loos, E., Kandler, O. 1966. In *Currents in Photosynthesis,* ed. J. B. Thomas, J. C. Goedheer, 243–51. Rotterdam: Donker
119. Ting I. P. 1971. See Ref. 16, 169–85
120. Tolbert, N. E. 1971. See Ref. 16, 458–71
121. Urbach, W., Hudson, M. A., Ullrich, W., Santarius, K. A., Heber, U. 1965. *Z. Naturforsch.* 20:890–98
122. Vishniac, W., Ochoa, S. 1952. *J. Biol. Chem.* 198:501–6
123. Walker, D. A. 1964. *Biochem. J.* 92:22C–23C
124. Walker, D. A. 1969. See Ref. 70, 1:250–57
125. Walker, D. A. 1974. *M.T.I. Int. Rev. Sci.,* Biochem. Sec., Vol. 11. In press
126. Walker, D. A., Cockburn, W., Baldry, C. W. 1967. *Nature* 216:597–99
127. Walker, D. A., Crofts, A. R. 1970. *Ann. Rev. Biochem.* 39:389–428
128. Walker, D. A., Hill, R. 1967. *Biochim. Biophys. Acta* 131:330–38
129. Wang, C. -T., Nobel, P. S. 1971. *Biochim. Biophys. Acta* 241:200–12
130. Werdan, K., Heldt, H. W. 1972. See Ref. 31, 1337–44
131. Werdan, K., Heldt, H. W., Geller, G. 1972. *Biochim. Biophys. Acta* 283:430–41
132. West, K. R., Wiskich, J. T. 1968. *Biochem. J.* 109:527–32
133. Wiesemann, R., Heber, U. Unpublished
134. Willenbrink, J., Kremer, P. 1973. *Planta* 113:173–78

Ann. Rev. Plant Physiol. 1974. 25:423–58

ENERGY CONSERVATION IN PHOTOSYNTHETIC ELECTRON TRANSPORT OF CHLOROPLASTS[1]

❖7573

A. Trebst

Abteilung Biologie, Ruhr-Universität Bochum, Germany

CONTENTS

INTRODUCTION 424
ELECTRON ACCEPTOR OF PHOTOSYSTEM I 426
    Endogenous Electron Acceptor 426
    Localization of the Acceptor Site of Photosystem I in the Membrane 428
ELECTRON DONOR OF PHOTOSYSTEM I 431
    Endogenous Electron Donor 431
    Artificial Electron Donors 432
    Cyclic Electron Flow Around Photosystem I 432
    Localization of the Donor Site of Photosystem I in the Membrane 433
ELECTRON ACCEPTOR OF PHOTOSYSTEM II 435
    Endogenous Electron Acceptor 435
    Artificial Electron Acceptors 436
    Localization of the Acceptor Site of Photosystem II in the Membrane 437
ELECTRON DONOR OF PHOTOSYSTEM II 438
    Endogenous Electron Donor 438
    Artificial Electron Donors 439
    Localization of the Donor Site of Photosystem II in the Membrane 440
FURTHER EVIDENCE FOR THE SIDEDNESS OF THE MEMBRANE 441
NONCYCLIC AND CYCLIC ELECTRON FLOW ACROSS THE THYLAKOID
    MEMBRANE 445
ENERGY CONSERVATION IN PHOTOSYNTHETIC ELECTRON FLOW 451

[1]Abbreviations used: CCP (carbonylcyanidephenylhydrazone); DAB (diaminobenzidine); DABS (*p*-(diazonium)-benzenesulfonic acid); DAD (diaminodurene); DBMIB (dibromothymoquinone); DCIP (dichlorophenolindophenol); DCMU (dichlorophenyldimethylurea); MV (methylviologen); PMS (methylphenazonium methosulfate); TMPD (*N*-tetramethyl-*p*-phenylenediamine).

INTRODUCTION

Photosynthetic electron flow in chloroplasts yields oxygen and NADPH (Hill reaction) and is coupled to ATP formation. The process is localized in the lamellar system (inner membrane) of the chloroplasts. The products of the light reactions (NADPH and ATP) in the lamellar system are used up by the enzymes of the CO_2 assimilation cycle localized in the matrix (stroma) of the chloroplasts.

The mechanism of the Hill reaction and of photophosphorylation is studied in washed, matrix free, isolated lamellar systems [osmotically shocked broken chloroplasts; class II chloroplasts designated type C according to Hall (107)]. Were it not for the use of artificial electron acceptors and donors, the discovery of both photosynthetic reactions of chloroplasts would have had to wait until the successful preparation of class I chloroplasts with an intact outer envelope. This is because ferredoxin—required for NADP reduction and possibly also the cofactor of physiological cyclic photophosphorylation—is lost during the preparation of broken chloroplasts. In describing photosynthetic oxygen evolution by chloroplasts, Hill in 1937 used ferricyanide as an artificial electron acceptor (124). Arnon discovered cyclic photophosphorylation in 1954 by adding menadione, an artificial cofactor, to broken chloroplasts in the light (6).

There are basically two types of electron donors and acceptors: electron donors feeding in before photosystem II or before photosystem I, and a feeding out to electron acceptors after photosystem II or after photosystem I. Cofactors of cyclic photophosphorylation are acceptors of photosystem I and donors for photosystem I at the same time. As Figure 1 indicates, such artificial or physiological electron donor and acceptor systems may be combined in any desired way to study a certain part of the native electron transport chain, provided the two components do not react with each other chemically. Figure 2 indicates a scheme for photosynthetic electron flow in which the possible position of certain carriers is indicated. This scheme shall not be discussed in detail here and should not be taken as the final word. It suffices for the points to be made in this review.

With new insights into the structure of the thylakoid membrane (181, 182, 204–206, 228), and particularly with the impact of the chemiosmotic theory of Mitchell (its relation to photosynthesis reviewed in 18, 73, 100, 121, 261, 313, 314), it became

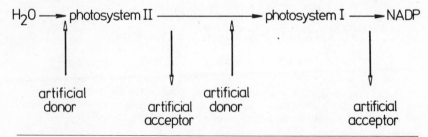

Figure 1 Native and artificial donors and acceptors in photosynthetic electron flow in the lamellar system of chloroplasts.

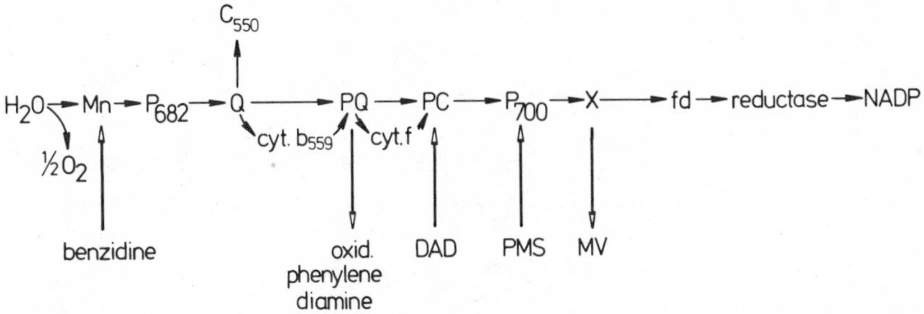

Figure 2   Functional location of some electron carriers in photosynthetic electron flow from water to NADP and the feed in and feed out of some artificial donors and acceptors. Abbreviations of the endogenous redox carriers appearing in this and the following electron flow schemes include: P_{700} and P_{682} = trapping centers of photosystems I and II; X and Q = primary electron acceptors of photosystems I and II; fd = ferredoxin; PC = plastocyanin; PQ = plastoquinone; C_{550} = compound absorbing at 550 nm.

obvious that more attention should be paid to the localization of functional parts of the electron flow system in the membrane, as has been pointed out by Racker (231). The relation of structure and function in chloroplasts has been reviewed recently by Park & Sane (228). Consideration of the topography of the membrane and particularly of the electron transport system has since then gained considerable interest. Witt and his colleagues proposed in 1968 that the two photosystems are crossing the membrane from the inside to the outside, yielding a positive charge inside and a negative charge outside. Hauska (112) offered a revised version of Racker's suggestion (231) as to the sides of the membrane involved in photosynthetic electron flow analogous to the one of mitochondria. The outer surface exposed in isolated lamellar systems of chloroplasts is the matrix side of the thylakoid of the grana and stroma lamellae (Figure 3). So far there is no procedure to obtain closed vesicles of chloroplast lamellae with the inner surface of the thylakoid turned outside. Disruption of the vesicle, of course, exposes the inner surface of such particles (like digitonin or French press fragmented or sonicated subchloroplast particles). Only very recently the properties of artificial electron donor and acceptor systems have been reevaluated in the light of the chemiosmotic theory. This means that the side of the membrane involved in the reduction of physiological as well as of artificial electron acceptors and equally in the oxidation of electron donors has to be considered. This has given new insight as to the number and location of energy conserving sites in noncyclic electron flow.

Many aspects of photosynthetic electron flow and energy conservation mechanisms have been reviewed recently in the *Annual Reviews of Biochemistry* (300), *Plant Physiology* (18, 21, 41, 61, 85, 127, 187, 209, 227, 228, 261) and *Microbiology* (121); also in *Current Topics in Bioenergetics* (14, 73, 100, 272), *Reviews of Bioenergetics* (2, 165), *Quarterly Review of Biophysics* (313); in Proceedings of photosynthesis meetings at Gatlinburg 1970 (229) and Stresa 1971 (87), at the Photobiology Congress at Bochum 1972 (254), and others (7, 59, 150, 181, 182, 205, 314).

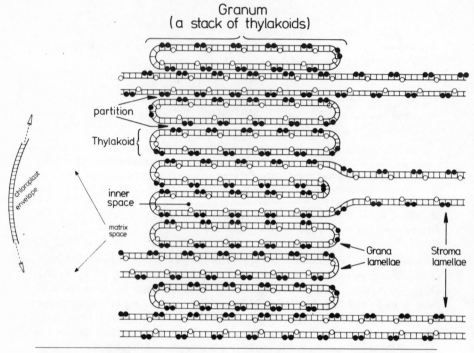

Figure 3 Schematic representation of the structure of the chloroplast lamellar system and the sides of membrane as referred to in the review (adopted from Mühlethaler).

This review will discuss the present status of the identification of the endogenous electron carriers at the donor and acceptor sites of the two photosystems and the evidence as to which side of the membrane might be involved and the methodical approach to obtain such evidence. By accepting then a sidedness of the membrane, a concept as to native and artificial energy-conserving sites in noncyclic and cyclic electron flow is presented.

ELECTRON ACCEPTOR OF PHOTOSYSTEM I

Endogenous Electron Acceptor

The reducing site of photosystem I provides a powerful reductant that rather unspecifically reduces a multitude of redox compounds. Among the first artificial compounds reduced were ferricyanide (124) and *p*-benzoquinone (301). Their reduction by chloroplast preparations in the light led to the discovery of photosynthetic oxygen evolution in cell-free systems long before the physiological electron acceptor of a Hill reaction was known. Besides benzo-, naphtho-, and anthraquinones, numerous dyes, DCIP, tetrazolium salts, methylred and dipyridylium salts are reduced (for summary see 283). With the dipyridylium salts the redox potential of the acceptor site of photosystem I has been measured to be around–550 mV (40, 179, 323). Certain acceptors of photosystem I with more positive redox potentials may also be reduced by photosystem II, as will be discussed later.

In vivo the acceptor for photosystem I in chloroplasts is ferredoxin (5, 279). It is now accepted that the ferredoxin-catalyzed reduction of NADP is the physiological Hill reaction and NADP the terminal acceptor of the electron transport chain of chloroplast lamellar systems. In blue-green algae, a flavodoxin called phytoflavin may replace ferredoxin in iron deficient cultures (48, 275). The reduction of NADP by ferredoxin is catalyzed by an enzyme, ferredoxin. NADP. oxido. reductase. This enzyme, crystallized by Shin et al (270), is bound to the chloroplast lamellae but is easily washed off by aging or fractionating the chloroplast. Avron & Jagendorf (17) earlier discovered the enzyme in chloroplasts via its diaphorase and transhydrogenase activity; its involvement in NADP reduction was demonstrated through an inhibition of NADP reduction by an antibody against the diaphorase, i.e. reductase (168, 253).

Ferredoxin forms a 1:1 complex with the ferredoxin-NADP reductase (42, 88, 212, 269). Via this complex ferredoxin may also be loosely bound to the membrane (123).

Soluble ferredoxin is not the primary acceptor of photosystem I. Recent experiments identified a "bound ferredoxin" as the primary acceptor by an absorption change at 430 nm and by ESR techniques as first observed by Hiyama & Ke (128) and Malkin & Bearden (193), respectively. The present status of the nature of the "bound ferredoxin" recently has been summarized and reviewed by Ke (165) and therefore need not be repeated here. The reaction mechanism between "bound ferredoxin" and soluble ferredoxin has not been clarified. Possibly factors described earlier in the literature as being involved in photosynthetic ferredoxin reduction may be participating. Neither the FRS (ferredoxin reducing substance) of Yocum & San Pietro (321, 322), ORS (oxygen reducing substance) of Honeycutt & Krogmann (132, 133), nor the S_{leth} of Regitz et al (238), which were thought to be related to the primary acceptor, are identical with the "bound ferredoxin." It seems possible that these factors may function after the bound ferredoxin. FRS was described as being required in addition to plastocyanin, ferredoxin, and Fd-NADP reductase in highly sonicated chloropasts in order to reduce NADP. Because FRS could be reduced first in the light in the absence of NADP, and NADP was then subsequently reduced in the dark, it seemed to have carrier function (321; see review 272). Unfortunately, it seems difficult to reproduce the exact conditions for liberation of FRS from the chloroplast membrane (290). FRS of Yocum and San Pietro was able to reverse the inhibition of an antibody prepared by Berzborn et al (37). By this experiment, a relation of FRS to S_{leth} of Regitz (238) was established (322). Berzborn et al (37) had described an antibody preparation against washed lamellae from *Antirrhinum* chloroplasts which in addition to antibodies against the Fd-NADP reductase and coupling factor contained a specific antibody inhibiting Hill reactions requiring ferredoxin (such as NADP, cytochrome *c*, or nitrite reduction by chloroplasts) but not the photoreduction of anthraquinone or methylviologen (37, 238).

Regitz et al (238) obtained a water-soluble fraction from ether-treated lyophilized chloroplasts, called S_{leth}, which would neutralize the antibody and inhibitions by it. S_{leth} therefore should contain the antigen responsible for the antibody formation and whose function close to the acceptor side of photosystem I in photosynthetic electron transport was inhibited by this antibody. Purification of S_{leth} led to a high molecular weight protein with an absorption at 275 (= HM_{275}) which carried the antigen properties, but so far it has no other detectable catalytic properties (239). Low molecular weight fractions which came off the membrane, together with the high molecular weight protein HM_{275}, were identified as flavonoids and p-coumaryl-meso-tartaric acid (221, 222). Whether these low molecular weight fractions constitute a lost prosthetic group of HM_{275} remains unclear.

At present the function of HM_{275} is best described as a protein required for reduction of soluble ferredoxin by chloroplast lamellae; it is not required for the reduction of methylviologen, anthraquinone, or ferricyanide (37, 238, 239), as judged by the influence on photosynthetic reactions of an antibody against it. This does not necessarily imply a functional role of HM_{275}, but possibly a structural role in that the reduction by chloroplasts of the soluble, charged, and relatively large ferredoxin requires a more definite structure at the reducing end of photosystem I than is needed for the reduction of low molecular weight Hill acceptors. Recently Selman et al (264) reported that DABS (see discussion on this chemical probe later) inhibits ferredoxin-dependent photoreductions but not the photoreduction of methylviologen. The relation of the compound labeled by DABS to HM_{275} has not yet been established, although the point of attack by DABS and the antibody described above seems to be the same.

S_{leth} and FRS are related to CRS, the cytochrome reducing substance of Fujita and co-workers (90, 91), and ORS, the oxygen reducing factor of Honeycutt & Krogmann (132, 133) in blue-green algae. This has been reviewed recently (272, 282, 322). Another component described for the function of photosystem I is a lipid requirement reported by Brand et al (50).

Localization of the Acceptor Site of Photosystem I in the Membrane

Lipophilic (quinones) as well as polar (ferricyanide or NADP and others) electron acceptors are easily reduced by the isolated lamellar system of chloroplasts. Their reaction with the endogenous acceptor of photosystem I is not limiting to the overall rate of a Hill reaction. This suggests that acceptors of photosystem I are reduced on the outside (matrix side) of the chloroplast thylakoid with a highly hydrophilic environment around the acceptor site of photosystem I. Of course, it makes physiological sense that the reduction of NADP occurs on the outside, i.e. the matrix side of the membrane, because the Calvin cycle enzymes which consume NADPH, formed in the light, are located in the matrix. However, there is more evidence that the reducing site of photosystem I is exposed in isolated lamellae of chloroplasts. Studies with antibodies proved particularly useful in determining the side of the membrane involved.

The use of an antibody against the ferredoxin-NADP reductase introduced the study of the photosynthetic membrane with the help of antibodies. Although at that time (168, 253) the aim was to clarify the role of the enzyme in photosynthetic electron transport, the results also gave the first information as to the sidedness of the Hill reaction. Obviously an antibody against a component of the membrane can react with its antigen only if the component is accessible to the antibody, i.e. located on the surface of the membrane vesicle. It is unlikely that a hydrophilic and large antibody can react with components buried in a membrane. It is also unlikely that an antibody can penetrate a membrane. The reaction of an antibody against a membrane component will tell which surface is involved as long as there is a closed vesicle, and therefore the inner space and inner surface are not accessible, and as long as no perturbation has occurred during preparation of the vesicle. In particles with no vesicle structure, however, both the inner and outer surface of the membrane are exposed. In addition, direct or indirect agglutination tests will indicate whether a component is on top of the membrane or in a crevice. This antibody technique is an approach to studying the structure of the membrane as introduced to chloroplasts by Menke (202, 202a) and Berzborn (31) and whose general background has been discussed recently by Koenig et al (176) and Berzborn (35). The antibody against the pure ferredoxin-NADP reductase was shown to inhibit the enzyme activity not only in the purified soluble state but also when the enzyme was still bound to the membrane (168, 253). A more detailed study by Berzborn (31–34) showed that the antibody against the reductase does precipitate the solubilized enzyme as expected but is not able to precipitate the chloroplasts. This means that though the antibody reacted with the enzyme on the membrane (because its function was inhibited) the antibody could not crosslink. Indirect agglutination tests proposed by Coombs (precipitation occurs by adding an antibody against the immunoglobulin of the rabbit after the antibody against the reductase had reacted) or the mixed agglutination test proposed by Uhlenbruck (precipitation by adding solubilized enzyme after the antibody had been reacted with the bound enzyme) were positive (see Figure 4). This led Berzborn to postulate that the ferredoxin-NADP reductase is located on the surface of the membrane but somewhat buried in a crevice or depression (32–34). The antibody reaches the antigen with only one of its two reaction sites and does not extend out of the crevice far enough to get to a second antigen. After removal of the coupling factor by EDTA, the antibody against the reductase would give direct agglutination (33). This indicates that the crevice for the reductase is partly formed by the coupling factor.

As already discussed, the ferredoxin-NADP reductase forms a stoichiometric complex with ferredoxin (42, 88, 212, 269). Because the reductase is bound to the membrane the complex leads also to a binding of ferredoxin on the membrane. This was shown directly by Hiedemann-Van Wyk & Kannangara (123) by an antibody against ferredoxin which was able to precipitate the chloroplasts. It proves that both the reductase and ferredoxin are bound to the outside of the membrane.

The antibody preparation against a component on the reducing site of photosystem I which is inhibiting ferredoxin reduction (37, 238) has been described above. Because this antibody does react with the thylakoid membrane, again this compound (and therefore S_{leth}) is located on the outside.

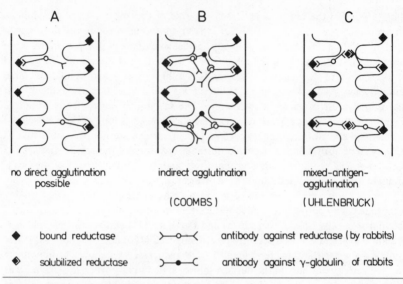

A	B	C
no direct agglutination possible	indirect agglutination (COOMBS)	mixed-antigen-agglutination (UHLENBRUCK)

◆   bound reductase   )—o—⟨   antibody against reductase (by rabbits)

◈   solubilized reductase   )—•—⟨   antibody against γ-globulin of rabbits

Figure 4 Schematic representation of the reaction of an antibody with its antigen in a membrane (adopted from Berzborn 33).

Recently also an antibody against an enriched P_{700} preparation (photosystem I pigment) has been described (231). The antibody does react with P_{700} because an externally added plastocyanin-stimulated ascorbate photooxidation was inhibited. Because also the chloroplasts were agglutinated, P_{700}-protein seems to be accessible from the outside.

Koenig et al (176) prepared antibodies against desoxycholate fractions of chloroplasts which showed differential activity of photosystem I or II. Of the antibodies against two different photosystem I fractions, one inhibited photosystem I activity in intact lamellae while the other did so only after disrupture of the membrane, suggesting that one antibody was against the inside and the other against the outside of photosystem I. Briantais & Picaud (58) prepared antibodies against enriched photosystem I and photosystem II preparations as obtained after fractionation of chloroplast membranes with triton. They showed that the antibody against the photosystem I fraction would also react with and precipitate the isolated lamellar system, whereas the antibody against photosystem II would do so to a much lesser extent (57, 58). They concluded that photosystem I is therefore accessible in the lamellar system. They take their results as proof for the binary model of Arntzen, Dilley & Crane (8) for the chloroplast lamellae. The binary model of the structure of the thylakoid membrane visualizes photosystem I particles arranged on the outer part (half) of the thylakoid on top of the photosystem II particle on the inner part (8). This model agrees well with the interpretation of electron microscope evidence (by freeze etch techniques) for two kind of particles in the thylakoid membrane (Mühlethaler 204–206, Branton & Park 54). The membrane is fractured along an interior layer by freeze etching and possibly also by the methods of chloroplast fragmentation [digitonin (8, 305), triton (56, 294), sonication (145), and French press (9, 10, 252)].

Dilley et al recently supported the model by using a chemical probe, labeled p-(diazonium)-benzene sulfonic acid (DABS) (74). This compound cannot penetrate into a membrane and therefore will label only reactive groups located on the outside of a membrane (27). After labeling with DABS fractionation of the chloroplast membrane into photosystem I and II particles yielded mainly DABS labeled particles containing photosystem I. Recently further experiments were able to localize one of the labeling points of DABS among the functional components of photosystem I because a DABS labeled photosystem I is still able to photoreduce methylviologen, but not NADP (264). Possibly then DABS is reacting with the component of the acceptor site of photosystem I described as S_{leth} by Regitz et al (238), as already discussed.

From the evidence with hydrophilic acceptors, antibodies, and chemical probes it is clear that photosystem I is oriented towards the outer surface (matrix side) of the membrane. More specifically, the acceptor site of photosystem I including ferredoxin, ferredoxin-NADP reductase, and an unknown (structural?) component of ferredoxin reduction (FRS, ORS, and S_{leth}, a site of DABS labeling) are exposed and accessible to a hydrophilic environment.

ELECTRON DONOR OF PHOTOSYSTEM I

Endogenous Electron Donor

The concept of two light reactions in series developed from the observation of Duysens (78) that cytochrome f is reduced by short wavelength light (photosystem II) and oxidized by long wavelength light (photosystem I). Because of a supposed temperature insensitivity of its photooxidation (the measured absorption change was probably due to a cytochrome b_{559} change), cytochrome f was proposed to be the immediate electron donor for photosystem I (60, 207, 312), but later work has shown a gradual displacement of cytochrome f by plastocyanin as the primary photooxidant of photosystem I (reviews 41, 187). Recently several groups reported on the stimulation of cytochrome f photooxidation by plastocyanin (19, 110, 125, 214, 230) in sonicated chloroplasts. However, since such experiments can be performed only in fragmented plastocyanin deficient chloroplasts, it was argued that plastocyanin would merely replace cytochrome f, which as the actual donor is spaced from the reaction center by the fragmentation procedure (86, 144, 208). Finally, in the development of the relative position of cytochrome f to plastocyanin, Haehnel (105) reported, on the basis of flash light experiments, that cytochrome f possibly is not located in the main electron flow from plastoquinone to P_{700} in contrast to plastocyanin (106), through which more than 90% of the electrons proceed. This seems to be in contradiction to recent experiments by Biggins (38) and Larkum & Bonner (184–186) on cytochrome f absorption changes in continuous light and their dependence on excitation conditions, inhibitors, and the type of chloroplasts. These authors supported a functional role of cytochrome f in cyclic as well as noncyclic electron flow.

A number of important plastocyanin inhibitors have recently been introduced: histones and polylysine (28, 49, 52), KCN (at $10^{-2}M$) (226) and low concentration of Hg^{++} (170, 172). It was shown that polylysine (52) as well as Hg (172) inhibit electron flow between cytochrome f and photosystem I in otherwise untreated chloroplasts, i.e. plastocyanin functions after cytochrome f also in intact chloroplast lamellae. One reaches the conclusion that the present evidence highly favors plastocyanin as the immediate electron donor for photosystem I.

Artificial Electron Donors

Artificial electron donors for photosystem I have been used extensively to study part reactions of photosystem I. The couple DCIP/ ascorbate was the first to be introduced by Vernon & Zaugg (297). They showed that $DCIPH_2$, kept reduced by ascorbate, reverses the inhibition of NADPH formation when photosystem II and the photooxidation of water is blocked by DCMU. Phenylenediamines like TMPD or DAD proved later to be a particularly active group of electron donors for photosystem I (281, 285, 306). Again catalytic amounts of phenylenediamines were used and kept reduced by excess ascorbate. Ascorbate (83, 161) as well as reduced cytochrome c (217) without a mediator are not electron donors for photosystem I in intact lamellar systems.

A major difference emerged as to the coupling of the donor systems. It was shown that the DCIP/ascorbate system (167, 190, 285, 286, 306) as well as the DAD/ascorbate system (285) were coupled to ATP formation, whereas the TMPD/ascorbate system was not (139, 281, 285, 306). Recently this was attributed to the chemical properties of the phenylenediamine (115), as will be discussed later. In fragmented chloroplasts these electron donor systems require plastocyanin (83, 153, 162, 298). Only DCIP at very high concentrations is able to bypass plastocyanin to a certain extent (83, 159).

The direct coupling to ATP formation of the electron donor systems to photosystem I has been questioned (13, 101, 102). Indeed, it seems likely that some of the high P/e_2 ratio reported in the early paper (286) is due to a superimposed cyclic electron flow. Some supported the view of direct coupling (114, 186, 267, 268, 277) and even postulated two coupling sites in the DCIP donor system (216). This question as to the coupling and the true P/e_2 ratio in donor systems for photosystem I will be taken up later in this review.

Cyclic Electron Flow Around Photosystem I

A number of artificial electron donors for photosystem I like DCIP or DAD also were shown to be cofactors of cyclic photophosphorylation if added to chloroplasts in the absence of ascorbate (284, 285). Indeed, the only difference between an electron donor system for photosystem I and a cyclic system is the way the donor is reduced. In the first case the donor is kept reduced by ascorbate, and an acceptor is added to be reduced in substrate amounts, whereas in the cyclic system the cofactor is acting as a donor as well as an acceptor. Cyclic photophosphorylation was discovered by Arnon et al when they added menadione or FMN (6, 307) to isolated chloroplasts. It was later shown that cyclic electron flow involves only photosystem I and is not inhibited by DCMU (see 18). Many quinones were found to be cofactors of cyclic electron flow (284). PMS turned out to be by far the best cofactor of cyclic photophosphorylation (146). By comparing the redox potential of quinones and other compounds and their ability to catalyze cyclic electron flow, it became apparent that the redox potential of a cyclic cofactor has to be more negative than zero volts. Kandler (155) and Trebst & Eck (284) concluded that the cofactor in its reduced state reacts with plastoquinone (which has a redox potential close to zero). A participation of plastoquinone was more directly shown by studies with petroleum ether-extracted chloroplasts (183) and recently with the plastoquinone antagonist dibromothymoquinone (46), which did inhibit such cyclic systems. However, there are notable exceptions to this. The cofactors of cyclic photophosphorylation PMS, as well as DAD and DCIP, have more positive redox potentials than zero volts. These cyclic systems are not inhibited by the plastoquinone antagonist DBMIB (46). Because, as discussed above, the DAD and DCIP systems require the addition of plastocyanin in fragmented chloroplasts, it is safe to assume that these systems close the cycle around photosystem I via plastocyanin. This is supported by the recently noted result that these systems are inhibited by the plastocyanin inhibitors KCN (226) or polylysine (49). Reduced PMS, on the other hand, was found to be able to react even directly with the donor site of P_{700} (314). This can be concluded also from recent experiments with KCN. High concentrations of KCN inhibit plastocyanin but still do not inhibit PMS catalyzed cyclic electron flow completely (226).

One may summarize that a cofactor of cyclic electron flow in isolated lamellar systems is an acceptor of photosystem I and closes the electron flow cycle back to the donor site of photosystem I by reacting in three different ways: (a) with plastoquinone, (b) plastocyanin, or (c) with P_{700}.

Cytochrome b_{563} usually has been implicated as a participant in cyclic electron flow (see bibliographies in 7, 18, 21, 41, 85, 127, 173, 175, 187, 228). Böhme & Cramer (44) recently produced direct evidence for an energy coupling site in cytochrome b_{563} oxidation. Several lines of experiments (38, 184) supported or schemes (particularly of Arnon 7, 175; see also 228) included cytochrome f in cyclic electron flow. Further support is also provided by the isolation of a cytochrome b_{563}-cytochrome f particle from chloroplasts (213). Because the oxidation of cytochrome b_{563} was inhibited by DBMIB, plastoquinone seems to be involved (44) in such a hypothetical cyclic system. The inclusion of plastoquinone, however, renders a cyclic system spatially and functionally separate from noncyclic flow more difficult to visualize.

Localization of the Donor Site of Photosystem I in the Membrane

Witt (313, 314) and Schliephake et al (255) were first to produce evidence for the sidedness of the chloroplast membrane according to the chemiosmotic theory. They found that the reaction centers of both photosystems I and II produce a charge separation across the membrane upon illumination, with the positive charge inside. Each photosystem would contribute half of the electric field generated (255). This indicates that the donor site and acceptor site of photosystem I should be located on different sides of the membrane, with the donor site inside or towards the inside of the membrane. The sidedness of photosystem I was substantiated by the experiments of Hauska et al (110, 113, 231) with an antibody against plastocyanin, the immediate electron donor for photosystem I. A specific antibody against plastocyanin is not able to react with plastocyanin in intact chloroplast lamellar vesicles, i.e. no inhibition of the Hill reaction or donor systems for photosystem I and also no agglutination occurs. Upon sonication in the presence of the antibody, inhibition did occur, which was explained by an opening of the membrane during the sonication procedure, liberating plastocyanin or permitting access of the antibody. An antibody against cytochrome f also did not react with intact chloroplast lamellae, but it did inhibit photophosphorylation when present during sonication of the chloroplasts (231).

Furthermore, the light-induced oxidation of cytochrome f stimulated by plastocyanin in sonicated chloroplasts is inhibited by the antibodies against cytochrome f or plastocyanin only when the antibody is present during sonication (110). Both antibodies reacted with externally added plastocyanin or cytochrome f. From this it was concluded that both plastocyanin and cytochrome f are not accessible from the outside and possibly are located inside the membrane (110, 112, 113, 231). Cramer recently reported that reduced cytochrome f—as opposed to cytochrome b_{559}—is only slowly reoxidized by ferricyanide in the dark, indicating a burial of cytochrome f in the membrane. Light cycles before the addition of ferricyanide, however, increased its accessibility and therefore the rate of oxidation (66).

The notion that the donor site of photosystem I is located in or inside the membrane is supported by recent experiments with charged and hydrophilic (vs lipophilic) electron donors for photosystem I. By comparing PMS and pyocyanine with their sulfo derivatives which have similar redox potentials but very different lipophilicity and polarity, Hauska found that sulfo-PMS or sulfopyocyanine are not cofactors of cyclic electron flow (111). The same is observed when 1, 2-or 1,4-naphthoquinones are compared in cyclic photophosphorylation with their sulfonic acid derivatives, lumiflavin with riboflavin and FMN and indophenol (DCIP) with sulfoindophenol (sulfo-DCIP) (115). The polar hydrophilic derivatives as against the parent lipophilic compounds are cofactors of pseudocyclic but not of cyclic photophosphorylation. From this it is deduced that polar derivatives are reduced by photosystem I, but their reduced forms are not oxidized by photosystem I. This was interpreted to indicate that the acceptor site of photosystem I is not accessible to polar hydrophilic compounds. Also sulfo-DCIP/ascorbate is not an electron donor system for photosystem I in intact chloroplast lamellae, but it does react in fragmented chloroplasts where the donor site of photosystem I is exposed (115). The hydrophilic ascorbate (83, 161) and the large protein cytochrome c (217) are also not electron donors in intact lamellae vesicles, but they are donors in fragmented chloroplasts.

The conclusion that plastocyanin is located in or inside the chloroplast inner membrane is not easily reconciled with the experiments with polylysine. It was shown that this compound inhibits photosystem I reactions (49) and specifically inhibits between cytochrome f and P_{700} (52). Because polylysine does react with solubilized plastocyanin (of chloroplasts but not of the positively charged plastocyanin of blue green algae) the inference that polylysine inhibits electron flow by blocking plastocyanin seems valid (52). However, recent experiments show that polylysine also inhibits sonicated chloroplasts devoid of plastocyanin (51). Polylysine (at low concentrations) even stimulated the activation of photosystem I activity by plastocyanin in such chloroplasts (51). This might be explained by assuming that polylysine, by blocking negative charges of the membrane, enables the negatively charged plastocyanin to get to its functional site. The inhibition of photosystem I activity by polycations is prevented by salt, trypsin, light, or lecithin coating, also suggesting that the inhibition depends on negatively charged goups on the surface of the membrane not identical with the plastocyanin itself (28). Neutralization of the negative charges on the outside of the membrane by reaction with a carbodiimid + glycine methyl ester (to be discussed later) protects photosystem I from inhibition by polylysine (29). Conformational changes also might be implicated, including an opening of the partition. There is therefore a possibility that polylysine inhibits plastocyanin function by conformational changes induced from the outside.

ELECTRON ACCEPTOR OF PHOTOSYSTEM II

Endogenous Electron Acceptor

The primary acceptor of photosystem II is the quencher of its fluorescence, designated Q by Duysens (77, 78), which is followed by a much larger pool of a secondary quencher A (see Amesz 2). The two pools are functionally separated by the inhibitor DCMU. There seems to be no disagreement that the large pool A is identical with plastoquinone, whose concentration in the membrane is about 10 to 20 times larger than the concentration of Q (see 2, 312) or about 5 molecules per electron transport chain (313). The large pool A, i.e. plastoquinone, acts as electron buffer between the two light reactions (312, 313). Recent results proved the important fact that several electron flow chains may feed electrons from photosystem II into this pool, i.e. two or more reaction centers of photosystem II may reduce the same plastoquinone molecule (70, 79, 194, 273, 274, 311, 312). The main experimental approach to this involves comparing the DCMU sensitivity at low and high light intensity. Siggel et al (273) estimated that as many as ten chains may be involved in this cooperation of several electron transport chains. The chemical nature of Q is not yet sufficiently clear. Stiehl & Witt suggested Q to be a separate small plastoquinone pool which is reduced to the semiquinone (276). Plastoquinone as a primary acceptor of photosystem II was supported by Kohl (177), who by ESR experiments concluded that a plastoquinone chromanoxylion is the primary acceptor. This was recently suggested also by Diner & Mauzerall (76). On the other hand, the experiments of Böhme & Cramer suggest that cytochrome b_{559} (in the low potential form) is located before the main pool of plastoquinone because its oxidation by photosystem I is inhibited by the plastoquinone antagonist DBMIB (43, 45). The latter result, though not the interpretation, has recently been supported by Anderson et al (4). Furthermore, cytochrome b_{559} acts as a secondary quencher of fluorescence in the presence of DCMU (67) and is still present in and reduced by highly purified photosystem II reaction center particles (166). Joliot & Joliot also found a relation of cytochrome b_{559} to a quencher of photosystem II in their elaborate scheme of the photoacts of photosystem II (148). The compound C_{550}, discovered by absorption changes at 550 nm by Knaff & Arnon (174), is related to the primary acceptor of photosystem II and probably a sensing pigment for the redox state of the quencher (see Butler 59). Extraction and reconstitution experiments suggest that C_{550} is β-carotene (223).

The midpoint redox potential(s) of the acceptor site of photosystem II has been reevaluated by Cramer & Butler, who report values of −35 mV and −270 mV (68). Amesz et al have also found about −150 mV for the redox potential of the quencher of photosystem II (3).

Artificial Electron Acceptors

Artificial electron acceptors may be reduced by photosystem II to yield a Hill reaction (oxygen evolution and reduction of an acceptor) without the participation of photosystem I. Ferricyanide and DCIP were often considered in the past to be electron acceptors of photosystem II (16, 188, 190, 197, 220, 249, 257, 312), but conflicting results emerged, particularly from measurement of the quantum requirement and enhancement because, contrary to the above authors, others did find enhancement (39, 98, 308). Govindjee & Bazzar (99), Kok et al (180), and Lien & Bannister (188) came to the conclusion that both photosystems, but photosystem I preferentially, reduce ferricyanide and DCIP. Rumberg et al (249) suggested that high concentrations of ferricyanide would be accepting electrons from photosystem II but only in flashing light experiments and at moderate frequencies (see also 152).

The problem of the specificity of photoreductions by photosystem II recently has been resolved. The reduction of ferricyanide and DCIP by photosystem II depends on the accessibility of these compounds to the acceptor site of photosystem II. In freshly prepared thylakoid membranes this side is very much covered up (as will be discussed in more detail below), and ferricyanide and DCIP are reduced preferentially by photosystem I. The rate of reduction by photosystem II, is only about 40% of the rate by photosystem I, according to experiments of Böhme et al (46) and those of Kimimura & Katoh (172), or even less than 10% according to Izawa et al (141) and Ouitrakul & Izawa (226). This is concluded from experiments with inhibitors which block electron flow from photosystem II to photosystem I, such as dibromothymoquinone (46, 282), KCN (226), or $HgCl_2$ (172). However, in fragmented chloroplasts (e.g. sonication), isolated photosystem II particles, or *Euglena* chloroplasts, this rate of photoreduction of ferricyanide or DCIP by photosystem II is increased (162, 163, 293) because now the acceptor site of photosystem II has been exposed. The photoreduction of ferricyanide or DCIP in sonicated spinach or in *Euglena* chloroplasts is no longer inhibited by DBMIB (46, 282). Therefore, in relating the rate of Hill reactions with polar acceptors to photoreductions by photosystem II and conclusions as to the efficiency of photosystem II, the state of the chloroplast employed in the experiments is of great importance.

Saha et al (251) have recently devised a general concept as to photoreductions of electron acceptors by photosystem I and II. They grouped Hill acceptors in classes according to lipophilicity and polarity. Hydrophilic acceptors turned out to be acceptors of photosystem I and lipophilic ones to be acceptors of photosystem II. Oxidized phenylenediamines and benzoquinones turned out to be excellent artificial electron acceptors of photosystem II (which does not mean that they may not be reduced also by photosystem I!). Saha et al (251) first concluded this from the $P/_{e_2}$ ratio obtained in photoreductions of oxidized phenylenediamines. Recently the concept of Saha et al has been proved correct by the use of the inhibitors already mentioned. In the presence of the plastocyanin antagonists $HgCl_2$ (161, 170, 172), KCN (226), and polylysine (225), photoreductions of oxidized phenylenediamines or certain benzoquinones occur at almost undiminished rates. The same has been observed when the plastoquinone antagonist DBMIB is employed (141, 287–289). Thus photoreductions by photosystem II can now be measured easily even in intact lamellar systems of chloroplasts by using these lipophilic acceptors and by blocking electron flow from photosystem II to photosystem I by one of the inhibitors. The importance of these experiments on photoreductions by photosystem II for the site of energy conservation in photosynthetic electron flow will be discussed later.

Photoreductions by photosystem II are still DCMU sensitive. Miles et al (203), however, reported that the photoreduction of Hg^{++} is DCMU insensitive. Brandon suggested from the effects of α-benzyl-α-bromo-malodinitrile on photosystem II that the compound may be also a DCMU insensitive acceptor of photosystem II (53).

Localization of the Acceptor Site of Photosystem II in the Membrane

The requirement of lipophilicity for an artificial electron acceptor for photoreductions by photosystem II indicates that the acceptor site of photosystem II is buried inside the lipophilic region of the membrane. Antibodies to photosystem II particles prepared by Briantais & Picaud (58) were less active in agglutinating intact chloroplast lamellae, and an antibody against an antigen on the surface of intact lamellae is not in the antiserum against photosystem II particles. From this the authors (58) supported the model of Arntzen et al (8), mentioned above. However, there is also evidence that the acceptor site of photosystem II is close to the surface of the thylakoid, though still in a lipophilic region and not in the hydrophilic environment (of the matrix). Indeed, the revised structural model of Mühlethaler (205) discusses an extension of the inside particle to the surface of the membrane. The antibody against photosystem II fractions from chloroplasts by Koenig et al (176) did inhibit photosystem II activity (though not necessarily on the acceptor site). Radunz, Schmidt, and Menke found that antibodies against chlorophyll *a* as well as against plastoquinone do react with photosystem II and plastoquinone respectively (232, 234, 235, 256). Though the rate of inhibition of photosynthesis by these antibodies is only about 15%, it seems to indicate that the acceptor site of photosystem II, and plastoquinone in particular, is located towards the outside and is accessible, although only to a small extent.

Earlier Witt and his colleagues at Berlin had already suggested, in view of the chemiosmotic theory, that on illumination photosystem II is transporting electrons across the membrane (313, 314), as already discussed in relation to the localization of photosystem I. Schliephake et al (255) observed a charge separation across the membrane upon illumination of either photosystems and proposed that the donor and acceptor sites of photosystem II (as well as of photosystem I) are located on different sites of the membrane, the acceptor site being outside. Grünhagen & Witt showed that the decay of this electric field corresponds to the rise of the ΔpH across the membrane (103). Junge & Ausländer (151, 152) produced evidence that ferricyanide reduction by photosystem II via plastoquinone (in flashing light experiments) occurs on the outside of the membrane. A statement in this paper refers to a covering protein layer as indicated by the conditions which facilitate the access of the polar ferricyanide to plastoquinone (152). Reinwald et al showed that the well-established proton pump of chloroplasts is due to a plastoquinone loop in the electron transport chain (240). Protons are taken up from the outside during the reduction of plastoquinone by photosystem II, and upon oxidation of plastohydroquinone inside protons are released. This indicates that the pair plastoquinone/plastohydroquinone is traversing the membrane, and from this it follows that plastoquinone is located and reduced on the outside close enough to a water phase to obtain protons. The pH dependence of the redox potential of the quencher Q indicated that the reduction of the quencher itself requires a proton uptake, possibly also from the outside (68).

Cytochrome b_{559} has been implicated as being located close to the quencher (45, 67). It is easily oxidized by, and therefore accessible to, ferricyanide in the dark as against cytochrome f, whose dark oxidation by ferricyanide is slow (66).

ELECTRON DONOR OF PHOTOSYSTEM II

Endogenous Electron Donor

The electron donor in photosynthesis of green plants of course, is water. From the oscillations in the yield of oxygen upon illumination of *Chlorella* or chloroplasts with single short flashes, a four quantum process in oxygen evolution is deduced. Four trapping centers are transformed consecutively from stage S_0 to S_3 upon illumination, which then on the fourth flash releases oxygen and returns to stage S_0. Stage S_1 is the most stable stage and therefore already the third flash releases the first molecule of O_2 after a dark period. Cheniae has recently summarized the biochemistry and biophysics of photosystem II and oxygen evolution (61). Manganese is involved in the process of water photooxidation. New experiments by Cheniae since his review (61) have clarified that there are 5 to 8 manganese atoms per photosystem II trapping centers in *Scenedesmus* and 4 to 6 in spinach chloroplasts rather than 2 to 3 (63).

The discovery of specific inhibitors [high concentrations of carbonylcyanide-phenylhydrazones (241, 316), NH_2OH (26, 80, 147), high NH_3, or methylamine concentrations (142) and others (160, 164)] between water oxidation and photosystem II and specific treatments inactivating water oxidation but not photosystem II [tris treatment (317, 320), gentle heating (47, 163, 171, 318), KCl treatment (12), and chaotropic reagents like perchlorate (191)] helped clarify the reactions on the donor site of photosystem II. The inhibition of water oxidation by antibodies and chemical probes deserves special discussion later. The mode of action of ADRY substances is to accelerate the deactivation reaction of the water splitting system Y, i.e. they decrease the lifetime of the higher stages of S (242, 243). Cheniae & Martin described in greater detail the dependence of the inactivation of oxygen evolution by hydroxylamine treatment on conditions (63). Ort & Izawa reported on a particularly effective but gentle treatment for inactivation of oxygen evolution by hydroxylamine + EDTA (224).

Artificial Electron Donors

In such inhibited or treated chloroplasts water may be replaced by artificial electron donors. Hydroquinones (319), phenylenediamines (319), benzidine (319), semicarbazide (116, 319), diphenylcarbazide (293, 295), hydrazobenzol (116, 117), hydrazine (117, 196), hydroxylamine (25, 26, 116, 292), cysteine (163), ascorbate (23, 47), diketogulonic acid (104), and Mn^{++}ions (22, 24, 104, 138, 169) have been reported as donors. Recently it was shown that H_2O_2 (135, 136) and tetraphenylboron (129, 130) are also electron donors for photosystem II. Several reaction sites between oxygen evolution and photosystem II have been implicated (12, 164, 171) on the basis of differential activity by donors with some of the inhibitors of inactivation treatments mentioned above. Instead of several sites between water and photosystem II, these results might rather reflect the degree of destruction (and of manganese extraction) on the cooperativity of the water oxidation complex. As Kok pointed out, artificial donors replace the complete water oxidation system rather than using part of its components. Restoration of electron flow from water to photosystem II also depends on the degree of the inactivation treatment. Simply poising the redox state (315) or adding manganese (137) restores electron flow after mild treatment, whereas after severe treatment and complete extraction of the endogenous manganese, or in severe manganese deficiency of the Euglena cells the chloroplasts were obtained from, no restoration of oxygen evolution and even no electron flow from artificial electron donors is possible (62, 119).

Some of the results obtained from the use of artificial electron donor systems for photosystem II are difficult to evaluate because a number of side reactions have not been taken into account sufficiently in studies on the mechanism of noncyclic flow or on the development of the photosynthetic apparatus.

1.Some of the artificial electron donor systems for photosystem II are also electron donors for photosystem I, such as hydroquinones or phenylenediamines and ascorbate (the latter depending on the structural integrity of the chloroplast preparation)

2. Some of the reported electron donors are active in fragmented chloroplasts or purified photosystem II particles only and are not very effective in intact thylakoid membranes. Vernon & Shaw (295) already pointed this out when they described the system DPC/DCIP as well suited to study only photosystem II activity. This means that the donor site (as well as the acceptor side) of photosystem II is not readily accessible in intact membranes by hydrophilic or charged donors.

3. Some electron donors (and also inhibitors before photosystem II) rapidly inactivate photosystem II. This happens with components like CCP or tetraphenylboron (129, 130). Such donors are therefore not useful for steady state experiments.

4. Some of the components, like hydrazine (196), are further oxidized chemically by molecular oxygen in chain reactions after initial oxidation by photosystem II. Of particular importance is the oxidation of electron donors by the superoxide anion radical which is formed by autoxidation of the reducing end of photosystem I by molecular oxygen. The superoxide radical will oxidize ascorbate (1, 81, 82, 84), for example, or sulfite (11). Elstner et al (81) have pointed out that the increased oxygen uptake observed when ascorbate is added to chloroplasts is probably due to such a superoxide radical oxidation rather than to an electron feed (see 23, 47). Because of cycling (82), stoichiometry of oxygen uptake to electrons transferred in such photooxidations is higher than 1:2 or 1:3 as calculated from a MV dependent pseudocyclic electron flow (84).

5. As mentioned above, mild inactivation treatments are reversible by redox state poising; then water is again the electron donor.

6. The oxidation products of an electron donor like diphenylcarbazone (from DPC) (271, 296) or azobenzene (116) may introduce additional effects.

Localization of the Donor Site of Photosystem II in the Membrane

The problem of accessibility of electron donors for photosystem II, as just discussed, is in agreement with the general notion that photosystem II is buried in a lipophilic area of the membrane and, according to the first binary model, even below photosystem I on the inside face of the membrane (8). Only lipophilic donors can approach photosystem II in intact chloroplast lamellae, but hydrophilic donors can also do so in fragmented chloroplasts (282). However, photosystem II is accessible to a certain extent from the matrix surface of the chloroplast lamellae. More specifically, the donor site of photosystem II seems to be exposed. This can be seen from studies with chemical probes (30, 74, 92, 93), with antibodies (55, 176, 234, 256), and with trypsin digestion (262, 263).

As already discussed, in the dark the nonpermeable DABS labels mainly photosystem I but not photosystem II (74). More detailed studies (30, 92, 93) have revealed that photosystem II is also labeled, but only in the light. The observed fourfold increases in DABS labeling of photosystem II in the light is interpreted to indicate a conformational change of photosystem II, exposing it to the outside. This conformational change would seem to expose the donor site of photosystem II, because DABS inhibits photoreductions at the expense of water, but not of DPC (92, 93). DCMU prevents the conformational change of photosystem II because there is little labeling of photosystem II in its presence. The DCMU inhibition of the increase in DABS labeling is not reversed by PMS catalyzed cyclic electron flow or proton uptake (no effect of uncouplers), indicating that not the energized state of the membrane, but the illumination of photosystem II as such is bringing about the assumed conformational change. Also in tris-washed chloroplasts, DABS labeling by photosystem II is increased in the light (93). Other chemical probes will be considered later.

The conclusion that the donor site of photosystem II is accessible from the outside to a small extent is also supported by the work with antibodies. Braun & Govindjee (55) reported that an antibody against photosystem II particles inactivates oxygen evolution to a small extent but does not influence artificial donor systems for photosystem II (55). This antibody does not agglutinate chloroplast lamellae (55), indicating that the exposure of water oxidation does occur in a crevice. According to Koenig et al (176), the antibody against photosystem II fractions from chloroplasts inhibited DPC oxidation in intact lamallae. An antibody against lutein, recently described by Radunz & Schmidt (234), inhibits photosystem II when water is the electron donor, but not when DPC is added. Again a conformational change of the donor site of photosystem II is implicated because the inhibition of the antibody depends on the absence of the uncoupler methylamine, i.e. opposite to DABS labeling. The antibody will agglutinate the chloroplast only in an indirect agglutination test (Coombs) indicating a crevice on the membrane surface (234).

Trypsin also inactivates specifically the donor site of photosystem II, inhibiting electron flow between water and DPC (262, 263). Electron flow through photosystem I is not effected, according to Selman et al (262, 263), whereas Strotmann et al (277, 278) did conclude that trypsin treatment inactivates (certain) cyclic electron flow around photosystem I. These experiments with digestive enzymes are possibly not as indicative about the side of the membrane involved as studies with antibodies or chemical probes because the enzymes might bring about a general breakdown of the membrane (195), although the experiments of Selman et al (263) do show a specific effect.

These experiments with antibodies, chemical probes, and trypsin indicate then that the donor site of photosystem II may be exposed to the outer surface, especially in the light. Giaquinta et al (92) suggested, therefore, that a conformational change of the water-splitting complex will release oxygen to the outside of the chloroplasts.

On the other hand, other experiments and considerations led to the hypothesis that the water-splitting reaction should be on the inside of the chloroplast inner membrane. This view has been particularly supported by Witt, Junge, and their colleagues (149, 152, 154, 255, 313, 314). As already discussed, illumination of photosystem II leads to a positive charge inside and a membrane potential across the membrane (255, 313, 314). Junge (149) and Junge & Ausländer (151, 152) provided more direct evidence that the water-splitting reaction releases protons inside the membrane. This is in agreement with recent work by Fowler (89), who showed that the third flash of light after a dark period liberates 1 mole of oxygen and 4 protons at the same time. Because of a time lag and the requirement for an uncoupler, Fowler suggests that the proton release occurs inside the membrane.

FURTHER EVIDENCE FOR THE SIDEDNESS OF THE MEMBRANE

The work with antibodies against components of the chloroplast membrane, as well as chemical probes, have proved to be valuable in studying components located on accessible sides of the membrane. The matrix side will be accessible in isolated chloroplast lamellae with an intact vesicle structure, but after fragmentation or even perturbation additional "faces" or even the inside become accessible. So far only antibodies affecting electron transport have been discussed. Antibodies against other components have added further evidence on the location of these compounds and the structure of the chloroplast in general. The first antibody against a chloroplast component to be studied in detail was the one against the coupling factor CF_1. The antibody preparation of Berzborn et al (37), discussed above, prepared against the whole thylakoid membrane, contained antibodies against CF_1 besides antibodies against the ferredoxin NADP reductase and the reducing side of photosystem I (S_{leth}). McCarty & Racker (201) were the first to prepare an antibody against purified CF_1 and to study its effect on the phosphorylating capacity of intact chloroplast lamellae. Their earlier results (201) had indicated that this mouse antibody against CF_1 inhibited ATP formation but did not inhibit the proton pump. Because CF_1 free chloroplasts (EDTA washed) show no proton uptake any longer, while chloroplasts inhibited by antibodies against CF_1 did, this was taken to indicate that CF_1, in addition to its function in ATP formation, plays a structural role (its removal leaving "holes" in the membrane) or even a role in energy conservation (201). Later, however, another antibody (from rabbits) against CF_1 (199) did inhibit the H^+ pump (or rather accelerated H^+ efflux). No inhibition of proton uptake by still another recent CF_1 antibody (or rather against subunits of CF_1) has been observed (210). It is interesting to note that polylysine, which inhibits ATP formation (71), also affects proton uptake, K^+ transport, and volume changes at higher concentrations, indicating that a distortion of the coupling factor located on the surface increases membrane permeability (71). The same has been observed by trypsin inactivation of the coupling system on the membrane, because trypsin not only inhibits ATP formation but also increases the decay of the pH gradient (263). On the other hand, Strotmann et al (277, 278), reporting on similar results, concluded that this was due to inhibition of electron flow, because they observed an inhibition of ATP formation in certain cyclic systems around photosystem I but not in noncyclic flow through photosystem I.

The antibodies against CF_1 agglutinate chloroplasts, as first reported by Kannangara et al (156). After removal of CF_1 the antibody no longer agglutinates (156). Another "structural role" for CF_1 became apparent from the work of Berzborn (33). As already mentioned, he concluded that the ferredoxin NADP reductase is located on the surface in a crevice or depression (32) which is partly formed by the knobs of CF_1 sticking out of the membrane and spacing two membrane surfaces (33). Recently, antibodies against subunits of CF_1 clarified the fine structure of the coupling factor CF_1 and led to the isolation and characterization of five subunits (36, 189, 210, 231). The location of the coupling factor on the matrix side of the thylakoid membrane is well established also by electron microscopy work, particularly by Moudrianakis (134). The knobs on the matrix side of the membrane are due to CF_1 as well as to ribulose diphosphate carboxylase, which is also loosely attached to the outer surface (134). This has been shown clearly by the antibody against the carboxylase prepared by Kannangara et al (156), which agglutinates isolated chloroplast lamellae.

Other components of the outside of the membrane localized by antibodies are galacto- and sulfolipids (122, 232, 233). Particularly the sulfolipid is located towards the matrix side, but as the results of Radunz & Berzborn (233) suggest, the sulfolipid, like the ferredoxin-NADP reductase, must be located in a depression of the membrane, because precipitation of the chloroplast by the antibody against sulfolipid occurs only in indirect agglutination tests (233). As against the reductase antibody, the sulfoquinovose antibody does not agglutinate chloroplasts directly, even when the coupling factor CF_1 is removed. Only after a trypsin treatment is direct agglutination possible (233).

The use of DABS as a chemical probe for components on the outside and accessible to hydrophilic components from the matrix side has been discussed extensively above. Other chemical probes now being investigated are carbodiimids and N-ethylmaleimide, which have been shown to react with the coupling system (198, 200, 291). Uribe (291) considered lipo-and hydrophilic carbodiimids, some of which also inhibit electron flow. Giaquinta et al (92) reported that CDIS (1-cyclohexyl-3-(2-morpholinoethyl)-carbodiimide metho-p-toluenesulfonate) will behave like DABS (labeling only in the light), whereas TNBS (2,4,6-trinitrobenzene sulfonate) and DSITS (4-4'-diisothiocyano-2-2'-disulfonic-stilbene) would also inhibit after dark incubation. The use of CDIS + glycine-methylester to neutralize negative surface charges (29) has already been mentioned. Possibly a further valuable chemical probe in the future will be labeling with iodine and lactoperoxidase, which changes the tyrosine to iodotyrosine with possibly the least harm to the membrane structure.

The role of the stacking and the partition between two thylakoids in the discussion of the accessibility of antibodies or chemical probes like polylysine to functional and structural components is of great importance, but not easily assessed (176). It is probable that components located in the partition are not able to react, directly or indirectly, with antibodies or polylysine, as pointed out by Menke, Radunz & Berzborn (35, 176, 233) and Berg et al (28). Since the results of Homann & Schmidt (131) and Wiessner & Amelunxen (309, 310), we are aware of the importance of stacking for photosystem II activity. The stroma lamellae contains predominantly only photosystem I which is therefore easily approached from the outside [see (228) on this important subject, which need not been discussed here in detail]. Because of the stacking, much of photosystem II in the grana stack and also photosystem I (see 28) is shielded. Not taking stacking into account may explain why some authors suggest little accessibility of photosystem II.

There is no doubt that photosynthetic activity occurs in the membrane bordering the partition. Tetrazolium salts (acceptors of photosystem I) are reduced in the partition [seen in the electron microscope by the insoluble formazane formed (266, 302)], though migration of the formazane does occur (266). Ferricyanide as seen by a histochemical method is also reduced by the grana and stroma lamellae, though no particular point as to the role of the partition has been made (108).

The use of DAB (diaminobenzidine), which upon oxidation forms an insoluble precipitate, will be of particular importance because microscopic studies will indicate where in the membrane the photooxidation occurs. DAB is an electron donor for photosystem I (64, 215, 219). Vigil et al (299) as well as Nir & Pease (218) observed a staining of the inside of the lamellae when DAB was oxidized by the chloroplasts, giving strong evidence for a sidedness of the electron flow system.

Other photosynthetic phenomena underline the sidedness of a closed membrane system of the chloroplasts. They are related to the movement of ions from or to the matrix space into or from the inner space of the thylakoid. After the discovery by Hind & Jagendorf (126) of a light dependent proton uptake and a dark formation of ATP by a pH gradient across the chloroplast membrane, numerous papers dealt with the pH gradient formed upon illumination of chloroplasts. This and the bearing on the chemiosmotic theory of energy conservation have been reviewed in (73, 100, 261, 300, 313, 314). For the discussion of the sidedness of the membrane one may select a few results particularly pertinent.

Measurements of the internal pH are now possible with reasonable accuracy. Evidently it is the internal pH rather than the external pH (i.e. of the buffer system employed in suspending chloroplasts) that controls the rate of electron flow (15, 244, 245, 247, 248). This means that the actual pH optimum of electron flow is not that of the externally added buffer and cannot be measured simply by adjusting the outside buffer. The amount of pH gradient depends on the pH outside; the Δ pH is about 2.5 - 3.5 at pH 8 outside (15, 244, 246, 248) and 1 - 1.5 at pH 6 outside (15). The Δ pH depends also on the internal buffer capacity (15, 157, 192) and may be increased by a number of compounds such as phenylenediamines (15) or pyridine (211). The control of electron flow by the internal pH easily explains older observations like the apparent shift of the pH optimum in uncoupled chloroplasts or fragmented chloroplasts, because the uncoupler breaks down the pH gradient and now the added buffer has to yield the optimal pH (244), or because the sidedness of the membrane is lost if upon fragmentation no vesicle is reformed. The inhibition of electron flow by uncouplers at high outside pH is also due to a shift of the internal pH into an unfavorable range (244).

Recently Bamberger et al found a more complex dependence and a control of both internal and external pH. In the presence of nigericin the rate of electron flow was inversely proportional to Δ pH (20). The authors concluded that there is a rate-controlling average pH in the membrane which together with the Δ pH is controlling electron flow. However, because of the sidedness of the membrane and the possibility of loops of the electron transport chain, the results of Bamberger et al may just indicate that redox reactions on the outside of the membrane have a different pH optimum than those inside. A dependence on a pH gradient was also proposed by Trebst & Reimer (289) for an artificial electron and hydrogen loop across the membrane. They interpret the inhibition by an uncoupler of the phenylenediamine-stimulated photoreduction of ferricyanide by photosystem II (i.e. in the presence of DBMIB) to indicate that a phenylenediamine/diimine loop is controlled by outside and inside pH (289). The excessively large stimulation of a donor system for photosystem I (DCIP/ascorbate) by an uncoupler possibly may also reflect the dependence of shuttles across the membrane on both external and internal pH. Reinwald et al (240) produced evidence that it is at the plastoquinone site that protons are pumped across the membrane with a ratio of 2 H^+ per plastoquinone. Upon reduction on the outside, plastoquinone would take up protons, the plastohydroquinone would be oxidized inside, and thereby release protons inside. This proton uptake by a quinone reduction was proposed as the mechanism for the rapid phase of proton uptake by Izawa & Hind (143). It appears also that one of the rapid proton binding sites in bacterial chromatophores is at the ubiquinone site (65). Recently Junge & Ausländer (152) provided additional evidence for two proton releasing sites inside and two sites for proton uptake outside by studying the dependence of photosystem I and/or II photoreductions on ficoll and sucrose.

NONCYCLIC AND CYCLIC ELECTRON FLOW ACROSS THE THYLAKOID MEMBRANE

In the foregoing discussion several phenomena point to the sidedness of the chloroplast inner membrane and to reactions across the membrane from and to outer and inner space. A definite conclusion as to a sidedness of components of the electron transport chain and of a zigzag of photosynthetic electron flow across the membrane, however, is not as immediately apparent. Table 1 summarizes results discussed in the previous sections that are particularly pertinent. According to the table there is agreement of the data to have the acceptor site of photosystem I extend into the hydrophilic environment of the matrix space. The donor site of photosystem I is not accessible from the outside, but there is not conclusive evidence that it is actually located on the inside. Under nonstacking conditions the donor site (i.e. plastocyanin) seems to be accessible even to polylysine. The acceptor site of photosystem II is not easily accessible from the outside towards hydrophilic electron acceptors. Antibodies against photosystem II particles and some components of photosystem II clearly indicate a certain accessibility of photosystem II. Antibodies against plastoquinone as well as the proton uptake from the outside upon its reduction by photosystem II suggest that the acceptor site of photosystem II is covered up by a protein lipid (?) layer but oriented towards the outside. The most conflicting results are obtained as to the location of the donor site of photosystem II. DABS labeling, antibody studies, and trypsin inactivation indicate an exposing of the water-splitting reaction to a certain extent. In addition, the DABS labeling suggests that a conformational change brought about by light exposes the water-splitting reaction, covered in the dark. On the other hand, proton release into the inner space in the water-splitting reaction, field formation, and energy coupling of photoreductions by photosystem II are easily explained if there is an orientation of the donor site of photosystem II towards the inside. A summary is given in Table I.

Rather than concluding that the present evidence is insufficient for a sidedness of the electron flow system correlated with energy conservation, the author takes the view of Witt and his colleagues because it seems to explain his own results most easily. The basic scheme of Witt and Junge and associates (152, 154, 255, 313, 314) proposes a zigzag of the two photosystems and the electron transport chain across the membrane with the acceptor site of photosystem I and II outside and the donor site of both photosystems inside. Some arguments perhaps may reconcile the new zigzag scheme with some of the experiments summarized in Table 1, which tend to argue against the scheme.

1. The donor site of photosystem I need not necessarily be located on the inside. An orientation towards the inner face is sufficient if only artificial electron donors

Table 1 Evidence for a sidedness of photosynthetic electron flow in the membrane

Located outside or oriented toward the outside.   Located inside or oriented toward the inside.

PHOTOSYSTEM I

Acceptor side

approach of hydrophilic acceptors

antibody against reductase (31–34)

antibody against ferredoxin (123)

antibody against S_{leth} (37, 238)

antibodies against subchloroplast
   particles (58, 176)

DABS labeling (74, 264)

field formation (255, 313, 314)

binary model (8, 205)

Donor side

polylysine inhibition of plastocyanin (52)

antibody against plastocyanin (113, 231)

antibody against cytochrome f (231)

slow chemical oxidation of cytochrome f
   by ferricyanide (66)

approach of lipophilic but not of
   hydrophilic donors (111, 115)

precipitation of DAB oxidation
   product (218, 299)

no DABS labeling (74)

field formation (255, 313, 314)

H+ release inside (at plastohydroquinone)
   (152, 240)

PHOTOSYSTEM II

Acceptor side

proton pump and proton uptake via
   plastoquinone (152, 240)

photoreductions by photosystem II
   (96, 141, 226, 251, 287–289)

antibody against plastoquinone and
antibody against chlorophyll
   (234, 235, 256)

antibody against subchloroplast
   particles (58, 176)

field formation (255, 313, 314)

accessibility of cytochrome b_{559} (66)

new version of binary model (8, 205)

relative inaccessibility to hydrophilic
   acceptors (282)

Donor side

DABS labeling (92, 93)

antibody against lutein (234)

antibodies against photosystem II
   particles (176)

trypsin digestion (262, 263)

field formation (255, 313, 314)

energy coupling to photoreductions
   (47, 287–289, 317)

proton release inside in the
   water-splitting reaction
   (89, 149, 152)

approach it from the inner face and, as in the reoxidation of plastohydroquinone in the native chain, release hydrogens inside. The proton uptake from the outside in plastoquinone reduction may very well occur through a protein lipid layer covering up the lipophilic quinone from the hydrophilic matrix.

2. Crevices and depressions in the surface of the membrane may temporarily expose sites actually inside the lipid layer. Such crevices are particularly indicated by the antibody studies against the Fd-NADP-reductase, some of the galacto- and sulfolipids and lutein, because these antibodies do not yield direct agglutination. No crevices have been identified yet on the inner surface. Crevices from the inside and outside actually may shorten the distance across the membrane, which seems necessary if the fixed photosystems are to charge across the membrane. One might speculate that the water-splitting reaction of photosystem II is located in the membrane close to crevices in such a way that upon illumination it actually releases oxygen to the outside but protons to the inside. The conformational changes of the water-splitting systems, as clearly indicated by the DABS labeling experiments, may expose the higher stages of S in the oxygen evolving reaction.

3. It seems possible that modification of a compound on the outside (by an antibody, a chemical probe, or digestion) leads to a structural rearrangement of the membrane and an inhibition of a functional component inside. It appears that some of the discrepancies as to the electron flow across the membrane listed in Table 1 stem from experiments in which it has not been proved that the treatment actually acts directly on a functional component.

The familiar zigzag scheme of photosynthetic electron flow in a redox potential scale may be depicted in a new version. In a premature and schematic way then, Figure 5 defines carriers in a zigzag of electron flow *across* the membrane. Two

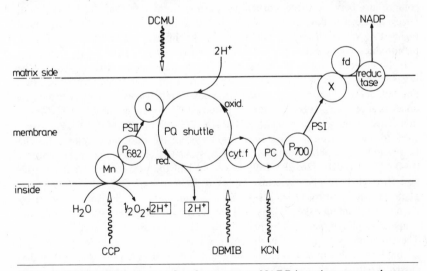

Figure 5 Photosynthetic electron flow from water to NADP in a zigzag across the membrane. Two proton releasing sites inside and the points of inhibition of some inhibitors of electron flow are indicated.

proton releasing sites inside and two sites taking up protons from the outside are indicated, as proposed by Junge (152). A plastoquinone loop connects the two photosystems across the membrane and is pumping hydrogens (protons) across the membrane as indicated by Reinwald et al (240). In the plastoquinone loop a shuttle of reducing equivalents and hydrogens from the outside to the inside occurs. The pH gradient thus generated yields favorable pH conditions for both enzymic reduction of plastoquinone and proton uptake from the outside and enzymic oxidation of plastohydroquinone and proton release on the inside. Thus, depending on conditions, internal and external pH and Δ pH would control the overall rate as observed (20).

The zigzag of the electron flow system across the membrane would ease the present discussion as to the number of energy conserving (ATP forming) sites in noncyclic and cyclic photophosphorylation. The two proton releasing sites inside at the water-splitting reaction and the plastoquinone loop, together with the two electrogenic transmembrane processes in the photosystems, may be considered the energy conservation sites in photosynthetic electron flow (Figure 5). As will be discussed later, two energy conserving sites are not necessarily equivalent to two ATP forming sites. Also, the indication of proton releasing sites in Figure 5 is no acceptance or proof of the chemiosmotic theory. Instead the two proton releasing sites could be represented also as fixed charges (72, 73, 158) or any other "squiggle" as long as that does not imply tight chemical coupling of electron flow and phosphorylation.

In noncyclic electron flow from water to NADP, both energy conserving sites will participate in and be responsible for coupled ATP formation. Two energy conserving sites not necessarily yielding two ATP per 2 electrons transferred would be a compromise between those workers supporting the notion that the $P/_{e_2}$ value in noncyclic electron flow from water to NADP is unity and others who have found higher $P/_{e_2}$ values as well as indications of two different "ATP coupling sites" in photoreductions by either photosystem II or photosystem I (including cyclic).

In photoreductions by photosystem II, only one energy conserving site at the water-splitting reaction would contribute to ATP formation. It has been shown that photoreductions by photosystem II with oxidized phenylenediamines or benzoquinones as acceptors—as Saha et al have proposed (251)—are coupled to ATP formation. This became clear when either DBMIB (287–289) or KCN (96, 97, 226) were used to block electron flow from photosystem II into photosystem I. The $P/_{e_2}$ ratio in such photoreductions by photosystem II obtained are in the range of 0.4–0.7 (96, 97, 226, 236, 287–289), i.e. about half the value of noncyclic electron flow through both photosystems. Trebst & Reimer (287, 289) also report on a photosynthetic control of such systems (i.e. stimulation of electron transport by uncoupler). Gimmler (94, 95), as well as Reeves & Hall (236), also report on the coupling of photoreductions by photosystem II and obtained evidence for control. The situation as to control is difficult to assess, however, because at high pH uncouplers inhibit photoreductions by photosystem II (97, 289). As already discussed, Trebst & Reimer (289) interpret this as evidence for a pH gradient-dependent phenylenediamine shuttle across the membrane (Figure 6). The coupling of

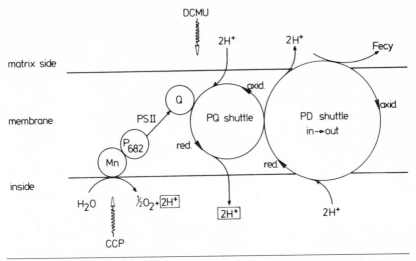

Figure 6 Photosynthetic electron flow from water to an acceptor (ferricyanide) in a photoreduction by photosystem II via a phenylenediamine shuttle.

photoreductions by photosystem II raises the question as to which electron flow reaction is coupled. A site between water and photosystem II had been proposed earlier (47). Also Kok et al (180) suggested an energy conserving site at photosystem II, as did experiments by others (178, 259, 260, 317). According to a theory of direct chemical coupling of electron flow to phosphorylation, such a site is difficult to specify. In view of the chemiosmotic theory and the zigzag scheme across the membrane, the protonreleasing site inside in the water-splitting reaction would be responsible for coupling of photoreductions by photosystem II. As Junge & Ausländer (152) show, in photoreductions by photosystem II protons are released inside.

In cyclic electron flow, according to the zigzag scheme across the membrane, also only one energy conserving site would participate. The site responsible would be the proton-releasing site at the plastoquinone loop, if in the cyclic system plastoquinone is participating (i.e. is DBMIB sensitive (46). As discussed above, certain cyclic photophosphorylation systems do not include plastoquinone. In such systems the native energy conserving site at plastoquinone would be replaced by an artificial energy conserving site. Such cofactors of cyclic photophosphorylation need to be lipophilic and should be able to release protons upon oxidation inside (111, 115). The shuttle of the cofactor itself through the membrane is the energy conserving site. Such systems are DBMIB insensitive (46) but KCN (226) sensitive systems with DAD or DCIP as cofactors or the DBMIB and KCN insensitive PMS system. Witt (314) has suggested a direct feeding of PMS into P_{700}, which would also explain the high light saturation of this cyclic system (18). The experiments of Krogmann & Olivero (183) with petrolether extracted chloroplasts do not necessarily indicate a participation of plastoquinone in the PMS cyclic electron flow system, because it seems quite possible that removal of plastoquinone by petrolether induces a leakiness of the membrane preventing a ΔpH to be built up. Three types of cyclic photophosphorylation schemes may then be conceived with three different energy conserving sites (Figure 7).

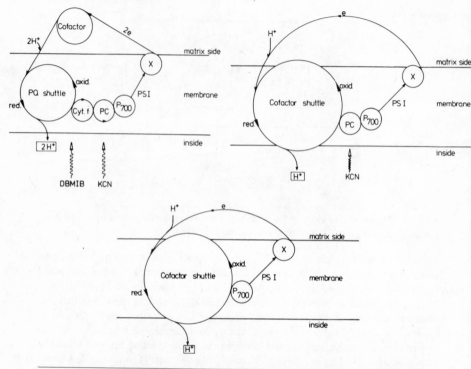

Figure 7   Three different ways of cyclic electron flow around photosystem I. The native (plastoquinone shuttle) and artificial energy conserving sites and the points of inhibition by some inhibitors are indicated.

In photoreductions by photosystem I at the expense of an artificial electron donor, coupling to ATP formation is also observed. Because cyclic electron flow also occurs in photoreductions with some mediators like DCIP and DAD (284, 285), a measurement of the true P/e_2 ratio for noncyclic flow is difficult. Using DAB as an electron donor, which does not cycle when the oxidized form is precipitating, Neumann (215) reported on a P/e_2 ratio of 0.8. Hauska et al (115) recently attributed the finding that TMPD/ascorbate as an electron donor system is not coupled to ATP/ formation to the fact that TMPD, contrary to DAD or $DCIPH_2$, is not carrying hydrogens across the membrane and liberating protons upon oxidation inside. From this it is proposed that in donor systems for photosystem I an artificial energy conserving site is induced by the donor if the donor is able to carry hydrogens across the membrane (Figure 8).

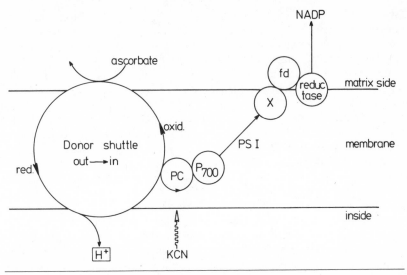

Figure 8 Photosynthetic electron flow in a photoreduction by photosystem I at the expense of an electron donor (ascorbate) via a donor shuttle releasing protons inside upon oxidation.

ENERGY CONSERVATION IN PHOTOSYNTHETIC ELECTRON FLOW

In adopting the zigzag scheme of electron flow across the membrane, two energy conserving sites—i.e. two proton releasing sites inside—have been discussed. As pointed out, a proton releasing site is not equivalent to an ATP coupling site because the "squiggle" formed in an energy conserving site does not necessarily lead to one equivalent of ATP. Not considering the membrane potential, the amount of ATP formed in noncyclic electron flow from H_2O to NADP or in photoreductions by either photosystem II or I alone, i.e. the P/e_2 ratio, will depend on how many protons are released inside per two electrons transferred and how many protons are required to form one ATP. This is a continuing controversy, and the inconsistencies in the experimental values make many authors hesitant to accept the chemiosmotic hypothesis.

There seems to be reasonable agreement that the proton/electron ratio is 2, i.e. 4 protons are released inside, when 2 electrons are moved across two photosystems from water to MV or NADP (see particularly reviews by Schwartz 26 and Dilley 73; Walker & Crofts 300; Crofts et al 69; and references 72, 119, 152, 158, 248, 280). There is less agreement as to the ratio of protons required for ATP formation. Earlier values pointed to 2 H^+/ATP [see review (261) and experiments by Schwartz (260)]. Rumberg et al (249, 258) and Junge et al (153) later found 3 H^+/ATP, and recently Rumberg & Schröder (250) settled on 4 H^+/ATP.

By computing a P/e_2 ratio from an accepted H^+/e ratio of 2 and from an H^+/ATP ratio of 2 or 3 or 4 respectively, one arrives at P/e_2 ratios of 2 or 1.33 or 1 respectively for noncyclic flow from water to NADP and a ratio of 1 or 0.7 or 0.5 for photoreductions by either photosystem II or I (including cyclic) alone. The observed values for noncyclic flow in the literature range from 1, as originally observed by Arnon in NADP, ferricyanide, and in the Mehler reaction to later P/e_2 ratios of two, though in some reports the computation of Izawa et al (140) (i.e. subtraction of a presumed uncoupled basal rate) has been applied. Recently (109, 236, 237, 303, 304) the conditions for obtaining P/e_2 ratios above 1 have been described. A value of 2 is also favored by Crofts et al in their review (69). Rumberg & Schröder (250) again settled for a P/e_2 ratio of 1. The values reported for photoreductions by photosystem II are in the range of 0.5 to 0.7 (96, 97, 226, 236, 287–289); this multiplied by 2 would correspond to a P/e_2 ratio in noncyclic flow between 1 and 1.3. It is apparent that according to the chemiosmotic theory whole numbers for the P/e_2 ratio are not necessarily expected (if the ratio of H^+/ATP is 3, then the value would be 1.33).

The H^+/e or $H^+/h\nu$ values in cyclic electron flow (or in noncyclic flow by photosystem I) is much less in agreement with the concept presented. The values in the literature are about 5 H^+ in the initial phase and 2.5 H^+/e (at the best) in the steady state (75). Heath (118), employing bromocresol purple as an indicator, recently reported on rather high values of about 3.5 $H^+/H\nu$, and only the efflux in the dark showed a value of 1.6. Though high proton uptake might reflect a neutralization of membrane charges which do not contribute to the "squiggle," a value of H^+/e or $H^+H\nu = 1$ should be expected according to the concept presented here. Strotmann et al (277) did come to a value of $H^+/e =1$ in the steady state after certain corrections and assumptions. A P/e_2 ratio of 0.5 (on the assumption of $H^+/ATP = 4$) should be expected for cyclic photophosphorylation. Indeed, such low values have been reported when $ATP/h\nu$ was measured directly (18, 261).

Of course, the P/e_2 ratio of noncyclic electron flow is of great importance for the overall stoichiometry of light reactions to CO_2 fixed in the dark assimilation of CO_2. According to the Calvin cycle, 3 ATP per NADPH are needed to reduce CO_2 to the level of a carbohydrate. If noncyclic electron flow has a P/e_2 ratio of only 1, additional ATP forming light reactions are required. Heber (120) recently came to the conclusion that the P/e_2 ratio in whole chloroplasts is close to 1 and proposed pseudocyclic electron flow to supply the extra ATP. On the other hand, the extensive and elaborate quantum requirement measurements for CO_2 assimilation in vivo by Senger (265) led to a value of 8, which would rather support the idea that the P/e_2 value of noncyclic electron flow is close to 2. It seems conceivable that the more flexible coupling of electron flow to ATP formation via a chemiosmotic mechanism would include a way to control and a mechanism to vary the P/e_2 ratio by changing the number of protons required for ATP formation under different physiological conditions.

Literature Cited

1. Allen, J. F., Hall, D. O. 1973. *Biochem. Biophys. Res. Commun.* 52:856–62
2. Amesz, J. 1973. *Biochim. Biophys. Acta* 301:35–51
3. Amesz, J., Van den Bos, P., Dirks, M. P. 1970. *Biochim. Biophys. Acta* 197:324–27
4. Anderson, J. M., Than-Nyunt, Boardman, N. K. 1973. *Arch. Biochem. Biophys.* 155:436–44
5. Arnon, D. I. 1965. *Science* 149:1460–70
6. Arnon, D. I., Whatley, F. R., Allen, M. B. 1955. *Biochim. Biophys. Acta* 16:607–8
7. Arnon, D. I. et al 1972. *Structure and Function of Oxidation Reduction Enzymes,* ed. A. Akeson, A. Ehrenberg, 237–56. Oxford, New York: Pergamon
8. Arntzen, C. J., Dilley, R. A., Crane, F. L. 1969. *J. Cell Biol.* 43:16–31
9. Arntzen, C. J., Dilley, R. A., Neumann, J. 1971. *Biochim. Biophys. Acta* 245:409–24
10. Arntzen, C. J., Dilley, R. A., Peters, G. A., Shaw, E. R. 1972. *Biochim. Biophys. Acta* 256:85–107
11. Asada, K., Kiso, K. 1973. *Eur. J. Biochem.* 33:253–57
12. Asada, K., Takahashi, M. 1971. *Photosynthesis and Photorespiration,* ed. M. D. Hatch, C. B. Osmond, R. O. Slatyer, 387–93. N.Y.: Wiley
13. Avron, M. 1964. *Biochem. Biophys. Res. Commun.* 17:430–32
14. Avron, M. 1967. *Curr. Top. Bioenerg.* 2:1–22
15. Avron, M. 1971. See Ref. 87, 2:861–71
16. Avron, M., Ben-Hayyim, G. 1969. *Progress in Photosynthesis Research,* ed. H. Metzner, 3:1185–96. München: Lichtenstern
17. Avron, M., Jagendorf, A. T. 1956. *Arch. Biochem. Biophys.* 65:475–90
18. Avron, M., Neumann, J. 1968. *Ann. Rev. Plant Physiol.* 19:137–66
19. Avron, M., Shneyour, A. 1971. *Biochim. Biophys. Acta* 226:498–500
20. Bamberger, E. S., Rottenberg, H., Avron, M. 1973. *Eur. J. Biochem.* 34:557–63
21. Bendall, D. S., Hill, R. 1968. *Ann. Rev. Plant Physiol.* 19:167–86
22. Ben-Hayyim, G., Avron, M. 1970. *Biochim. Biophys. Acta* 205:86–94
23. Ben-Hayyim, G., Avron, M. 1970. *Eur. J. Biochem.* 15:155–60
24. Ben-Hayyim, G., Avron, M. 1971. *Photochem. Photobiol.* 14:389–96
25. Bennoun, P., Bouges, B. 1971. See Ref. 87, 1:569–76
26. Bennoun, P., Joliot, A. 1969. *Biochim. Biophys. Acta* 189:85–94
27. Berg, H. C. 1969. *Biochim. Biophys. Acta* 183:65–78
28. Berg, S., Cipollo, D., Armstrong, B., Krogmann, D. W. 1973. *Biochim. Biophys. Acta* 305:372–83
29. Berg, S., Dodge, S., Krogmann, D. W., Dilley, R. A. In press
30. Bering, C. L., Dilley, R. A., Dodge, S. 1973. *Plant Physiol.* Suppl. 51:362
31. Berzborn, R. J. 1967. Thesis Köln
32. Berzborn, R. J. 1968. *Z. Naturforsch.* 23b:1096–1104
33. Ibid 1969. 24b:436–46
34. Berzborn, R. J. 1969. See Ref. 16, 1:106–14
35. Berzborn, R. J. 1972. *Habilitationsschrift* 1–149. Univ. Bochum
36. Berzborn, R. J. 1972. *Hoppe-Seyler's Z. Physiol. Chem.* 353:693
37. Berzborn, R., Menke, W., Trebst, A., Pistorius, E. 1966. *Z. Naturforsch.* 21b:1057–59
38. Biggins, J. 1973. *Biochemistry* 12:1165–70
39. Biggins, J., Sauer, K. 1964. *Biochim. Biophys. Acta* 88:655–57
40. Black, C. C. 1966. *Biochim. Biophys. Acta* 120:332–40
41. Boardman, N. K. 1970. *Ann. Rev. Plant Physiol.* 21:115–40
42. Böger, P. 1971. See Ref. 87, 1:449–58
43. Böhme, H., Cramer, W. A. 1972. *Biochemistry* 11:1155–60
44. Böhme, H., Cramer, W. A. 1972. *Biochim. Biophys. Acta* 283:302–15
45. Böhme, H., Cramer, W. A. 1971. *FEBS Lett.* 15:349–51
46. Böhme, H., Reimer, S., Trebst, A. 1971. *Z. Naturforsch.* 26b:341–52
47. Böhme, H., Trebst, A. 1969. *Biochim. Biophys. Acta* 180:137–48
48. Bothe, H. 1969. See Ref. 16, 3:1483–91
49. Brand, J., Baszynski, T., Crane, F. L., Krogmann, D. W. 1972. *J. Biol. Chem.* 247:2814–19
50. Brand, J., Krogmann, D. W., Crane, F. L. 1971. *Plant Physiol.* 47:135–38
51. Brand, J., San Pietro, A. 1973. *Biochim. Biophys. Acta* 325:255–65
52. Brand, J., San Pietro, A., Mayne, B. C. 1972. *Arch. Biochem. Biophys.* 152:426–28
53. Brandon, P. C., Elgersma, O. 1973. *Biochim. Biophys. Acta* 292:753–62

54. Branton, D., Park, R. B. 1967. *J. Ultrastruct. Res.* 19:283–303
55. Braun, B. Z., Govindjee 1972. *FEBS Lett.* 25:143–46
56. Briantais, J. M. 1969. *Physiol. Veg.* 7:135–80
57. Briantais, J. M. 1972. *Chloroplast Fragments,* ed. G. Jacobi, 155–67. Göttingen
58. Briantais, J. M., Picaud, M. 1972. *FEBS Lett.* 20:100–4
59. Butler, W. L. 1973. *Accounts Chem. Res.* 6:177–84
60. Chance, B., Bonner, W. D. 1963. *Photosynthetic Mechanisms of Green Plants,* ed. B. Kok, A. Jagendorf, 66–81. Washington: Nat. Acad. Sci., Nat. Res. Counc.
61. Cheniae, G. M. 1970. *Ann. Rev. Plant Physiol.* 21:467–98
62. Cheniae, G. M., Martin, I. F. 1970. *Biochim. Biophys. Acta* 197:219–39
63. Cheniae, G. M., Martin, I. F. 1971. *Plant Physiol.* 47:568–75
64. Chua, Nam-Hai 1972. *Biochim. Biophys. Acta* 267:179–89
65. Cogdell, R. J., Jackson, J. B., Crofts, A. R. 1972. *Bioenergetics* 4:413–29
66. Cramer, W. A. 1973. Presented at Gordon Res Conf. Photosyn. Tilton/N.H.
67. Cramer, W. A., Böhme, H. 1972. *Biochim. Biophys. Acta* 256:358–69
68. Cramer, W. A., Butler, W. L. 1969. *Biochim. Biophys. Acta* 172:503–10
69. Crofts, A. R., Wraight, C. A., Fleischmann, D. E. 1971. *FEBS Lett.* 15:89–100
70. Delvieu, M. J., de Kouchkovsky, Y. 1971. *Biochim. Biophys. Acta* 226:409–21
71. Dilley, R. A. 1968. *Biochemistry* 7:338–46
72. Dilley, R. A. 1970. *Arch. Biochem. Biophys.* 137:270–83
73. Dilley, R. A. 1971. *Curr. Top. Bioenerg.* 4:237–71
74. Dilley, R. A., Peters, G. A., Shaw, E. R. 1972. *J. Membrane Biol.* 8:163–80
75. Dilley, R. A., Vernon, L. P. 1967. *Proc. Nat. Acad. Sci. USA* 57:395–400
76. Diner, B., Mauzerall, D. 1973. *Biochim. Biophys. Acta* 305:353–63
77. Duysens, L. N. M. 1963. See Ref. 60, 1–17
78. Duysens, L. N. M. 1964. *Progr. Biophys. Mol. Biol.* 14:1–104
79. Duysens, L. N. M. 1970. See Ref. 87, 1:19–25
80. Elstner, E. F., Heupel, A., Vaklinova, S. 1970. *Z Pflanzenphysiol.* 62:173–83
81. Ibid, 184–200

82. Elstner, E. F., Kramer, R. 1973. *Biochim. Biophys. Acta* 314:340–53
83. Elstner, E. F., Pistorius, E., Böger, P., Trebst A. 1968. *Planta* 79:146–61
84. Epel, B. L., Neumann, J. 1972. See Ref. 254, 237
85. Fork, D. C., Amesz, J. 1969. *Ann. Rev. Plant Physiol.* 20:305–28
86. Fork, D. C., Murata, N. 1971. *Photochem. Photobiol.* 13:333–44
87. Forti, G., Avron, M., Melandri, A., Eds. 1971. *Proc. 2nd Int. Congr. Photosyn. Res.,* Stresa. The Hague: Dr. W. Junk, N.V. Vol. 1–3
88. Foust, P. G., Mayhew, S. G., Massey, V. 1969. *J. Biol. Chem.* 244:964–70
89. Fowler, C. F. 1973. *Biophys. Soc. Abstr.* 13:64a
90. Fujita, Y., Murano, F. 1967. *Plant Cell Physiol.* 8:269–81
91. Fujita, Y., Myers, J. 1967. *Arch. Biochem. Biophys.* 119:8–15
92. Giaquinta, R. T., Dilley, R. A., Anderson, B. J. 1973. *Biochem. Biophys. Res. Commun.* 52:1410–17
93. Giaquinta, R. T., Dilley, R. A., Anderson, B. J. In press
94. Gimmler, H. 1973. *Z. Pflanzenphysiol.* 68:289–307
95. Ibid, 385–90
96. Gould, J. M., Izawa, S. 1973. *Eur. J. Biochem.* 37:185–92
97. Gould, J. M., Ort, D. R. 1973. *Biochim. Biophys. Acta* 325:157–66
98. Govindjee, R. 1963. See Ref. 60, 318–34
99. Govindjee, Bazzaz, M. 1967. *Photochem. Photobiol.* 6:885–94
100. Greville, G. D. 1969. *Curr. Top. Bioenerg.* 3:1–78
101. Gromet-Elhanan, Z. 1968. *Arch. Biochem. Biophys.* 123:447–56
102. Gromet-Elhanan, Z., Redlich, N. 1970. *Eur. J. Biochem.* 17:523–28
103. Grünhagen, H. H., Witt, H. T. 1970. *Z. Naturforsch.* 25b:373–86
104. Habermann, H. M., Handel, M. A., McKellar, P. 1968. *Photochem. Photobiol.* 7:211–24
105. Haehnel, W. 1973. *Biochim. Biophys. Acta* 305:618–31
106. Haehnel, W. 1973. *Abstr. Int. Cong. Biochem. Stockholm,* 217
107. Hall, D. O. 1972. *Nature* 235:125–26
108. Hall, D. O., Edge, H., Kalina, M. 1971. *J. Cell Sci.* 9:289–303
109. Hall, D. O., Reeves, S. G., Baltscheffsky, H. 1971. *Biochem. Biophys. Res. Commun.* 43:359–66
110. Hauska, G. A. 1971. *Abstr. 1st Eur. Biophys. Congr.* Baden, ed. E. Broda,

A. Locker, H. Springer-Lederer, 4:61–65
111. Hauska, G. A. 1972. *FEBS Lett.* 28:217–20
112. Hauska, G. A. 1972. *Angew. Chem.* 84:123–24
113. Hauska, G. A., McCarty, R. E., Berzborn, R. J., Racker, E. 1971. *J. Biol. Chem.* 246:3524–31
114. Hauska, G. A., McCarty, R. E., Racker, E. 1970. *Biochim. Biophys. Acta* 197:206–18
115. Hauska, G. A., Trebst, A., Draber, W. 1973. *Biochim. Biophys. Acta* 305: 632–41
116. Haveman, J., Donze, M. 1971. See Ref. 87,1:81–91
117. Haveman, J., Duysens, L. N. M., Van der Geest, T. C. M., van Gorkom, H. J. 1972. *Biochim. Biophys. Acta* 283: 316–27
118. Heath, R. L. 1972. *Biochim. Biophys. Acta* 256:645–55
119. Heath, R. L., Hind, G. 1969. *Biochim. Biophys. Acta* 189:222–33
120. Heber, U. 1973. *Biochim. Biophys. Acta* 305:140–52
121. Henderson, P. J. F. 1971. *Ann. Rev. Microbiol.* 25:393–428
122. Hiedemann-Van Wyk, D. 1971. *Z. Naturforsch.* 26b:1052–54
123. Hiedemann-Van Wyk, D., Kannangara, C. G. 1971. *Z. Naturforsch.* 26b:46–50
124. Hill, R. 1937. *Nature* 139:881–82
125. Hind, G. 1968. *Biochim. Biophys. Acta* 153:235–40
126. Hind, G., Jagendorf, A. T. 1965. *J. Biol. Chem.* 240:3195–3201
127. Hind, G., Olson, J. M. 1968. *Ann. Rev. Plant Physiol.* 19:249–82
128. Hiyama, T., Ke, B. 1971. *Proc. Nat. Acad. Sci. USA* 68:1010–13
129. Homann, P. H. 1971. See Ref. 87, 1:126–32
130. Homann, P. H. 1972. *Biochim. Biophys. Acta* 256:336–44
131. Homann, P. H., Schmidt, G. H. 1967. *Plant Physiol.* 42:619–32
132. Honeycutt, R. C., Krogmann, D. W. 1970. *Biochim. Biophys. Acta* 197: 267–75
133. Ibid 1972. 256:467–76
134. Howell, S. H., Moudrianakis, E. N. 1967. *Proc. Nat. Acad. Sci. USA* 58:1261–68
135. Inoué, H., Nishimura, M. 1971. *Plant Cell Physiol.* 12:739–47
136. Inoué, H., Wakamatsu, K., Nishimura, M. 1971. *Plant Cell Physiol.* 12:457–60

137. Itoh, M., Yamashita, K., Nishi, T., Konishi, K., Shibata, K. 1969. *Biochim. Biophys. Acta* 180:509–19
138. Izawa, S. 1970. *Biochim. Biophys. Acta* 197:328–331
139. Izawa, S., Connolly, T. N., Winget, G. D., Good, N. E. 1966. *Brookhaven Symp. Biol.* 19:169–87
140. Izawa, S., Good, N. E. 1968. *Biochim. Biophys. Acta* 162:380–91
141. Izawa, S., Gould, J. M., Ort, D. R., Felker, P., Good, N. E. 1973. *Biochim. Biophys. Acta* 305:119–28
142. Izawa, S., Heath, R. L., Hind, G. 1969. *Biochim. Biophys. Acta* 180:388–98
143. Izawa, S., Hind, G. 1967. *Biochim. Biophys. Acta* 143:377–90
144. Jacobi, G. 1970. *Ber. Deut. Bot. Ges.* 83:451–63
145. Jacobi, G., Lehmann, H. 1968. *Z. Pflanzenphysiol.* 59:457–76
146. Jagendorf, A. T., Avron, M. 1959. *Arch. Biochem. Biophys.* 80:246–57
147. Joliot, P. 1968. *Biochemie des Sauerstoffs,* ed. B. Hess, H. J. Staudinger, 307–12. Springer-Verlag
148. Joliot, P., Joliot, A. 1973. *Biochim. Biophys. Acta* 305:302–16
149. Junge, W. 1972. See Ref. 254, 34
150. Junge, W. 1973. *Excited States in Photosynthesis and Vision,* ed. D. O. Hall, F. Kaufman. London: University Press
151. Junge, W., Ausländer, W. 1973. *Abstr. 9th Int. Congr. Biochem. Stockholm,* 243
152. Junge, W., Ausländer, W. *Biochim. Biophys. Acta.* In press
153. Junge, W., Rumberg, B., Schröder, H. 1970. *Eur. J. Biochem.* 14:575–81
154. Junge, W., Witt, H. T. 1968. *Z. Naturforsch.* 23b:244–54
155. Kandler, O. 1960. *Ann. Rev. Plant Physiol.* 11:37–54
156. Kannangara, C. G., Van Wyk, D., Menke, W. 1970. *Z. Naturforsch.* 25b:613–18
157. Karlish, S. J. D., Avron, M. 1968. *Biochim. Biophys. Acta* 153:878–88
158. Karlish, S. J. D., Avron, M. 1971. *Eur. J. Biochem.* 20:51–57
159. Katoh, S. 1963. See Ref. 60, 262–77
160. Katoh, S. 1972. *Plant Cell Physiol.* 13:273–86
161. Katoh, S. 1972. *Biochim. Biophys. Acta* 283:293–301
162. Katoh, S., San Pietro, A. 1966. *The Biochemistry of Copper,* ed. J. Peisach, P. Aisen, W. E. Blumberg, 407–22. N.Y.: Academic

163. Katoh, S., San Pietro, A. 1967. *Arch. Biochem. Biophys.* 122:144–52
164. Katoh, S., Satoh, K., Ikegami, I., Kimimura, M., Takamiya, A. 1971. See Ref. 87, 1:525–37
165. Ke, B. 1973. *Biochim. Biophys. Acta* 301:1–33
166. Ke, B., Vernon, L. P., Chaney, T. H. 1972. *Biochim. Biophys. Acta* 256: 345–57
167. Keister, D. L. 1965. *J. Biol. Chem.* 240:2673–77
168. Keister, D. L., San Pietro, A., Stolzenbach, F. E. 1962. *Arch. Biochem. Biophys.* 98:235–44
169. Keller, J., Bachofen, R. 1969. See Ref. 16, 2:1013–21
170. Kimimura, M., Katoh, S. 1972. *Biochim. Biophys. Acta* 283:279–92
171. Kimimura, M., Katoh, S. 1972. *Plant Cell Physiol.* 13:287–96
172. Kimimura, M., Katoh, S. 1973. *Biochim. Biophys. Acta* 325:167–74
173. Knaff, D. B. 1972. *FEBS Lett.* 23:92–94
174. Knaff, D. B., Arnon, D. I. 1969. *Proc. Nat. Acad. Sci. USA* 63:963–69
175. Ibid 1969. 64:715–22
176. Koenig, F., Menke, W., Craubner, H., Schmid, G. H., Radunz, A. 1972. *Z. Naturforsch.* 27b:1225–38
177. Kohl, D. H., Wood, P. M. 1969. *Plant Physiol.* 44:1439–45
178. Kok, B., Cheniae, G. M. 1966. *Curr. Top. Bioenerg.* 1:1–47
179. Kok, B., Datko, E. A. 1965. *Plant Physiol.* 40:1171–77
180. Kok, B., Malkin, S., Owens, O., Forbush, B. 1966. *Brookhaven Symp. Biol.* 19:446–59
181. Kreutz, W. 1970. *Advan. Bot. Res.* 3:53–169
182. Kreutz, W. 1972. *Angew. Chem.* 13: 597–648
183. Krogmann, D. W., Olivero, E. 1962. *J. Biol. Chem.* 237:3292–95
184. Larkum, A. W. D., Bonner, W. D. 1972. *Biochim. Biophys. Acta* 256: 385–95
185. Ibid, 396–408
186. Ibid 1972. 267:149–59
187. Levine, J., Reimann, B. E. F. 1969. *Ann. Rev. Plant Physiol.* 20:289–304
188. Lien, S., Bannister, T. T. 1971. *Biochim. Biophys. Acta* 245:465–81
189. Lien, S., Berzborn, R. J., Racker, E. 1972. *J. Biol. Chem.* 247:3520–24
190. Losada, M., Whatley, F. R., Arnon, D. I. 1961. *Nature* 190:606–10
191. Lozier, R., Baginsky, M., Butler, W. L. 1971. *Photochem. Photobiol.* 14: 323–28

192. Lynn, W. S. 1968. *Biochemistry* 7: 3811–20
193. Malkin, R., Bearden, A. J. 1971. *Proc. Nat. Acad. Sci. USA* 68:16–19
194. Malkin, R., Michaeli, G. 1971. See Ref. 87, 1:149–67
195. Mantai, K. E. 1970. *Plant Physiol.* 45:563–66
196. Mantai, K. E., Hind, G. 1971. *Plant Physiol.* 48:5–8.
197. Mayne, B. C., Brown, A. H. 1963. *Studies on Microalgae and Photosynthetic Bacteria*, ed. J. Ashida, 347–52. Tokyo Press
198. McCarty, R. E., Fagan, J. 1973. *Biochemistry* 12:1503–7
199. McCarty, R. E., Fuhrman, J. S., Tsuchiya, Y. 1971. *Proc. Nat. Acad. Sci. USA* 68:2522–26
200. McCarty, R. E., Pittman, P. R., Tsuchiya, Y. 1972. *J. Biol. Chem.* 247: 3048–51
201. McCarty, R. E., Racker, E. 1966. *Brookhaven Symp. Biol.* 19:202–14
202. Menke, W. 1967. *Arbeitsgemeinsch. Forsch Landes NRW* 171:1–25
202a. Menke, W. 1972. Jahrbuch der Max-Planck-Gesellschaft zur Förderung der Wissenschaften E. V., 132–55. Max-Planck Institut für Züchtungsforschung, Köln-Vogelsang
203. Miles, D. et al 1973. *Biochem. Biophys. Res. Commun.* 50:1113–19
204. Mühlethaler, K. 1971. See Ref. 87, 2:1423–29
205. Mühlethaler, K. 1971. *Int. Rev. Cytol.* 31:1–19
206. Mühlethaler, K. 1972. See Ref. 254, 28
207. Müller, A., Witt, H. T. 1961. *Nature* 189:944–45
208. Murata, N., Fork, D. C. 1971. *Biochim. Biophys. Acta* 245:356–64
209. Myers, J. 1971. *Ann. Rev. Plant Physiol.* 22:289–312
210. Nelson, N., Deters, D. W., Nelson, H., Racker, E. 1973. *J. Biol. Chem.* 248:2049–55
211. Nelson, N., Nelson, H., Haim, Y., Neumann, J. 1971. *Arch. Biochem. Biophys.* 145:263–67
212. Nelson, N., Neumann, J. 1968. *Biochem. Biophys. Res. Commun.* 30: 142–47
213. Nelson, N., Neumann, J. 1972. *J. Biol. Chem.* 247:1817–24
214. Nelson, N., Racker, E. 1972. *J. Biol. Chem.* 247:3848–53
215. Neumann, J. 1973. *FEBS Lett.* 36: 61–64
216. Neumann, J., Arntzen, C. J., Dilley, R. A. 1971. *Biochemistry* 10:866–73

217. Nieman, R. H., Vennesland, B. 1959. *Plant Physiol.* 34:255–62
218. Nir, I., Pease, D. C. 1973. *J. Ultrastruct. Res.* 42:534–50
219. Nir, I., Seligman, A. M. 1970. *J. Cell Biol.* 46:617–20
220. Nishimura, M., Sakurai, H., Takamiya, A. 1964. *Biochim. Biophys. Acta* 79: 241–48
221. Oettmeier, W., Heupel, A. 1972. *Z. Naturforsch.* 27b:177–83
222. Ibid, 586–87
223. Okayama, S., Butler, W. L. 1972. *Plant Physiol.* 49:769–74
224. Ort, D. R., Izawa, S. *Plant Physiol.* In press
225. Ort, D. R., Izawa, S., Good, N. E., Krogmann, D. W. 1973. *FEBS Lett.* 31:119–22
226. Ouitrakul, R., Izawa, S. 1973. *Biochim. Biophys. Acta* 305:105–18
227. Packer, L., Murakami, S., Mehard, C. W. 1972. *Ann. Rev. Plant Physiol.* 21:271–304
228. Park, R. B., Sane, P. V. 1971. *Ann. Rev. Plant Physiol.* 22:395–430
229. Pearlstein, R. M. 1971. *Proc. Int. Congr. Photosyn. Unit,* Gatlinburg, Tenn. 1970. In *Photochem. Photobiol.* 14:231–464
230. Plesnicar, M., Bendall, D. S. 1973. *Eur. J. Biochem.* 34:483–88
231. Racker, E., Hauska, G. A., Lien, S., Berzborn, R. J., Nelson, N. See Ref. 87, 2:1097–1113
232. Radunz, A. 1971. See Ref. 87, 2: 1613–18
233. Radunz, A., Berzborn, R. 1970. *Z. Naturforsch.* 25b:412–19
234. Radunz, A., Schmid, G. H. 1973. *Z. Naturforsch.* 28c:36–44
235. Radunz, A., Schmid, G. H., Menke, W. 1971. *Z. Naturforsch.* 26b:435–46
236. Reeves, S. G., Hall, D. O. 1973. *Biochim. Biophys. Acta* 314:66–78
237. Reeves, S. G., Hall, D. O., West, J. 1971. See Ref. 87, 2:1357–69
238. Regitz, G., Berzborn, R., Trebst, A. 1970. *Planta* 91:8–17
239. Regitz, G., Oettmeier, W. 1971. See Ref. 87, 1:499–506
240. Reinwald, E., Stiehl, H. H., Rumberg, B. 1968. *Z. Naturforsch.* 23b:1616–17
241. Renger, G. 1970. *Z. Naturforsch.* 25b:966–71
242. Renger, G. 1972. *Biochim. Biophys. Acta* 256:428–39
243. Renger, G. 1972. *Eur. J. Biochem.* 27:259–69
244. Rottenberg, H., Grunwald, T., Avron, M. 1971. *FEBS Lett.* 13:41–44
245. Rottenberg, H., Grunwald, T., Avron, M. 1972. *Eur. J. Biochem.* 25:54–63
246. Rottenberg, H., Grunwald, T., Schuldiner, S., Avron, M. 1971. See Ref. 87, 2:1035–47
247. Rumberg, B., Reinwald, E., Schröder, H., Siggel, U. 1968. *Naturwissenschaften* 55:77–79
248. Rumberg, B., Reinwald, E., Schröder, H., Siggel, U. 1969. See Ref. 16, 3: 1374–82
249. Rumberg, B., Schmidt-Mende, P., Skerra, B., Vater, J., Weikard, J., Witt, H. T. 1965. *Z. Naturforsch.* 20b:1086–1101
250. Rumberg, B., Schröder, H. 1972. See Ref. 254, 36
251. Saha, S., Ouitrakul, R., Izawa, S., Good, N. E. 1971. *J. Biol. Chem.* 246:3204–9
252. Sane, P. V., Goodchild, D. J., Park, R. B. 1970. *Biochim. Biophys. Acta* 216: 162–78
253. San Pietro, A. 1963. *Ann. NY Acad. Sci.* 103:1093–1105
254. Schenck, G. O. 1972. *Abstr Int. Congr. Photobiol.* Bochum
255. Schliephake, W., Junge, W., Witt, H. T. 1968. *Z. Naturforsch.* 23b:1571–78
256. Schmid, G. H. 1971. See Ref. 87, 2:1603–12
257. Schmidt-Mende, P., Witt, H. T. 1968. *Z. Naturforsch.* 23b:228–35
258. Schröder, H., Muhle, H., Rumberg, B. 1971. See Ref. 87, 2:919–30
259. Schwartz, M. 1967. *Biochim. Biophys. Acta* 131:548–58
260. Schwartz, M. 1968. *Nature* 219:915–19
261. Schwartz, M. 1971. *Ann. Rev. Plant Physiol.* 22:469–84
262. Selman, B. R., Bannister, T. T. 1971. *Biochim. Biophys. Acta* 253:428–36
263. Selman, B. R., Bannister, T. T., Dilley, R. A. 1973. *Biochim. Biophys. Acta* 292:566–81
264. Selman, B. R., Giaquinta, R. T., Dilley, R. A. In press
265. Senger, H. 1971. See Ref. 87, 1:723–30
266. Shumway, L. K., Park, R. B. 1969. *Exp. Cell Res.* 56:29–32
267. Shavit, N. 1971. See Ref. 87, 2:1221–31
268. Shavit, N., Shoshan, V. 1971. *FEBS Lett.* 14:265–67
269. Shin, M., San Pietro, A. 1968. *Biochem. Biophys. Res. Commun.* 33:38–42
270. Shin, M., Tagawa, K., Arnon, D. I. 1963. *Biochem. Z.* 338:84–96
271. Shneyour, A., Avron, M. 1971. *Biochim. Biophys. Acta* 253:412–20
272. Siedow, J., Yocum, C. F., San Pietro, A. 1973. *Curr. Top. Bioenerg.* 5:107–23

273. Siggel, U., Renger, G., Rumberg, B. 1971. See Ref. 87,1:753–62
274. Siggel, U., Renger, G., Stiehl, H. H., Rumberg, B. 1972. *Biochim. Biophys. Acta* 256:328–35
275. Smillie, R. M. 1963. *Plant Physiol.* 37:716–21
276. Stiehl, H. H., Witt, H. T. 1969. *Z. Naturforsch.* 24b:1588–98
277. Strotmann, H., von Gösslen, C. 1972. *Z. Naturforsch.* 27b:445–55
278. Strotmann, H., Wenninger, R., von Gösslen, C. 1972. *FEBS Lett.* 21: 289–92
279. Tagawa, K., Arnon, D. I. 1962. *Nature* 195:537–43
280. Telfer, A., Evans, M. C. W. 1972. *Biochim. Biophys. Acta* 256:625–37
281. Trebst, A. 1964. *Z. Naturforsch.* 19b:418–21
282. Trebst, A. 1971. See Ref. 87, 1:399–417
283. Trebst, A. 1972. *Methods Enzymol.* 24b:146–65
284. Trebst, A., Eck, H. 1961. *Z. Naturforsch.* 16b:455–61
285. Trebst, A., Pistorius, E. 1965. *Z. Naturforsch.* 20b:143–47
286. Trebst, A., Pistorius, E. 1967. *Biochim. Biophys. Acta* 131:580–82
287. Trebst, A., Reimer, S. 1973. *Biochim. Biophys. Acta* 305:129–39
288. Trebst, A., Reimer, S. 1973. *Z. Naturforsch.* 28c:710–16
289. Trebst, A., Reimer, S. 1973. *Biochim. Biophys. Acta* 325:546–57
290. Tsujimoto, H. Y., Chain, R. K., Arnon, D. I. 1973. *Biochem. Biophys. Res. Commun.* 51:917–23
291. Uribe, E. G. 1972. *Biochemistry* 11: 4228–35
292. Vaklinova, S., Tomova, N., Nicolova, E., Dechov, G. 1964. *C. R. Acad. Bulgare Sci.* 17:1051–57
293. Vernon, L. P., Shaw, E. R. 1969. *Biochem. Biophys. Res. Commun.* 36: 878–84
294. Vernon, L. P., Mollenhauer, H., Shaw, E. R. 1968. *Regulatory Functions of Biological Membranes*, ed. J. Järnefelt, 11:57–71. Elsevier
295. Vernon, L. P., Shaw, E. R. 1969. *Plant Physiol.* 44:1645–49
296. Ibid 1972. 49:862–63
297. Vernon, L. P., Zaugg, W. S. 1960. *J. Biol. Chem.* 235:2728–33
298. Vernon, L. P., Shaw, E. R., Limbach, D. 1966. *Curr. Photosyn. Proc. 2nd West.-Eur. Conf. Photosyn. 1965,* 121–28
299. Vigil, E. L., Arntzen, C. J., Swift, H. 1972. *Proc. 4th Int. Congr. Histochem. Cytochem.* Kyoto, ed. T. Takeuchi 139–40
300. Walker, D. A., Crofts, A. R. 1970. *Ann. Rev. Biochem.* 39:389–428
301. Warburg, O., Lüttgens, W. 1944. *Naturwissenschaften* 32:301
302. Weier, T. E., Stocking, C. R., Shumway, L. K. 1966. *Brookhaven Symp. Biol.* 19:353–74
303. West, K. R., Wiskich, J. T. 1968. *Biochem. J.* 109:527–32
304. West, K. R., Wiskich, J. T. 1973. *Biochim. Biophys. Acta* 292:197–205
305. Wessels, J. S. C. 1969. See Ref. 16, 1:128–36
306. Wessels, J. S. C. 1964. *Biochim. Biophys. Acta* 79:640–42
307. Whatley, F. R., Allen, M. B., Arnon, D. I. 1955. *Biochim. Biophys. Acta* 16: 605–6
308. Whittingham, C. P., Bishop, P. M. 1961. *Nature* 192:426–27
309. Wiessner, W., Amelunxen, F. 1969. *Arch. Mikrobiol.* 66:14–24
310. Ibid. 67:357–69
311. Williams, W. P. 1971. See Ref. 87, 1:745–52
312. Witt, H. T. 1967. *Nobel Symposium No. 5,* ed. S. Claesson, 261–316. Interscience
313. Witt, H. T. 1971. *Quart. Rev. Biophys.* 4:365–77
314. Witt, H. T., Rumberg, B., Junge, W. 1968. See Ref. 147, 262–306
315. Yamashita, K., Tsuji, I., Tomita, G. 1970. Presented at Photosyn. Unit Conf. Gatlinburg, Tenn.
316. Yamashita, K., Konishi, K., Itoh, M., Shibata, K. 1969. *Biochim. Biophys. Acta* 172:511–24
317. Yamashita, T., Butler, W. L. 1968. *Plant Physiol.* 43:1978–86
318. Ibid, 2037–40
319. Ibid 1969. 44:435–38
320. Yamashita, T., Horio, R. 1968. *Plant Cell Physiol.* 9:267–84
321. Yocum, C. F., San Pietro, A. 1969. *Biochem. Biophys. Res. Commun.* 36: 614–20
322. Yocum, C. F., San Pietro, A. 1970. *Arch. Biochem. Biophys.* 152–57
323. Zweig, G., Avron, M. 1965. *Biochem. Biophys. Res. Commun.* 19:397–400

Ann. Rev. Plant Physiol. 1974. 25:459–86

THE METABOLISM OF
AROMATIC COMPOUNDS

❖7574

Helen A. Stafford

Reed College, Portland, Oregon

CONTENTS

INTRODUCTION 460
PRE-AROMATIC PATHWAY TO PHENYLALANINE AND TYROSINE 460
C_6-C_3 PATHWAYS 462
  Hydroxylation-Methoxylation Sequence 462
      The ammonia lyases 462
      Aromatic hydroxylations 465
      Cinnamate-4-hydroxylase 466
      4-Hydroxycinnamate-3-hydroxylase 466
      Ferulate-5-hydroxylase 467
      O-methyltransferase activity 468
      General comments on the cinnamic acid sequence 468
  Formation of Glucose and Quinic Acid Esters 469
  Miscellaneous C_6-C_3 Transformations 470
  Special Roles of the Cinnamic Acid Derivatives 470
  Ortho-Hydroxylation to Coumarins 470
  Activation of Carboxyl Groups via Coenzyme A Ligases 471
  Carboxyl Reduction Pathway to Lignin Precursors 471
LIGNIN 472
  Characteristics of the C_6-C_3 Polymer 472
  Enzymatic Components Required to Form Lignin 473
      Peroxidase 473
      H_2O_2 474
      Oxidative Polymerization to Lignin in Cell-Free Systems 474
      Subcellular Events Leading to the Formation of Lignin in Walls 474
CHAIN-SHORTENING PATHWAYS 475
  C_6-C_2 Pathway to Cyanogenic Glycosides 475
  C_6-C_1 Pathways to Quinones 475
C_{15}-FLAVONOID PATHWAY 476
  The Enzymology of Flavonoid Biosynthesis 476
  The Role of the Chloroplast 478
  Conclusion about Flavonoid Biosynthesis 478

SPECIAL ROLES OF PEROXIDASE AND POLYPHENOLOXIDASE................. 478
    Peroxidase 478
    Polyphenoloxidase Complex 480
CONCLUSIONS.. 482

INTRODUCTION

About 14 years have passed since Neish's review of the pathways of aromatic compounds in this series (104). Our knowledge of these pathways in 1960 was based entirely on isotopic tracer techniques at the tissue level. A major breakthrough occurred in the following year when Neish (105) and Koukol & Conn (76) published their cell-free demonstration of the novel enzymes capable of deaminating phenylalanine and tyrosine, respectively. The peak of this descriptive cell-free enzymology may have occurred in 1973 with the demonstration of the reduction pathway to lignin precursors (23, 91) and the condensation of a coenzyme A (CoA) derivative of hydroxylated cinnamic acids with that of malonyl CoA to produce a C_6-C_3-C_6 flavonoid (77). The earlier work in cell-free enzymology has been reviewed by Conn (17) and Higuchi (61).

This review concentrates on the highlights of the cell-free enzymology of phenolic acid in higher plants, citing gaps in our information and summarizing the fragmentary knowledge of the in vivo state and intracellular localization of these enzymes. Evidence of possible multienzyme complexes in the soluble or particulate fraction is emphasized (36). The regulatory control by light of some of these enzymes has been reviewed recently (143, 155, 188); the data concerning hormonal control are still fragmentary and are not included.

Special attention is given to two enzymes known to be involved in the metabolism of phenolic compounds, i.e. peroxidase and polyphenoloxidase. Peroxidase is a confusing enzyme because of its numerous multiple forms and its versatile catalytic abilities. Polyphenoloxidase is another versatile enzyme whose cell-free diphenol oxidations are all too easily demonstrated, but whose in vivo function for the diphenoloxidase activities is unclear. New orientations toward the role of these enzymes may come from the recent indication that they are associated with a variety of cellular membranes.

An overall view of the metabolic pathways to be discussed is shown in Figure 1.

PRE-AROMATIC PATHWAY TO PHENYLALANINE AND TYROSINE

Since the enzymes that synthesize aromatic amino acids have been reviewed recently (118, 184), they are not discussed in detail here. Parts of this sequence of reactions might be expected to exist as a multienzyme complex, but although all of the individual steps have now been demonstrated, most of them in higher plants are easily solubilized as separate enzymes. The intracellular localization and regulation of these activities are largely unknown.

The *arom* cluster in *Neurospora*, however, is an excellent example of a multienzyme complex (64). The *arom* cluster encodes four to five enzymes of the shikimate

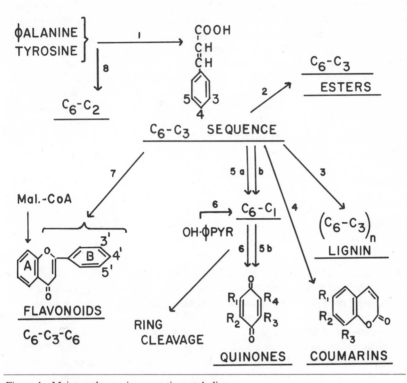

Figure 1   Major pathways in aromatic metabolism

1. C_6-C_3 hydroxylation-methoxylation sequence forming cinnamate, *p*-coumarate, caffeate, ferulate, and sinapate via NADPH and SAM.
2. Ester formation via UDPG.
3. Lignin formation via peroxidase and H_2O_2 after reduction of carboxyl groups via CoA, ATP, and NADPH.
4. *Ortho*-hydroxylation to coumarins.
5. Chain-shortening pathways involving C_6-C_1 skeletons: a & b - conversion to benzoate and *p*-hydroxybenzoate after activation by CoA and ATP prior to β oxidation; b - conversion to the aromatic skeleton in ubiquinone.
6. Chain-shortening pathway from 4-hydroxyphenylpyruvate (OH-φ-PYR) via homogentisate and homoarbutin to the C_6-C_1 skeleton in plastoquinone.
7. Synthesis of B ring and heterocyclic ring of flavonoids after activation by CoA and ATP prior to condensation with malonyl CoA (Mal-CoA).
8. Chain-shortening pathway to C_6-C_2 cyanogenic glycosides, prunasin, and dhurrin.

pathway which catalyzes five steps leading ultimately to chorismate, after the initial condensation step involving erythrose-4-P + PEP. The activities are associated with an aggregate of about 230,000 mol wt, made up of two sets of the enzymes which can be separated into a series of smaller fragments. Only two of the activities are found associated in the algae and higher plants examined by the same group. One could argue that the complex isolated from such plant cells is unstable or that proteases break it down during extraction, rather than there being any basic difference in the state of the enzymes in these different organisms. This multienzyme complex found in the so-called soluble fraction of extracts from *Neurospora* is of particular interest because it illustrates catalytic facilitation, in which the rates of an overall sequence starting with the initial precursor is greater than any of the subsequent steps with known intermediates (31).

C_6-C_3 PATHWAYS

Hydroxylation-Methoxylation Sequence

Phenylalanine $\xrightarrow{1}$ cinnamate $\xrightarrow{2}$ p-coumarate[1] $\xrightarrow{3}$ caffeate $\xrightarrow{4}$ ferulate $\xrightarrow{5}$

5-hydroxyferulate $\xrightarrow{6}$ sinapate

The sequence of six chemical reactions converting phenylalanine to sinapic acid involves three hydroxylations (steps 2, 3, and 5) and two methylations (steps 4 and 6) following the initial ammonia lyase step (step 1) (Table 1). This is an unusual sequence in that some of the phenolic compounds involved are not only intermediates leading to sinapate, but are also final products themselves, which are either accumulated as esters or used in other pathways such as lignin and flavonoid biosynthesis. The regulation of the activity of such a sequence must be complex, and one might expect that one or more multienzyme complexes are involved (159). All the cinnamate derivatives of the sequence are in the *trans* form.

THE AMMONIA LYASES

Phenylalanine $\longrightarrow$ cinnamate + NH$_3$ (PAL)
Tyrosine $\longrightarrow$ 4-hydroxycinnamate + NH$_3$ (TAL)
                    (p-coumarate)

These activities have been widely studied and reviewed (13, 48, 188). Only major controversial points are emphasized here.

Universality and mechanism of light effects on PAL activity   PAL activities of many dicots are controlled by phytochrome or a blue light high irradiance response (HIR) (97, 143, 188). The light-induced response is characterized by an initial increase followed by a decrease to produce a bell-shaped curve of activity with developmental

[1]The majority of workers use the shorter, trivial names for the compounds in the C_6-C_3 sequence. But the name 4-hydroxycinnamate is far more informative than p-coumarate when considering the enzymatic reactions involved. I use the two names interchangeably for the substrate, but call the enzyme involved 4-hydroxycinnamate hydroxylase (HCH).

Table 1 Enzymes of the major pathways of aromatic metabolism in higher plants

Enzyme	Cofactors
C_6–C_3 sequence	
1. Phenylalanine and tyrosine ammonia lyases (PAL and TAL)	–
2. t-cinnamate–4-hydroxylase (cytochrome b_5 and P_{450})[a]	NADPH
3. 4-hydroxycinnamate–3-hydroxylase (p–coumarate hydroxylase)[a]	Ascorbate, NADPH, or reduced pteridines
4. O–methyltransferase	SAM, Mg^{2+}
5. [Ferulate–5-hydroxylase] [a,b]	?
Ester formation	
1. UDPG: glycosyltransferase	–
Carboxyl group activation	
1. CoA ligase for p-coumarate, ferulate, and (sinapate)	ATP, CoASH, NADPH, Mg^{2+}
Lignification sequence	
1. p-coumaroyl, feruloyl, and [sinapoyl] :CoA reductases	–
2. p-coumaryl, coniferyl, and [sinapyl] alcohol oxidoreductases	NADPH
3. [H_2O_2 generating system]	–
4. Peroxidase	
C_{15} flavonoid sequence (starting with malonyl CoA and p-coumaroyl CoA)	
1. "Chalcone synthetase"	–
2. Chalcone-flavanone isomerase	–
3. "Flavanone dehydrogenase"	–
4. 3′- and 4′- B–ring hydroxylases (polyphenoloxidase?)[a,c]	Ascorbate
5. 3′-O-methyltransferase (luteolin 3′-O-methyltransferase)[d]	SAM
6. Glycosyltransferases	
(UDPG: flavonoid 7-O-glycosyltransferase)[d]	–
(UDPG: flavonol 3-O-glycosyltransferase)[d]	–
(UDP-apiose: 7-O-glucosylapigenin (1 → 2) apiosyltransferase)[d]	–
(UDP-D-apiose synthase)[d]	–
7. Acyltransferase	
(malonyl–CoA: flavonoid glycoside malonyltransferase)[d]	–

[a] Mixed function oxidases (mono-oxygenases).
[b] [   ] = hypothetical enzymes.
[c] Nonspecific, act also on C_6–C_3 compounds.
[d] (Enzymes) necessary for the biosynthesis of the flavone glycosides apiin and gravebioside A plus initial steps 1–4 (38).

time. But evidence of a light-induced control is rare or missing in monocot tissues, at least in those with light-sensitive first internodes (mesocotyls).[2] A recent report from McClure's laboratory, using shoots of barley seedlings, is the first case of phytochrome control of these activities in a monocot, but the increases are not great (94, 140). Furthermore, etiolated barley shoots differ from those of corn, *Sorghum,* etc. The latter have long first internodes attached below short coleoptiles, which can be easily separated. In contrast, the first internode of barley is microscopic, and the etiolated shoot consists of an elongated coleoptile enclosing both the second internode and inner young leaves (159). It is not clear whether the lack of a phytochrome effect in most monocots studied is due to control by another system, or whether inactivation masks any increase in activity.

Etiolated seedling tissues, especially the first internode of monocots and the hypocotyl of some dicots, have been widely used for the above studies (97, 159). Some confusion may exist in the literature due to different pretreatments and ambiguity as to what tissue was extracted. Care must be taken both in reading the literature and in reporting experiments to clarify these problems.

Mechanisms postulated for the light-induced increases (or prevention of inactivation) have been reviewed recently (143, 155, 188). Engelsma has reported that Mn^{2+} can substitute for the blue light HIR of PAL in hypocotyls of gherkin (27). The Mn^{2+}-induced increase in PAL activity was quite striking, but the effects on the concentration of hydroxycinnamic acids in the hypocotyl were even greater. Engelsma's interpretation that the increase in PAL was due to the removal of hydroxycinnamic acid by complexing with Mn^{2+} is not completely satisfactory, since both PAL and *p*-coumarate initially have parallel increases (27). These are provocative data, and should be considered along with the Attridge & Smith report of an already formed but inactive PAL in gherkin seedlings (5). Peroxidase activities such as monophenol and NADPH oxidase might also be involved in such Mn-dependent effects (32, 160).

Intracellular state and localization of PAL and TAL activities   Highly purified PAL enzymes isolated from wheat, corn, and potato consist of one tetramer with both PAL and TAL activities in the monocots, and only PAL in the case of the dicot (55–57, 103, 123). No light effects were detectable in either of the monocot preparations in contrast to the dicot potato tissue. While the tetramer isolated from wheat was composed of two different subunits (103), the corn and potato enzymes contained similar subunits (56). The latter data do not explain why corn has a dual catalytic role when its subunits are similar to those of potato. Each subunit had a molecular weight of 83,000, and it was suggested that there are two active sites per fully active tetramer. These was evidence of a higher molecular weight form in potato, but not in corn (56). One wonders whether an enzyme with high TAL activity might not be discarded sometimes in earlier purification steps. For instance, protamine sulfate used to remove nucleic acids precipitated TAL activity (105).

[2]Although the use of the term "mesocotyl" for the first internode of grasses is widespread, it is an inaccurate term since the single cotyledon is attached at the base of the internode (159).

Ammonia lyases are associated with high molecular weight and particulate fractions in other plant preparations (72, 73, 129, 130, 139, 160). Kindl (72) has reported one high molecular weight form with a high TAL relative to PAL activity, and another form of less than 100,000 mol wt with a low TAL to PAL activity in barley shoots. Details of the separation of these forms were inadequate; the small form, however, could be the subunit described above.

PAL "isozymes" from *Quercus* roots have been reported to be associated with two different cytoplasmic fractions. One of the isozymes associated with microbodies gave rise to C_6-C_1 products (the benzoate pathway); the other, associated with microsomes, gave rise to the C_6-C_3 products and contained cinnamate hydroxylase activity. The two isozymes differed in their sensitivities to vanillic (microbody isozyme) and caffeic acid (microsomal isozyme) (2). Glyoxysomes isolated from *Ricinus* contained PAL activity and also produced chain-shortening products (73, 129). In green leaves, brief reports have appeared of PAL and TAL activities in peroxisomes of sunflower leaves (128) and in highly purified chloroplasts of barley (94, 139).

Artifacts are a constant concern when multiple molecular weight forms or activities associated with particulate fractions are found. They can be caused by aggregation by salts and phenolics (4) or by degradation via proteases (33, 124). Adsorption of phenolic compounds can also alter mobilities during electrophoresis and column chromatography (56, 172). There is no a priori reason to believe that either the smaller or larger aggregate is the in vivo form. Schopfer (142) has argued that a large aggregate (4×10^6 mol wt) of PAL activity detected in extracts of *Sinapis* eluted from Sepharose columns with 20 mM *tris* was an artifact due to the dilute buffer. Elution with 0.1 M KCl and 50 g/liter sucrose gave a form with a molecular weight of about 3×10^5, similar to that obtained in the purified preparations cited above. While his interpretation of these results may be correct, it is equally plausible that the small form represents the dissociation of a native aggregate at the higher osmotic concentration. High salt concentrations can dissociate membrane-associated aggregates or polymeric form of proteins, including ribosomes (87). The isolation of a purified tetrameric form is not proof of the in vivo state of an enzyme.

It is often forgotten that side reactions might interfere with assay methods for enzymes of the C_6-C_3 sequence. A recent word of warning comes from Erez (28). The PAL assay followed at 290 nm in borate buffer can involve the conversion of phenylalanine to phenylpyruvate via transaminases if keto acids are present. This leads to erroneous readings due to an enol tautomer-borate complex. Similar problems might occur with tyrosine as substrate.

AROMATIC HYDROXYLATIONS   Reviews of hydroxylases are provided by Hayaishi (58) and Hamilton (47). The three hydroxylation steps of the C_6-C_3 sequence are probably all mixed function oxidases or mono-oxygenases catalyzing the general reaction

$$SH + O_2 + AH_2 \longrightarrow SOH + H_2O + A$$

Two of the three have been identified in cell-free preparations.

CINNAMATE-4-HYDROXYLASE

Cinnamate $+ O_2 +$ NADPH $+ H^+ \longrightarrow$ 4-hydroxycinnamate $+$ NADP$^+ +$ H$_2$O

The basic work with this enzyme in etiolated peas and *Sorghum* shoots comes from the laboratory of Conn, working with Russell (131, 133) and Potts (117). Although initially considered a pteridine-dependent hydroxylase (131), it was subsequently found to be a cytochrome b_5 and P$_{450}$ type associated with microsomal or light membrane fractions. Evidence for the presence of cytochrome P$_{450}$ was based on the CO difference spectrum and the photodissociation of the CO complex (117). The demonstration of an NIH shift, characteristic of some hydroxylations of non-phenolic aromatic substrates, has been shown by two groups (132, 185). The peroxidase-catalyzed hydroxylation of cinnamate, requiring dihydroxyfumarate, does not show such a shift (21). Light controls the activity of the P$_{450}$ cinnamate hydroxylase in some tissues (133) but not in others (14). The activity appears to decline in mature pea plants (133) and in excised and incubated first internodes (H. A. Stafford, unpublished data). This may not be a physiological response but rather an inactivation upon extraction, since both tissues are still producing large amounts of phenolic compounds requiring cinnamate hydroxylase. This enzyme activity is difficult to demonstrate in cell-free extracts of some plants and is frequently studied only in a tissue slice system (54).

While the above data are based on activities found in a high-speed particulate fraction, there is one recent report of a soluble cinnamic hydroxylase in fresh potato discs. Upon aging the slices, the localization was microsomal (14).

4-HYDROXYCINNAMATE-3-HYDROXYLASE

4-hydroxycinnamate $+ O_2 +$ ascorbate $\longrightarrow$ 3,4-dihydroxycinnamate
$+$ dehydroascorbate $+$ H$_2$O

Tissue extracts capable of hydroxylating 4-hydroxycinnamate to caffeic acid in higher plants, regardless of whether they are associated with a diphenol function, have been demonstrated in potato (86, 114), *Saxifraga* (135), beet (112, 175), and *Sorghum* (161, 163). In all but *Sorghum,* the activities are considered inseparable from the diphenoloxidase activities. Generally ascorbate, NADPH, or reduced pteridine are required electron donors (137, 163, 174). In light-treated chloroplast preparations, however, the cofactor was not required, presumably because of an endogenous supply of NADPH by photosynthesis (7). Nonenzymatic ascorbate-dependent hydroxylations can interfere unless agents such as serum albumin are added (10).

A major problem is whether there is a separate hydroxylase that has no diphenoloxidase activity. While the monophenol activities in beet preparations (175) coincide with those of the diphenol, the two activities are often separable in *Sorghum* extracts. But, so far, no hydroxylase preparation has been found that is devoid of chlorogenic acid oxidase activity (161, 163). An enzyme specific for the hydroxylation of 4-hydroxycinnamate would be comparable to the mammalian system in which there is a classical tyrosinase with both monophenol and diphenol functions and a separate pteridine-dependent hydroxylase activity (100).

The strict requirement of some plant monophenol hydroxylases for external hydrogen donors such as ascorbate or NADPH might be cited as evidence of a separate or modified enzyme, since Mason's model for monophenol hydroxylation requires diphenoloxidase activity (92 and later discussion). Data from beet leaf preparations support Mason's model, since diphenol activity was required for the hydroxylation step and catecholoxidase activity could be expressed during the hydroxylation under certain conditions (175, 176). But the double step has never been observed in *Sorghum* leaf preparations, even with preparations containing both activities when assayed independently (161, 163). There may be two monophenol hydroxylating enzymes, one specific for 4-hydroxycinnamate, and the other associated with a diphenoloxidase. It will be necessary to separate the two monophenol functions to determine their specificities. One would suspect that the polyphenolase enzyme would have the broader monophenol specificity. A specific hydroxylase might be an evolutionary product of the combined function. A separate 4-hydroxycinnamate hydroxylase would have a selective advantage, since the diphenoloxidase activity would remove a necessary intermediate in the C_6-C_3 sequence.

The hydroxylase activity in beet leaf preparations has been purified 100-fold by ammonium sulfate and DEAE- and CM-cellulose treatment, and a constant ratio of this hydroxylase to diphenoloxidase activity was maintained throughout the purification (175). Hydroxylase activity in *Sorghum* extracts at pH 6 was associated with a minimum of three molecular weight forms or fractions. One was sometimes associated with an active chlorogenic acid oxidase activity, while the others had very low diphenoloxidase activities. The type found in first internode tissues was a small molecular weight form, according to its elution from Agarose A-15 M. An intermediate-sized form was found in etiolated leaves. Activity in green leaves was partly in a microsomal fraction and partly in the void volume fraction from Agarose A-15 M columns. Six hours of light were sufficient to convert significant amounts of the etiolated leaf form to that of green leaves. Mixing experiments indicated that artifacts due to extraction were not involved. If extractions were made at pH 8 rather than 6, 40–80% of the hydroxylase activity was associated with a crude chloroplast fraction (161). Parish likewise reported an association of beet leaf hydroxylase with both chloroplast and supernatant fractions (112). The only other case of a known molecular weight for this enzyme is that of 18,000 for the hydroxylase isolated from *Streptomyces* (102). Thus, as in the case of ammonia lyases, this hydroxylase activity appears to be found in different cellular compartments in various molecular weight fractions.

FERULATE-5-HYDROXYLASE   In this third hydroxylation of the sequence, 3-methoxy, 4-hydroxy-cinnamate (ferulate) is converted to 3-methoxy,4,5,-hydroxy-cinnamate (5-hydroxyferulate). No information is available concerning the cell-free enzymology of this step, although tracer evidence predicts its presence (148, 149). The product is not accumulated in detectable amounts in plant tissues. If the entire C_6-C_3 sequence occurs on the surface of a multienzyme complex leading to sinapate, one might expect that 5-hydroxyferulate would not accumulate because of the presence of a methyltransferase which would tend to catalyze both methylation steps of the sequence (159).

O-METHYLTRANSFERASE ACTIVITY

> 3,4,-dihydroxycinnamate + CH_3 donor $\longrightarrow$ 4-hydroxy,3-methoxycinnamate
> (caffeate)   (ferulate)
> 5-hydroxyferulate + CH_3 donor $\longrightarrow$ 4-hydroxy,3,4-methoxycinnamate
>   (sinapate)

The two steps in the C_6-C_3 basic sequence requiring O methylation are those producing ferulic and sinapic acids. Recent reports following the initial demonstration by Nelson & Finkle in 1964 (106) indicate that there may be at least two enzymes capable of methylating hydroxy groups at positions 3 and 5 in higher plants (150). All require S-adenosylmethionine (SAM) as a methyl donor and Mg^{2+}. They differ in substrate specificity, but both were *meta*-specific. The one found in gymnosperms methylated the 3 position of caffeate more effectively than 5-hydroxyferulate, while both were methylated in angiosperms. Such a difference might be expected, since these two groups differ in the absence and presence of the syringyl unit in their lignins. The methylation step was considered the block to the production of syringyl units in gymnosperms rather than the preceding hydroxylation step. Separate enzymes in pampas grass methylate the *meso* and *para* positions, respectively (30).

A methyltransferase, purified 85-fold from parsley suspension cultures, was a small protein of about 48,000 mol wt (24). Although caffeate was a better substrate than luteolin and its 7-O-glucoside, the affinity of the enzyme was greater for the C_{15} than for the C_6-C_3 compound. Two peaks of activity were found after elution from Sephadex G-100, but only one band was detected after disc electrophoresis or isoelectric focusing. Interpretation of phenolic pathways is complicated by the fact that O demethylation can occur (148), although there is an indication of the separation of anabolic and catabolic pathways (52).

GENERAL COMMENTS ON THE CINNAMIC ACID SEQUENCE   Does this hydroxylation-methylation sequence exist in one or more multienzyme forms capable of binding with membranes of the cytoplasm or organelles? The fragmentary direct and indirect evidence for this and speculations concerning their existence have been discussed recently (159).

Preliminary evidence of a sequence of reactions leading to ferulate, starting from either ^{14}C-labeled phenylalanine or tyrosine, was reported for a crude particulate fraction from *Sorghum*. The individual enzymatic steps were demonstrated in that or similar particulate fractions (160, 161, 163). Evidence of compartmentation from experiments using isotopes (25) and differential centrifugation (2, 73), and the coordinated increases of the activities of the C_6-C_3 sequence (43) might also suggest that multienzyme complexes exist.

None of the data for the intracellular physical state or localization of these enzymes are definitive, and these activities might just be easily adsorbed to various particulates upon grinding. But the concept of one or more multienzyme complexes associated with membranes is a useful working hypothesis. The specific tyrosine hydroxylase of brain tissues might aid in the interpretation of the plant data. This protein can reversibly associate with either a soluble, membrane, or particulate aggregate, and readily attaches to all types of cellular fractions (79).

Formation of Glucose and Quinic Acid Esters

The substrates used to demonstrate the cell-free activities of enzymes of the C_6-C_3 sequence leading to cinnamic acid derivatives are the free acids or their salts. But, although some isotopic tracer data at the tissue level indicated that the interconversions were at the level of free acids, other data indicated that esters were intermediates.

Data concerning intermediates in the formation of chlorogenic acid (3-O-caffeoyl-D-quinic) are controversial. There is an indication that there may be three pathways, one involving free acids and the other two esters (165). Levy & Zucker (86) postulated that the intermediates in potato tuber slices were all quinic acid intermediates from the level of cinnamic acid. But Kojima et al (75) reported that an initial intermediate in sweet potato tubers was β-1-cinnamoyl-D-glucose. It is not clear whether the formation of chlorogenic acid is a special case, and if so, why.

The tracer data of El-Basyouni (25) were interpreted as evidence of protein-bound esters as intermediates in the hydroxylation-methoxylation sequence after activation of the carboxyl group. Zenk et al (186) argued that this was in conflict with the cell-free enzymic data which indicated catalysis at the level of free acids. But another interpretation of the tracer data is that intermediates occurred only on the surface of a multienzyme complex, and that phenylalanine gave a higher overall rate of incorporation into hydroxylated cinnamic acids of ethanol insoluble residues than cinnamic acid due to catalytic facilitation (31). Perhaps similar effects due to compartmentation might explain the data concerning chlorogenic acid biosynthesis.

There is no cell-free evidence that the esters are better substrates in these hydroxylation reactions than the free acids, but since glucose esters are not readily available, no one has used them for comparative studies. In the one study made with both free acids and quinic esters, the hydroxylation of 4-hydroxycinnamate was similar to the free acid and the ester (114).

Glucose esters (1-O-acyl derivatives) of the hydroxycinnamic acids are common in higher plants. The activating agent is UDP-glucose (19). Presumably quinic acid esters could be formed from glucose esters.

In spite of the above tracer data at the tissue level indicating that esters are intermediates in the C_6-C_3 sequence, the esterification reaction is best considered as a terminal step. Possibly the conversion to esters occurs directly from the surface of the enzyme-product complex, and the accumulation of esters in the vacuole might be dependent upon this esterification.

Miscellaneous C_6-C_3 Transformations

While fungi have polyphenol oxidases capable of hydroxylating tyrosine (92, 141), tyrosine hydroxylase activity has been identified in only a few higher plants such as potato (114) and banana (99). Recent work with banana tissue indicated that the activity was found in both soluble and particulate fractions in the pulp. Both optical isomers of tyrosine were hydroxylated, and ascorbate was the most effective reductant. The product, dihydroxyphenylalanine (DOPA), could be subsequently oxidized by the associated diphenoloxidase function. Phenylalanine hydroxylase activity in higher plants is weak or nonexistent (54, 101, 170).

Special Roles of the Cinnamic Acid Derivatives

While the postulated role of monophenols and diphenols as cofactors and inhibitors, respectively, of IAA oxidase is well known, other potential regulatory functions of these compounds are being reported. A possible generalization is that p-coumarate is the key intermediate leading to both flavonoids and hydroxylated coumarins, rather than the corresponding hydroxylated cinnamic acids. This implies that hydroxylation and methylation occur at the C_{15} and coumarin levels.

Ferulic acid may play a special role in cell wall metabolism other than in lignified cell walls. In 1970, Lamport reviewed cell wall linkages that might be under cellular control (81). One of these was a Ca^{2+} chelate bridge between protein and ferulic acid, the latter being ester-linked to polysaccharide. Such a ferulic complex has been identified in wheat flour glycoprotein, and a mechanism of oxidative gelation of such protein was described in a model system based upon caffeic acid (111). Ferulic acid has also been identified as an esterified component of a complex carbohydrate polymer (85), and as an alkaline-sensitive component of peptide sequence from barley globulins (173).

Ortho-Hydroxylation to Coumarins

Tissue level studies of this biosynthetic pathway are discussed by Brown (12). The cell-free enzymology of these pathways represents a major gap in our knowledge of the metabolism of phenolic compounds in higher plants. While previous studies have indicated that coumarins are derived from their corresponding cinnamic acids, Sato et al (138) now conclude from tissue level studies that the major route to natural dihydroxycoumarins such as daphnetin and esculetin is via p-coumarate rather than caffeate. Subsequent steps from p-coumarate to coumarin glycosides would involve *ortho* hydroxylation leading to ring cyclization.

Two reports have appeared, however, which indicate that the diphenol function of a polyphenoloxidase can produce coumarins in cell-free systems. Sato studied the formation of esculetin from *cis*-caffeic acid in crude chloroplast preparations from *Saxifraga* stolons (136). But since this plant never accumulates caffeic or esculetin, the reaction may have no physiological significance in that plant. It is significant that related compounds such as cinnamic, p-coumaric, or ferulic acids were not converted to their respective coumarin derivatives. Sato concluded that the initial step in esculetin formation was not the production of a hydroxyl-group *ortho* to the side chain, but an *ortho*-quinone of *cis*-caffeic acid. He postulates that subsequently 3,4,6-trihydroxy-*cis*-cinnamic acid is formed by hydration, followed by lactonization to form esculetin. The reaction forming esculetin in the presence of a *cis-trans* mixture of caffeic acid was inhibited by ascorbic acid and other phenolase inhibitors such as diethyldithiocarbamate. The phenolase activities and esculetin synthesis were always associated in the same ratios during purification via ammonium sulfate precipitation. A similar relationship was observed with phenolase preparations from mushroom.

A second quite different example was the synthesis of a coumarin by crystalline β-tyrosinase from *Escherichia coli*. At pH 7.8, S-methyl-L-cysteine plus resorcinol and added pyridoxal phosphate produced 3,4,-dihydro-3-amino-7-hydroxycoumarin (171).

A recent report indicated that chloroplast preparations from *Meliotus* leaves catalyzed in the presence of NADPH the *ortho*-hydroxylation of *trans*-cinnamic to *o*-coumaric (*o*-hydroxycinnamic acid) (35). Subsequently, coumarin would be formed after glucosylation and conversion to the *cis* isomer and glucosidase activity (74).

Activation of Carboxyl Groups via Coenzyme A Ligases

$$R \cdot CH{:}CH \cdot COOH + ATP + CoA \cdot SH \rightarrow R \cdot CH{:}CH \cdot CO \sim S \cdot CoA + AMP + PP_i$$

Activation of the carboxyl group is required for many reactions involving cinnamic acids and their derivatives (186). In higher plants, cell-free evidence indicates that CoA esters are produced in the presence of ATP by CoA ligases.

Evidence of the activation of the carboxyl group of acetate, p-coumarate, and ferulate has been reported by Hahlbrock et al (44, 45). The assay was based on the formation of hydroxamic acid in the presence of the above substrates, CoA, ATP, and $MgSO_4$. In cell suspension cultures of soybean and parsley, the activity of the acetate:CoA ligase was independent of light treatment, while that of p-coumarate, cinnamate, and ferulate were light dependent, indicating that at least two enzymes were involved in the above activations. A comparable activation of cinnamate by a so-called cinnamoyl-CoA synthetase has been demonstrated in beet leaf extracts; it was specific for cinnamate, showing no activity with the hydroxylated derivatives (177).

The CoA esters of p-coumarate and ferulate can be used in the reduction pathway to lignin precursors, discussed in the next section. The p-coumaroyl CoA ester may also be the main entrance into the C_{15} pathway to flavonoids and possibly coumarin biosynthesis. Cinnamoyl and p-coumaroyl CoA esters may function in the chain-shortening sequence in which benzoic and hydroxybenzoic acids are formed by β oxidation.

Carboxyl Reduction Pathway to Lignin Precursors

The activation mechanism for the initial step of this reaction differs in fungi and higher plants. Zenk & Gross demonstrated an arylaldehyde:NADP oxidoreductase requiring ATP in *Neurospora*. The enzyme had a broad specificity, but cinnamate was the best substrate. It was postulated that an enzyme-AMP complex was formed followed by an alkaline-sensitive protein-bound cinnamate ester as an intermediate complex. A second enzyme, an arylalcohol:NADPH oxidoreductase, converted the aldehyde to the alcohol (40, 186).

The reduction pathway in higher plants involved activation by the CoA ligases described in the previous section, followed by

$$R \cdot CH:CH \cdot CO \sim S\ CoA + NADPH + H^+ {\longrightarrow} R \cdot CH:CH \cdot CHO + CoA-SH$$
$$+ NADP^+$$
$$R \cdot CH:CH \cdot CHO + NADPH + H^+ {\longrightarrow} R \cdot CH:CH \cdot CH_2OH + NADP^+$$

The above overall reaction has now been demonstrated by two groups (23, 91). Both coumaroyl CoA and feruloyl CoA were converted to their respective alcohols in the presence of NADPH and a supernatant fraction after centrifugation at 10,000 X g isolated from cell suspension cultures of soybean. NADH gave about 0.1 the activity of NADPH. Starting with ferulic acid, ATP, CoASH, Mg^{2+}, and NADPH were required. It was not clear in these double-step reactions whether free aldehyde was produced.

Lignin does contain aldehyde groups. Earlier tracer work indicated an aldehyde intermediate (11), and a specific aromatic alcohol dehydrogenase was reported in potato tuber extracts (22). Recently one of the above groups has characterized three separate enzyme activities in cambial tissues of *Salix*, which convert ferulate to coniferyl alcohol: ferulate CoA ligase, ferulate-CoA reductase, and coniferyl alcohol oxidoreductase (39).

LIGNIN

Characteristics of the C_6-C_3 Polymer

In spite of a vast literature, lignin is a poorly understood natural product. Other than being a polymer of C_6-C_3 phenolic units found in cell walls, its structure is unclear and the three-dimensional view is only speculative. Information concerning the lignins of woody plants has overwhelmed the literature, and knowledge concerning lignins of herbaceous plants is meager. One basic limitation is that lignin must be altered chemically for extraction from the cell walls of plants. Another problem is that most of the assay methods do not differentiate between monomers or polymers, but depend only on a free functional group such as a terminal aldehyde or benzylalcohol group. Total analyses by gravimetric methods (Klason lignin, etc) are often undependable for herbaceous and young tissue (134, 156).

The recent book on lignins, edited by Sarkanen & Ludwig, is an excellent account of the present status of lignin, with a useful section on herbaceous tissues, a subject frequently ignored by wood chemists (134). Degradative aspects of lignins are considered by Higuchi (61) and Steelink (166). The 1966 review by Brown (11) is still helpful.

The classical concept of lignin is that the basic core is a polymer made up of phenylpropyl units of one or more of the following moieties: *p*-hydroxyl-, guaiacyl-, and syringyl-aldehyde and alcohol units. Grasses and dicots such as *Populus* also contain large amounts of esters of phenolic acids associated with the lignin core, consisting in grasses of *p*-coumaric and ferulic acid (78, 147, 148). While others have postulated that the acids are linked to the α- or benzyl-carbon, the Japanese group argue that *p*-coumaric acid is linked to the terminal carbon of the side chain of the lignin core. They also postulate that because these ester linkages are limited to certain groups, there must be specific acylating enzymes controlling their formation (147).

Other workers, however, consider that ester groups in lignin can arise from dehydrogenation products during the peroxidase-catalyzed reaction (115). Thus, no additional enzymatic reactions would be required to explain the existence of ester linkages. The oxidative gelation of glycoproteins and the polysaccharide-ferulic-Ca^{2+}-protein complex might be useful in any consideration of ester linkages (111).

It has also been argued that there may be an acid lignin in addition to the classical core of aldehyde-alcohol groups, since ferulic acid alone in a paper-peroxidase model system can produce phenolic products similar to those found in grasses (157). Ferulic acid can also substitute for the dianisidine substrate in producing a yellow color associated with some of the major peroxidase bands isolated electrophoretically (162, and unpublished data). The yellow product was not further studied.

Lignin may be a heterogeneous polymer even in one cell type and especially in diverse types such as tracheids and sclerenchyma (156). It is also becoming quite clear that phenolic compounds such as ferulic acid are associated with plant cell walls that give no classical lignin histochemical test such as that with phloroglucinol (53, and unpublished data of Stafford and Lamppa).

Not only are phenolic acids esterified to the lignin core, but the core itself is probably covalently attached to a carbohydrate, presumably with components of the hemicellulose matrix. The nature of this linkage is unknown or controversial, but recent data of a complex isolated from *Eucalyptus* indicate a benzyl-ether or benzyl-glycosidic type of linkage between lignin and carbohydrate (96). Carbohydrate-associated esters of ferulic acid are released from *Lolium* cell walls by cellulase in a series of H_2O-soluble compounds ranging from a molecular weight of 300 to 50,000. The carbohydrate moiety contained xylose, arabinose, and glucose. The ferulic component appeared more accessible to cellulase than *p*-coumaric acid. Hartley postulated that the esters are lignin-carbohydrate units (53).

Enzymatic Components Required to Form Lignin   (Table 1)

PEROXIDASE   This component is undoubtedly the main agent of oxidative polymerization of precursors to form the lignin complex (51, 60). Detection of wall-localized peroxidase activity has been frequently demonstrated in both cell-free wall preparations and histochemical tissue preparations (60, 162), but not all wall-localized enzymes are necessarily concerned with lignification (see section on peroxidase). The particular peroxidase isozyme involved would be found ultimately in the wall, but would also be expected to appear at least initially in the cytoplasm.

H_2O_2 The specific source of the supply used in lignification is unknown. H_2O_2 production at the appropriate site may be the major limiting factor in lignification and may account for the lack of classical or core lignin in many cells that do have a wall-localized peroxidase and an ample supply of phenolic precursors (156). A flavoprotein system would be a likely source of H_2O_2, but polyamine oxidase (154) and an uncoupled NADPH-dependent hydroxylase (9) should also be considered. Boveris et al (9), using cytochrome c peroxidase as an indicator of H_2O_2 production in liver cell fractions, found that microsomes had the highest physiological level of H_2O_2 formation, with peroxisomes a close second. Such techniques should be repeated with higher plant tissues.

Enzymes may be required to form the ester linkages as postulated by Shimada et al (147), or for the linkages to the hemicellulose matrix, but nothing is known about them.

Oxidative Polymerization to Lignin in Cell-Free Systems

Knowledge in this area has been slow due to the above-mentioned difficulties in detection methods. Earlier work, using the *dehydrierungspolymerizat* (DHP) technique of Freudenberg, has been summarized by Sarkanen et al (134). This approach is limited because of the long incubation periods involved, but it is useful for a study of the early intermediates during the peroxidase-catalyzed oxidation. A more rewarding technique is the use of inert macromolecular matrices, first introduced by Siegel (151). This model system should be re-explored with modern chromatographic matrices analogous to cell wall carbohydrates and bound peroxidase. A third partially cell-free technique is the use of cell suspension cultures that secrete macromolecular fibrils containing carbohydrates and phenolic compounds. But the original report identifying these as lignofibrils has subsequently been withdrawn in favor of pectofibrils (83). Both reports illustrate difficulties due to inadequate detection methods. Another report of soybean callus complexes with an apparent lignin content of 11% needs substantiation (98). The latter workers used the inadequate Klason and nitrobenzene analyses, but substantiated this assay with the quinone-imine reagent (indicative of benzylalcohol groups) and the phloroglucinol test (free aldehyde groups). But there was no proof of the presence of a polymeric rather than monomeric form. Both secretion products were rich in galacturonic acids. This is potentially a very useful approach that needs to be actively pursued. Cell suspension cultures of soybean have been effectively used by the Freiburg group as a source of enzyme for C_6-C_3 and flavonoid biosynthesis (77), and macromolecules containing peroxidase and hydroxyproline activity were secreted from similar cultures (110).

Subcellular Events Leading to the Formation of Lignins in Walls

A speculative view of subcellular events leading to lignins, based on the fragmentary biochemical and cytological evidence, has been discussed recently (159). This involves an interaction between vesicles derived from the endoplasmic reticulum, dictyosomes, microtubules, and the wall (46, 59, 116, 125). The actual site of oxidative polymerization to lignin is still unclear, although most workers believe that it occurs entirely outside the plasmalemma and in the wall. Some believe that only the initial formation of mesomeric free radicals from anions of alcohols such as coniferyl alcohol is enzymatically controlled, and that the subsequent polymerizations are nonenzymatic (11). But the enzyme peroxidase and phenolic substrates are widespread in plant cells and walls, even in aquatic plants that do not form lignins (51, 157). Therefore, regulation may go beyond the initial peroxidation steps. The lignin precursors from the reduction sequence must be transported independently and come in contact with both peroxidase and the H_2O_2-producing system at the appropriate time and place. While it is easier to visualize this process in a tracheid cell whose cytoplasm is undergoing degradation, it is far more difficult to envisage the metabolic control, compartmentalization, and transport that must be coordinated in differentiating protoxylem cells with active cytoplasm, where lignification is localized in narrow rings or spirals of secondary wall.

CHAIN-SHORTENING PATHWAYS

Towers & Rao (170) recently have reviewed pathways involving chain shortening and ring cleavage of aromatic compounds. Only two of these will be mentioned here.

C_6-C_2 Pathway to Cyanogenic Glycosides

Prunasin and dhurrin are derived from phenylalanine and tyrosine, respectively. The biosynthetic steps involved, based on tissue-level studies, have been reviewed by Conn & Butler (18), and the prunasin pathway is summarized in Figure 6 of Towers & Rao (170). Recent data from Conn's laboratory (abstract form only) indicate that a particulate fraction from *Sorghum* can convert tyrosine to p-hydroxymandelonitrile, the aglycone of dhurrin (95). The pathway is postulated to occur via N-hydroxylation, decarboxylation, and dehydrogenation to the aldoxime, which is converted to the nitrile and then hydroxynitrile. The initial N-hydroxylation may require NADPH (95, 170), and the glucosidic linkage oxygen is believed to be derived from O_2 by action of an oxygenase on a nitrile in the final step prior to glucosidation via UDPG (121, 187). Dhurrin accumulates in etiolated shoots of *Sorghum* and is known to be subsequently metabolized (8). But the fate is unknown, except that the HCN produced can be converted into asparagine (15). Phenolic glycosides such as dhurrin may substitute for sucrose as glycosyl donors in the UDP-glucose pyrophosphorylase reaction (41) and in the synthesis of ethyl-β-glucoside (88).

C_6-C_1 Pathways to Quinones

Fragmentary evidence of the enzymology of these pathways leading to the aromatic moiety of quinones in higher plants is beginning to appear. According to tracer techniques at the tissue level (37), p-hydroxyphenylpyruvate, homogentisate, and possibly homoarbutin are intermediates in the path leading to plastoquinones of chloroplasts. In the other path leading to ubiquinones of mitochondria, p-hydroxycinnamate and p-hydroxybenzoate are intermediates. Both ultimately require a condensation with polyprenol units to form the quinones, with the retention of either the C_6-C_1 or C_6 skeleton (170).

Homogentisate (a C_6-C_2 compound) is produced in vertebrates by p-hydroxy-phenylpyruvate oxidase or hydroxylase in a complex reaction (170). Fellman et al (29) have isolated from chicken liver a tetramer of about 180,000 mol wt which forms homogentisate from 4-hydroxyphenylpyruvate, and can also hydroxylate phenylpyruvate and 3,4,-dihydroxyphenylpyruvate in the presence of ascorbate or GSH and 2,6-dichlorophenolindophenol. Kindl & Ruis (73) reported that plant glyoxysomes produce homogentisate from tyrosine, but little supporting data were supplied. Since p-hydroxyphenylpyruvate is a precursor and product of tyrosine via other enzymes, the ammonia lyases are not obligatory for this chain-shortening pathway.

The pathway to p-hydroxybenzoate has been demonstrated in rat liver mito-chondria in the presence of p-hydroxycinnamate, ATP, Mg^{2+}, cytochrome c, GSH, and KCN. A requirement for CoA was assumed, but it was not necessary to add CoA (119). This is of interest in the light of CoA ligases demonstrated recently in higher plants which activate cinnamate and p-coumarate. Kindl & Ruis (73) re-ported the conversion of tyrosine to p-hydroxybenzoate in plant glyoxysomes, presumably involving TAL, p-coumarate:CoA ligase, and β oxidation. One of the two phenylalanine ammonia lyases studied by Alibert et al (2) was reported to be localized in plant microbodies. Phenylalanine was converted to benzoate via β oxidation and would represent a third chain-shortening pathway leading to non-phenolic C_6-C_1 compounds, presumably involving cinnamate:CoA ligase. The per-cent recovery of the total activity was not reported, only the specific activity.

These results are suggestive of compartmentation and the chain-shortening path-ways to quinones and other compounds should become an active area of the cell-free enzymology of higher plants.

C_{15}-FLAVONOID PATHWAY

Three reviews of the physiology of flavonoids have appeared recently (49, 94, 155). Some cell-free enzymology was discussed, and only this aspect and the possible special role of chloroplasts will be emphasized here.

The Enzymology of Flavonoid Biosynthesis (Table 1)

The most exciting new information is the demonstration by Kreuzaler & Hahlbrock (77) of the synthesis of a flavonoid from C_6-C_3 and C_2 precursors for the first time in cell-free extracts. The stumbling block had been the initial condensation step, the subsequent chalcone-flavanone isomerizations and various glycosylations have been known for some time. The condensation step involved the two predicted CoA precursors, the CoA ester of a monophenol and malonyl CoA. It was necessary to use the CoA esters, since free CoA was inhibitory.

For the above demonstration of flavonoid synthesis, the 15,000 X g supernatant fraction made from extracts of cell suspensions of parsley was used. They obtained a 20% yield of the flavanone, naringenin (5, 7, 4'-trihydroxyflavanone), from ^{14}C-malonyl CoA and p-coumaroyl CoA. ATP was not required for the condensation step. They postulate that only two enzymes were involved, the initial chalcone synthetase that condensed malonyl CoA molecules with p-coumaroyl CoA to form an intermediate enzyme-bound β-triketo acid which was considered the immediate precursor of a chalcone. The chalcone can then be isomerized by chalcone-flavanone isomerase to give the corresponding flavanone, naringenin (77).

Further changes are necessary to produce the flavone glycosides apin (3':4'-dihydroxy B ring) and gravebioside B (4'-hydroxy-3'-methoxy B ring) found in parsley. This work of the Freiburg group has been summarized by Grisebach (38). They now have identified and partially purified 10 enzymes postulated for the biosynthesis of the above glycosides from the level of the initial condensation step (Table 1). The later steps will, of course, vary with the particular flavonoid involved. This entire sequence represents exciting advances by a dedicated group of workers. Further details of this work by the Freiburg group are awaited with interest.

Peroxidase has been implicated in chalcone oxidations (120). The O glycosylation which occurs toward the end of the biosynthetic sequence of flavonoids has also been studied in other tissues. A fourfold purification of UDP-glucose:quercetin glucosyl-transferase was obtained from maize pollen and was active with both kaempferol and quercetin in the presence of mercaptoethanol and Ca^{2+} (82). The C glycosylation step has not yet been demonstrated in vitro. The glucose moiety of some flavonoids is acylated in a terminal step (42).

If the B ring of the C_{15} pathway is supplied by p-coumaroyl CoA and not the other appropriately hydroxylated cinnamoyl units, the subsequent hydroxylations would have to occur at the C_{15} level. Crude preparations rich in phenolase activity isolated from beet leaves can hydroxylate dihydrokaempferol more effectively than kaempferol and naringenin (127). Ascorbate was the hydrogen donor. The yield of flavonoids with the diphenol B ring was about 5%. Such data does not prove an in vivo function for this enzyme since it could be due to an overloading of a relatively nonspecific hydroxylase present in the preparations. The presence of an active diphenol function is deleterious to the flavonoid pathway just as it would be in the C_6-C_3 sequence. The broad specificity of the methyltransferases for C_6-C_3 compounds is a similar problem (24). Flavonoids appear to be degraded in several types of cell cultures with the B ring appearing in benzoic acid derivatives in a manner similar to C_6-C_3 compounds (62).

Acetyl CoA can be formed in a variety of ways, including acetate:CoA ligase. The source of malonyl CoA is probably acetyl-CoA-carboxylase. The latter reaction is catalyzed by three proteins which exist in higher plants as single enzymes or as a multienzyme complex of about 400,000 mol wt that can aggregate to form higher molecular weight units. The activity has been found both in nongreen tissues such as wheat germ and in chloroplasts (144).

The enzymatic data from cell suspension cultures used by the Freiburg group is an excellent example of the interdependent regulation by light of the 8–10 enzymes directly involved in the synthesis of a flavone glycoside. The development of the enzymes of the C_6-C_3 sequence prior to the activities of the C_{15} sequence is of considerable significance. Furthermore, the acetate:CoA ligase activity producing acetyl CoA was not light dependent, indicating that light affects the B ring and not the A ring (43).

Many questions concerning the enzymology remain unanswered: (*a*) What is the intracellular state and localization of these enzymes? (*b*) Do the intermediate steps occur only on the surface of a multienzyme complex specific for each aglycone, or is the "grid hypothesis" valid in vivo (49)? (*c*) Is the monophenol *p*-coumaroyl CoA ester the precursor of all forms of the B ring so that subsequent hydroxylations and methylations must take place at the C_{15} level, and are these hydroxylations and methylations catalyzed by generalized enzymes or specific ones operating only at the C_{15} level? (*d*) When does C glycosylation take place; and is glycosylation in vivo part of the above multienzyme complex or is it related to the process of accumulation of these products in cell vacuoles?

The Role of the Chloroplast

Flavonoids and *p*-coumaroyl esters of tartaric acid have been reported in chloroplasts and etioplasts (108, 109, 178). Furthermore, one report claimed that 6-methylsalicylic acid was formed in barley chloroplasts via malonyl CoA and was interpreted as evidence of the condensation of malonyl units forming the B ring of flavonoids with another malonyl CoA unit when blocked by a lack of *p*-coumaroyl-CoA for condensation to form the C_{15} molecule (69). A flavonoid-like compound has been associated with FRS in Photosystem I (94, 108). Many of these studies, however, have not ruled out artifacts caused by adsorption of phenolics during extraction. These plant tissues were often extracted at pH 8 without using any adsorbents for phenolics, but class I chloroplasts were obtained in some cases. These reports are suggestive and exciting and need to be thoroughly investigated. If flavonoids are part of the electron-transport machinery of photosynthesis, this could explain the evolutionary origin of the condensation step peculiar to green plants. Subsequently, during evolution this flavonoid product has become associated with new functions in nongreen portions of the plant, and is accumulated in large amounts in plants with large central vacuoles.

Conclusion about Flavonoid Biosynthesis

Descriptive enzymology of flavonoids is well under way. Biochemical genetics, which started in the early 1900s with the work of Onslow, can at last be completed. Genic and nongenic modifiers controlling flavonoid biosynthesis studied by McClintock (93) and the more recent light-controlled phenomena (49, 155, 188) can now be studied at the molecular level.

SPECIAL ROLES OF PEROXIDASE AND POLYPHENOLOXIDASE

Peroxidase

The Fe-porphyrin enzyme, peroxidase, catalyzes the oxidation of a wide variety of compounds peroxidatically with H_2O_2, or oxidatively with O_2 as an oxidase (or peroxidase-oxidase) (183). It is not clear how many of these in vitro activities are in vivo functions. Plant peroxidases are characterized by a large number of forms (isozymes) separable electrophoretically which do not appear to be artifacts. Many of them are strongly positive charged (cathodic forms) even at pH 8–9. But catalase (16) and cytochrome P_{450} (63) can act as peroxidases, and polyphenoloxidase can be a pseudoperoxidase (67).

Shannon's group (70) originally divided a series of isozymes from horseradish into two groups, based on the ratio of activities with oxaloacetic acid (oxidatic) and o-dianisidine (peroxidatic). The anodic group was more active with dianisidine relative to oxaloacetic acid, but had lower affinities for both these substrates than the cathodic group. In 1971, the anodic group was subdivided to make a total of three groups with different primary structure indicating control by separate genes (146). All consisted of single polypeptide chains with no subunits, each having a molecular weight of about 40,000. No sulfhydryl groups were detectable, and the three disulfide groups were intrachain rather than interchain. While glycoproteins associated with the isozymes during earlier stages of purification were removed in subsequent steps, peroxidase is still considered to be a glycoprotein. Welinder's group reported the presence of eight sites of carbohydrate attachment. They have established the amino acid sequences of some of the tryptic peptides (179). Neither group reports the presence of any hydroxyproline in these purified peroxidase preparations.

Although peroxidases are easily solubilized, they are localized in the cell wall and are at least loosely bound to a variety of membranes, according to differential centrifugation of cell-free extracts (cited in 162), ion exchange of cathodic forms from the negatively charged walls prior to breaking of the protoplast (3, 162), and electron microscopy (46, 60, 107). Using diaminobenzidine (DAB), several electron microscope studies indicate an association with membranes of endoplasmic reticulum, nucleus, vacuoles, tonoplast, dictyosomes, various vesicular bodies, ribosomes, and polysomes. The technique, however, is not without pitfalls. Any localization in chloroplasts is suspect because DAB is photochemically oxidized (60) and catalase and polyphenoloxidase can interfere. The above workers have used inhibitors in an attempt to detect such artifacts.

What is the function of the various multiple forms (or isozymes)? Certainly one of the wall-localized cathodic forms could be involved in the peroxidatic activity of lignification. For example, one might suspect that one of the slow-moving cathodic forms found in both walls and cytoplasm in the vascular stele of first internodes of *Sorghum* might be the one. The large amounts of another fast-moving cathodic form found in walls and cytoplasm of the nonlignified cortical cells must have another function (162).

Other potential functions of peroxidase could be due to its IAA oxidase activities. Phenolic compounds are well-known cofactors (monophenols) and inhibitors (diphenols) of this oxidase activity. The light-reversible characteristics of the P_{670} intermediate studied by Yamazaki (181) are intriguing as a possible primitive phytochrome system. The roles of Mn^{2+} and phenols in this complex IAA oxidase reaction have been recently discussed by the same group (182). Interaction in IAA oxidation by phenolics such as ferulic, hydroxycinnamic acids, and scopoletin add to the complexity of this system, especially as some of these effects are only on the lag phase (26, 34, 153). Peroxidase also oxidizes 4-hydroxycinnamate to unknown products if GSH (or mercaptoethanol) is present (160). While the physiological significance, if any, of this reaction is unknown, it could function in control of the level of 4-hydroxycinnamate, and unfortunately can interfere in enzymatic assays involving this substrate. Peroxidase will also interfere with some assays because of its NADPH oxidase activities (32, 183). Most of these oxidase activities of peroxidase involve decarboxylation of the substrates, including C_6-C_3 compounds such as phenylpyruvate (65).

Polyphenoloxidase Complex

Monophenol + AH_2 + $O_2\longrightarrow$diphenol + H_2O + A
Diphenol + $\frac{1}{2}$ $O_2\longrightarrow$$o$-quinone + H_2O
o-quinones$\longrightarrow$pigmented polymers

This complex is perhaps best known for its diphenoloxidase activities demonstrated upon injury and when aqueous extracts are prepared from many higher plant tissues. But the physiological role(s) of this Cu-containing o-diphenoloxidoreductase in higher plants is not clear. In mushroom, where tyrosine is probably the natural monophenol substrate in the initial hydroxylation reaction, the subsequent diphenoloxidase activity is undoubtedly involved in the production of black pigments of spores. Tyrosine is hydroxylated in only a few higher plants. However, other diphenols might produce melanin and tanning pigments in seed coats and outer tissues of higher plants (113, 170). While both activities are frequently closely associated in higher plants (174, 175), the diphenol activity can be found alone (1, 113, 163). The possibility and advantage of a separate monophenol hydroxylase for C_6-C_3 pathways have been discussed previously. Since esters of caffeic acid are common plant constituents, an attractive potential role for the diphenol activity (as a chlorogenic acid oxidase) is that of a NADPH-oxidizing system acting in conjunction with a quinone reductase (1). The above oxidase was characteristic of younger rather than older stem tissues in tobacco (164). The association of diphenoloxidases with chloroplast grana is discussed below. Polyphenoloxidase may be a primitive enzyme which has evolved into proteins with many functions.

There is considerable variability in the substrate specificities of various diphenoloxidases. Esters of caffeic acid are probably the most common natural substrate in higher plants; DOPA is also an active substrate (113, 158) but accumulates in relatively few plants such as legumes and bananas (99, 122).

Models of the mechanism of catalysis by polyphenoloxidase are based mainly on tyrosinase isolated from mushroom. This enzyme is a tetramer containing 4 Cu atoms per 120,000 daltons, with 2 Cu atoms at each active site (71, 141). Four states of the enzyme have been tentatively identified, including a resting state [Cu $(II)_2$], a kinetically required intermediate, deoxygenated and oxygenated forms [Cu $(I)_2O_2$] (66, 90). Diphenol or ascorbate reduces the resting form, but only o-diphenols convert the oxygenated form to the postulated hydroxylating intermediate (92). Because of the close structural relationship with hemocyanin, Mason speculates that tyrosinase could have a common evolutionary origin with hemocyanin and might function as a primitive O_2 transport enzyme (66, 141). This is of particular interest because of the speculative role of diphenoloxidase in photosynthesis (169).

While some of the multiple forms in higher plants appear to be tetramers and their dissociating units (50), others may not be (145, 164, 168). But electrophoretic studies of multiple forms of polyphenoloxidases are plagued with difficulties. If acrylamide gels are used without sufficient washing to remove excess polymerizing agents, peroxidase can react either as an oxidase or a peroxidase, depending on the amount of H_2O_2 (145, 172). Staining techniques are not very satisfactory, but DOPA, chlorogenic acid, and catechol are frequently used with or without intensifying agents. Gel stains for monophenolase activities are not satisfactory, and nonenzymatic reactions are a severe problem with some gels.

In addition to beet and *Sorghum* preparations discussed under hydroxylases (112, 113, 161, 163, 174), potato polyphenoloxidases have been studied extensively. They act with a variety of mono- and diphenols, including tyrosine and chlorogenic acid. Patil & Zucker (114) isolated two fractions differing in affinity to DEAE-cellulose. The higher molecular weight form of 100,000 was purified 1000-fold. Balasingam isolated three molecular weight forms of the diphenoloxidase on Bio-gel P-300, and the higher molecular weight form contained equivalent amounts of nucleic acid (6). Two other cases of association with nucleic acid have been reported (113, 167). Ruis (128) isolated soluble, peroxisomal, and microsomal forms.

Although artifacts have not been ruled out, polyphenoloxidases appear to be deeply embedded or loosely bound to a variety of cellular membranes. Electron microscope studies indicated that DOPA oxidase was either restricted to thylakoid membranes (20) or was found also in both outer and inner membranes of chloroplasts (113). Such a localization cannot be applied to nongreen tissues except in leucoplasts, and staining so far is limited to DOPA as substrate. Diphenol oxidase activities have been reported in chloroplasts (50, 112, 113, 129, 152, 167) or associated with microsomes (1, 128) or unidentified membrane fragments (161). The membrane-associated (chloroplast ?) catechol oxidase of apple peel was solubilized by a combination of Triton X-100 and butanol treatment (167).

A membrane localization is consistent with the latency of many diphenoloxidases (152). Tolbert has reported three groups of DOPA oxidases in isolated chloroplasts. One is stimulated by aging, trypsin, uncoupling agents, and light (spinach); another is stimulated by light and inhibited by trypsin (pea), while the third was insensitive to the above agents (corn) (169). Since the activities decreased from the first to the third group, it is possible that appropriate activators have not been found for these. Other activating agents are anionic detergents (180) and denaturating agents such as urea and manoxal (84, 126).

The localization of some of the *o*-diphenoloxidase activities with chloroplasts affects the in vitro physical state and activity of ribulosediphosphate carboxylase. When this enzyme is isolated, special precautions are taken to inhibit the diphenoloxidase during extraction (68). Van Loon (172) reported the isolation electrophoretically of a slow migrating band of pholyphenolase activity that was interpreted as an artifact due to an association of Fraction I protein with diphenoloxidase. One wonders whether such complexes should always be considered artifacts.

CONCLUSIONS

A speculative overview of biochemical and subcellular events in cells producing major phenolic compounds has been presented recently, using fragmentary data concerning the cell-free enzymology and electron microscopy (159). A basic premise of this overview was that activities of a biochemical sequence might be expected to be associated with a multienzyme complex, found either in the cytosol or associated with a cytoplasmic membrane system or specific organelle.

Aside from direct evidence by isolation and purification of such complexes, indirect evidence can be drawn from the existence of correlative increases in the activities of a sequence, the presence of a series of multiple forms or isozymes associated with various particulate as well as the so-called soluble fractions. Isotopic tracer data with tissue or cell-free systems might also indicate the existence of complex-bound intermediates compartmented from more inactive metabolic pools (metabolic channeling), or that an initial substrate in a sequence gives a much higher overall reaction rate than the intermediate (catalytic facilitation) (31).

There must be a high degree of compartmentation involving the metabolism of aromatic compounds in cells of higher plants, since many of the pathways indicated in Figure 1 might occur at the same time. Many phenolic compounds with similar hydroxylation and methylation patterns are accumulated independently (158). Some of the enzymes can also exist in inactive states or are separated from their substrates as in the case of the ammonia lyases or polyphenoloxidases. Potentially competitive synthetic and degradative pathways arising from a common intermediate need to be spatially separated, as postulated for the C_6-C_3 chain-shortening pathways to C_6-C_1 derivatives in the microbodies, and the C_6-C_3 hydroxylation-methoxylation sequence with the endoplasmic reticulum or vesicles derived from it. There might even be a series of C_6-C_3 complexes with appropriate enzymes, each capable of synthesizing one specific C_6-C_3 compound such as p-coumarate, caffeic, ferulic, or sinapic acid (159).

CoA and NADPH must be key controlling factors in the regulation of these pathways of aromatic metabolism. Supply centers for NADPH would be the pentose shunt in the cytosol and plastids, photosynthesizing chloroplasts, isocitrate dehydrogenases of the cytosol, and mitochondria; centers for CoA would be chloroplasts, mitochondria, and glyoxysomes. These cofactors either have to diffuse or be transported to the various sites needed in phenolic pathways, or preferably the complexes themselves might have binding sites permitting attachment to the appropriate organelles and membranes (79).

The problem of artifacts is mentioned several times in this review. Tissues of higher plants are particularly subject to such test-tube phenomena because of the large central vacuole filled with many products, especially phenolic compounds. Phenolic compounds interfere with protein and enzyme assays (89). Adsorption to proteins and nucleic acids are especially bothersome. Dialysis, Sephadex G-25 or G-50 treatment, or precipitation with ammonium sulfate or TCA may not remove these artifacts once they are formed. Well-documented procedures to prevent this are necessary and may differ for different tissues (4, 6, 68, 80, 89), but they are frequently ignored by plant biochemists and physiologists. However, a tendency to adsorb or bind to other compounds should not always be considered an artifact; the tendency toward such associations might be reflecting valid in vivo relationships of significance.

Many reports of intracellular localization of enzyme activities use specific activity (units per mg protein) as the only basis for expression of enzyme activity. This is a measure of purity and not total activity of a fraction. Changes in specific activity can be due solely to alterations in unrelated proteins. The percent of total activity in various fractions should be reported, even though inhibitors and activators can cause difficulties if the crude extract is used as the 100% level.

The descriptive enzymology of aromatic metabolism has begun to flourish. While the data reviewed above are fragmentary, they suggest that multienzyme complexes may be involved in aromatic pathways in higher plants. The challenge for the future is to validate this working hypothesis and determine the in vivo state and localization of these enzymes or complexes in order to understand their regulation in the cell.

Literature Cited

1. Alberghina, F. A. M. 1964. *Phytochemistry* 3:64–72
2. Alibert, G., Ranjeva, R., Boudet, A. 1972. *Biochim. Biophys. Acta* 279:282–89
3. Abeles, F. B., Leather, G. R. 1971. *Planta* 97:87–91
4. Anderson, J. W. 1968. *Phytochemistry* 7:1973–88
5. Attridge, T. H., Smith, H. 1973. *Phytochemistry* 12:1569–74
6. Balasingam, K., Ferdinand, W. 1970. *Biochem. J.* 118:15–23
7. Bartlett, D. J., Poulton, J. E., Butt, V. S. 1972. *FEBS Lett.* 23:265–67
8. Bough, W. A., Gander, J. E. 1971. *Phytochemistry* 10:66–77
9. Boveris, A., Oshino, N., Chance, B. 1972. *Biochem. J.* 128:617–30
10. Breslaw, R., Lukens, L. N. 1960. *J. Biol. Chem.* 235:292–96
11. Brown, S. A. 1966. *Ann. Rev. Plant Physiol.* 17:223–44
12. Brown, S. A. 1966. In *Biosynthesis of Aromatic Compounds,* ed. G. Billek, 15–24. New York: Pergamon
13. Camm, E. L., Towers, G. H. N. 1973. *Phytochemistry* 12:961–73
14. Ibid, 1575–80
15. Castric, P. A., Farnden, K. J. F., Conn, E. E. 1972. *Arch. Biochem. Biophys.* 152:62–69
16. Chance, B., Oshino, N. 1971. *Biochem. J.* 122:225–33
17. Conn, E. E. 1964. *Biochemistry of Phe-*
    nolic Compounds, ed. J. B. Harborne, 399–435. New York: Academic
18. Conn, E. E., Butler, G. W. 1969. In *Perspectives in Phytochemistry,* ed. J. B. Harborne, T. Swain, 48–74. New York: Academic
19. Corner, J. J., Swain, T. 1965. *Nature* 207:634–35
20. Czaninski, Y., Catesson, A. 1972. *J. Microsc.* 15:409–14
21. Daly, J. W., Jerina, D. M. 1970. *Biochim. Biophys. Acta* 208:340–42
22. Davies, D. A., Ugochukwu, E. N., Patil, K. D., Towers, G. H. N. 1973. *Phytochemistry* 12:531–36
23. Ebel, J., Grisebach, H. 1973. *FEBS Lett.* 30:141–43
24. Ebel, J., Hahlbrock, K., Grisebach, H. 1972. *Biochim. Biophys. Acta* 268:313–24
25. El-Basyouni, S. Z., Neish, A. C. 1965. *Phytochemistry* 5:683–91
26. Engelsma, G. 1964. *Nature* 202:88–89
27. Engelsma, G. 1972. *Plant Physiol.* 50:599–602
28. Erez, A. 1973. *Plant Physiol.* 51:409–11
29. Fellman, J. H., Fujita, T. S., Roth, E. S. 1972. *Biochim. Biophys. Acta* 284:90–100
30. Finkle, B. J., Kelly, S. H. 1974. *Arch. Biochem. Biophys.* In press
31. Gaertner, F. H., Ericson, M. C., DeMoss, J. A. 1970. *J. Biol. Chem.* 245:595–600
32. Gamborg, O. L., Wetter, L. R., Neish,

A. C. 1961. *Can. J. Biochem. Physiol.* 39:1113–24

33. Gardner, G., Pike, C. S., Rice, H. V., Briggs, W. R. 1971. *Plant Physiol.* 48:686–93
34. Gelinas, D. A. 1973. *Plant Physiol.* 51:967–72
35. Gestetner, B., Conn, E. E. 1973. *Abstr. Phytochem. Soc. N. Am.* Ann. Meet. Asilomar, Calif.
36. Ginsburg, A., Stadtman, E. R. 1970. *Ann. Rev. Biochem.* 39:429–72
37. Goodwin, T. W. 1971. In *Structure and Function of Chloroplasts,* ed. M. Gibbs, 215–76. New York: Springer-Verlag
38. Grisebach, H. 1974. *Recent Advan. Phytochem.* 8. In press
39. Gross, G. G., Stockigt, J., Mansell, R. L., Zenk, M. H. 1973. *FEBS Lett.* 31:283–86
40. Gross, G. G., Zenk, M. H. 1969. *Eur. J. Biochem.* 8:413–19
41. Gustafson, G. L., Gander, J. E. 1972. *J. Biol. Chem.* 247:1387–97
42. Hahlbrock, K. 1972. *FEBS Lett.* 28:65–68
43. Hahlbrock, K. et al 1971. *Biochim. Biophys. Acta* 244:7–15
44. Hahlbrock, K., Grisebach, H. 1970. *FEBS Lett.* 11:62–64
45. Hahlbrock, K., Kuhlen, E., Lindl, T. 1971. *Planta* 99:311–18
46. Hall, J. L., Sexton, R. 1972. *Planta* 108:103–20
47. Hamilton, G. A. 1969. *Advan. Enzymol.* 32:55–96
48. Hanson, K. R., Havir, E. A. 1972. *Recent Advan. Phytochem.* 4:45–85
49. Harborne, J. B. 1973. In *Phytochemistry II,* ed. L. P. Miller, 344–80. New York: Van Nostrand-Reinhold 2:344–80
50. Harel, E., Mayer, A. M. 1968. *Phytochemistry* 7:199–204
51. Harkin, J. M., Obst, J. R. 1973. *Science* 180:296–97
52. Harms, H., Haider, K., Berlin, J., Kiss, P., Barz, W. 1972. *Planta* 105:342–51
53. Hartley, R. D. 1973. *Phytochemistry* 12:661–65
54. Hasegawa, S., Maier, V. P. 1972. *Phytochemistry* 11:1365–70
55. Havir, E. A., Hanson, K. R. 1968. *Biochemistry* 7:1896–1903
56. Ibid 1973. 12:1583–91
57. Havir, E. A., Reid, P. D., Marsh, H. V. 1971. *Plant Physiol.* 48:130–36
58. Hayaishi, O. 1969. *Ann. Rev. Biochem.* 38:21–44

59. Hepler, P. K., Fosket, D. E. 1972. *Am. J. Bot.* 57:85–96
60. Hepler, P. K., Rice, R. M., Terranova, W. A. 1972. *Can. J. Bot.* 50:977–83
61. Higuchi, T. 1971. *Advan. Enzymol.* 34:207–83
62. Hosel, W., Shaw, P. D., Barz, W. 1972. *Z. Naturforsch.* 27:946–54
63. Hrycay, E. G., O'Brien, P. J. 1973. *Arch. Biochem. Biophys.* 153:480–94
64. Jacobson, J. W., Hart, B. A., Doy, C. H., Giles, N. H. 1972. *Biochim. Biophys. Acta* 289:1–12
65. Jaynes, T. A., Haskins, F. A., Gorz, H. J. 1972. *Phytochemistry* 11:563–69
66. Jolley, R. L., Evans, L. H., Mason, H. S. 1972. *Biochem. Biophys. Res. Commun.* 46:878–84
67. Jolley, R. L., Evans, L. H., Mason, H. S. 1973. *J. Biol. Chem.* In press
68. Jones, W. T., Lyttleton, J. W. 1972. *Phytochemistry* 11:1595–96
69. Kannangara, C. G., Henningsen, K. W., Stumpf, P. K., von Wettstein, D. 1971. *Eur. J. Biochem.* 21:334–38
70. Kay, E., Shannon, L. M., Lew, J. Y. 1967. *J. Biol. Chem.* 242:2470–73
71. Kertesz, K., Rotilio, G., Brunori, M., Zito, R., Antonini, E. 1972. *Biochem. Biophys. Res. Commun.* 49:1208–15
72. Kindl, H. 1970. *H. S. Z. Physiol. Chem.* 351:792–98.
73. Kindl, H., Ruis, H. 1971. *Phytochemistry* 10:2633–36
74. Kleinhofs, A., Haskins, F. A., Gorz, H. J. 1967. *Phytochemistry* 6:1313–18
75. Kojima, M., Uritani, I. 1972. *Plant Cell Physiol.* 13:1075–84
76. Koukol, J., Conn, E. E. 1961. *J. Biol. Chem.* 236:2692
77. Kreuzaler, F., Hahlbrock, K. 1972. *FEBS Lett.* 28:69–72
78. Kuc, J., Nelson, O. E. 1964. *Arch. Biochem. Biophys.* 105:103–13
79. Kuczenski, R. T. 1973. *J. Biol. Chem.* 248:5074–80
80. Lam, T. H., Shan, M. 1970. *Biochem. Biophys. Res. Commun.* 39:965–68
81. Lamport, D. T. A. 1970. *Ann. Rev. Plant Physiol.* 21:235–70
82. Larson, R. L., Lonergan, C. M. 1972. *Planta* 103:361–64
83. Leppard, G. C., Colvin, J. R. 1971. *J. Polymer Sci.* 36:321–62
84. Lerner, H. R., Mayer, A. M., Harel, E. 1972. *Phytochemistry* 11:2415–21
85. Levand, O., Heinicke, R. M. 1968. *Phytochemistry* 7:1659–62
86. Levy, C. C., Zucker, M. 1960. *J. Biol. Chem.* 235:2418–25

87. Lin, C. Y., Key, J. L. 1971. *Plant Physiol.* 48:547–52
88. Liu, T., Castelfranco, P. 1970. *Plant Physiol.* 45:424–28
89. Loomis, W. D. 1974. *Methods Enzymol.* 31. In press
90. Makino, N., Mason, H. S. 1973. *J. Biol. Chem.* 248:5731–35
91. Mansell, R. L., Stockigt, J., Zenk, M. H. 1973. *Z. Pflanzenphysiol.* 68:286–88
92. Mason, H. 1957. *Advan. Enzymol.* 19:79–233
93. McClintock, B. 1967. *Develop. Biol. Suppl.* 1:84–112
94. McClure, J. 1974. In *The Flavonoids*, ed. J. B. Harborne, T. J. Mabry. London: Chapman & Hall. In press
95. McFarlane, I. J., Lees, E. M., Conn, E. E. 1973. *Abstr. Phytochem. Soc. N.A.U.* Ann. Meet. Asilomar, Calif.
96. Merewether, J. W. T., Samsuzzaman, L. A. M. 1972. *Holzforschung* 26:11–17
97. Mohr, H. 1972. *Lectures on Photomorphogenesis.* New York: Springer-Verlag
98. Moore, T. S. Jr. 1973. *Plant Physiol.* 51:529–36
99. Nagatsu, I., Sudo, Y., Nagatsu, T. 1972. *Enzymologia* 43:25–31
100. Nagatsu, T., Levitt, M., Udenfriend, S. 1964. *J. Biol. Chem.* 239:2910–17
101. Nair, P. M., Vining, L. C. 1965. *Phytochemistry* 4:401–11
102. Nambudiri, A. M. D., Bhat, J. V., Rao, P. V. S. 1973. *Biochem. J.* 130:425–33
103. Nari, J., Mouffet, C., Pinna, M., Ricard, J. 1972. *FEBS Lett.* 23:220–24
104. Neish, A. C. 1960. *Ann. Rev. Plant Physiol.* 11:55–80
105. Neish, A. C. 1961. *Phytochemistry* 1:1–24
106. Nelson, R. F., Finkle, B. J. 1964. *Phytochemistry* 3:321–25
107. Nougarede, A. 1971. *C. R. Acad. Sci. Paris* 273:864–67
108. Oettmeier, W., Heupel, A. 1972. *Z. Naturforsch.* 27:177–82
109. Ibid, 586–87
110. Olson, A. C., Evans, J. J., Frederick, D. P., Jansen, E. F. 1969. *Plant Physiol.* 44:1594–1600
111. Painter, T. J., Neukom, H. 1968. *Biochim. Biophys. Acta* 158:363–81
112. Parish, R. W. 1972. *Eur. J. Biochem.* 31:446–82
113. Parish, R. W. 1972. *Z. Pflanzenphysiol.* 66:176–88
114. Patil, S. S., Zucker, M. 1965. *J. Biol. Chem.* 240:3938–43

115. Pew, J. C., Connors, W. J. 1969. *J. Org. Chem.* 34:585–89
116. Pickett-Heaps, J. D. 1968. *Protoplasma* 65:181–205
117. Potts, R. 1973. *4-Hydroxylation of cinnamic acid by Sorghum microsomes*, 1–77. PhD thesis. Univ. California, Davis
118. Preiss, J., Kosuge, T. 1971. *Ann. Rev. Plant Physiol.* 21:433–66
119. Ranganathan, S., Ramasarma, T. 1971. *Biochem. J.* 122:487–93
120. Rathmill, W. G., Bendall, D. S. 1972. *Biochem. J.* 127:125–32
121. Reay, P. F., Conn, E. E. 1970. *Phytochemistry* 9:1825–27
122. Rehr, S. S., Janzen, D. H., Feeny, P. P. 1973. *Science* 181:81–82
123. Reid, P. D., Havir, E. A., Marsh, H. V. Jr. 1972. *Plant Physiol.* 50:480–84
124. Rice, H. V., Briggs, W. R. 1973. *Plant Physiol.* 51:927–38
125. Robards, A. W., Kidwai, P. 1969. *New Phytol.* 68:343–49
126. Robb, D. A., Swain, T., Mapson, L. W. 1966. *Phytochemistry* 5:665–75
127. Roberts, R. J., Vaughan, P. F. T. 1971. *Phytochemistry* 10:2649–52
128. Ruis, H. 1972. *Phytochemistry* 11:53–58
129. Ruis, H., Kindl, H. 1970. *H. S. Z. Physiol. Chem.* 351:1425–27
130. Ruis, H., Kindl, H. 1971. *Phytochemistry* 10:2627–31
131. Russell, D. W., Conn, E. E. 1967. *Arch. Biochem. Biophys.* 122:256–68
132. Russell, D. W., Conn, E. E., Sutter, A., Grisebach, H. 1968. *Biochim. Biophys. Acta* 170:210–12
133. Russell, D. W. 1971. *J. Biol. Chem.* 246:3870–78
134. Sarkanen, K. V., Ludwig, C. H., Eds. 1971. *Lignins*, 1–916. New York: Wiley-Interscience
135. Sato, M. 1966. *Phytochemistry* 5:385–89
136. Ibid 1967. 6:1363–73
137. Ibid 1969. 8:353–62
138. Sato, M., Hasegawa, M. 1972. *Phytochemistry* 11:657–62
139. Saunders, J. A., McClure, J. W. 1972. *Am. J. Bot.* 59(s):673
140. Saunders, J. A., McClure, J. W. 1973. *Plant Physiol.* 51:407–8
141. Schoot Uiterkamp, A. J. M., Mason, H. S. 1973. *Proc. Nat. Acad. Sci.* 70:993–96
142. Schopfer, P. 1971. *Planta* 99:339–46
143. Schopfer, P. 1972. In *Phytochrome*, ed. W. Shropshire Jr., 486–514. New York: Academic

144. Sedgwick, B. 1973. *Annual Proceedings of the Phytochemical Society, No. 9,* ed. B. V. Milborrow, 178–217. New York: Academic
145. Sheen, S. J. 1973. *Plant Physiol.* 51: 839–44
146. Shih, J. H. C., Shannon, L. M., Kay, E., Lew, J. Y. 1971. *J. Biol. Chem.* 246:4546–51
147. Shimada, M., Fukuzuka, T., Higuchi, T. 1971. *Tappi* 54:72–78
148. Shimada, M. 1972. *Wood Res.* 53:19–65
149. Shimada, M., Fushiki, H., Higuchi, T. 1972. *Phytochemistry* 11:2247–52
150. Ibid, 2657–62
151. Siegel, S. M. 1957. *J. Am. Chem. Soc.* 79:1628–32
152. Siegenthaler, P., Vaucher-Bonjour, P. 1971. *Planta* 100:106–23
153. Sirois, J. C., Miller, R. W. 1972. *Plant Physiol.* 49:1012–18
154. Smith, T. A. 1970. *Biochem. Biophys. Res. Commun.* 41:1452–56
155. Smith, H. 1973. See Ref. 144, 303–21
156. Stafford, H. A. 1962. *Plant Physiol.* 37:643–49
157. Ibid 1964. 39:350–60
158. Stafford, H. A. 1969. *Phytochemistry* 8:743–52
159. Stafford, H. A. 1974. *Recent Advan. Phytochem.* 8. In press
160. Stafford, H. A., Baldy, R. 1970. *Plant Physiol.* 45:215–22
161. Stafford, H. A., Bliss, M. *Plant Physiol.* 52:453–58
162. Stafford, H. A., Bravinder-Bree, S. 1971. *Plant Physiol.* 49:950–56
163. Stafford, H. A., Dressler, S. 1972. *Plant Physiol.* 49:590–95
164. Stafford, H. A., Galston, A. W. 1970. *Plant Physiol.* 46:763–67
165. Steck, W. 1968. *Phytochemistry* 7: 1711–17
166. Steelink, C. 1972. *Recent Advan. Phytochem.* 4:239–71
167. Stelzig, D. A., Akhtar, S., Ribeiro, S. 1972. *Phytochemistry* 11:535–39
168. Takeo, T., Baker, J. E. 1973. *Phytochemistry* 12:21–24
169. Tolbert, N. E. 1973. *Plant Physiol.* 51:234–44
170. Towers, G. H. N., Rao, P. V. S. 1972. *Recent Advan. Phytochem.* 4:1–43
171. Ueno, T., Fukami, H., Ohkishi, H., Kumagai, H., Yamada, H. 1970. *Biochim. Biophys. Acta* 206:476–79
172. Van Loon, L. C. 1971. *Phytochemistry* 10:503–7
173. Van Sumere, C. F., De Pooter, H., Ali, H., Degrauw-van Bussel, M. 1973. *Phytochemistry* 12:407–11
174. Vaughan, P. F. T., Butt, V. S. 1969. *Biochem. J.* 113:109–15
175. Ibid 1970. 119:89–94
176. Ibid 1972. 127:641–47
177. Walton, E., Butt, V. S. 1971. *Phytochemistry* 10:295–304
178. Weissenbeck, G., Fleing, I., Ruppel, H. G. 1972. *Z. Naturforsch.* 27:1216–24
179. Welinder, K. G. 1973. *FEBS. Lett.* 30:243–45
180. Yamaguchi, M., Huang, P. M., Campbell, J. S. 1970. *Can. J. Biochem.* 48:198–202
181. Yamazaki, H., Ohishi, S., Yamazaki, I. 1970. *Arch. Biochem. Biophys.* 136: 41–46
182. Yamazaki, H., Yamazaki, I. 1973. *Arch. Biochem. Biophys.* 154:147–65
183. Yokota, K., Yamazaki, I. 1965. *Biochim. Biophys. Acta* 105:301–12
184. Yoshida, S. 1969. *Ann. Rev. Plant Physiol.* 20:40–62
185. Zenk, M. H. 1967. *Z. Pflanzenphysiol.* 57:477–78
186. Zenk, M. H., Gross, G. G. 1972. *Recent Advan. Phytochem.* 4:88–106
187. Zilg, H., Tapper, B. A., Conn, E. E. 1972. *J. Biol. Chem.* 247:2384–86
188. Zucker, M. 1972. *Ann. Rev. Plant Physiol.* 23:133–56

Ann. Rev. Plant Physiol. 1974. 25:487–513

METABOLISM OF AUXIN IN HIGHER PLANTS

❖7575

Elnora A. Schneider and F. Wightman

Department of Biology, Carleton University, Ottawa, Canada

CONTENTS

INTRODUCTION 487
BIOSYNTHESIS OF INDOLEACETIC ACID 488
  Evidence for the Presence of Indoleacetic Acid in Plants 488
  Tryptophan as the Primary Precursor of Indoleacetic Acid 488
  Pathways leading from Tryptophan to Indoleacetic Acid 489
    The indolepyruvic acid pathway 489
    The tryptamine pathway 491
    The indoleacetaldoxime pathway 493
    The tryptophol pathway and indolelactic acid 494
  Role of Epiphytic Microorganisms in Indoleacetic Acid Biosynthesis 495
CATABOLISM OF INDOLEACETIC ACID 496
  Oxidation 496
    Molecular site of indoleacetic acid oxidase activity 496
    Products of the oxidation of indoleacetic acid 497
    Mechanism of action of horseradish peroxidase 499
    Effects of naturally occurring cofactors, inhibitors, and hormones on peroxidase
      and indoleacetic acid oxidase activity 501
    Cellular location of peroxidase and indoleacetic acid oxidase 503
  Bound Forms of Indoleacetic Acid 505
    Indoleacetylaspartic acid and indoleacetylglucose 505
    Indole compounds of maize seeds 505
    Indoleacetic acid-nucleic acid complexes 505
NATURAL AUXINS OTHER THAN INDOLEACETIC ACID 506
CONCLUSIONS 507

INTRODUCTION

The most recent reviews on the subject of indoleacetic acid (IAA) metabolism are those of Hare (74) on IAA oxidase, Shantz (217) on the chemistry of naturally occurring growth substances, and Scott (213) on auxins and roots. In the present review, we shall consider the evidence obtained in recent years for the pathways of IAA biosynthesis in plants, the oxidative and nonoxidative routes for the catabolism of this growth hormone, and, finally, the natural occurrence of auxins other than IAA in higher plants.

BIOSYNTHESIS OF INDOLEACETIC ACID

Evidence for the Presence of Indoleacetic Acid in Plants

The small amount of indoleacetic acid (IAA) present in vegetative tissues has always caused difficulty in the rigorous chemical identification and quantitative estimation of this compound. Most workers have used the classical methods of alcohol, ether, or ethylacetate extraction of the tissue followed by ether fractionation, chromatography, and bioassay. If such identifications are accepted as valid, then IAA has been found to be present in *Marchantia* (210), *Picea* buds (231), *Pinus* buds and shoots (3), *Populus* shoots and roots (34), *Salix* cuttings (263), ash and sycamore vascular tissue (219), *Alnus* roots (32), walnut buds (106), rose shoots (144), tomato shoots (209) and fruits (82), bean cotyledons and leaves (268), cotton stems and leaves (273), tobacco stems (13), *Solanum nigrum* stems and leaves (265), cucumber hypocotyls (85), *Begonia* leaves (77), maize roots (68), and shoots of wheat (156), sugar cane (264), and barley (209). Recently, Greenwood et al (69) have conclusively identified the auxin present in diffusates from maize coleoptile tips as IAA by mass spectrometry.

Quantitative measurements of the concentration of IAA in plants have been made mainly by bioassay of chromatographically purified extracts; the amounts found usually range between one and 100 μg/kg fresh weight of tissue (3, 12, 34, 68, 82, 144, 161, 162, 165, 207, 209, 210, 219, 241, 263, 264, 268).

Tryptophan as the Primary Precursor of Indoleacetic Acid

Tryptophan (TPP), because of its close chemical similarity to IAA, has been considered the most likely precursor of auxin, especially since the demonstration by Thimann (243) that cultures of *Rhizopus suinus* would readily form IAA when supplied with tryptophan. This protein amino acid is probably of ubiquitous occurrence in plants, though remarkably few determinations of the level of free TPP in plants appear to have been made. The amount of free TPP in leaves appears to be about one thousand-fold greater than that of IAA; wheat leaves contain 20 μg/g fresh weight (92), barley leaves 20–46 μg/g fresh weight (209), tomato shoots 12 μg/g fresh weight (209), *Solanum nigrum* leaves 2–17 μg/g fresh weight (265), and bean shoots 30 μg/g fresh weight (209). In vivo metabolism experiments have shown that ^{14}C-TPP can be converted to ^{14}C-IAA by watermelon slices (25), cabbage shoots (99, 274), tomato shoots (60, 275), *Lens* root (173), lime fruits (88), tobacco shoots (167), cucumber hypocotyls (221), wheat leaves (92), maize coleoptiles (122), barley shoots (60), bean shoots (19), and bean roots (143). Cell-free preparations of mung bean (277), tobacco (167), and pea seedlings (146) have also been shown to carry out this conversion. On the other hand, Winter (281) and Thimann & Grochowska (247) found that sterile *Avena* coleoptile tips did not elongate when supplied with TPP, and these workers therefore concluded that TPP was not a precursor of IAA in this tissue. Recent work by Black and Hamilton (19) has shown that sterile *Avena* coleoptile tissues can convert ^{14}C-TPP to ^{14}C-IAA, although the yield of ^{14}C-IAA is low. These experiments indicate that exogenously supplied TPP does not fully equilibrate with and elevate the internal free TPP pool in coleoptile tissue which is important for IAA biosynthesis. Perhaps the strongest support for the role of TPP as the native precursor of IAA has been provided by the work of Erdmann & Schiewer (36), who found that when ^{14}C-indole and ^{3}H-labeled serine or ^{14}C, ^{3}H-TPP were fed to sterile pea plants, the relative labeling ratio (^{3}H/^{14}C)IAA:(^{3}H/^{14}C)TPP observed when these compounds were extracted from the plants was the same in each case, showing that no bypass from indole to IAA had occurred.

Pathways Leading from Tryptophan to Indoleacetic Acid

If we accept that IAA occurs in plants and that its primary precursor is tryptophan, then how is the conversion from amino acid to auxin carried out? Evidence has been obtained for four possible pathways, which will be discussed in turn below; the key intermediates after which these pathways have been named are indolepyruvic acid (IPyA), tryptamine (TNH$_2$), indoleacetaldoxime (IAOx), and tryptophol (TOL). The principal lines of evidence for the existence of each pathway are: (*a*) presence of the intermediates as native compounds in plants; (*b*) biological activity of the intermediates; (*c*) in vivo interconversions of the intermediates; and (*d*) isolation of the enzymes catalyzing the postulated reactions.

THE INDOLEPYRUVIC ACID PATHWAY   Indolepyruvic acid is notoriously unstable, especially under alkaline conditions, and no isolation of the keto acid as a native compound from vegetative tissues has yet been made. Stowe & Thimann (236) claimed to have identified IPyA in maize kernels, and although this report was later confirmed by Winter (280), experiments by Srivastava (229) and Stowe, Vendrell & Epstein (237) were unable to produce the same observation. On the other hand, good evidence for the occurrence of indoleacetaldehyde (IAAld) as a native compound of vegetative tissues has been obtained from extracts of pea seedlings (109, 181, 183) and cucumber seedlings (W. K. Purves, personal communication). Since IAA is among the many products of chemical breakdown of IPyA in solution, it is difficult to draw valid conclusions on the biological activity of this compound. Some IAA is also formed spontaneously when IAAld is incubated in aqueous solution, but Larsen & Rajagopal (110) estimated that the amount of IAA formed was not

I	II	III	IV

$$R \cdot CH_2 \cdot CHNH_2 \cdot COOH \xrightarrow{a} R \cdot CH_2 \cdot CO \cdot COOH \xrightarrow{b} R \cdot CH_2 \cdot CHO \xrightarrow{c} R \cdot CH_2 \cdot COOH$$

Figure 1   I = Tryptophan, II = Indolepyruvic acid.
III = Indoleacetaldehyde, IV = Indoleacetic acid.
a = Tryptophan aminotransferase.
b = Indolepyruvic acid decarboxylase.
c = Indoleacetaldehyde dehydrogenase or oxidase.

sufficient to account for the activity they observed for the acetaldehyde in four test systems. In all cases, however, the biological activity of IAAld was much lower than that of IAA.

Demonstration of the conversion of ^{14}C-TPP to ^{14}C-IPyA in vivo is difficult because of the relatively small amounts of IPyA formed and its instability during extraction and chromatographic analysis. Dannenburg & Liverman (25) were the first to feed ^{14}C-TPP to plant tissues (watermelon slices), and they found a radioactive compound in acid ether extracts, after ammoniacal chromatography, which they identified as IPyA. Unfortunately, this first report of IPyA formation is unreliable since the keto acid is known to break down completely during ammoniacal chromatography, and it is probable that the radioactive acidic compound observed by Dannenburg & Liverman was malonyltryptophan, which was first reported as a tryptophan metabolite by Good & Andreae in 1967 (63). In other in vivo metabolism experiments, incubation of young lime fruits with ^{14}C-TPP resulted in the formation of a radioactive metabolite which had the same Rf as authentic IPyA on a silica gel column and showed biological activity in the oat coleoptile test (88). IPyA was also reported as a metabolite of ^{14}C-TPP in primary leaves of wheat seedlings (92), but since very small amounts of tissue were used in this experiment, if IPyA was present, it must have been formed in unusually high amounts in order to be detectable.

Gibson, Schneider & Wightman (60) were able to demonstrate unequivocally the in vivo conversion of ^{14}C-TPP to ^{14}C-IPyA in barley and tomato shoots. After feeding ^{14}C-TPP to the shoots, unlabeled carrier IPyA was added to the acid ether-soluble metabolites, and the 2,4-dinitrophenylhydrazone was prepared to stabilize the IPyA. The IPyA hydrazone was then identified by thin-layer chromatography and shown to be radioactive. The in vivo conversion of ^{14}C-TPP to ^{14}C-IAAld has been shown in lime fruits (88) and tomato and barley shoots (60), but this is not conclusive evidence for the operation of the IPyA pathway in these tissues, since IAAld may also arise via the tryptamine pathway. Conversion of IPyA to IAAld in vivo has not been demonstrated, but it has been shown that numerous species of higher and lower plants produce IAA when fed with (unlabeled) IAAld (182).

The first step in the indolepyruvic acid pathway involves the transamination of TPP to yield IPyA, and there is now considerable evidence that this reaction is catalyzed by a multispecific aminotransferase which can utilize TPP, tyrosine, phenylalanine, and the nonaromatic amino acids, aspartic and glutamic acids, as amino-group donors. Gamborg (52) partially purified (50 to 60-fold) an aromatic aminotransferase from mung bean seedlings and demonstrated that the preparation could also transaminate several nonaromatic amino acids, including aspartic and glutamic acids. The product of tryptophan transamination by the mung bean aromatic aminotransferase was shown to be IPyA, by IR spectroscopy of its 2,4-dinitrophenylhydrazone derivative (277, 278). Forest & Wightman (43) purified 600-fold an aromatic aminotransferase from bush bean seedlings and showed by gel electrophoresis that only a single protein was present in the final preparation. In addition to its activity with all three aromatic amino acids, this purified enzyme was also found to transaminate aspartic and glutamic acids at a high rate, and inclusion of aspartic acid in a reaction mixture with equimolar amounts of any of the aromatic amino acids resulted in strong inhibition of the aromatic aminotransferase activity (44). The results from several other investigations of tryptophan aminotransferase in plants indicate that this enzyme may generally exhibit substrate multispecificity with respect to the three aromatic amino acids (45). The enzyme also appears to be widely distributed in the plant kingdom; Truelsen (249) has demonstrated its presence in 30 species from 16 families.

The second enzyme required for the IPyA pathway, IPyA decarboxylase, has been purified 234-fold from yeast and can be separated from classical pyruvate decarboxylase by DEAE-cellulose chromatography (239). Qualitative evidence for the presence of IPyA decarboxylase in a crude supernatant fraction from tomato shoots was obtained by Gibson, Schneider & Wightman (60), but isolation and purification of this enzyme from higher plant tissues has not yet been achieved. The last step in the IPyA pathway, conversion of IAAld to IAA, could be catalyzed by a mutase, a dehydrogenase, or an oxidase. Wightman & Cohen (277) demonstrated the presence of an NAD-dependent IAAld dehydrogenase in mung bean seedlings. This enzyme was separable from the enzyme converting IAAld to tryptophol by pH precipitation, and therefore was not a dismutase. An IAAld oxidase from oat coleoptiles has been purified 18-fold by Rajagopal (185). Like the mung bean enzyme, this oxidase was found mainly in the cytoplasmic supernatant fraction; however, the oat enzyme appears to be very different from the mung bean enzyme in its pH optimum, lack of NAD dependence, and stability to ionizing radiation [the mung bean enzyme was shown by Gordon (65) to be sensitive to low doses of ionizing radiation, whereas activity of the oat enzyme was actually enhanced]. The oat enzyme is active only in the presence of oxygen, and therefore also differs from potato aldehyde oxidase (67), which could not oxidize aldehydes in the presence of oxygen since it was destroyed by the H_2O_2 formed. Although oxygen is necessary for the oat IAAld oxidase reaction, the oxygen atom introduced into the aldehyde molecules appears to arise from water, since electron transfer to phenazine methosulfate can occur under anaerobiosis with concurrent IAA formation. The pathway of electron transport to oxygen under natural conditions is unknown (186).

THE TRYPTAMINE PATHWAY   Evidence for the natural occurrence of TPP, IAAld, and IAA has been considered above. Tryptamine (TNH_2) was first isolated from *Acacia* by White (269) and has since been found in at least 11 other species (209). Tryptamine is not detectable, however, in many common plants such as pea, bean, squash, and cabbage (209).

Skoog (226) was the first to observe that TNH_2 was active, after a certain lag period, in the *Avena* curvature test. In more recent studies, this compound was

I → V → III → IV

$R \cdot CH_2 \cdot CHNH_2COOH \xrightarrow{d} R \cdot CH_2 \cdot CH_2 \cdot NH_2 \xrightarrow{e} R \cdot CH_2CHO \xrightarrow{c} R \cdot CH_2 \cdot COOH$

Figure 2   I, III, IV, c, see Figure 1. V = Tryptamine, d = Tryptophan decarboxylase, e = Tryptamine oxidase.

again found to evoke an elongation response in oat coleoptile segments (247) and in hypocotyl segments from nine other species (41). Tobacco (167), tomato, and barley shoots (60) have been shown to convert ^{14}C-TPP to ^{14}C-TNH$_2$, and ^{14}C-TNH$_2$ to ^{14}C-IAA. The participation of IAAld in this pathway in tomato and barley shoots was clearly demonstrated by Gibson, Schneider & Wightman (60) by adding unlabeled carrier IAAld to the neutral ether extracts from both ^{14}C-TPP and ^{14}C-TNH$_2$-fed shoots, preparing the corresponding IAAld-2,4-dinitrophenylhydra- zones and showing that both hydrazones were radioactive. The participation of IAAld in this metabolic pathway may also be indirectly inferred from the fact that ^{14}C-TNH$_2$ gives rise to tryptophol-^{14}C in tomato shoots (60) and cucumber hypoco- tyls (221), presumably through ^{14}C-IAAld as an intermediate.

The initial reaction of the tryptamine pathway is catalyzed by the enzyme trypto- phan decarboxylase. Reed (193) reported the presence in etiolated pea epicotyls of an enzyme which decarboxylated TPP, but the product of this reaction was not TNH$_2$. However, TNH$_2$-forming tryptophan decarboxylases are present in tobacco buds (168), cucumber hypocotyls (220), and barley and tomato shoots (60). The tomato shoot tryptophan decarboxylase was purified 86-fold by Gibson, Barrett & Wightman (59) and shown to be separable from tryptophan aminotransferase by ammonium sulfate fractionation. This partially purified enzyme required pyridoxal phosphate for activity and could decarboxylate L-TPP and 5OH-L-TPP, but not D-TPP, L-tyrosine, or L-phenylalanine. It therefore seems to be a more specific enzyme than tryptophan aminotransferase.

The further conversion of TNH$_2$ to indoleacetaldehyde requires the participation of an amine oxidase. Some in vivo evidence for the participation of an amine oxidase in reactions leading to plant growth has been obtained by using inhibitors. For example, the amine oxidase inhibitors, Marsilid and Catron, caused partial inhibi- tion of TNH$_2$-induced growth in oat coleoptile segments (247). In addition, the growth of pea seedlings was strongly inhibited by the 1,1-dimethylhydrazides of succinic and maleic acids (B995 and C-011), and the treated seedlings showed a considerable decline in amine oxidase activity (194). An amine oxidase was purified from pea seedlings by Mann (130, 131), and was shown to catalyze the oxidative deamination of a wide variety of amines, including tryptamine (78). The enzyme was a pink, copper-containing protein, and the copper was shown to be necessary for activity. Since carbonyl reagents were found to act as inhibitors, Mann (131) sug- gested that the prosthetic group of the enzyme consisted of a complex between copper and carbonyl group. Kinetic studies by Yamazaki, Swindell & Reed (282), using the pea seedling enzyme, suggest that oxidative catalysis involves the amine substrate reacting with the amine oxidase to form the corresponding aldehyde and a modified form of the enzyme which is subsequently oxidized by oxygen. F. W. Percival and W. K. Purves (personal communication) have recently shown by ion exchange chromatography that three peaks of amine oxidase activity can be demon- strated in the cytoplasmic supernatant fraction of cucumber seedlings. All three fractions were capable of oxidizing TNH$_2$ and showed differences in substrate specificity, K_m values for TNH$_2$, pH optima, and molecular weight. This appears to be the first report of the presence of more than one amine oxidase in a single plant species.

THE INDOLEACETALDOXIME PATHWAY   The indoleacetaldoxime-indoleacetonitrile pathway for the conversion of tryptophan to IAA is characteristic of the Brassicaceae (99), although the related pathway to glucobrassicin is also found in the Capparaidaceae, Tovariaceae, and Resedaceae (211). The distribution of oxime pathways in the plant kingdom is discussed in detail in a recent review of the metabolism of oximes by Mahadevan (127). Since indoleacetonitrile (IAN) is readily formed by myrosinase-catalyzed breakdown of glucobrassicin during tissue extraction, it is not certain that IAN is a normal constituent of *Brassica* plants, but it is probably present in small amounts (101). The occurrence of indoleacetaldoxime (IAOx) as a natural constituent was demonstrated by Kindl (93), who isolated this compound from cabbage and also showed that radioactive IAOx was present in cabbage plants grown in a $^{14}CO_2$ atmosphere.

Indoleacetaldoxime has been found to promote growth in wheat coleoptile and pea stem segments (40). Indoleacetonitrile is a very active growth promoter of oat, wheat, and maize coleoptile segments (16, 214) and also of cabbage, radish and turnip (139), cucumber, sunflower, *Impatiens,* and *Salvia* hypocotyl tissues (6). Several species, however, such as pea, tomato, and broad bean, show little growth response to this compound, and this lack of activity appears due to the inability of these plants to convert IAN to IAA (214, 244, 274). Glucobrassicin is also active as a growth promoter in the oat and wheat coleoptile tests (98, 228), but the activity of this compound on cabbage hypocotyls is small (228).

In vivo metabolism experiments have shown that radioactive TPP can be converted to IAOx (93), to IAN (100, 274) and to glucobrassicin (99, 102) in cabbages. ^{14}C-IAN can be converted to IAA in cabbage (274), wheat, and corn (39). Feeding of unlabeled IAOx to a range of plants representing 17 families resulted in the accumulation of large amounts of IAN in eight species, and traces of the compound were found in many others (187). Every plant tested converted the oxime to IAA

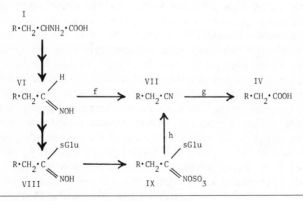

Figure 3   I, IV, see Figure 1.
VI = Indoleacetaldoxime, VII = Indoleacetonitrile,
VIII = Desthioglucobrassicin, IX = Glucobrassicin,
f = Indoleacetaldoxime hydro-lyase,
g = Nitrilase, h = Myrosinase.

and tryptophol, but only one species (*Amaranthus*) accumulated IAAld. In another investigation of this pathway, woad leaves were shown to incorporate ^{3}H-IAOx into desthioglucobrassicin and glucobrassicin (128).

It is possible to convert TPP to IAOx by a horseradish peroxidase/dihydroxy-fumarate system (93), but this system is probably not responsible for formation of the aldoxime in vivo. Indoleacetaldoxime hydro-lyase, which catalyzes the conversion of IAOx to IAN, was first demonstrated in banana leaves by Mahadevan (126) and has been partially purified from *Giberella* (97, 222, 223). The purified enzyme was shown to be specific for IAOx and required pyridoxal phosphate; activation of the enzyme by freezing and by several compounds unrelated to the substrate suggested that it may be a metabolically regulated enzyme composed of subunits (223). Cell-free preparations from oat coleoptiles have been shown to convert IOAx to IAAld, indicating that an alternate pathway for the metabolism of IAOx exists in noncruciferous plants (187). The enzyme nitrilase, which converts IAN to IAA, has been found only in the families Gramineae, Cruciferae, and Musaceae (129, 248), and is not highly specific. Myrosinase, which converts glucobrassicin to IAN, is found mainly in cruciferous plants. Since the formation of IAN by myrosinase activity does not occur at pH values above 5.2, it would seem that the in vivo role of this enzyme is rather limited (212).

THE TRYPTOPHOL PATHWAY AND INDOLELACTIC ACID   Rayle & Purves (190) extracted tryptophol (TOL) from green shoots of cucumber seedlings and proved its identity by gas chromatography and mass spectrometry. TOL is also a natural constituent of shoots of sunflower (181) and tomato (209, 257). Indolelactic acid (ILA) has been found as a native compound only in tomato (33, 209, 275). Tryptophol acts as a growth promoter in oat (108) and wheat coleoptile tissues (274), in pea epicotyl, and in tomato, beet, radish, sunflower, melon, squash, and cucumber hypocotyl tissues (190, 192). On the other hand, ILA is only weakly active in the oat, wheat, and maize coleoptile tests and in the pea stem test (7, 245, 274).

In vivo metabolism experiments have shown that ^{14}C-TPP is a good precursor of ILA and TOL in tomato shoots (60, 275) and that ^{14}C-TOL can be converted

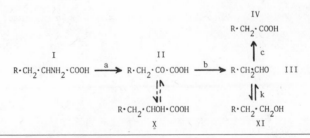

Figure 4 I, II, III, IV, a, b, c, see Figure 1.
X = Indolelactic acid, XI = Tryptophol,
k = Tryptophol dehydrogenase or oxidase.

to ^{14}C-IAA by cucumber hypocotyl tissue (191). When ILA-3-^{14}C was fed to tomato shoots, radioactive IAA was found in acid ether extracts of the tissue, but since a large percentage of the radioactivity was found in the free TPP fraction, the pathway by which the ^{14}C-IAA had arisen could not be determined (60). ILA has been suggested as a direct precursor of TOL in tomato shoots (275); however, no ILA decarboxylase was detected in this issue in later investigations and this pathway now seems unlikely (60).

In studies to determine whether the metabolism of IAAld to TOL and IAA is catalyzed by a dismutase or two separate dehydrogenase enzymes, Wightman & Cohen (277) described the partial purification of an alcohol dehydrogenase from mung bean seedlings which catalyzed the reversible reduction of IAAld to TOL. NADH was required for the reduction reaction. Similar enzymes extracted from oat coleoptile tissue (184) and cucumber seedlings (W. K. Purves, personal communication) required either NADH or NADPH for activity. The cucumber enzyme appeared to be highly specific for IAAld. A tryptophol oxidase, purified more than 3000-fold from cucumber shoots by Vickery & Purves (262), has been shown to catalyze the aerobic oxidation of TOL to form IAAld and H_2O_2. The reaction was irreversible and had no cofactor requirements other than the presence of an electron acceptor. Inhibitor studies suggested that the enzyme may be a flavoprotein with a metal ion and SH groups necessary for full activity. The enzyme was found to be inhibited by its product IAAld, and the inhibition was overcome by O_2 but not by TOL, suggesting a ping-pong Bi-Bi reaction mechanism. IAA and several synthetic auxins also inhibited the enzyme, while gibberellins had no effect (166).

Role of Epiphytic Microorganisms in Indoleacetic Acid Biosynthesis

The extensive work of Libbert and co-workers has shown that plants are colonized by many species of bacteria (123). These bacteria are capable of metabolizing TPP to IAA (271, 272) and also of converting TNH_2 to TOL and IAA (121). In addition, sterile plants appear to contain less extractable auxin (119) and diffusible auxin (120) than nonsterile controls. On the other hand, sterile plants do contain some auxin (119, 120, 183, 210), and IAAld and TOL have been shown to be native constituents of sterile pea plants (183). Furthermore, ^{14}C-TPP can be converted to ^{14}C-IAA by sterile maize (122) and oat coleoptiles (19), cucumber hypocotyls (221), runner bean roots (143), and duckweed plants (F. Wightman and K. W. Joy, personal communication). Sterile cucumber hypocotyl segments can convert TOL to IAA and TNH_2 to TOL and IAA (221), and sterile pea stems can metabolize TPP to IPyA, IAAld, and TOL (118). Cell-free extracts of sterile mung bean seedlings exhibited tryptophan aminotransferase activity identical to that shown by similar extracts of nonsterile plants, and both enzymic preparations showed the same capacity to metabolize ^{14}C-TPP to ^{14}C-IAA (277). TPP decarboxylase is present in cucumber hypocotyls which are free of epiphytic bacteria, and the internal bacteria of this plant do not possess this enzyme (220). It appears, therefore, that plants can synthesize IAA independently, although the amount of IAA formed may be affected by the presence of bacteria.

CATABOLISM OF INDOLEACETIC ACID

Oxidation

MOLECULAR SITE OF INDOLEACETIC ACID OXIDASE ACTIVITY   It has been realized since the early 1950s (49, 61) that IAA can be oxidized by plant peroxidases, and since that time there has been continued discussion of the molecular site of IAA oxidase activity. Two alternative possibilities, which are not mutually exclusive, have been considered: first, that IAA oxidase activity and peroxidase activity reside on the same molecule; and second, that molecules exist that have IAA oxidase activity but are devoid of peroxidase activity.

Clearly, resolution of this problem requires rigorous purification of the peroxidase and IAA oxidase activities. This purification is complicated by the fact that many plants contain several isoenzymes of peroxidase (4, 9, 24, 29, 30, 35, 37, 38, 47, 64, 73, 80, 84, 91, 111, 134, 138, 142, 158, 161, 164, 165, 175, 199, 203, 216, 218, 230, 240, 258, 270). IAA oxidase may also occur in several molecular forms. McCune (135) found four bands of IAA oxidase activity after starch gel electrophoresis of maize extracts. Sequeira & Mineo (215), using an SE-Sephadex C-50 column, found one major and several minor peaks of IAA oxidase activity in tobacco root extracts and also in a crystalline horseradish peroxidase (HRP) preparation. Using similar methods, Penel & Greppin (164) found nine to ten peaks of IAA oxidase activity in spinach leaf extracts. Meudt (136) found at least two peaks of IAA oxidase activity after Sephadex G-100 filtration of a tobacco leaf extract. Endo (35) showed that proteins separated by starch gel electrophoresis could be stained for IAA oxidase activity by coupling an unidentified intermediate of IAA degradation with a diazonium salt to form an insoluble colored complex. Using this method, he demonstrated the presence of several bands of IAA oxidase activity in turnip, radish, and morning glory roots. In more recent studies using Endo's staining procedure combined with polyacrylamide gel electrophoresis, isoenzymes of IAA oxidase have been found in broad bean roots (203) and pear fruits (47).

Thus it is clear that both peroxidase and IAA oxidase can exist in multiple molecular forms, and it appears that these isoenzymes can be divided into at least four classes on the basis of their relative peroxidase and IAA oxidase activities (196, 284).

1.   Typical peroxidases that catalyze peroxidation reactions at a very high rate while also oxidizing IAA much more slowly in the absence of added H_2O_2, e.g. horseradish peroxidase.

2.   Enzymes that have both high peroxidase and high IAA oxidase activity, e.g. turnip peroxidase P_7 (196). Yamazaki (284) has pointed out that these enzymes appear to be rather basic, have a relatively low molecular weight, and show spectra characteristic of thermal mixtures of high-spin and low-spin states.

3.   Peroxidases that show no IAA oxidase activity; electrophoretically separated proteins showing peroxidase activity but no IAA oxidase activity have been found in root extracts (35, 203), *Pharbitis* callus cultures (287), and pear fruit (47).

4.   IAA oxidases that have no peroxidase activity; Sequeira & Mineo (215) found a peak of IAA oxidase activity after gel filtration of a tobacco root preparation and

of crystalline HRP which did not show peroxidase activity towards guaiacol. Hoyle (80), however, was unable to confirm the presence of this peroxidase-free IAA oxidase. Van der Mast (257) found two IAA oxidase fractions in pea roots, and one of these was free of peroxidase activity.

A somewhat different approach to the question of the sites of peroxidase and IAA oxidase activity was taken by Siegel & Galston (224), who found that when the heme prosthetic group of HRP was removed by treatment with acidified acetone, the apoenzyme still had IAA oxidase activity but had lost its activity towards peroxidase substrates such as guaiacol. Peroxidase activity could be partially restored by recombining the heme and the apoenzyme. This result was confirmed by Hoyle (80), but Ku, Yang & Pratt (96) found that if the prosthetic group of the HRP was removed by acid butanone, the apoenzyme had almost no IAA oxidase activity.

It appears, then, that plants contain several peroxidase isoenzymes, some of which are also able to oxidase IAA at various rates and that in one or two cases, enzymes have been demonstrated which have IAA oxidase activity but not peroxidase activity. Ricard, Mazza & Williams (196) have made the interesting suggestion that a sequence of proteins may exist having progressively fewer acidic groups in the heme cleft, with an associated change in activity from peroxide activation (most acidic) to oxygen activation to oxygen carrying (most basic). This type of explanation may account for the almost continuous series of behavior exhibited by these plant hemoproteins.

PRODUCTS OF THE OXIDATION OF INDOLEACETIC ACID

Oxindoles   Hinman & Lang (79), in a study of the products of the oxidation of IAA by horseradish peroxidase (HRP), found that the course of the reaction was highly dependent on the substrate concentration, the main product at IAA concentrations below $2 \times 10^{-4}M$ being 3-methyleneoxindole.

Hinman & Lang proposed a reaction scheme (Figure 5) in which the first step is a one-electron enzymatic oxidation of IAA (IV) by peroxidase, with the formation of an indolenine hydroperoxide (XII). In subsequent nonenzymatic steps, the hydroperoxide is converted via an indolenine epoxide (XIII) to oxindole-3-carbinol (XV) and finally to 3-methyleneoxindole (XVI). At higher substrate concentrations (up to $10^{-2}M$ IAA) the principal product was an unidentified neutral indole.

Several authors (72, 136, 137, 151, 252) have discussed the possibility that oxidation products of IAA, rather than IAA itself, may be active in growth regulation. Moyed and co-workers hypothesized that the stimulatory and inhibitory effects of IAA may have a common biochemical origin. In a model system, growth of *Schizosaccharomyces pombe* was inhibited by 3-methyleneoxindole (48). The inhibition was transitory, as 3-methyleneoxindole was enzymatically converted to the nontoxic compound 3-methyloxindole (48, 232). The **inhibitory** effect of 3-methyleneoxindole was attributed to its reactivity with the -SH groups of proteins (232), and Tuli & Moyed (250) showed that this property could also result in the release of regulatory enzymes from feedback control, which might result in the **acceleration** of metabo-

Figure 5   IV = Indoleacetic acid, XII = Indolenine hydroperoxide,
XIII = Indolenine epoxide, XV = Oxindole-3-carbinol,
XVI = 3-Methyleneoxindole, XVII = Indolealdehyde.

lism and growth. Binding of ^{14}C-3-methyleneoxindole to the proteins of pea seed-lings was demonstrated by Basu & Tuli (11). Demorest & Stahmann (31) have found that 3-methyleneoxindole can also react with the -SH groups of arginine-rich histones, which might also result in regulatory effects.

Extending their work to higher plants, Tuli & Moyed (252) suggested that IAA is converted to 3-methyleneoxindole, which at low concentrations stimulates growth by desensitization of regulatory proteins, but at higher concentrations inhibits such processes as root growth. The duration of both responses would be controlled by the inactivation of 3-methyleneoxindole by reduction to 3-methyloxindole. In support of this hypothesis, it was shown that intact pea seedlings and extracts of these plants convert IAA to 3-hydroxymethyloxindole (251). Dehydration of 3-hydroxy-methyloxindole to 3-methyleneoxindole can occur nonenzymatically, but an enzyme catalyzing this conversion has been partially purified from wheat germ (10). Conversion of IAA to 3-methyleneoxindole by crude cell-free extracts from corn coleoptiles was also reported by Hager & Schmidt (72). A highly specific 3-methyleneoxindole reductase has been purified from peas (152) and shown to exist in several isoenzymic forms (153). One of these isoenzymes was noncompetitively inhibited by 2,4-D whereas another was competitively inhibited by NAA. These synthetic auxins might therefore control the level of 3-methyleneoxindole in the plant by their effect on the reduction of this compound to the inactive substance, 3-methyloxindole (252). Tuli & Moyed (252) have also shown that low concentrations of 3-methyleneoxindole are tenfold more effective than IAA in promotion of growth in pea and mung bean stem sections, while higher concentrations are inhibitory. In complete contradiction to the work of Moyed and co-workers, however, Skytt-Andersen, Moller & Hansen (227) found that 3-methyleneoxindole had no effect, either positive or negative, on the growth of pea stem and oat first internode sections, or on the initiation of roots by pea stem cuttings. Thimann (246) also reported inability to demonstrate any growth-regulatory activity for this compound. These conflicting results remain to be explained.

Indolealdehyde   In contrast to the oxindoles, indolealdehyde is a relatively stable compound, and has been demonstrated as a native constituent of shoots of barley, tomato (209), and *Equisetum* (22). Exogenously supplied ^{14}C-IAA can be converted to indolealdehyde-^{14}C by shoots of tomato (275) and barley (208), by pea stem sections (125), pea roots (150), and bean stems (27). The ability of plant enzymes to convert IAA to indolealdehyde has also been demonstrated in preparations from lupin (238), pea (180), lentil (171), Japanese radish (149), and maize (14). Magnus, Iskric & Kveder (125) found that the indolealdehyde formed by pea stem sections could also be reversibly reduced to indole-3-methanol (in a reaction analagous to the formation of tryptophol from indoleacetaldehyde) and also irreversibly oxidized to indole-3-carboxylic acid. The oxidation of indolealdehyde to indolecarboxylic acid also occurs in shoots of tomato (F. Wightman, unpublished data) and barley (208).

Indoleglycollic acid and indoleglyoxylic acid have been suggested as intermediates between IAA and indolealdehyde (42), but the formation of these compounds from IAA in plants has never been proved satisfactorily; indeed, they were shown to be absent from the radioactive metabolites obtained after feeding IAA-2-^{14}C to barley shoots (208). Hinman & Lang (79) considered that indolealdehyde (Figure 5, XIV) might arise from the epoxide intermediate (XIII) if ring opening occurred before rather than after hydration.

Acetophenones   The products expected if cleavage of the pyrrole ring occurs, *o*-formamidoacetophenone and *o*-aminoacetophenone have been isolated after chemical oxidation of IAA (2). The only evidence to date, however, of the possible occurrence of an acetophenone as a plant metabolite is that provided by Collet (23), who reported that incubation of pea root tips with ^{14}C-IAA resulted in the formation of a radioactive compound with chromatographic properties and a uv spectrum similar to those of *o*-formamidoacetophenone.

MECHANISM OF ACTION OF HORSERADISH PEROXIDASE   According to the scheme of Hinman & Lang (79), the first product of the peroxidase-catalyzed oxidation of IAA is an IAA free radical (IAA·). The mechanism by which this free radical is produced is complicated by the fact that the reaction of IAA with HRP results in the formation of other spectroscopically distinct forms of peroxidase known as Compounds I, II, and III (for discussion of the structures and properties of these compounds, see 163, 204). Some authors have considered Compounds I and II to be the catalytically active forms (46), while others have emphasized the role of Compound III (140, 198, 285). Recently, Yamazaki & Yamazaki (283) proposed a reaction scheme which attempts to reconcile these conflicting views. In this scheme, the initial slow reaction involves the direct reduction of HRP by IAA in the presence of O_2 with the formation of Compound III (oxyferroperoxidase) (140, 197, 283).

$$\text{Ferriperoxidase} + \text{IAA} \longrightarrow \text{Ferroperoxidase} + \text{IAA·} \qquad 1.$$
$$\text{Ferroperoxidase} + O_2 \longrightarrow \text{Compound III} \qquad 2.$$

In the steady state of IAA oxidation, a more important pathway for the formation of Compound III may be the reaction of HRP with IAA peroxide radical.

$$\text{Ferriperoxidase} + \text{IAA.OO·} \longrightarrow \text{Compound III} + \text{IAA(ox)} \qquad 3.$$

The relative affinity of Compound III for IAA is very high (286), and this compound may react with a second molecule of IAA to give free peroxidase (140, 198, 286).

$$\text{Compound III} + \text{IAA} \longrightarrow \text{Ferriperoxidase} + \text{IAA·} + H_2O_2 \qquad 4.$$

However, the spectral data of Yamazaki & Yamazaki (283) indicate that after several seconds of reaction, Compound II predominates. The precursor of Compound II, Compound I, may be formed either from Compound III (reaction 5) or by a reaction between HRP and IAA peroxide (reaction 6). Compound I is then reduced by a molecule of IAA to give Compound II (reaction 7). Compound II may return to the native oxidation state of HRP with the formation of another IAA free radical (reaction 8), or may be irreversibly converted into the pigment P-670 in a side reaction.

$$\text{Compound III} + \text{IAA} \longrightarrow \text{Compound I} + \text{IAA·} \qquad 5.$$
$$\text{Ferriperoxidase} + \text{IAA.OOH} \longrightarrow \text{Compound I} + \text{IAA(ox)} \qquad 6.$$
$$\text{Compound I} + \text{IAA} \longrightarrow \text{Compound II} + \text{IAA·} \qquad 7.$$
$$\text{Compound II} + \text{IAA} \longrightarrow \text{Ferriperoxidase} + \text{IAA·} \qquad 8.$$

An important feature of the scheme of Yamazaki & Yamazaki is the involvement of IAA peroxide radical as an intermediate, a proposal compatible with the earlier schemes of Maclachlan & Waygood (124), Ray (189), and Hinman & Lang (79).

$$\text{R·} + O_2 \longrightarrow \text{ROO·} \qquad 9.$$
$$\text{ROO·} + \text{HR} \longrightarrow \text{ROOH} + \text{R·} \qquad 10.$$

In some peroxidase-oxidase reactions the products of reaction 9 seem to be R^+ and OO^- (superoxide anion). However, it has been shown that superoxide dismutase, which rapidly destroys superoxide anion by disproportionation, does not affect the HRP-IAA reaction (140, 283). Hence, free superoxide anion cannot be an intermediate. Similarly, since the reaction is not inhibited by catalase (46), free H_2O_2 is not required for the reaction. The participation of IAA peroxide also accounts for the requirement for molecular oxygen during the oxidation of IAA. Thus, although IAA peroxide radical has not been demonstrated directly, its participation as an intermediate would explain much of the available experimental data.

The scheme of Yamazaki & Yamazaki involves the production of IAA free radical at four separate points (reactions 1, 5, 7, and 8), and this radical might also be produced by reaction 4, which is not included in Yamazaki & Yamazaki's current scheme. No conclusive evidence, in the form of EPR spectra, for the formation of these radicals during the enzymatic reaction has yet been obtained, although Borg (21) reported observing a transient EPR spectrum during the oxidation of IAA in acid. Fox, Purves & Nakada (46) found that sodium bisulfite, a free radical trap, inhibited the oxidation of IAA by HRP, a result consistent with the presence of free radical intermediates. The rapid reaction of IAA free radicals with oxygen to form IAA peroxide may explain the difficulty experienced in obtaining EPR spectra.

Thus the oxidation of IAA by HRP appears to occur via an initial slow reaction involving Compound III, whose function may be to supply IAA peroxide or some other form of peroxide which is not attacked by catalase. Reaction of HRP with IAA peroxide can then occur, and oxidation of IAA can proceed rapidly via the cycle formed by reactions 6, 7, and 8.

EFFECTS OF NATURALLY OCCURRING COFACTORS, INHIBITORS, AND HORMONES ON PEROXIDASE AND INDOLEACETIC ACID OXIDASE ACTIVITY The activities of peroxidase and IAA oxidase can be altered by many naturally occurring compounds such as phenols (both free and bound), coumarins, manganese salts, and plant acids. Investigations with phenols generally support the view that monophenols act as cofactors of IAA oxidase, while o- and p-dihydric phenols and polyphenols are IAA oxidase inhibitors. (58, 172, 174, 176, 202). Unfortunately, many of these studies have been made with crude enzyme preparations. The molecular size of naturally occurring phenolic IAA oxidase inhibitors ranges from free, low molecular weight compounds such as chlorogenic, ferulic, and protocatechuic acids, to the high molecular weight "auxin protectors" reported by Phipps (169, 170) and Stonier & Yoneda (235). Phipps (170) described a thermostable, nondialyzable IAA oxidase inhibitor from tobacco which appears to be a protein-Fe-chlorogenic acid-rutin complex and also may contain carbohydrate (J. Phipps, personal communication). Stonier and co-workers have isolated three "protectors" from stems and leaves of *Pharbitis nil:* protector A (Mol wt 200,000), protector I (mol wt 8,000), and protector II (mol wt 2000) (235). Protector A may be a precursor of the other two compounds (288). These protectors induce a lag in the oxidation of IAA by HRP, rather than affecting the rate of oxidation (233). The active site of protector II from *Pharbitis* is probably an o-dihydroxphenol, since it is inactivated by polyphenoloxidase, but not by lipase or protease (234). Gradients of protector activity diminishing from younger to older tissue are found in *Pharbitis* (288) and tobacco (170), and similar gradients of low molecular weight inhibitors have been reported in cotton, peach, and rhubarb (147). Stonier (233) suggests that auxin protectors act as antioxidants which "interact with H_2O_2 and and which can also keep manganese in a reduced state."

Scopoletin, a naturally occurring coumarin, has been shown to inhibit sweet potato IAA oxidase at higher concentrations, whereas lower concentrations were stimulatory (81). Schafer, Wender & Smith (206) isolated two anionic isoperoxidases from tobacco callus cultures, and showed that the activity of one isoenzyme (A_3) was stimulated by scopoletin, while the other was unaffected. Scopoletin appears, in fact, to be the substrate for isoenzyme A_3 (195). Thus stimulatory or inhibitory effects may be due to the relative concentrations of scopoletin and individual isoenzymes in each tissue. In a study of the reaction between scopoletin and purified HRP, Sirois & Miller (225) found that scopoletin inhibited IAA oxidation in a nonlinear, competitive manner. More recently (141), the coumarin was found to react stoichiometrically with Compound II, converting this compound back to ferriperoxidase. It was found that this reaction was responsible for the spectral shift which was observed in dilute peroxidase solutions on addition of inhibitory concentrations of scopoletin. Addition of a tenfold excess of IAA to the scopoletin-inhibited HRP resulted in rapid oxidation of the scopoletin, conversion of the enzyme to an active intermediate compound, and rapid degradation of the IAA (225). It seems probable that protector substances such as coumarins and phenolic derivatives of cinnamic acid (e.g. ferulic acid) can react preferentially with both Compound II and Compound III. The protectors are themselves oxidized, and during this period a lag in the oxidation of IAA is observed. When the concentration of protector falls to a low level, IAA can be oxidized at a rate close to that of controls lacking protector (57, 205; R. W. Miller, personal communication).

Manganese has been found to be a cofactor for many IAA oxidase systems (50), and the manganese nutrition of cotton has been found to affect levels of IAA oxidase in this plant. At toxic levels of manganese, IAA oxidase activity was increased and IAA oxidase inhibitor activity decreased (148). In addition, plants deficient in manganese had very high IAA oxidase activity and no detectable inhibitor activity, and a native cofactor was found in the deficient plants (242). Thus the manganese status of the plant may affect IAA oxidase activity directly or via its effect on natural cofactors and inhibitors of the system.

After filtration through Sephadex G-75, cotton IAA oxidase is stimulated by low concentrations of malate, succinate, fumarate, and other plant acids (105). The authors suggest that this stimulation may be due to the inhibition of catalase activity by the acids. Rubery (201) found that Sephadex G-25 filtration of liquid medium from crown-gall tissue cultures gave a protein peak that had peroxidase activity but showed little IAA oxidase activity unless malic acid or related compounds were added in the presence of Mn^{2+} and a monohydric phenol. This effect was not due to inhibition of endogenous catalase. Rubery suggests that malic acid may increase the efficiency of oxidation of ferriperoxidase to Compound II by indoleacetyl peroxy radicals. ·

Plant growth hormones have never been shown to have a direct effect on peroxidase or IAA oxidase activity in vitro, but considerable effects on the levels of these enzymes in vivo have been demonstrated in a wide variety of tissues. The results of many experiments on the effects of auxins, gibberellins, and cytokinins on IAA oxidase and peroxidase activity are summarized in Table 1; the effect of ethylene

Table 1 Effects of growth hormones on peroxidase and IAA oxidase

Ref.	Tissue	Enzyme	Effect
IAA (ref. marked * used 2,4-D)			
51	Tobacco pith culture	2 cathodic isoperoxidases 3rd cathodic isoperoxidase	Represses Induces
112	*Pelargonium* pith culture	Peroxidase	Inhibits, later promotes
165	*Lens* root ribosomes	2 basic isoperoxidases Acid peroxidase	Stimulates de novo biosynthesis No effect
53	*Lens* root ribosomes	Peroxidase	Promotes
200	Tobacco tissue culture	2 anodic isoperoxidases	Induces (2,4-D does not induce)
270	Wheat coleoptile	3 peroxidases, 1 with IAA oxidase activity	Inhibits
114	Tobacco callus	Fast-moving IAA oxidases Slow-moving IAA oxidases	Low concs. promote High concs. promote
116*	Tobacco callus	Fast-moving IAA oxidases Slow-moving IAA oxidases	Low concs. promote High concs. promote
54	*Lens* embryo	Isoperoxidases	Promotes, but inhibits one isoenzyme
138	Tobacco leaf	Cell wall isoperoxidase	Promotes
Gibberellin			
255	Sunflower seedling	IAA decarboxylation	No effect
256	*Coleus* stem	IAA decarboxylation	No effect
86	Cucumber seedling	IAA oxidase	Inhibits
159	Dwarf pea buds	IAA oxidase	Promotes to level in tall peas
20	Wheat seedling	IAA oxidase	Promotes
18	Dwarf pea internodes	Peroxidase	Inhibits
115	Tobacco callus	Fast-moving IAA oxidases	Promotes
75	Barley endosperm	Peroxidase	Promotes
56	*Lens* root	IAA oxidase Peroxidase	Promotes Inhibits
112	*Pelargonium* pith culture	Peroxidase	Inhibits, but with IAA may promote
51	Tobacco pith culture	Peroxidase isoenzymes	Increases total activity; no effect on pattern
83	Dwarf bean seedlings	IAA oxidase Peroxidase	Inhibits Promotes
55	Barley seedlings	IAA oxidase Peroxidase	Promotes Promotes
113	Tobacco callus	IAA oxidase isoenzymes	0.2 μm optimal; higher concs. inhibit
54	*Lens* embryo axis	Cathodic isoperoxidases	Promotes

on the levels of auxin in the plant was recently summarized by Abeles (1). It is difficult to draw any general conclusions from this data, but it is clear that all the hormones can often have quite specific effects on enzyme activity and even on the activities of individual isoenzymes. The effect of the hormone is often concentration-dependent, and there may be interaction between hormones (51, 112, 114).

CELLULAR LOCATION OF PEROXIDASE AND INDOLEACETIC ACID OXIDASE   Part of the peroxidase activity of the cell is soluble (165, 178), but peroxidases may also be associated with the cell wall and with various subcellular organelles. The presence of peroxidase activity in the cell wall has been shown by histochemical techniques (157, 266) and by direct extraction, either in situ (138, 230) or after isolation of the cell walls (199, 230, 270). The isoenzyme composition of wall-bound peroxidase may be different from that found in the cytoplasm; in both tobacco (138) and sorghum (230), the activities of one or two of the isoenzymes were much higher in the walls than in the cytoplasm, whereas in peas (199), a covalently bound wall peroxidase fraction was found in which all the isoenzymes were qualitatively different from those of the cytoplasm and from the peroxidase which is ionically bound to the cell walls. In cabbage roots, the wall fraction contained an IAA oxidase with conventional kinetic properties, while the cytoplasmic enzyme was allosteric (179).

Cytochemical studies have shown that peroxidase activity may be associated with many of the membranous components of the cell, such as the plasmalemma and the tonoplast, and that peroxisomes give a particularly strong reaction (157). Extraction of peroxidases from tobacco leaf tissue was greatly improved by the presence of the anionic detergent sodium deoxycholate, again suggesting the association of the enzyme with membranes (29). The IAA oxidases of pea roots are bound to membranes but can be reversibly removed by treatment with KCl (259). Plesnicar, Bonner & Storey (178) found that while 90% of the peroxidase activity of mung bean seedlings was soluble, 6% was associated with microsomes and about 0.5% was in the mitochondrial fraction. Activity was not associated with the mitochondria per se, but with a denser, lysosomal-like particle which contaminated the fraction. In wheat embryos, both soluble and ribosome-linked peroxidases were found. Part of the ribosome-linked peroxidase was easily solubilized, but the remainder could be removed only by treatment with EDTA. The two types of ribosome-linked peroxidases showed different kinetic properties (104). In *Lens* roots, about 67% of the peroxidase activity was particulate, and the microsomal fraction was found to contain the greatest specific activity of peroxidase. Three peroxidase isoenzymes were bound to the ribosomes and could be removed by EDTA treatment; these isoenzymes were not found in the other fractions (165).

It therefore appears that peroxidases may be associated with many cellular compartments, and the finding that some isoenzymes are specific to various areas of the cell again suggests that this enzyme carries out many different reactions. Unfortunately, the intracellular location of IAA oxidase activity has not yet been explored to the same extent as that of the peroxidases.

Bound Forms of Indoleacetic Acid

INDOLEACETYLASPARTIC ACID AND INDOLEACETYLGLUCOSE   When exogenously supplied IAA is metabolized by plants, many more compounds can be detected than can be accounted for by the oxidative pathways discussed above (27, 208). One important metabolite in *Colchicum* leaves (289), and probably in barley leaves (208) and pea and bean stems (27), is 1-(indole-3-acetyl)-β-D-glucose. Another prominent IAA conjugate is indoleacetylaspartic acid (IAA-Asp), first discovered by Andreae & Good (5), and subsequently reported from numerous plant species, both as a native component (94, 160, 267) and after feeding IAA (see references in 145). The product of ^{14}C-IAA metabolism by barley seeds has been identified as the IAA-L-aspartic acid isomer by comparison with an authentic synthetic sample (145, 154). The interesting compound monomethyl-4-chloroindolyl-3-acetyl-L-aspartate has been isolated from immature seeds of pea (76). Also present were 4-chloroindolyl-3-acetate and methyl-4-chloroindolyl-3-acetate (132, 133). These compounds are the first naturally occurring chlorinated auxins that have been isolated from plants.

Synthesis of IAA-Asp by a cell-free system from peas was reported by Lantican & Muir (107); however, this claim has been disputed by Venis (261), who was unable to repeat these observations. Biosynthesis of the aspartate from exogenously supplied IAA can be induced in pea tissue by pretreatment of the sections with any active auxin, whereas inactive auxin analogs are without effect (261).

INDOLE COMPOUNDS OF MAIZE SEED   These compounds, which have been extensively studied by Bandurski and co-workers, have been divided into groups A and B on the basis of molecular weight and solubility (103). Each group contains about half the total indoles of the seed. The compounds found in group A are lipid soluble and of high molecular weight, corresponding to the "bound auxin" of Haagen-Smit et al (70, 71) and Berger & Avery (17). These compounds have been partially purified by column chromatography on silica gel, polystyrene divinylbenzene resin, and LH-Sephadex (177). IAA was found to be in ester linkage to a β-1,4- linked cellulosic glucan of variable chain length. Two or more lipids, a nitrogen-containing compound other than IAA, and two compounds which may have been phenols were also present. The compounds of group B, which are water soluble and of low molecular weight, have also been purified by column chromatography and gas-liquid chromatography (GLC). Nine compounds were present and these could be divided into three groups: IAA myoinositols, IAA myoinositol arabinosides, and IAA myoinositol galactosides (8, 103, 155, 253, 254).

INDOLEACETIC ACID-NUCLEIC ACID COMPLEXES   Early workers (15) found that when pea stem sections were incubated with ^{14}C-IAA, radioactivity was associated with a phenol-extractable fraction coincident with 4S RNA (tRNA) by sucrose density gradient centrifugation. Later, however, (28) it was found that the ^{14}C label could be completely separated from tRNA by Sephadex G-100 chromatography, and so the hypothesis of the formation of an IAA-tRNA complex could no longer be supported. Key & Ingle (87) found that radioactivity from IAA-2-^{14}C was incorporated into all fractions of the nucleic acids of soybean hypocotyl and artichoke tuber tissue. However, since the incorporation of labeled IAA into nucleic acid was greatly inhibited by actinomycin D, and since most of the activity was recovered in the ribonucleotides from the RNA hydrolysates, it was concluded that most of the labeling of nucleic acids resulted from incorporation of products of IAA catabolism rather than direct binding of IAA itself. Kobayashi & Yamaki (95) treated mung bean hypocotyls with IAA-2-^{14}C and found radioactivity coincident with the tRNA and rRNA fractions on MAK columns. The radioactivity remained with the tRNA after rechromatography on DEAE and BD-cellulose, and IAA-^{14}C could be recovered by alkaline hydrolysis. In an attempt to confirm this work, Davies (26) administered ^{3}H-IAA of high specific activity to light-grown pea stem sections, and separated the phenol-extractable material on MAK columns. No radioactivity was found in the tRNA or rRNA, and preparation of polyribosomes showed that no labeling was associated with the rRNA, mRNA, or tRNA of this fraction. A conflict thus exists between the experimental results obtained in different laboratories, and its resolution must await further work.

NATURAL AUXINS OTHER THAN INDOLEACETIC ACID

Evidence is slowly accumulating for the natural occurrence in some plants of substances that exhibit high auxin activity and yet appear to be nonindolic in chemical structure. For example, Vendrig (260) demonstrated the presence in *Coleus* plants of nonindolic substances with strong auxin activity which he identified as steroid-like compounds on the basis of their chromatographic and chromogenic properties. Khalifah and co-workers reported the isolation of a substance from developing citrus fruits which showed appreciable activity in the oat coleoptile curvature test (89, 117) and was nonindolic in nature (90). Since they could not detect free IAA in citrus fruit extracts, these workers considered that the unknown active substance might be the natural auxin of this tissue, and accordingly they referred to the substance as "citrus auxin." Goren & Goldschmidt (66) found that the auxin system of the citrus fruit was complex and changed in pattern during fruit development. Prominent zones of growth promotion that did not coincide with IAA were present on chromatograms of fruit extracts, and some of these zones were also distinct from Khalifah's citrus auxin. Several auxins were also present in petals and roots, but in young elongating shoots and in the bark and wood of older branches only a single auxin, behaving identically to authentic IAA-2-^{14}C in eight chromatographic solvent systems, could be detected (62). Thus it seems that citrus plants do contain IAA but that several other unknown auxins may also be present, especially in reproductive tissues.

In another approach to the problem of the possible occurrence in plants of auxins other than IAA, Wightman & Rauthan (279) have examined the possibility that phenylalanine might be metabolized in shoot tissues to the auxin, phenylacetic acid (PAA), via a sequence of reactions similar to those involved in the conversion of tryptophan to IAA. Tracer metabolism experiments with excised shoots and cell-free extracts have confirmed that significant amounts of PAA-^{14}C are formed in the shoot tissues of tomato, pea, sunflower, tobacco, barley, and maize plants during the metabolism of phenylalanine-3-^{14}C. Many of the radioactive metabolites formed in tomato shoots have been identified (188), and it appears that the main biosynthetic pathway from phenylalanine to PAA involves the intermediary formation of phenyl-pyruvic acid and phenylacetaldehyde. Bioassay evidence has also been obtained from extracts of unfed tomato and sunflower shoots that PAA occurs naturally in these plants in amounts greater than that of IAA. Since phenylacetic acid has been shown by many workers to exhibit auxin-like activity in a range of vegetative and fruit tissues (for review of literature see 276), the demonstration of the ready formation of this substance from phenylalanine in a range of vegetative shoots may have important implications for further research on the hormonal control of plant growth and development.

CONCLUSIONS

1. IAA has been conclusively shown to be a natural constituent of at least one plant species. There is an urgent need for the application of modern techniques for the separation, identification, and quantitation of this compound.

2. In most plants, IAA is probably synthesized from tryptophan via in-dolepyruvic acid and indoleacetaldehyde, while tryptamine and indoleacetaldoxime may be important intermediates in some species. The relative importance of these alternative pathways is not known.

3. Considerable purifications of tryptophan aminotransferase and amine oxi-dase and lesser purifications of several other enzymes of the pathways have been achieved. Further studies of these enzymes should determine their specificity and, most importantly, may reveal a control mechanism for the biosynthesis of IAA.

4. Many strains of epiphytic bacteria can synthesize IAA. However, experi-ments carried out under sterile conditions have shown that higher plants are capable of the independent synthesis of this compound.

5. IAA oxidase activity is usually associated with various isoenzymes of perox-idase, although at least two IAA oxidases that lack peroxidase activity have been reported.

6. The principal product of the oxidation of IAA appears to be 3-methyleneox-indole, although indolealdehyde is also found. 3-Methyleneoxindole has been as-signed an important role in growth regulation by some authors, while others have found it to be inactive.

7. The oxidation of IAA by horseradish peroxidase appears to involve the formation of Compounds I, II, and III of the enzyme, and indoleacetylperoxy radicals may be important intermediates.

8. The oxidation of IAA is affected by phenolic compounds of both high and low molecular weight, coumarins, manganese, plant acids, and growth hormones. The auxin protector activity of coumarins and some phenols appears to involve the preferential reaction of these compounds with peroxidase Compounds II and III.

9. The metabolism of exogenously supplied IAA by plants results in the formation of many compounds, some of which have been identified as IAA conjugates and others which remain unknown. At least nine naturally occurring IAA conjugates have been isolated from maize seed; the function of these compounds is not known. The question of a direct interaction between IAA and nucleic acids remains controversial.

10. Some plants may contain auxins that are nonindolic in nature, such as phenylacetic acid and citrus auxin.

ACKNOWLEDGMENTS

The authors wish to thank Dr. R. W. Miller of Agriculture Canada for his help in the preparation of this manuscript.

Literature Cited

1. Abeles, F. 1972. *Ann. Rev. Plant Physiol.* 23:259–92
2. Abramovitch, R. A., Ahmed, K. S. 1961. *Nature* 192:259–60
3. Alden, T. 1971. *Physiol. Plant.* 25:54–57
4. Alvarez, M. R., King, D. O. 1969. *Am. J. Bot.* 56:180–86
5. Andreae, W. A., Good, N. E. 1955. *Plant Physiol.* 30:380–82
6. Ballin, G. 1962. *Planta* 58:261–82
7. Ballin, G. 1967. *Flora Jena A* 158:407–12
8. Bandurski, R. S., Ueda, M., Nicholls, P. B. 1969. *Ann. NY Acad. Sci.* 165:655–67
9. Bar-Akiva, A., Sagiv, J. 1969. *Experientia* 25:474–75
10. Basu, P. S., Tuli, V. 1972. *Plant Physiol.* 50:503–6
11. Ibid, 507–9
12. Bayer, M. H. 1969. *Plant Physiol.* 44:267–71
13. Bayer, M. H., Ahuja, M. R. 1968. *Planta* 79:292–98
14. BeMiller, J. N., Colilla, W. 1972. *Phytochemistry* 11:3393–3402
15. Bendana, F. E., Galston, A. W., Kaur-Sawhney, R., Penney, P. J. 1965. *Plant Physiol.* 40:977–83
16. Bentley, J. A., Housley, S. 1952. *J. Exp. Bot.* 3:393–405
17. Berger, J., Avery, G. S. 1944. *Am. J. Bot.* 31:199–203
18. Birecka, H., Galston, A. W. 1970. *J. Exp. Bot.* 21:735–45
19. Black, R. C., Hamilton, R. H. 1971. *Plant Physiol.* 48:603–6
20. Bolduc, R. J., Cherry, J. H., Blair, B. O. 1970. *Plant Physiol.* 45:461–64

21. Borg, D. C. 1965. *Proc. Nat. Acad. Sci. USA* 53:829–36
22. Bourdoux, P., Vandervorst, D., Hootele, C. 1971. *Phytochemistry* 10:1934–35
23. Collet, G. F. 1968. *Can. J. Bot.* 46:969–78
24. Conklin, M. E., Smith, H. H. 1971. *Am. J. Bot.* 58:688–96
25. Dannenburg, W. N., Liverman, J. L. 1957. *Plant Physiol.* 32:263–69
26. Davies, P. J. 1971. *Plant Cell Physiol.* 12:785–89
27. Davies, P. J. 1972. *Physiol. Plant.* 27:262–70
28. Davies, P. J., Galston, A. W. 1971. *Plant Physiol.* 47:435–41
29. de Jong, D. W. 1972. *Plant Physiol.* 50:733–37
30. de Jong, D. W., Olson, A. C., Hawker, K. M., Jansen, E. F. 1968. *Plant. Physiol.* 43:841–44
31. Demorest, D. M., Stahmann, M. A. 1972. *Biochem. Biophys. Res. Commun.* 47:227–33
32. Dullaart, J. 1970. *J. Exp. Bot.* 21:975–84
33. Dye, M. H., Clark, G., Wain, R. L. 1962. *Proc. Roy. Soc. B* 155:478
34. Eliasson, L. 1969. *Physiol. Plant.* 22:1288–1301
35. Endo, T. 1968. *Plant Cell Physiol.* 9:333–41
36. Erdmann, N., Schiewer, U. 1971. *Planta* 97:135–41
37. Evans, J. J. 1968. *Plant Physiol.* 43:1037–41
38. Ibid 1970. 45:66–69
39. Evans, M. L., Rayle, D. L. 1970. *Plant Physiol.* 45:240–43

40. Fawcett, C. H. 1964. *Nature* 204: 1200–1
41. Ferenczy, L., Matkovics, B. 1961. *Acta Biol. Budapest* 12:107–18
42. Fischer, A. 1954. *Planta* 43:288–314
43. Forest, J. C., Wightman, F. 1972. *Can. J. Biochem.* 50:813–29
44. Ibid 1973. 51:332–43
45. Ibid 1974. In press
46. Fox, L. R., Purves, W. K., Nakada, H. I. 1965. *Biochemistry* 4:2754–63
47. Frenkl, C. 1972. *Plant Physiol.* 49: 757–63
48. Fukuyama, T. T., Moyed, H. S. 1964. *J. Biol. Chem.* 239:2392–97
49. Galston, A. W., Bonner, J., Baker, R. S. 1953. *Arch. Biochem. Biophys.* 42: 456–70
50. Galston, A. W., Hillman, W. S. 1961. *Handbuch der Pflanzenphysiologie XIV,* ed. W. Ruhland, 647–70. Berlin, Gottingen, Heidelberg: Springer
51. Galston, A. W., Lavee, S., Siegel, B. Z. 1968. *Biochemistry and Physiology of Plant Growth Substances,* ed. F. Wightman, G. Setterfield, 455–72. Ottawa: Runge. 1642 pp.
52. Gamborg, O. L. 1965. *Can. J. Biochem.* 43:723–30
53. Gaspar, T. 1970. *Physiol. Veg.* 8:641–48
54. Gaspar, T., Khan, A. A., Fries, D. 1973. *Plant Physiol.* 51:146–49
55. Gaspar, T., Verbeek, R., van Onckeen, H. 1969. *Physiol. Plant.* 22:1200–6
56. Gaspar, T., Xhaufflaire, A. 1967. *Planta* 72:252–57
57. Gelinas, D. A. 1973. *Plant Physiol.* 51:967–72
58. Gelinas, D., Postlethwait, S. N. 1969. *Plant Physiol.* 44:1553–59
59. Gibson, R. A., Barrett, G., Wightman, F. 1972. *J. Exp. Bot.* 23:775–86
60. Gibson, R. A., Schneider, E. A., Wightman, F. 1972. *J. Exp. Bot.* 23:381–99
61. Goldacre, P. L. 1951. *Aust. J. Sci. Res. B* 4:293–302
62. Goldschmidt, E. E., Monselise, S. P., Goren, R. 1971. *Can. J. Bot.* 49:241–45
63. Good, N. E., Andreae, W. A. 1967. *Plant Physiol.* 32:561–66
64. Gordon, A. R., Allridge, N. A. 1971. *Can. J. Bot.* 49:1487–96
65. Gordon, S. A. 1956. *The Chemistry and Mode of Action of Plant Growth Substances,* ed. R. L. Wain, F. Wightman, 65–75. London: Butterworths. 312 pp.
66. Goren, R., Goldschmidt, E. E. 1970. *Physiol. Plant.* 23:937–47
67. Green, D. E. 1941. *Mechanisms of Biological Oxidations.* Cambridge Univ. Press
68. Greenwood, M. S., Hillman, J. R., Shaw, S., Wilkins, M. B. 1973. *Planta* 109:369–74
69. Greenwood, M. S., Shaw, S., Hillman, J. R., Ritchie, A., Wilkins, M. B. 1972. *Planta* 108:179–83
70. Haagen-Smit, A. J., Leech, W. D., Bergren, W. R. 1941. *Science* 93: 624–25
71. Haagen-Smit, A. J., Leech, W. D., Bergren, W. R. 1942. *Am. J. Bot.* 29:500–6
72. Hager, A., Schmidt, R. 1968. *Planta* 83:347–71
73. Hamill, D. E., Brewbaker, J. L. 1969. *Physiol. Plant.* 22:945–58
74. Hare, R. C. 1964. *Bot. Rev.* 30:129–65
75. Harmey, M. A., Murray, A. M. 1968. *Planta* 83:387–89
76. Hattori, H., Marumo, S. 1972. *Planta* 102:85–90
77. Heide, O. M. 1967. *Physiol. Plant.* 20:886–902
78. Hill, J. M., Mann, P. J. G. 1964. *Biochem. J.* 91:171–82
79. Hinman, R. L., Lang, J. 1965. *Biochemistry* 4:144–58
80. Hoyle, M. C. 1972. *Plant Physiol.* 50:15–18
81. Imbert, M. P., Wilson, L. A. 1970. *Phytochemistry* 9:1787–94
82. Iwahori, S. 1967. *Plant Cell Physiol.* 8:15–22
83. Jain, M. L., Kadkade, P. G., Van Huysse, P. 1969. *Physiol. Plant.* 22:1038–42
84. Kasinsky, H. E., Hackett, D. P. 1968. *Phytochemistry* 7:1147–50
85. Katsumi, M., Chiba, Y., Fukuyama, M. 1969. *Physiol. Plant.* 22:993–1000
86. Katsumi, M., Sano, H. 1968. *Physiol. Plant.* 21:1348–55
87. Key, J. L., Ingle, J. 1968. See Ref. 51, 711–22
88. Khalifah, R. A. 1967. *Physiol. Plant.* 20:355–60
89. Khalifah, R. A., Lewis, L. N., Coggins, C. W. 1963. *Science* 142:399–400
90. Khalifah, R. A., Lewis, L. N., Coggins, C. W., Radlick, P. C. 1965. *J. Exp. Bot.* 16:511–17
91. Khan, A. A., Gaspar, T., Roe, C. H., Bouchet, M., Dubucq, M. 1972. *Phytochemistry* 11:2963–69
92. Kim, W. K., Rohringer, R. 1969. *Can. J. Bot.* 47:1425–33
93. Kindl, H. 1968. *Hoppe Seyler's Z. Physiol. Chem.* 349:519–20

94. Klämbt, H. 1960. *Naturwissenschaften* 47:398
95. Kobayashi, K., Yamaki, T. 1972. *Plant Cell Physiol.* 13:49–65
96. Ku, H. S., Yang, S. F., Pratt, H. K. 1970. *Plant Physiol.* 45:358–59
97. Kumar, S. A., Mahadevan, S. 1963. *Arch. Biochem. Biophys.* 103:516–18
98. Kutacek, M., Bulgakov, R., Oplistilova, K. 1966. *Biol. Plant.* 8:252–55
99. Kutacek, M., Kefeli, V. I. 1968. See Ref. 51, 127–52
100. Kutacek, M., Kefeli, V. I. 1970. *Biol. Plant.* 12:145–58
101. Kutacek, M., Prochazka, Z. 1964. *Régulateurs naturels de la croissance végétale, C.N.R.S.* Paris 123:445–56
102. Kutacek, M., Prochazka, Z., Grünberger, D., Stajkova, R. 1962. *Collect. Czech. Chem. Commun.* 27:1278–83
103. Labarca, C., Nicholls, P. B., Bandurski, R. S. 1965. *Biochem. Biophys. Res. Commun.* 20:641–46
104. Lanazani, G. A., Galante, E. 1964. *Arch. Biochem. Biophys.* 106:20–24
105. Lane, H. C., King, E. E. 1968. *Plant Physiol.* 43:1699–1702
106. Langrova, V., Sladky, Z. 1971. *Biol. Plant.* 13:361–67
107. Lantican, B. P., Muir, R. M. 1969. *Physiol. Plant.* 22:412–23
108. Larsen, P. 1947. *Nature* 159:842–46
109. Larsen, P., Aasheim, T. 1961. *Plant Growth Regulation,* ed. R. Klein, 43–55. Ames: Iowa State Univ. Press
110. Larsen, P., Rajagopal, R. 1964. See Ref. 101, 221–33
111. Lavee, S., Galston, A. W. 1968. *Plant Physiol.* 43:1760–68
112. Lavee, S., Galston, A. W. 1968. *Am. J. Bot.* 55:890–93
113. Lee, T. T. 1971. *Plant Physiol.* 47:181–85
114. Ibid. 48:56–59
115. Lee, T. T. 1971. *Can. J. Bot.* 49:687–93
116. Lee, T. T. 1972. *Plant Physiol.* 49:957–60
117. Lewis, L. N., Khalifah, R. A., Coggins, C. W. 1965. *Plant Physiol.* 40:500–5
118. Libbert, E., Fischer, E., Drawert, A., Schröder, R. 1970. *Physiol. Plant.* 23:278–86
119. Libbert, E., Kaiser, W., Kunert, R. 1969. *Physiol. Plant.* 22:432–39
120. Libbert, E., Manteuffel, R. 1970. *Physiol. Plant.* 23:93–98
121. Libbert, E., Schröder, R., Drawert, A., Fischer, E. 1970. *Physiol. Plant.* 23:287–93
122. Libbert, E., Silhengst, P. 1970. *Physiol. Plant.* 23:480–87
123. Libbert, E., Wichner, S., Schiewer, U., Risch, H., Kaiser, W. 1966. *Planta* 68:327–34
124. Maclachlan, G. A., Waygood, E. R. 1956. *Can. J. Biochem. Physiol.* 34:1233–50
125. Magnus, V., Iskric, S., Kveder, S. 1971. *Planta* 97:116–25
126. Mahadevan, S. 1963. *Arch. Biochem. Biophys.* 100:557–58
127. Mahadevan, S. 1973. *Ann. Rev. Plant Physiol.* 24:69–88
128. Mahadevan, S., Stowe, B. B. 1972. *Plant Physiol.* 50:43–50
129. Mahadevan, S., Thimann, K. V. 1964. *Arch. Biochem. Biophys.* 107:62–68
130. Mann, P. J. G. 1954. *Biochem. J.* 59:609–20
131. Ibid 1961. 79:623–31
132. Marumo, S., Abe, H., Hattori, H., Munakata, K. 1968. *Agr. Biol. Chem.* 32:117–18
133. Marumo, S., Hattori, H., Abe, H., Munakata, K. 1968. *Nature* 219:959–60
134. Mazza, G., Charles, C., Bouchet, M., Ricard, J., Raynaud, J. 1968. *Biochem. Biophys. Acta* 167:89–98
135. McCune, D. C. 1961. *Ann. NY Acad. Sci.* 94:723–30
136. Meudt, W. J. 1967. *Ann. NY Acad. Sci.* 144:118–28
137. Meudt, W. J. 1972. *Plant Growth Substances 1970,* ed. D. J. Carr, 110–16. Berlin, Heidelberg, New York: Springer. 837 pp.
138. Meudt, W. J., Stecher, K. J. 1972. *Plant Physiol.* 50:157–60
139. Michel, B. 1957. *Plant Physiol.* 32:632–39
140. Miller, R. W., Parups, E. V. 1971. *Arch. Biochem. Biophys.* 143:276–85
141. Miller, R. W., Sirois, J. C. 1974. *Arch. Biochem. Biophys.* In press
142. Misawa, M., Martin, S. M. 1972. *Can. J. Bot.* 50:1245–52
143. Mitchell, E. K., Davies, P. J. 1972. *Plant Cell Physiol.* 13:1135–38
144. Moe, R. 1971. *Physiol. Plant.* 24:374–79
145. Mollan, R. C., Donnelly, D. M. X., Harmey, M. A. 1972. *Phytochemistry* 11:1485–88
146. Moore, T. C. 1969. *Phytochemistry* 8:1109–20
147. Morgan, P. W. 1964. *Plant Physiol.* 39:741–46
148. Morgan, P. W., Joham, H. E., Amin, J. V. 1966. *Plant Physiol.* 41:718–24
149. Morita, Y., Kameda, K., Mizuno, M. 1962. *Agr. Biol. Chem.* 26:442

150. Morris, D. A., Briant, R. E., Thomson, P. G. 1969. *Planta* 89:178–97
151. Moyed, H. S., Tuli, V. 1968. See Ref. 51, 289–300
152. Moyed, H. S., Williamson, V. 1967. *Plant Physiol.* 42:510–14
153. Moyed, H. S., Williamson, V. 1967. *J. Biol. Chem.* 242:1075–77
154. Murray, A., Harmey, M. A. 1970. *Sci. Proc. Roy. Dublin Soc. B.* 2:275.
155. Nicholls, P. B. 1967. *Planta* 72:258–64
156. Norris, R. F. 1966. *Can. J. Bot.* 44:675–84
157. Nougarède, A. 1971. *C. R. Acad. Sci. Paris* 273:864–67
158. Novacky, A., Hampton, R. E. 1968. *Phytochemistry* 7:1143–45
159. Ockerse, R., Waber, J. 1970. *Plant Physiol.* 46:821–24
160. Olney, H. O. 1968. *Plant Physiol.* 43:293–302
161. Olson, A. C., Evans, J. J., Frederick, D. P., Jansen, E. F. 1969. *Plant. Physiol.* 44:1594–1600
162. Pegg, G. F., Selman, I. W. 1959. *Ann. Appl. Biol.* 47:222–31
163. Peisach, J., Blumberg, W. E., Wittenberg, B. A., Wittenberg, J. B. 1968. *J. Biol. Chem.* 243:1871–80
164. Penel, C., Greppin, H. 1972. *Plant Cell Physiol.* 13:151–56
165. Penon, P. et al 1970. *Phytochemistry* 9:73–86
166. Percival, F. W., Purves, W. K., Vickery, L. E. 1973. *Plant Physiol.* 51:739–43
167. Phelps, R. H., Sequeira, L. 1967. *Plant Physiol.* 42:1161–63
168. Phelps, R. H., Sequeira, L. 1968. See Ref. 51, 197–212
169. Phipps, J. 1965. *C. R. Acad. Sci* 261:3864–67
170. Phipps, J. 1966. *Le catabolisme auxinique chez le tabac: ses modalités dans la plante saine, et parasitée par le virus de la mosaïque.* Toulouse: Imprimerie du Commerce
171. Pilet, P. E. 1960. *Physiol. Plant.* 13:766–75
172. Pilet, P. E. 1964. *Phytochemistry* 2:617–21
173. Pilet, P. E. 1964. See Ref. 101, 543–58
174. Pilet, P. E. 1966. *Phytochemistry* 5:77–82
175. Pilet, P. E., Lavanchy, P. 1969. *Physiol. Veg.* 7:19–29
176. Pilet, P. E., Mato, M. C. 1967. *Ann. Physiol. Veg.* 9:369–75
177. Piskornik, Z., Bandurski, R. S. 1972. *Plant Physiol.* 50:176–82
178. Plesnicar, M., Bonner, W. D., Storey, B. T. 1967. *Plant Physiol.* 42:366–70.
179. Raa, J. 1971. *Physiol. Plant.* 25:130–34
180. Racusen, D. 1955. *Arch. Biochem. Biophys.* 58:508–9
181. Rajagopal, R. 1967. *Physiol. Plant.* 20:655–60
182. Ibid, 928–90
183. Ibid 1968. 21:378–85
184. Ibid, 1076–96
185. Ibid 1971. 24:272–81
186. Rajagopal, R., Larsen, P. 1972. See Ref. 137, 102–9
187. Rajagopal, R., Larsen, P. 1972. *Planta* 103:45–54
188. Rauthan, B. S. 1972. *Studies on the biosynthesis of phenylacetic acid in higher plants.* MSc thesis. Carleton Univ., Ottawa
189. Ray, P. M. 1962. *Arch. Biochem. Biophys.* 96:199–209
190. Rayle, D. L., Purves, W. K. 1967. *Plant Physiol.* 42:520–24
191. Ibid, 1091–93
192. Rayle, D. L., Purves, W. K. 1968. See Ref. 51, 153–61
193. Reed, D. J. 1968. See Ref. 51, 243–58
194. Reed, D. J., Moore, T. C., Anderson, J. D. 1965. *Science* 148:1469–71
195. Reigh, D. L., Wender, S. H., Smith, E. C. 1973. *Phytochemistry* 12:1265–68
196. Ricard, J., Mazza, G., Williams, R. J. P. 1972. *Eur. J. Biochem.* 28:566–78
197. Ricard, J., Nari, J. 1966. *Biochim. Biophys. Acta* 113:57–70
198. Ibid 1967. 132:321–29
199. Ridge, I., Osborne, D. J. 1970. *J. Exp. Bot.* 21:843–56
200. Ritzert, R. W., Turin, B. A. 1970. *Phytochemistry* 9:1701–5
201. Rubery, P. H. 1972. *Biochim. Biophys. Acta* 261:21–34
202. Runkova, L. V., Lis, E. K., Tomaszewski, M., Antoszewski, R. 1972. *Biol. Plant.* 14:71–81
203. Sahulka, J. 1970. *Biol. Plant.* 12:191–98
204. Saunders, B. C., Holmes-Siedle, A. G., Stark, B. P. 1964. *Peroxidase.* London: Butterworths. 271 pp.
205. Schaeffer, G. W., Buta, J. G., Sharpe, F. 1967. *Physiol. Plant.* 20:342–47
206. Schafer, P., Wender, S. H., Smith, E. C. 1971. *Plant Physiol.* 48:232–33
207. Scharf, P., Gunther, G. 1970. *Biochem. Physiol. Pflanz.* 161:320–29
208. Schneider, E. 1965. *Studies on the biosynthesis and degradation of 3-indoleacetic acid and gramine in barley shoots.* PhD thesis. Carleton Univ., Ottawa. 237 pp.
209. Schneider, E., Gibson, R. A., Wightman, F. 1972. *J. Exp. Bot.* 23:152–70

210. Schneider, M. J., Troxler, R. F., Voth, P. D. 1967. *Bot. Gaz.* 128:174–79
211. Schraudolf, H. 1965. *Experientia* 21:520
212. Schraudolf, H., Weber, H. 1969. *Planta* 88:136–43
213. Scott, T. K. 1972. *Ann. Rev. Plant Physiol.* 23:235–58
214. Seeley, R. C., Fawcett, C. H., Wain, R. L., Wightman, F. 1956. See Ref. 65, 234–47
215. Sequeira, L., Mineo, L. 1966. *Plant Physiol.* 41:1200–8
216. Shannon, L. 1968. *Ann. Rev. Plant Physiol.* 19:187–210
217. Shantz, E. M. 1966. *Ann. Rev. Plant Physiol.* 17:409–38
218. Sheen, S. J. 1969. *Phytochemistry* 8:1839–47
219. Sheldrake, A. R. 1971. *J. Exp. Bot.* 22:735–40
220. Sherwin, J. E. 1970. *Plant Cell Physiol.* 11:865–72
221. Sherwin, J. E., Purves, W. K. 1969. *Plant Physiol.* 44:1303–9
222. Shukla, P. S., Mahadevan, S. 1968. *Arch. Biochem. Biophys.* 125:873–83
223. Ibid 1970. 137:166–74
224. Siegel, B. Z., Galston, A. W. 1967. *Science* 157:1557–59
225. Sirois, J. C., Miller, R. W. 1972. *Plant Physiol.* 49:1012–18
226. Skoog, F. 1937. *J. Gen. Physiol.* 20:311–34
227. Skytt-Andersen, A., Moller, I. B., Hansen, J. 1972. *Physiol. Plant.* 27:105–8
228. Skytt-Andersen, A., Muir, R. M. 1966. *Physiol. Plant.* 19:1038–48
229. Srivastava, B. I. S. 1964. *Plant Physiol.* 39:781–85
230. Stafford, H. A., Bravinder-Bree, S. 1972. *Plant Physiol.* 49:950–56
231. Steen, I. 1972. *Physiol. Plant.* 26:92–97
232. Still, C. C., Fukuyama, T. T., Moyed, H. S. 1965. *J. Biol. Chem.* 240:2612–18
233. Stonier, T. 1970. *Colloq. Int. C.N.R.S.* 193:423–35
234. Stonier, T., Singer, R. W., Yang, H. M. 1970. *Plant Physiol.* 46:454–57
235. Stonier, T., Yoneda, Y. 1967. *Ann. NY Acad. Sci.* 144:129–35
236. Stowe, B. B., Thimann, K. V. 1954. *Arch. Biochem. Biophys.* 51:499–516
237. Stowe, B. B., Vendrell, M., Epstein, E. 1968. See Ref. 51, 173–82
238. Stutz, R. L. 1958. *Plant Physiol.* 33:207–12
239. Sukanya, N. K., Vaidyanathan, C. S., Mahadevan, S. 1971. *Indian J. Biochem. Biophys.* 8:235–38
240. Takeo, T., Kato, Y. 1971. *Plant Cell Physiol.* 12:217–23
241. Tal, M., Imber, D. 1970. *Plant Physiol.* 46:373–76
242. Taylor, D. M., Morgan, P. W., Joham, H. E., Amin, J. V. 1968. *Plant Physiol.* 43:243–47
243. Thimann, K. V. 1935. *J. Biol. Chem.* 109:279–91
244. Thimann, K. V. 1953. *Arch. Biochem.* 44:242–43
245. Thimann, K. V. 1958. *Plant Physiol.* 33:311–21
246. Thimann, K. V. 1972. *Hormonal Regulation in Plant Growth and Development. Proc. Advan. Study Inst. Izmir 1971*, ed. H. Kaldewey, Y. Vardar, 155–70. Weinheim: Verlag Chem. 524 pp.
247. Thimann, K. V., Grochowska, M. 1968. See Ref. 51, 231–42
248. Thimann, K. V., Mahadevan, S. 1964. *Arch. Biochem. Biophys.* 105:133–41
249. Truelsen, T. A. 1973. *Physiol. Plant.* 28:67–70
250. Tuli, V., Moyed, H. S. 1966. *J. Biol. Chem.* 241:4564–66
251. Tuli, V., Moyed, H. S. 1967. *Plant Physiol.* 42:425–30
252. Tuli, V., Moyed, H. S. 1969. *J. Biol. Chem.* 244:4916–20
253. Ueda, M., Bandurski, R. S. 1969. *Plant Physiol.* 44:1175–81
254. Ueda, M., Ehmann, A., Bandurski, R. S. 1970. *Plant Physiol.* 46:715–19
255. Valdovinos, J. G., Ernest, L. C. 1967. *Physiol. Plant.* 20:682–87
256. Valdovinos, J. G., Ernest, L. C., Perley, J. E. 1967. *Physiol. Plant.* 20:600–7
257. Van der Mast, C. A. 1969. *Acta Bot. Neer.* 18:620–26
258. Ibid 1970. 19:363–73
259. Ibid, 546–59
260. Vendrig, J. C. 1967. *Ann. NY Acad. Sci.* 144:81–93
261. Venis, M. A. 1972. *Plant Physiol.* 49:24–27
262. Vickery, L. E., Purves, W. K. 1972. *Plant Physiol.* 49:716–21
263. Vieitez, E. et al 1967. *Physiol. Plant.* 20:232–44
264. Vlitos, A. J., Most, B. H. 1972. See Ref. 246, 473–86
265. Wakhloo, J. L. 1965. *Planta* 65:301–14
266. Wardrop, A. B. 1957. *Tappi* 40:225–43
267. Weaver, G. M., Jackson, H. O. 1963. *Can. J. Bot.* 41:1405–18
268. Wheeler, A. W. 1968. *J. Exp. Bot.* 19:102–7
269. White, E. P. 1944. *N.Z.J. Sci. Technol. B* 25:137–62

270. Whitmore, F. W. 1971. *Plant Physiol.* 47:169–71
271. Wichner, S., Libbert, E. 1968. *Physiol. Plant.* 21:227–41
272. Ibid, 500–9
273. Wiese, M. V., deVay, J. E. 1970. *Plant Physiol.* 45:304–9
274. Wightman, F. 1962. *Can. J. Bot.* 40:689–718
275. Wightman, F. 1964. See Ref. 101, 191–212
276. Wightman, F. 1973. *Nitrogen Metabolism in Plants.* Biochem. Soc. Symp. 38:247–75
277. Wightman, F., Cohen, D. 1968. See Ref. 51, 273–288b
278. Wightman, F., Fowden, L. 1966. *IUPAC Symp. Chem. Natur. Prod. Stockholm,* 166–67
279. Wightman, F., Rauthan, B. S. 1974. *Plant Growth Substances 1973.* Sci. Counc. Jap. In press
280. Winter, A. 1964. *Arch. Biochem. Biophys.* 106:131–37
281. Winter, A. 1966. *Planta* 71:229–39
282. Yamazaki, E. F., Swindell, R., Reed, D. J. 1970. *Biochemistry* 9:1206–10
283. Yamazaki, H., Yamazaki, I. 1973. *Arch. Biochem. Biophys.* 154:147–59
284. Yamazaki, I., Nakajama, R., Honma, H., Tamura, M. 1968. *Structure and Function of the Cytochromes,* ed. K. Okunuki, M. D. Kamen, I. Sekuzu, 552. Univ. Tokyo Press
285. Yamazaki, I., Piette, L. H. 1963. *Biochim. Biophys. Acta* 77:47–64
286. Yokota, K., Yamazaki, I. 1965. *Biochim. Biophys. Acta* 105:301–12
287. Yoneda, Y., Endo, T. 1969. *Plant Cell Physiol.* 10:235–37
288. Yoneda, Y., Stonier, T. 1967. *Plant Physiol.* 42:1017–20
289. Zenk, M. H. 1961. *Nature* 191:493–94

COMMONWEALTH SCIENTIFIC AND INDUSTRIAL
RESEARCH ORGANIZATION – AUSTRALIA

Ann. Rev. Plant Physiol. 1974. 25:515–39

PHLOEM TRANSPORT: PHYSICAL CHEMICAL OR IMPOSSIBLE

❖7576

Ian F. Wardlaw

CSIRO Division of Plant Industry, Canberra, A.C.T., 2601 Australia

CONTENTS

CHARACTERISTICS OF THE CONDUCTING SIEVE ELEMENTS.................... 516
Sieve Tube Fine Structure 517
Tissue Fixation and Turgor Changes 517
Nature and Properties of Fine Structure 518
Phloem Blockage.. 518
THE METABOLIC CONTROL OF PHLOEM TRANSPORT......................... 519
Vein Loading and Metabolite Retention..................................... 520
Sieve Tube Chemistry... 520
Energy Requirements for Translocation 520
  Electroosmosis. 521
  Protoplasmic Streaming... 521
  Contractile Proteins... 521
Available Energy.. 521
Metabolic Inhibitors 522
Temperature.. 522
SIEVE TUBE WATER RELATIONS... 524
Solute Concentrations... 524
Sieve Tube Pressure and Turgor Gradients 525
Water Movement.. 527
Translocation under Water Stress 528
PATTERNS, PROFILES, AND TRANSPORT ATTRIBUTES 528
Patterns and Profiles.. 529
Bidirectional Movement 529
Speed of Movement... 530
Comparison and Properties of Mobile Material.............................. 530
Viruses 532
SOURCES, SINKS, AND HORMONAL CONTROL OF TRANSPORT................. 533
Response to Sink Removal... 533
Hormonal Control of Transport 534
CONCLUSION 535

The ability of sieve elements to transport sugars and other metabolites from the leaves to areas of plant growth is not in question, and many estimates for fruits and storage organs indicate a carrying capacity of about 20 g sucrose/cm² sieve tube/ hour. The radial thickness of the phloem in a tree is often 1 mm or less, yet the sieve tubes, each around 20 μ in diameter, which together may occupy about half this space, are competent to transfer photosynthate over distances of up to 300 ft. Yet the current trend to explore different possible mechanisms of translocation and the failure to reach general agreement on these is an indication of the inconclusive nature of the data at present available on the phloem transport system. As a consequence there are also considerable gaps in our understanding of how genetic and environmental factors limit growth, how nutrients and growth regulators circulate in plants, and how diseases may spread.

The proposed mechanisms of transport have been detailed in several recent reviews (19, 31, 111) and can be divided into two broad groups: 1. Mechanisms not requiring pathway energy, i.e. "physical" in the sense that movement is controlled directly by inputs and outputs from the sources and sinks, and only requiring metabolic energy along the pathway for maintenance of the conducting tissue. 2. Mechanisms requiring pathway energy, i.e. "chemical" in the sense that energy available from respiration along the pathway is used directly in the transfer of sugars, while the sources and sinks have only a regulatory role. Both these groups can be subdivided further on the basis of a requirement for water movement: (*a*) Mass flow, in which water with metabolites in solution moves through the sieve elements. This includes the "pressure flow" suggested by Münch, "electroosmosis" proposed independently by Spanner and Fensom, and "tubular persistaltic flow" controlled by contractile proteins as described by Thaine and Fensom. (*b*) Limited water flow, in which the overall movement of metabolites may be largely independent of water movement. This is a feature of both "interfacial flow" proposed by van den Honert and "cytoplasmic streaming" advocated by Canny.

It is evident from this brief outline that clarification is needed both of the metabolic control of transport and of the water relations of the sieve elements. For this reason an attempt has been made in the sections that follow to reassess our understanding in these and other areas, such as fine structure and source sink relationships, that are relevant to the mechanism of translocation.

CHARACTERISTICS OF THE CONDUCTING SIEVE ELEMENTS

Many studies have emphasized the problem of relating phloem structure to function, a particularly important aspect of our understanding of the mechanism of translocation. Structural studies are complicated not only by problems of tissue fixation and artifacts caused by the surging of sieve tube contents with sudden turgor changes, but also by the developmental changes that occur as the cell matures and the problem of identifying the cells that are actively transporting assimilates (37, 51). There are often strong disagreements in interpretation of observations on phloem structure, as for example in the case of "transcellular strands" (39, 171, 173), and it may have been a little premature of Siddiqui & Spanner (156) to conclude that "the electron microscrope evidence for sieve tube structure is virtually conclusive against the pressure-flow hypothesis of Münch," and that "the only hypothesis which seems to be consistent with it is the electroosmotic theory."

Many aspects of phloem structure have been excellently summarized in recent reviews by Behnke (4), Eschrich (43), and Weatherley & Johnson (196), and the examples that follow have been selected to illustrate different points of view and to complement these earlier reviews.

Sieve Tube Fine Structure

The nature and extent of the fine structure in sieve elements is still imperfectly understood (30, 196) and probably varies between species. Thus P-protein which occurs either as 240 Å diameter microtubules or as 60 to 150 Å diameter microfilaments, although present in many species, has not been identified in mature sieve elements of barley (49), corn (158), or *Welwitschia* (48). The transcellular strands described by Thaine (171, 172) and von Parker (186) have not received general support (111) and perhaps cannot be considered as universal in sieve tube elements. However, their role in translocation should not be rejected entirely until more is known of fixation techniques and cell preservation. A parietal endoplasmic reticulum, 200-400 Å in diameter, has been identified in most species (32, 160, 196), although Spanner & Jones (162) have suggested that many of the laminar stacks regarded as endoplasmic reticulum are in fact "brush borders" of plasmalemma displaced from the wall, a finding that they feel is relevant to potassium exchange in electroosmosis. This suggestion has been contested by Evert, Eschrich & Eichhorn (50), again emphasizing the problems of interpretation of fine structure.

Tissue Fixation and Turgor Changes

It is clear that fixation procedures must be adapted to accommodate the physical and chemical properties of the sieve elements.

Initial fixation in buffered glutaraldehyde solution, followed by post fixation in osmium tetroxide, has now become a fairly standard procedure instead of the less satisfactory potassium permanganate (86), although Thaine (174) claimed that this has failed to preserve strands of cytoplasm in phloem exudate. Phloem exudates generally have been found with pH values of around 8.0, but with a few exceptions (187) fixatives have been buffered in the pH range from 6.5 to 7.0. If surface charge is critical in the separation of membranes, then variations in pH and ionic balance could affect phloem strands (90) and their arrangement within the lumen.

It is clear that rapid surging, which results in the massive displacement of the structural material within the sieve tube, must be prevented if the sieve tube fine structure is to be accurately described. In many instances an attempt has been made to obtain an osmotic balance by pretreatment of tissue in 0.3 M sucrose, or to stabilize the fine structure by freeze drying prior to fixation, and on occasions the tissue has been fixed on the intact plant (85, 196). A rather drastic treatment used by Siddiqui & Spanner (156, 157) has been to plunge the material into boiling water prior to fixation, while in contrast Evert, Eschrich & Eichhorn (50) found that surging could be minimized quite simply by starving the plant prior to fixation.

Nature and Properties of Fine Structure

Much of the work on the chemical and physical properties of sieve tube contents has centered around the nature of the P-proteins (52, 187, 202). The filamentous protein isolated from *Heracleum* phloem, either by fractionation or in exudate, was shown to have an isoelectric point of 4.9 (209), which would indicate that in a sieve tube at pH 8.0 the protein would be negatively charged. This was substantiated by the observation that pepsin, but not trypsin, digested the fibrillar material in the phloem of tomato and New Zealand spinach (210). Bowling (12, 13) has obtained evidence for a potential gradient of approximately 19 mV across the sieve plates of *Vitis vinifera*. Although this observation apparently supports the concept of electroosmosis, MacRobbie (111) has pointed out that if the protein has a net charge, a displacement of sieve tube contents on cutting could account for the observed sawtooth pattern of potential gradients.

It has been suggested that the movement of sugar through the sieve tubes may be mediated by the action of contractile proteins, and a detailed discussion of the many aspects of this proposal can be seen in the review by MacRobbie (111). Probably one of the earliest suggestions for a system of this nature came from Kuo & Lou (100), but more recently attention has been focused on the models proposed by Hejnowicz (78), Thaine (174), and Fensom (53). Although a similarity has been seen between P-protein microtubules and actin-like contractile protein (129), studies on response to temperature, vinblastine, colchicine, heavy meromysin subfragment 1, and cytochalasin B (93, 153, 206, 207) lend little support to this suggestion. Also, as mentioned earlier, there are some plants in which P-protein would appear to be entirely absent from the mature sieve elements.

Phloem Blockage

It has been suggested that the slow movement of ^{14}C-assimilates in *Laminaria* (154) in comparison with *Macrocystis* (134, 135) could be related to the smaller sieve plate pores in *Laminaria* (211), although there is no direct evidence for such an association. Weatherley & Johnson (196) point out that with sieve tubes of radius 12 μ carrying a 10% sugar solution at 100 cm h^{-1} a pressure gradient of 0.25 atm m^{-1} is to be expected, but this gradient will be increased by an additional 0.32 atm m^{-1} with the inclusion of 60 sieve plates per centimeter, each 0.5 μ thick and with pores of radius 2.5 μ. A series of parallel filaments, each 100 Å thick and separated by 200 Å, passing through the pores, even with only 20 plates per centimeter, would result in a pressure drop of 280 atm m^{-1}, which is untenable for mass flow. Tammes, van Die & Ie (170) have taken up this question of sieve tube blockage and pressure flow in *Yucca flaccida*. From measurements of the rate of exudation of a 16% sucrose solution at the cut surface of the inflorescence stalk they estimated a speed of movement of 44 cm h^{-1}. In *Yucca* with sieve plates set at an oblique angle the total pore area is slightly larger than the lumen. With fully unobstructed pores it was estimated that a linear velocity of 128 cm h^{-1} would occur with a pressure drop of 1 atm over a length of 100 cm. If the pores were traversed by 250 Å filaments 1000 Å apart, the pressure drop over 1 m becomes 5.6 atm, which the authors feel would be reasonable for the exuding inflorescence stalk with an apparent pressure drop of 16 atm. Thus a knowledge of the actual separation and spacial arrangement of the filaments both in the sieve tube lumen and within the sieve plate pores is important in our understanding of solution flow in this system. The demonstration of flow or particle movement through sieve plates with extreme pressure gradients (167, 185) does not appear to have relevance to the intact system.

Early in their development sieve tubes do have a cytoplasmic component with a complex network of membranes and organelles, and evidence has been presented by Kollmann (96, 97) and Kollmann & Dörr (98) that the translocation of photosynthate may occur in the youngest phloem cells adjacent to the cambium in *Metasequoia glyptostroboides* and *Juniperus communis*. In these experiments actively transporting sieve tubes were identified by microautoradiography of frozen dried tissue following the uptake of $^{14}CO_2$ by the leaves, and also by locating the stylet position of actively feeding aphids. However, even these results have been subject to dispute (31, 51), based on the location and identification of mature sieve elements and the characteristics of functional stylets.

Another related topic which warrants special consideration is the formation of callose around sieve plate pores and the effect that this has on phloem transport. The classical example usually discussed is the deposition of callose in the phloem of trees that overwinter and its disappearance as sugar transport recommences in the spring, prior to the formation of new sieve elements (196). Cause and effect have not necessarily been separated in this instance, in that reduced translocation may have resulted in callose formation. Currier & Webster (34) found that although ultrasonic treatment induced callose formation in cotton phloem, growth was not affected. Also, callose deposits induced in *Cucurbita* by injecting the petioles with boron failed to reduce the transport of ^{14}C-labeled assimilates or fluorescein (44). However, in this latter experiment there was some evidence for greater accumulation and lateral movement at the site of the block. In contrast it was found that there was a good relationship between callose formation and disappearance in response to high temperatures and the translocation of assimilates through the stem of cotton (114, 115). Since some callose was always evident in untreated plants, and partial callose blocking did not result in reduced transport, it was suggested that quite severe restrictions were necessary to inhibit transport. More information on the relation between pore size as modified by callose and the rate of translocation of assimilates could provide useful information in studies on the mechanism of translocation.

THE METABOLIC CONTROL OF PHLOEM TRANSPORT

It is difficult to determine exactly how the energy available to a cell is partitioned between those factors required for maintenance and specialist activities such as nectary secretion and starch storage. It is certainly not clear how much if any of the energy available to the phloem is directly responsible for the movement of sugars through the sieve elements.

Vein Loading and Metabolite Retention

A special characteristic of the sieve elements is their ability to accumulate specific metabolites (101, 126) against a concentration gradient (152, 177) and to retain these effectively during translocation. There appear to be similar energy requirements for vein loading both in the leaf and along the path of transport (6, 7, 178, 181). Brovchenko (14, 15) concluded that there was at least a partial breakdown of sucrose prior to its entry into the minor veins of sugar beet, although Hatch & Glasziou (77) found that this did not occur in sugar cane leaves. Recently, from studies based on aphid stylet exudates, Gardener & Peel (59) have proposed that sucrose may enter the sieve elements of willow either by direct loading from the free space via the companion cells (a movement involving the splitting of sucrose), or indirectly through storage parenchyma where phosphorylation reactions may be involved.

To some extent the exchange of assimilates along the pathway of transport is dependent on factors such as maturity of the tissue (63), its ability to photosynthesize (188, 193), and the demand for or supply of assimilates elsewhere in the plant (144, 191), i.e. the establishment of a lateral gradient. One consequence of the ability of the sieve elements to retain metabolites actively is that the pattern of movement of assimilates through the plant is in part governed by vascular connections (190).

Sieve Tube Chemistry

Although the role of the companion cell in sieve tube function is often mentioned, attempts to relate metabolism to sugar movement have been concerned largely with the sieve tube. Sieve element biochemistry has been reviewed specifically by Eschrich (43) and more generally by Crafts & Crisp (31). Many enzymes, including ATPase, have been identified by histochemistry (99, 100). In the sieve cells of *Cucurbita maxima,* ATPase activity is associated with cell surfaces, P-protein, and cell wall regions, while in veins of the leaf heavy deposits of ATPase can be observed in the wall between the sieve elements and companion cells, which suggests an association with vein loading (65). A wide range of enzymes and high levels of ATP have been detected in sieve tube exudates (45, 58, 60, 89). However, the observation by Lehmann (103) that enzymes may move from the companion cells into sieve tubes or exudates in response to cutting indicates that caution is needed in the interpretation of many enzyme distribution studies.

The presence of enzymes and ATP is by itself not evidence for the metabolic control of transport, although their absence could be an argument against it. However, metabolism is also implicated in cell maintenance, as even in "enucleate" sieve cells there may be some protein synthesis (128). Also, one group of enzymes, the acid phosphatases, could be important in the rapid formation of callose produced in response to injury (43).

Energy Requirements for Translocation

With many of the proposed mechanisms of transport, estimates have been made of the energy required to maintain the known rates of specific mass transfer. For purposes of comparison, Weatherley & Johnson (196) extended their calculations on the pressure gradients associated with mass flow through sieve elements to obtain an estimate of energy expenditure. This indicated that an available energy supply of 0.05 g glucose/day/cm³ sieve tube would allow a flow of 100 cm hr⁻¹ with a pressure gradient of 3.3 atm cm⁻¹ through a willow sieve element.

ELECTROOSMOSIS This mechanism has been discussed in some detail by MacRobbie (111) in relation to the recent papers by Tyree & Fensom (179) and Spanner (161). In addition to commenting on the problem of K^+ recycling and the apparent need for a high K^+ flux across the side walls of sieve tube elements, MacRobbie (111) calculated that sieve cells 500 μ in length would require half the available ATP to recycle the K^+, but if only 100 μ long they would require twice the available ATP, and these values do not take into account ATP required for processes other than transport. Tyree & Fensom (179), in calculating the energy dissipation required to move a 1 cm³ volume of sap a distance of 1 m at 80 cm hr⁻¹, based on electrical and hydraulic conductivities and an index of ion sap interaction, estimated that this value was 1000 times greater than the energy stored in the sucrose being translocated.

PROTOPLASMIC STREAMING Canny (18) calculated that the required energy supply needed for streaming rates of 50 cm hr⁻¹, i.e. acceptable for a mechanism of streaming in transcellular strands, would amount to 1.6 mg sucrose per cm³ of sieve tube sap, which compares favorably with the experimental value of 50 mg of sucrose cm⁻³ day⁻¹.

CONTRACTILE PROTEINS Aikman & Anderson (1) estimated that to maintain a flow of 10% sucrose solution along microtubules, due to a peristaltic action controlled by contractile proteins, 1.5×10^{-3} moles of sucrose m⁻³ sec⁻¹ would be utilized in providing the necessary energy, an estimated 2% of the sucrose being transported. For a somewhat more intricate system, Fensom (53) estimated that the energy dissipation of the microtubule system would require an input of 4.5×10^{-3} g sucrose cm⁻² hr⁻¹ per centimeter length of sieve tube. The energy dissipation for the complementary volume flow would be less than 1×10^{-4} g sucrose cm⁻² hr⁻¹ per centimeter length of sieve tube, again well within the capacity of the system.

Available Energy

The mitochondria of conducting bundles in sugar beet petioles have a high level of oxidative phosphorylation in comparison with the parenchyma, and low levels of DNP were found to stimulate O_2 uptake (133). However, there are relatively few experiments that provide quantitative data on the energy available within the transport system. Duloy & Mercer (36) recorded a respiration rate for the isolated vascular tissue of *Cucurbita pepo* of about 2000 μl O_2/g fresh weight/hr, while in grapevine Canny & Markus (21) obtained values for CO_2 evolution of 220 to 230 μl/g fresh weight/hr, which were in agreement with the earlier work on *Pelargonium* and *Heracleum*. However, Crafts & Crisp (31) have criticized respiratory measurements on isolated plant parts because of possible injury responses. From measurements of $^{14}CO_2$ respired during the transport of ^{14}C assimilates through the petiole of vine, Canny (16) estimated that the breakdown of translocated sucrose was about 0.5 mg cm^{-3} of phloem per hour, or 0.3 to 5.0% of the sugar passing through the petiole.

Metabolic Inhibitors

The main concern in the use of locally applied inhibitors has been in relation to their penetration and localization at the point of application. Inconsistent results have been obtained with dinitrophenol (DNP), which uncouples oxidative phosphorylation (74, 151). The respiratory inhibitor cyanide can be extremely mobile and in many instances where translocation has been stopped may have acted via the assimilating source leaf. However, careful experimentation does suggest that cyanide can act in a reversible manner directly on the conducting pathway (79). Cyanide treatments may result in callose formation in sieve elements (182); however, as it was shown that recovery of translocation on removal of the inhibitor was not associated with a concurrent reduction in the levels of callose, it would seem that the initial stoppage was not the result of callose blockage. Qureshi & Spanner (151) found no evidence for callose formation in *Saxifraga* stolons in response to DNP concentrations (5 X 10^{-3} *M*) that prevented translocation.

Gardner & Peel (60) examined the effect of various metabolic inhibitors on the rate of exudation of sugars and ATP from aphid stylets inserted in willow bark strips. Both DNP (10^{-4} *M*) and oligomycin (20 μg/ml) caused a sudden drop in exudation without any prior change in ATP levels, and the effect was reversed on removal of the inhibitors. Sodium floride (10^{-3} *M*), which inhibits glycolysis, had an erratic effect on exudation, and in only two out of nine effective experiments did ATP concentration fall prior to the effect on exudation. From these results the authors tentatively suggest that ATP formed by oxidative phosphorylation may only indirectly influence translocation. Reduced oxygen levels failed to modify the transport of fluorescein in *Pelargonium* (180); however, it is possible that tissue oxygen levels were inadequately reduced, and Qureshi & Spanner (150) did obtain an effect of nitrogen flushing on the movement of ^{137}Cs and ^{14}C assimilates through the stolon of *Saxifraga*. Sij & Swanson (159) obtained a transient reduction in assimilate movement through the petiole of squash when this was flushed with nitrogen, and in agreement with Gardner & Peel (60) they concluded that energy was required only for maintenance of the sieve elements. A further depression in these latter experiments after 24 hr of low oxygen was associated with permanent damage to the petiole.

Temperature

As a metabolic inhibitor, temperature has the advantage that penetration can always be ensured and spread from the site of application easily monitored.

Early evidence suggested that transport was stopped at low temperature (0-3°C) (175) and that there was in fact an optimum temperature for translocation (199). More recently it has come to be accepted that the response to a localized cold block may be transient (61, 200), or that temperature may have little direct effect on translocation (193). In the latter experiment it was considered that a 2 cm cold zone was adequate to observe a reduction in the speed of movement of assimilates, but the insensitivity of transport to temperature has since been reconfirmed for the movement of ^{32}P through a 10 cm cold zone (2°C) on the stem of wheat. However, although there is no clear effect of temperature on the longitudinal transport of assimilates, there is a marked effect on lateral transfer and radial movement (57, 166, 193).

There is the possibility of a homeostatic adjustment of energy-releasing processes at low temperature (61), or a change in concentration gradient across the temperature block. The latter does not appear to account for the recovery in Canada thistle observed by Bayer (see 61) or the lack of response in *Lolium temulentum* (193). The failure of Coulson & Peel (29) to observe a falloff in the respiratory loss of ^{14}C at low temperatures during the transport of ^{14}C-labeled assimilates, although suggesting that respiration of the conducting system was insensitive to temperature, could be confounded by an effect of temperature on the availability of respiratory substrates from different parts of the phloem. Subsequently Coulson et al (28) noted that although translocation through the petiole of sugar beet at 0.7 to 2.5°C returned to normal rates in 2 to 3 hr, there was no recovery of respiration (10% of controls) and no apparent change in petiole ATP levels (0.7 nmoles/10 mg petiole fresh weight). The authors concluded from their estimates of ATP and respiration in relation to sugar movement that the energy available reflected the requirement for structural maintenance and was inadequate for sugar translocation. In a detailed study of temperature effects, Giaquinta & Geiger (64) noted that above a critical temperature of 10°C for bean and 0°C for sugar beet, the effect of temperature on the rate of mass transfer and speed of movement of ^{14}C assimilates was consistent with the response of a physical process and to be expected from changes in viscosity of sugar solutions. In sugar beet even the initial "physical" response was transient and disappeared after 90 min. In bean the petiole respiration showed a Q_{10} of about 3.85 over the entire temperature range of 0 to 25°C, unlike assimilate velocity and mass transfer with Q_{10} values of 1.1 and 1.3 respectively in the range 10 to 25°C, and a dramatic increase below 10°C. The apparent diffusion coefficient for assimilate movement in bracken with a Q_{10} of 2.95, determined by Whittle (203), is not strictly comparable in this instance, as the temperature of the whole plant was altered and the response could well be an indirect one due to growth. Giaquinta & Geiger (64), using freeze substitution techniques, also noted that quite distinct structural changes occurred in the sieve elements of bean at low temperatures. At 25°C the sieve plate pores were apparently open, while after a 30-min treatment at 0°C the pores were found to be plugged with cytoplasmic material. This observation should be kept in mind when considering the effect of metabolic inhibitors on transport, where the only work on blockage has been in relation to callose formation.

The ability of the conducting system to function adequately at low temperatures, the failure to obtain consistent evidence with metabolic inhibitors, and the apparent lack of available energy for more than "maintenance" requirements in some systems suggests that the movement of assimilates is not directly influenced by metabolism in the sieve elements or surrounding cells.

SIEVE TUBE WATER RELATIONS

Several early studies on translocation analyzed assimilate movement into actively growing organs such as fruits and tubers and relied on reasonable estimates of the concentration of solute to estimate the speed of movement of assimilates through the conducting system (31). Implicit in this type of calculation was the premise that all the sieve tubes were functional and that there was a mass movement of both water and sucrose, although it was impossible to test this directly. With the advent and use of radioactive tracers, more direct estimates indicate that a speed of movement of 250 cm hr^{-1} is possible (31), but a value of half or even one fifth of this would be acceptable. This would mean that the sucrose concentration in the sieve elements of the potato stolon, based on the observation of tuber growth by Dixon & Ball (see 194), could be in the range of 20 to 50% and not 10% as originally suggested.

Solute Concentrations

The concentration of solutes in a sieve element has been determined directly from phloem exudates or from plasmolytic studies and estimates of specific mass transfer.

(i) Phloem exudates commonly contain 10 to 25% dry matter, about 90% of which is soluble sugars (31). However, it is clear that no fixed value can be assumed, and extremes may range from almost no sucrose in willow plants kept in the dark to 50% when a 25% solution is passed through the xylem (197). Normal seasonal variation of sugar concentrations in willow is apparently in the range 5 to 25% (143). Exudation from sieve elements has been used as an argument in favor of mass flow (31, 196), but it would also appear valid to suggest that any longitudinal transfer of sugar, no matter what the mechanism, could result in exudation of solution over a prolonged period with lateral movement of the water from the adjacent free space. This also raises the possibility, suggested by Zimmermann (213), that exudates from cut surfaces underestimate the sugar concentration in the intact sieve tube, and there is some support for this contention in the observed rapid movement of THO laterally through the bark of willow to an exuding stylet (141). The "effective length" of phloem supplying a willow aphid feeding on a sieve element, beyond which blockage has no effect on exudation, can be lengthened from about 16 cm up to 40 cm by applying an additional pressure gradient of 4 atm through the xylem (138). These values may represent the volume of storage tissue required to maintain an adequate supply of assimilates, but they may also indicate the limit of mass flow through the sieve elements for a particular drop in pressure.

(ii) Plasmolysis experiments, although suggesting a means of estimating sugar concentrations in situ, are difficult to carry out in practice because the sieve tubes are generally not readily accessible for observation without a major disturbance to the surrounding tissues. Currier, Esau & Cheadle (33) found that 0.5 and 1.0 M sucrose were sufficient to plasmolyze the sieve elements of some species, while in dormant *Vitis* 2.0 M sucrose was necessary; but the exact relation between sugar concentrations and plasmolysis is a little uncertain from the above experiments. However, Geiger et al (62), using freeze substitution techniques for fixation of the plasma membrane, observed that plasmolysis in both the sieve elements and companion cells of the sugar beet leaf resulted from bathing in 1.0 to 1.1 M mannitol, which suggests an osmotic potential of about 30 atm.

(iii) The only published analysis of sugar movement based on specific mass transfer that is complete enough to allow an estimate of sieve tube sugar concentration is that of Geiger, Saunders & Cataldo (63). Transfer through the petiole of sugar beet was found to be 4.8 g dry wt/cm^2 sieve tube/hr, moving at a speed of 54 cm/hr (estimated from the movement of ^{14}C assimilates) and indicated a concentration of 8.9 g sucrose/100 cm^3 of sieve tube volume, which compares favorably with a sieve tube exudate concentration of 8.8% (wt/vol) determined separately. This last comparison suggests that dilution of exudates by the lateral movement of water may not always be an important consideration. Similar estimates, based on specific mass transfer rates, have been made on the leaves of several grass species and in *Chloris* concentrations could be as high as 38% (wt/vol) (110).

The similarity of maximum values recorded for specific mass transfer (20 g dry wt/cm^2 sieve tube/hr) has led to the suggestion that this may represent an upper limit to the carrying capacity of the phloem. However, Passioura & Ashford (private communication) have observed values up to 200 g/cm^2 sieve tube/hr in wheat dependent on a restricted root system.

Sieve Tube Pressure and Turgor Gradients

Although assimilate movement appears to be controlled by sugar gradients from source to sink (31, 111), the evidence is not clear whether this movement is also in the direction of a turgor pressure gradient within the sieve tube system.

(i) Solute concentrations, as mentioned earlier, can range from 5 to 50% (wt/vol), and Mittler (119, 120) estimated that a pressure of 20 to 40 atm would be required to maintain a sap flow of 1 to 3 mm^3 hr^{-1} through a willow aphid stylet 1.8 mm long and ranging in radius from 0.6 μ at the distal end to 1.8 μ near the head. This calculated potential is not strictly in agreement with the osmotic potential of exudates from the severed stylets.

It has been suggested by Eschrich (40, 43) that callose may have a variable water holding capacity dependent on the level of Ca^{2+} and may play a part in regulating turgor pressure within the sieve element, but this effect requires more direct confirmation. With the recent work on the role of K$^+$ as an osmoticum in regulating stomatal movements in leaves (56, 83), it is possible that K$^+$ could also play a role in the water relations of the sieve tube, with malate the balancing anion (71). Again the evidence is slight, but Hoad & Peel (82) found that there was an inverse relation between sugar and potassium levels in the sieve elements of willow bark.

(ii) Pressure gradients down the length of a conducting system are difficult to establish experimentally, largely because of the inaccessibility of the sieve elements and the fact that turgor is a product of osmotic potential within the cell and water potential outside the cell, each with its own independent gradient. This interaction can be seen best in aphid stylet exudate studies where increased xylem pressures enhance exudation (145) and the addition of an osmoticum to the xylem decreases the volume of exudation (197). Also, the rates of phloem exudation are sensitive to variation in both transpiration (144) and root moisture stress (72, 119).

Kaufmann & Kramer (88) attempted to measure both the water potential and osmotic potential of the bark of yellow poplar and red maple at different heights. Their results indicated that although the osmotic potential of the phloem fell with height, this was balanced by a characteristic drop in water potential (less negative) towards the base of the tree. There is some difficulty, however, in accepting their measurements of osmotic potentials as these were based on the whole of the phloem and may or may not be representative of the sieve tubes. An attempt was made by Hammel (73) to measure sieve tube turgor directly in the bark of red oak by inserting a hollow needle attached to a calibrated closed capillary into the secondary phloem. This is similar in principle to the direct manometric measurements of turgor pressure in *Nitella* made by Green & Stanton (66). The mean gradient down the trunk represented a drop in pressure of 1 to 2 atm for a distance averaging 4.8 meters, which is on the borderline of acceptability for a mass flow of sugar solution over this distance (196). Hammel's (73) measurements of turgor show considerable variation and are clearly influenced by factors like transpiration. In stating that "It is not certain that the turgor pressure gradients in each section of the phloem system were adequate to account for a flux, even under the most favorable pressure gradients," he was far more cautious about the significance of his results in relation to a mechanism of mass flow than were Crafts & Crisp (31). Should pressure flow be occurring in trees, the present data would argue in favor of a slow speed of movement, and this is supported by the evidence of Canny, Nairn & Harvey (22), who concluded from tracer studies that assimilate movement in *Acer* occurs at about 2 cm hr^{-1}. Zimmermann (214), who unlike Canny has argued in favor of a pressure flow mechanism, estimated higher rates of 30 to 70 cm hr^{-1} for American ash based on time course studies of the ratios of transportable sugars with height.

In a recent paper Eschrich, Evert & Young (46) questioned the necessity for a pressure gradient down the sieve tubes to drive a mass flow of solution in response to a sugar concentration gradient, their main contention being that for the nonequilibrium situation of a moving front of sugar solution in a semipermeable tube, water inflow will occur behind the front in response to an osmotic potential gradient and move out through the membrane ahead of the front in response to the hydrostatic potential gradient, resulting in little pressure difference between the ends of the tube. Weatherley (195) has challenged this assessment of mass flow in response to a sugar concentration gradient, but has defined a system that does not appear to take account of the semipermeability of the conducting element. However, the argument tends to be academic in relation to the actual presence or absence of pressure gradients in the conducting system; as with any solution flow through a small tube, gradients of hydrostatic pressure will be established as a consequence of frictional resistance. One area where this proposal would appear to be relevant is in relation to the detection of solution flow using tritiated water, where lateral displacement and cycling of THO could be misleading. Certainly further thought is needed on the properties of mass flow through very small diameter semipermeable tubes where sugar is being continuously supplied and removed.

Water Movement

In all but a few of the proposed mechanisms of translocation, sugar would move in solution with water over long distances, and detection of water movement would be an argument in favor of this mass flow. As was discussed earlier, the significance of sieve tube exudation should be considered only as circumstantial evidence until it can be shown more directly that the water actually moves over long distances.

Direct evidence: Tritiated water (THO) has been used as a tracer for water movement in phloem tissue, but unfortunately it has failed to yield clear-cut evidence either for or against mass flow. Much of this work has been discussed by Crafts & Crisp (31) and MacRobbie (111), but perhaps the most detailed analysis has been that of Choi & Aronoff (26), who showed that following the uptake of THO by the leaflet of soybean, tritium-labeled sugars were readily translocated, but the THO profile virtually ceased a few centimeters from the feeding chamber. These authors concluded that the THO profile was consistent with self-diffusion of water through the petiole and not mass flow of water through the sieve tubes with lateral exchange of THO. This conclusion has since been challenged by Cataldo et al (24), based on the validity of the use by Choi & Aronoff of the constant for THO diffusion through water, rather than the permeability of the sieve tube wall to water, in determining lateral exchange. Although this modification would indicate that movement could have been by mass flow, it would appear that the profiles obtained by Choi & Aronoff still could be the result of diffusion, so the problem has not been resolved. Cataldo, Christy & Coulson's (23) supplementary data need further ratification, and in any further studies it would be of value to know what effect an increased demand for photosynthate would have on both the THO and ^{14}C-assimilate profiles.

In a series of experiments using bark strips from willow, Peel et al (141) failed to obtain evidence even after 8 hr for the movement of THO through the sieve elements to an aphid stylet about 8 cm from the site of application, though ^{14}C-sucrose and ^{32}PO$_4$ applied simultaneously were evident in the exudate within 1 hr. Subsequently Peel (139) noted that when gradients of ^{35}S, ^{32}P, and THO were established in segments of willow stems, the specific activity of ^{35}S and ^{32}P in the exudate from a stylet situated at the end of the segment with the greater activities could be raised by ringing the bark to isolate the low activity end of the segment, although it had no effect on the level of THO in the exudate. This evidence further suggested that while metabolites could move longitudinally through the bark, the water for exudation was derived from the immediate vicinity of the stylet and not by concurrent movement with the assimilates. There is a need to evaluate, for this system, the losses of THO that will occur by diffusion through the membrane and by exchange of tritium with hydrogen. Allowing for the exchange envisaged by Cataldo et al (24) it would appear that THO is unlikely to be evident within 8 hrs in the exudate from a stylet 8 cm from the source, on the basis of a mass flow of solution at 8 cm hr^{-1} in a sieve element 23 μ in diameter (Mrs. I. Sofield, personal communication).

Indirect evidence: By following the pattern of *heat transfer* from a 1 mm zone on the isolated bundle of *Heracleum,* Ziegler & Vieweg (212) concluded that a mass flow of solution was occurring in the sieve elements in the expected direction of assimilate utilization. However, their estimate of the speed of movement based on a test system in which fluorescein migrated along strands of hemp needs further justification. A second indirect method (204) in which evaluation of the movement of phloem mobile and xylem mobile nutrients has been used to analyze the patterns of water movement in sprouting potato tubers has been used by Wiersum. The evidence is only correlative and probably would be meaningful only if a negative result had been obtained.

Translocation under Water Stress

According to van den Honert (183), one reason for doubting the hypothesis of mass flow as proposed by Münch was the observation that nitrogenous substances were rapidly transported out of wilted petals. More recently it has been possible to demonstrate the rapid translocation of photosynthate under water stress conditions that cause the wilting of leaves (189, 191), although this is dependent on maintaining the demand for assimilates. The transfer of assimilates through the peduncle to the ear in wheat can occur actively when the relative water content of the leaves and stem tissue has fallen as low as 60% (192), which may be equated with a water potential of –20 to –30 atm (208). It was first felt that the result was an argument against mass flow of sugar solutions in the phloem (189), and it is clear that exudation from sieve elements is sensitive to xylem water potentials. However, further consideration suggests that in a closed system pressure gradients could be maintained in the sieve tube system under water stress as long as xylem water potentials are increased more or less uniformly between the source and the sink. In this regard the response of exudates to water stress is probably not typical of the intact system, and movement will be limited only when the xylem water potential is greater than the osmotic potential of the sieve element and plasmolysis occurs. Thus the observation that transport can occur under a plant water deficit of about 20 to 30 atm suggests that the osmotic potential of the sieve elements is greater than this. Also, the concept of concurrent water and solute movement through the sieve element into expanding tissue must be treated with caution when it is realized that under water stress extension growth is reduced more than the supply of carbohydrates (191).

PATTERNS, PROFILES, AND TRANSPORT ATTRIBUTES

It is self-evident that for a compound to be phloem-mobile it must readily enter the conducting elements. However, not all those compounds listed by Crafts & Crisp (31) as present in the phloem are necessarily translocated in significant amounts (31, Table 6.1). It is generally conceded that the hexose sugars, glucose and fructose, are minor components of the sugar fraction (177), and the evidence is not very good for some of the sugar or organic phosphates that have been identified in phloem (8). Also, although protein and enzymes are identified in some exudates, they may be immobile in the intact system. Phloem mobility of nitrogen, phosphorus, and potassium, as well as many of the minor elements (67, 68, 136), is implied by their remobilization from the leaves following an initial uptake by the roots. However, more direct evidence has come from time course studies using radioactive tracers to define the nature of the translocated material (8, 201), and in this way Clauss, Mortimer & Gorham (27) obtained evidence for the mobility of sucrose, serine, and glycine through the petiole of soybean.

Patterns and Profiles

Following the application of radioactive tracer to one part of a plant (typically a leaf), it is possible to analyze and describe mathematically the pattern of distribution of radioactivity both with distance from the point of application and with time from application. In doing this it is hoped that some of the characteristics of transport may be defined and clarified in relation to mechanisms. Canny (19) and MacRobbie (111) recently have reviewed the theoretical aspects and interpretation of experimental profiles so that little detail needs to be added here.

Tracer movement through the conducting system will depend on a number of features, including the time course output from the leaf (source), speed and direction of movement of the carrier system, exchange between the moving and stationary phases (including lateral transfer to adjacent cells), and retardation effects due to the physical dimensions and chemical attributes of both the transport system and the mobile material. MacRobbie (111) has entered arguments in favor of a mass flow of solution based on a correspondence between input and output of tracer along a conducting pathway, similarity of ^{14}C-time profiles with distance, uniform velocity with distance, and a steady rate of solution flow as indicated by exudation from aphid stylets.

Kinetic studies have provided a useful guide to the problems of translocation, but they have been limited to some extent because they have relied too much on a wide range of published data instead of experiments specifically designed for analysis, in which the factors known to be associated with transport such as source and sink activity and lateral transfer rates are varied. In line with this, Canny (19) has suggested that specific mass transfer between comparable sources and sinks should be measured when the distance between these is varied, although no experimental system was suggested.

Bidirectional Movement

Evidence for the movement of metabolites simultaneously in two directions within a single sieve element would be a strong argument against many of the proposals relating to mass flow. However, evidence that appears to support bidirectional movement is inconclusive and subject to alternative explanations (111), such as lateral transfer between elements conducting in opposite directions (41, 176) or movement to a common sink, such as an aphid stylet, from opposite directions (20, 80). Peterson & Currier (147) concluded that individual bundles of *Vicia faba* conducted K-fluorescein and ^{14}C unidirectionally, although movement through different bundles could be in opposite directions. This is similar to the observations made by Bonnemain (9) on differences in the direction of movement of ^{14}C assimilates in the internal and external phloem of tomato. More recently, Qureshi & Spanner (149) concluded that the movement of cesium along the stolon of *Saxifraga*, although nonpolar, was unidirectional and the direction could be changed by altering the source/sink relationships.

Speed of Movement

Estimates of the speed of movement of assimilates through the phloem extend up to 7200 cm hr^{-1}, but generally fall in the range 2 to 250 cm hr^{-1} (31). The difficulties in using radioactive tracers to measure speed of movement have been discussed adequately by Canny (17), but if lateral exchange along the pathway is small and the demand for assimilates reasonably high, a mean speed can be estimated by following the progress of a tracer profile with distance from the site of application (122, 188). Movement of the front of activity away from the site of application with time, although unsatisfactory in theory, can also be used as a rough estimate in some situations (22, 111, 112). Nelson, Perkins & Gorham (127) proposed a dual transport mechanism based on the observation of a slow moving component (100 cm hr^{-1}) and a rapid moving component (7200 cm hr^{-1}) in soybean; however, this rapid movement was challenged by Canny (17), and Moorby, Ebert & Evans (122) failed to obtain any evidence for this in soybean using ^{11}C as a tracer. More recently, Fensom (53) has proposed a mechanism involving three concurrent pathways of movement, including a small but rapid surface mobile component, to account for the data he obtained following the injection of tracers into isolated phloem strands of *Heracleum*.

Comparison and Properties of Mobile Material

An important aspect of transport that needs further clarification are the properties of different metabolites that enhance or inhibit their phloem mobility.

(i) Carbohydrates: Only nonreducing sugars such as sucrose or stachyose appear to be actively translocated in the phloem (31, 177). It is not clear whether this is related to metabolic stability or differential retention by the sieve element, although Arnold (2) has suggested that sucrose acts as a protected derivative of glucose. The sugar alcohols, sorbitol and mannitol, with similar dimensions to the hexose sugars are translocated in several plant species (130, 198).

(ii) Anions and cations: Three widely differing anions stand out as being readily mobile in the phloem: PO_4^{3-}, 2,4-dichlorophenoxyacetic acid (2,4-D), and fluorescein (3, 8, 31, 112), and the evidence would suggest that they can move rapidly in association with neutral sugar molecules through the sieve elements. The same cannot be said for cations. First, the divalent cations such as Ca^{2+} and Sr^{2+} are phloem immobile (31, 116, 149), although selective uptake by the sieve elements could be the controlling factor (82, 102, 140). When applied at high enough concentrations, calcium can be induced to enter the sieve tube system of *Yucca* (205); however, high levels of Ca^{2+} in the sieve tubes are likely to be untenable with the movement of PO_4^{3-}, as this could be precipitated out of solution with sap pH values of around 8.0 (108). In contrast to the divalent cations, the monovalent cations

K$^+$, Rb$^+$, and Cs$^+$ do appear to be readily mobile in the sieve elements, with the first of these (K$^+$) occurring naturally at high levels (71, 143, 169).

Although the pattern of movement of monovalent cations to a sink organ may resemble that of sugars (68, 70, 146), it can be seen from studies on exogenously applied tracers such as ^{137}Cs that their movement, although in the same direction as ^{14}C assimilates, shows little similarity because of differences in timing and exchange (150). Following the application of ^{32}PO$_4$$^{3-}$ and ^{86}Rb$^+$ to the flag leaf of wheat (Figure 1), it can be seen that although the rise in activity in the stem below the ear is quite rapid for both isotopes, after the removal of the supply of tracer from the leaf there is a distinct fall off in ^{32}P activity but not ^{86}Rb. This suggests that the ^{32}P represents a pulse of mobile label passing through the stem, but the ^{86}Rb profile represents a pattern of accumulation possibly developed by rapid exchange with a small amount of material. The ^{137}Cs profile observed in *Nymphoides* after a much longer time interval (163) shows much the same characteristics as the ^{86}Rb. There are two possible explanations for the differences in mobility between the monovalent cations and sugars. First there could be a very high exchange rate between the sieve elements and adjacent cells, which would fit in with the suggested role of K$^+$ in water relations. Second, cations may be absorbed onto the negatively charged membranous structures occurring in the sieve elements (209). This absorption could explain why Fensom & Davidson (54) found a rapid movement of sucrose but not K$^+$ when these were injected into a single sieve element of *Heracleum*.

(iii) Amino acids: Assuming there are grounds for accepting that anions move more readily than cations through the sieve elements, then it might be reasonable

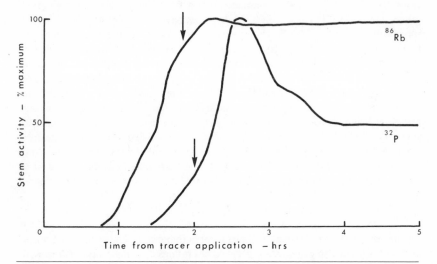

Figure 1 The rise in radioactivity with time in the stem below the ear of wheat, following the application of either ^{86}Rb or ^{32}P to the flag leaf blade. The arrows indicate the time of removal of the uptake area. Scales have been adjusted to give similar peak activities for the two isotopes (R. Dunstone unpublished).

to suggest that the lower the isoelectric point of the amino acid the greater will be its mobility. Unfortunately, there is little critical data available on the relative phloem mobility of different amino acids, although many such as glutamine, glycine, serine, and proline with isoelectric points around 5 to 6, and aspartic and glutamic acids with values around 2 to 3, do appear to be mobile (31, 118, 168), also their distribution patterns are similar to that of sugars from the same leaf (87, 132, 136). The more basic amino acids such as lysine, histidine, and arginine with high isoelectric points (7.5 to 9.0) have not been identified in high concentrations in sieve tube sap, and little appears to be known of their actual mobility in phloem.

(iv) Growth substances: The movement of synthetic growth regulators has been covered in detail by Crafts & Crisp (31), but attention may be drawn to the review by Mitchell & Linder (117), where the effect of structural alterations to herbicides in relation to their penetration and translocation has been discussed. Unfortunately, the evidence does not separate the two processes, but it would be of interest to know if structural changes had altered movement within the transport system. Field & Peel (55), in examining the mobility of several growth regulators in willow, concluded that they differed largely in their ability to be transferred into the sieve elements.

The information available on the movement of naturally occurring hormones is probably more relevant to their role in regulating growth than to an understanding of translocation. Indole acetic acid may move either from the shoot apex in a polar direction at speeds of 1 to 2 cm hr^{-1}, or from mature leaves more rapidly through the sieve elements in association with the assimilates (10, 42, 106, 123, 184). Gibberellins appear to move in the assimilate stream from mature leaves to centers of growth (25, 113), and gibberellin-like substances have been identified in the phloem sap of several species (71, 95). Cytokinins are considered to be relatively immobile in plant tissues other than the xylem stream (31); however, Phillips & Cleland (148) recorded cytokinin-like activity in exudates from aphids feeding on *Xanthium* plants. Abscisic acid (ABA) will move slowly (2–4 cm hr^{-1}) through isolated petioles (35, 84), and ABA also has been identified in the phloem sap of willow and *Ricinus* (71, 81) and may be moving with the assimilates. The floral stimulus is also suspected of being phloem mobile, moving in the sieve elements in association with sugars (91, 92, 164, 165). No direct proof of this is possible of course until the floral stimulus has been identified. The reason that the floral stimulus appears to move more slowly (2 cm hr^{-1}) and independently of the assimilates in *Lolium temulentum* (47) may, like the cations, be related to its charge distribution or lateral permeability.

Viruses

The pattern of virus movement in plants is often found to resemble that of carbohydrates (155), but one of the more perplexing findings in translocation is the well-documented report by Bennett (5) that sugar beet curly top virus, inoculated into the plant by a leaf hopper, may move through the sieve elements at a speed in excess of 60 cm hr^{-1}. Particles of beet yellows virus 20–30 nm in diameter have been identified by electronmicroscopy in sieve elements of the phloem (38), but this probably follows multiplication. The discontinuity of spread in virus down a stem from an infected leaf (155) suggests that transport over long distances may be restricted to relatively few particles. Kluge (94) was able to establish that sieve tube sap from cucumber plants infected with *Cucumis* virus 2A carried infectivity that could not be removed in dialysis or phosphodiesterase treatment and contained particles 345 X 23 mμ, which led him to the conclusion that the virus moved as an intact particle.

SOURCES, SINKS, AND HORMONAL CONTROL OF TRANSPORT

Placing in perspective the role of the source, sink, and pathway in controlling translocation is not a simple matter, although it is important to a consideration of the mechanism of translocation. The plant is an integrated system, and a change in the function of one part may result in a complex set of changes throughout the whole. Thus a reduction in sink size may result in a change in the pattern of distribution of leaf assimilates, favoring an alternative sink, or even a reduction in the rate of source leaf photosynthesis (69, 190). This response is further complicated by the possible role of hormones in directing and controlling the movement of sugars along the pathway, i.e. a directive message produced in the sink. An important factor that must also be remembered in considering the role played by source and sinks in the movement of assimilates is that the transport pathway itself is a sink with varying demands for metabolites. This depends on factors such as cell metabolism and wall thickening and the ability to store excess assimilates, which in turn depend on the maturity of the tissue (125).

Response to Sink Removal

It has been shown that translocation of ^{14}C assimilates and other metabolites will occur in detached leaves (75, 104) where the sink, although not entirely removed for the reasons indicated earlier, is severely restricted. This has led to the suggestion that considerable push for translocation occurs within the leaf (75).

With a reduction in sink size, there is a reduction in the speed of movement of assimilates through the conducting system (75, 188). The effect of variable demand on the speed of movement of assimilates is clearly seen by comparing the movement of ^{14}C assimilates from the flag leaf through the stem to the ear of wheat in intact plants and plants with one third of the grain removed from the ear (Figure 2). The same relation between speed of movement and demand for assimilates can also be obtained by preventing ear photosynthesis with DCMU, where the important factor is that the demand for assimilates through the peduncle can be increased without altering grain growth and presumably without altering hormone production. Similarly, in several species the removal of competitive sources by defoliation has been shown to stimulate the rate of translocation from the remaining leaves (76, 109, 110).

These responses are difficult to reconcile with a pathway controlled mechanism of transport unless the effects are regulated by changes in hormonal output from the

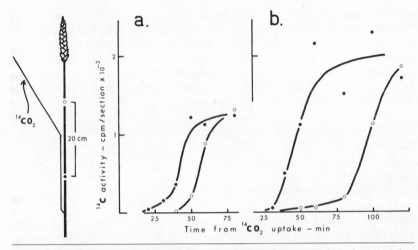

Figure 2 Profiles of ^{14}C activity with time at two points (20 cm apart) on the stem below the ear of wheat, following the uptake of $^{14}CO_2$ by the flag leaf blade. (a) Control plants ear intact; (b) plants with 1/3 of the grain removed from the ear (Wardlaw unpublished).

sink. However, the observations that the transport of sugars and their exudation from cut surfaces may occur over long time intervals, as for example in *Yucca* (170), or through aphid stylets in completely isolated systems such as willow bark strips (140), would appear to exclude hormone directed transport. Furthermore, by adjusting aphid colony size on willow stems, Peel & Ho (142) were able to demonstrate a sink size effect on mass transfer of sugars through the bark. In addition, it was found that a small aphid colony, when in competition with a large colony, had to rely more on stored sugars for a direct supply of assimilates from the shoot.

Hormonal Control of Transport

Moorby (121) and Peel (140) have reviewed much of the literature directly related to the hormonal control of translocation, and it is apparent that auxins are the hormones most likely to be associated with assimilate movement.

Recently Bowen & Wareing (11) have noted that species differ in their transport response to a range of applied auxins, and they observed a general relation between the movement of these down the stem and the movement of metabolites in the opposite direction. Although auxin may stimulate transport directly in these decapitated test systems, an alternative explanation for the enhanced movement is that the auxin prevents senescence of the transport system (137). The recent observation by Morris, Kadir & Barry (124) that a TIBA ring applied to the stem of intact pea seedlings inhibits the basipetal movement of ^{14}C-IAA, but not the movement of ^{14}C sugars into the top of the shoot, is further evidence that in the decapitated test system IAA is associated with the maintenance of the transport system and not directly with assimilate movement. Lepp & Peel (105, 107) found that labeled sugars move away from a site of IAA application on willow bark strips and that IAA enhanced the loading of sugars into the sieve elements. However, they did find some evidence for a stimulatory effect of IAA on the longitudinal movement of sugar through the sieve elements of willow when these were supplied together, although the effect was only apparent in sections placed vertically. This evidence needs further clarification.

CONCLUSION

To this point the impossible has not been mentioned, yet it still might be needed to explain phloem transport. In summary it must be said that much of the data on structure in relation to function are still open to problems of interpretation. There may be a structural continuum passing from one cell to the next through the sieve plate pores, but this may still allow a mass flow of sugar solution. Metabolic inhibitors can stop transport within the sieve tube system, but whether this is a direct effect on the transport mechanism is still an open question. Also, there are no conclusive data to suggest that transport through the sieve elements is stimulated by hormone export from actively growing sinks. The data on the effect of IAA on the movement of metabolites into decapitated stumps of pea and bean plants possibly results from an effect on the senescence of the vascular tissue. The finding that active transport can occur at very low temperatures suggests that pathway metabolism does not play a direct role in phloem transport, a conclusion that is reinforced by the observation that the speed of movement varies with the demand by the sink.

Two mechanisms have been proposed that do not require the direct intervention of metabolic energy along the pathway, pressure or volume flow (31, 46), and interfacial flow of assimilates along surfaces (183). Some doubt, in addition to that relating to structure, has been placed on the mass flow hypothesis by the failure to obtain reliable evidence for the movement of tritiated water in sieve elements. Also it is difficult to envisage how the mass flow of sugar solution through a small tube would be unaffected by the viscosity changes resulting from a 20°C drop in temperature. The physical system proposed by van den Honert has been criticized on the grounds that neutral sucrose molecules are not surface active. Although this does appear to limit the usefulness of van den Honert's proposal, a recent reassessment of the importance of van der Waals forces and the relation of these to adsorbed layers by Ninham & Richmond (131) has led to calculations (Richmond & Wardlaw, in preparation) that suggest sucrose could be adsorbed onto material like P-protein, wetting the surface and thus enabling the sugar to be rapidly equilibrated throughout the sieve tube system. Movement would depend on the supply and utilization of assimilates and would occur in the direction of the gradient with minimal water movement and be dependent on absolute temperature. Thus interfacial flow possibly in association with pressure flow could provide an effective means of transporting sugars and other metabolites from source to sink.

ACKNOWLEDGMENTS

The ideas and suggestions in this review have evolved in part through discussions and correspondence with many people directly or indirectly concerned with the problem of translocation. I am particularly grateful to Dr. R. King and Dr. J. Passioura for their constructive criticism of an earlier draft of this manuscript.

Literature Cited

1. Aikman, D. P., Anderson, W. P. 1971. *Ann. Bot.* 35:761–72
2. Arnold, W. N. 1968. *J. Theoret. Biol.* 21:13–20
3. Bauer, L. 1953. *Planta* 42:367–457
4. Behnke, H. D., 1966. In *Viruses of Plants,* ed A. Beemster, J. Dijkstra. Amsterdam: North-Holland
5. Bennett, C. W. 1934. *J. Agr. Res.* 48: 665–701
6. Bieleski, R. L. 1966. *Plant Physiol.* 41: 455–66
7. Ibid, 447–54
8. Ibid 44:497–502
9. Bonnemain, M. J. L. 1965. *Compt. Rend.* 260:2054–57
10. Ibid 1971. 273:1699–1702
11. Bowen, M. R., Wareing, P. F. 1971. *Planta* 99:120–32
12. Bowling, D. J. F. 1968. *Planta* 80:21–26
13. Bowling, D. J. F. 1969. *Biochim. Biophys. Acta* 183:230–32
14. Brovchenko, M. I., 1965. *Fiziol. Rast.* 12:270–78
15. Ibid 1967. 14:415–24
16. Canny, M. J. 1960. *Ann. Bot.* 24:330–44
17. Ibid 1961. 25:152–67
18. Ibid 1962. 26:603–17
19. Canny, M. J. 1971. *Ann. Rev. Plant Physiol.* 22:237–60
20. Canny, M. J., Askham, M. J. 1967. *Ann. Bot.* 31:409–16
21. Canny, M. J., Markus, K. 1960. *Aust. J. Biol. Sci.* 13:292–99
22. Canny, M. J., Nairn, B., Harvey, M. 1968. *Aust. J. Bot.* 16:479–85
23. Cataldo, D. A., Christy, A. L., Coulson, C. L. 1972. *Plant Physiol.* 49:690–95
24. Cataldo, D. A., Christy, A. L., Coulson, C. L., Ferrier, J. M. 1972. *Plant Physiol.* 49:685–89
25. Chin, T. Y., Lockhart, J. A. 1965. *Am. J. Bot.* 52:828–33
26. Choi, I. C., Aronoff, S. 1966. *Plant Physiol.* 41:1119–29
27. Clauss, H., Mortimer, D. C., Gorham, P. R. 1964. *Plant Physiol.* 39:269–73
28. Coulson, C. L., Christy, A. L., Cataldo, D. A., Swanson, C. A. 1972. *Plant Physiol.* 49:919–23
29. Coulson, C. L., Peel, A. J. 1971. *Ann. Bot.* 35:9–15
30. Crafts, A. S. 1968. *Science* 160:325–27
31. Crafts, A. S., Crisp, C. E. 1971. *Phloem Transport in Plants.* San Francisco: Freeman
32. Cronshaw, J., Esau, K. 1967. *J. Cell Biol.* 34:801–15
33. Currier, H. B., Esau, K., Cheadle, V. I. 1955. *Am. J. Bot.* 42:68–81
34. Currier, H. B., Webster, D. H. 1964. *Plant Physiol.* 39:843–47
35. Dörffling, K., Böttger, M. 1968. *Planta* 80:299–308
36. Duloy, M. D., Mercer, F. V. 1961. *Aust. J. Biol. Sci.* 14:391–401
37. Esau, K., Cheadle, V. I., Risley, E. B. 1962. *Bot. Gaz.* 123:233–43
38. Esau, K., Cronshaw, J., Hoefert, L.L. 1967. *J. Cell Biol.* 32:71–87
39. Esau, K., Engleman, E. M., Bisalputra, T. 1963. *Planta* 59:617–23
40. Eschrich, W. 1965. *Planta* 65:280–300
41. Ibid 1967. 73:37–49
42. Ibid 1968. 78:144–57
43. Eschrich, W. 1970. *Ann. Rev. Plant Physiol.* 21:193–214
44. Eschrich, W., Currier, H. B., Yamaguchi, S., McNairn, R. B. 1965. *Planta* 65:49–64
45. Eschrich, W., Evert, R. F., Heyser, W. 1971. *Planta* 100:208–21
46. Eschrich, W., Evert, R. F., Young, J. H. 1972. *Planta* 107:279–300
47. Evans, L. T., Wardlaw, I. F. 1966. *Planta* 68:310–26
48. Evert, R. F., Bornman, C. H., Butler, V., Gilliland, M. G. 1973. *Protoplasma* 76:1–21
49. Evert, R. F., Eschrich, W., Eichhorn, S. E. 1971. *Planta* 100:262–67
50. Ibid 1973. 109:193–210
51. Evert, R. F., Eschrich, W., Medler, J. T., Alfieri, F. J. 1968. *Am. J. Bot.* 55: 860–74
52. Evert, R. F., Tucker, C. M., Davis, J. D., Deshpande, B. P. 1969. *Am. J. Bot.* 56:999–1017
53. Fensom, D. S. 1972. *Can. J. Bot.* 50: 479–97
54. Fensom, D. S., Davidson, H. R. 1970. *Nature* 227:857–58
55. Field, R. J., Peel, A. J. 1972. *New Phytol.* 71:249–54
56. Fischer, R. A., Hsiao, T. C. 1968. *Plant Physiol.* 43:1953–58
57. Ford, J., Peel, A. J. 1966. *J. Exp. Bot.* 17:522–33

58. Gardner, D. J. C., Peel, A. J. 1969. *Nature* 222:774
59. Gardner, D. J. C., Peel, A. J. 1971. *Phytochemistry* 10:2621–25
60. Gardner, D. J. C., Peel, A. J. 1972. *Planta* 107:217–26
61. Geiger, D. R. 1969. *Ohio J. Sci.* 69:356–66
62. Geiger, D. R., Giaquinta, R. T., Sovonick, S. A., Fellows, R. J. 1974. *Plant Physiol.* 56. In press
63. Geiger, D. R., Saunders, M. A., Cataldo, D. A. 1969. *Plant Physiol.* 44:1657–65
64. Giaquinta, R. T., Geiger, D. R. 1973. *Plant Physiol.* 51:372–77
65. Gilder, J., Cronshaw, J. 1973. *Planta* 110:189–204
66. Green, P. B., Stanton, F. W. 1967. *Science* 155:1675–76
67. Greenway, H., Gunn, A. 1966. *Planta* 71:43–67
68. Greenway, H., Pitman, M. G. 1965. *Aust. J. Biol. Sci.* 18:235–47
69. Habeshaw, D. 1973. *Planta* 110:213–26
70. Hafez, A., Rains, D. W. 1972. *Agron. J.* 64:413–17
71. Hall, S. M., Baker, D. A. 1972. *Planta* 106:131–40
72. Hall, S. M., Milburn, J. A. 1973. *Planta* 109:1–10
73. Hammel, H. T. 1968. *Plant Physiol.* 43:1042–48
74. Harel, S., Reinhold, L. 1966. *Physiol. Plant.* 19:634–43
75. Hartt, C. E., Kortschak, H. P. 1964. *Plant Physiol.* 39:460–74
76. Hartt, C. E., Kortschak, H. P., Burr, G. O. 1964. *Plant Physiol.* 39:15–22
77. Hatch, M. D., Glasziou, K. T. 1964. *Plant Physiol.* 39:180–84
78. Hejnowicz, Z. 1970. *Protoplasma* 71:343–64
79. Ho, L. C., Mortimer, D. C. 1971. *Can. J. Bot.* 49:1769–75
80. Ho, L. C., Peel, A. J. 1969. *Ann. Bot.* 33:833–44
81. Hoad, G. V. 1967. *Life Sci.* 6:1113–18
82. Hoad, G. V., Peel, A. J. 1965. *J. Exp. Bot.* 16:433–51
83. Humble, G. D., Raschke, K. 1971. *Plant Physiol.* 48:447–53
84. Ingersoll, R. B., Smith, O. E. 1971. *Plant Cell Physiol.* 12:301–9
85. Jarvis, P., Thaine, R. 1971. *Nature (New Biol.)* 232:236–37
86. Johnson, R. P. C. 1966. *Planta* 68:36–43
87. Joy, K. W., Antcliff, A. J. 1966. *Nature* 211:210–11

88. Kaufmann, M. R., Kramer, P. J. 1967. *Plant Physiol.* 42:191–94
89. Kennecke, M., Ziegler, H., Rongine de Fekete, M. A. 1971. *Planta* 98:330–56
90. Kidwai, P., Robards, A. W. 1969. *J. Exp. Bot.* 20:664–70
91. King, R. W., Evans, L. T., Wardlaw, I. F. 1968. *Z. Pflanzenphysiol.* 59:377–88
92. King, R. W., Zeevaart, J. A. D. 1973. *Plant Physiol.* 51:727–38
93. Kleinig, H., Dörr, I., Weber, C., Kollmann, R. 1971. *Nature (New Biol.)* 229:152–53
94. Kluge, M. 1967. *Planta* 73:50–61
95. Kluge, M., Reinhard, E., Ziegler, H. 1964. *Naturwissenschaften* 51:145–46
96. Kollmann, R. 1965. *Planta* 65:173–79
97. Kollmann, R. 1967. *Z. Pflanzenphysiol.* 56:401–9
98. Kollmann, R., Dörr, I. 1966. *Z. Pflanzenphysiol.* 55:131–41
99. Kuo, C-F. 1964. *Acta Bot. Sinica* 12:100–6
100. Kuo, C-F., Lou, C-H. 1966. *Acta Bot. Sinica* 14:41–46
101. Kursanov, A. L., Brovchenko, M. I., Pariskaya, A. N. 1959. *Fiziol. Rast.* 6:527–36
102. Läuchli, A. 1968. *Planta* 83:137–49
103. Lehmann, J. 1973. *Planta* 111:187–98
104. Leonard, O. A., Glenn, R. K. 1968. *Plant Physiol.* 43:1380–88
105. Lepp, N. W., Peel, A. J. 1970. *Planta* 90:230–35
106. Ibid 1971. 96:62–73
107. Ibid. 97:50–61
108. Lipmann, F., Tuttle, L. C. 1944. *J. Biol. Chem.* 153:571–82
109. Lovell, P. H., Oo, H. T., Sagar, G. R. 1972. *J. Exp. Bot.* 23:255–66
110. Lush, W. M. 1973. *The translocation of assimilates in grasses.* MS thesis. Australian National Univ., Canberra
111. MacRobbie, E. A. C. 1971. *Biol. Rev.* 46:429–81
112. Marshall, C., Wardlaw, I. F. 1973. *Aust. J. Biol. Sci.* 26:1–13
113. McComb, A. J. 1964. *Ann. Bot.* 28:669–87
114. McNairn, R. B. 1972. *Plant Physiol.* 50:366–70
115. McNairn, R. B., Currier, H. B. 1968. *Planta* 82:369–80
116. Middleton, L. J. 1959. *Int. J. Radiat. Biol.* 1:387–402
117. Mitchell, J. W., Linder, P. J. 1963. *Residue Rev.* 2:51–76
118. Mittler, T. E. 1953. *Nature* 172:207
119. Mittler, T. E. 1957. *J. Exp. Bot.* 34:334–41

120. Mittler, T. E. 1967. *Ann. Entomol. Soc. Am.* 60:1112–14
121. Moorby, J. 1968. In *The Transport of Plant Hormones,* ed. Y. Vardar. Amsterdam: North Holland
122. Moorby, J., Ebert, M., Evans, N. T. S. 1963. *J. Exp. Bot.* 14:210–20
123. Morris, D. A., Kadir, G. O. 1972. *Planta* 107:171–82
124. Morris, D. A., Kadir, G. O., Barry, A. J. 1973. *Planta* 110:173–82
125. Müller, K., Leopold, A. C. 1966. *Planta* 68:186–205
126. Nelson, C. D., Clauss, H., Mortimer, D. C., Gorham, P. R. 1961. *Plant Physiol.* 36:581–88
127. Nelson, C. D., Perkins, H. J., Gorham, P. R. 1959. *Can. J. Bot.* 37:1181–89
128. Neumann, S., Wollgiehn, R. Z. 1964. *Z. Naturforsch. B* 19:1066–71
129. Newcomb, E. H. 1969. *Ann. Rev. Plant Physiol.* 20:253–88
130. Nicholson, N. L., Briggs, W. R. 1972. *Am. J. Bot.* 59:97–106
131. Ninham, B. W., Richmond, P. 1973. *Trans. Faraday Soc.* In press
132. Oghoghorie, C. G. O., Pate, J. S. 1972. *Planta* 104:35–49
133. Palladina, T. A., Shapochka, O. F. 1970. *Sov. Plant Physiol.* 17 (Transl.): 640–42
134. Parker, B. C. 1965. *J. Phycol.* 1:41–46
135. Parker, B. C., Huber, J. 1965. *J. Phycol.* 1:172–79
136. Pate, J. S. 1973. *Soil Biol. Biochem.* 5:109–19
137. Patrick, J. W., Wareing, P. F. 1970. In *Plant Growth Substances* 1970, ed. D. J. Carr. Berlin: Springer
138. Peel, A. J. 1965. *J. Exp. Bot.* 16:249–60
139. Peel, A. J. 1970. *Physiol. Plant.* 23:667–72
140. Peel, A. J. 1972. *Pestic. Sci.* 3:631–41
141. Peel, A. J., Field, R. J., Coulson, C. L., Gardner, D. J. C. 1969. *Physiol. Plant.* 22:768–75
142. Peel, A. J., Ho, L. C. 1970. *Physiol. Plant.* 23:1033–38
143. Peel, A. J., Weatherley, P. E. 1959. *Nature* 184:1955–56
144. Peel, A. J., Weatherley, P. E. 1962. *Ann. Bot.* 26:633–46
145. Ibid 1963. 27:197–211
146. Penot, M. 1972. *Physiol. Vég.* 10:687–96
147. Peterson, C. A., Currier, H. B. 1969. *Physiol. Plant.* 22:1238–50
148. Phillips, D. A., Cleland, C. F. 1972. *Planta* 102:173–78
149. Qureshi, F. A., Spanner, D. C. 1971. *Planta* 101:133–46

150. Ibid 1973. 110:131–44
151. Ibid. 111:1–12
152. Roeckl, B. 1949. *Planta* 36:530–50
153. Sabnis, D. D., Hart, J. W. 1973. *Planta* 109:127–33
154. Schmitz, K., Lüning, K., Willenbrink, J. 1972. *Z. Pflanzenphysiol.* 67:418–29
155. Schneider, I. R. 1965. *Advan. Virus Res.* 11:163–221
156. Siddiqui, A. W., Spanner, D. C. 1970. *Nature* 226:88
157. Siddiqui, A. W., Spanner, D. C. 1970. *Planta* 91:181–89
158. Singh, A. P., Srivastava, L. M. 1972. *Can. J. Bot.* 50:839–46
159. Sij, J. W., Swanson, C. A. 1973. *Plant Physiol.* 51:368–71
160. Sokolova, S. V. 1968. *Sov. Plant Physiol.* 15 (Transl.):631–38
161. Spanner, D. C. 1970. *J. Exp. Bot.* 21:325–34
162. Spanner, D. C., Jones, R. L. 1970. *Planta* 92:64–72
163. Spanner, D. C., Prebble, J. N. 1962. *J. Exp. Bot.* 13:294–306
164. Stigter, H. C. M. De 1966. *Z. Pflanzenphysiol.* 55:11–19
165. Takeba, G., Takimoto, A. 1966. *Bot. Mag. Tokyo* 79:811–14
166. Tammes, P. M. L. 1969. *Acta Bot. Neer.* 18:224–29
167. Tammes, P. M. L., Ie, T. S. 1971. *Acta Bot. Neer.* 20:309–17
168. Tammes, P. M. L., van Die, J. 1964. *Acta Bot. Neer.* 13:76–83
169. Tammes, P. M. L., van Die, J. 1966. *Proc. Ned. Akad. Wetensch.* 69:656–59
170. Tammes, P. M. L., van Die, J., Ie, T. S. 1971. *Acta Bot. Neer.* 20:245–52
171. Thaine, R. 1961. *Nature* 192:772–73
172. Thaine, R. 1962. *J. Exp. Bot.* 13:152–60
173. Thaine, R. 1964. *New Phytol.* 63: 236–42
174. Thaine, R. 1969. *Nature* 222:873–75
175. Thrower, S. L. 1965. *Aust. J. Biol. Sci.* 18:449–61
176. Trip, P., Gorham, P. R. 1968. *Plant Physiol.* 43:877–82
177. Trip, P., Nelson, C. D., Krotkov, G. 1965. *Plant Physiol.* 40:740–77
178. Turkina, M. V. 1961. *Fiziol. Rast.* 8:649–57
179. Tyree, M. T., Fensom, D. S. 1970. *J. Exp. Bot.* 21:304–24
180. Ullrich, W. 1961. *Planta* 57:402–29
181. Ibid 1962. 57:713–17
182. Ibid 1963. 59:387–90
183. Van den Honert, T. H. 1932. *Proc. Ned. Akad. Wetensch.* 35:1104–11
184. Van Overbeek, J. 1956. *Ann. Rev. Plant Physiol.* 7:355–72

185. Van Went, J. L., Tammes, P. M. L. 1972. *Acta Bot. Neer.* 21:321–26
186. Von Parker, J. 1964. *Naturwissenschaften* 51:273–74
187. Walker, T. S., Thaine, R. 1971. *Ann. Bot.* 35:773–90
188. Wardlaw, I. F. 1965. *Aust. J. Biol. Sci.* 18:269–81
189. Ibid 1967. 20:25–39
190. Wardlaw, I. F. 1968. *Bot. Rev.* 34:79–105
191. Wardlaw, I. F. 1969. *Aust. J. Biol. Sci.* 22:1–16
192. Ibid 1971. 24:1047–55
193. Wardlaw, I. F. 1972. *Planta* 104:18–34
194. Weatherley, P. E. 1972. *Physiol. Vég.* 10:731–42
195. Weatherley, P. E. 1973. *Planta* 110:183–87
196. Weatherley, P. E., Johnson, R. P. C. 1968. *Int. Rev. Cytol.* 24:149–92
197. Weatherley, P. E., Peel, A. J., Hill, G. P. 1959. *J. Exp. Bot.* 10:1–16
198. Webb, K. L ., Burley, J. W. A. 1962. *Science* 137:766
199. Webb, J. A. 1967. *Plant Physiol.* 42:881–85
200. Webb, J. A. 1971. *Can. J. Bot.* 49:717–33
201. Webb, J. A., Gorham, P. R. 1964. *Plant Physiol.* 39:663–72
202. Weber, C., Kleinig, H. 1971. *Planta* 99:179–82
203. Whittle, C. M. 1964. *Ann. Bot.* 28:339–44
204. Wiersum, L. K. 1967. *J. Exp. Bot.* 18:160–62
205. Wiersum, L. K., Vonk, C. A., Tammes, P. M. L. 1971. *Naturwissenschaften* 58:99
206. Williamson, R. E. 1972. *Planta* 106:149–57
207. Wooding, F. B. P. 1969. *Planta* 85:284–98
208. Yang, S. J., De Jong, E. 1968. *Can. J. Plant Sci.* 48:89–95
209. Yapa, P. A. J., Spanner, D. C. 1972. *Planta* 106:369–73
210. Ibid. 107:89–96
211. Ziegler, H., Ruck, I. 1967. *Planta* 73:62–73
212. Ziegler, H., Vieweg, G. H. 1961. *Planta* 56:402–8
213. Zimmermann, M. H. 1957. *Plant Physiol.* 32:288–91
214. Zimmermann, M. H. 1969. *Planta* 84:272–78

Ann. Rev. Plant Physiol. 1974. 25:541–66

PHYTOTOXINS PRODUCED BY PLANT PARASITES

❖7577

Gary A. Strobel

Department of Plant Pathology, Montana State University Bozeman, Montana 59715

"The deeper we search, the more we find there is to know, and as long as human life exists I believe it always will be so."

Einstein

CONTENTS

INTRODUCTION 542
GLYCOSIDE PHYTOTOXINS 544
    Helminthosporoside 544
    Oligosaccharides 545
    Glycopeptides 546
    Lipomucopolysaccharides 547
    Polysaccharides 548
TERPENOID PHYTOTOXINS 548
    Helminthosporal 548
    Diacetoxyscirpenol 549
    Fusicoccin 549
    Ophiobolins 552
    Helminthosporium maydis Toxins 552
AMINO ACID DERIVED PHYTOTOXINS 554
    Lycomarasmine 554
    Tabtoxins 555
    Tentoxin 557
    Rhizobitoxine 558
    Periconia Toxins 559
    Pseudomonas phaseolicola Toxins 559
    Helminthosporium carbonum Toxins 560
    Syringomycin 561
MISCELLANEOUS TOXINS 562
SUMMARY 563

INTRODUCTION

Man depends upon hundreds of different plants to supply his everyday needs for food, fiber, and recreation. Each plant may have more than a score of plant diseases caused by fungi, bacteria, viruses, or nematodes (52). Each disease may represent a unique host-parasite relationship. Thus the total number of parasite-host combinations that exist in nature is immense. It may be that only a limited amount of progress has been made on toxins in plant disease because there are so many systems from which an investigator can choose. The result is that no large group of scientists has made a concerted effort on any one system.

In order to explain the symptoms of the host-parasite relationship, the concept that a pathogen may produce a toxin was expounded by DeBary in 1886 (24). In the early part of the twentieth century many papers appeared indicating that plant pathogens were producing phytotoxic compounds. The more easily cultured pathogenic bacteria and fungi were the subject of these reports. The early workers generally tested extracts of culture fluid on plants susceptible to the pathogen being investigated. If all or some of the normal symptoms developed, workers concluded that a toxin was involved in the disease. These investigators did not realize that microbes may produce many toxic compounds in enriched culture media that may not be produced in a susceptible host. Eventually, Dimond & Waggoner (31) suggested that conclusive evidence for the role of a toxic substance in a plant disease could only come when a disease-inducing substance is isolated from an infected host and identified. Their argument was good and incontrovertible.

Plant pathologists had spent considerable time proposing generalized names for toxins prior to having adequate data on the chemical and biological nature of such compounds. Such terms as vivotoxins, pathotoxins, phytotoxins, mycotoxins, and host-specific toxins have appeared in the literature. The latter was defined by Pringle & Scheffer (88) as a metabolic product of a pathogenic microorganism which is toxic only to the host susceptible to that pathogen. A vivotoxin was defined by Dimond & Waggoner (31) as a substance produced in the infected host by the pathogen which functions in the production of disease, but it is not itself the initial inciting agent of disease. Since some toxins may be unstable in the host, Wheeler & Luke (148) proposed that the criteria to properly test the toxin theory should include a consideration that toxin concentrations are adequate to induce all of the symptoms in the host: that both the toxin and the host exhibit similar suscept specificity, and that a positive correlation exists between toxin production and pathogenicity. A toxin fulfilling these requirements is described as a pathotoxin. The term phytotoxin was proposed by these workers to denote a compound that is nonspecific, expresses a low order of activity, or incites few or none of the symptoms incited by the pathogen.

There appears to be merit in many of the proposals for naming particular classes of toxins, however, in this review the simple term phytotoxin will be used in a broad sense in reference to any compound produced by the parasite that interferes with the metabolism of the host. Substances having enzymatic activity or toxic compounds produced by the host in response to the parasite will not be discussed.

This reviewer believes that the following points need to be carefully considered relative to establishing the role of any toxin in a plant disease:

1. Preparations of the toxin should produce some or all of the symptoms normally associated with the disease. To say that all symptoms need to be produced by a toxin implies that it is the only factor responsible for disease development.

2. Ultimately the investigator should isolate and identify the toxic substance or substances. This information will aid in establishing by direct chemical means when, where, and how much of the toxin is produced in plants infected by the pathogen. Organic synthesis of the compound may also be possible to further establish its identity.

3. The investigator should establish means for isolating the toxin from diseased plants and determining actual amounts present by chemical tests or quantitative bioassay tests. As will be seen later in this chapter, the amount of toxin capable of being produced by the pathogen, and its location in the plants, are critical factors in establishing the role of any toxin in disease development.

4. The mere demonstration of a substance having toxic properties from a diseased plant should not imply to the investigator that it played a causal role in disease development. For instance, many toxic compounds such as phenols, quinones, and organic acids are produced in the advanced stages of the disease and probably play no role whatever in disease development.

5. Tests should be conducted on the host range of the toxin relative to that of the pathogen itself. It may also be desirable to relate the pathogenicity of various strains, isolates, and mutants of the pathogen to their ability to produce the toxin in question. This would provide additional evidence for the role of a toxin in the disease.

The fact that a phytotoxic substance is produced by a fungus or bacterium warrants further investigation. Of basic interest concerning all such compounds are the following questions: (*a*) what physiological functions of the plant cell are affected; (*b*) what is the initial site of action of the toxin in the plant cell; (*c*) what functional group or groups on the toxin are necessary for activity: and (*d*) how is the toxin biosynthesized or degraded?

Numerous reports concerning phytotoxic compounds produced by pathogenic bacteria and fungi have appeared in the chemical and biological literature in the past 5 years. Little or no work had been done on toxic substances that may be associated with parasitic nematodes, and there is no work implicating toxic substances in diseases caused by plant viruses.

The upsurge of recent interest in phytotoxins resulted in a symposium sponsored by NATO in 1970. A compilation of papers on phytotoxins in plant diseases came from this symposium (151). In addition, there are already several reviews of the extensive biological work done on the host-specific toxin of *Helminthosporium victoriae* (63, 88, 109, 147, 148). This review, however, will deal primarily with toxins of other pathogenic bacteria and fungi.

GLYCOSIDE PHYTOTOXINS

The prominent structural feature of some toxins is the presence of one or more glycosidic bonds. Substances such as polysaccharides, glycopeptides, and small glycosides are included in this category of compounds.

Helminthosporoside

Steiner & Byther (117) reported that a host-specific toxin was produced by *Helminthosporium sacchari,* the casual agent of eye spot disease of sugar cane. The fungus causes eye-shaped lesions on leaves followed by the development of long reddish brown streaks or runners extending from the lesion toward the leaf tip. Since the fungus could be isolated only from the lesion and not the "runner" areas, the suggestion was made that a toxin was involved in the symptomatology. These workers partially purified a substance that was capable of producing runners only on susceptible clones of sugar cane. It could, therefore, be called a host-specific toxin. Steiner & Strobel (118) isolated this toxin from cultures of *H. sacchari* and named it helminthosporoside (Figure 1). They devised a biological assay for its quantification based on the degree of symptom expression on susceptible cane leaves. Helminthosporoside, (2-hydroxycyclopropyl-α-galactopyranoside) was isolated from naturally infected sugar cane leaves in amounts that could account for symptoms of eye spot (129).

One of the first visible symptoms on susceptible leaves treated with helminthosporoside is water clearing and the formation of water droplets on both leaf surfaces within 30 min after toxin application. Studies of Strobel, Hess & Steiner (128), however, showed that no visible ultrastructural effects were noticeable until at least one hr after toxin application. Those changes that were detected after 1 hr were slight alterations in chloroplast membranes. Furthermore, after the administration of ^{14}C-toxin to leaves of both resistant and susceptible clones, there was no difference in the amount of ^{14}C recoverable as helminthosporoside from these two clones of cane. This suggested that toxin breakdown was not a factor in resistance to toxin action. In addition, the labeled toxin moved as well in the vascular system of susceptible as in resistant sugar cane leaves.

Strobel (125a) demonstrated that membrane preparations from susceptible clones of sugar cane bound helminthosporoside-^{14}C and that there was no binding by similar preparations from resistant clones. Furthermore, in vivo binding of the toxin occured in susceptible clones and not resistant ones. Membranes from clones giving

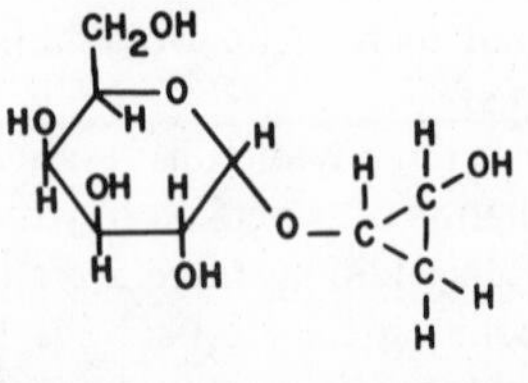

Figure 1   Proposed structure for helminthosporoside.

an intermediate reaction to the toxin likewise had only intermediate amounts of binding activity. Symptom production by the toxin, as well as binding of the toxin to membrane preparations, was reduced in the presence of a number of α-galactosides. The binding activity was associated with a membrane-bound protein that was purified and shown to have molecular weight of 48,000 and to consist of four identical subunits. Scatchard plots derived from equilibrium dialysis experiments were used to demonstrate the presence of at least two toxin binding sites on the protein. The protein has a K_m for helminthosporoside of 10^{-5} and an isoelectric point near pH 5.0. Resistant clones have a comparable protein with the same molecular weight, which is immunologically indistinguishable from the binding protein of susceptible clones (126). The two proteins, however, differ slightly in their mobility on disc gel electrophoresis. The protein from resistant clones is also a four subunit protein, but its amino acid composition differs by four residues. While freshly prepared protein from resistant plants does not bind helminthosporoside, binding can be observed upon treatment of the protein with mild detergent. It has been suggested that the protein from resistant clones possesses helminthosporoside binding sites, but these were most likely masked by virtue of a change in the tertiary or quaternary structure of the protein resulting from alteration in amino acid composition. There is considerable evidence which supports the idea that the binding protein is associated with the plasma membrane (125b).

The mechanism of toxin action may be the result of an induced conformational change on the membrane binding protein upon binding with the toxin (125a). Such a change might then affect that local environment of the membrane and induce local phase transitions in membrane lipids resulting in abnormal cellular permeability. This would ultimately account for the rapid appearance of water and solutes on the surfaces of toxin-treated leaves. If other organelles, such as lysosomes, possess this protein, they too may ultimately be affected and the net result may be complete cellular disruption due to the release of autolytic enzymes.

Even though the presence of the active binding protein in a given cane variety is invariably linked to susceptibility to the toxin, several important questions remain unanswered, including: (a) what is the physiological role of the binding protein in the plant; (b) how is the genetic information for the binding protein inherited; and (c) is it possible that some clones have hybrid binding proteins. There is no question that the toxin plays an important and definite role in the symptomatology of eye spot disease and is ultimately involved in determining host specificity. However, a question remains relative to the role of this toxin in the initial establishment of the pathogen in the host, even though in other diseases in which a host-specific toxin is involved the toxin appears necessary for successful establishment of the parasite (155).

An interesting practical result of some of this work is the use that helminthosporoside has in screening sugar cane varieties for disease resistance (17).

Oligosaccharides

Didymella applanata infects the leaves and canes of raspberry plants. Culture filtrates of the fungus were shown to produce toxic effects on cane sprouts comparable to those occurring in natural infections (105). The toxic component was isolated by column chromatography employing Sephadex G-25 followed by absorption chromatography on a Norite R11 column The compound has a molecular weight of less than 2500, and several sugars were noted after hydrolysis, silization, and gas chromatography. The compound does not contain nitrogen and is active in concentrations as low as 1 mg/l.

Glycopeptides

Spencer & Gorin (115) demonstrated that crude culture preparations of *Corynebacterium sepedonicum* and *C. insidiosum* contained wilt-including polysaccharides. A toxic compound having a molecular wieght of 21,400 was purified from cultures of *C. sepedonicum* (123). The toxin appeared to be a highly branched glycopeptide as shown by NMR. This was confirmed by the work of Strobel, Talmadge & Albersheim (130) in which the toxin was methylated, hydrolyzed, reduced, and acetylated. The monomers were separated by gas chromatography and analyzed by mass spectroscopy. The carbohydrate portion consists mainly of mannose and glucose with mannose accounting for about one half of the branch points and virtually all of the terminal residues. The peptide portion is linked glycosidically from threonine to a terminal mannose residue. The most probable structure of the toxin is that of a single highly branched oligosaccharide chain attached to a single peptide (7–9 amino acids). The evidence suggests that the peptide chain may vary in its amino acid content since five peptides were isolated from base-treated toxin preparations. Strobel (124) isolated the toxin from infected potato plants and showed by a number of techniques that the toxin from infected plants was identical to the one obtained from culture filtrates. Furthermore, there was enough of the toxin in infected plants to account for symptom production in a wilt bioassay test employing potato cuttings. The toxin contains about 10% 2-keto-3-deoxygluconic acid, which appears to be vital for its biological activity since methyl esterification of the toxin rendered it inactive (53).

Plugging of vascular elements and increased viscosity of tracheal fluids is said to be the cause of wilting induced by polysaccharide-like toxins from many sources (30). Strobel & Hess (127), however, presented evidence for an involvement of *C. sepedonicum* glycopeptide in membrane dysfunction. Electrolyte leakage, ultrastructural breaks, passage of ^3H_2O through intact plant cuttings, and autoradiographic studies on tissues treated with ^3H-toxin supported the hypothesis that the toxin adversely affects cellular membranes. Comparable ultrastructural alterations were observed in plants infected with *C. sepedonicum* (50). No evidence could be found for vascular plugging. As Duniway (32) pointed out, no critical gross water relation studies have been conducted on glycopeptide toxin-induced wilting in host plants. Evidence of this type should corroborate or refute the ideas for the proposed mechanisms of toxin action from the aspect of gross water movement in the plant.

The phytotoxic glycopeptide of *C. insidiosum* was purified and characterized by Ries & Strobel (97). The organism produces profuse quantities of this toxin in culture media. A molecular weight of 5×10^6 was calculated for this toxin by both light scattering and gel column techniques. The molecule is blue due to the chelation of approximately 75 moles of copper/mole of toxin. It consists primarily of L-fucose, mannose, glucose, galactose, and has an unidentified keto-deoxy acid. A single peptide with glycine as the sole NH_2-terminal amino acid is covalently linked through the hydroxyl of threonine to a sugar residue in the molecule. There appears to be at least 77 peptide chains per mole of toxin. L-Fucose comprises about 40% of the toxin with 20% as glucose, 20% as galactose, and 4% as mannose. Sadowski & Strobel (103) successfully demonstrated the presence of a guanosine diphosphate-L-fucose glycopeptide fucosyltransferase in membrane preparations of *C. insidiosum*. The enzyme transferred L-fucose from GDP-L-fucose to preparations of a partially hydrolyzed toxin which served as a primer. This toxic glycopeptide is present in alfalfa plants infected with *C. insidiosum* (98). It is also a wilt-inducing compound, and it not only affects alfalfa, but a wide range of plant species. Interestingly enough, however, if used in low concentrations on alfalfa cuttings, it selectively causes wilting in susceptible but not in bacterial wilt-resistant clones (122). This fact should enable plant breeders to rapidly sort our wilt-resistant clones in alfalfa breeding projects.

Toxic glycopeptides have also been isolated from *Corynebacterium michiganese* (94). Of at least three toxic glycopeptides produced by this organism, one has a molecular weight greater than 200,000, another approximating 130,000, and one of about 30,000. The compounds vary in their content of hexose and all contain small peptides having several common amino acids. All three toxins have an ability to cause wilting in young tomato cuttings. The compounds are antigenically related. Using ^{14}C-toxin treated tomato cuttings in radioautographic experiments, Rai & Strobel (95) effectively showed that the toxins became generally distributed throughout the plant prior to wilting. The greatest toxin concentrations, however, occurred at leaf margins, which is significant in view of the fact that leaves of naturally infected plants often show chlorosis and necrosis at leaf margins. Acid-fushin dye moved at the same rate in treated and nontreated cuttings. These experiments along with microscopic observations suggested that plugging of vessels was not involved as a mechanism of wilting. Immunological studies showed the presence of the glycopeptide toxins in plants infected with *C. michiganense.*

Toxin glycopeptides with a molecular weight range of 25,000–30,000 have been isolated from culture filtrates of *Ceratocystis ulmi,* the causal agent of Dutch elm disease (96). Other larger molecular weight polysaccharides were also found in cultures of *C. ulmi* (104). The small molecular weight substances appear to have one peptide chain as demonstrated by oxidation of the glycopeptide with sodium periodate and isolation of the products by paper electrophoresis. The major sugar residues present in the glycopeptide toxins are mannose and galactose. The application of the low molecular weight toxins to young elm shoots at concentrations on the order of 10^{-5} *M* results in leaf discoloration, vascular browning, and formation of gums and tyloses in the vascular elements. These symptoms are similar to those appearing in susceptible trees after inoculation with a spore suspension of *C. ulmi.*

Lipomucopolysaccharides

Keen & Williams (55) isolated a lipomucopolysaccharide from cell-free fluids of *Pseudomonas lachrymans* and showed that it induced the typical water soaking of cucumber leaves of the type normally associated with the pathogen itself. Further, the compound was toxic to mice with an LD_{50} of 7.5 $\mu g/g$ body weight. The compound was shown to be homogeneous by a number of criteria and to have a molecular weight in the range of 3.5–4 X 10^6 million. The toxin complexed with proteins at neutral to alkaline pH, which may have some bearing upon its ability to induce water soaking in treated leaves. Conceivably, water soaking symptoms could result from local toxin-membrane interactions rendering the plasmalemma more permeable to water. Of course, additional studies on this interesting compound may elucidate its involvement in the disease and its exact mode of action in plant tissues.

Polysaccharides

Numerous toxic compounds having a polysaccharide backbone as the bulk of their structure have been reported from many fungi and bacteria (61, 150). The structures of many of these substances are poorly characterized, and only a small amount of physical data is available. This is not to mention the total lack of extensive work needed to show their involvement in plant disease and their mode of action. Ultimately, more complete chemical data on these compounds may result in the determination that these polysaccharides are polymers of a more complex nature involving residues other than sugars. For instance, although the extracellular polysaccharide of *Xanthomonas campestris* was originally reported not to possess nitrogen, more careful analysis by Sutton & Williams (132) indicated that it was associated with 0.04–0.08% organic nitrogen. Thus it is possible that the high molecular weight polysaccharide of *X. campestris* is a glycopeptide. The majority of the polysaccharide is mannose and glucose, and a compound having about the same proportionate ratio of mannose to glucose was isolated from cabbage plants infected with this bacterium. Furthermore, there was a positive antigenic relationship between the compound from cultures and the preparations from infected plants. Plugging of vascular elements was the suggested mode of action of this toxic polysaccharide (131). Isolates not having an ability to produce the polysaccharide were markedly restricted in their multiplication in the leaves. Sutton & Williams (132) postulated that the polysaccharide may also act to protect bacteria from preformed inhibitory substances in the leaves or to prevent the bacteria from eliciting the formation of inhibitors.

TERPENOID PHYTOTOXINS

A number of phytotoxins have structures clearly of terpenoid origin. These compounds have been found in a number of pathogenic fungi including the genera Helminthosporium, Fomes, and Fusicoccum. Some of the finest chemical, biosynthetic, and mode of action studies on phytotoxins have been conducted on certain members of this group of compounds. A review of these toxins has appeared (22).

Helminothosporal

Helminthosporium sativum causes seedling blight, root rot, leaf spot, and head blight on wheat and barley. Ludwig (62) demonstrated that the action of the fungus in producing chlorosis and necrosis was dependent upon the presence of a toxin produced by this pathogen. The toxin is nonspecific in that it affects a number of cereals. Furthermore, the pathogenicity of various fungus isolates was related to their capacity to produce the toxin.

The toxin, termed helminthosporal, was isolated by DeMayo, Spencer & White (26) and characterized as a sesquiterpenoid having an empirical formula of $C_{15}H_{22}O_2$, and a structure was proposed by DeMayo, Spencer & White (27). Biosynthesis of this toxin proceeds via mevalonate (25). Taniguchi & White (135) showed that helminthosporal inhibits respiration in root tissues of barley and wheat at a site between flavoprotein dehydrogenase and cytochrome c. The reduction of cytochromes b, c, a, and a_3 was inhibited as indicated by the absorption maxima of these enzymes in the presence of the toxin. It apparently has a dual effect on both electron transfer and oxidative phosphorylation. Nevertheless, many questions relating to the biological specificity of the toxin, its production in host plants, and its role in disease production remain to be answered.

Diacetoxyscirpenol

This compound and some compounds closely related to it, all known as the trichothecanes, have been shown to have phytotoxic as well as mammalian toxicity. It is commonly produced by species of *Fusarium* on stored grain. Aspects of its structural determination, as well as those of related compounds, are reviewed by Casinovi (22) and Bamburg & Strong (13). The most comprehensive studies on the phytotoxicity of diacetoxyscirpenol have been done by Brian et al (16), who showed that the toxin prevented the growth of cress seedling roots at 100 μg/ml. These workers also demonstrated that this toxin significantly reduced the toxic effects of 0.5 μg/ml indoleacetic acid. Furthermore, the growth-promoting effects of indoleacetic acid were significantly reduced by concentrations of the toxin as low as 0.04 μg/ml, suggesting that the toxin can effectively block the response of the plant to indoleacetic acid. Other trichothecanes are produced by plant parasitic fungi. These include crotocin, nivalenol, fusarenone, T-2 toxin, and HT-2 toxin. Nevertheless, the isolation of a trichothecane from an infected host plant has not yet been accomplished, making their involvement in plant diseases still questionable. The interesting antibiotic, dermatitic, insecticidal, and other toxic properties of these and related compounds are discussed by Bamburg & Strong (13).

Fusicoccin

Fusicoccum amygdali causes wilting and desiccation of shoots on infected almond and peach trees. Since these foliar symptoms appear on leaves remotely located from fungus infected nodes, toxins elaborated by the pathogen have been designated as the cause of such damage (43). Cultures of the actively growing fungus produced a phytotoxin which was isolated, partially characterized, and called fusicoccin by Ballio et al (10). It was later shown by Ballio et al (7) to be a glucoside of a carbotricyclic terpene with a molecular weight of 680 and a structure shown in Figure 2. The introduction of fusicoccin into the xylem of peach and almond shoots

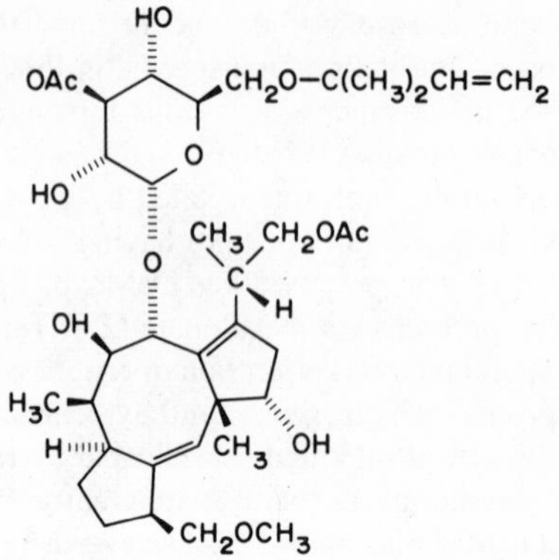

Figure 2   Structure of fusicoccin.

produces symptoms closely resembling those following infection by *F. amygdali* (43). The toxin affects a wide range of plants in very dilute solution (2 μg/ml). Graniti (43) established a bioassay test for the toxin using four-leafed cuttings from young tomato plants. This test has served other investigators in biological studies with the toxin and its derivatives.

Using thin-layer chromatography, Ballio et al (9) showed that culture filtrates of *F. amygdali* consistently yielded small amounts of six substances resembling fusicoccin with lower R_f values in an 8% isopropanol:chloroform solvent system. Some of these compounds were identified, and one, termed isofusicoccin, was shown to be nearly as phytotoxic as fusicoccin; mondeacetylofusicoccin and dideacetylfusicoccin were 12 and 100 times less active, respectively. More recently, Ballio et al (8) described the structrue of allofusicoccin; however, no information was presented relative to its phytotoxicity.

In order to determine which portion or portions of the fusicoccin molecule are necessary for phytotoxicity, Ballio et al (6) prepared 16 derivatives of the parent compound and tested their ability to wilt young tomato cuttings. With the exception of hydrogenation of the *trans*-pentenyl group, any structure modification, including partial or full deacetylation, acetylation, removal of the *trans*-pentenyl group, and removal of the glucosidic moiety, virtually abolished phytotoxicity. Fusicoccin and a number of closely related derivatives stimulate water uptake in cuttings of etiolated pea seedlings (12). Interestingly enough, hydrogenation, or removal of the *trans*-pentenyl group, as well as partial or total deacetylation of fusicoccin, dihydrofusicoccin, and de-*trans*-pentenylfusicoccin, gave compounds toxic activity comparable to that of fusicoccin. Acetylation products of these compounds did not stimulate water uptake and the glucose moiety appeared necessary for activity. These results suggest that the toxin may be acting at two levels: (*a*) water uptake, and (*b*) transpiration. Other work (12) has shown that fusicoccin produces a pronounced increase in the wet weight of pea internodes, an increase in the rate tissue elongation, and enhances tissue deformability, suggesting that it may either possess auxin-like activity or promote such activity.

Lado et al (59) confirmed the observation that toxin-treated pea segments showed increased water uptake over nontreated controls in leaf discs of tomato, clover, and tobacco. Since the osmotic pressure values of treated tissues were lower than those of the control, the authors concluded that fusicoccin acts to irreversibly extend the cell wall. They showed that fusicoccin lacks the ability possessed by auxins to inhibit cell elongation in root tissues.

Procacci & Graniti (93), using a modification of Hygen's drying technique, showed that fusicoccin increased both stomatal and cuticular transpiration in toxin-treated plants. By using both silicon rubber impressions and measuring leaf water potential, Turner & Graniti (145) and Graniti & Turner (44) demonstrated that fusicoccin induced stomata to open wider in treated than in control leaves. They concluded that the water requirement for increased transpiration was greater than could be supplied by the conducting vessels and that the leaf water potential declined until the loss of turgor was visible. These workers also showed that fusicoccin induced stomates to open in the dark. Ballio et al (11) were the first to suggest that fusicoccin affects the permeability of plant cell membranes in the advanced stages of toxin action. Graniti & Turner (44) reasoned that the toxin may induce membrane changes causing the permeability of the membranes in the epidermal cells to be greater than that of the guard cells. This would result in an increase in turgor in the guard cells causing the stomata to open.

Recently, however, evidence presented by a number of workers (34, 35, 106) shows that potassium ion accumulation is required for stomatal opening in the light. Turner (144) investigated potassium uptake in leaves of *Phaseolus vulgaris* treated with fusicoccin. He demonstrated that the toxin stimulated the uptake of potassium by guard cells in both the light and dark, confirming the idea that potassium is necessary for stomatal opening. The effects of the toxin on stomatal opening could be reversed by the action of 2,4-dinitrophenol in both the light and the dark (144). These results indicated that for the normal stomatal opening process, ATP from both photosynthetic phosphorylation and oxidative phosphorylation is involved as an energy source in driving the uptake of potassium. Turner's results on potassium uptake have been confirmed by Natr (70), who also showed that photosynthetic rates were increased in toxin treated plants which he related to a decrease in the stomatal resistance to CO_2 transfer. Chain, Mantle & Milborrow (23) also confirmed Turner's observations on toxin-induced stomatal opening in tomato, but hastened to point out that leaves whose stomata were closed by application of absicisic acid still wilted in response to treatment with fusicoccin. These workers suggested that the most satisfactory hypothesis for the toxin action would involve a decrease in resistance of the plasmalemma to the passage of water and that the stomatal opening process is a secondary effect.

To this reviewer it seems apparent that the rapid increase in the stomatal apera-ture induced by toxin application is a primary affect of the toxin on the leaf. Such a phenomenon implies an involvement of potassium transport which is regulated by the energy balance of the guard cell. It appears likely that the toxin affects one or more systems associated with cellular energy production. This is not to deny the fact that by affecting the permeability of the plasmalemma to water, cellular energy production also may be altered.

Aside from the academic questions associated with the mode of action of fusicoc-cin, Turner (143) successfully showed the practical possibility of using fusicoccin as a means of hastening the drying time of alfalfa.

Ophiobolins

Orsenigo (72) isolated Ophiobolin A from cultures of *Cochliobolus miyakanus,* the perfect stage of *Helminthosporium oryzae.* Although *H. oryzae* causes brown spot of rice seedlings, the toxin causes a loss of pigment from beet root discs within 15 min, suggesting irreversible damage to plant membranes. Orsenigo & Pavan (73) demonstrated that this toxin also inhibits the growth of rice roots and coleoptiles. The shoots of treated rice seedlings became chlorotic within 24 hr as contrasted to wilting induced by fusicoccin under similar donditions (72). The absolute structure of Ophiobolin A was deduced by X-ray crystallographic analysis by Nozoe et al (71) and confirmed by Canonica et al (20). Ophiobolin A (Figure 3) has a basic terpenoid structure with an eight-membered ring, making it similar in respect to fuscicoccin. Thus biological correlations between Ophiobolin A and other compounds is limited because of its sophisticated and unique structure.

At least four ophiobolin-like structures besides Ophiobolin A are known from *H. oryzae.* Ophiobolin B (Figure 3) is the biological precursor of Ophiobolin A, and, likewise, Ophiobolin C (Figure 3) can be transformed to Ophiobolin A (18).

The isoprene origin of these toxins was demonstrated by Canonica et al (21); they showed that mevalonic acid-2-^{14}C was incorporated into Ophiobolin A to the extent of 3–10% of the original label administered to the fungus culture. They successfully showed by degradation, coupled with the localization of ^{14}C in the toxin, that the ophiobolins are derived from five mevalonic acid units. In a series of unique experi-ments using cultures of *H. oryzae* grown in an atmosphere enriched with ^{18}O, Canonica et al (19) showed that the OH group at position 14 of Ophiobolin B and the ethereal oxygen of Ophiobolin A are derived from the atmosphere while the hydroxy group at position 3 comes from water. More details on the stereochemistry and biosynthesis of these interesting toxins are given by Canonica (18).

Detailed biochemical and physiological studies on the mode of action of these toxins have not been made.

Helminthosporium maydis Toxins

In 1970, *H. maydis* caused an epidemic of Southern corn leaf blight in the United States (136). The pathogen was devastating on corn carrying Texas male sterile

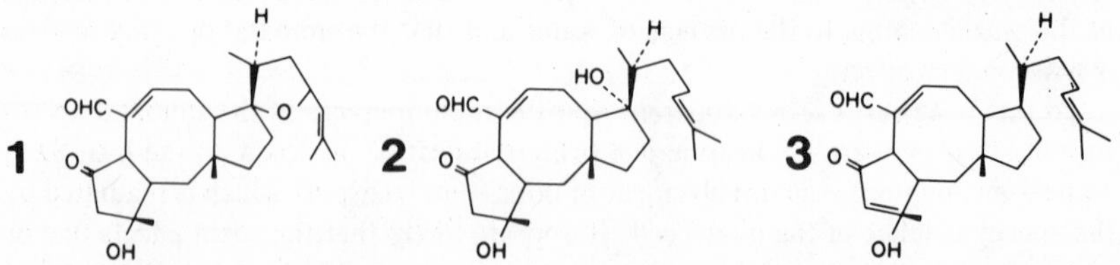

Figure 3 The ophiobolins: 1 = Ophiobolin A, 2 = Ophiobolin B, 3 = Ophiobolin C.

cytoplasm, while corn with normal cytoplasm, was resistant. A host-specific toxin had been associated with this organism (114), and a number of workers suggested that the toxin was responsible for the rapid graying, chlorosis, and necrosis associated with this disease. Using a leaf bioassay test, Karr, Karr & Strobel (54) isolated four host-specific toxins from *H. maydis* and showed numerous criteria of purity for at least three of these compounds. Two toxins, labeled I and II, reacted positively with all of the reagents commonly used in terpenoid identification and gave UV, IR, NMR, and mass spectral data comparable to those of known tetracyclic triterpenoids. Toxins I and II differed only slightly in spectral properties and molecular weight, whereas toxin III appeared to be a glycoside of either toxin I or II. All four compounds were recovered from leaf and stem tissues infected with *H. maydis.* The future development of information explaining the relationship between the action of the toxins and corn carrying Texas male sterile cytoplasm will be interesting.

Miller & Koeppe (69) showed that isolated mitochondria from corn carrying Texas male sterile cytoplasm were severely affected by crude preparations of the toxins from *H. maydis,* and that mitochondria from corn with normal cytoplasm were not affected. The effects on susceptible mitochondria included a loss of phosphorylating ability and severe swelling. Koeppe, Malone & Miller (56) have demonstrated that toxin preparations also adversely affect mitochondria in vivo within 1 hour after treatment. Arntzen et all (3) suggested that since the mitochondria in situ were not rapidly affected by the toxins of *H. maydis,* the primary site of toxin action must be elsewhere in the cell. They indicated that toxin preparations inhibited root growth in 30 min, and respiration was inhibited only after 2 hr of treatment. Likewise, only high concentrations of the toxins after prolonged treatment produced a decrease in cellular ATP and an increase in ion leakage. Mertz & Arntzen (67) demonstrated that the toxin preparations caused a rapid (less than 10 min) decrease in K^+ uptake and H^+ efflux in cells. On the other hand, phosphate uptake was affected much later, ca 60 min. The toxin preparations caused a rapid and only partial depolarization of the electrochemical membrane potential in cells. These data were taken as evidence that one of the earliest effects of the toxin was to impair the transport of ions across the plasmalemma. Changes in mitochondrial activity occurred later.

Toxin preparations rapidly inhibited CO_2 fixation probably as a result of impairment of stomatal functioning, the latter being consistent with a toxin-inhibited, light-induced K^+ uptake by guard cells (2). Toxin inhibition of K^+-stimulated ATPase activity has also been observed (141). Caution, however, must be taken in relating these results to symptoms of the disease since most physiological studies to date have been conducted with only partial purified toxin preparations. Thus it is conceivable that the differential effects observed between normal and Texas male sterile cytoplasm derived corn are entirely related to cultural products of the fungus that may not play a role in disease development yet are host-specific. Furthermore, since several toxins are known from this fungus, it is possible that besides individual toxin effects, there may be combined or even synergistic effects on corn tissues. For instance, a root growth inhibiting component of crude culture fluids does not produce lesions on susceptible leaves;[1] yet a root bioassay utilizing crude culture fluids has been useful in screening corn varieties for disease resistance (149).

AMINO ACID DERIVED PHYTOTOXINS

Phytotoxic substances that are derived from amino acids are produced by pathogenic fungi and bacteria. Several of these compounds appear to have host-specificity. In other cases, the peptide toxins exhibit not only plant but also animal toxicity.

Lycomarasmine and Related Compounds

The earlier work on lycomarasmine was done by Gaumann and his associates at the ETH in Zurich (38, 39). Lycomarasmine is produced by the wilt pathogen *Fusarium oxysporum* and is obtained from cultures in amounts of 200–300 mg/l after 6 weeks. It was the first so-called wilting toxin isolated and identified. A molecular weight of 277 and an empirical formula of $C_9H_5O_2N_3$ had beeen established for it by the earlier workers, and these formulae have recently been confirmed by rate of diffusion measurements of the Na salt and X-ray analysis of the copper complex (48). This phytotoxin is insoluble in water and many of the more common organic solvents. After acid hydrolysis, equimolar amounts of aspartic acid, glycine, and pyruvic acid are produced. No acetic acid is produced after Kuhn-Roth oxidation, and the toxin cannot be reduced catalytically. Woolley (152) concluded that the toxin was a derivative of asparagine because aspartic acid was not obtained after a Hoffman degradation and hydrolysis. Woolley proposed a structure for lycomarasmine and synthesized the compound by organic means. The synthetic product was quite soluble in water in contrast to its natural counterpart. However, the synthetic product was active in the wilt bioassay. Based on the inconsistent results of solubility tests, some question could be raised as to the accuracy of the original structure proposed by Woolley. Using the powerful technique of NMR spectroscopy in a comparative study of lycomarasmine with aspartic acid, N-acetyl aspartic acid and N (β-carboxy-β-aminoethyl) aspartic acid, Hardegger et al (48) determined what is currently accepted as the correct formula for lycomarasmine (figure 4).

Gaumann (37) described the effects of 0.01 M lycomarasmine as an immediate 33% decrease in both transpiration and absorption of H_2O by treated tomato cuttings. Following this initial response, an increase of both H_2O uptake and water

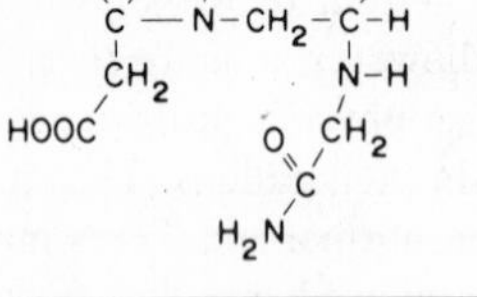

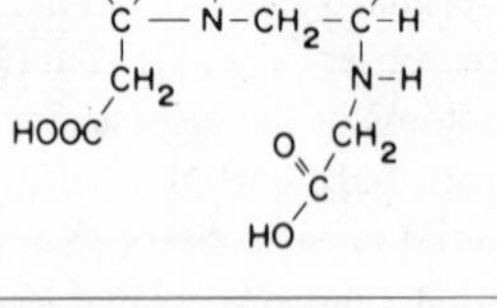

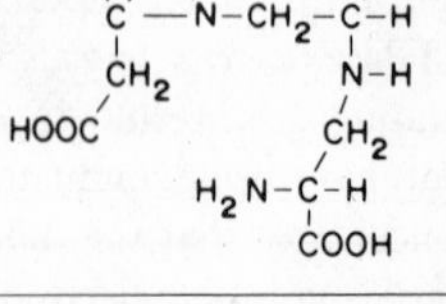

Figure 4   Lycomarasmine and its derivatives: 1 = lycomarasmine, 2 = Aspergillomarasmine B or lycomarasmic acid, 3 = Aspergillomarasmine A.

[1]Karr, A., Strobel, G. A. Unpublished results.

loss occurred over a 4-hr period. There was a net loss of H_2O since transpiration exceeded water intake and symptoms of desiccation appeared. Exceedingly large doses of lycomarasmine are needed to damage healthy tomato cuttings. Such treatments cause an upward curling of leaflets which become withered and desiccated followed by necrotic spotting in areas between veins. The wilting activity of this toxin is enhanced by ferric ions.

The role of lycomarasmine in the development of disease symptoms has been disputed by a number of workers. Scheffer (107), for instance, claims that even if the parasite produced the toxin in plants at the rate that it does in cultures, not enough toxin would be produced to induce symptoms even after 6 weeks. In normal disease development, necrotic spots seldom appear before the petioles wilt. In contrast, lycomarasmine first induces necrotic spots, and the petioles do not wilt. Furthermore, wilted leaves removed from infected plants and placed in H_2O often recover their turgidity; irreversible wilt is caused by lycomarasmine. It would seem that even though the role of lycomarasmine in the disease symptomatology is in some doubt, the fact that it possesses biological activity should still be of interest and investigated more thoroughly with modern techniques.

Two biologically active compounds were isolated from cultures of *Aspergillus flavus-oryzae* (45, 46, 99). These compounds were called aspergillomarasmine A and B, and after elemental analysis and acid hydrolysis, were shown to be related to lycomarasmine. In fact, aspergillomarasmine B turned out to be identical to lycomarasmic acid, and aspergillomarasmine A differed from B as shown in Figure 4. The elegant chemical work by the French investigators on the aspergillomarasmines was conducted on a nonpathogenic fungus and has paved the way for later workers who have shown the presence of these toxic compounds in cultures of plant pathogens. Ballio et al (5) described aspergillomarasmine B from *Colletotrichum olivarum,* the anthracnose pathogen of olive trees, and Bousquet et al (14) described aspergillomarasmine A from a strain of *C. gloesporioides* that attacks willows. Thus, although both substances cause wilt in the tomato assay tests, much more work could be done relative to their involvement in plant disease, their mode of action, and biosynthesis.

Tabtoxins

Wildfire is a highly infectious disease of tobacco plants caused by *Pseudomonas tabaci.* Leaves of plants infected by this disease are covered by circular yellow lesions about 1 cm in diameter. The causal organism can be isolated from these lesions. Cell-free culture filtrates are capable of producing the symptoms of the disease, and, in fact, symptoms can be produced on a number of plant species. Woolley, Pringle & Braun began the first systematic work on the isolation of the toxin (153). They developed a bioassay test and a method for concentrating the toxin. On the basis of the chemical reactions of the purified toxin, Woolley, Schaffner & Braun (154) proposed that the toxin was α-lactylamino-β-hydroxy-ε-aminopimelic acid lactone. Although subsequent work disproved the structure, it represented a foundation for later investigations of this toxin. Using ion-exchange chromatography in conjunction with a bioassay test, Stewart (120) was able to

```
          H  O  H  H                                      NH2
          |  ||  |  |                                      |
     H2N-C-C-N-C-COOH                                  H-C-COOH
          |        |                                       |
          CH2    H-C-OH                                    CH2
  1       |       |                    2                   |
          CH2     CH3                                      CH2
      O   |                                                |
       \  C-C-OH                                      H2N-C-COOH
          |  |                                             |
      H-N-CH2                                              CH2
                                                           |
                                                           OH
```

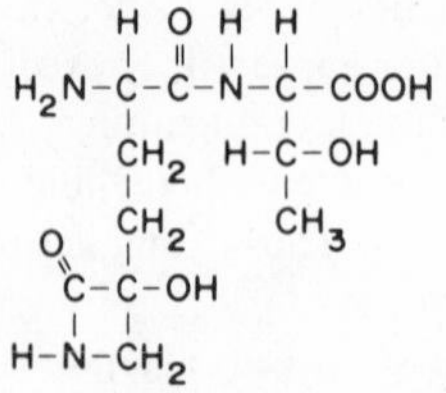

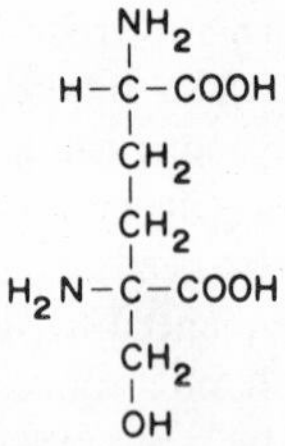

Figure 5 Tabtoxin and its derivatives: 1 = tabtoxin, 2 = tabtoxinine.

isolate the pure toxin as an off-white, fluffy noncrystalline powder. Based upon extensive NMR experiments coupled with basic compositional data and other spectroscopic observations, Stewart showed what is now accepted as the correct structural formula of tabtoxin (Figure 5). Hydrolysis of tabtoxin yields tabtoxinine and threonine (Figure 5). The structure of tabtoxin was recently confirmed by Taylor, Schones & Durbin (137). Furthermore, these workers isolated the serine analog of tabtoxin and proposed the name 2-serine-tabtoxin. It, too, is capable of inducing chlorosis in plants and has the same relative specific biological activity as tabtoxin.

Crude toxin preparations from *P. tabaci* have been called the "wildfire toxin." Since at least two toxins have been isolated from such preparations, the name wildfire toxin no longer seems appropriate. Sinden & Durbin (112) showed that *P. coronafaciens,* which attacks oats, also produces both tabtoxin and 2-serine-tabtoxin. In addition, *P. garcae,* a varient of *P. coronafaciens* attacking timothy, and a pseudomonad from wheat rhizosphere also produce these toxins.

Braun (15) originally suggested that the toxin could be regarded as a naturally occurring antimetabolite of methionine since in some plants its toxic action could be overcome by methionine. The hypothesis that the toxin was serving as a natural metabolite was fraught with several difficulties; namely, the proposed structure bore little resemblance to methionine, and pretreatment of tobacco leaves with methionine failed to prevent symptom production upon subsequent treatment with the toxin.

Sinden & Durbin (111) reopened studies on the mode of action of the wildfire toxin and proceeded to show that crude toxin preparations inhibited glutamine synthetase prepared from rat brains and pea. They demonstrated that toxin inhibition of glutamine synthetase is a mixed type of kinetics that is partially competitive and partially noncompetitive with respect to the formation of glutamic acid. They showed that toxin concentrations necessary to inhibit the enzymes in vitro were also able to produce chlorosis in tobacco leaves. Treated leaves accumulated ammonia to concentrations about seven times those in control leaves. Both chlorosis and ammonia buildup were prevented by injections of high concentrations of L-glutamine into leaves. They suggested that glutamine protected plants either by inhibiting the cellular uptake of the toxic compound or by preventing glutamine synthetase from being inhibited. They speculated that the results of the enzyme inhibition is a buildup of ammonia and perhaps other nitrogen-containing compounds which by themselves are detrimental to the leaf. There is now some evidence that pure tabtoxin does not inhibit glutamine synthetase suggesting another role for its toxicity.[2] This also implicates the presence of another toxic product in cultures of *Pseudomonas tabaci* that inhibits glutamine synthetase and points out the importance of using purified toxins in mode of action studies.

Tentoxin

Templeton (138) has recently reviewed work on this interesting compound produced by *Alternaria tenuis*. This organism produces an irreversible variegated seedling chlorosis in cotton, citrus, and other seedlings. The striking symptoms of this disease could be reproduced experimentally with sterile culture filtrates of the fungus. Cotton seedlings with more than 35% chlorotic areas usually die (36). The period of time that cucumber seeds are soaked in toxin solution directly affects the amount and pattern of chlorosis in developing cotyledons (139). A workable bioassay for tentoxin was developed by evaluating the amount of chlorophyll in toxin-treated seedlings that were incubated for 4 days at room temperature (42).

The most detailed procedure for the isolation of tentoxin is outlined by Templeton (138), and procedures for the preparation of large amounts of the toxin have also been described (102). A cyclic peptide with four amino acid residues was proposed as the structure for tentoxin (138, 140). Although a sequence of the amino acids in the peptide has been suggested (140), recent work by Koncewicz et al (57) has shown the structure of tentoxin to be cyclo-N-methyl-dehydrophenylalanyl-L-N-methylalanyl. Evidence for this structure was derived by using the established sequencing and mass spectrometric techniques.

Templeton et al (139) observed that cucumber seedlings were more sensitive to this toxin in darkness than under continuous light. These seedlings exposed 48 hr after the initiation of germination were insensitive to the toxin. As a result of this, as well as the overall symptom expression of affected seedlings, they suggested that the activity of the toxin was associated with some step late in chloroplast development. They proposed that the toxin may: (*a*) interfere with chlorophyll synthesis but not plastid development; or (*b*) interfere with plastid development thereby affecting chlorophyll synthesis indirectly. The work of Halloin et al (47) showed that cucumber seedlings, highly sensitive to the toxin, exhibited no interference with the conversion of protochlorophyll to chlorophyll, although a 90 percent reduction in chlorophyll content occurred. In cabbage, which is insensitive to the toxin, there was a slight stimulation in the chlorophyll content of toxin-treated tissues. Electron microscopy revealed that the treatment of cucumber cotyledons with toxin resulted in an abnormal development of lamellae and prolamellar bodies and yielded deformed plastids. These investigators noted that abnormal amounts of starch formed in both toxin-treated cucumber and cabbage plastids. Since starch accumulated it is possible that a toxin-mediated influence occurs on allosteric effectors of ADP glucose-pyrophosphorylase such as 3-PGA or inorganic phosphate as shown by MacDonald & Strobel (64) in rust-infected wheat.

[2]R. D. Durbin, personal communication.

Relative to the effect of the toxin on photosynthetic processes, Arntzen (1) has shown that tentoxin inhibits cyclic photophosphorylation but not reversible proton accumulation by chloroplasts of lettuce. Relatively low toxin concentrations inhibited coupled electron flow in the presence of ADP and phosphate. There was no effect on basal electron flow or on uncoupled electron transport. Arntzen suggested that tentoxin is an energy transfer inhibitor acting at the terminal steps of ATP synthesis. This explanation may ultimately account for chlorosis in the treated plants in that a synthesis of ATP in the plastid would be required for normal chloroplast development.

Recently, Durbin & Uchytil (33) have pointed out that immersion of leaves of common bean, mung bean, and cucumber in 200-μm tentoxin results in stomatal closure within 1 hr. Conversely, the stomates of cabbage, turnip, and raddish seedlings were not strongly affected by this toxin. Furthermore, in CO_2-free air in the dark, the opening of stomata of only susceptible plants was significantly inhibited. The chlorophyll content of (200 μM for 6 hr) leaves declined at the same rate as the leaves of control plants over a 5-day period. The chlorophyll data are in partial conflict with the previous observations made on the mode of action of this toxin. At the present time it seems difficult to resolve the problem until more information is abailable.

Rhizobitoxine

Certain strains of *Rhizobium japonicum* fix nitrogen in root nodules of soybean plants in a normal fashion and simultaneously synthesize a toxin that induces chlorosis in new leaf growth (77). Owens & Wright (77, 78) isolated a chlorosis-inducing toxin from chlorotic leaves of diseased plants, from nodules, and from bacterial cultures. The toxin, called rhizobitoxine by Owens, Guggenheim & Hilton (75), is not host-specific since it produces chlorosis symptoms in seedlings of many plants (77). Furthermore, it seems to be the sole cause of chlorosis in plants infected with disease-producing strains of *R. japonicum.* The disease is described by interactions of the host bacterium that are not a part of the normal symbiotic relationship.

The structure of rhizobitoxine was showed by Owens & Thompson to be 2-amino-4-(2-amino-3 hydroxypropyl)-*trans*-but-3-enoic acid (76). Experiments with *Salmonella typhirmurium* suggested that rhizobitoxine interferes with the metabolism of cystathionine (75). This suggestion was supported by the observation that supplementation with homocysteine or methionine prevented the inhibitory effect of the toxin on the growth of *S. typhimurium.* Furthermore, the toxin inhibited the activity of purified β-cystathionase from spinach in an active-site-directed irreversible manner (40, 41). The K_i for the dissociation of the enzyme-pyridoxal phosphate-toxin complex is 8 X 10^{-5}. Cystathionine, djenkolate, and β-cyanoalanine protect the enzyme from inactivation by the toxin, a fact consistent with the supposition that these compounds and the toxin compete for the active site on the enzyme. The experiments suggest that chlorotic symptoms in the infected soybeans result from the inability of the plant to form methionine. This would be a consequence of toxin inhibition of the enzymatic cleavage of cystathionine to form homocysteine, a precursor of methionine. Further studies on the specificity of the toxin will be needed to firmly establish its role as a specific inhibitor of β-cystathionase. Likewise, more information on its biosynthesis and those factors in infected plants which regulate its synthesis would be desirable.

Periconia Toxins

Periconia circinata, the causal agent of milo disease of *Sorghum* produces a host-specific toxin (87). All symptoms of the disease are caused by toxin preparations making it, among others, a useful model for studying the disease process. Using Dowex column chromatography, Pringle & Scheffer (90) demonstrated at least two host-specific toxins of *P. circinata.* At least one of the toxin components from this organism was crystallized (89). Satisfactory criteria for homogeneity of the crystalline toxin preparation were not presented, yet approximately 80% of the weight of the crystalline sample after acid hydrolysis could be accounted for as alanine, aspartic acid, glutamic acid, and serine, suggesting a peptide nature of the toxic component. Elution profiles from Sephadex G-25 column implied a molecular weight of approximately 2000. A criticism of this molecular weight estimate is that only the column technique was used to obtain the figure. Considerable error may occur with molecular weight estimations taken from Sephadex elution data since compounds may be retained because of their charged properties. Also there is a possibility that the toxin is something other than a peptide having a molecular weight in the range of 2000. If it is a peptide, then other experiments such as enzyme digestion, amino acid sequencing, and peptide synthesis should be conducted to show accurately the nature and chemistry of the toxin.

Some work on the mode of action of these toxins has been conducted by Mansour (66), who showed that increased respiration, electrolyte leakage, decreased ability to incorporate amino acids, and interference with membrane functions occurred in toxin-treated tissues. Adequate explanations with experimental data to account for the host-specificity as well as the primary site or sites of toxin attack are yet to be presented by people working on these interesting compounds.

Pseudomonas phaseolicola Toxins

P. phaseolicola is a pathogen of bean plants which causes chlorotic halos in infected host leaves. Hoitink, Pelletier & Coulson (51) showed that sterile culture filtrates of this bacterium induced halos characteristic of the disease. They also showed that a dilution series of the toxin gave a positive correlation with halo areas produced as a function of concentration. The toxic principle appeared to be thermostable and dialyzable. Rudolph (100) originally reported that the toxin was a polysaccharide with a molecular weight of 2100; it is composed of about 80% glucose, and a mixture of rhamnose, fructose, and peptide nitrogen. However, it appears that this substance produces symptoms somewhat unlike the halo areas shown by other investigators (81). Patil (80) resolved the partially purified halo-inducing toxin into two distinct anionic fractions by DEAE cellulose chromatography and both fractions possessed toxic activity. One of the two fractions yielded three known and two unknown amino acid residues upon acid hydrolysis. Although Patil has presented fairly convincing evidence for the peptide nature of a halo-inducing toxin, quantitative data on amino acid content, as well as structural data relative to the arrangement and nature of the amino acids, awaits further studies. Further, the chemical and biological relationships between the toxin prepared by Rudolph and the ones prepared by Patil need to be resolved.

In leaves either infected by *P. phaseolicola* or treated with crude toxin preparations, there is an accumulation of L-ornithine and chlorosis (101). Patil (79) suggested that the accumulation of ornithine may be a result of the toxin inhibition of ornithine carbamoyltransferase. The relationship between ornithine accumulation and chlorosis production is not clear, but a suggestion was made that reduction in the level or arginine observed in chlorotic halos, consistent with ornithine accumulation, may be detrimental to the synthesis of enzymes required for chlorophyll synthesis. This is partially supported by the fact that pretreatment of leaves with 10 μM citrulline 3 hr prior to, or simultaneously with, toxin injection resulted in no chlorotic halos. Patil explains this phenomenon as an alleviation of the citrulline deficiency normally resulting after toxin treatment because of the inhibition of ornithine carbamoyltransferase.

In additional studies with more highly purified preparations of toxin, Patil, Tam & Sakai (82) noted that ornithine did not accumulate in tissues treated with the purified toxin, suggesting that still other inhibitors or toxins may be produced by the pathogen. Nevertheless, L-arginine still protected leaves from toxin-induced chlorosis, indicating that the toxin-induced chlorosis is a reversible process most likely involved with chlorophyll biosynthesis.

Tam & Patil (133) have conducted kinetic studies on the inhibition of ornithine carbamoyltransferase by the purified toxic peptide of *P. phaseolicola*. Using the enzymes prepared from acetone powders of bean plants, they showed that the toxin induces a hyperbolic competitive inhibition for carbamoylphosphate and a noncompetitive inhibition relative to ornithine. The authors provide evidence for the binding of the toxin to a site on the enzyme other than the catalytic ones.

Helminthosporium carbonum Toxins

Scheffer & Ullstrup (110) successfully demonstrated the production of a host-specific toxin by *H. carbonum*. They showed that seedling growth and development of susceptible corn lines was greatly inhibited by culture filtrates of this fungus. Only corn lines normally susceptible to the pathogen were affected by the filtrates. High concentrations of the filtrate caused necrosis of susceptible corn root tips and had no effect on resistant seedlings. Leaf damage was evident in susceptible inbred lines treated with the filtrate diluted 50:1. Some suggestions were made that victoxinine was produced by *H. carbonum*. Importance was placed on the presence of this compound since it is also a portion of the host-specific toxin of *H. victoriae*. However, more recent work shows that victoxinine is not present in cultures of *H. carbonum* (92). Pringle & Scheffer (91) isolated that host-specific toxin of *H. carbonum*, and Pringle (86) described it as being a cyclic peptide containing proline and alanine in a ratio of 1:2 with two unstable amino acids, one of which was identified as α-amino-2,3-dehydro-3-methylpentanoic acid. Since the molecular weight of the toxin was estimated to be about 700, it is conceivable that proline and alanine occur as one and two residues per mole, respectively. The remaining un-known compound was suggested to be a hydroxy amino acid, and its breakdown during hydrolysis may have accounted for such compounds as ammonia, glycine, and unknown products. Although Pringle quantitatively accounted for alanine and proline in the toxin preparations, data on the remaining 70% of the weight of the samples were not presented. In view of this, as well as lack of adequate criteria of toxin purity presented by Pringle and Scheffer in their original report, there is a possibility that the toxin itself is a contaminant of their preparations and is some-thing other than a cyclic peptide.

Using the perfect stage of *H. carbonum, Cochliobolus carbonum,* crosses of race 1 with race 2 indicated that the toxin-producing ability of race 1 was qualitatively determined by one gene (108). The amount of toxin produced was controlled by several genes. Furthermore, genetic analysis of interspecific hybrids of *C. carbonum* with *C. victoriae* showed that a different gene pair controlled toxin production in *C. carbonum.* The host pathogenicity of each hybrid was positively correlated with its ability to produce one or both host-specific toxins.

Kuo, Yoder & Scheffer (58) showed that in susceptible corn infected with *H. carbonum* and susceptible corn treated with *H. carbonum* toxin, both the toxin and the fungus caused an increased capacity of susceptible tissues to fix CO_2 in the dark. Furthermore, cell-free preparations from toxin-treated corn leaves fixed more CO_2 with ribulose-5-phosphate, ATP, CO_2, and Mg^{+2} in the reaction mixture than did the control from nontreated tissues. Since no increase in CO_2 fixation was evident when toxin was added to extracts from nontreated corn tissues, it is apparent that the effect of the toxin is a secondary one and probably involves one or more regulatory factors associated with RuDPase (85). These results are comparable to those of Malca, Huffaker & Zscheile (65), who demonstrated that extracts from corn tissue infected with *H. carbonum* taken before the onset of symptom expression had a greater capacity to fix CO_2 in the dark than did control extracts.

Recently, Yoder & Scheffer (156, 157) demonstrated that toxin treated susceptible corn roots took up and retained more NO_3^-, Na^+, Cl^-, 3-*o*-methylglucose and leucine than did control roots. Their data suggested that the toxin does not cause derangement of the plasmalemma but instead results in specific changes in permea-bility to certain solutes. This work represents an excellent start in discovering the basis of susceptibility of corn to the *H. Carbonum* toxin. It should be followed up by water relations studies and an examination for the involved site or sites on the plasmalemma.

Syringomycin

DeVay & Strobel (29) showed that a wide spectrum antibiotic is produced by certain isolates of *Pseudomonas syringae* that are pathogenic on stone fruit trees. That virulence of *P. syringae* isolates was highly correlated with antibiosis toward *Geotrichum candidum* was demonstrated by DeVay et al (28). Further, they presented evidence that the antibiotic substance in crude extracts from bacterial cultures was phytotoxic. The antibiotic phytotoxin was named syringomycin: its properties have been described by Sinden, DeVay & Backman (113). Although no exhaustive tests were presented as criteria of homogeneity of the final toxin preparations, the authors used a number of procedures that conceivably could have resulted in a pure toxin. Syringomycin was described as a low molecular weight, ninhydrin-reacting compound which yielded eight known and one unknown amino acid after acid hydrolysis. Its broad antibiotic activity was labile at pH values above 8.0. Organisms, including filamentous fungi, unicellular algae, bacteria, and *Daphina* species among others, were inhibited by low levels of the toxin. The growth of *G. candidum* was completely inhibited at 24 µg/ml.

Syringomycin produced symptoms on leaves of peach shoots that were immersed in an aqueous solution containing 600 µg/ml (28). The symptoms of necrosis and browning were very similar to those produced in stems inoculated with *P. syringae.* A substance having some properties identical to those of syringomycin was isolated from diseased host tissues. The results of this work strongly implicated syringomycin as a contributory factor in producing symptoms associated with the disease. Penner, DeVay & Backman (83) demonstrated that syringomycin binds salmon sperm and calf thymus DNA but not calf thymus histone. The antibiotic inhibited RNA polymerase, uridylic acid incorporation in *G. candidum,* and the synthesis of the RNA phage MS2 in *E. coli.* Although effects of the toxin seemingly point to an involvement with DNA and RNA metabolism or function, the primary effect of the toxin appeared to be on cellular membranes (4). This contention is supported by evidence which included (*a*) electron micrographs of toxin-treated cells of *G. candidum* showing massive disruption of membrane integrity; (*b*) microautography of cells treated with ^{14}C toxin showing localization of label over the plasmelemma and nuclear membranes; and (*c*) reversal of the effects of the toxin on cells by treatment with certain sterols and phospholipids. Further evidence is required to verify the hypothesis that the membrane or specific membrane components are the primary site of toxin activity.

MISCELLANEOUS TOXINS

A review on the chemical and biological properties of the alternaria toxins by Templeton has appeared (138). Alternariol monomethyl ether is a metabolite of *A. tenuis* causing brown lesions and necrosis on Japanese pear and tobacco (84, 142). Tenuazonic acid, another toxin of *A. tenuis,* was first isolated and characterized by Stickings (121) and later synthesized by Harris, Fisher & Folkers (49). Mikami et al (68) showed that small amounts of this acid could induce chlorotic halos on tobacco leaves. Zinniol (116) is a phytotoxic metabolite of *A. zinnae.*

The concept of a toxin being host-specific was first exemplified by the work of Tanaka (134) on Japanese pear trees susceptible to *Alternaria kikuchiana.* Recent studies have shown that the toxin causes a rapid loss of electrolytes from susceptible tissues but little or no loss from resistant tissues (74). The earliest effect of the toxin was suggested to be on the plasmalemma. The common toxic metabolites of the other species of alternaria were not host-specific in their action and caused only slight changes in electrolyte loss. The host-specificity of this metabolite may lend itself very nicely to isolation and chemical studies.

Hydrogen cyanide (HCN) is a common phytotoxic product of a number of basidiomycetous fungi. A sterile psychrophilic basidiomycete pathogenic on a number of forage crops, winter wheat, and turf grass is capable of releasing HCN (60). Isolates unable to form HCN are not pathogenic. The organism produces two glucosidases and an oxynitrilase which collectively liberate HCN from cyanogenic glucosides (119). The degradation of glycine has been proposed as another source of HCN from this fungus (146).

A review of the naphthazarin toxins of *Fusarium* spp. has been published (151). These compounds are phytotoxic red pigments with a common naphthazarin structure. At least six of these compounds have been isolated, and they vary in biological activity. Correlations between toxin formation and pathogenicity have been found. In addition, some of these compounds have been isolated from diseased plants in quantities sufficient to cause damage to healthy tissues.

Workers throughout the world report toxic activity associated with numerous pathogenic fungi and bacteria. Such work paves the way for more thorough and comprehensive chemical and biological work on compounds posessing toxic properties. This review has not dealt with such reports because of their preliminary nature.

SUMMARY

Phytotoxins representing a diversity of classes of chemical compounds have been isolated from plant pathogenic bacteria and fungi. The structures of these compounds have been well characterized and several have been synthesized by organic synthesis. The association of the phytotoxin with the disease process has been made in a number of cases by isolating the toxin from diseased tissues and showing a relationship between pathogenicity of the organisms as it relates to toxin production.

Phytotoxins, especially the ones that are host-specific, have proven to be extremely useful tools in studying host-parasite interactions in as much as pathogen specificity in a given host or hosts is entirely related to the specificity of the toxin. In such cases the potential of explaining the plant disease susceptibility and disease resistance is apparent.

Toxins also appear to be tools useful in studying some of the activities of the healthy plant, not to mention their usefulness as agents in disease screening programs in plant breeding and selection.

ACKNOWLEDGMENTS

The author is a Public Health Service Career Development Awardee 1k4-GM-42, 457-05 from the National Institute of General Medical Sciences. Gratitude is expressed to the CSRS of the USDA for grant 216-15-23 and to the NSF for grant GB 12956, both of which deal with phytotoxins in plant diseases. This report represents paper number 462 of the Montana Agricultural Experiment Station.

The author wishes to thank D. Mathre, T. Kosuge, A. Karr, F. Pinkerton, and S. Kent for helpful suggestions and criticism on this manuscript, and Miss Teressa Arnold for her help in preparing it.

Literature Cited

1. Arntzen, C. J. 1972. *Biochim. Biophys. Acta* 283:539–42
2. Arntzen, C. J., Haugh, M. F., Bobick, S. 1973. *Plant Physiol.* 52:569–74
3. Arntzen, C. J., Koeppe, D. E., Miller, R. J., Peverly, J. H. 1973. *Physiol. Plant Pathol.* 3:444–47
4. Backman, P. A., DeVay, J. E. 1971. *Physiol. Plant Pathol.* 1:215–33
5. Ballio, A. et al 1969. *Phytopathol. Mediter.* 8:187–96
6. Ballio, A., Bottalico, A., Framondina, M., Graniti, A., Randazzo, G. 1971. *Phytopathol. Mediter.* 10:26–32
7. Ballio, A. et al 1968. *Experientia* 24:631–35
8. Ibid 1972. *Experientia* 28:126–27
9. Ballio, A., Casinovi, C. G., Randazzo, G., Rossi, C. 1970. *Experientia* 26:349–51
10. Ballio, A. et al 1964. *Nature* 203:297
11. Ballio, A., Graniti, A., Pocchiari, F., Silano, V. 1968. *Life Sci.* 7:751–60
12. Ballio, A., Pocchiari, F., Russi, S., Silano, V. 1971. *Physiol. Plant Pathol.* 1:95–104
13. Bamburg, J. R., Strong, F. M. 1971. *Microbial Toxins,* ed. S. Dadis, A. Ciegler, S. J. Ajl, 7:207–92. New York: Academic. 401 pp.
14. Bousquet, J. F., Vegh, I., Pouteau-Thouvenot, M., Barbier, M. 1971. *Ann. Phytopathol.* 3:407–8
15. Braun, A. C. 1950. *Proc. Nat. Acad. Sci. USA* 36:423–27
16. Brian, P. W. et al 1961. *J. Exp. Bot.* 12:1–12
17. Byther, R. S., Steiner, G. W. 1972. *Phytopathology* 62:466–70
18. Canonica, L. 1972. See Ref. 151, 157–73
19. Canonica, L. et al 1967. *Tetrahedron Lett.* 3371–76
20. Canonica, L., Fiecchi, A., Kienle, M. G., Scala, A. 1966. *Tetrahedron Lett.* 11:1211–18
21. Ibid, 1329–33
22. Casinovi, C. G. 1972. See Ref. 151, 105–25
23. Chain, E. B., Mantle, P. G., Milborrow, B. V. 1971. *Physiol. Plant Pathol.* 1:495–514
24. DeBary, A. 1886. *Bot. Z.* 44:377–474
25. DeMayo, P., Robinson, J. R., Spencer, E. Y., White, R. W. 1962. *Experientia* 18:359–60
26. DeMayo, P., Spencer, E. Y., White, R. W. 1961. *Can. J. Chem.* 39:1608–12
27. DeMayo, P., Spencer, E. Y., White, R. W. 1962. *J. Am. Chem. Soc.* 84:494–95

28. DeVay, J. E., Lukezic, F. L., Sinden, S. L., English, H., Coplin, D. L. 1968. *Phytopathology* 58:95–101
29. DeVay, J. E., Strobel, G. A. 1962. *Phytopathology* 52:360 (abstr.)
30. Dimond, A. E. 1970. *Ann. Rev. Phytopathol.* 8:301–22
31. Dimond, A. E., Waggoner, P. E. 1953. *Phytopathology* 43:229–35
32. Duniway, J. 1973. *Phytopathology* 63:458–66
33. Durbin, R. D., Uchytil, T. F. 1972. *Phytopathology* 62:755 (abstr.)
34. Fischer, R. A. 1968. *Science* 160:794–85
35. Fujino, M. 1967. *Sci. Bull. Fac. Educ. Nagasaki Univ.* 18:1–47
36. Fulton, N. D., Bollenbacher, K., Templeton, G. E. 1960. *Phytopathology* 50:575 (abstr.)
37. Gaumann, E. 1951. *Advan. Enzymol.* 11:401–37
38. Gaumann, E., Naef-Roth, S., Kern, H. 1955. *Phytopathol. Z.* 24:373–74
39. Gaumann, E., Naef-Roth, S., Miescher, G. 1950. *Phytopathol. Z.* 16:257–88
40. Giovanelli, J., Mudd, S. H. 1970. *Biochim. Biophys. Acta* 227:654–70
41. Giovanelli, J., Owens, L. D., Mudd, S. H. 1971. *Biochim. Biophys. Acta* 227:671–84
42. Grable, C. I., Templeton, G. E., Meyer, W. L. 1966. *Phytopathology* 56:897 (abstr.)
43. Graniti, A. 1962. *Phytopathol. Mediter.* 1:182–85
44. Graniti, A., Turner, N. C. 1970. *Phytopathol. Mediter.* 9:160–67
45. Haenni, A. L., Barbier, M., Lederer, E. 1962. *Compt. Rend.* 255:1476–78
46. Haenni, A. L. et al 1965. *Helv. Chim. Acta* 48:729–50
47. Halloin, J. M., DeZoeten, G. A., Gaard, G., Walker, J. C. 1969. *Plant Physiol.* 45:310–14
48. Hardegger, E., Liechti, P., Jackman, L. M., Boller, A., Plattner, P. A. 1963. *Helv. Chim. Acta* 46:60–74
49. Harris, S. A., Fisher, L. V., Folkers, K. 1965. *J. Med. Chem.* 8:478–82
50. Hess, W. M., Strobel, G. A. 1970. *Phytopathology* 60:1428–31
51. Hoitink, H. A. J., Pelletier, R. L., Coulson, J. G. 1966. *Phytopathology* 56:1062–65
52. *Index of Plant Diseases in the United States* 1969. Washington, D. C.: Crops Res. Div., ARS, USDA, Agr. Handbook No. 165. 531 pp.

53. Johnson, T. B., Strobel, G. A. 1970. *Plant Physiol.* 45:761–64
54. Karr, A., Karr, D., Strobel, G. A. 1974. *Plant Physiol.* In press
55. Keen, N. T., Williams, P. H. 1971. *Physiol. Plant Pathol.* 1:247–64
56. Koeppe, D. E., Malone, C. P., Miller, R. J. 1973. *Plant Physiol.* (*Suppl.*) 51:10 (abstr.)
57. Koncewicz, M. et al 1973. *Biochem. Biophys. Res. Commun.* 53:653–58
58. Kuo, M. S., Yoder, O. C., Scheffer, R. P. 1970 *Phytopathology* 60:365–68
59. Lado, P., Pennachioni, A., Rasi Caldogno, F., Russi, S., Silano, V. 1972. *Physiol. Plant Pathol.* 2:75–85
60. Lebeau, J. 1972. See Ref. 151, 437–39
61. Lousberg, J. J. Ch., Salemink, C. A. 1972. See Ref 151, 127–37
62. Ludwig, R. A. 1957. *Can. J. Bot.* 35:291–303
63. Luke, H. H., Gracen, V. E. 1972. See Ref. 13, 8:141–54
64. MacDonald, P., Strobel, G. A. 1970. *Plant Physiol.* 46:126–35
65. Malca, I., Huffaker, R. C., Zscheile, F. P. Jr. 1964. *Phytopathology* 54:663–69
66. Mansour, I. S. 1968. PhD thesis, Michigan State Univ. East Lansing
67. Mertz, S. M., Arntzen, C. J. 1973. *Plant Physiol.* (Suppl) 51:16 (abstr.)
68. Mikami, Y., Nishijima, Y., Iimura, H., Suzuki, A., Tamura, S. 1971. *Agr. Biol. Chem.* 35:611–18
69. Miller, R. J., Koeppe, D. E. 1971. *Science* 173:67–69
70. Natr, L. 1971. *Photosynthetica* 5(3):195–99
71. Nozoe, S. et al 1965. *J. Am. Chem. Soc.* 87:4968–70
72. Orsenigo, M. 1957. *Phytopathol. Z.* 29:180–96
73. Orsenigo, M., Pavan, D., 1958. *Ann. Fac. Agr. Univ. Catt. Sacro Cuore,* 19–54
74. Otani, H., Nishimura, S., Kohmoto, K. 1973. *J. Fac. Agr. Tottori Univ.* 8:14–20
75. Owens, L. D., Guggenheim, S., Hilton, J. L. 1968, *Biochim. Biophys. Acta* 158:219–25
76. Owens, L. D., Thompson, J. F. 1972. *J. Chem. Soc. Chem. Commun.* 714
77. Owens, L. D., Wright, D. A. 1965. *Plant Physiol.* 40:927–30
78. Ibid. 40:931–33
79. Patil, S. S., Tam, L. Q., Kolattukudy, P. E. 1972. See Ref. 151, 365–71
80. Patil, S. S. 1972. *Phytopathology* 62:782 (abstr.)
81. Patil, S. S., Tam, L. Q., Kolattukudy, P. E. 1972. See Ref. 151, 365–71
82. Patil, S. S., Tam, L. Q., Sakai, W. S. 1972. *Plant Physiol.* 49:803–7
83. Penner, D., DeVay, J. E., Backman, P. A. 1969. *Plant Physiol.* 44:806–8
84. Pero, R. W., Main, C. E. 1969. *Phytopathology* 60:1570–73
85. Preiss, J., Kosuge, T. 1970. *Ann. Rev. Plant Physiol.* 21:433–66
86. Pringle, R. B. 1971. *Plant Physiol.* 48:756–59
87. Pringle, R. B., Scheffer, R. P. 1963. *Phytopathology* 53:785–87
88. Pringle, R. B., Scheffer, R. P. 1964. *Ann. Rev. Phytopathol.* 2:133–56
89. Pringle, R. B., Scheffer, R. P. 1966. *Phytopathology* 56:1149–51
90. Ibid 1967. 57:530–32
91. Ibid, 1169–72
92. Ibid 1970. 60:565–66
93. Procacci, R., Graniti, A. 1966, *Proc. 1st Congr. Med. Phytopathol. Union, Bari, Italy*
94. Rai, P. V., Strobel, G. A. 1969. *Phytopathology* 59:47–52
95. Ibid, 53–57
96. Rebel, H. 1969. Thesis. State Univ. Utrecht, Netherlands
97. Ries, S. M., Strobel, G. A. 1971. *Plant Physiol.* 49:676–84
98. Ries, S. M., Strobel, G. A. 1972. *Physiol. Plant Pathol.* 2:133–42
99. Robert, M. et al 1962. *Bull. Soc. Chim. Fr.* 187–88
100. Rudolph, K. 1969. *Naturwissenschaften* 56:569–70
101. Rudolph, K., Stahmann, M. A. 1966. *Phytopathol. Z.* 57:29–46
102. Saad, S. M., Halloin, J. M., Hagedorn, D. J. 1969. *Phytopathology* 59:1048 (abstr.)
103. Sadowski, P., Strobel, G. A. 1973. *J. Bacteriol.* 115:668–72
104. Salemink, C. A., Rebel, H., Kerling, L. C. P., Tchernoff, V. 1965. *Science* 149:202–3
105. Salemink, C. A., Sehuring, F., Kerling, L. C. P., Schippers, B. 1966. *Experientia* 22:248–50
106. Sawhney, B. L., Zelitch, I. 1969. *Plant Physiol.* 44:1250–1354
107. Scheffer, R. P. 1952. PhD thesis. Univ. Wisconsin, Madison
108. Scheffer, R. P., Nelson, R. R., Ullstrup, A. J. 1967. *Phytopathology* 57:1288–91
109. Scheffer, R. P., Samaddar, K. R. 1970 *Recent Advan. Phytochem.* 3:123–42
110. Scheffer, R. P., Ullstrup, A. J. 1965. *Phytopathology* 55:1037–38

111. Sinden, S. L., Durbin, S. L. 1968. *Nature* 219:379–80
112. Sinden, S. L., Durbin, R. D. 1970. *Phytopathology* 60:360–68
113. Sinden, S. L., DeVay, J. E., Backman, P. A. 1971. *Physiol. Plant Pathol.* 1:199–213
114. Smedegard-Peterson, V., Nelson, R. R. 1969. *Can. J. Bot.* 47:951–57
115. Spencer, J. F. T., Gorin, P. A. J. 1961. *Can. J. Microbiol.* 7:185–88
116. Starratt, A. N. 1968. *Can. J. Chem.* 46:767–70
117. Steiner, G. W., Byther, R. S. 1971. *Phytopathology* 61:691–96
118. Steiner, G. W., Strobel, G. A. 1971. *J. Biol. Chem.* 246:4350–57
119. Stevens, D. L., Strobel, G. A. 1968. *J. Bacteriol.* 95:1094–1102
120. Stewart, W. W. 1971. *Nature* 229:174–78
121. Stickings, C. E. 1958. *Biochem. J.* 72:332–40
122. Straley, C., Straley, M., Strobel, G. A. 1974. *Phytopathology.* In press
123. Strobel, G. A. 1967. *Plant Physiol.* 42:1433–41
124. Strobel, G. A. 1970. *J. Biol. Chem.* 245:32–38
125a. Ibid 1973. 248:1321–28
125b. Strobel, G. A. 1974. *Proc. Nat. Acad. Sci. USA.* In press
126. Strobel, G. A. 1973. *Proc. Nat. Acad. Sci. USA* 70:1673–88
127. Strobel, G. A., Hess, W. M. 1968. *Plant Physiol.* 43:1673–88
128. Strobel, G. A., Hess, W. M., Steiner, G. W. 1972. *Phytopathology* 62:339–45
129. Strobel, G. A., Steiner, G. W. 1972. *Physiol. Plant Pathol.* 2:129–32
130. Strobel, G. A., Talmadge, K. W., Albersheim, P. 1972. *Biochim. Biophys. Acta* 261:365–74
131. Sutton, J. C., Williams, P. H. 1970. *Can. J. Bot.* 48:391–401
132. Ibid. 48:645–51
133. Tam, L. Q., Patil, S. S. 1972. *Plant Physiol.* 49:808–12
134. Tanaka, S. 1933. *Mem. Coll. Agr. Kyoto Univ.* 28:1
135. Taniguchi, T., White, G. A. 1967. *Biochem. Biophys. Res. Commun.* 28:879–85
136. Tatum, L. A. 1971. *Science* 171:1113–15
137. Taylor, P. A., Schones, H. K., Durbin, R. D. 1972. *Biochim. Biophys. Acta* 286:107–17
138. Templeton, G. E. 1972. See Ref. 13, 8:169–92
139. Templeton, G. E., Grable, C. I., Fulton, N. D., Bollenbacher, K. 1967. *Phytopathology* 57:516–18
140. Templeton, G. E., Grable, C. I., Fulton, N. D., Meyer, W. L. 1967 *Proc. Mycotoxin Res. Seminar.* Washington, D. C.: USDA
141. Tipton, C. L., Mondal, M. H., Uhlig, J. 1973. *Biochem. Biophys. Res. Commun.* 51:725–28
142. Torikata, H. et al 1969. *Ann. Phytopathol. Soc. Jap.* 35:62:66
143. Turner, N. C. 1970. *Agron. J.* 62:538–41
144. Turner, N. C. 1972. *Nature* 235:341–42
145. Turner, N. C., Graniti, A. 1969. *Nature* 223:1070–71
146. Ward, E. W. B., Thorn, G. D. 1966. *Can. J. Bot.* 44:95–104
147. Wheeler, H., Hanchey, P. 1968. *Ann. Rev. Phytopathol.* 6:331–50
148. Wheeler, H., Luke, H. H. 1963. *Ann. Rev. Microbiol.* 17:223–42
149. Wheeler, H., Williams, A. S., Young, L. D. 1971. *Plant Dis. Rep.* 55:667–71
150. Wood, R. K. S. 1967. *Physiological Plant Pathology.* Oxford: Blackwell. 570 pp.
151. Wood, R. K. S., Ballio, A., Graniti, A., Eds. 1972. *Phytotoxins in Plant Diseases.* New York: Academic. 530 pp.
152. Woolley, D. W. 1948. *J. Biol. Chem.* 176:1291–98
153. Woolley, D. W., Pringle, R. B., Braun, A. C. 1952. *J. Biol. Chem.* 197:409–17
154. Woolley, D. W., Schaffner, G., Braun, A. C. 1955. *J. Biol. Chem.* 215:485–93
155. Yoder, O. C., Scheffer, R. P. 1969. *Phytopathology* 59:1954–59
156. Yoder, O. C., Scheffer, R. P. 1973. *Plant Physiol.* 52:513–17
157. Ibid, 518–23

Ann. Rev. Plant Physiol. 1974. 25:567–86

PHYSIOLOGY OF MYCORRHIZA ❖7578

Franz H. Meyer

Institute for Landscape Management and Nature Conservation, 3 Hannover, Herrenhäuser Str. 2, Federal Republic of Germany

CONTENTS

INTRODUCTION 567
    Definition of Mycorrhiza 567
    Occurrence of Mycorrhiza in the Plant Kingdom 568
    Anatomical Features 569
ADVANTAGES OF ECTOMYCORRHIZA TO SYMBIOSIS PARTNERS 570
    Nutrient Requirements of Ectomycorrhizal Fungi 570
    The Significance of Ectomycorrhiza for the Host Tree 572
RECIPROCAL RELATIONSHIPS IN ECTOMYCORRHIZAE 574
    Ectomycorrhiza, a Form of Alleloparasitism 574
    Carbohydrate Physiology of Ectomycorrhizae 575
        Substances released by the fungi 575
        Translocation of carbohydrates 576
CONDITIONS FOR ECTOMYCORRHIZA FORMATION 578
    Factors Determined by the Fungus 579
    Factors Determined by the Higher Plant 580
    Soil Factors 582
ARE ECTOMYCORRHIZAE TYPICAL MANIFESTATIONS OF SOILS POOR IN
      NUTRIENTS? 582
CONCLUSION 583

INTRODUCTION

Definition of Mycorrhiza

Against the attack of soil fungi the tender roots are sensitive because of their structure, for cutin layers and corresponding barriers are formed only in older roots. On the other hand, the roots spread within a substrate which offers favorable conditions for existence to many fungi. Therefore, numerous fungi may penetrate into the younger parts of roots. Many authors name an infected root a mycorrhiza, provided that the higher plant suffers no damage by the fungus infection and that the infection remains restricted to the root cortex.

There is a broad spectrum of possibilities for the mode of coexistence of plant roots and fungi. The intruded fungus may behave like a harmless parasite which has pierced the cortex cells in order to gain nutrients. The higher plant may localize the invaded fungus to the cortex tissue, but the fungus is able to withdraw organic substances from the host plant without damaging it further.

In other cases the reaction of the higher plant is more specific. It synthesizes inhibitory compounds during its metabolic response to fungal attack and, as a consequence of this, may digest the penetrated mycelia. Through this digestion the host plant regains organic compounds previously taken away. There is also the possibility that the higher plant during lysis of mycelia regains mineral or organic nutrients which the fungus has drawn from the soil. In such cases symbiosis may render advantages to the host plant.

As early as 1911, Bernard (6) noted the production of antifungal compounds in orchid tubers in response to fungal infection. Specific inhibitory substances in orchid tubers were detected by Gäumann et al (19).

There are further examples in the plant kingdom that the host plant reverses the procedure and utilizes the original assailant. The fungus must then procure the energy requirements for the higher plant, as is the case in nonchlorophyllous orchids. For instance, in *Galeola septentrionalis* the intruder (*Armillaria mellea*) usually is known as a parasite, but here the higher plant became a parasite of the fungus (Hamada 25). Campbell (14) found the nonchlorophyllous *Monotropa uniflora* also associated with *Armillaria mellea*. When a mycorrhizal fungus is connected as well with the roots of a nonchlorophyllous angiosperm, as with the roots of a green plant, the former can indirectly parasitize the latter via the shared mycelium (Björkman 9, Trappe 110). Reid & Woods (92) gave evidence that within an ecosystem between mycorrhizal root systems an exchange of organic substances may take place.

Occurrence of Mycorrhiza in the Plant Kingdom

As mentioned above, with respect to the coexistence of higher plants and fungi there are many transitions from harmless parasitism of fungi to unilateral dependence of higher plants on the mycorrhizal fungus. In comparison with most other parts of higher plants, the tender roots can be infected quite easily, and therefore numerous cases of mycorrhiza in the plant kingdom have been recorded. Janse (34) and Maeda (50) checked the different systematic categories of plants for the occurrence of mycorrhiza and found that more than 80% of taxa are mycorrhizal ones. The mycorrhiza was absent in the Centrospermae, Plumbaginales, Cruciferae, Helobiae, Farinosae, and Cyperales. This fact deserves further attention, especially the question of whether these taxa produce specific antifungal substances. In a few taxa which have both marshy and dry habitats, the mycorrhizae have been shown to be absent in plants growing on marshy land (Droseraceae, Oenotheraceae, Halorrhagaceae).

In general, root hairs cease to form as soon as a mycorrhiza is established. This means that the active surface for nutrient and water uptake is diminished. However, in some cases to be discussed later, fungal hyphae act as additional absorbing organs.

The prevalence of mycorrhiza in the plant kingdom and the fact that the root stops root hair formation after fungal infection should be considered in experiments on plant nutrition. The uptake of nutrients via a root system under natural environmental conditions is greatly influenced by the state of symbiosis. "Needless to say, extrapolation of results obtained from laboratory or greenhouse studies in soil without mycorrhizal fungi to field application is dangerous" (Marx 54).

Anatomical Features

In most of the mycorrhizae the mycelia pierce into the interior of the cortex cells. As the mycorrhizal fungus attacks the host primarily in the same way as a parasite, the intracellular hyphae might be considered as haustoria, which we often notice in the pathogenic fungi. It appears that the host plant attempts to resist the invading hyphae by forming a cap of membraneous substance at the place of penetration. The localized secretion of membrane substance certainly represents a defense reaction and may be successful in encasing the penetrating fungus.

In some mycorrhizae a high content of tannins—whose secretion is also considered to be a defense mechanism—is obvious. The nucleus of infected cortex cells often swells and exhibits hyperchromicity. This is an indication that the metabolic activity of the nucleus increases. In general, the fungus settles in the outer layers of the root cortex, but when it tries to penetrate further into the inner layers of the root cortex, it can be overcome by the resistance of the host. This defense is seen under the light microscope as disintegration of hyphal coils (tolypophagy) or of arbuscules (thamniscophagy).

By lysing the hyphae of the endophyte, the host plant gains in organic compounds. On the basis of their results with the orchid *Dactylorhiza purpurella,* Hadley & Williamson (24) proposed the hypothesis that the transfer of nutrients from fungus to host occurs before digestion sets in, and that lysis is only a defense reaction and not a prerequisite for growth stimulus of the host plant.

In the endodermis the mycorrhizal fungi find an insurmountable barrier. Should a fungus surpass this barrier, it is no more a case of mycorrhiza but rather of pure parasitism against which the resistance of the higher plant failed. In mycorrhizae not only does the stele remain fungus free, but also the apical meristem.

Two main groups of mycorrhizae may be recognized: the ectomycorrhiza and endomycorrhiza. In the endomycorrhiza the fungal associate lives with one part of its mycelium within the root cells, i.e. intracellular, while in the ectomycorrhiza it develops among the cortex cells of the root (intercellular). In the endomycorrhiza as well as in the ectomycorrhiza the fungal mycelium invades not only the roots, but a more or less larger part thrives outside the roots in the soil.

In the ectomycorrhiza the mycelium between the root cells forms a network known as the Hartig net. This net creates a large common surface of contact between fungus and higher plant and thus facilitates the exchange of substances. Furthermore, in ectomycorrhiza the root is often surrounded by a fungal network, the fungus mantle. This sheath encloses the root apices and tender parts of roots without leaving any gap, so that there is no direct contact between the younger roots and the soil and all nutrients absorbed into the host must pass through the fungus mantle.

Between ecto- and endomycorrhiza there are anatomical transitions that can be named ectendomycorrhiza. In some ectendomycorrhizae distinct fungal partners have been described (Laiho 37, Mikola 77, Wilcox 116). Endomycorrhizae vary more than ectomycorrhizae and are by far the more prevalent type. Ectomycorrhizae are more unique and exhibit a rather definite pattern. Ectomycorrhizae appear to be a more advanced form of symbiosis than endomycorrhizae. We must keep in mind that endomycorrhiza and especially the ectomycorrhiza originated from a reciprocal parasitism. In the case of ectomycorrhiza there is a fairly balanced symbiosis that proved to be advantageous to both partners. For many partners of ectomycorrhiza symbiosis became obligatory, and they are unable to fulfil their life cycle in the absence of their symbiotic partner. Examples for this are given below.

The manyfoldness of endomycorrhiza shall not be discussed here in detail, but it is of interest to note how the fairly balanced reciprocal parasitism of ectomycorrhiza has developed, how it functions, and what the advantages are for the symbiosis partners.

ADVANTAGES OF ECTOMYCORRHIZA TO SYMBIOSIS PARTNERS

Nutrient Requirements of Ectomycorrhizal Fungi

The nutrient requirements of ectomycorrhizal fungi have been tested extensively on pure cultures. The results of these experiments show that the typical ectomycorrhizal fungi differ quite considerably from other ecological groups of woodland fungi, i.e. the lignicolous fungi and the litter-decaying fungi. Lignicolous and litter-decaying fungi may use cellulose and most of them also lignin as a carbon source. In contrast to these groups of fungi, the fermentative properties of typical ectomycorrhizal fungi are less. In general, they are incapable of lignin destruction and only a few of them may decompose cellulose; they are dependent to a high degree upon simple carbohydrates. Rarely, or only to a small extent, can these fungi utilize the complex organic material on the top soil of a forest (litter and dead branches) as a source of energy. In this respect they are at a disadvantage in competition with litter-decaying fungi when living asymbiotically. As the content of soluble carbohydrates in litter is very small, we can assume that they must have another source. As early as 1885, Frank (18) stated that ectomycorrhizal fungi gain the requisite amount of soluble carbohydrates from the roots of trees by attacking the roots like parasites. Melin & Nilsson (66) provided direct evidence by means of radioactive carbon that a translocation of carbon compounds takes place from the higher plant into the fungal associate.

Romell (95) gave experimental hints as to what extent ectomycorrhizal fungi are dependent on their host tree. Along the border of quadratical plots between the trees metal plates were driven deep into the soil in order to sever the roots within these plots from their parent trees so that no assimilates could flow into the isolated roots. Within the plots there was no further occurrence of fruit bodies of ectomycorrhizal fungi, with one exception, namely *Xerocomus subtomentosus*. This experiment shows that most ectomycorrhizal fungi form their fruit bodies only in symbiosis, and therefore in this respect they are dependent on their host tree.

The behavior of *Xerocomus subtomentosus* obliterates the border between the symbiotic and saprophytic fungi. With this fungus an artificial mycorrhiza could be initiated (Modess 83), and this fungus is capable of forming fruit bodies when living saprophytically.

Investigations on the fermentative potentialities of ectomycorrhizal fungi confirmed that there are subtle transitions between the saprophytic and the ectomycorrhizal fungi. Many ectomycorrhizal fungi exhibit their best growth in pure culture in the presence of glucose, while more complex carbohydrates are less useful for them (Hacskaylo 22, Melin 59, Norkrans 88). But there are also undoubtedly ectomycorrhizal fungi which can utilize lignin and cellulose to a significant extent, such as *Tricholoma fumosum* (Norkrans 88), *Xerocomus subtomentosus,* and *Lactarius deliciosus* (Lindeberg 45). Other ectomycorrhizal fungi (*Tricholoma imbricatum, Tricholoma vaccinum*) displayed a very weak production of cellulase only after adding starter glucose. This behavior suggests that an adaptive enzyme formation is involved.

Under certain circumstances the hyphae of the Hartig net penetrate through the cell wall and enter into root cells. A higher share of such so-called ectendomycorrhizae can be observed when ectomycorrhizae age or in trees which live under unfavorable environmental conditions (Bergemann 5, Meyer 68). Norkrans (88) and Melin (60) suggested that these penetrations might be induced after the available glucose in the roots is diminished. As in the case of the starter glucose in the culture substrate of *Tricholoma imbricatum* and *Tricholoma vaccinum,* the mycorrhizal fungi might be stimulated to produce cellulase after the consumption of most of the soluble sugar.

The differences in enzyme production between the saprophytic and ectomycorrhizal fungi are in several cases qualitative ones, but are often only of a quantitative nature. This fact, which also has been confirmed by Lyr (49) and Lundeberg (48), leads to the conclusion that the ectomycorrhizal fungi might have been derived from the litter-decomposing ones. During symbiosis with tree roots from which they obtain soluble sugars, they have lost most of their original saprophytic capabilities by adaptation to the new mode of life in successive degrees. During the course of adaptation to the symbiotic existence, the properties that are advantageous in symbiosis must have been correspondingly increased. This is expressed by the production of auxins in which the symbiotic fungi are mostly superior to the saprophytic ones (Moser 85).

Lundeberg (48) demonstrated that even within one fungal species (*Xerocomus subtomentosus*) physiological races can occur with differing abilities to decompose the humus compounds. To induce a stronger growth of pines Björkman (10) recommended adding those mycorrhizal fungi that also are able to break down humus compounds.

It can be assumed that distinct mycorrhizal fungus species may influence their host tree in different ways, according to their various enzymatic properties. Therefore, it would be desirable to inoculate seedlings with the more beneficial fungus partners (cf. Lamb & Richards 39, Moser 84), but up to now little has been known about the efficiency of various mycorrhizal fungi. In this connection the findings of Dominik (17) are of interest, i.e. that a host tree in its particular stages of development may harbor special symbiotic partners.

Fungi that display distinct differences from the saprophytic ones in respect to their enzymatic capabilities, and that form their fruit bodies only in symbiosis, we may call obligatory ectomycorrhizal fungi, while those that exhibit only quantitative differences and build up their fruit bodies as well under symbiotic as under saprophytic conditions we may name facultative ectomycorrhizal. According to these considerations the fungi of the forest soils (except for the pure parasites) may be classified as follows (Meyer 69):

1. Pure saprophytic litter fungi (e.g. *Mycena* spp.).
2. Predominantly saprophytically living, but also mycorrhiza-forming fungi (e.g. *Phallus impudicus* or *Collybia peronata*).
3. Mycorrhizal fungi with a broad host range, but which can also form fruit bodies in a saprophytic mode of nutrition (e.g. *Xerocomus subtomentosus, Scleroderma aurantium*).
4. Mycorrhizal fungi which undergo a symbiosis with several genera of trees and which the fruit bodies develop only under symbiotic association (e.g. *Amanita muscaria* or *Russula xerampelina*).
5. Species which are bound as symbionts only to a few genera of trees or to just one genus (e.g. *Suillus tridentinus* or *Lactarius porninsis* only with *Larix*).

The Significance of Ectomycorrhiza for the Host Tree

As already mentioned, in ectomycorrhizae root hairs are not developed and the fungal sheath completely covers the root apices and adjoining tender parts of roots. Therefore, nutrient salts and water must pass through the fungal associate on their course from soil to plant root. By using isotope techniques, Melin & Nilsson (63–65), Melin et al (67), and Mejstrik & Benecke (57) gained unequivocal proof that the ectomycorrhizae actually represent absorptive organs of trees and that the hyphae spreading from the fungal sheath into the soil act in analogous manner to root hairs in salt absorption. Furthermore, fungal hyphae are able to dissolve silicate minerals and little soluble phosphates (Henderson & Duff 32, Meyer & König 76). Wilde (117) suggests that in addition to the uptake of mineral nutrients from the soil, another beneficial effect of ectomycorrhiza lies in the solubilizing action of mycelial extensions. This problem was discussed by Voigt (114), who points to the fact that in infertile soils with a low level of ions in solution and on exchange sites ectomycorrhizae are most advantageous to higher plants. The process of uptake of mineral nutrients from soil and the movement from fungus to host has been intensively studied and described by Harley (27) and co-workers and by Bowen (12).

In the experiments of Lamb & Richards (39), inoculation of pine seedlings enhanced growth and nutrient uptake even where it did not result in mycorrhiza formation. The authors explain this as a rhizosphere effect.

The fungal sheath is also regarded as protecting the tender roots from pathogenic fungi (Levisohn 41). The possible role of ectomycorrhizae as biological deterrents to root pathogens was discussed by Zak (120). He suggested that several factors are involved in the protecting activity of ectomycorrhizal fungi; among these are the physical barrier of the fungus mantle, the secretion of antibiotics, and the support of a protective rhizosphere population of bacteria and fungi. Furthermore, during symbiosis the root cells are induced to produce substances that maintain the symbiotic equilibrium between root cells and mycorrhizal fungi. These substances may also inhibit pathogenic fungi. Marx & Davey (56) and Marx (53) gave proof of the capability of ectomycorrhizal fungi of *Pinus taeda* and *Pinus echinata* to protect the tender roots against the pathogenic *Phytophthora cinnamomi.* Marx (52) identified an antifungal and antibacterial compound (diatretyne nitrile), produced by the mycorrhizal fungus *Leucopaxillus cerealis,* that at 2 ppm totally inhibited the germination of zoospores of *Phytophthora cinnamomi.* Root pathogens (*Pythium* and *Fusarium* spp.) predominated in the rhizosphere of nonmycorrhizal roots of *Betula alleghaniensis* and were absent in the rhizosphere of mycorrhizae (Katznelson et al 35). Pure culture tests with *Rhizopogon vinicolor* i. a. revealed a strong inhibition of *Phytophthora cinnamomi, Pythium debaryanum,* and *P. sylvaticum* and a moderate inhibition of *Fomes annosus* and *Poria weirii* (Zak 121). Marx (55) proposed a list of ectomycorrhizal fungi with antibiotic activity and thoroughly discussed the mechanism of resistance of mycorrhiza to root diseases.

Krywolap et al (36) have shown that *Cenococcum graniforme* produced an antibacterial substance in pure culture and in symbiosis. This antibiotic was present not only in the mycorrhiza, but also in roots, stems, and needles of red and white pines, and they speculated that it could protect the pines to some degree against bacteria.

There are many observations that under natural environmental conditions tree seedlings devoid of mycorrhiza were stunted or died away. The first report of this kind was given by Melin (58), who observed that pine and spruce seedlings planted on freshly drained peat bogs were stunted as long as ectomycorrhizal fungi were absent. Pine species and other ectomycorrhizal conifers without ectomycorrhiza repeatedly displayed yellowed needles and were only weakly developed; in some cases their cultivation was not possible at all. Most of these observations were made in parts of the world where pines had not been cultivated and where soils have been found devoid of ectomycorrhizal fungi (Mikola 81). Other studies made where soils had been in agricultural use for long periods or where soil had been fumigated showed that conifers grew slowly and were chlorotic (Afscharpour et al 1, Henderson & Stone 31, Trappe & Strand 111). The cessation of growth could not be avoided by shading, irrigation, or manuring of various kinds. Only after the introduction of suitable ectomycorrhizal fungi did the plants recover. A detailed study on the necessity and methods of introduction of ectomycorrhizal fungi was made in different parts of the world by Mikola (79). By planting exotic tree species, new fungal species have been introduced to many countries (Mikola 80, Singer 99).

As mentioned above, one beneficial effect of ectomycorrhizae on the host trees lies in the mobilization and the transfer of mineral nutrients from soil into the higher plant. Therefore, the stunted growth in the absence of ectomycorrhizal fungi should be avoided by adding adequate amounts of mineral nutrients and trace elements. But by these methods the sickness of higher plants without ectomycorrhiza could not be avoided (Dale et al 16, Vozzo & Hackskaylo 115). On the other hand, it is possible to cultivate tree seedlings aseptically without any ectomycorrhizal fungus if a suitable nutrient solution is present. Under such circumstances they grow normally. Therefore, the higher plant is not absolutely bound to an ectomycorrhizal associate, but in natural surroundings it has to withstand the attack of many soil fungi. Because of their tender structured cell walls younger roots are not able to resist soil fungi physically, and in the absence of true ectomycorrhizal fungi they are invaded by other fungi. As a consequence of this infection no more root hairs are formed and the plant tries to expel the intruder by secreting antibiotic compounds like tannins. Lack of root hairs and cell walls impregnated with tannins hampers the absorptive function of the root. Slowly growing tree seedlings in sandy soils often exhibit such structures in their roots. The less vigorous growth of pine and spruce seedlings in soils lacking true ectomycorrhizal fungi may be traced, at least partially, to this phenomenon (Meyer 74).

Although the ectomycorrhizal fungus withdraws soluble carbohydrates from his host tree, this symbiosis is not harmful to the tree. Among all the soil fungi that are capable of entering tree roots, the invasion of ectomycorrhizal fungi is the least evil. Action and counteraction of both partners have reached in the long run a competitive balance that is beneficial to tree and fungus.

Under natural conditions ectomycorrhizal trees can unfold their competitive power only in the presence of a suitable fungal partner. In a large number of species, especially within the families of Pinaceae and Fagaceae, members with ectomycorrhiza have been selected in evolution against members without ectomycorrhizae. These trees are the main components of forests in rigorous climates and in the region of the timberline (Meyer 74, Moser 86).

RECIPROCAL RELATIONSHIPS IN ECTOMYCORRHIZAE

Ectomycorrhiza, a Form of Alleloparasitism

As mentioned earlier, the fungus enters the root like a parasite in order to procure the necessary carbohydrates. Against this offense a defensive force of the tree is operating. Only when the powers of offense and defense maintain a balance can both partners live eusymbiotically with each other. This mode of existence may appear like a peaceful coexistence in which both partners benefit. But the presence of a balance of forces is made obvious when environmental conditions change and thus favor one of the partners. The weaker one is then exploited to a larger degree than formerly. For instance, after a dry period that weakened tender roots, certain mycorrhizal fungi can enter cortex cells and utilize the cortex so that this mycorrhiza can no longer act as an absorbing organ (Meyer 68). In 1925 Melin (59) stated that ectomycorrhiza represents more a reciprocal exploitation than a reciprocal benefit. Therefore, he considered this kind of living together a double parasitism or alleloparasitism. Relatively little is known about the chemical substances that provoke this balance of forces and about the metabolites that enable both the partners to exploit each other. Some data on the interaction of the associates follow.

Carbohydrate Physiology of Ectomycorrhizae

SUBSTANCES RELEASED BY THE FUNGI Most of the ectomycorrhizal fungi have only restricted or no ability to break down and utilize the complex organic compounds in the litter or soil. They enter the roots like parasites to obtain nourishment. Undoubtedly these are not offered spontaneously to the fungus so that the host tree may get mineral salts in return. In the realm of ectomycorrhiza there is only a "taking away" or a "giving up" under compulsion. The question arises as to how the fungus succeeds in intervening in the metabolism of its host.

The first hints on this matter were given by Slankis (102, 103). He observed that the presence of auxin ((β-indolacetic acid) in root cultures free from fungus causes anatomical and morphological changes characteristic for ectomycorrhizae, i. e. radial elongation of outer cells, reduced growth in length along with an increase in diameter of the roots, and absence of root hairs on the swollen root parts. A corresponding morphogenesis could be induced by adding cell-free culture medium of an ectomycorrhizal fungus (Levisohn 40, Slankis 101, Turner 112). This proves that a substance with auxin character has been released by the mycelium into the culture medium. Because generally in roots the concentration of auxin lies above the optimum, and because an addition of auxin causes inhibition of the elongation of roots, the typical morphology of mycorrhizae may be traced back, at least partially, to the secretion of compounds of auxin nature through the fungus. Slankis (105) pointed out that the characteristic morphology of ectomycorrhizae is a consequence of the interaction between the fungus auxin and certain metabolites of the higher plant. In the experiments of Slankis there was an accelerated elongation and a decrease in diameter after a delay of addition of auxin for more than 2 weeks.

Moser (85) and Ulrich (113) demonstrated the ability of ectomycorrhizal fungi to synthesize indole auxins in pure culture if tryptophan is provided as a precursor. The findings of Moser show that the ability to produce auxin is more common among the ectomycorrhizal fungi and less among the saprophytes. Certain ectomycorrhizal fungi synthesize β-indolacetic acid even in the absence of tryptophan (Ulrich 113). The differences in auxin production between symbiotic and saprophytic fungi are more of a quantitative nature, and it seems that this capability increases in the course of symbiotic life.

The auxin concentrations necessary for the formation of mycorrhizal structures must be considered extremely high in comparison to the normal physiological ones (Slankis 104). Besides morphological changes, these high concentrations may evoke alterations in the metabolism of the host tree.

Auxin causes numerous changes in metabolism, but only some points of special meaning for symbiotic relationships shall be discussed here. The investigations of Borthwick et al (11), Stuart (108), Alexander (2) and Bausor (3) show that an addition of auxin to plants enhances the hydrolysis of starch into sugars. Furthermore, auxin apparently effects the translocation of sugar from the starch reservoir to those locations where the auxin is secreted (Cleland 15, Thimann 109). Auxins normally are formed in growing buds and young growing shoots where they serve to maintain the supply of sugars to the growing parts. According to the findings of

Slankis (105), auxin supplied externally to one part of the root system unfolds its action throughout the whole root system.

Besides auxin, other compounds may be involved in symbiotic relationships. Miller (82) found a definite production of cytokinins in five of seven tested mycorrhizal fungi, while two mycorrhizal fungi (*Cenococcum graniforme, Thelephora terrestris*) and 22 nonmycorrhizal fungi apparently released no cytokinins. The possible role of cytokinins in symbiosis is discussed by Miller (82), Hacskaylo (21), and Slankis (106). Cytokinins, among other things, may prevent maturation and suberization of infected root tips and thus apparently help mycorrhizae exhibit a longer life span than nonmycorrhizal rootlets. Furthermore, cytokinins, like auxins, may influence the mobilization of organic compounds to the point of cytokinin application. The role of cytokinins in ectomycorrhiza needs further elucidation.

Levisohn (43) tested the influence of gibberellins on ectomycorrhiza. Different soils were inoculated with *Giberella fujokuroi* and young seedlings of *Pinus sylvestris* grown in these soils. The inoculation resulted in a decrease of true ectomycorrhizae and a simultaneous increase of a "parasitic association." These findings show that byproducts of microorganisms may influence the interactions between the symbiotic partners. Therefore, in experiments on ectomycorrhiza, the activity of the microorganisms in the culture substrate should be considered. The partially contradicting results in experiments on ectomycorrhiza (for instance, influence of fertilizers) might be based on the different population of microorganisms in the culture substrate.

TRANSLOCATION OF CARBOHYDRATES   The analysis of sugar content of different parts of *Fagus sylvatica* seedlings grown in various soil types led to the idea that the mycorrhizal fungus plays an important role in the sugar economy of its host plant (Meyer 68). The concentration of soluble sugars in tender roots of a root system tends to increase with the frequency of ectomycorrhizae[1] on the root system (Björkman 7, Hacskaylo & Snow 23, Harley & Waid 29, Meyer 68). Considering the effects of auxin as mentioned above, this increased sugar level in roots may be the result of auxin production by symbiotic fungi.

This conception is supported by an experiment in which the roots of a single beech tree spread simultaneously into two substrates with different microbial activity, namely mull from eutrophic brown earth and mor from podsol (Meyer 68). A different frequency of mycorrhiza and parallel to this a different sugar content in roots was the result. The rise of sugar level in those parts with higher frequency of mycorrhiza must be a consequential effect of the fungal infection.

In the region of the root tips the symbiotic fungi withdraw sugars for their own requirements, and at the same time they induce an enhancement of the sugar level in the more distal root parts so that in root systems infected by mycorrhizal fungi there is a steep gradient in the concentration of soluble carbohydrates from top root over lateral roots to tender roots (Meyer 68). In mycorrhizae respiration is superior to that of nonmycorrhizal roots (Mikola 78, Routien & Dawson 96, Schweers &

---

[1]Frequency of ectomycorrhiza = the percentage of root tips converted into ectomycorrhizae.

Meyer 97). Mycorrhizal respiration is sensitive to oxygen deficiency (Harley et al 28).

There may be a competition between the mycorrhizal fungi and the growing buds and young shoots of a tree in respect to the effect of the auxin produced. In spring and the beginning of summer large amounts of carbohydrates are necessary for leaf and shoot growth and for diameter increase. During this time, although there is a sufficient moisture content in the soil, fruiting bodies of mycorrhizal fungi appear only very seldom, but those of saprophytic fungi appear quite often. However, in late summer and autumn, when leaves and shoots have been built up and the annual increment is almost finished, the mycorrhizal fungi in their auxin secretion may be able to compete successfully with the auxin production of the top of the tree and as a consequence of it form their fruiting bodies (Meyer 73). In the experiments of Hacskaylo (20) the development of young sporophores of *Telephora terrestris* attached to pine seedlings was arrested as soon as the pines were covered with a black bag.

Another important factor in the carbohydrate physiology of mycorrhizae is the ability of fungal partners to convert the absorbed sugars into compounds which the higher plant cannot influence. Rexhausen (93) found a rich presence of glycogen in the inner parts of the fungous mantle and in the Hartig net, but none in the noninfected roots. By withdrawing soluble carbohydrates from the roots and converting them into insoluble ones, which are not utilizable by the host plant, the mycorrhizal fungus also induces a gradient in the concentration of soluble carbohydrates in the plant roots. Within the soluble fraction of beech mycorrhizae Lewis & Harley (44) found two specific carbohydrates, namely mannitol and trehalose. These substances were not present in the host plant. From the findings of Rexhausen (93) and Lewis & Harley (44) it follows that the three important storage carbohydrates in the fungal partner (glycogen, mannitol, trehalose) constitute a sink into which the soluble carbohydrates of the tree flow and from which the host cannot reabsorb them.

The fungal partner intervenes into the carbohydrate metabolism of its host plant also by acting as a sink. This enhances the translocation of sugars to the root tips. But simultaneously the content of soluble sugars in main roots increases in comparison to uninfected roots. This increase must be traced back to the auxin secretion of mycorrhizal fungi. Both these facts, namely the rise in sugar level in main roots and the conversion of carbohydrates in the region of root tips, promote the transport of sugars.

The activities of the symbiotic fungi suggest that there is a faster and greater flow of assimilates to the infected roots than in plants without mycorrhizae. This was proved by Nelson (87). The trial plants (*Pinus resinosa* with and without mycorrhizae) assimilated $^{14}CO_2$ for 1 hour. Twenty-five hours later the percentage of radioactive photosynthate translocated to the roots was examined. In a plant with mycorrhizae 54% of the labeled photosynthate had been moved to the roots, while in a plant without mycorrhizae only 5% had been moved.

The experiments of Schweers & Meyer yielded similar results (97). The trial plants (*Pinus sylvestris* with different frequencies of mycorrhiza) were exposed for 6 ½ hr to $^{14}CO_2$, and thereafter the activity in the different parts of the plants was determined. The results (see Table 1) indicate that mycorrhizae considerably enhance the transport of labeled assimilates towards the roots. Furthermore, there is the tendency toward increased photosynthesis in plants with mycorrhiza. This result conforms with the theory that the activity of a sink can influence the rate of photosynthesis.

Table 1 Distribution of labeled carbon in needles, shoots, and roots of *Pinus sylvestris*. Activity (counts/min) per mg carbon

Trial plant	Needles	Shoots	Roots	Ratio, Shoot/ Root
without mycorrhiza	141,359 (94.54%)	7,895 (5.28%)	265 (0.18%)	29.79
without mycorrhiza	117,203 (95.51%)	5,324 (4.34%)	181 (0.15%)	29.41
with mycorrhiza (3%)	340,880 (95.30%)	15,181 (4.25%)	1,622 (0.45%)	9.36
with mycorrhiza (3%)	85,308 (96.38%)	2,863 (3.24%)	399 (0.38%)	8.45
with mycorrhiza (10%)	571,265 (84.39%)	58,323 (8.62%)	47,349 (6.99%)	1.23

CONDITIONS FOR ECTOMYCORRHIZA FORMATION

The formation of ectomycorrhiza is a subtle process which is controlled by a complex constellation of interacting factors. In this process of mycorrhiza formation the higher plant, the symbiotic fungus, and the environmental conditions are closely interlinked to each other and must be regarded as a complex system. In experiments exploring the conditions of mycorrhiza formation the natural environmental conditions should be maintained as far as possible. For instance, addition of sand to the natural substrate provides unlikely ecological conditions and thus influences the results considerably. The same may be true in substrates like vermiculite and terralite or gravel, which are ideal for experiments on plant nutrition or for testing the influence of ectomycorrhiza on host plants in comparison to aseptically grown plants (cf Lister et al 46, Schweers & Meyer 97). However, in such artificial substrates the microbial conditions and those for mycorrhiza formation are quite different from natural sites.

There are many theories on mycorrhiza formation and most of them regard only the higher plant and its internal state as decisive. Stahl (107) considered ectomycorrhiza as a special manifestation of nutritionally poor soils. Here the competition between higher plants and soil microorganisms for the scarce nutrients is especially intense. Stahl pointed out that in poor soils the higher plant could procure the essential nutrients with the aid of symbiotic fungi much more easily. Melin (59) found that the activity of fungi attacking the roots is a decisive factor in mycorrhiza formation.

Hatch (30), Björkman (7), Hacskaylo & Snow (23), and Shemakhanova (98) gave experimental evidence that the content of mineral salts in the soil effects the symbiotic relationships. Hatch (30) postulated that the soil conditions exert an influence on the internal relationship of nitrogen, phosphorus, potassium, and calcium in the plant and that an imbalance of these elements determines whether a mycorrhiza is formed. Björkman (7) thoroughly reexamined the existing theories of mycorrhiza formation and considered the content of soluble carbohydrates within the roots as the decisive factor. The sugar content is influenced by the supply of nitrogen and phosphorus, which promotes the synthesis of proteins in the plant and thereby lessens the content of sugars. Lack of soluble carbohydrates adversely effects mycorrhiza formation. A lessened intensity of assimilation under reduced daylight works in a similar manner. According to the carbohydrate theory proposed by Björkman, the formation of mycorrhiza is controlled by the status of the host plant "through the surplus of energy nourishments present in the roots of trees." Meyer (68) emphasized that in the process of mycorrhiza formation many factors are involved on behalf of the higher plant as well as on behalf of the fungal partner. These factors, on the other hand, are regulated by the environment (soil conditions etc). Meyer stated: "Mycorrhiza formation is promoted by all factors that enable the fungus to obtain the necessary organic compounds more easily from the higher plant." Most of these regulating factors are incompletely known and need further study. The factors now recognized as important are discussed in the following paragraphs.

Factors Determined by the Fungus

A suitable fungal associate must be active. The activity is reduced or even completely arrested through specific inhibitory substances which occur in nondecayed litter (Bendz 4, Olsen et al 89) and row humus (mor) (Melin 59, Levisohn 42) or which are secreted by certain saprophytic fungi (Brian et al 13) and by endophytic fungi of *Calluna* (Handley 26).

Specific metabolic manifestations must correspond with those of the host so that the fungus can intervene in the metabolism of its host plant, for instance, by the secretion of auxin. Auxin production is influenced by various soil factors. Moser (85) found that a high nitrogen concentration in the substrate lessens the production of fungus auxin. This may explain the low content of ectomycorrhizae in certain soils rich in nitrogen. Slankis (105) convincingly demonstrated that at high nitrogen concentrations the renewed elongations on ectomycorrhizal roots regain a nonmycorrhizal state, and he traces this back to inhibited auxin production. Slankis (106) cited experimental data showing that the endogenous auxin content in higher plants tends to rise with increased availability of nitrogen. In this connection it appears that the mycorrhizal fungi with their reduced auxin production are no longer able to compete successfully with the auxins of the higher plant (cf influence of seasons on formation of fungus fruit bodies as mentioned above). On the other hand, the synthesis of auxin by the symbiotic fungi is accelerated by various soil organisms (Moser 85). According to Meyer (68, 70) the frequency of mycorrhiza rose in three different soil types along with the total microbial activity. Comparing roots with the same mycorrhiza frequency within the different layers of a profile, those within the microbially more active fermentation and humus layer contain relative more sugar and often are more swollen and stunted than those within the B-horizon, and the fermentation layer is superior to the humus layer (Figure. 1). The observations mentioned above indicate that the conditions for the formation of ectomycorrhiza are more advantageous in microbially active forest soils. In such soils the ectomycorrhiza also proved to be more stable against the influence of fertilizers, because it was not diminished to the same extent as in sandy, infertile soils of low microbial activity (Meyer 68). The additional secretion of growth substances by accompanying microorganisms may be one reason for this. The living conditions and composition of microorganisms in the mycorrhizosphere has been described by Rambelli (90).

An established mycorrhiza seems to promote the formation of mycorrhizae on the newly developed root apices in a manner similar to active microflora in the soil. This idea is supported by an experiment in which the roots of the same plant spread simultaneously into two different soil types, namely microbially most active mull and less active raw humus. The mycorrhiza frequency increased in raw humus when at the same time other roots of the same plant grew in mull. After fertilization, mycorrhiza frequency decreased in 2-year-old seedlings below the level in 1-year-old seedlings (Meyer 68).

Factors Determined by the Higher Plant

Favorable light conditions promote the formation of mycorrhiza. In the experiments of Björkman (7) mycorrhiza frequency decreased considerably at light intensities below 23% of full daylight. According to Björkman, the decrease is caused by a lack of soluble carbohydrates. It may be that light intensity also influences the formation of mycorrhiza by way of the synthesis of compounds other than sugar, for instance by plant hormones. The establishment of the specific physiological state in ectomycorrhiza seems to result "from an interaction between the fungus auxin and the host plant metabolites, other than soluble sugars" and it seems "that certain of these metabolites are not formed at low light intensities" (Slankis 105). In this field there are many open questions. Furthermore, the reduction of ectomycorrhizae under low light intensities may also be due to retarded root growth, since decreased illumination adversely affects the production of new roots (Hoffmann 33). The absence of newly developed mycorrhizae in the girdling experiment of Björkman (8) also may be a consequence of restricted root growth (Meyer 68).

The root secretes certain substances which diffuse into the immediate surroundings of the root and which stimulate the activity of fungi. The so-called M factor is such a stimulating compound (Melin 61). In its influence on hyphal growth the M factor can be replaced by diphosphopyridine nucleotide (Melin 62).

It can be assumed that in the process of ectomycorrhiza formation antibiotics secreted by the higher plant are involved and that these substances control the settlement of the symbiotic fungi. The defensive power of the host plant by means of such antibiotics must achieve a critical level against the fungus seeking entrance. It should not be so great that the fungus is destroyed, but also not so small that the

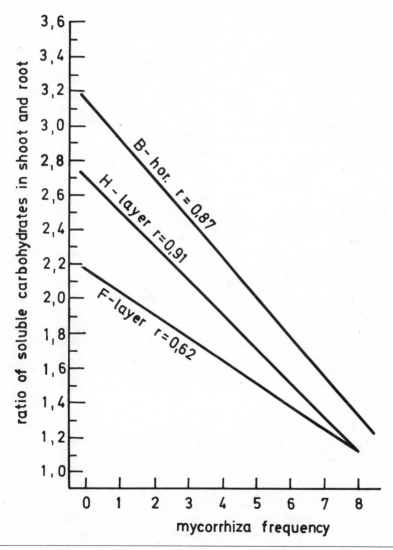

Figure 1   Relation between mycorrhiza frequency (determined at 10% interval) and ratio of soluble carbohydrates in shoot and root of beech plants grown in B-horizon, humus layer, and fermentation layer of eutrophic brown-earth and podsol (after Meyer 68).

plants suffer damage at the hands of the fungus. The formation and action of antibiotics as mentioned above deserves further investigation.

Soil Factors

The activity of both partners in symbiosis is greatly influenced by soil properties. Ectomycorrhizal fungi require an adequately aerated substrate (Meyer 74, Read 91), and most of them need an acidic soil for good development (Modess 83). But not quite all the mycorrhizal fungi develop best in an acidic soil. Richards (94) found ectomycorrhizal fungi in neutral and weakly alkaline soils as long as the nitrification remained weak. In chestnut-colored alkaline soils (Kastannosem) ectomycorrhizas in *Quercus* occur abundantly (Lobanow 47).

Most of the ectomycorrhizal fungi develop poorly in the presence of a water deficit. After dry periods of at least 3 weeks it often can be observed that the fungus mantle and the outer cortex layers shrink. After the soil has been remoistened ectomycorrhizas regenerate from the renewed elongations of roots. The dark-colored *Cenococcum graniforme,* on the other hand, is impaired by a water deficit to a lesser extent (Worley & Hacskaylo 118). Its abundant occurrence in raw humus is a consequence of periodic water deficit in this substrate, which is caused by densely interwoven roots (Meyer 71). Soil temperature affects formation and structure of mycorrhizae (Marks & Foster 51).

The soil properties not only affect both partners directly but also the symbiotic relationships. Rexhausen (93) and Bergemann (5) compared conifers cultivated on sand, poor in nutrients, and in forest soil, rich in humus. Morphology and anatomy of mycorrhizae in both substrates differed considerably, and parallel to this was the growth of conifers. In sand the conifers exhibited a weak growth, the fungus mantle was absent, the outer cortex cells were filled with tannins, and in autumn a relatively intense intracellular infection was noticed. In forest soil the fungus mantle was thick and the Hartig net stretched less deeply into the cortex. Thus in the sand the fungus apparently behaved more like a parasite and the symbiotic balance was not fairly established.

ARE ECTOMYCORRHIZAE TYPICAL MANIFESTATIONS OF SOILS POOR IN NUTRIENTS?

Most theories on mycorrhiza formation state that nutritional properties of soils greatly influence the symbiotic relationships (Björkman 7, Hatch 30, Shemakhanova 98, Stahl 107). A lack of nutritional elements, especially nitrogen and phosphorus, was considered as decisive for ectomycorrhiza formation. This might evoke the idea that in soils poor in nutrients the higher plant "allows" the fungus to enter the roots in order to obtain the necessary minerals. Observations in forests seem to confirm such theories. In nutritionally poor soils ectomycorrhizae are most frequent, while in fertile soils less ectomycorrhizae can be detected.

The results of Meyer (68) seem to contradict these theories. In infertile podsol the frequency of mycorrhizae (see footnote on page 576) was low and in eutrophic brown-earth it was high. As mentioned above, in eutrophic brown-earth the prerequisites for the activity of ectomycorrhizal fungi are better than in podsol, where ectomycorrhizae also are less stable. Similar results were obtained by Wright (119). On Douglas fir seedlings mycorrhiza formation was stimulated by a soil of high fertility with a balanced content of nutrients. Therefore, it is inappropriate to consider ectomycorrhizae as a typical manifestation of soils poor in nutrients.

The fact that ectomycorrhizae are especially conspicuous in poor soils can be attributed not to better conditions for ectomycorrhiza formation, but to the rooting peculiarities of trees in these substrates. As shown by Meyer (72) and by Meyer & Göttsche (75), the rooting habits of *Fagus sylvatica* and *Picea abies* vary considerably in different soil types. The more disadvantageous the site and the biological conditions the more root tips have to be formed by the trees to obtain the necessary amounts of minerals and water, and the more the roots concentrate in the upper parts of the profile, where especially within the fermentation layer minerals are rendered available to plant roots in the course of decomposition of plant debris. Thus the number of root tips of beech increases from the eutrophic brown-earth with about 500 root tips per 100 ml of soil to the podsol with 45,600 in the fermentation layer. In forest soils poor in nutrients mycorrhizae are conspicuous because of the shallow and dense rooting habits. But as stated above, the conditions for mycorrhiza formation are not as good as in biologically more active soils. The share of the so-called pseudomycorrhizae (roots not converted into true ectomycorrhizae) is greatest in podsol. The pseudomycorrhizae may indicate an imbalance between mycorrhizal fungus and host plant; they have a shorter life than true mycorrhizae (Laiho & Mikola 38) and are less efficient in absorbing water and nutrients (Meyer 74).

The frequency of the true ectomycorrhizae is directly related to the conditions of mycorrhiza formation, these being favorable in mull (eutrophic brown-earth) and unfavorable in mor (podsol), and the number of root tips corresponds inversely to the nutritional state of the soil: good in mull, bad in mor. These statements support the theory of Melin (59), that the initial constitution of ectomycorrhiza took place in forest soils with high microbial activity and that the well-balanced symbiosis enabled the trees to advance towards soils and regions with suboptimal site quality.

Forests growing under less favorable environmental conditions often harbor a high percentage of ectomycorrhizal trees or are entirely ectomycorrhizal. This, for instance, is the case in the region of the timberline in the boreal zones and the mountains (Moser 86). Here symbiosis is obligatory for tree and fungus, as is often the case with the symbiotic partners of lichens. Therefore, Singer & Morello (100) placed the reciprocal relationship between ectomycorrhizal trees and their fungal partners alongside the lichens and coined the term "ectotroph" for the complex tree/fungus organism.

CONCLUSION

Ectomycorrhiza is a symbiosis far from being fully elucidated; there exist many statements that are partially contradicting. One reason for this might be the fact that an ectomycorrhiza is governed by a complex of interlinking physiological and ecological factors and that at least three main factor groups must be considered: the host plant, the symbiotic fungus, and the environment. Experimental data from the field or greenhouse often cannot be replicated because the environmental conditions are not known sufficiently. Results obtained from exact experiments under laboratory conditions often cannot be transferred directly to the natural environment because decisive factors were quite different in the laboratory (e.g. a sterilized artificial rooting substrate like terralite). Experiments in the field or greenhouse and in the laboratory should complement and control each other. The controversial points of view will in the future perhaps become partially reconciled when in generalizing the experimental results some additional factors are included like composition and activity of the accompanying population of microorganisms, daylength and seasons, soil type and soil properties, and treatment of plants before the beginning of experiments. In addition to these more ecological points, those compounds which control symbiosis and are involved in symbiotic relationships need further investigation.

Literature Cited

1. Afscharpour, F., Retzlaff, E., Meyer, F. H. 1967. *Nachrichtenbl. Deut. Pflanzenschutzdienstes* 19:4–6
2. Alexander, T. R. 1938. *Plant Physiol.* 13:845–58
3. Bausor, S. S. 1942. *Bot. Gaz.* 104: 115–21
4. Bendz, G. 1956. *Physiol. Plant.* 9: 243–46
5. Bergemann, J. 1955. *Z. Weltforstwirt.* 18:184–202
6. Bernard, N. 1911. *Ann. Sci. Nat. Bot. Ser. 9,* 14:221–34
7. Björkman, E. 1942. *Symb. Bot. Upsal.* 6(2):1–190
8. Björkman, E. 1944. *Sv. Bot. Tidskr.* 38:1–14
9. Björkman, E. 1960. *Physiol. Plant.* 13:308–29
10. Björkman, E. 1970. *Stud. Forest. Suec.* 83:1–24
11. Borthwick, H. A., Hammer, K. C., Parker, M. W. 1937. *Bot. Gaz.* 98:491–519
12. Bowen, G. D. 1973. *Ectomycorrhizae,* ed. G. C. Marks, T. T. Kozlowski, 151–205. New York: Academic. 444 pp.
13. Brian, P. W., Hemming, H. G., McGowan, J. C. 1945. *Nature* 155:637–38
14. Campbell, E. O. 1971. *Mich. Bot.* 10:63–67
15. Cleland, R. E. 1961. *Encyclopedia of Plant Physiology,* ed. H. Ruhland, 14:754–83. Berlin, Göttingen, Heidelberg: Springer. 1357 pp.
16. Dale, J., McComb, A. L., Loomis, W. E. 1955. *Forest Sci.* 1:148–57
17. Dominik, T. 1959. *Soc. Sci. Stetinensis* 1:1–17
18. Frank, A. B. 1885. *Ber. Deut. Bot. Ges.* 3:128–45
19. Gäumann, E., Nüesch, J., Rimpau, R. H. 1960. *Phytopathol. Z.* 38:274–308
20. Hacskaylo, E. 1965. *Forest Sci.* 11: 401–4
21. Hacskaylo, E. 1971. *Proc. 1st N. Am. Conf. Mycorrhizae,* USDA Misc. Publ. 1189, 175–82
22. Hacskaylo, E. 1973. See Ref. 12, 207–30
23. Hacskaylo, E., Snow, A. G. 1959. *Northeast. Forest. Exp. Sta. Pap.* 125:1–13
24. Hadley, G., Williamson, B. 1971. *New Phytol.* 70:445–55
25. Hamada, M. 1939. *Jap. J. Bot.* 10:151–211
26. Handley, W. R. C. 1963. *Forest. Comm. Bull.* 36:1–70
27. Harley, J. L. 1969. *The Biology of Mycorrhiza.* London: Hill. 334 pp.
28. Harley, J. L., McCready, C. C., Brierley, J. K., Jennings, D. H. 1956. *New Phytol.* 55:1–28
29. Harley, J. L., Waid, J. S. 1955. *Plant Soil* 7:96–112
30. Hatch, A. B. 1937. *Black Rock Forest Bull.* 6:1–168
31. Henderson, G. S., Stone, E. L. 1970. *Soil Sci. Soc. Am. Proc.* 34:314–18
32. Henderson, M., Duff, R. B. 1963. *J. Soil Sci.* 14:236–46
33. Hoffmann, G. 1967. *Arch. Forstw.* 16:745–49

34. Janse, J. M. 1897. *Ann. Jard. Buiten-zorg* 14:202–5
35. Katznelson, H., Rouatt, J. W., Peterson, E. A. 1962. *Can. J. Bot.* 40:377–82
36. Krywolap, G. N., Grand, L. F., Casida, L. E. Jr. 1964. *Can. J. Microbiol.* 10:323–28
37. Laiho, O. 1965. *Acta Forest. Fenn.* 79(3):1–35
38. Laiho, O., Mikola, P. 1964. *Acta Forest. Fenn.* 77(2):1–33
39. Lamb, R. J., Richards, B. N. 1971. *Aust. Forest.* 35:1–7
40. Levisohn, I. 1953. *Nature* 172:316–17
41. Levisohn, I. 1954. *New Phytol.* 53:284–90
42. Levisohn, I. 1957. *Nature* 179:1143–44
43. Ibid 1960. 186:987–88
44. Lewis, D. H., Harley, J. L. 1965. *New Phytol.* 64:224–69
45. Lindeberg, G. 1948. *Physiol. Plant.* 1:196–205
46. Lister, G. R., Slankis, V., Krotkov, G., Nelson, C. D. 1968. *Ann. Bot.* 32:33–43
47. Lobanow, N. W. 1960. *Mykotrophie der Holzpflanzen.* Berlin: VEB Deut. Wiss. 352 pp.
48. Lundeberg, G. 1970. *Stud. Forest. Suec.* 79:1–95
49. Lyr, H. 1963. *Int. Mykorrhiza Symp. Weimar 1960,* 123–45
50. Maeda, M. 1954. *Kumamoto J. Sci. Ser. B.* 3:57–84
51. Marks, G. C., Foster, R. C. 1973. See ref. *12, 1–41*
52. Marx, D. H. 1969. *Phytopathology* 59:411–17
53. Marx, D. H. 1971. *Proc. 1st N. Am. Conf. Mycorrhizae,* USDA Misc. Publ. 1189, 81–96
54. Marx, D. H. 1972. *Agrichem. Age* 15:13–14,16
55. Marx, D. H. 1973. See Ref. 12, 351–82
56. Marx, D. H., Davey, C. B. 1969. *Phytopathology* 59:559–65
57. Mejstrik, V., Benecke, U. 1969. *New Phytol.* 68:141–49
58. Melin, E. 1917. *Norrl. Handbibl.* 7:1–426
59. Melin, E. 1925. *Untersuchungen über die Bedeutung der Baummykorrhiza.* Jena: Fischer. 152 pp.
60. Melin, E. 1953. *Ann. Rev. Plant Physiol.* 4:325–46
61. Melin, E. 1954. *Sv. Bot. Tidskr.* 48:86–94
62. Melin, E. 1963. *Tree Growth,* ed. T. T. Kozlowski, 247–63. New York: Ronald. 442 pp.
63. Melin, E., Nilsson, H. 1950. *Physiol. Plant.* 3:88–92

64. Melin, E., Nilsson, H. 1954. *Sv. Bot. Tidskr.* 48:555–58
65. Ibid 1955. 49:119–22
66. Ibid 1957. 51:166–86
67. Melin, E., Nilsson, H., Hacskaylo, E. 1958. *Bot. Gaz.* 119:241–46
68. Meyer, F. H. 1962. *Mitt. Bundesforschungsanst. Forst. Holzwirt.* 54:1–73
69. Meyer, F. H. 1963. *Ber. Deut. Bot. Ges.* 76:90–96
70. Meyer, F. H. 1963. *Int. Mykorrhiza Symp. Weimar 1960,* 285–95
71. Meyer, F. H. 1964. *Soil Biology,* ed. A. Jongerius, 23–31. Amsterdam: Elsevier. 540 pp.
72. Meyer, F. H. 1967. *Forstarchiv* 38:286–90
73. Meyer, F. H. 1968. *Transport of Plant Hormones,* ed. Y. Vardar, 320–30. Amsterdam: North Holland
74. Meyer, F. H. 1973. See Ref. 12, 79–105
75. Meyer, F. H., Göttsche, D. 1971. *Integrated Experimental Ecology,* ed. H. Ellenberg, 48–52. Berlin: Springer. 214 pp.
76. Meyer, L., König, E. 1960. *Landwirt. Forsch.* 13:7–24
77. Mikola, P. 1965. *Acta Forest. Fenn.* 79(2):1–56
78. Mikola, P. 1967. *Proc. Int. Union Forest Res. Organ. 14th,* 100–11
79. Mikola, P. 1969. *Unasylva* 23:35–48
80. Mikola, P. 1969. *Karstenia* 10:169–76
81. Mikola, P. 1973. See Ref. 12, 383–411
82. Miller, C. O. 1971. *Proc. 1st N. Am. Conf. Mykorrhizae,* USDA Misc. Publ. 1189, 168–74
83. Modess, O. 1941. *Symb. Bot. Upsal.* 5(1):1–146
84. Moser, M. 1959. *Forstwiss. Zentralbl.* 78:193–202
85. Moser, M. 1959. *Arch. Mikrobiol.* 34:251–69
86. Moser, M. 1967. *Mitt. Forstl. Bundesversuchsanst, Wien* 75:357–80
87. Nelson, C. D. 1964. *The Formation of Wood in Forest Trees,* ed. M. H. Zimmermann, 243–59. New York: Academic
88. Norkrans, B. 1950. *Symb. Bot. Upsal.* 11(1):1–126
89. Olsen, R. A., Odham, G., Lindeberg, G. 1971. *Physiol. Plant.* 25:122–29
90. Rambelli, A. 1973. See Ref. 12, 299–349
91. Read, D. J. 1972. *New Phytol.* 71:49–53
92. Reid, C. P. P., Woods, F. W. 1969. *Ecology* 50:179–87
93. Rexhausen, L. 1920. *Beitr. Biol. Pflanz.* 14:19–58

94. Richards, B. N. 1961. *Nature* 190: 105–6
95. Romell, L. G. 1938. *Sv. Bot. Tidskr.* 32:89–99
96. Routien, J. B., Dawson, R. F. 1943. *Am. J. Bot.* 30:440–51
97. Schweers, W., Meyer, F. H. 1970. *Ber. Deut. Bot. Ges.* 83:109–19
98. Shemakhanova, N. M. 1962. *Mycotrophy of Woody Plants.* Transl. From Russ., Israel Prog. Sci. Transl. Jerusalem 1967. 429 pp.
99. Singer, R. 1964. *Nova Hedwigia* 7:93–132
100. Singer, R., Morello, J. H. 1960. *Ecology* 41:549–51
101. Slankis, V. 1948. *Physiol. Plant.* 1:390–400
102. Slankis, V. 1949. *Sv. Bot. Tidskr.* 43:603–7
103. Slankis, V. 1951. *Symb. Bot. Upsal.* 11(3):1–63
104. Slankis, V. 1963. *Int. Mykorrhiza Symp. Weimar 1960,* 175–83
105. Slankis, V. 1971. *Proc. 1st N. Am. Conf. Mycorrhizae,* USDA Misc. Publ. 1189, 151–67
106. Slankis, V. 1973. See Ref. 12, 231–98.

107. Stahl, E. 1900. *Jahrb. Wiss. Bot.* 34:539–668
108. Stuart, N. W. 1938. *Bot. Gaz.* 100:298–311
109. Thimann, K. V. 1972. *Plant Physiol.* 6B:1–365
110. Trappe, J. M. 1971. *Quart. Rev. Biol.* 46:219–25
111. Trappe, J. M., Strand, R. F. 1969. *Forest. Sci.* 15:381–89
112. Turner, P. D. 1962. *Nature* 194:551–52
113. Ulrich, J. M. 1960. *Physiol. Plant.* 13:429–43
114. Voigt, G. K. 1971. *Proc. 1st N. Am. Conf. Mycorrhizae,* USDA Misc. Publ. 1189, 122–31
115. Vozzo, J. A., Hacskaylo, E. 1971. *Forest. Sci.* 17:239–45
116. Wilcox, H. 1971. *Proc. 1st N. Am. Conf. Mycorrhizae,* USDA Misc. Publ. 1189, 54–68
117. Wilde, S. A. 1954. *Soil Sci.* 78:23–31
118. Worley, J. F., Hacskaylo, E. 1959. *Forest Sci.* 5:267–68
119. Wright E. 1971. *Ore. State Univ. Forest Res. Lab. Res. Bull.* 13:1–36
120. Zak, B. 1964. *Ann. Rev. Phytopathol.* 2:377–92
121. Zak, B. 1971. *Can. J. Bot.* 49:1079–84

REPRINTS

The conspicuous number aligned in the margin with the title of each article in this volume is a key for use in ordering reprints.

Available reprints are priced at the uniform rate of $1 each postpaid. Payment must accompany orders less than $10. A discount of 20% will be given on orders of 20 or more. For orders of 200 or more, any Annual Reviews article will be specially printed.

The sale of reprints of articles published in the Reviews has been expanded in the belief that reprints as individual copies, as sets covering stated topics, and in quantity for classroom use will have a special appeal to students and teachers.

AUTHOR INDEX

A

Aach, H. J., 404
Aasheim, T., 489
Abdel-Al, M. S. M., 287
Abdul-Baki, A. A., 175, 176, 200, 211
Abe, H., 505
Abeles, F. B., 185, 285, 286, 479, 504
Abelson, P. H., 367
Abercrombie, M. J., 341, 347
Abo El-Nil, M. M., 143, 148
Abrahamsen, M., 168, 185
Abramovitch, R. A., 499
Abrol, Y. P., 286
Ackrell, B. A. C., 105
Adams, P. A., 204, 218
Addicott, F. T., 184, 260-62, 264, 274, 278, 284-87, 290-94, 300
Addink, C. C. J., 197, 201
Adelman, M. R., 310, 314, 338, 340, 341, 349
Adelstein, R. S., 338, 339
Advani, V. R., 228, 229
Afscharpour, F., 573
Agrawal, K. M. L., 213
Ahmed, K. S., 499
Ahuja, M. R., 146, 488
Aikman, D. P., 521
Aist, J. R., 318, 320, 326, 328
Akazawa, T., 229, 231
Akhtar, S., 481
Aksenovich, A. V., 242
Alben, J. O., 229
Alberghina, F., 174, 182
Alberghina, F. A. M., 480, 481
Albersheim, P., 206, 212, 214, 216, 546
Albert, S., 341
Alden, T., 488
Aldrich, H. C., 320
Aldridge, N. A., 234, 250
Alexander, T. R., 575
Alfieri, F. J., 516, 519
Ali, H., 470
Alibert, G., 465, 468, 476
Allard, R. W., 228, 250
Allaway, W. G., 41
Allen, J. F., 440
Allen, M. B., 394, 424, 432
Allen, N. S., 348, 349
Allen, P., 145
Allen, P. J., 318
Allen, R. D., 310, 321, 337, 340, 348, 349
Alléra, A., 340, 341, 351
Alleweldt, G., 157
Allison, A. C., 341, 345
Allison, R. M., 95, 96
Allridge, N. A., 496
Allsopp, A., 153
Altman, A., 286, 291, 297
Altschul, A. M., 173
Alvarez, M. R., 496
Amagase, S., 382, 383
Amar, L., 71, 75
Amelunxen, F., 443
Amen, R. D., 167, 171, 284
Amesz, J., 425, 433, 435, 436
Amin, J. V., 502
Amir, J., 380
Ammirato, P. V., 147, 154
Amrhein, N., 316
Anai, M., 92
Andersen, K. S., 34, 37
Andersen, L., 298
Anderson, B. J., 440, 441, 443, 446
Anderson, J. D., 171, 175, 176, 187, 492
Anderson, J. M., 37, 142, 159, 405, 435
Anderson, J. W., 383, 465, 482
Anderson, L. E., 228, 229
Anderson, W. P., 54, 73, 521
Andreae, W. A., 218, 490, 505
Andreasson, D. C., 143
Andrew, C. S., 56
Andrews, D. J., 395, 405
Aneja, S., 144
Anojulu, C. C., 184, 298
Anstine, W., 250, 251
Antcliff, A. J., 532
Antoine, A. D., 92
Antonini, E., 480
Antonova, E. K., 234
Antoszewski, R., 229, 263, 274, 501
App, A. A., 181
Appleby, C. A., 84, 93, 94, 104, 106
Ap Rees, T., 175, 177, 233
Aprison, M. H., 96
Arditti, J., 138, 139, 292
Arias, I. M., 370
Armstrong, B., 432, 435, 443
Armstrong, D. J., 380
Armstrong, J. E., 184
Arney, S. E., 290
Arnold, W. N., 530
Arnon, D. I., 82, 87, 90, 94, 95, 394, 424, 425, 427, 432, 433, 436
Arnon, R., 250
Arnott, H. J., 336
Arntzen, C. J., 430-32, 437, 440, 443, 446, 553, 558
Aronoff, S., 527
Arquembourg, P. C., 229, 247
Arrigoni, O., 200
Arslan, N., 201
Asada, K., 179, 229, 438-40
Asahi, T., 177
Asahira, T., 383
Ascarelli, I., 229
Aschoff, J., 116
Ash, J. F., 310, 341, 343, 347, 349
Ashida, J., 201, 209
Ashton, F. M., 172, 174, 183, 382, 383, 387
Askham, M. J., 529
Aslam, M., 368, 374
Asmundson, C. M., 268, 274
Aspinall, D., 184, 274, 284, 290, 291, 293, 294
Atal, C. K., 144
Atanasov, A. I., 142
Atkins, B. D., 200
Atkinson, D. E., 118, 412
Attardi, G., 181
Attridge, T. H., 464
Aubert, J.-P., 97
Audrain, L., 384
Audus, L. J., 196, 218
Ausländer, W., 436, 438, 441, 445, 446, 448, 449, 451
Austin, R. B., 168, 187
Avadhani, P. N., 44, 49, 119
Avants, J. K., 233
Avers, C. J., 326, 342
Avery, G. S., 505
Avron, M., 424, 425, 427, 431-33, 436, 439, 440, 444, 448, 449, 451, 452
Awwad, H. K., 370
Axelrod, B., 229
Axelrod, D., 49
Axelrod, J., 117, 345
Aylor, D. E., 335, 336
Azari, P. R., 384
Azhar, S., 216

B

Ba, L.-T., 159
Baba, S., 333

Baccari, V., 174
Baccarini-Melandri, A., 128
Bachofen, R., 439
Back, A., 293, 294
Backman, P. A., 561, 562
Backs, D., 147, 154
Badr, S. A. M., 292
Baginsky, M., 438
Bahl, O. P., 213
Baic, D., 41, 324, 329, 333
Bain, J. M., 34, 37, 172, 177, 185, 186
Baisted, D. J., 186
Bajaj, Y. P. S., 142, 144
Bajer, A. S., 310, 318, 321, 323, 325, 341
Baker, D. A., 73, 525, 531, 532
Baker, D. B., 211
Baker, D. N., 30
Baker, J. E., 234, 481
Baker, J. H., 67
Baker, P. C., 340
Baker, R. H., 174
Baker, R. S., 496
Bal, A. K., 181
Balasingam, K., 481, 482
Balce, L. V., 175
Baldev, B., 142
Baldry, C. W., 30, 32, 46, 47, 394, 397, 400, 401, 403, 406, 409, 410, 416
Baldy, R., 464, 465, 468, 479
Ball, E., 147
Ball, E. A., 138, 139
Ballade, P., 142, 161
Ballal, S. K., 228, 229
Ballantine, J., 39
Ballard, L. A. T., 170, 171, 177
Ballin, G., 493, 494
Ballio, A., 543, 549-51, 555, 563
Baltscheffsky, H., 452
Balz, J. P., 385
Bamberger, E. S., 394, 395, 403, 444, 448
Bamburg, J. R., 215, 549
Bandurski, R. S., 213, 505
Bange, G. G. J., 59, 65, 73
Bangham, A. D., 394
Bannister, L. H., 336
Bannister, T. T., 436, 440-42, 446
Bar-Akiva, A., 496
Barba, R., 144, 159
Barber, D. A., 56, 64, 66, 73
Barber, G. R., 180-82
Barber, J. T., 379, 380
Barbier, M., 555
Barendse, G. W. M., 183
Barker, H. A., 96
Barkley, G. M., 197-99, 201-

4, 207
Barlow, H. W. B., 290
Barlow, P. W., 333
Barnes, M. F., 289
Barnsley, G. E., 286
Barr, R., 365-68
Barrett, G., 492
Barry, A. J., 534
Bartlett, D. J., 466
Bartlett, L., 260
Barton, L. V., 167
Barton, R., 310
Barz, W., 468, 477
Barzilai, E., 183
Bassham, J. A., 47, 130, 394, 395, 397, 398, 400, 401, 403, 407, 415
Basu, P. S., 498
Baszynski, T., 432-34
Bates, D. C., 229
Battaile, J., 83
Bauer, K., 58
Bauer, L., 530
Bauer, W. D., 212, 214, 216
Baun, L. C., 228, 231, 239, 240
Bausor, S. S., 575
Bayer, M. H., 488
Bayley, S. T., 211
Bazzaz, M., 436
Bazzaz, M. K., 36, 37
Beale, S., 379
Bearden, A. J., 427
Beasley, C. A., 287
Beauchesne, G., 156, 157
Beavers, H., 119
Bechet, J., 371
Bech-Hansen, C. W., 318
Beck, G. E., 229-31
Beck, R., 341
Becker, W. M., 175
Becking, J. H., 92, 108
Beckman, L., 231, 248
Beevers, H., 43, 74, 174, 185, 187, 366, 406
Beevers, L., 172, 183, 291, 293, 299, 374, 375
Behal, F. J., 248
Behnke, H. D., 517
Behnke, O., 313, 338, 340, 341, 345, 350-52
Beisel, W. R., 117
Belderok, B., 168
Belitser, N. V., 385
Belitz, H. D., 172
Bellenger, N., 75
Bellin, S. A., 263, 265
BeMiller, J. N., 499
Ben-Aziz, A., 229
Benbadis, M-C., 323, 325
Bendall, D. S., 425, 431, 433, 477
Bendall, J. R., 310, 347
Bendana, F. E., 505
Bendz, G., 579
Benecke, U., 572

Benemann, J. R., 81, 92-95
Ben-Hamida, F., 382
Ben-Hayyim, G., 436, 439, 440
Ben-Jaacov, J., 141, 159
Bennet-Clark, T. A., 211
Bennett, C. W., 532
Bennoun, P., 438, 439
Ben-Shaul, Y., 185, 186
Benson, A., 87
Benson, A. A., 75
Ben-Tal, Y., 218
Bentley, J. A., 493
Bentrup, F. W., 201, 205
Benveniste, K., 229, 247
Berberich, M. A., 98
Berg, H. C., 431
Berg, S., 432, 435, 443
Bergemann, J., 571, 582
Berger, J., 505
Bergersen, F. J., 81, 83, 85, 89, 91-95, 99, 106, 108
Bergren, W. R., 505
Bering, C. L., 440
Berjak, P., 181, 186
Berl, S., 348
Berlier, Y., 56
Berlin, C. M., 385
Berlin, J., 468
Berliner, J., 314
Berman, T., 186
Bernard, N., 568
Berry, J. A., 30, 44, 46
Berry, R. W., 313
Bers, E. P., 228
Bertsch, W., 139
Berzborn, R. J., 425, 427-31, 434, 442, 443, 446
Betina, V., 345
Bettex-Galland, M., 340
Betz, A., 117
Bevilacqua, R. L., 176
Bewley, J. D., 186, 285, 286
Bex, J. H. M., 298
Bhalla, P. R., 154
Bhandari, M. C., 284
Bhardwaj, S. N., 286
Bhat, J. V., 467
Bhatia, C. R., 228, 229, 247, 380
Bhatty, R. S., 172
Bianchetti, R., 178, 179, 182
Bianchi, L. M., 124
Bidwell, R. G. S., 200, 365-70, 372
Biegert, F., 326
Bieleski, R. L., 54, 67, 520, 528, 530
Bielinska-Czarnecka, M., 283
Biggins, D. R., 83, 86, 88-90
Biggins, J., 431, 433, 436
Bigot, C., 153
Bilderback, D. E., 239, 240

Bingham, F. T., 61
Binnie, S. W., 283
Bird, I. F., 46, 396, 404
Birecka, H., 503
Birk, Y., 186
Birt, L. M., 74
Bisalputra, T., 35, 37, 40, 516
Bishoff, R., 337, 338, 341, 348
Bishop, D. G., 34, 37
Bishop, P. M., 436
Biswas, B. B., 179, 182
Biswas, S., 179
Bitters, W. P., 145
Bittner, S., 276
Björkman, E., 568, 571, 576, 579, 580, 582
Björkman, O., 44, 46, 405
Björling, G., 248
Black, C. C., 27, 30-32, 35-37, 43, 45, 46, 48, 405, 427
Black, I. B., 117
Black, M., 167, 182, 186, 199, 208
Black, P. H., 348
Black, R. C., 488, 489, 495
Black, R. F., 29
Blair, B. O., 503
Blake, J. D., 212
Blasco, F., 56, 66
Blasik, L. M., 340, 351
Bliss, M., 466-48, 481
Bloomberg, R., 229
Bluemink, J. G., 345
Blumberg, W. E., 500
Blumenfeld, A., 287, 291
Blundell, J. B., 291
Boardman, N. K., 37, 405, 425, 431, 433, 435
Bobick, S., 553
Bock, R. M., 243, 370
Boe, A. A., 299
Böger, P., 427, 429, 432, 434
Bogorad, L., 379
Böhme, H., 433, 435, 436, 438-40, 446, 449
Boiteux, A., 116, 117, 125
Bolduc, R. J., 503
Boll, W. G., 146
Bollenbacher, K., 557
Boller, A., 554
Bolton, E. T., 367
Bomsel, J. L., 118, 177, 179
Bond, G., 96, 106
Bone, D. H., 102, 103
Boniforti, R., 59
Bonnell, K. F., 207
Bonnemain, M. J. L., 530, 532
Bonner, J., 203, 208, 217, 337, 381, 496
Bonner, W. D., 177, 431-33, 504

Bonnet-Masimbert, M., 272
Bonnett, H. T., 142, 148, 160, 328, 329
Bonneville, M. A., 348
Bonotto, S., 118
Boone, C. W., 350
Boos, W., 72
Bopp, M., 142
Borecka, H., 284, 300
Borg, D. C., 501
Borisy, G. G., 310, 313-15, 324, 341
Bornman, C. H., 145, 274, 283, 286, 517
Boroughs, H., 381
Borriss, H., 167
Borst-Pauwels, G. W. F. H., 65
Borthwick, H. A., 575
Bose, T. K., 292
Böszörményi, Z., 74
Bothe, H., 89, 95, 100, 427
Botrill, D. E., 201
Bottalico, A., 550
Böttger, M., 285, 286, 295, 532
Bouchet, M., 168, 229, 496
Bouck, G. B., 320, 328, 329, 336
Boudet, A., 465, 468, 476
Boudreaux, G. J., 174
Bouges, B., 439
Bough, W. A., 475
Boulter, D., 181
Bouniols, A., 151, 155, 158
Bourdoux, P., 499
Bousquet, J. F., 555
Bovee, E. C., 310, 337
Boveris, A., 474
Bovey, F., 181
Bowen, C. C., 318, 320, 323, 326
Bowen, G. D., 572
Bowen, J. E., 57, 59-61, 66, 74
Bowen, M. R., 274, 296, 534
Bowling, D. J. F., 518
Braatz, R., 350
Bracciocurti, G., 59
Bracker, C. E., 70, 205, 328
Bradbeer, J. W., 285
Braden, W. G., 316
Bradley, M. O., 342, 345, 348, 350
Bradley, S., 105
Brady, A. C., 340, 341
Brady, C. J., 380
Brand, J., 428, 432-35, 446
Brand, K., 117
Brandon, P. C., 437
Brangeon, J., 36
Branton, D., 430
Braselton, J. P., 318
Braten, T., 321, 323

Braun, A. C., 555, 556
Braun, B. Z., 440, 441
Braun, J. W., 299
Brauner, L., 201, 217
Bravinder-Bree, S., 229, 473, 479, 496, 504
Bray, C. M., 181, 182
Bray, D., 338, 339, 348, 351
Bray, R. C., 90-92
Breidenbach, R. W., 174, 177
Brennan, J. R., 328, 333, 335
Breslaw, R., 466
Brewbaker, J. L., 250, 496
Brian, P. W., 549, 579
Briant, R. E., 499
Briantais, J. M., 430, 431, 437, 446
Brice, J. M., 105
Brierley, J. K., 577
Briggs, D. E., 184
Briggs, W. R., 167, 465, 530
Brill, W. J., 82-85, 90, 102, 103, 108
Bristow, J. M., 145
Britten, R. J., 366, 367
Brossard, D., 161
Brostrom, C. O., 382
Broughton, W. J., 104
Brovchenko, M. I., 520
Brown, A. H., 436
Brown, A. P., 409
Brown, C. B., 117, 130
Brown, C. M., 81, 96-98, 100
Brown, D. L., 320, 336
Brown, D. M., 229
Brown, E. G., 177, 186
Brown, J. E., 30, 32
Brown, J. R., 96
Brown, R. H., 40, 41
Brown, S. A., 470, 472, 475
Brown, W., 29
Brown, W. V., 30, 34, 36
Brownbridge, M. E., 196
Brownell, P. F., 49
Bruce, V. G., 129
Brulfert, A., 323
Brulfert, J., 120, 121
Brunori, M., 480
Bruton, J., 117
Bryan, J., 310, 312-15, 347
Buchanan, B. B., 47
Buchowicz, J., 181
Bucke, C., 46, 47, 400, 403, 406
Buckley, I. K., 340, 348, 351
Budilova, E. V., 229, 234
Budowski, P., 229
Bui, P. T., 88, 90
Bukovac, M. J., 286, 292
Bulard, C., 272

Bulen, W. A., 82, 83, 88, 90, 94
Bulgakov, R., 493
Bulis, M. G., 181
Bull, T. A., 47, 370, 377
Bünning, E., 116, 129, 326
Burden, R. S., 260, 266, 272, 276, 277, 279, 284, 290, 297, 299
Burdett, A. N., 185
Burg, E. A., 200, 207
Burg, S. P., 197, 200, 201, 207
Burger, W. C., 172, 382, 383, 387
Burgess, J., 311, 315, 321, 325, 326
Burk, D., 105
Burkholder, G. O., 311
Burley, J. W. A., 530
Burma, D. P., 95, 96
Burman, S., 179
Burns, R. C., 81-83, 85-90, 92, 103
Burnside, B., 340, 341, 345
Burr, G. O., 27, 533
Burris, R. H., 82, 83, 86, 88, 89, 95, 96, 99, 102, 104
Burstrom, H. G., 197, 198, 201, 203, 217
Burton, P. R., 311, 341
Buta, J. G., 502
Butenko, R. G., 141, 142
Butler, G. W., 475
Butler, V., 517
Butler, W. L., 425, 436, 438, 439, 446, 449
Butt, V. S., 119, 466, 467, 471, 480, 481
Byers, B., 311, 312
Byrne, O. R., 294
Byther, R. S., 544, 545

C

Cahn, R. S., 260
Caldwell, B. E., 294
Caldwell, M., 30
Calvin, M., 395, 404, 412, 413
Camm, E. L., 462, 466
Cammack, R., 91
Campbell, E. O., 568
Campbell, J. S., 481
Campbell, L. C., 49
Campeau, M. A., 231, 245, 248, 249
Cande, W. Z., 198, 327, 342, 345
Cannon, F. C., 101
Canny, M. J., 516, 521, 522, 526, 529, 530
Canonica, L., 552
Cantor, C. R., 315, 316
Canvin, D. T., 403
Caponetti, J. D., 379, 380

Carahan, J. E., 95, 104
Cardell, R. R., 340, 348
Carell, E. F., 228
Carlin, L., 227
Carlson, K., 313-15
Carns, H. R., 262, 285, 290
Carolin, R., 30, 31
Carpenter, S., 299
Carr, A. H., 155
Carr, D. J., 32, 208
Carr, N. G., 100, 105
Carroll, E. W. Jr., 229, 247
Carter, G. E., 171, 284
Carter, O., 144
Carter, O. G., 56
Carter, S. B., 338, 345
Cartwright, B., 64
Caruso, J. L., 146
Carvalho, A., 32
Casida, L. E. Jr., 573
Casinovi, C. G., 548-50
Caso, O. H., 141, 158
Cassio, D., 384
Castelfranco, P., 174, 177, 475
Castle, J. E., 95, 104
Castric, P. A., 475
Cataldo, D. A., 520, 523, 525, 527
Catedral, E. F., 229
Catesson, A., 481
Cathey, H. M., 292
Catsimpoolas, N., 383
Celati, C., 119, 121, 122, 128, 130
Ceulen, M. T. E., 92
Chabaud, J. P., 299
Chafe, S. C., 329
Chain, E. B., 289, 551
Chain, R. K., 427
Chakravorty, A. K., 181
Champagnat, M., 138-40, 161
Champigny, M. L., 119
Chance, B., 117, 125, 412, 431, 474, 479
Chandra, G. R., 175, 184, 239
Chaney, T. H., 436
Chang, C-M., 341
Chang, J. L. L., 184
Chang, Y. P., 261, 262, 276, 286
Chant, S. R., 229
Chao, S. E., 229, 231, 234, 238, 240
Chapman, J. A., 181
Charles, C., 496
Charlton, W. A., 146, 159
Charnock, J. S., 72
Chatt, J., 93
Chatterjee, S., 286
Chatterjee, S. K., 286
Chaturvedi, H. C., 146
Cheadle, V. I., 328, 329,

516, 524
Chen, C. H., 88, 89, 95
Chen, D., 180, 181, 298, 368
Chen, H. R., 143, 207
Chen, J. C. W., 342, 345, 349
Chen, J. H., 229
Chen, J.-S., 84, 86, 87, 93
Chen, L. L., 383
Chen, S. L., 229, 230, 232-34, 247, 379, 380
Chen, S. S. C., 169, 171, 178, 184
Chen, T. M., 374
Cheniae, G., 93
Cheniae, G. M., 425, 438, 439, 449
Cherry, J. H., 174, 177, 178, 181, 205, 503
Cherry, J. P., 228
Cheruel, J., 292
Chetram, R. S., 170
Cheung, Y. S., 398, 404, 417
Chiba, Y., 488
Chin, T. Y., 172, 183, 291, 532
Ching, K. K., 177
Ching, T. M., 173, 177
Chlapowski, F. J., 348
Choi, I. C., 527
Chrispeels, M. J., 175, 184, 289, 345
Christiansen, G. S., 211
Christodoulou, C., 248
Christopher, J., 229
Christy, A. L., 523, 527
Chua, N.-H., 443
Churchill, M. E., 138, 139
Chylan, H., 146
Cipollo, D., 432, 435, 443
Civen, M., 117, 130
Clark, G., 494
Clarke, N., 187
Clauss, H., 520, 529
Claver, F. K., 283
Cleland, C. F., 532
Cleland, R., 197, 198, 201-9, 211-14, 216, 218
Cleland, R. E., 575
Cleland, S., 311, 319
Cleland, W. W., 54
Clements, R. L., 380
Cleveland, L. R., 311
Cline, M. G., 197, 206, 213, 219, 297
Cloney, R. A., 340, 341
Cloud, P. E., 107
Clowes, F. A. L., 367
Cockburn, W., 394, 397, 400, 401, 403, 406, 409, 410, 416, 419
Cocking, E. C., 201
Codd, G. A., 119
Coffey, M. D., 318
Cogdell, R. J., 445

Coggins, C. W., 506
Cohen, C., 311, 350
Cohen, D., 169, 186, 488, 490, 491, 495
Cohen, G. N., 130
Cohen, I., 350
Cohen, M. H., 129
Cole, F. E., 229, 247
Cole, G. T., 342
Colilla, W., 499
Collet, G. F., 291, 499
Collin, H. A., 196, 197
Collins, D. M., 176, 177
Collins, G. G., 187
Colombo, R., 203, 206, 214
Colot, H. V., 317
Colowick, S. P., 385
Colquhoun, A. J., 293, 294
Colson, B., 320, 326
Colvin, J. R., 474
Combier, H. Y., 92
Come, D., 168, 169, 171
Comly, L. T., 340, 341, 348, 351
Commings, D. E., 311
Conchie, J., 214
Conklin, M. E., 234, 496
Conn, E. E., 460, 466, 471, 475
Connolly, T. N., 432
Connors, W. J., 473
Constabel, F., 144
Conti, M. A., 338, 339
Cook, D. A., 72
Cook, K. A., 82-90
Coombe, B. G., 274, 292
Coombs, J., 27, 30, 32, 46, 47, 397, 406, 407
Coombs, T. L., 383
Cooper, B. R., 63
Cooper, D. A., 386
Cooper, M. J., 289
Cooper, P. J., 289
Cooper, T. G., 174
Cooper, W. C., 286, 292
Coplin, D. L., 561, 562
Corgan, J. N., 283
Cornaggia, M. P., 178, 182
Cornelius, M. J., 46, 396, 404
Corner, J. J., 469
Cornforth, J. W., 260-64, 274, 275, 278, 285, 286, 299
Corvazier, P., 231, 239, 240
Cosloy, S. D., 75
Cottenie, J., 185
Couillard, P., 340
Coulomb, P., 385
Coulson, C. L., 523, 524, 527
Coulson, J. G., 559
Courtice, A. C., 68
Cowie, D. B., 367
Cox, E. L., 74, 374
Crabb, D., 170

Cracker, L. E., 285, 286
Crafts, A. S., 516, 517, 519-21, 524-28, 530, 532, 535
Craig, A. S., 40, 93
Cram, W. J., 60-63, 68
Cramer, W. A., 433-36, 438, 446
Crane, F. L., 428, 430-34, 437, 440, 446
Crane, J. C., 284
Craubner, H., 429, 430, 437, 440, 441, 443, 446
Crawford, R. M., 327, 336
Cresswell, C., 175
Cretney, W. C., 84, 86, 90, 96
Criddle, R. S., 174, 177
Crisp, C. E., 516, 517, 519-21, 524-28, 530, 532, 535
Crofts, A. R., 395, 397, 405, 425, 444, 451, 452
Cronshaw, J., 311, 325, 328, 329, 339, 342, 346, 349, 517, 532
Crook, E. M., 197, 200
Crookston, R. K., 30, 31
Crossland, C. J., 49
Cseh, E., 74
Culp, L. A., 348
Cumming, B. G., 116, 129
Cummins, W. R., 197, 208, 289
Cunningham, B. A., 228, 229
Currier, H. B., 519, 524, 529
Cusanovich, M. A., 87
Cutter, E. G., 321, 325, 326
Cutting, J. A., 104
Czaninski, Y., 481
Czapski, J., 229

D

Daesch, G., 90, 98, 102-6
Dahlen, J. V., 86
Dahlhelm, H., 216
Dahmen, W. J., 382, 383, 387
Dainty, J., 67
Dainty, R. H., 96-98
Dale, J., 574
Dales, S., 313
Dalle, J. P., 265, 275, 285
Dalton, H., 81, 84-86, 88-90, 98, 102, 103, 105
Daly, J. M., 229
Daly, J. W., 466
Dalziel, K., 72
D'Amato, F., 159
Danckwardt-Lillieström, C., 142
Daniel, R. M., 93, 94
Daniels, D., 200, 202, 206, 211, 213, 216
Dannenburg, W. N., 488, 490

Darley, W. M., 336
Dart, P. J., 104, 106-8
Dasberg, S., 170, 171
Datko, A. H., 211
Datko, E. A., 427
Datta, A., 197, 200
Datta, S. C., 168
Daussant, J., 231, 239, 240
Davey, C. B., 573
Davidson, H. R., 531
Davidson, O. W., 139
Davies, D. A., 472
Davies, D. R., 384
Davies, E., 200
Davies, P., 341, 345
Davies, P. J., 196, 198, 251, 488, 495, 499, 505, 506
Davis, J. D., 518
Davis, L. A., 264, 274, 285-87
Davis, L. C., 83, 84, 90, 102, 103
Davis, R. F., 205
Dawson, B. M. C., 187
Dawson, G. W., 272
Dawson, R. F., 576
Day, J. M., 104, 107, 108
Dayhoff, M. O., 87
De, D. N., 38, 329, 334
DeBary, A., 524
Debbas, G., 350
DeBusk, A. G., 228
Dechov, G., 439
Decker, K., 98
de Duve, C., 366
Degrauw-van Bussel, M., 470
de Greef, J., 185
De Groot, N., 180, 181
De Jong, D. W., 233, 247, 496, 504
De Jong, E., 528
Dekhuijzen, H. M., 216
Dekker, E. E., 175
de Kouchkovsky, Y., 435
DeLaat, S. W., 345
Dela Fuente, R. K., 197, 201, 211
De Leo, P., 293, 294
Delincee, H., 229
Delvieu, M. J., 435
DeMaggio, A. E., 283, 328, 379, 380
DeMayo, P., 549
Demorest, D. M., 498
DeMoss, J. A., 462, 469, 482
Dennis, F. G., 284
De Petris, S., 341
De Pooter, H., 470
DeRosier, D. J., 338
Desai, P., 141
Desborough, S., 228
Deshpande, B. P., 325, 518
De Stigter, H. C. M., 532
Deters, D. W., 442
Detlefsen, M. A., 181

Detroy, R. W., 86, 88
Deuel, T. F., 97
Devanathan, T., 83
DeVay, J. E., 286, 488, 561, 562
DeVries, G. H., 341
De Vries, J., 92
Dey, B., 176, 184
Dey, P. M., 213
Deysson, S., 323, 325
DeZoeten, G. A., 557
Dharmawardene, M. W. N., 90, 99, 100, 102
DiBella, F., 316
Dickinson, D. B., 74
Dickinson, W. J., 235
Diegelmann, R. F., 345
Diemer, R., 217
Dietz, R., 323
Digby, J., 289
Dilley, R. A., 424, 425, 430-32, 435, 437, 440-44, 446, 448, 451, 452
DILWORTH, M. J., 81-114; 88, 94, 103, 104, 106
Dimond, A. E., 542, 546
Diner, B., 435
Dingle, J. T., 385
Diouris, M., 57
Dirks, M. P., 436
Dixon, M., 248
Dixon, R. O. D., 88, 95
Dixon, R. Q., 101
Dmeter, S., 37
Dobereiner, J., 104, 107, 108
Dobra, W. A., 197
Dodge, B. O., 320, 326
Dodge, J. D., 321, 323
Dodge, S., 435, 440, 443
Doemeny, P. A., 92
Doerschug, M. R., 141, 148
Doi, E., 385
Doig, R. I., 174
Doireau, P., 178
Domanska, J., 283
Dominik, T., 572
Donachie, W. D., 130
Donaldson, I. G., 341, 347, 348
Donnelly, D. M. X., 505
Donze, M., 105, 439, 440
Dörffling, K., 184, 285, 286, 292, 295, 300, 532
Dorner, R. W., 378
Dörr, I., 346, 347, 518, 519
Doudoroff, M., 100
Dover, G. A., 326
Dovrat, A., 186
Dowler, M. J., 198, 200, 201, 211, 213
Downes, R. W., 48
Downton, W. J. S., 29, 30, 32, 35-37, 39, 46
Doy, C. H., 101, 228, 460
Doyle, D., 243, 252, 364,

365, 368-71, 383, 386
Draber, W., 260, 262, 264, 432, 434, 446, 449, 450
Dragonetti, C., 245
Drake, M., 67
Dramer, D., 30
Drawert, A., 495
Drawert, F., 229
Dressler, S., 466-68, 480, 481
Drinkwater, W. O., 142, 148
Drozd, J. W., 98, 101-3, 106
Drury, R. E., 299
Drysdale, J. W., 385
Dubbs, D. R., 385
Dubourdieu, M., 87
Dubucq, M., 168, 229, 496
Duckett, J. G., 336
Duckworth, W. C., 383
Duff, R. B., 572
Duffus, C. M., 184, 232, 233, 247
Duffus, J. H., 184
Duggar, B. M., 151
Dullaart, J., 488
Duloy, M. D., 521
Duncan, I., 172
Duniway, J., 546
Durand, B., 299
Durand, H., 199, 201-3, 297
Durbin, R. D., 556, 558
Durbin, S. L., 556
Dure, L. S. III, 180, 181, 285, 287, 298, 383
Durley, R. C., 274
Durzan, D. J., 176, 181, 234
Duysens, L. N. M., 431, 435, 439
Dye, M. H., 494
Dyer, T. A., 46, 396, 404

E

Eady, R. R., 82-90
Eagles, C. F., 282
Earle, E. D., 142, 148
East, J. W., 179
Eastwood, D., 179, 180, 183, 295
Ebashi, S., 310, 350
Ebel, J., 460, 468, 472, 477
Ebert, M., 530
Echave Llanos, J. M., 117
Eck, H., 432, 433, 450
Edge, H., 443
Edgerton, L. J., 286
Edmondson, D. E., 87
Edmunds, L. N. Jr., 118, 119, 130
Edwards, D. G., 56, 62, 63, 66, 68
Edwards, G. E., 46, 405, 406
Edwards, K. L., 218

Edwards, M. M., 171
Efron, D., 180, 181
Efron, Y., 230, 239
Egan, J. M., 228
Eggman, L., 337
Ehmann, A., 505
Ehret, C. F., 126
Ehwald, R., 66
Eichhorn, S. E., 517
Eidt, D. C., 283, 300
Eiduson, S., 117
Eilrich, G. L., 374
Eipper, B. A., 316
Eisenberg, E., 350
Eisinger, W. R., 198
El-Antably, H. M. M., 282, 283, 292, 293
El-Basyouni, S. Z., 368, 468, 469
Eldan, M., 177, 178, 182
Eleg, J. H., 401, 403
Elgersma, O., 437
Eliasson, L., 274, 488
Eling, W., 117
Elkin, L., 37
Ellis, R. A., 320
Ellis, R. J., 378
Ellison, J. H., 143, 159
Elmerich, D., 97
Elseewi, A., 61
El-Sharkawy, M., 29
El Sheraky, A. S., 370
Elstner, E. F., 432, 434, 438, 440
Elzam, O. E., 58, 60, 61, 66, 72
Emmerson, J., 340, 341, 345
Enari, T. M., 382, 383, 387
Endo, M., 310, 350
Endo, T., 228, 229, 234, 236, 496
Engel, P. C., 72
Engelbrecht, A. H., 174
Engelsma, G., 370, 376, 464, 479
Engleman, E. M., 516
English, H., 561, 562
Engvild, K. C., 146
Enoch, H., 171
Enright, J. T., 129
Entenman, C., 364, 365
Entsch, B., 37
Epel, B. L., 440
Epele, M. E., 117
Epstein, E., 54, 55, 58-62, 64-68, 71-73, 489
Erdmann, N., 489
Erez, A., 465
Erickson, R. O., 197, 217, 311, 335
Ericson, M. C., 462, 469, 482
Erikson, C. E., 229
Ernest, L. C., 503
Esan, E. B., 144, 146, 148, 161

Esashi, Y., 171, 185
Esau, K., 31, 321, 325, 328, 329, 342, 346, 350, 352, 416, 417, 524, 532
Eschrich, W., 516, 517, 519, 520, 525, 529, 530, 535
Eshel, A., 64, 68
Eshhaz, Z., 74
Esnault, R., 197, 198, 200
Espiritu, L. G., 231, 248, 253
Estabrook, R. W., 117, 125
Estensen, R. D., 345
Etherton, B., 205
Etiènne, E. M., 350
Evans, H. J., 83-85, 87, 89, 90, 92-95, 99, 100, 104, 105
Evans, J. J., 250, 474, 488, 496
Evans, L. H., 479, 480
Evans, L. T., 292, 532
Evans, M. C. W., 83, 86, 89, 91, 95, 102, 451
EVANS, M. L., 195-223; 197-99, 201-7, 210, 211, 213-16, 297, 493
Evans, N. T. S., 530
Evans, W. J., 179
Evenari, M., 168, 170, 180, 181
Even-Chen, Z., 276
Everhart, L. P. Jr., 313
Everson, R. G., 403
Evert, R. F., 325, 517-20, 526, 535
Evins, W. H., 184, 187, 299

F

Fagan, J., 443
Faludi-Daniel, A., 37, 46
Fan, D. F., 196, 197, 200, 211, 213, 381
Farineau, J., 405
Farkas, G. L., 228
Farnden, K. J. F., 475
Fawcett, C. H., 493
Fay, P., 102, 105
Feder, J., 383
Feely, J., 180
Feeney, R. E., 367, 383, 387
Feeny, P. P., 480
Feierabend, J., 129
Feigin, R. D., 117
Feit, H., 313, 314
Felder, M. R., 230, 237, 238, 250, 251, 253
Felker, P., 436, 437, 446
Fell, H. B., 385
Fellenberg, G., 147, 149
Fellman, J. H., 476
Fellows, R. J., 524
Feng, K. A., 153
Fensom, D. S., 346, 347, 518, 521, 530, 531
Ferdinand, W., 72, 481, 482

Ferenczy, L., 492
Fernandez, H. L., 311
Fernandez, N. O., 274, 290
Ferrandi, L., 59
Ferri, M. V., 229
Ferrier, J. M., 523, 527
Fiecchi, A., 552
Field, R. J., 524, 527, 532
Fielding, A. H., 92
Fields, M. A., 229
Filner, B., 378
Filner, P., 127, 239, 252, 316, 364, 370, 371
Finch, J. T., 339, 346, 350
Findlay, G. P., 65
Findlay, J. A., 263
Fine, R. E., 313, 314, 338
Finkle, B. J., 468
Firenzuoli, A. M., 174
Firn, R. D., 264, 272, 276, 279
Fischer, A., 499
Fischer, E., 499
Fischer, R. A., 525, 551
Fisher, J. D., 69, 71, 205
Fisher, L. V., 562
Fisher, M. L., 206
Fisher, R. J., 102, 106
Fishler, M. C., 364, 365
Fishman, B., 117
Fitzpatrick, D. F., 350
Fleing, I., 478
Fleischmann, D. E., 451, 452
Flesher, D., 238, 374, 379
Flick, B., 292
Flinn, A. M., 182, 385
Floyd, G. L., 321
Fock, H., 403
Folds, J. D., 248
Folk, J. E., 383
Folkers, K., 562
Folkes, B. F., 367-69
Fonnesbech, M., 139
Foote, M., 378
Forbush, B., 436, 449
Ford, J., 523
Forde, B., 39
Forde, H. I., 284
Forer, A., 313, 338, 341, 345, 351, 352
Forest, J. C., 490, 491
Fork, D. C., 435, 431, 433
Forrence, L. E., 285
Forsyth, W. G. C., 93
Forti, G., 200, 425
Fosket, D. E., 328, 329, 333-35, 376, 474
Foster, J. F., 384
Foster, R. C., 582
Foster, R. J., 205
Fottrell, P. F., 99
Fountain, D. W., 285, 286
Foust, P. G., 427, 429
Fowden, L., 174, 180, 182, 367, 385
Fowke, L. C., 318, 327

Fowler, C. F., 86, 441, 446
Fox, J. L., 86
Fox, L. R., 500, 501
Framondina, M., 550
Francesconi, R. P., 117
Frank, A. B., 570
Franke, W. W., 311, 320, 342, 348
Frankland, B., 181
Frater, R. B., 341
Frazier, W. A., 92
Frearson, P. M., 385
Frederick, D. P., 474, 488, 496
Frederick, S., 43
Fredrick, J. F., 228, 229
Freebairn, H. T., 185
Freeberg, J. A., 283
Freed, J. J., 352
Freedland, R. A., 371
Freeling, M., 230, 239
Frenkel, C., 229, 496
Fridborg, G., 141, 159
Fried, M., 59
Frieden, C., 97
Friend, J., 264, 279
Fries, D., 503
Fritz, P., 226
Froscio, M., 316
Frydenberg, O., 240
Fuchs, S., 274
Fuchs, Y., 274, 293
Fuchsman, W. H., 92
Fuge, H., 311
Fuhrman, J. S., 442
Fujimura, T., 144
Fujino, M., 144, 551
Fujita, M., 383
Fujita, T. S., 476
Fujita, Y., 428
Fukami, H., 272, 471
Fukui, H., 275, 281, 285, 286, 299
Fukushima, H., 378, 382
Fukuyama, M., 488
Fukuyama, T. T., 497
Fukuzuka, T., 473, 474
Fuller, G. L., 219, 264
Fuller, M. S., 320
Fuller, R. C., 86
Fuller, R. W., 117
Fulton, C., 313, 314, 323
Fulton, N. D., 557
Funahashi, S., 186
Funk, S. K., 383
Furuya, M., 167
Fushiki, H., 467, 468

G

Gaard, G., 557
Gabbott, P. A., 286
Gaber, S. D., 170
Gaertner, F. H., 462, 469, 482
Gail, M. H., 350

Galante, E., 504
Galbraith, M. N., 272
Gall, J., 321
Gallon, J. R., 90, 95, 105
Galson, E. C., 261, 262, 267, 276, 284, 286
Galston, A. W., 143, 196, 197, 205, 207, 229, 250, 251, 480, 481, 496, 497, 502-5
Gamborg, O. L., 144, 151, 159, 297, 464, 480, 490
Gan, J. C., 367
Ganapathy, P. S., 146, 253
Gander, J. E., 475
Ganguly, S. N., 262
Ganot, D., 75, 203, 210
Garay, A., 37
Garber, E. D., 228, 229, 248
Garber, M. J., 211
Gardner, D. J. C., 520, 522, 524, 527
Gardner, G., 465
Gardner, I. C., 96
Garg, G. K., 172, 382, 383, 387
Garlick, P. J., 365
Garmston, M., 264, 265, 280, 281
Garnier-Dardart, J., 119-21
Garrett, K., 229
Garrett, L. R., 383
Gartner, J. B., 283
Garz, J., 179
Gaskin, F., 315, 316
Gaskin, P., 261, 264, 274, 275
Gaspar, T., 168, 229, 298, 496, 503
Gassman, M., 379
Gast, A., 217
Gaudin, C., 56, 66
Gauhl, E., 46
Gäumann, E., 554, 568
Gautheret, R. J., 147, 151, 153, 156-58
Gawadi, N., 341
Gawlik, S. R., 328, 336
Gayler, K. R., 200
Gazit, S., 291
Gebert, R. A., 117
Gee, R., 70
Geiger, D. R., 520, 522-25
Gelinas, D. A., 479, 501, 502
Geller, E., 117
Geller, G., 402, 412, 414, 415, 418
Gelman, A. L., 214
Generalova, M. V., 181
Gepstain, S., 175, 183
Gerbandy, S. J., 229
Gerhardt, B. P., 174
Gerson, D. F., 65
Gertman, E., 293
Gestetner, B., 186, 471
Gesundheit, Z., 177, 179

Ghetie, V., 182
Ghosh, A., 117, 125
Giaquinta, R. T., 440, 441, 443, 446, 524
Gibbons, I. R., 312-14, 336
Gibbins, L. N., 179, 180
Gibbs, M., 37, 46, 394, 395, 401, 403, 404, 406, 412
Gibson, R. A., 488, 490-92, 494, 495, 499
Gientka-Rychter, A., 174
Gilbert, A. M., 118
Gilchrist, D. G., 228
Gilder, J., 520
Giles, N. H., 460
Gill, R. H., 321, 328, 329
Gillbank, L. R., 197, 200, 209, 214
Gilliland, M. G., 517
Gimmler, H., 448
Gingell, D., 348, 350
Ginsburg, A., 460
Giovanelli, J., 551, 558
Girbardt, M., 318, 328
Givah, C. V., 177
Gladner, J. A., 383
Glass, L., 129
Glass, R. D., 370
Glasziou, K. T., 200, 364, 370, 371, 377, 520
Glenn, R. K., 533
Glinka, Z., 203, 219, 295
Goddard, J., 317
Godfrey, C. A., 104
Goff, C. W., 316, 317
Goldacre, P. L., 496
Goldberg, A. L., 382, 384
Goldman, R. D., 340, 341, 345, 352
Goldney, D. C., 41
Goldschmidt, E. E., 276, 506
Goldsmith, M. H. M., 327, 342, 345
Goldstein, L. D., 375
Gomperts, B., 72
Good, J., 293, 299, 300
Good, N. E., 432, 436, 437, 446, 448, 452, 490, 505
Goodchild, D. J., 37, 39, 93, 106, 405, 407, 431
Goodman, D. B. P., 316
Goodman, R. N., 328, 336
Goodwin, B. C., 123, 125, 129
Goodwin, T. W., 172, 277, 280, 475
Gorbunoff, M. J., 384
Gordon, A. R., 234, 496
Gordon, A. S., 72
Gordon, J. K., 102, 103
Gordon, S. A., 197, 491
Goren, R., 286, 291, 297, 506
Goren, R. R., 276
Gorham, P. R., 520, 529, 530

Gorin, P. A. J., 546
Göring, H., 66
Gorini, L., 384
Gorski, J., 247
Gorter, C. J., 143
Gorz, H. J., 471, 480
Göttsche, D., 583
Gould, J. M., 436, 437, 446, 448, 452
Gould, S. E. B., 172, 178
Govindjee, 36, 37, 436, 440, 441
Govindjee, R., 436
Grabe, D. F., 178
Graber, P. J., 175
Grable, C. I., 557
Gracen, V. E., 43, 543
Gracen, V. E. Jr., 40, 41
Graham, D., 378
Grand, L. F., 573
Granick, S., 379
Graniti, A., 543, 549-51, 563
Grant, B. R., 74, 403
Grant, F. W., 143
Graves, J. S., 205
Gray, B. H., 86
Gray, J. L., 386
Gray, R. H., 320
Green, D. E., 491
Green, P. B., 197, 208, 328, 333, 335, 336
Green, T. R., 186
Greenhouse, G., 317
Greenway, H., 529, 531
Greenwood, C. T., 385
Greenwood, D., 396
Greenwood, M. S., 488
Greenwood, R. M., 93
Gregory, F. G., 119, 120
Grellet, F., 181
Gremona, T., 228
Greppin, H., 496
Gresshoff, P. M., 101
Greville, G. D., 424, 425, 444
Grieve, A. M., 378
Grimstone, A. V., 310, 311
Grimwood, B. G., 247
Grinblat, U., 145
Grisebach, H., 228, 460, 463, 466, 468, 471, 472, 477
Grisolia, S., 385
Groat, J. I., 184
Grochowska, M., 488, 492
Grochowska, M. J., 283, 284, 295
Gromet-Elhanan, Z., 432
Gross, D., 46, 260
Gross, G. G., 469, 471, 472
Gross, K. W., 317
Gross, P. R., 317
Grossman, A., 379
Grossman, S., 229, 383, 387
Grove, S. N., 328

Gruber, M., 172
Grünberger, D., 493
Grünhagen, H. H., 438
Grünsfelder, M., 56
Grunwald, T., 444
Grushvitskii, R. V., 141
Guardiola, J. L., 179
Guerrero, M. G., 92
Guerrier, D., 120, 121
Guerrini, A. M., 228
Guggenheim, S., 558
Guha, S., 146, 148
Guignard, J., 159
Guiraud, G., 56
Guitton, Y., 181
Gunckel, J. E., 142, 148
Gunckel, J. P., 139
Gunn, A., 529
Gunther, G., 488
Gupta, G. R. P., 146-48
Gupta, S., 292
Gurney, E., 101
Gustafson, G. L., 475
Guthrow, C. E. Jr., 316
Gutterman, Y., 168, 170
Guttes, E., 320
Guttes, S., 320
Guttierrez, M., 405, 406
Guzman, C. A., 229

H

Ha, D. B. D., 153
Haagen-Smit, A. J., 505
Haapala, H., 47
Haard, N. F., 234
Haber, A. H., 187
Haber, J. E., 315
Haberer-Liesenkötter, I.,
  395, 412, 413
Haberlandt, B., 29
Habermann, H. M., 439
Habeshaw, D., 47, 533
Haccius, B., 146, 156
Hacker, M., 173
Hackett, D. P., 496
Hackett, W. P., 139, 142,
  144, 148, 159
Hacskaylo, E., 571, 572, 574,
  576, 577, 579, 582
Hadfield, K. L., 88
Hadley, G., 569
Haehnel, W., 431
Haenni, A. L., 555
Hafez, A., 531
Hagedorn, D. J., 557
Hageman, R. H., 238, 374,
  375, 379
Hagen, C. E., 170
Hagen, G. L., 146
Hager, A., 197, 199, 203-6,
  210, 497, 498
Hahlbrock, K., 228, 460, 474,
  476, 477
Haider, K., 468
Haim, Y., 444
Haissig, B. E., 283

Hale, C. R., 274, 292
Halevy, A. H., 143, 274,
  293
Hall, D. O., 397, 424, 440,
  443, 448, 452
Hall, G. S., 187
Hall, J. L., 474, 479
Hall, R. E., 72
Hall, S. M., 525, 531, 532
Hall, T. C., 229-31
Hallam, N. D., 177
Hallier, U. W., 394-404, 406,
  409, 412
Halloin, J. M., 557
Halperin, W., 147, 154,
  161
Halvorson, H. O., 243, 315,
  370
Hamada, K., 144
Hamada, M., 568
Hamann, J. R., 124
Hamill, D. E., 250, 496
Hamilton, G. A., 465
Hamilton, R. H., 200, 201,
  488, 489, 495
Hammel, H. T., 526
Hammer, K. C., 575
Hampton, R. E., 496
Hanchey, P., 543
Hancock, C. R., 290
Hancock, J. G., 67, 74
Handel, M. A., 439
Handley, W. R. C., 579
Handro, W., 146, 147
Hansen, D., 69-71, 205
Hansen, H. J., 172, 381
Hansen, J., 499
Hanson, J. B., 67, 201, 205
Hanson, K. R., 128, 462,
  464, 465
Hansson, G., 70
Hanzely, L., 318, 321
Harada, H., 146, 147, 292
Harada, N., 260
Harada, T., 143
Harborne, J. B., 476, 478
Hardegger, E., 554
Hardeland, R., 118
Hardin, J. W., 205
Hardy, R. W. F., 82, 83,
  85-89, 91, 92, 103
Hare, R. C., 487
Harel, E., 173, 175, 177, 179,
  180, 182, 230, 385, 481
Harel, S., 522
Harkin, J. M., 473, 475
Harley, J. L., 366, 572, 576,
  577
Harmey, M. A., 503, 505
Harms, H., 468
Harrington, J. F., 185
Harris, C. E., 86
Harris, D., 107, 108
Harris, J. W., 228, 229
Harris, P., 318
Harris, S. A., 562
Harrison, A., 196, 203

Harrison, S. C., 311
Hars, R., 118
Hart, B. A., 460
Hart, G. E., 229, 230,
  236
Hart, J. W., 314, 347, 518
Hart, M. A., 229
Hartley, B. S., 383
Hartley, R. D., 473
Hartley, R. W. Jr., 370
Hartmann, H. T., 286, 292
Hartmans, K. J., 282
Hartt, C. E., 27, 533
Hartung, W., 216, 217
Harvey, B. L., 159
Harvey, M., 526, 530
Harvey, M. J., 409
Harvey, W. H., 379, 380
Harwood, J. L., 182, 186
Hasegawa, M., 470
Hasegawa, P. M., 140, 143,
  154, 156-59
Hasegawa, S., 466, 470
Hashimoto, T., 283
Haskins, F. A., 471, 480
Hassid, W. Z., 213
Hastings, J. W., 116
Haswell, A. D., 345
Hata, T., 385
Hatakeyama, I., 209
Hatano, S., 338, 340, 350
Hatch, A. B., 579, 582
Hatch, M. D., 27, 29, 46,
  368, 394, 395, 398, 405-7,
  411, 520
Hattori, A., 102
Hattori, H., 505
Haugh, M. F., 553
Haughton, P. M., 203, 204,
  209
Haupt, W., 129, 345
Hauska, G. A., 425, 430-32,
  434, 442, 446, 449, 450
Haveman, J., 105, 439, 440
Havir, E. A., 462, 464,
  465
Hawker, J. S., 228
Hawker, K. M., 496
Hawkes, R. B., 350
Haxo, F. T., 118
Hayaishi, O., 465
Hayashi, R., 385
Hayashi, T., 341
Haynes, R., 367, 387
Haystead, A., 89, 90, 100,
  105
Hayward, A. C., 93
Healey, F. P., 412
Heath, G. A., 93
Heath, I. B., 336
Heath, R. L., 438, 439, 451,
  452
Heaysman, J. E. M., 341,
  347, 348
Heber, M., 394
HEBER, U., 393-421; 394-
  404, 406-14, 416-18, 452

Hebert, R. R., 85, 92
Heckman, R. A., 263, 265
Hege, B. P., 263, 265
Heide, O. M., 291, 488
Heijneker, H. L., 92
Heilmeyer, L. M. G., 350
Heimer, Y. M., 374
Heinemann, M. A., 383
Heinicke, R. M., 470
Heinz, D. E., 264, 274
Heinz, D. J., 144, 159
Hejnowicz, Z., 217, 349, 518
Heldt, H. W., 394, 395, 397, 398, 400-4, 406-12, 414-18
Helgeson, J. P., 199, 215
Hellebust, J. A., 118, 366, 367, 370, 372
Hellendoorn, M., 159
Heller, C. G., 340
Heller, R., 151
Helmi, S. A., 370
Hemberg, T., 282, 298
Hemming, H. G., 579
Henderson, G. S., 573
Henderson, H. M., 229
Henderson, M., 572, 573
Henderson, P. J. F., 424, 425
Henderson, R. F., 216
Henderson, T. R., 216
Hendricks, S. B., 170, 177, 186
Henningsen, K. W., 172, 478
Henry, W. H., 286, 292
Henshall, J. D., 172
HEPLER, P. K., 309-62; 310-12, 318, 319, 321, 323-29, 333-35, 341, 343, 346, 347, 349, 473, 474, 479
Hershko, A., 382
Hertel, R., 199, 201, 205
Herth, W., 342, 348
Hesketh, J. D., 29, 30
Heslop, A. J., 286
Heslop-Harrison, J., 321, 325, 326
Hess, B., 116, 117, 125
Hess, W. M., 544, 546
Heupel, A., 428, 438, 440, 478
Hew, C. S., 37, 46, 406
Hewitt, E. J., 92
Heydecker, J. C., 170
Heydecker, W., 170
Heyes, J. K., 199
Heyn, A. N. J., 211, 329
Heyser, W., 520
Heywood, J., 92
Hiatt, A. J., 57-60, 65-67
Hiedemann-Van Wyk, D., 427, 429, 442, 446
Hield, H. Z., 286
Higgins, J., 124, 125
Higinbotham, N., 54, 73, 74, 205
Higuchi, T., 460, 467, 468, 472-74
Hildebrandt, A. C., 141, 143, 147, 148, 151, 158
Hill, G. P., 141, 142, 524, 525
Hill, J. M., 492
Hill, R., 401, 424-26, 433
Hill, R. E. E., 92
Hill, S., 98, 105, 106
Hillel, D., 171
Hilliard, J. H., 32, 40, 41, 43
Hillman, J., 282, 283, 292, 293
Hillman, J. R., 282, 283, 294, 296, 488
Hillman, W. S., 126, 127, 131, 502
Hilton, J. L., 558
Himmelhoch, S. R., 383
Hind, G., 425, 431, 433, 438-40, 444, 445, 451
Hinkson, J. W., 94
Hinman, R. L., 497, 499, 500
Hinssen, H., 338, 340, 346
Hird, F. J. R., 74
Hiron, R. W. P., 286-88, 290, 291
Hirt, G., 413
Hitchcock, C., 173
Hiyama, T., 427
Ho, C., 72
Ho, H. H., 229
Ho, L. C., 522, 529, 534
Hoad, G. V., 282, 296, 525, 530, 532
Hobday, S. M., 172
Hoch, G., 395, 412
Hoch, H. C., 320
Hock, B., 174
Hocking, T. J., 282, 296
Hodge, A., 34
Hodges, T. K., 69-71, 205
Hoefert, L. L., 532
Hoelzl, J., 186
Hoerhammer, L., 186
Hoffmann, G., 580
Hoffmann-Berling, H., 340
Hofstra, G., 33
Hoitink, H. A. J., 559
Hokanson, R., 197, 211
Holberton, D. V., 350
Holden, D. J., 144
Holleman, J. M., 366, 369, 372
Hollings, M., 160
Holm, R. E., 284
Holmes, R. S., 226
Holmes-Siedle, A. G., 500
Holmsen, T. W., 368
Holowinsky, A. W., 120
Holsten, R. D., 83, 85, 87-89, 92, 103
Holtzer, H., 337, 338, 340, 341, 345, 348
Holtzer, S., 345
Holubowicz, T., 299
Holzer, H., 97
Homann, P. H., 439, 443
Honeycutt, R. C., 427, 428
Honma, H., 496
Honold, G. R., 380
Hootele, C., 499
Hope, A. B., 65
Hopkins, W. G., 207
Horak, J., 141, 159
Horavka, B., 292
Horecker, B. L., 378
Horiguchi, T., 172, 173, 387
Horio, R., 438
Horn, D. H. S., 272
Horton, R. F., 289
Hosada, H., 228
Hosel, W., 477
Hotchkiss, R. D., 227
Hotta, Y., 370, 380
Housley, S., 493
Houssais, J. F., 181
Howard, K. L., 320
Howard, R. L., 83-85, 87, 93, 94, 100, 104
Howell, R., 171
Howell, S. H., 442
Hoyle, M. C., 496, 497
Hoysler, V., 291
Hrycay, E. G., 479
Hsiao, A., 170
Hsiao, T. C., 525
Hsiung, I., 170
Hu, A. S. L., 243, 370
Hu, C. Y., 141, 148
Huang, A. H. C., 43, 406
Huang, B., 313, 314, 336
Huang, K. P., 228
Huang, P. M., 481
Huang, R. C., 175
Huang, T. C., 82, 84, 85, 89, 96
Huart, R., 101
Hubbard, J. S., 97
Huber, J., 518
Huber, W., 32
Huddle, J. D., 172, 382
Hudock, G. A., 378
Hudson, M. A., 394-404, 406, 409, 412
HUFFACKER, R. C., 363-92; 368, 371, 374, 375, 378, 383, 561
Hughes, H., 147
Humble, G. D., 525
Humpherson, P. G., 328
Humphreys, J. S., 97
Hung, C-Y., 321, 325, 326, 342
Hunter, N. W., 248
Hurwitz, J., 378
Hurwitz, L., 350
Hutchinson, J., 104
Huxley, H. E., 310, 337-40, 346, 347, 349, 350
Hwang, J. C., 88, 89, 95

Hyeon, S. B., 260

I

Ibrahim, R. K., 368
Ichida, A. A., 320
Ie, T. S., 518, 519, 534
Ighe, U., 71
Ihle, J. N., 180, 181, 285, 287, 298, 383
Iimura, H., 562
Ikegami, I., 438, 439
Ikuma, H., 171
Ilan, I., 175, 183, 205, 206, 208
Imai, A., 380
Imaseki, H., 229
Imber, D., 260, 289, 290, 296, 448
Imbert, M. P., 502
Ina, K., 272
Incoll, L., 47
Ingersoll, R. B., 268, 289, 296, 297, 532
Ingle, J., 381, 506
Ingold, C. K., 260
Ingram, V. M., 341, 347
Inoue, H., 439
Inoué, S., 315, 318, 321
Intuwong, O., 138, 139, 148
Inui, M., 275, 281
Irving, R. M., 299
Ishikawa, H., 337, 338, 340, 341, 345, 348
Iskric, S., 499
Isoe, S., 260
Israel, D. W., 83-85, 87, 100, 104
Ito, S., 340, 341
Itoh, M., 438, 439
Ivanova, M. A., 229, 234
Iwahori, S., 488
Izawa, S., 432, 433, 436-39, 445, 446, 448, 449, 452

J

Jackman, L. M., 554
Jackman, R. H., 59
Jacks, T. J., 173, 175, 385
Jackson, E. K., 87-89, 91, 92, 103
Jackson, G. A. D., 283, 284, 291
Jackson, H. O., 505
Jackson, J. B., 445
Jackson, M. B., 276, 286, 294
Jackson, W. A., 368, 379, 381, 413
Jackson, W. T., 217, 314, 318, 321, 323, 325, 336
Jacobi, G., 431
Jacobs, G., 145
Jacobs, M., 101
Jacobs, S., 30, 31
Jacobs, W. P., 281, 294,

295, 352
Jacobsen, J. V., 172, 231, 239, 240, 250, 251, 290, 298, 383
Jacobson, J. W., 460
Jacobson, K. B., 227
Jacobson, L., 49, 63
Jacoby, B., 69, 70
Jacquiot, C., 147, 153
Jaffe, L. F., 345
Jaffe, M. F., 157
Jagendorf, A. T., 427, 444
Jahn, T. L., 310, 337
Jain, M. L., 503
Jain, S. K., 326
Jaiswal, V. S., 293
Jakob, K. M., 181
Jangaard, N. O., 283
Janick, J., 147
Janse, J. M., 568
Jansen, E. F., 474, 488, 496
Janzen, D. H., 480
Jarosch, R., 341, 347-49
Jarvis, B. C., 181
Jarvis, P., 517
Jaspars, E. M. J., 240
Jayakar, M., 141
Jaynes, T. A., 233, 371, 377, 480
Jeanjean, R., 56, 66
Jeffay, H., 367, 382
Jeffrey, D., 292
Jelaska, S., 142, 148
Jeng, D., 83, 88
Jenkinson, I. S., 200, 217
Jenner, C. F., 187
Jennings, D. H., 49, 577
Jennings, P. H., 375
Jenny, H., 63
Jensen, R. G., 394, 395, 397, 400, 401, 403, 407
Jerina, D. M., 466
Jerusalem, C., 117
Jeschke, W. D., 58, 59, 63, 73, 407
Jessen, H., 340, 341
Joham, H. E., 68, 69, 502
Johansen, C., 67, 68
Johanson, L., 68, 69
John, H. A., 341
Johnson, E. A., 345
Johnson, G. S., 338, 339
Johnson, H. B., 119
Johnson, H. N., 228
Johnson, H. S., 29
Johnson, H. W., 395, 405, 411
Johnson, K. D., 187, 200, 203, 211, 213, 219
Johnson, M. C., 30, 34, 36
Johnson, M. D., 34
Johnson, M. L., 228
Johnson, R. E., 285
Johnson, R. P. C., 346, 347, 517-19, 521, 524, 526
Johnson, T. B., 546

Johnson, U. G., 321, 323, 326
Johnsson, A., 126
Johnston, I. R., 197, 200
Johri, B. M., 144, 147, 154
Johri, M. M., 298
Jolchine, G., 119
Joliot, A., 436, 438, 439
Joliot, P., 436, 438
Jolley, R. L., 479, 480
Jones, C. W., 105
Jones, G. T., 117
Jones, J. B., 143, 154, 159
Jones, P. C. T., 130
Jones, R. F., 229
Jones, R. J., 219, 264, 289
Jones, R. L., 184, 187, 517
Jones, W. T., 481, 482
Jordan, W. R., 374, 375
Jost, M., 385
Joy, K. W., 367-69, 371, 532
Juliano, B. O., 175, 228, 231, 239, 240
Julien, P., 181
Junge, W., 424, 425, 432, 433, 436-38, 441, 444-46, 448, 449, 451
Jungermann, K., 98

K

Kadir, G. O., 532, 534
Kadkade, P. G., 503
Kadouw, A. M., 228, 229
Kadyrov, Ch. Sh., 263, 267
Kagawa, T., 187
Kahn, A., 378
Kajiyama, S., 83
Kalina, M., 443
Kaloshina, G. S., 232
Kameda, K., 499
Kamen, M. D., 92
Kaminski, W., 284, 285
Kamisaka, S., 184, 197, 198, 200, 211
Kamitsubo, E., 341
Kamiya, N., 310, 337, 340, 341, 347-49
Kamra, S. K., 170
Kanai, R., 41
Kandler, O., 395, 407, 412, 413, 433
Kane, R. E., 313, 314
Kaneshiro, T., 102
Kang, B. G., 197, 201
Kannan, S., 59, 66
Kannangara, C. G., 374, 378, 379, 427, 429, 442, 446, 478
Kao, K. N., 159
Kaplan, N. O., 227
Karlish, S. J. D., 444, 448, 451
Karlsson, H. G., 126
Karpilov, Yu. S., 27
Karr, A., 553

Karr, D., 553
Karssen, C. M., 184, 284
Karyakina, T. I., 232
Kasai, Z., 179
Kasier, W., 495
Kasinsky, H. E., 496
Kaska, N., 282
Kasprzyk, Z., 186
Kassel, B., 172
Kastenschmidt, J., 172, 382, 383
Katayama, M., 186
Katchalski, E., 180, 181
Kato, H., 147
Kato, Y., 229, 496
Katoh, S., 432, 434, 436-39
Katsumi, M., 200, 488, 503
Katsumura, S., 260
Katterman, F. R. H., 228
Katunuma, N., 383
Katz, M., 211, 293
Katznelson, H., 573
Kauffman, S. A., 129
Kaufman, P. B., 41, 204, 218, 324, 329, 333
Kaufmann, M. R., 526
Kaul, K., 143, 148
Kaumeyer, J. F., 317
Kaur, R., 207
Kaur-Sawhney, R., 505
Kauzmann, W., 125
Kavanau, J. L., 342
Kawashima, N., 378, 380, 382
Kay, E., 229, 251, 479
Kay, W. W., 42
Ke, B., 425, 427, 436
Keegstra, K., 212, 214, 216
Keen, N. T., 547
Keenan, T. W., 70, 205
Kefeli, V. I., 263, 267, 488, 493
Kefford, N. P., 141, 158
Keister, D. L., 427, 429, 432
Keith, A. D., 72
Keller, C. J., 378
Keller, J., 439
Kelly, M., 82, 83, 86, 88-90
Kelly, R. J., 171, 284
Kelly, S. H., 468
Kemp, J. D., 366, 372, 373
Kende, H., 183, 187, 289, 380
Kender, W. J., 299
Kennecke, M., 520
Kennedy, G. S., 108
Kennedy, I. R., 83, 88, 90, 95, 96, 98, 99, 104
Kennedy, R., 36, 42, 45
Kenney, J., 383
Kentzer, T., 186
Kerling, L. C. P., 546, 547
Kern, H., 554
Kertesz, K., 480

Kessel, R. J. H., 155
Kessler, D., 338, 340
Keswani, C. L., 380
Ketchum, P. A., 92
Ketring, D. L., 185, 282
Key, J. L., 198, 200, 366, 369, 372, 381, 465, 506
Keys, A. J., 46, 396, 403, 404, 407, 412, 417
Khalifah, R. A., 488, 490, 506
Khan, A. A., 168, 183, 184, 229, 284, 298, 496, 503
Khanna, P., 142
Khavkin, E. E., 379
Kholdebairn, B., 73
Kidby, D. K., 99, 106
Kidwai, P., 474, 517
Kielley, W. W., 350
Kienle, M. G., 552
Kiermayer, O., 311, 327, 328, 334
Kihlman, B. A., 314, 316
Kim, K. K., 139
Kim, S. J., 174
Kim, W. K., 488, 490
Kim, Y. S., 371
Kimimura, M., 432, 436-39
Kindinger, J. I., 211
Kindl, H., 465, 468, 476, 481, 493, 494
King, A., 335
King, D. O., 496
King, E. E., 502
King, J., 74
King, J. P., 283
King, R. W., 532
Kint, J., 185
Kirk, M., 394, 395, 397, 400, 401, 403
Kirk, P. R., 404, 407, 411
Kirkland, W. L., 341
Kirsi, M., 172, 387
Kirsop, B. H., 170
Kisaki, T., 404
Kiso, K., 440
Kiss, P., 468
Kit, S., 385
Kitabchi, A. E., 383
Kitagishi, K., 172, 173, 387
Kito, K., 383
Kitto, G. B., 227
Kivilaan, A., 213
Kjaergaard-Pedersen, L., 98
Klämbt, H., 505
Klaus, G. G., 345
Klein, A. O., 378
Klein, S., 167, 168, 171, 176, 180, 185, 186
Kleinhofs, A., 471
Kleinig, H., 346, 347, 518
Kleinkopf, G. E., 371, 378, 383, 384
Kletzien, R. F., 345
Klevecz, R. P., 130

Klingenberg, M., 412, 417, 418
Klucas, R., 94, 95, 105
Klug, A., 310
Kluge, M., 119, 120, 130, 532, 533
Knaff, D. B., 433, 436
Knappe, J., 87
Knight, E., 87-89
Knipe, D. M., 340, 341, 345, 352
Knyl, J. S., 293, 294
Kobayashi, K., 506
Kobayashi, S., 209
Koch, A. L., 365, 368
Koch, B. L., 83, 86, 88, 94, 99
Kochar, T. S., 154
Kochba, J., 145, 146
Kocholaty, W. F., 386
Koenig, F., 429, 430, 437, 440, 441, 443, 446
Koeppe, D. E., 553
Kohl, D. H., 435
Kohlenbach, H. W., 144
Köhler, D., 196
Kohmoto, K., 562
Kojima, M., 469
Kok, B., 395, 412, 427, 436, 449
Kolattukudy, P. E., 559
Kolehmainen, L., 172, 382, 383
Koller, D., 167-70, 176
Kollmann, G. E., 299
Kollmann, R., 346, 347, 518, 519
Kolloffel, C., 177, 178
Kominami, E., 383
Kominami, S., 383
Komnick, H., 310, 340, 347, 348, 350, 351
Konar, A., 144
Konar, R. N., 142, 144, 145, 148
Koncewicz, M., 557, 559
König, E., 572
Koningsberger, V. J., 196
Konishi, K., 438, 439
Kopin, I. J., 345
Koreeda, M., 260
Korn, E. D., 338-41, 348-51
Kornberg, H. L., 42
Kortschak, H. P., 27, 32, 35, 36, 533
Koshimizu, K., 275, 281, 285, 286, 299
Kostel, P. J., 92
Kosuge, T., 228, 371, 401, 460, 561
Koukol, J., 460
Kovacs, E. I., 162
Kowallik, K., 320
Kozlowski, T. T., 167
Kraayenhof, R., 408
Kramer, P. J., 526
Kramer, R., 440

Krause, G., 403, 404, 406, 408-10, 412-14, 418
Krauss, A., 197, 199, 203-6, 210
Kreishman, G. P., 72
Kreitner, G. L., 321, 336
Krekule, J., 292
Krelle, E., 291
Kremer, P., 398, 399
Kretovich, V. L., 232
Kreutz, W., 424, 425
Kreuzaler, F., 460, 474, 476, 477
Kriedemann, P. E., 219, 264
Krikorian, A. D., 335, 336
Krishmaro, N., 174, 176
Krishna Murti, C. R., 216
Krishnan, A., 345
Kristensen, B. I., 340, 350
Krogmann, D. W., 427, 428, 432-35, 443, 449
Krosing, M., 147, 154
Krotkov, G., 520, 528, 530, 578
Krywolap, G. N., 573
Ku, H. S., 234, 497
Kubai, D. F., 321, 323
Kuc, J., 473
Kuczenski, R. T., 469, 482
Kuehl, W. M., 338, 339
Kuhlen, E., 471
Kuiper, P. J. C., 70
Kukulezanka, K., 143
Kumagai, H., 471
Kumamoto, J., 72, 268, 274
Kumar, S. A., 494
Kunert, R., 495
Kunisaki, J. T., 139
Kunisawa, R., 102, 103
Kunitake, G., 119
Kuo, C.-F., 518, 520
Kuraishi, S., 380
Kuriyama, Y., 386
Kuroda, K., 341, 342, 348
Kursanov, A. L., 520
Kurz, W. G. W., 90, 95, 105
Kust, C. A., 174
Kutacek, M., 488, 493
Kveder, S., 499
Kylin, A., 70
Kyuwa, K., 178, 238

L

Labarca, C., 505
Labavitch, J., 201, 212
Labeyrie, F., 384
Lacks, S., 182
Lacy, H. J., 290
Lado, P., 174, 182, 203, 206, 214, 551
LAETSCH, W. M., 27-52; 28-38, 41-45, 47, 48
LaFountain, J., 342
Lahiri Majumder, A. N., 179

Laidman, D. L., 174, 179, 180, 183, 187, 295
Laiho, O., 570, 583
Lakshmanan, K. K., 146, 156
Lal, M., 153, 154
Lam, S., 147
Lam, T. H., 482
Lamb, R. J., 572
Lamberti, A., 92
Lamport, D. T. A., 210, 470
Lanazani, G. A., 504
Landa, Z., 141, 159
Landis, S. C., 311, 312
Landon, E. J., 350
Lane, H. C., 502
Lang, A., 183, 377
Lang, J., 497, 499, 500
Langford, G. A., 340
Langhans, R. W., 141, 159
Langrova, V., 488
Lantelme, F., 72
Lantican, B. P., 505
Larkum, A. W. D., 431-33
Larsen, F. E., 286
Larsen, P., 489, 491, 493, 494
Larson, R. L., 477
Larson, S., 403, 406, 410, 418
LaRue, T. A. G., 90, 95, 105, 297
Lathwell, D. J., 56
Laties, G. G., 54, 59-64, 67, 68, 71, 73, 74
Latzko, E., 37, 46, 404, 406
Läuchli, A., 54, 73, 530
Laude, H. M., 375
Laux, A., 345
Lavanchy, P., 496
Lavee, S., 196, 197, 496, 503, 504
Leach, C. K., 100
Leadbeater, B., 321, 323
Leadbetter, E., 92
Leather, G. R., 285, 479
Lebeau, J., 563
Lebowitz, M. M., 352
Lechevallier, D., 179
LeComte, J. R., 82, 83, 88, 90
Ledbetter, M. C., 309-11, 328, 334
Lederberg, S., 315
Lederer, E., 555
Ledoux, L., 101
Lee, B., 68
Lee, D. K., 92
Lee, E. Y. C., 228
Lee, H. J., 174
Lee, K. B., 174
Lee, S., 213
Lee, T. T., 153, 233, 234, 503, 504
Lee, Y. C., 228

Leech, R. M., 397, 401, 404, 407, 411, 418
Leech, W. D., 505
Leedale, G. F., 321
Lees, E. M., 475
LeGall, J., 87
Leggett, J. E., 56, 66
Legrand, B., 157
Lehmann, H., 431
Lehmann, J., 520
Lehmann, K., 179
Lehner, K., 404, 416, 417
Lehninger, A. L., 418
Leigh, R. A., 64, 68
Leighton, F., 366
Leimenstall, G., 98
Lembi, C. A., 205, 211
Lenton, J. R., 265, 274, 275, 282, 296
Leonard, O. Z., 533
Leonard, R. T., 67, 69-71, 205
Leopold, A. C., 171, 185, 197, 199, 201-4, 207, 211, 218, 219, 264, 297, 533
Le Page-Digivry, M. T., 272, 283, 284
Lepp, N. W., 532, 534
Leppard, G. C., 474
Lepper, R. J., 321
Lerbs, V., 318
Lerner, H. R., 481
Leroux, R., 156
Leshem, Y., 229
Lessie, P. E., 320
Letouze, R., 156, 157
Levand, O., 470
Levine, J., 425, 431, 433
Levine, M., 147
Levine, R. P., 378
Levisohn, I., 572, 575, 576, 579
Levites, E. V., 242
Levitt, M., 467
Levvy, G. A., 214
Levy, C. C., 466, 469
Lew, J. Y., 229, 251, 479
Lewak, S., 233, 284
Lewis, D. H., 577
Lewis, D. R., 328
Lewis, L. N., 286, 506
Lex, M., 81, 95, 102, 105
Li, H. C., 297
Libbert, E., 186, 291, 488, 495
Licari, G. R., 107
Lie, R. F., 92
Lieberman, M., 345
Liechti, P., 554
Liedtke, M. P., 380
Lien, S., 425, 430, 434, 436, 442, 446
Light, E. N., 201, 205, 289
Limbach, D., 432
Lin, C. Y., 465
Lin, D. C., 396
Lin, S., 345

Linask, J., 71, 73, 74
Linck, A. J., 153
Linck, R. W., 312
Lindeberg, G., 571, 579
Lindemann, E. G. P., 139
Linder, P. J., 532
Linderstrom-Lang, K., 384
Lindl, T., 471
Ling, G. N., 71
Linser, H., 147, 161
Linskens, H. F., 321
Lioret, C., 119
Lipe, W. N., 284
Lipmann, F., 530
Lipp, A. E. G., 171, 177
Lis, E. K., 501
List, A. L. Jr., 197, 201, 217
Lister, G. R., 578
Little, C. H. A., 283, 300
Littlefield, J. W., 382, 385
Liu, A. Y., 43
Liu, E., 229, 231, 237, 245, 251, 253
Liu, T., 475
Liverman, J. L., 488, 490
Livshits, N. D., 263, 267
Ljones, T., 82, 83, 86, 88, 89
Lobanow, N. W., 582
Lockhart, J. A., 532
Loeffler, J. E., 283, 284, 297
Loening, U. E., 381
Loewenberg, J. R., 229, 230, 232-34, 247, 379, 380
Loewus, F., 179
Loewy, A. G., 337
Loneragan, J. F., 68
Lonergan, C. M., 477
Long, S. P., 46
Long, T. J., 229
Longo, C. P., 174, 244, 245
Longo, G. P., 233, 244-47
Lonski, J., 185
Loomis, W. D., 83, 482
Loomis, W. E., 574
Loos, E., 407
Loos, G. M., 381
Lord, J. M., 187
Losada, M., 92, 432, 436
Lott, J. N. A., 177
Lou, C.-H., 518, 520
Lousberg, J. J. Ch., 548
Lovell, P. H., 168, 533
Lovett, J. S., 320
Loveys, B. R., 219, 264
Lovlie, A., 321
Lowe, D. J., 90-92
Lowry, O. H., 394
Lozier, R., 438
Lu, B. C., 318, 320
Luchtel, D., 345
Ludueña, M. A., 310, 340, 347, 348, 350
Ludueña, R. F., 313

Ludwig, C. H., 472, 474
Ludwig, R. A., 548
Luh, B. S., 229
Luke, H. H., 542, 543
Lukens, L. N., 466
Lukezic, F. L., 561, 562
Lundeberg, G., 571
Lundegårdh, H., 196, 203, 214
Lüning, K., 518
Lüscher, E. F., 340
Lüscher, F., 338
Lush, W. M., 525, 533
Lustinec, J., 141, 159
Lüttge, U., 54, 58, 60, 61, 64, 65, 67, 205
Lüttgens, W., 426
Luykx, P., 310
Lyman, R. L., 172
Lyndon, R. F., 379
Lynn, W. S., 444
Lyon, J. L., 184, 260-62, 285, 286, 290-92, 300
Lyons, J. M., 72
Lyr, H., 571
Lyttleton, J. W., 39, 46, 407, 481, 482

M

Ma, S., 144
Maas, E. V., 59-61
MacDonald, I. R., 60, 67
MacDonald, P., 557
Macdonald-Brown, D. S., 81, 96-98
MacGregor, A. W., 385
Machnik, J., 284, 292
MacKay, W. D., 263
Mackender, R. O., 401
Macklon, A. E. S., 60
Macko, V., 380
Maclachlan, G. A., 196, 197, 200, 211, 213, 381, 500
MacLennan, D. H., 366
MacMillan, J., 261, 262, 264, 274-76
MacRobbie, E. A. C., 54, 65, 73, 346, 407, 516-18, 521, 525, 527, 529, 530
Madansky, C., 92
Maeda, E., 144
Maeda, M., 568
Magee, W. E., 96
Mager, M., 117
Magnus, V., 499
Mague, T. H., 104
Mahadevan, S., 491-94
Maherchandani, N., 180
Maheshwari, P., 142
Maheshwari, S. C., 146-48, 292
Mahl, M. C., 102, 103
Maier, V. P., 466, 470
Main, C. E., 562
Maitra, S. C., 328, 329, 334

Majumdar, S. K., 143
Majumder, A. L., 182
Makino, N., 480
Malawista, S. E., 345
Malca, I., 561
Maletsky, S. I., 242
Malhotra, S. K., 177
Malhotra, S. S., 177
Malkin, R., 427, 435
Malkin, S., 436, 449
Mallaby, R., 263, 264, 274, 275
Malnassy, P., 159
Malone, C. P., 553
Maltzahn, K. E., 153
Manasek, F. J., 341, 345
Mandal, N. C., 179
Mandelstam, J., 365, 369, 382
Mani, J. C., 265, 275, 285
Mann, H. E., 142, 148
Mann, P. J. G., 492
Mano, Y., 173
Mansell, R. L., 460, 472
Mansfield, T. A., 219, 264, 274, 289, 290, 299
Mansour, I. S., 559
Mantai, K. E., 439-41
Manteuffel, R., 495
Mantle, P. G., 289, 551
Manton, I., 320, 321
Manuel, J., 293, 299, 300
Mapes, M. O., 143, 147, 154, 168
Mapson, L. W., 177, 481
Marak, J., 320
Marasas, W. F. O., 215
Marchaim, U., 186
Marchalonis, J. J., 86
Marchant, H. J., 320, 321, 328, 336
Marcus, A., 180, 181, 184, 364, 371
Marcus, L., 83, 102, 106
Maretzki, A., 74
Margara, J., 141, 142, 151, 155, 157, 158
Margulies, M. M., 378
Marinoff, P., 205
Markert, C. L., 226, 253
Markowitz, D., 123, 124, 130
Marks, G. C., 582
Markus, G., 384, 385
Markus, K., 521
Marre, E., 174, 181, 182, 200, 203, 206, 214
Marschner, H., 54
Marsh, H. V. Jr., 375, 464
Marshall, C., 530
Marshall, D., 199
Marshall, D. R., 228, 250
Marshall, J. J., 228
Marston, M. E., 138
Martin, C., 383
Martin, G. C., 283, 284, 286, 292

Martin, I. F., 438, 439
Martin, S. M., 229, 496
Marumo, S., 505
Marushige, K., 379
Marushige, Y., 379
Marx, D. H., 569, 573
Marx-Figini, M., 328, 334
Marzluf, G. A., 379
Mascarenhas, J. P., 216, 342
Mason, B. J., 59
Mason, H. S., 467, 470, 479, 480
Mason, M. I. R., 283, 284, 297
Massey, V., 427, 429
Massini, P., 395, 404, 412, 413
Masteller, V. J., 144
Masters, C. J., 226
Masters, M., 130
Mastronuzzi, E., 174
Masuda, Y., 184, 197, 198, 200, 211, 279
Mathieu, Y., 395, 406, 409
Matile, P., 172, 175, 385
Matkovics, B., 492
Mato, M. C., 501
Matsubara, H., 87, 141, 148
Matsubara, K., 92
Matsuki, T., 83
Mattas, R. E., 375
Mattox, K. R., 321
Mauzerall, D., 435
Mavrides, C., 379
Mayak, S., 274, 293
MAYER, A. M., 167-93; 167-69, 172-80, 182, 183, 187, 230, 385, 387, 481
Mayer, L., 145
Mayevsky, A., 186
Mayhew, S. G., 427, 429
Mayne, B. C., 405, 432, 434-36, 446
Mazia, D., 312
Mazurczuk, W., 293, 294
Mazus, B., 181
Mazza, G., 496, 497
McCarthy, W. J., 181
McCarty, R. E., 432, 434, 442, 443, 446
McClintock, B., 478
McClure, F. T., 366
McClure, J., 464, 465, 476, 478
McClure, J. W., 464, 465
McComb, A. J., 532
McComb, A. L., 574
McCown, B. H., 229-31
McCown, D. D., 229-31
McCready, C. C., 295, 577
McCully, E. K., 318, 320
McCully, M. E., 342, 348, 349
McCune, D. C., 496
McDaniel, R. G., 200, 247

McDonald, C. E., 383
McDonald, K., 318, 320
McEwen, T. J., 229
McFarlane, A. S., 369
McFarlane, I. J., 475
McGowan, J. C., 579
McIntosh, J. R., 311, 312, 319, 324, 334, 336
McKay, D., 125
McKellar, P., 439
McKenna, C. E., 92
McLaughlin, D. J., 318, 326, 328, 336
McLean, J., 34
McLeod, A. M., 178, 184
McLeod, G. C., 118, 378
McManus, G. M., 340, 351
McMeans, J. L., 262, 290
McNairn, R. B., 519
McNutt, N. S., 348
Means, G. E., 383
Mears, K., 147, 154, 168
Mecke, D., 97
Medler, J. T., 516, 519
Mee, G. W. P., 144, 159
Meers, J. L., 81, 96-98
Meguro, H., 260
Mehard, C. W., 425
Mehlhorn, R. J., 72
Mehra, A., 143
Mehra, P. N., 143, 147
Meier, D. D., 161
Meier, H., 175
Meijer, C. L. C., 59, 73
Meijer, G., 197, 201
Mejstrik, V., 572
Melandri, A., 425
Melandri, B. A., 128
Melchers, G., 159
Melin, E., 570-74, 578-80, 583
Mellenthin, W. M., 292
Melville, J. C., 172, 249
Menke, W., 427-30, 437, 440-43, 446
Menon, M. K. C., 153, 154
Mense, R., 295
Menzel, H., 197, 199, 203-6, 210
Mer, C. L., 203
Mercer, F. V., 34, 172, 177, 185, 186, 521
Merewether, J. W. T., 473
Merrett, M. J., 119
Mertz, S. M., 553
Meselson, M., 92
Mestre, J., 159
Meudt, W. J., 496, 497, 503, 504
Meunier, J. C., 228
MEYER, F. H., 567-86; 64, 571-74, 576-83
Meyer, F. J., 29
Meyer, H., 179, 180, 182, 187, 230
Meyer, L., 572
Meyer, M. M., 283, 291

Meyer, W. L., 557
Meyerhof, O., 105
Meza, I., 312-14
Mia, A. J., 176, 181, 234
Mičekova, D., 345
Michaeli, G., 435
Michel, B., 493
Michniewicz, B. M., 265, 270
Middleton, L. J., 530
Miescher, G., 554
Mikami, Y., 562
Mikola, J., 172, 382, 383, 387
Mikola, P., 570, 573, 576, 583
MILBORROW, B. V., 259-307; 187, 260-65, 269, 272, 274-81, 284-92, 551
Milburn, J. A., 525
Miles, D., 437
Miller, C. O., 148, 149, 151-54, 160, 576
Miller, M. R., 284
Miller, R. A., 144, 151, 159
Miller, R. E., 93, 97, 98
Miller, R. J., 553
Miller, R. W., 479, 500, 502
Millington, W. F., 328, 336
Millward, D. J., 365
Milovancev, M., 402, 412, 414, 415, 417, 418
Mims, C. W., 320
Minami, Y., 385
Mineo, L., 496
Misawa, M., 229, 496
Mishra, N. C., 229
Misra, L. P., 157
Mitaki, T., 378
Mitchell, D. L., 290
Mitchell, E. K., 488, 495
Mitchell, J. E., 320
Mitchell, J. W., 532
Mitchell, P., 418
Mitra, G. C., 146, 153, 157
Mitra, R., 228, 229, 247
Mitsui, T., 275, 281, 285, 286, 299
Mittelheuser, C. J., 219, 289, 297
Mittler, T. E., 525, 532
Mizel, S. B., 345
Mizrahi, Y., 287, 380
Mizukami, I., 321
Mizuno, M., 499
Modess, O., 571, 582
Moe, R., 488
Moeller, M., 172, 382, 383
Moens, P. B., 320
Moestrup, O., 336
Mohan Ram, H. Y., 293
Mohr, H., 462, 464
Mohr, H. C., 139
Mole-Bajer, J., 310, 318, 321, 323, 325, 341

Mollan, R. C., 505
Mollenhauer, H. H., 30, 32, 35, 37, 431
Møller, F., 226
Moller, I. B., 499
Mondal, M. H., 553
Monin, J., 184
Monselise, S. P., 506
Montgomery, M. W., 228
Mooney, P., 99
Moorby, J., 530, 534
Moore, D. P., 59
Moore, G. L., 386
Moore, K., 368
Moore, K. G., 168
Moore, P. B., 338
Moore, R. T., 320
Moore, T. C., 488, 492
Moore, T. S. Jr., 474
Mooseker, S. M., 311, 312, 338, 340, 341, 348
Morales, M., 125
Moravkova-Kiely, J., 378
Morel, C., 119-22, 128, 130
Morel, G., 138-40
Morel, G. M., 138, 139
Morello, J. H., 583
Morgan, C. M., 260
Morgan, D., 260
Morgan, J. M., 338
Morgan, P. W., 185, 282, 501, 502
Mori, K., 260
Morita, Y., 499
Morohashi, Y., 176
Morran, L., 289
Morré, D. J., 198, 205, 211, 217, 342, 348, 381
Morris, D. A., 499, 532, 534
Morris, J. A., 88, 90
Morrison, M., 229
Morrison, W. L., 386
Mortenson, L. E., 81-91, 93, 95, 96, 98, 102-6
Mortimer, D. C., 520, 522, 529
Morton, R. K., 179
Mory, Y. Y., 181
Moser, H., 29
Moser, I., 129
Moser, J. W., 321
Moser, M., 571, 572, 574, 575, 579, 583
Moses, J. A., 340, 351
Moss, D. N., 33
Mossberg, Y., 177
Most, B. H., 261, 264, 274, 288, 488
Motta, J. J., 318
Mottet, M. K., 248
Moudrianakis, E. N., 442
Mouffet, C., 464
Moulder, J. E., 315
Mounetou, B., 138, 139
Mousseron-Canet, M., 265,

267, 275, 285, 298, 299
Moustafa, E., 90
Moutschen, J., 182
Mower, H. F., 95, 104
Moyed, H. S., 497-99
Moyse, A., 119
Mudd, S. H., 551, 558
Muhle, H., 451
Mühlethaler, K., 342, 346, 349, 424, 425, 430, 437, 446
Muir, R. M., 493, 505
Muir, W. H., 147, 159
Mukerji, S. K., 120, 229
Mukherji, S., 176
Müller, A., 431
Müller, K., 533
Müller, W., 311
Mulliken, J. A., 174
Multani, J. S., 84, 86, 87, 90, 93
Munakata, K., 505
Munkres, K. D., 229, 247
Munro, H. N., 117, 385
Munson, T. O., 88, 102
Murakami, S., 425
Murano, F., 428
MURASHIGE, T., 135-66; 140, 143, 145, 146, 151, 153, 154, 156-61
Murata, N., 431
Murayama, K., 196, 197, 199, 201, 202, 207
Murison, G., 235
Murphy, M. J., 229
Murphy, P. M., 86, 88
Murphy, R. A., 316
Murray, A. M., 503, 505
Murray, A. W., 316
Murray, M. G., 186
Murthy Reddy, K. B. S., 143, 148
Myers, J., 412, 425, 428

N

Nachmias, V. T., 338-40, 347-51
Nadler, K., 379
Naef-Roth, S., 554
Nagai, R., 310, 334, 341, 350
Nagao, M., 270
Nagaro, H., 173
Nagatani, H., 97, 98, 101
Nagatsu, I., 470, 480
Nagatsu, T., 467, 470, 480
Nagl, W., 291
Nagy, A. H., 46
Nair, P. M., 367, 470
Nairn, B., 526, 530
Nakada, H. I., 500, 501
Nakagawa, H., 147
Nakai, Y., 228
Nakajama, R., 496
Nakajima, H., 340
Nakanishi, K., 260

Nakano, R., 146, 159, 160
Nakayama, F., 144
Nakayama, T. O. M., 179
Nakos, G., 85
Nambudiri, A. M. D., 467
Naqvi, S. M., 297
Narayana, R., 143, 148
Narayanan, A., 177, 179
Narayanaswami, S., 141, 147
Nari, J., 464, 500
Naslin, L., 384
Nason, A., 92
Nataraja, K., 143, 145, 148
Natr, L., 551
Nawa, Y., 177
Naylor, A. W., 156
Naylor, J. M., 180, 184
Neales, T., 47
Nebel, B. J., 156
Negbi, M., 170, 171, 180, 186
Neilson, A. H., 102, 103
Neirinckx, L. J. A., 65
Neish, A. C., 368, 460, 464, 468, 469, 480
Nelson, C. D., 33, 520, 528, 530, 577, 578
Nelson, D. R., 345
Nelson, H., 175, 442, 444
Nelson, N., 425, 427, 429-31, 433, 434, 442, 444, 446
Nelson, O. E., 228, 229, 233, 371, 377, 473
Nelson, R. F., 468
Nelson, R. R., 553, 561
Nemec, P., 345
Netien, G., 147
Neukom, H., 470, 473
Neumann, J., 424, 425, 427, 429, 431-33, 440, 443, 444, 449, 450, 452
Neumann, K. H., 147, 161
Neumann, P. M., 197, 200
Neumann, S., 520
Neurath, H., 383, 386
Newcomb, E. H., 43, 175, 310, 323-25, 328, 329, 333, 335, 346, 352, 518
Newcomb, W., 147, 153
Newman, D. J., 87
Newton, J. W., 95
Ng, E. K., 208
Nicholls, P. B., 505
Nichols, B. W., 173
Nicholson, N. L., 530
Nickell, L. G., 144, 159
Nicklas, R. B., 310
Nicklas, W. J., 348
Nicolova, E., 439
Nielsen, G., 238, 240
Nielsen, L. E., 340, 350
Nieman, R. H., 71, 432, 434
Nikolaeva, M. G., 167
Nilson, J. P., 380
Nilsson, H., 572

Ninham, B. W., 535
Nir, I., 443, 446
Nishi, T., 144, 159, 439
Nishijima, C., 286
Nishijima, Y., 562
Nishikawa, K., 231, 240
Nishimura, M., 436, 439
Nishimura, S., 562
NISSEN, P., 53-79; 54-67, 69, 71, 72, 75
Nissl, D., 196, 197, 199, 201, 202, 297
Nitsan, J., 379
Nitsch, C., 144, 151, 153, 203, 265, 292
Nitsch, J. P., 144, 146, 148, 151, 153, 203
Nizeki, M., 143
Nobel, P. S., 394-96, 398, 403, 404, 406, 417
Nobs, M., 44
Nobuhara, M., 231, 240
Noddle, R. C., 263-65, 277, 280, 287, 288
Noguchi, M., 117
Nooden, L. D., 198, 381
Nordby, O., 321, 323
Norkrans, B., 571
Norris, F. W., 179, 180
Norris, R. F., 488
Norstog, K., 143, 144
Northcote, D. H., 210, 315, 321, 324, 325, 328, 329, 334
Norton, J. P., 146
Norton, W. T., 341
Nosoh, Y., 83
Notton, B. A., 92
Nougarède, A., 479, 504
Novacky, A., 496
Novais, M. C., 283
Noy, R. J., 95
Nozoe, S., 552
Nüesch, J., 568
Nugent, N. A., 86
Nyman, B., 173

O

Oaks, A., 366, 367, 369, 372, 374, 375
Obendorf, R. L., 378
Oberoi, Y. P., 142, 148
O'Brien, P. J., 479
O'Brien, T. P., 32, 185, 310, 328, 329, 342, 348, 349, 367
Obst, J. R., 473, 475
Och, F. F., 229
Ochoa, S., 95, 394
Ockerse, R., 251, 503
O'Connell, P. B. H., 380
Odham, G., 579
Oertli, J. J., 59, 61, 65, 73
Oeser, A., 175
Oettmeier, W., 428, 478
Ogata, E. S., 311, 312
Ogata, G., 59-61

Ogawa, Y., 285, 286, 299
Oghoghorie, C. G. O., 532
O'hEocha, C., 229
Ohishi, S., 479
Ohkishi, H., 471
Ohkuma, K., 260-62, 268, 271, 278, 285, 292
Ohmann, E., 380
Ohmori, M., 102
Ohmura, T., 171
Ohnuma, J., 338, 340
Ojama, K., 151
Oka, Y., 385
Okada, T. A., 311
Okayama, S., 436
Okukuki, K., 384
Okunuki, K., 384
Olah, L. V., 318
Olausson, B., 197, 198, 201, 217
Oleniuk, F. H., 74
Olive, J. L., 265, 275, 285
Olive, L. S., 342
Oliver, P. T. P., 345
Olivero, E., 433, 449
Olmsted, J. B., 310, 312-15, 324
Olney, H. O., 505
Olsen, R. A., 579
Olson, A. C., 233, 247, 474, 488, 496
Olson, J. M., 425, 433
Olson, L. W., 315
Omura, T., 386
O'Neal, D., 37, 46, 406
O'Neil, C. H., 340
Ongun, A., 395, 398, 405
Onwueme, I. C., 375
Oo, H. T., 533
Oosawa, F., 338, 350
Opik, H., 177, 185
Opit, L. J., 72
Oplistilova, K., 493
Oppenheim, J., 83, 102, 106
Ordin, L., 49, 211
Oritani, T(akashi), 293, 294
Oritani, T(akayuki), 260, 263, 268, 269, 271, 293, 294
Orme-Johnson, W. H., 86, 90, 91, 102
Orsenigo, M., 552
Ort, D. R., 436, 437, 439, 446, 448, 452
Ory, R. L., 172, 174, 381, 383
Osborne, D. J., 177, 181, 276, 285, 286, 293, 294, 298, 496, 504
Oshino, N., 474, 479
Osmond, C. B., 27, 37, 44, 49, 58, 60, 67, 119, 120, 130, 405
O'Sullivan, S. A., 233, 246, 247
Otani, H., 562
Ottesen, M., 384, 385

Ouitrakul, R., 432, 433, 436, 437, 446, 448, 449, 452
Overstreet, R., 59
Owens, L. D., 551, 558
Owens, O., 436, 449
Owens, O. v. H., 395, 412
Ozbun, J. L., 228

P

Packer, L., 405, 425
Padma, A., 234
Pai, C., 228
Painter, T. J., 470, 473
Palade, G. E., 118, 386
Paleg, L. G., 184, 187, 274, 284, 290, 291, 293, 294
Palevitch, D., 187
PALEVITZ, B. A., 309-62; 310, 318, 326, 327, 341-43, 346, 347, 349
Palladina, T. A., 522
Pallaghy, C. K., 64, 65, 205
Pallas, J. E., 41
Palmer, G., 82, 84-86, 89-91
Palmer, G. H., 184
Palmer, J. K., 380
Palmer, J. M., 200
Palmer, R. L., 286
Palmiano, E. P., 175, 228, 231, 239, 240
Palta, H. K., 147
Pan, S., 92
Pandey, K. K., 251
Paneque, A., 92
Paolillo, D. J., 336
Paranjothy, K., 293, 294, 298
Pardee, A. B., 71, 124
Parejko, R. A., 86, 89, 90, 103
Pareyri, C., 323
Parish, R. W., 466, 467, 480, 481
Pariskaya, A. N., 520
Park, R. B., 38, 378, 424, 425, 431, 433, 443
Parkash, V., 298
Parker, B. C., 518
Parker, C. A., 99, 103, 108
Parker, M. W., 575
Parkhouse, R. M. E., 345
Parkman, S. B., 179
Parlange, J.-Y., 335, 336
Parshall, G. W., 88, 89, 91, 92
Partanen, C. R., 159
Parthasarathy, M. V., 342, 346, 349
Parups, E. V., 500
Passery, M., 46
Passoneau, J. V., 394
Pastan, I., 338, 339
Pate, J. S., 99, 367, 529, 532

Patil, K. D., 472
Patil, R. B., 102
Patil, S. S., 466, 469, 470, 481, 559
Patrick, J. W., 534
Pattee, H. H., 124
Patterson, B. D., 198
Paul, D. C., 316, 317
Paul, K. G., 229
Paulet, P., 146, 148
Pauli, A. W., 375
Paulson, R. E., 185
Paupardin, C., 153
Pavan, D., 552
Pavlidis, T., 116, 124, 125
Payne, J. F., 181
Payne, P. I., 181
Peak, J. G., 247
Peak, M. J., 247
Pearce, J., 100
Pearlstein, R. M., 425
Pearson, H. W., 105
Pearson, J. A., 298, 299
Pease, D. C., 310, 443, 446
Peel, A. J., 520, 522-25, 527, 529-34
Peel, J. L., 96-98
Pegg, G. F., 488
Pegrum, S. M., 341, 347, 348
Peisach, J., 500
Pelletier, R. L., 559
Peloquin, J. G., 315
Peloquin, S. J., 228
Penel, C., 496
Pengra, R. M., 102
Penn, N. W., 382
Pennachioni, A., 214, 551
Penner, D., 172, 174, 183, 199, 562
Penney, P. J., 505
Penny, P., 197-99, 201, 207
Penon, P., 488, 496, 503, 504
Penot, M., 57, 521
Penth, B., 56
Percival, F. W., 495
Perdue, J. F., 338, 345, 350
Perez, C. M., 228, 231, 239, 240
Perkins, F. O., 320
Perkins, H. J., 530
Perley, J. E., 503
Pero, R. W., 562
Peron, P., 229
Perry, M. M., 340, 341
Perry, T. O., 294
Perry, V. M., 265, 274, 275, 282
Persson, L., 71
Petering, L. B., 41, 204, 218, 324, 329, 333
Peterkofsky, B., 345
Peters, G. A., 431, 440, 446

Peterson, C., 177
Peterson, C. A., 529
Peterson, E. A., 573
Peterson, J. B., 320
PETERSON, L. W., 363-92; 371, 378, 383
Pettersson, S., 71
Petzelt, C., 312
Peverly, J. H., 553
Pew, J. C., 473
Pfaff, E., 412, 417, 418
Pfeifhofer, A. O., 38
Pfruener, H., 201, 205
Phelps, R. H., 488, 492
Phillips, D. A., 84, 93, 94, 104, 299, 532
Phillips, I. D. J., 282
Phipps, J., 501
Picaud, M., 430, 437, 446
Picciurro, G., 59
Pichichero, M. E., 342
Pickett-Heaps, J. D., 310, 316-18, 320, 321, 323-25, 327-29, 333, 334, 336, 341, 352, 474
Pieniazek, J., 275, 283-86, 291, 292, 295, 297, 300
Pieniazek, N., 292
Pierik, R. L. M., 142, 148
Pietila, K., 382
Piette, L. H., 500
Pihlaja, D. J., 311, 313
Pike, C. S., 465
Pilet, P. E., 297-300, 488, 496, 499, 501
Pillai, S. K., 143
Pine, M. J., 382
Pinevich, V. V., 228
Pinfield, N. J., 173, 184
Pinna, M., 464
Pinsky, A., 383, 387
Pirson, A., 129
Piskornik, Z., 505
Pistorius, E., 229, 427-29, 432, 434, 442, 446, 450
Pitelka, D. R., 336
Pitelka, L. F., 229, 247
Pitman, M. G., 49, 65, 68, 73, 529, 531
Pitot, H. C., 117
Pittendrigh, C. S., 126, 129
Pittman, P. R., 443
Plagemann, P. G., 345
Plattner, P. A., 554
Plesnicar, M., 431, 504
Pocchiari, F., 550, 551
Poglazov, B. F., 340
Poincelot, R. P., 46, 406
Poisson, J., 272, 276
Polevoy, V. V., 199, 201
Poljakoff-Mayber, A., 167-69, 174, 176-79, 182
Pollard, C. J., 175, 184, 298
Pollard, T. D., 310, 338-41, 347, 348, 350, 351

Polle, E. O., 63
Pollock, B. M., 170
Polya, G. M., 37, 405
Polyakova, E. V., 242
Pon, N. G., 378, 394
Pool, R. M., 286
Poole, B., 366
Poole, R. J., 65
Pope, D., 199, 208
Popjak, G., 278
Porter, D., 320
Porter, H. K., 404
Porter, K. R., 309-11, 321, 323, 326, 328, 334, 336, 340, 348, 351
Postgate, J. R., 81-90, 95, 98, 101-3, 105-7
Postlethwait, S. N., 501
Potchen, E. J., 370
Potter, V. R., 117
Potts, R., 466
Poulson, R., 172, 183, 299
Poulton, J. E., 466
Pousset, J. L., 272, 276
Pouteau-Thouvenot, M., 555
Pouwels, P. H., 92
Powell, L. E., 265, 270, 274, 283
Powell, R. G., 75
Power, J. B., 201
Prabha, C., 157
Pradet, A., 118, 177, 179
Prasad, S., 177
Prathapasenan, G., 174
Pratje, E., 350
Pratt, E. A., 228
Pratt, H. K., 234, 497
Pratt, M. J., 205
Prebble, J. N., 531
Preddie, E. C., 228
Preiss, J., 228, 371, 401, 460, 561
Prelog, V., 260
Prentice, N., 172, 382, 383
Presley, H. J., 174, 180, 182, 385
Pressey, R., 233, 377
Preston, R. D., 328, 336
Price, H. D., 72
Price, I., 32, 35, 36
Price, V. E., 370
Pridham, J. B., 213
Primrose, S. B., 101
Pringle, J. W. S., 310, 347, 350
Pringle, R. B., 542, 543, 555, 559, 560
Probst, E., 338
Procacci, R., 551
Prochazka, Z., 493
Promila, 144
Protopopova, E. M., 181
Prusiner, S., 98
Pryce, R. J., 262, 272, 274, 276

Pucher, G. W., 364
Puiseux-Dao, S., 118
Pupillo, P., 128, 228
Puputti, E., 382, 383, 387
Purves, W. K., 488, 492,
  494, 495, 500, 501
Puszkin, S., 348
Pusztai, A., 172, 173
Pye, K., 117, 123
Pyliotis, N., 36

Q

Quail, P. H., 231, 238, 243,
  251, 252
Quarles, R. H., 187
Quatrano, R. S., 345
QUEIROZ, O., 115-34; 116,
  119-22, 127-30
Quispel, A., 81
Qureshi, F. A., 522, 530

R

Raa, J., 504
Racker, E., 425, 430-32,
  434, 442, 446
Racusen, D., 378, 499
Radin, T., 374
Radler, F., 157
Radley, M., 183, 184
Radlick, P. C., 506
Radola, B. J., 229
Radunz, A., 429, 430, 437,
  440-43, 446
Raff, R. A., 317
Ragland, T. E., 229, 247
Rai, P. V., 547
Railton, I. D., 300
Rains, D. W., 54, 58-60,
  65-68, 531
Raison, J. K., 72, 179
Rajagopal, R., 489-91, 493-
  95
Raja Harun, R. M., 186
Raju, M. V. S., 142, 148
Raju, N. B., 318
Raju, P. N., 104, 105
Ramaiah, P. K., 181, 234
Ramasarma, T., 476
Rambelli, A., 580
Rancillac, M., 141
Randazzo, G., 550
Rangan, T. S., 145
Ranganathan, S., 476
Rangaswamy, N. S., 144,
  145
Ranjeva, R., 465, 468, 476
Ranson, S. L., 119, 196
Rao, G. R., 174
Rao, P. S., 141, 146, 147
Rao, P. V. S., 368, 467, 470,
  475, 476, 480
Raper, J. R., 229-33, 247
Rapley, L., 395, 397, 398,
  400, 401, 403, 404, 406,
  407, 410-12, 415, 416

Rapoport, M. I., 117
Rappaport, L., 283, 300
Rapport, E., 320
Raschke, K., 289, 525
Rasi Caldogno, F., 203, 206,
  214, 551
Rasmussen, H., 316
Rasmussen, H. P., 33
Raste, A. P., 146
Rathmill, W. G., 477
Ratner, A., 69, 70
Raudaskoski, M., 328, 342
Rauthan, B. S., 506, 507
Ravel, J. M., 97
Raven, J. A., 73
Rawson, K. S., 129
Ray, P. M., 196-201, 203,
  204, 206, 208, 211-15, 297,
  327, 342, 345, 500
Rayle, D. L., 197, 199-211,
  213, 214, 216, 218, 219,
  493-95
Raymond, P., 179
Raynaud, J., 147, 496
Read, D. J., 582
Read, P. E., 291
Reau, P., 320
Reay, P. F., 475
Rebagay, G. R., 234
Rebeiz, C. A., 174
Rebel, H., 547
Rebello, J. L., 97
Rebhun, L. I., 310, 334, 341,
  350, 352
Rechcigl, M. Jr., 370
Reddy, G. M., 234
Reddy, M. M., 228, 229
Redlich, N., 432
Reed, D. J., 492
Reed, J., 176
Rees, D. A., 172, 178
Reeves, S. G., 448, 452
Regitz, G., 427-29, 431,
  446
Rehm, M. M., 197, 206, 213,
  219, 297
Rehr, S. S., 480
Reid, C. P. P., 568
Reid, J. S. G., 175, 178
Reid, P. D., 464
Reigh, D. L., 502
Reighard, J. A., 336
Reimann, B. E. F., 425,
  431, 433
Reimer, S., 433, 436, 437,
  444, 446, 448, 449, 452
Reimers, F. E., 379
Reiner, J. M., 364, 365
Reinert, J., 147, 153, 154,
  161
Reinert, R. A., 139
Reinhard, E., 532
Reinhold, L., 71, 74, 75,
  197, 203-5, 210, 213-15,
  219, 295, 522
Reinwald, E., 438, 444, 446,
  448

Rejman, E., 181
Renard, M., 231, 239, 240
Renaud, F. L., 312, 314
Renger, G., 435, 438, 439
Retig, N., 229, 232
Retzlaff, E., 573
Rexhausen, L., 577, 582
Rexroth, A. K., 365, 369,
  371
Reyer, H., 228
Rhamstine, E., 143
Rhea, R. P., 340
Rhoades, M. M., 32
Ribeiro, S., 481
Ricard, J., 228, 464, 496,
  497, 500
Ricardo, C. P., 233
Rice, E. L., 184, 284, 297
Rice, H. V., 167, 465
Rice, R. M., 473, 479
Rice, R. V., 340, 341
Richards, B. N., 572, 582
Richards, G. N., 212
Richards, R. L., 92, 93
Richardson, M., 182
Richmond, A. E., 287, 293,
  294, 380
Richmond, P., 535
Richmond, P. A., 335
Richter, G., 118
Rickenberg, H. V., 96
Ridge, I., 496, 504
Ridley, S. M., 397, 418
Rieber, M., 180, 181
Ried, A., 395, 412
Ries, S. K., 374
Ries, S. M., 546, 547
Rigaud, J., 94
Rijven, A. H. G. C., 298
Riker, A. J., 141, 151
Rimpau, R. H., 568
Ringo, D. L., 315
Rippka, R., 102, 103
Ris, H., 320, 321, 323
Risch, H., 495
Risley, E. B., 516
Ritchie, A., 488
Ritenour, G. L., 374
Rittenberg, D., 364
Ritzert, R. W., 234, 503
Robards, A. W., 311, 328,
  329, 334, 474, 517
Robb, D. A., 481
Robb, S. M., 144, 148
Robbins, E., 317
Robbins, G. S., 382
Robert, M., 555
Roberts, B. E., 177
Roberts, D. L., 263, 265
Roberts, D. W. A., 380
Roberts, E. H., 167, 170,
  171, 176, 177
Roberts, G. R., 403, 404
Roberts, J. B., 93
Roberts, L. W., 310, 328,
  329, 333
Roberts, R. B., 367

Roberts, R. J., 477
Robertson, D. E., 72
Robinow, C. F., 318, 320
Robinson, D. G., 328, 336
Robinson, D. R., 261-64, 274, 277, 280, 284, 288, 292
Robinson, J. M., 394, 401, 407, 409
Robinson, J. R., 549
Robinson, P. M., 264, 292
Robinson, R., 89, 105
Robinson, S. L., 386
Robison, W. G., 311
Rocha, V., 229, 246, 247, 253
Roe, C. H., 168, 229, 496
Roeckl, B., 520
Rogers, L. J., 280
Rohrbaugh, L. M., 297
Rohringer, R., 488, 490
Roisen, F. J., 316
Roland, J. C., 300
Rolfe, B. G., 101
Rolnick, A., 320, 326
Romberger, J. A., 155
Romell, L. G., 570
Rongine de Fekete, M. A., 32, 520
Rosado-Alberio, J., 34, 37
Rose, I. A., 95
Rosen, R., 123, 131
Rosen, W. G., 328
Rosenbaum, J. L., 313-15
Rosenberg, M., 345
Rosenblum, E. D., 95, 96
Ross, C., 186
Ross, J., 311
Rossi, C., 550
Rossini, L. M., 153
Rostgaard, J., 340, 341
Roth, E. S., 476
Roth, L. E., 311, 313
Rothberg, L., 171, 180
Rothwell, K., 261, 268, 285, 286, 290, 292, 299
Rotilio, G., 480
Rottenberg, H., 444, 448
Rouatt, J. W., 573
Routien, J. B., 576
Rowan, K. S., 197, 200, 209, 214, 383
Rowe, A. J., 314
Rubery, P. H., 376, 502
Rubin, B. A., 229, 234
Rubin, R. W., 316
Rubinstein, B., 201, 205
Ruck, I., 518
Rücker, W., 153
Rudich, J., 229, 232
Rudnicki, R., 263, 274, 275, 282-85, 292, 300
Rudolph, K., 559, 560
Rüegg, J. C., 347
Ruesink, A. W., 196, 199, 201, 211
Ruis, H., 465, 468, 476, 481

Rumberg, B., 424, 425, 432, 433, 435-38, 441, 444-46, 448, 451, 452
Rungie, J. M., 70
Runkova, L. V., 501
Rupley, J. A., 383
Ruppel, H. G., 396, 478
Rushkin, E., 170
Russell, D. W., 466
Russell, S. A., 83-85, 87, 89, 90, 92-95, 99, 100, 104
Russi, S., 214, 550, 551
Russo, V. E. A., 205
Ryan, C. A., 382, 385, 386
Ryback, G., 260-64, 274, 275, 277, 285, 286, 299
Rychter, A., 233
Ryugo, K., 292

S

Saad, S. M., 557
Sabar, Z., 229, 247
Sabharwal, P. S., 143, 145, 148, 154
Sabnis, D. D., 314, 347, 352, 518
Sacher, J. A., 293, 294, 367, 369, 380
Sacristan, M. D., 159
Sadowski, P., 547
Sadri, H. A., 268
Sae, S. W., 228, 229
Saffe de Vilchez, I. F., 117
Safran, H., 145, 146
Saftner, R. A., 215
Saga, K., 143
Sagar, G. R., 533
Sagawa, Y., 138, 139, 148
Sagiv, J., 496
Saha, S., 436, 437, 446, 448
Sahulka, J., 496
St. Angelo, A. J., 172, 173, 381, 383
St. John, R. T., 103
St. Thomson, K., 205
Saka, H., 144
Sakai, A., 320, 321
Sakai, R. K., 248
Sakai, W. S., 560
Sakan, T., 260
Sakato, Y., 272
Sako, N., 228, 230, 232-34
Sakurai, H., 436
Salamini, F., 228, 229
Salemink, C. A., 546-48
Salomon, D., 216
Salsac, L., 58
Saltman, P., 119
Samaddar, K. R., 215, 543
Sammler, P., 66
Samsuzzaman, L. A. M., 473
Sands, R. H., 90
Sane, P. V., 424, 425, 431,

433, 443
Sanger, J. W., 336, 340, 341, 345
Sankhla, D., 293, 294, 297
Sankhla, N., 293, 294, 297
Sano, H., 200, 229, 503
San Pietro, A., 425, 427-29, 432, 434-36, 438, 439, 446
Santarius, K. A., 394-404, 406-12, 414, 416-18
Sanyal, T., 262
Sarid, S., 180, 181
Sarkanen, K. V., 472, 474
Sarkissian, I. V., 200, 229, 298
Sarma, V. R., 384
Sartirana, M. L., 179, 182
Sasaki, R. M., 87
Sasaki, T., 228
Sasakuma, T., 144
Satir, P., 310, 311, 336
Sato, H., 315
Sato, M., 466, 470
Satoh, K., 438, 439
Satoh, Y., 174
Satter, R., 205
Sauer, F., 394, 395, 398, 401, 403, 404, 406, 407, 411, 412, 415, 417, 418
Sauer, K., 379, 436
Saunders, B. C., 250, 500
Saunders, J. A., 464, 465
Saunders, M. A., 520, 525
Saunders, P. F., 167, 169, 184, 265, 274, 275, 282, 290, 296, 299
Sauvaire, Y., 56
Savageau, M. A., 131
Sawanobori, T., 345
Sawhney, B. L., 551
Sax, K. B., 197
Scala, A., 552
SCANDALIOS, J. G., 225-58; 172, 226, 227, 229-34, 236-40, 242, 243, 246-53
Schachter, B., 401, 403
Schaeffer, G. W., 502
Schafer, P., 229
Schaffner, G., 555
Scharf, P., 488, 502
Scheffer, R. P., 215, 542, 543, 545, 555, 559-61
Schenck, G. O., 425
Schenk, R. U., 151
Schertz, K. F., 229
Schieferstein, R. H., 283
Schiereck, P., 105
Schiewer, U., 489, 495
Schiff, J. A., 128
Schill, L., 228
Schimke, R. T., 243, 252, 364, 365, 368-71, 382, 383, 385, 386
Schippers, B., 546
Schjeide, O. A., 321
Schlesinger, G., 92
Schlessinger, D., 382

Schliephake, W., 433, 438, 441, 445, 446
Schlosser, S. A., 143
Schmid, A., 186
Schmid, G. H., 429, 430, 437, 440, 441, 443, 446
Schmidt, R., 497, 498
Schmidt-Mende, P., 436, 451
Schmitz, K., 518
Schnarrenberger, C., 175
SCHNEIDER, E. A., 487-513; 488, 490-92, 494, 495, 499, 505
Schneider, I. R., 532, 533
Schneider, M. J., 488, 495
Schnepf, E., 327, 336, 345
Schnetkamp, P., 65
Schoch, E., 30
Schoenheimer, R., 364
Schofield, J. G., 345
Schones, H. K., 556
Schoot Uiterkamp, A. J. M., 470, 480
Schopfer, P., 128, 460, 462, 464, 465
Schor, S., 118
Schrader, L. E., 174, 374, 375
Schraudolf, H., 153, 493, 494
Schrauzer, G. N., 92
Schröder, H., 432, 444, 451, 452
Schröder, R., 495
Schroeder, C. A., 142
Schroeder, T. E., 340, 341, 345, 348
Schuldiner, S., 444
Schulman, H. M., 104
Schultz, G., 181
Schulz, G. V., 334
Schurmann, P., 47
Schwabe, W. W., 129, 283, 292
Schwartz, D., 230, 236, 239, 298
Schwartz, M., 424, 425, 444, 449, 451, 452
Schweers, W., 577, 578
Schweiger, E., 118
Schweiger, H. G., 118
Schwender, S., 31
Schwendimann, M., 174
Sckerl, M. M., 283
Scott, B. I. H., 217
Scott, T. K., 217, 218, 487
Scott, W. A., 228
Scully, R. M. Jr., 139
Sedgwick, B., 477
Seeley, R. C., 493
Seeley, S. D., 274, 283
Seevers, P. M., 229
Segal, H. L., 371
Segal, L., 203
Segel, I. H., 72, 75

Seghal, C. B., 147, 154
Sehuring, F., 546
Seibert, M., 157
Seidle, A. G. H., 250
Seidler, R. J., 104, 105
Seiler, L., 217
Seitz, K., 377
Seligman, A. M., 443
Selman, B. R., 440-42, 446
Selman, G. G., 340
Selman, I. W., 488
Selvig, S. E., 317
Semadeni, E., 385
Semenoff, S., 154
Semenova, M. A., 229, 234
Sen, D. N., 284
Sen, S. P., 197, 200
Senger, H., 452
Sequeira, L., 488, 492, 496
Seravin, L. N., 310
Seth, P. N., 292
Setlik, I., 395, 412
Setterfield, G., 41, 211
Sexton, R., 474, 479
Shabde, M. N., 143, 154, 159
Shah, S. P. J., 280
Shah, S. S., 325, 326
Shah, V. K., 82-85, 90, 102, 103, 108
SHAIN, Y., 167-93; 172, 173, 175, 182, 385, 387
Shan, M., 482
Shannon, J. C., 198, 200
Shannon, L. M., 226, 229, 251, 380, 479, 496
Shannon, M. S., 228, 229
Shantz, E. M., 487
Shapiro, B. M., 97
Shapochka, O. F., 522
Sharp, L. W., 321, 323
Sharp, W. R., 142, 148
Sharpe, F., 502
Shashi, B. B., 228
Shatokhin, I. L., 59
Shavit, N., 432
Shaw, C. R., 226, 227
Shaw, E. R., 431, 432, 436, 439, 440, 446
Shaw, P. D., 477
Shaw, R., 377
Shaw, S., 488
Sheen, S. J., 234, 481, 496
Shelanski, M. L., 310, 311, 313-17, 341
Sheldrake, A. R., 488
Shelton, E., 338, 340
Shemakhanova, N. M., 579, 582
Sheridan, J. D., 345
Sheridan, W. F., 144
Sherwin, J. E., 488, 492, 495
Shetairwy, S. K., 370
Shevchenko, V. V., 181

Shewry, P. R., 173
Shibata, K., 438, 439
Shield, J. A., 294
Shiga, Y., 143
Shigematsu, K., 141, 148
Shigenaga, M., 320
Shigenaka, Y., 311, 313
Shih, C. Y., 300
Shih, J. H. C., 229, 479
Shih, T.-C., 340
Shii, C., 144
Shilo, R., 143
Shimada, M., 467, 468, 473, 474
Shimada, T., 144
Shimizu, M., 97, 98, 101
Shimoda, C., 200
Shimokoriyama, M., 176
Shin, M., 427, 429
Shiroya, T., 178
Shive, W., 97
Shneyour, A., 431, 440
Shoji, T., 139
Shoji, T., 139
Shone, M. G. T., 73
Short, K., 196, 197
Shoshan, V., 432
Shtarkshall, R. A., 75
Shukla, P. S., 494
Shumway, L. K., 34, 396, 443
Shyamala, G., 172
Siddiqui, A. W., 516, 517
Sidelnikova, L. I., 232
Siedow, J., 425, 427, 428
Siegel, B. Z., 196, 197, 250, 251, 497, 503, 504
Siegel, N., 199, 201, 215
Siegel, S. M., 474
Siegelman, H. W., 387
Siegenthaler, P., 481
Siekevitz, P., 118, 382, 386
Siggel, U., 435, 444, 451
Sij, J. W., 521
Silaeva, A. M., 33
Silano, V., 214, 550, 551
Silhengst, P., 488, 495
Silver, W. S., 107
Silverstein, R., 90
Silverton, E. W., 384
Silvey, S. K. G., 105
Simard-Duquesne, N., 340
Simon, E. W., 186
Simonet, J. M., 320
Simonis, W., 63
Simonsen, J., 143
Simpkins, I., 196, 197
Simpson, G. M., 279, 280
Sinden, S. L., 556, 561, 562
Singer, R., 573, 583
Singer, R. W., 501
Singh, A. P., 324, 328, 329, 333, 336, 517
Singh, B. N., 184
Singh, N., 383
Singh, U. P., 145, 146

Singleton, J. R., 320, 326, 328
Sinnott, E. W., 326
Sinoto, Y., 147
Sinska, I., 284
Sircar, P. K., 262
Sircar, S. M., 176, 184, 262
Sirois, J. C., 479, 502
Sisken, J. E., 317
Sivori, E. M., 274, 290
Skerra, B., 436, 451
Skoog, F., 151-66, 380, 491
Skou, J. C., 69
Skupin, J., 381
Skwarku, B., 186
Skytt-Andersen, A., 493, 499
Slack, C. R., 27, 29, 46, 368, 394-96, 398, 405-7
Sladky, Z., 488
Slankis, V., 575, 576, 579, 580
Slater, J. H., 117
Slatyer, R. O., 27, 48
Slepko, G. I., 90
Slepyan, L. I., 141
Sliwowski, J., 186
Sloger, C., 294
Slusarek, L., 313, 314
Sluys, J. V., 177
Smalley, E. B., 215
Smedegard-Peterson, V., 553
Smillie, R. M., 34, 37, 378, 380, 427
Smith, B. E., 82-92
Smith, B. N., 30
Smith, D. L., 182, 385
Smith, E. C., 229, 502
Smith, E. L., 229
Smith, F. A., 33
Smith, G. M., 92
Smith, H., 460, 464, 476, 478
Smith, H. H., 234, 496
Smith, O. E., 260-62, 268, 274, 278, 285, 289, 290, 292, 294, 296, 297, 532
Smith, R. C., 58, 61
Smith, R. J., 139
Smith, R. V., 83, 86, 89, 91, 95, 102
Smith, S. S., 86
Smith, T. A., 184, 279, 474
Smock, R. M., 292
Snaith, S. M., 214
Snell, F. M., 124
Snoddy, H. D., 117
Snow, A. G., 576, 579
Sodek, L., 229
Soedigo, R., 172
Sofer, W. H., 235
Sokolova, S. V., 74, 517
Solomos, T., 177
Sondheimer, E., 128, 261-65, 267, 270, 275, 276, 281, 284, 286, 298
Sonvico, V., 274, 290
Soofi, G. S., 181, 298

Sorger, G. J., 102, 103
Sovonick, S. A., 524
Spangler, R. A., 124
Spanner, D. C., 346, 516-18, 522, 530, 531
Spear, I., 119, 120
Spedding, D. J., 176
Spencer, D., 37
Spencer, E. Y., 549
Spencer, F. S., 211
Spencer, J. F. T., 546
Spencer, M., 177
Spichiger, J., 175
Spiegel-Roy, P., 145, 146
Spiller, H., 87
Splittstoesser, W. E., 231
Spolter, H., 119
Spooner, B. S., 310, 340, 341, 347, 348, 350
Sprent, J. I., 175, 184
Spring, A., 197, 200, 209, 214
Springer, A., 345
Spudrich, J. A., 339, 345, 346, 350
Spurr, A. R., 73, 286
Spyridakis, A., 384
Srivastava, B. I. S., 489
Srivastava, L. M., 185, 324, 328, 329, 333, 336, 517
Staba, E. J., 142
Stadtman, E. R., 97, 98, 460
Staehlin, L. A., 348
STAFFORD, H. A., 459-86; 229, 234, 462, 464-68, 472-75, 479-82, 496, 504
Stahl, C. P., 199, 201, 215
Stahl, E., 578, 582
Stahmann, M. A., 228, 230, 232-34, 380, 498, 560
Stajkova, R., 493
Stanforth, D. W., 299
Stanley, S. O., 96-98
Stanton, F. W., 526
Staritsky, G., 145
Stark, B. P., 250, 500
Starratt, A. N., 562
Stebbins, G. L., 49, 325, 326
Stecher, K. J., 496, 503, 504
Steck, W., 469
Steelink, C., 472
Steen, I., 274, 488
Steer, B. T., 117
Steinberg, D., 382
Steiner, G. W., 544, 545
Stelzig, D. A., 481
Stephens, R. E., 310-15, 317
Sterling, W. R., 370
Stern, H., 370, 380
Stetler, D. A., 35, 328
Stetten, G., 315
Stevens, D., 374, 375
Stevens, D. L., 563

Stevens, F. C., 229
Steward, F. C., 143, 147, 154, 168, 365-68, 379, 380
Stewart, E. R., 185
Stewart, G. R., 283
Stewart, K. D., 321
Stewart, S. A., 231
Stewart, W. D. P., 81, 83, 89, 90, 93, 95, 99, 100, 102, 105
Stewart, W. W., 555
Steyer, B., 186
Stichel, E., 145
Stickings, C. E., 562
Stiefel, E. I., 93
Stiehl, H. H., 435, 438, 444, 446, 448
Stigbrand, T., 229
Still, C. C., 497
Stiller, M. L., 119
Stillman, J., 143
Stitts, C., 119
Stobart, A. K., 173, 184
Stock, R., 72
Stockem, W., 310, 340, 347, 348, 350, 351
Stockigt, J., 460, 472
Stocking, C. R., 34, 37, 394-96, 398, 401, 404-7, 409-11, 418, 443
Stohr, H., 173
Stokes, D. M., 407
Stolarek, J., 200
Stolzenbach, F. E., 427, 429
Stone, E. L., 573
Stonier, T., 501
Storey, B. T., 504
Stösser, R., 286, 292
Stowe, B. B., 207, 489, 494
Strahs, K., 340, 341, 345
Straley, C., 547
Straley, M., 547
Strand, R. F., 573
Strandberg, G. W., 102, 103
Strange, J. L., 365, 369, 371
Strauss, N., 97
Street, H. E., 146, 196, 197, 217
Streicher, S. L., 81, 93, 101
STROBEL, G. A., 541-66; 544-47, 553, 557, 561, 563
Stroman, J., 341, 345
Stromeyer, C. T., 229, 247
Strong, F. M., 215, 549
Strotmann, H., 408, 417, 432, 441, 442, 452
Stuart, N. W., 575
Stumpf, P. K., 182, 186, 228, 370, 381, 478
Sturani, E., 180
Stutz, R. L., 499
Subramanian, D., 88
Sudo, Y., 470, 480
Sukanya, N. K., 491
Sulzman, F. M., 119, 130
Summers, K. E., 336
Sumner, D. C., 184
Sumpter, N. A., 229

Sun, N. C., 320, 323, 326
Surer, J. M., 117
Sussex, I. M., 141, 148
Sussman, A. S., 229
Sussman, M., 370, 380
Sussman, R. R., 370, 380
Suszka, B., 283
Suszynska, G., 143
Sutcliffe, J. F., 179
Suter, R. B., 129
Sutter, A., 466
Sutton, D. W., 366, 372, 373
Sutton, J. C., 548
Suzer, S., 379
Suzuki, A., 562
Suzuki, S., 228
Suzuki, Y., 178, 238
Svensson, S. G., 229
Swain, R. R., 175
Swain, T., 469, 481
Swanson, C. A., 521, 523
Sweeney, B. M., 116, 118,
  129, 196-98, 201, 203
Sweeney, E. W., 385
Swick, R. W., 365, 369, 371
Swift, H., 443, 446
Swift, J. G., 185
Syono, K., 159
Szarek, S. R., 119
Sze, H., 183, 387
Szepesi, B., 371

T

Tabor, C. A., 155
Tadano, T., 67
Tadokoro, K., 228
Tagawa, K., 427
Taiz, L., 184
Takagi, Y., 92
Takahashi, E., 144, 159
Takahashi, M., 229, 438, 439
Takamiya, A., 436, 438, 439
Takata, M., 340
Takatori, F. H., 140, 143,
  154, 156-59
Takayanagi, K., 185
Takeba, G., 532
Takeo, T., 229, 234, 481,
  496
Takeuchi, M., 41, 147
Takimoto, A., 532
Tal, M., 260, 289, 290, 296,
  488
Talmadge, K. W., 212, 214,
  216, 546
Tam, L. Q., 559, 560
Tamaki, E., 117, 378, 382
Tamas, I. A., 200
Tammes, P. M. L., 518, 519,
  523, 530-32, 534
Tamura, M., 496
Tamura, S., 270, 283, 313,
  317, 562
Tan, K. K., 44, 49, 119
Tanada, T., 201, 205, 218,
  274, 295, 299

Tanaka, H., 350
Tanaka, K., 179, 320
Tanaka, S., 562
Tanaka, Y., 229, 231
Taniguchi, T., 549
Tanimoto, E., 200
Tanner, W., 174, 407
Tapper, B. A., 475
Tarantola, V. A., 370
Tatchell, E. C., 336
Tatum, E. L., 228, 229
Tatum, L. A., 552
Tavares, J., 380
Tavener, R. J. A., 174, 183
Taylor, A., 40
Taylor, D. M., 502
Taylor, E. L., 345
Taylor, E. W., 310, 313-15,
  338, 340, 341, 349
Taylor, H. F., 184, 260, 266,
  272, 276, 277, 279, 284, 290,
  297, 299
Taylor, K. B., 83
Taylor, P. A., 556
Taylorson, R. B., 170, 177,
  186
Tazawa, M., 154, 338
Tchernoff, V., 547
Telfer, A., 83, 86, 91, 451
Teller, D. C., 86
Tempest, D. W., 96-98
Templeton, G. E., 557, 562
ten Hoopen, H. J. G., 387
Teo, C. K. H., 139
Terborgh, J., 118
Terranova, W. A., 473, 479
Terry, W. D., 384
Thaine, R., 346, 516-18
Than Nyunt, 435
Thauer, R. K., 98
Thellier, M., 65
Thielke, C., 318
Thiessen, W. E., 262, 278,
  285
Thimann, K. V., 119, 120,
  171, 196-98, 201, 203, 206,
  211, 342, 381, 383, 488, 489,
  492-94, 499, 575
Thoa, N. B., 345
Thoiron, B., 65
Thom, M., 74
Thomas, E., 146
Thomas, M., 119
Thomas, N. S. T., 341
Thomas, S. M., 175, 177
Thomas, T. H., 187
Thompson, A. D., 346, 347
Thompson, C. S., 350
Thompson, J. F., 558
Thompson, R. G., 346, 347
Thomson, C. M., 340
Thomson, J. F., 215, 216
Thomson, P. G., 499
Thorion, A., 65
Thorn, G. D., 563
Thorneley, R. N. F., 85, 89,
  92

Thorpe, T. A., 161
Threlkeld, S. F. H., 228,
  229
Thrower, S. L., 522
Tietz, A., 300
Tilney, L. G., 311-15, 317,
  336, 338, 340, 341, 348
Timasheff, S. N., 384
Tinelli, E. T., 262, 263, 276
Ting, I. P., 119, 229, 246,
  247, 253, 287, 407, 409
Tinklin, I. G., 283
Tipton, C. L., 553
Tobin, N. F., 37
Tolbert, N. E., 43, 175, 247,
  404, 409, 480, 481
Tollin, G., 87
Tomaszewska, E., 285
Tomaszewski, M., 501
Tomita, G., 439
Tomkins, G. M., 382
Tomova, N., 439
Toole, V. K., 170
Torii, K., 59-61, 64, 67
Torikata, H., 139, 156, 562
Torrey, J. G., 142, 148, 159-
  61
Towers, G. H. N., 368, 462,
  466, 470, 472, 475, 476, 480
Towill, L. R., 229, 230, 232-
  34, 247, 379, 380
Trappe, J. M., 568, 573
Trautschold, I., 172
Traverso, S., 228
Traverso-Cori, A., 228
Travis, R. L., 368, 374, 375
Traylor, T. G., 92
Trayser, K. A., 385
TREBST, A., 423-58; 426-29,
  431-34, 436-40, 442, 444,
  446, 448-50, 452
Treffry, T., 185
Tregunna, E. B., 29, 30, 32,
  35-37, 39, 40, 46
Trelease, R. N., 175
Trewavas, A., 365, 369, 370,
  373, 380
Trewavas, A. J., 197, 198,
  200, 294
Trimmer, B. M., 117, 130
Trinick, M. J., 106
Trip, P., 520, 528-30
Triplett, L. L., 187
Trippi, V. S., 229
Trofimenkoff, D., 102
Troughton, J. H., 37
Trown, P. W., 378
Troxler, R. F., 488, 495
Trucco, E., 126
Truchet, G., 83, 106
Truelsen, T. A., 491
Tsai, C. Y., 228, 229
Tse, A., 139
Tso, M.-Y. W., 82, 83, 86,
  88
T'so, P. O., 337
Tsuchiya, Y., 442, 443

Tsui, C., 153
Tsuji, H., 177, 178
Tsuji, I., 439
Tsujimoto, H. Y., 427
Tsukamoto, Y., 383
Tsunewaki, K., 144, 228
Tubb, R. S., 98, 101-3
Tucker, C. M., 518
Tucker, D. J., 274, 289, 290, 299
Tucker, D. P. H., 159, 160
Tucker, J. B., 311
Tuli, V., 497-99
Tung, D. A., 248
Tung, H. F., 380
Turetskaya, R. Kh., 263, 267
Turin, B. A., 234, 503
Turkina, M. V., 74, 520
Turner, F. R., 336
Turner, G. L., 83, 89, 91, 92, 94, 99, 106
Turner, N. C., 215, 551, 552
Turner, P. D., 575
Turner, W. B., 200
Tuttle, L. C., 530
Tyree, M. T., 521
Tyson, H., 229
Tzou, D. S., 284

U

Uchytil, T. F., 558
Udenfriend, S., 467
Udvardy, J., 228
Ueda, H., 139, 156
Ueda, K., 177, 178, 196, 197, 199, 201, 202, 207
Ueda, M., 505
Ueno, T., 471
Ugochukwu, E. N., 472
Uhlenbeck, G., 123
Uhlig, J., 553
Uhrstrom, I., 197, 198, 201, 207, 217
Ulitzur, S., 177, 179
Ullmann, J., 292
Ullrich, W., 394, 396, 400, 401, 403, 407, 520, 522
Ullstrup, A. J., 560, 561
Ulrich, J. M., 575
Ulrich, R., 117, 130
Upadhya, M. D., 380
Urbach, W., 394, 396, 400, 401, 403, 407
Uribe, E. G., 443
Uritani, I., 229, 469
Urmantzeva, W. W., 142
Ursprung, H., 227, 235
Usuda, H., 41
Usui, N., 340, 348

V

Vaidyanathan, C. S., 491
Vaklinova, S., 438-40

Valdovinos, J. G., 503
Valentily, S., 176
Valentine, R. C., 81, 86, 87, 93-95, 97, 98, 101
Valio, R. F. M., 272
Vallee, B. L., 383
Vallée, M., 72
Vandecasteele, J.-P., 83, 89
Van den Bos, P., 436
Vanden Driessche, T., 116, 118, 126
Van den Honert, T. H., 528, 535
Vandepeute, J., 229, 247
Van der Geest, T. C. M., 439
Vanderhoef, L. N., 199, 201, 215
Van der Mast, C. A., 494, 496, 497, 504
Van der Veen, R., 292
Vandervorst, D., 499
Vanderwoude, W. J., 211, 342, 348
Van de Walle, C., 181
van Die, J., 518, 531, 532, 534
Van Dorp, B., 92
Vanes, A., 282
van Gorkom, H. J., 439
Van Huysse, P., 503
van Huystee, R. B., 229
Van Loon, L. C., 465, 481
Vannereau, A., 323
Vanni, P., 174
van Onckelen, H., 503
Van Overbeek, J., 283, 284, 297, 532
Van Staden, J., 183, 274, 283
Van Steveninck, M. E., 41
Van Steveninck, R. F. M., 41, 219, 286, 289, 297
Van Sumere, C. F., 185, 470
van Well, P., 65
Van Went, J. L., 519
Van Wie, D. G., 312, 324, 334
Van Wyk, D., 396, 442
Varner, J. E., 127, 169, 172, 175, 178, 182, 184, 187, 218, 231, 239, 240, 243, 250-52, 289, 295, 298, 299, 364, 370, 371, 383
Vasil, I. K., 141, 147
Vasseur, J., 162
Vater, J., 436, 451
Vaucher-Bonjour, P., 481
Vaughan, M., 382
Vaughan, P. F. T., 466, 467, 477, 480, 481
Veerabhadrappa, P. S., 228
Vega, J. M., 92
Vegh, I., 555
Veldstra, H., 240
Vender, J., 96
Vendrell, M., 489

Vendrig, J. C., 506
Venere, R. J., 184
Venis, M. A., 200, 505
Venkataraman, R., 292
Vennesland, B., 432, 434
Verbeek, R., 503
Verleur, J. D., 229
Verma, D. P. S., 229
Vermeersch, J., 177, 179
Vernon, L. P., 431, 432, 436, 439, 440, 452
Vesell, E. S., 226
Vesk, M., 30, 31
Vetter, H., 87
Vickery, H. B., 364
Vickery, L. E., 495
Vidaver, W., 170
Vidaver, W. E., 185
Vieitez, E., 488
Vieweg, G. H., 528
Vigil, E. L., 443, 446
Vilchez, C. A., 117
Villiers, T. A., 170, 181, 184-86, 298
Vining, L. C., 367, 470
Vinograd, J. R., 337
Virupaksha, T. K., 172, 382, 383, 387
Vishniac, W., 394
Visuri, K., 382
Vlitos, A. J., 35, 488
Vlodawsky, L., 173, 175, 385
Vogel, H. J., 367
Vogel, R., 172
Voight, G. K., 572
Volcani, T., 180
Volk, R. J., 368, 381, 431
Volz, M., 63
von Gösslen, C., 432, 441, 442, 452
Vonk, C. A., 530
von Mayersbach, H., 116
Von Noort, G., 378
Von Parker, J., 517
von Stosch, H. A., 320
Von Traitteur, R., 327, 345
Von Wettstein, D., 320, 478
von Willert, K., 65
Voraurai, P., 138
Vorob'eva, I. A., 340
Vose, P. B., 59, 171
Voth, P. D., 488, 495
Vozzo, J. A., 574

W

Waber, J., 503
Wacek, V., 228
Wada, S., 200, 209, 211
Wagenknecht, A. C., 95
Waggoner, P. E., 542
Wagner, E., 116
Wagner, G., 201, 205, 345
Wagner, H., 186
Waid, J. S., 576
Wain, R. L., 261, 268, 279, 285, 286, 290, 292, 299,

493, 494
Waisel, Y., 64, 68
Wakamatsu, K., 439
Wakhloo, J. L., 488
Waksman, B. H., 345
Walbot, V., 180
Waldron, J. C., 370, 377
Walker, D. A., 27, 28, 30, 47, 119, 394, 395, 397, 400, 401, 403, 406, 407, 409, 410, 416, 418, 425, 444, 451
Walker, J., 99
Walker, J. C., 557
Walker, N. A., 65
Walker, T. S., 346, 517, 518
Walkey, D. G. A., 141, 146
Wall, J. R., 248, 249
Wall, J. S., 95
Wallace, W., 99, 374, 375
Waller, J. P., 384
Wallraff, H. G., 118
Walsby, A. E., 102, 105
Walter, T. J., 182
Walther, W. G., 118, 119
Walton, D. C., 181, 261-65, 267, 275, 276, 281, 286, 298, 376
Walton, E., 471
Wang, B. S. P., 176
Wang, C. S., 229-33, 247
Wang, C.-T., 394, 395, 398, 403, 404, 406, 417
Wang, C. Y., 292
Wang, J., 383
Wang, S. Y., 292
Wanka, F., 321
Warburg, O., 426
Warchalewski, J., 381
Ward, E. W. B., 563
WARDLAW, I. F., 515-39; 47, 520, 523, 528, 530, 532, 533
Wardrop, A. B., 329, 504
Ware, D. A., 85, 89
Ware, S. M., 200
Wareing, P. F., 167, 169, 171, 184, 260, 262, 264, 282, 283, 292-94, 298-300, 534
Warner, F. D., 310, 311
Warner, H. L., 197, 201, 218, 219, 297
Wassarman, P. M., 227
Wassner, H. P., 172
Waters, L., 180
Watson, M. W., 336
Waygood, E. R., 500
Weatherley, P. E., 346, 517-21, 524-26, 531
Weaver, E., 229
Weaver, G. M., 505
Weaver, R. H., 286
Webb, E. C., 248
Webb, J. A., 522, 529
Webb, K. L., 530
Weber, C., 346, 347, 518
Weber, G., 130
Weber, H., 494

Webster, D. H., 519
Wedding, R. T., 233, 246, 247
Weder, J., 172
Weedon, B. C. L., 260, 263, 292
Weeks, D. P., 180
Weier, T. E., 34, 37, 396, 443
Weigl, J., 56, 73
Weihing, R. R., 338, 340
Weikard, J., 436, 451
Weil, J., 383, 387
Weis, J. S., 157
Weisenberg, R. C., 310, 313-17, 324, 341
Weiss, G., 260
Weissbach, A., 378
Weissenboeck, G., 478
Welch, R. M., 61
Welinder, K. G., 479
Welkie, G. W., 30
Wells, J. R. E., 383
Wells, K., 320, 328
Weltman, J. K., 86
Wender, S. H., 229, 297, 502
Wenninger, R., 441, 442
WENT, F. W., 1-26
Werdan, K., 401, 402, 412, 414-16, 418
Werle, E., 172
Werner, D., 92, 93
Wessells, N. K., 310, 334, 338, 340, 341, 345, 347, 348, 350
Wessels, J. S. C., 431, 432
West, J., 452
West, K. R., 30, 408, 452
West, N. B., 248
West, S. H., 32, 40, 41, 43
West, W. C., 142, 148
Westergaard, M., 320
Wetherell, D. F., 147, 153, 154, 161
Wetter, L. R., 464, 480
Wever, R., 126-28, 131
Whatley, F. R., 394, 424, 432, 436
Wheeler, A. W., 488
Wheeler, C. T., 104
Wheeler, H., 542, 543, 554
Whelan, W. J., 228
Whisler, J., 286
Whitaker, D. R., 213
Whitaker, J. R., 229
White, E. P., 491
White, G. A., 549
White, P. R., 151, 154, 155
White, R. K., 328, 336
White, R. W., 549
Whitmore, F. W., 229, 251, 496, 503, 504
Whitt, G. S., 226, 253
Whittingham, C. P., 396, 403, 404, 407, 412, 417, 436

Whittle, C. M., 523
Wiame, J. M., 371
Wichner, S., 495
Wiersum, L. K., 528, 530
Wiese, M. V., 286, 488
Wiessner, W., 443
WIGHTMAN, F., 487-513; 488, 490-95, 499, 506, 507
Wilcox, H., 570
Wilde, S. A., 572
Wildman, S. G., 378
Wiley, L., 172, 183
Wilfret, G. J., 143
Wilkes, E., 317
Wilkins, M. B., 119-21, 282, 296, 488
Willemot, C., 370, 381
Willemsen, R. W., 184, 284
Willenbrink, J., 395, 396, 398-401, 403, 404, 413, 518
Willetts, N. S., 382
Williams, A. S., 554
Williams, B. W., 142, 148
Williams, G. R., 395, 398, 412
Williams, J. A., 316
Williams, P. H., 318, 320, 328, 546, 548
Williams, R. J. P., 496, 497
Williams, R. O., 312
Williams, S. G., 179, 180
Williams, W. P., 435
Williamson, B., 569
Williamson, F. A., 64
Williamson, K. I., 93
Williamson, R. E., 342, 345-47, 518
Williamson, V., 498, 499
Willis, C., 71
Wills, E. J., 345
Wilmar, C., 159
Wilson, A. T., 176, 177
Wilson, C. L., 328
Wilson, C. M., 229
Wilson, E. B., 321
Wilson, H. J., 311, 321
Wilson, J. R., 129
Wilson, L., 310, 312-15, 345, 347
Wilson, L. A., 502
Wilson, P. W., 86, 88-90, 95, 96, 102, 103, 106
Wilson, S. B., 177
Wilson, W. D., 384
Wimber, D. E., 139, 154
Winfree, A. T., 116, 125
Winget, G. D., 432
Wingstrand, K. G., 340, 341
Winnacker, E. L., 96
Winne, D., 63
Winter, A., 488, 489
Winter, H. C., 82, 90
Winter, K., 49
Winton, L. L., 146
Wise, B., 229
Wiskich, J. T., 70, 408, 452
Witman, G. B., 313, 314

Witt, H. T., 424, 425, 431, 433, 435-38, 441, 444-46, 451
Wittenberg, B. A., 500
Wittenberg, J. B., 500
Wittmann, W., 108
Witz, D. F., 86, 88
Witztum, A., 170, 171, 180
Wochok, Z. S., 146, 152, 328
Wohlfarth-Botterman, K-E., 310, 340, 341, 347, 348, 350, 351
Wohlman, A., 348
Wolf, J., 316
Wolf, N., 283
Wolk, C. P., 102, 105
Wollgiehn, R. Z., 520
Wolpert, L., 310, 340, 347, 348
Wolter, K. E., 146
Wong, E., 228
Wong, J. T., 73
Wong, M. K., 284
Wong, P., 93-95
Wong, T. C., 229
Woo, K. C., 36, 37, 405
Wood, H. L., 380
Wood, K. R., 229
Wood, P. M., 435
Wood, R. K. S., 543, 548, 563
Wood, T. C., 75
Woodcock, C. L. F., 327, 328
Woodfin, B. M., 216
Woodin, T. S., 228
Wooding, F. B. P., 328, 329, 346, 347, 518
Woods, F. W., 568
Woodstock, L. W., 178
Woolfitt, J. M. G., 141, 146
Woolfolk, C. A., 97
Woolhouse, H. W., 374, 378, 379
Woolley, D. E., 338, 340
Woolley, D. W., 554, 555
Wooten, G. F., 345
Worley, J. F., 582
Wraight, C. A., 451, 452
Wray, J. L., 127, 252, 364, 370, 371
Wrenn, J. T., 340, 341
Wright, D. A., 558
Wright, E., 583
Wright, S. T. C., 229, 279, 286-88, 290, 291
Wright, V., 105

Wu, C., 97
Wurm, G., 141, 142, 145, 147
Wurtman, R. J., 117
Wyatt, J. T., 105
Wyen, N. V., 228
Wyn Jones, R. G., 64, 68

X

Xavier Filho, J., 172
Xhaufflaire, A., 503

Y

Yakovleva, L. V., 263, 267
Yakuma, T., 143
Yamada, H., 471
Yamada, K. M., 340, 341, 345, 348
Yamada, T., 147
Yamada, Y., 144, 159
Yamaguchi, H., 181
Yamaguchi, M., 481
Yamaguchi, S., 519
Yamaki, T., 197, 200, 203, 506
Yamamoto, R., 200, 211
Yamamoto, T., 384
Yamamoto, Y., 130, 167
Yamashita, K., 260, 263, 268, 269, 271, 438, 439
Yamashita, T., 438, 439, 446, 449
Yamazaki, E. F., 492
Yamazaki, H., 479, 500
Yamazaki, I., 478-80, 496, 500
Yamazaki, R. K., 247
Yanagishima, N., 200
Yang, H. M., 501
Yang, N. S., 247
Yang, S. F., 234, 497
Yang, S. J., 528
Yang, Y.-Z., 338, 350
Yapa, P. A. J., 346, 518, 531
Yates, M. G., 84, 90, 94
Yates, R. A., 124
Yatsu, L. Y., 173, 175, 385
Yemm, E. W., 366
Yen, L.-F., 340
Yoch, D. C., 86, 87, 94, 102
Yocum, C. F., 425, 427, 428
Yocum, C. S., 41, 324, 329, 333

Yoda, S., 201
Yoder, O. C., 545, 561
Yokota, K., 478, 480, 500
Yomo, H., 240, 298
Yoneda, Y., 141, 234, 496, 501
Yoshida, R., 293, 294
Yoshida, S., 460
Yoshinaga, M., 345
Young, J. H., 526, 535
Young, J. L., 182
Young, L. D., 554
Yu, S. A., 229
Yuan, L. H., 97
Yuan, R., 92
Yue, S. B., 380
Yuwiler, A., 117

Z

Zak, B., 573
Zanobin, A., 174
Zaugg, W. S., 432
Zeevaart, J. A. D., 282, 288, 532
Zeiger, E., 327
Zeigler, R., 201
Zelitch, I., 27, 95, 96, 551
Zenk, M. H., 196, 197, 199, 201-3, 297, 460, 466, 469, 471, 472, 500
Zenkteler, M., 146-48
Zickler, D., 320, 328
Ziegler, H., 32, 128, 518-20, 528, 532
Ziegler, I., 128
Zielke, H. R., 367, 371, 374, 375
Zilg, H., 475
Zilversmit, D. B., 364, 365
Zimmerer, R. P., 200, 201
Zimmermann, M. H., 524, 526
Ziola, B., 211
Zito, R., 480
Ziv, M., 143
Zscheile, F. P. Jr., 561
Zsoldos, F., 59
Zucconi, F., 286, 292
Zucker, M., 127-29, 367, 371, 375, 376, 378, 379, 460, 462, 464, 466, 469, 470, 478, 481
Zuiches, C. A., 247
Zumft, W. G., 87
Zwar, J. A., 298
Zweig, G., 427

SUBJECT INDEX

A

Abscisic acid (ABA)
and abscission of leaf, 285-87
analogs of
and compounds related to, 272
data on, 265-72
and isomeric reduction products, 264
quantitative determination, 274
and structural requirements, 264-65
biosynthesis of
in a cell free system, 280-81
chemical reactions of, 263-64
chemistry and physiology of, 259-307
effects on
fungi, 300
isolated enzymes, 297-99
nucleic acids, 297-99
permeability, 295
proteins, 297-99
flowering and, 292-93
fruit set development and, 291-92
interaction with
auxin, 299
cytokinin, 299
gibberellin, 299
metabolism of, 275-81
occurrence of
in cellular compartments, 281
physical properties of, 261-62
physiological role of, 281-95
properties of optical isomers, 262-63
rapid growth responses to, 219
senescence and, 293-95
and stimulation of growth, 291
and tissue culture
inhibitors of callus growth, 297
and transport in plants, 295-97
and ultrastructure changes in, 299-300
and wilting, 287-89
Abscission, leaf
stimulation of

by abscisic acid, 285-87
Acetylcholine
effect on cell elongation, 216
Acid pH
auxin and
cell wall chemistry, 210-14
effects on
plant growth, 203-4
root growth, 218
relationship to auxin, 204-10
Adenine nucleotide translocator, 417
ADH isozyme
developmental expression of, 235-36
effect of genetic background on, 237-38
ADP
and adenine nucleotide translocator, 417
adenylates and
from chloroplasts, 407-9
ATP/ADP ratio
and nitrogenase, 105-6
lipid metabolism
and glyoxylate cycle, 173-74
and malate/OAA shuttle, 412
microfilaments and, 337
mitochondria and, 418
and PGA/DHAP shuttle, 410
role in seed germination, 177
tentoxin and, 557-58
Air pollution
effects of
on plant growth, 20-24
and natural smog, 22-24
Aitken condensation nuclei (ACN), 22
Alleloparasitism
see Ectomycorrhiza fungi
Amino acid derived phytotoxin, 554-62
Amino acids
deamination of
and carbohydrate metabolism, 176
derived by
plant parasites, 554-61
labeling of, 369-70
and protein turnover, 368
Ammonia assimilation
routes of, in dinitrogen fixation
activity in, 96-100

glutamate dehydrogenase (GDH), 96-100
glutamine synthetase (GS), 96-100
and GOGAT activity, 96-100
and tracer studies, for legumes, 96
and tracer studies, for nonlegume modules, 95-96
Ammonia uptake
in nitrogen-fixing organisms, 98-100
AMP
controlling assembly of microtubules, 316-17
cyclic
in motility of microtubules, 316-17
effects on cell elongation, 316-17
α-Amylase, 239-41
β-Amylase, 239-41
Aromatic compounds
C_6-C_3 pathways, 460-83
activation of carboxyl groups via coenzyme A ligases, 471
and ammonia lyases, 462-64
and aromatic hydroxylations, 465-66
carboxyl reduction pathway to lignin precursors and, 471-72
and cinnamate-4-hydroxylations, 466
cinnamic acid derivatives' special roles, 470
cinnamic acid sequence and, 468-69
ferulate-5-hydroxylase and, 467-68
formation of glucose and, 469-70
4-hydroxycinnamate-3-hydroxylase, 466-67
O-methyltransferase activity, 468
ortho-hydroxylation to coumarins, 470
quinic acid esters, 469-70
C_{15}-flavonoid pathway, 476-78
biosynthesis of enzymology, 476-78
and chloroplast's role, 478
and photosystem I, 478
chain-shortening pathways

C_6-C_2, to cyanogenic glycosides, 475
C_6-C_1, to quinones, 475-
76
and lignin
characteristics of C_6-C_3
polymers, 472-73
and enzymatic components
required to form, 473-74
oxidative polymerization
to cell-free systems, 474
subcellular events and formation of, 474-75
peroxidase and, 478-80
polyphenoloxidase complex
and, 480-82
pre-aromatic pathway
to phenylalanine, 460-62
to tyrosine, 460-62
Aseptic tissue cultures
explants of, 148, 150
in plant propagation, 139
Aspartate, 36, 45
ATP
acid responses to hormonal
activity, 205
activity in cross-bridges,
312
adenine nucleotide translocator and, 417
in aromatic compounds, 476
ATP/ADP ratio
in nitrogenase, 105-6
in C_3 plant photosynthesis,
403
effect on growth, 205
and enzyme
activation, 178
synthesis, 178
formation in
chloroplasts, 424
mineral cations, 73
and K^+ recycling
for translocation, 521
level
during seed germination,
177-78
malate/OAA shuttle and,
412-14
and metabolic
control of phloem transport,
520
enzyme rhythms, 130
mitochondria and, 418
and oxidative phosphorylation,
522
PGA/DHAP shuttle and, 410
in photosynthetic electron
transfer of chloroplasts,
424, 442, 448, 450-52
and protein synthesis
in seed germination, 180-
82
in seed germination, 177-81
variations in
unicells, 118-19
ATPase

in biochemistry of micro-
filaments, 338-40, 347,
351, 353
inhibition of
and helminthosporium may-
dis toxins, 553
Atriplex
C_3-C_4 species, 48
rosea, 43, 44
Auxin
and cell wall chemistry,
210-14
in control of phloem transport, 534
growth responses to
effect of, on cell wall
extensibility, 198
and factors, 9
modification of, 199-202
relation to acid pH, 204-10
interaction with ABA, 299
metabolism of
and biosynthesis of indoleacetic acid, 488-96
and catabolism of indole-
acetic acid, 496-506
in higher plants, 487-513
in plant propagation media,
152
as regulator of root growth,
217-18
solar transport of, 6
translocation of growth
factors across graft union,
9-10
use in analyzing phototropism,
8-9

B

Boric acid
and carbohydrate metabolism
in control of seed germination, 175
inorganic uptake mechanism
and barley roots, 66
data on, 57-59, 61
evidence for unstirred
layer, 63
kinetics for, 71
multiphasic isotherm, 57
multiphasic mechanisms
for, 61
in sugar cane tissue, 61

C

Carbohydrate metabolism
in seed germination
interaction with gibberellic
acid, 175-76
Carbon dioxide
metabolite exchange, 27
promotion of plant growth,
203-4
proton gradient, 414
Catalase isozyme system

biochemical properties of,
245
developmental control of, 242
differential control of, 243
genetic control of, 242
subcellular localization of,
243-45
tissue specificity of, 246
Chlorenchyma
location of
in C_4 plants, 30-31
around vascular bundles, 28
Chlorophyll
and synthesis, 379
Chloroplasts
export of energy from
envelope permeability in,
407-9
malate/OAA shuttle in, 410
PGA/DHAP shuttle in, 410
interrelations with cytoplasm,
393-418
interrelations with mitochondria, 418
sidedness of membrane, 441-
45
structure of
dimorphic, 34-37
and peripheral reticulum,
37-42
see also Electron transport
Cinnamic acid sequence, 468-
70
see also Aromatic compounds
Circadian clock
Went, F. W., on, 14-15
Circadian rhythms
in chloroplasts of unicells
and photosynthesis, 117-19,
123
and synthesis of RNA, 118
variation in ATP and, 118-
19
compartmentation and, 129
crassulacean acid metabolism
and, 119-22
feedback models and, 124-
25
light and metabolic circadian
periodicity, 126-29
and metabolic patterns, 13-
14, 115 34
physiological significance
of circadian metabolic
rhythms, 130-31
and problems of circadian
periodicity, 126-29
Compartmentation
and circadian rhythms, 129
fluxes in giant algal cells
and, 54
models of, 64
see also Uptake mechanisms
Constant infusion method
for studying protein turnover,
369
Continuous labeling method

for studying protein turnover, 369
Crassulacean acid metabolism (CAM)
in C$_4$ photosynthesis, 42, 44, 47-49
effect of short days on, 121-22
induction of
by photoperiodism, 121
rhythm of carbon dioxide fixation, 120, 123
output, 121
storage step in, 120
Cross-bridges
ATP activity in, 312
in microtubules, 311-12, 335-36
Crypto-succulents, 47-48
Cytochalasin B (CB)
effect on microfilaments, 342-46
Cytokinins
interaction with abscisic acid, 299
and maintaining protein, 380
in plant propagation media, 152
in seed germination, 183
Cytoplasmic streaming
and microfilaments, 342-43, 347, 353

D

Degradation
of abscisic acid, 275-77
"Delay block"
and circadian periodicity, 126-27
Density labeling
to measure protein turnover, 370-71
Diacetoxyscirpenol, 549
Dicarboxylate translocator, 416-17
Diffusion
and carrier mechanisms, 65
across plasmalemma, 61, 62
in potato slices, 67
in unstirred layers, 63
Dimorphic chloroplasts, 36-37
Dinitrogen fixation, 81-114
ammonia uptake, 98-100
evolution within nitrogen-fixing systems, 107-8
in legume root nodule, 81, 108
nitrogenase enzyme
ATP binding and, 90-92
components of, 84-86
cross-reactions of, 86-88
electron transfer in, 90-92
molybdenum function in, 92-93
properties of, 88-90

purification of, 82-83
population increase and, 82
routes of ammonia assimilation in
glutamate dehydrogenase (GDH) activity in, 96-98, 100
glutamine synthetase (GS) activity in, 96-100
GOGAT activity in, 96-100
tracer studies of, for legumes, 96
tracer studies of, for non-legumes, 95-96
DNA
effects of abscisic acid on, 297-99
synthesis and replication of, 181-82
syringomycin, 562
Dormancy
abscisic acid effect on, 282-85
and senescence, 293
Dual labeling
to estimate protein turnover, 370
Dual uptake models, 54, 57
by barley roots, 61, 75
kinetics of, 61
see also Uptake; Uptake mechanisms

E

Ecology
of desert plants, 18
of mycorrhiza, 19
Ectomycorrhizal fungi, 570-74
nutrient requirements of, 570-74
significance of
for host tree, 572-74
see also Mycorrhiza
Electron acceptors
of photosystem I
endogenous, 425-28
localization of site in membrane, 428-50
of photosystem II, 435-38
artificial, 436
endogenous, 435-36
Electron donors
in nitrogenase, 93-95
of photosystem I
artificial, 432
endogenous, 431
location of donor site on membrane, 433
of photosystem II
artificial, 439
endogenous, 438
localization of donor site in membrane, 440
Electron flow
across thylakoid membrane,

445-51
energy conservation in, 451-52
Electron transfer
in nitrogen-fixing systems, 90-92
Electron transport
energy conservation in, 423-58
noncyclic and cyclic
electron flow across thylakoid membrane, 445-51
photosynthetic
of chloroplasts, 423-58
electron acceptor of photosystem I, 425-31
electron acceptor of photosystem II, 435-38
electron donor of photosystem I, 431-35
electron donor of photosystem II, 438-41
sidedness of the membrane, 445-51
Envelope permeability
toward adenylates, 407-9
toward pyridine nucleotides, 409
Explants
of aseptic tissue culture, 148, 150

F

Feedback inhibition
in C$_4$ photosynthesis, 47
Ferulate-5-hydroxylase
and C$_6$-C$_3$ pathways of aromatic compounds, 467-68
Flowering
and ABA growth promotion of, 292
Froelichia tissue cultures
C$_3$ and C$_4$ photosynthesis in, 42
Fruit set
development and abscisic acid, 291-92
Fungal toxins
effect on cell elongation, 214-16
Fusicoccin
and increase in stomatal and cuticular transpiration, 551-52
influences of, 549
as stimulator of
cell elongation, 214-15
water uptake, 214
structure of, 550

G

Gibberellic acid
and ABA, 291
rapid growth responses to, 218

in seed germination, 183-85

Gibberellins
as flower growth stimulus, 293
in plant propagation media, 152
and senescence, 294

Glucose ester
of abscisic acid, 275-76, 281

Glutamate dehydrogenase (GDH)
in ammonia incorporation
of nitrogen-fixing systems, 96-100

Glutamine synthesis (GS)
in ammonia incorporation
of nitrogen-fixing systems, 96-100

Glycoside phytotoxins, 544-48
see also specific phytotoxins

GOGAT
in ammonia incorporation
of nitrogen-fixing systems, 96-100

Greenhouses, 10-12, 15-17, 20

H

Heavy meromyosin (HMM), 337-38, 341, 349

Heavy water
effects on cell elongation, 215-16

Helmithosporium carbonum
toxin, 560-61

Helminthosporium maydis
toxins, 552-53

Helmithosporoside, 544

Hormones
activity of
and gibberellic acid, 183-84
in seed germination, 183-84
and auxin
effects of on cell wall extensibility, 198
modification of timing, 199
rapid response to, 197-99
control of phloem transport, 534
and nonhormonal factors
acid and cell wall chemistry, 210-14
acid response, 204-10
fusicoccin, 214-15
promotion of growth by carbon dioxide, 203-4
protein synthesis and, 196
rapid responses
to plants, 195-223
in roots, 217-18
RNA and transferase activity, 218-19
techniques for measuring rapid responses, 196-97
timing responses to, 195-96

see also Auxin; Fusicoccin

I

Indoleacetic acid (IAA)
biosynthesis of
role of epiphytic microorganisms, 495
tryptophan in, 488-89
catabolism of
bound forms in, 505-6
oxidation in, 496-504
see also Auxin

Intermediates, C_3-C_4, 44

Invertase
turnover of, 377

Iron-sulfur protein
comparison with nitrogenase
enzyme, 86-87

Isotopic
methods in protein turnover, 365

Isozymes
cellular development, 225-26
cellular differentiation, 226
classification of, 227
definition of, 226
in development and differentiation, 225-58
genetics of, 235
number of, in plants, 227-35
physiochemical nature of, 226
systems of
alcohol dehydrogenase, 235-39
α- and β-amylase, 239-42
biochemical analysis of, 251
catalase, 242-46
and enzyme polymorphism, 252
investigation of subcellular distribution, 254
malate dehydrogenase (MDH), 246-48
as natural marker systems, 252
peptidases, 248-50
peroxidases, 250-52
see also specific isozymes

K

Kalanchoe
compartmentation of, 129
crassulacean acid metabolism in, 117, 120-23, 129

Kinetic analysis
of uptake
to study protein turnover, 369
see also Protein turnover; Uptake mechanisms

Kranz anatomy
and bundle sheaths, 30-31,

43
effect of, on translocation of photosynthate into vascular tissue, 33
exceptions to common type, 30
photorespiration, and reassimilation of CO_2 as a result of, 43
physiological aspects of photosynthesis, 29

Krebs cycle
malate dehydrogenase in, 246

L

Leaf anatomy
of bundle sheaths, 30-33
of C_4 plants, 28-33
and CO_2 fixation pathways, 44
as indicator of
C_3 syndrome, 44
C_4 syndrome, 44
Kranz-type, 28-29
mesophyll, 30-32
as CO_2 trap, 46
relation to carbon metabolism, 48

Legume root nodule
dinitrogen fixation in, 81-108

Light reactions
and bundle sheaths, 36-37
effect of, on circadian rhythm, 126-29
enzyme induction and, 127-29
in tissue cultures, 156-57

Lignins, 472-75
characteristics of, 472-73
enzymatic compounds required to form, 473-74
formation of, in walls, 474-75

Lipid metabolism
and glyoxylate cycle
and ADP, 174
in Douglas fir seeds, 173

Lipomucopolysaccharides, 547
see also Glycoside phytotoxins

Liver enzymes
circadian rhythms in, 117-18

Lycomarasmine, 554

Lysosomes
regulation of protein breakdown, 385-86

M

Maize seeds
and indoleacetic acid, 505

Malate
and CAM, 119-20
dehydrogenase (isozyme

system), 246-48
groups of, 36, 44-45
malate/OAA shuttle
and ATP, 412-14
and metabolite transfer,
410-12
and NADP, 411
Mass flow hypothesis
in phloem transport, 526-28
Membrane binding
functions in protein turnover,
386
Membranes
properties of
controlling seed germina-
tion in, 185-87
and endoplasmic reticulum,
186-87
Meristem
in tissue cultures, 136-37
Mesophyll, 30-31
Metabolism
of abscisic acid
biosynthesis, 277-80
biosynthesis, in a cell-free
system, 280-81
and degradation, 275-77
glucose ester, 275-76
metabolite C, 276-77
mevalonate, 277-78, 280
phaseic acid, 276-77
of aromatic compounds, 459-
86
and ATP control of phloem
transport, 520
of auxin
in higher plants, 487-513
carbohydrate
and boric acid, in control
of seed germination, 175
and circadian periodicity,
115-32
enzyme control in, 126-29
crassulacean acid, 120-23
and circadian rhythm, 13-
14, 119-22
in C_4 photosynthesis, 42,
44, 47-49
Metabolite C, 276-77
Metabolite exchange
ATP respiration and, 394
between chloroplasts and
cytoplasm, 393-421
and C_4 plants during photosynthesis, 405-7
carriers of
adenine nucleotide trans-
locator as, 417
and carriers mediating
transfer of amino acids,
417
transfer of sugars, 417
and dicarboxylate translocator, 416-17
and phosphate translocator,
415
CO_2 and, 27

DHAP and, 27
enzymatic control of, 27-28
export of energy from chloroplast envelope towards
adenylates, 407-9
malate/OAA shuttle, 410-
12
PGA/DHAP shuttle, 410
pyridine nucleotides, 409
methods for study of
in vitro, 397-98
in vivo, 395-97
and PGA, 27
photosynthesis of C_3 plants,
398-405
in vitro, 398
in vivo, 398
proton gradient and
CO_2, 414
pH, 414-15
and relationships between
chloroplasts and
CO_2 in photosynthesis, 418
mitochondria, 418
Mevalonate
effect on fruit set, 292
relation to ABA, 277-78, 280
Michaelis-Menten kinetics,
54-55, 63-65
Microbodies
C_4 photosynthesis
distribution in, 43-44
structure in, 43-44
Microfilaments, 337-51
ATPase activity in, 338-40
biochemistry of, 338-40
cooperation with micro-
tubules, 351-52
effect of cytochalasin B (CB)
on, 342-46
morphology of, 340-42
motility of, 347-51
relation of P-protein to,
346-47
Microtubules, 310-37
biochemistry of, 312-15
and cell
nuclear migrations, 326-27
polarity, 324-28
shape, 335-36
wall formation, 328-35
control of assembly, 315-17
by equilibrium process,
315
within cell, 317
cooperation with microfilaments, 351-52
mechanism of action, 336
morphology of, 310-12
organizing centers (MTOC),
317-24
and cell wall formation,
335
morphology of, 317-18
polymerization, 324
Mineral cations
and anions in uptake mech-

anisms, 66
ATPases and, 70
ATP formation, 73
bacterial effects on, 64
data on, 57-59
evidence for unstirred
layer and, 63
kinetics for, 71
and multiphasic isotherms,
57
Mitochondria
in bundle sheaths of C_4 dicots,
43
relation with chloroplasts,
418
Models
of feedback in circadian
rhythms, 124-26
see also Uptake models
Molybdenum
functions of
in nitrogen-fixing systems,
92-93
Monocots, C_4, 43
Multiphasic isotherms
and binding of sugars, 75
chloride uptake and, 57
counterions and, 67
mineral cation and, 57
and phosphate uptake, 57, 66
and sulphate uptake, 57
see also Uptake mechanisms
Multiphasic series model
supplements to, 65
versus parallel model, 62
see also Uptake; Uptake
mechanisms
Mycorrhiza
advantages of ectomycorrhiza
to symbiosis partners,
570-74
nutrient requirements of,
570-72
significance of, for the host
tree, 572-74
anatomical features of
cortex cells, 569
ectomycorrhiza, 569-70
endomycorrhiza, 570
and conditions for ectomycorrhizal formation, 578-82
factors determined by the
fungus, 579-80
factors determined by the
higher plant, 580-82
definition of, 567
occurrence of, in plant kingdom, 568
and coexistence of fungi
in higher plants, 568
and infection, 568
root hair formation and,
568
uptake of nutrients and, 569
physiology of, 567-86
poor nutrient soils, 582
reciprocal relationships in

ectomycorrhiza
  and alleloparasitism, 574
  and substances released
    by fungi, 575-76
  and translocation of carbo-
    hydrates, 576-78
  see also Ectomycorrhizal
    fungi
Myosin
  in microfilaments, 338-40

N

NADP
  and aromatic compounds,
    471
  and chloroplasts, 424
  malate dehydrogenase, 247
  malate/OAA shuttle, 411
  PGA/DHAP shuttle, 410
  pyridine nucleotides, 409
NADPH
  and aromatic compounds,
    471, 474, 482
  and chloroplasts, 424, 427,
    442
  and indoleacetic acid, 495
  pyridine nucleotides, 409
  rise of, during seed germin-
    ation, 176
Nitrate reductase
  turnover of, 374-75
Nitrogenase
  electron donor system in,
    93-95
  enzyme
    ATP binding in, 90-92
    comparisons with iron-
      sulfur proteins, 86-87
    components of, 84-86
    electron transfer in, 90-92
    molybdenum functions in,
      92-93
    properties of, 88-90
    purification of, 82-83
  genetics of, 100-1
  physiological control of
    ATP/ADP ratio in, 104-6
  synthesis of, 102-4
Nutrient medium
  amino acids in, 152
  auxins in, 152
  carbohydrate requirements
    of, 151
  chemical composition of, 150
  cytokinins in, 152
  gibberellins in, 152
  natural complexes in, 152
  pH of, 155
  physical qualities of, 154-55
  salt requirements of, 151

O

Oligosaccharides, 545
Ophiobolins, 552
Optical rotary dispersion

of abscisic acid, 262
Orchids
  culture propagation of, 138-
    40
Organic uptake mechanisms
  amino acids
    by carrot root cells, 74
    of glycine, alanine, and
      phenylalanine, 74
    by sugar cane cells, 48
  cations, 71
  choline sulfate
    by barley roots, 75
    by filamentous fungi, 75
  multiphasic, 73
  of solutes by higher plants,
    54, 75-76

P

Parallel model
  of uptake
    as compromise between
      series model, 65
    supplements to, 65
    versus series model, 62
    see also Uptake; Uptake
      mechanisms
Pathways
  C_6-C_1 to quinones, 475-76
  C_6-C_2 to cyanogenic glyco-
    sides, 475
  C_6-C_3, 462-72
  C_{15}-flavonoid, 476-78
  photosynthetic reductive
    pentose phosphate, 46
  tryptophan
    to IAA, 489-95
Pea stems
  rapid responses to plant
    hormones
    and IAA, 207-8
Peptidases
  aminopeptidase, 248
  endopeptidase, 249
  peroxidases, 250-52
Pericoma toxins, 559
Periodicity, circadian
  and "delay block," 126
  Higgins-Pavlidis model, 127
  and light, 126-29
  Wever's model, 126
  and "Zeitgeber," 126
Peripheral reticulum (PR)
  in C_3 plants
    of Atriplex rosea, 39
    profiles of, 40
  in C_4 plants
    and glutaraldehyde, 37
    and $KMnO_4$ fixation, 37
    syndrome of, 37-42
    tissue culture of Froelichia
      gracillus, 41-42
    and carboxylating enzyme
      system
    in chloroplasts of mesophyll
      cells, 41

and chloroplast structure
  of C_3 plants, 39-41
  of C_{14} plants, 37-39
  and envelope, 37-38, 40
  and function of PR, 41-42
  effects of fixation procedures
    on, 37
  and freeze-fracture studies,
    38
  and guard cells, 41
  as influenced by light inten-
    sity, 39
  involved in transport system
    between
    chloroplasts, 42
    cytoplasm, 42
Permeability
  ABA increase of, 295-97
Peroxidase
  in aromatic metabolism,
    478-80
Phenylalanine ammonia lyase
  turnover of, 375-77
Phloem transport, 515-39
  attributes of
    and biodirectional move-
      ment, 529
    and comparison of mobile
      material, 530-32
    properties of mobile mate-
      rial, 530-32
    speed of movement, 530
    viruses and, 532
    water movement, 527
  hormonal control of, 534-35
  metabolic control of
    and available energy, 521-
      22
    energy required for trans-
      location, 520-21
    inhibitors of, 522
    and metabolite retention,
      520
    and sieve tube chemistry,
      520
    temperature, 522
    vein loading, 520
  patterns of, 528-29
  profiles of, 528-29
  sieve elements, 516-19
    fine structure properties,
      518
    and phloem blockage, 518-
      19
    tissue fixation and, 517
    tubal fine structure, 517
    turgor changes and, 517
  sinks
    response to removal of,
      533
  sources
    and hormonal control of
      transport, 533-34
    and sinks, 533-34
Phosphate translocator, 415
Phosphate uptake
  and aging in celery, 67

in barley roots, 69
and glucose, 70
from dilute solutions
affected by bacteria, 64
and long distance transport
in wheat seedlings, 61
Michaelis-Menten kinetics
and, 63
multiphasic isotherm and,
57, 66
phase patterns for, 71-72
of plants, 55
potato slices, 57
and sulphate, 55-56
in tissues, 55
see also Sulphate uptake;
Uptake; Uptake mecha-
nisms
Phosphorous metabolism
in seed germination, 179-80
see also Phytin
Photoperiodism
and CAM, 121
Photorespiration
in bundle sheath cells, 46
in C_4 plants, 43, 45
and CO_2 loss, 48
C_3 Photosynthesis
transfer of metabolites
during, 398-405
see also Pathways; Peripheral reticulum
C_4 Photosynthesis
C_3-C_4 intermediates and,
44-45
and chloroplast structure in,
34-42
bundle sheaths, 36, 41
dimorphic, 36-37
in peripheral reticulum
(PR), 37-42
feedback inhibition in, 47
and leaf anatomy
bundle sheaths, 30-31, 43,
45-46, 48
Kranz-type, 28-31, 33, 43-
45, 47
starch sheath (endodermis),
31-33
stomata and, 30
metabolite transfer during,
405-7
microbodies and
distribution of, 43-44
structure of, 43-44
mitochondria and
distribution of, 43-44
structure of, 43-44
plants of
as crypto-succulents, 47-50
structural basis of, 45-47
see also Pathways; Peripheral reticulum
Photosynthetic reductive
pentose phosphate pathway,
46
Photosystem I

artificial electron donors
in, 439-40
and circadian rhythm, 119
electron acceptors of, 426-
31
electron donors of, 431-35
Photosystem II
artificial electron donors
of, 439-40
and chloroplast structure,
36-37
and circadian rhythm, 119
electron acceptor of, 435-
38
electron donor of, 438-41
Phototropism
analyzing, in terms of auxin,
8-9
Phytin
in seed germination
and ATP formation, 179
and phytase formation, 179-
80
Phytotoxins
as produced by plant parasites, 541-66
amino acid derived, 554-
61
glycoside, 544-48
miscellaneous, 562-63
terpenoid, 548-54
Plant propagation
and disease-free plants,
160
explants of stage I, 148-50
future prospects of, 160-62
influence of temperature on,
157-58
light requirements of, 156-
57
and multiplication of propagula, 140-47
nutrient medium of, 150-54
of orchids, 138, 140
physical qualities of medium
in, 154-55
reproduction of genetically
aberrant plants, 159-60
stages of tissue culture
method, 138-40
tables of plants in, 141-47
see also Tissue culture
Plasmalemma
and binding of
phosphate, 71
sulphate, 71
and data about, 62
and diffusion across, 61-63
kinetic control shifting and,
63
measuring uptake across,
61
multiphasic series model,
63
and vessicles, 64
Polyphenoloxidase
in aromatic metabolism,

480-82
Polysaccharides, 548
Precursor pools
problems of methodology in
protein turnover, 365-68
rate of inactivation of PAL
in, 377
in total protein turnover, 372
Protease inhibitors
in seed germination, 172-
73
P-Protein
relation of
to microfilaments, 346-47
in sieve tubes, 518
Protein turnover, 363-92
of enzymes for chlorophyll
synthesis
inhibitors of, 375, 379
kinetic studies of, 379
invertase
half-life of, 377
regulation of, 377
methods for studying
constant infusion (continuous
labeling), 369-70
density labeling, 370-71
dual labeling, 370
kinetic analysis of changes
in enzyme activity, 371
kinetic analysis of uptake,
369
nitrate reductase (NR)
degradation of, 374
induction of, 374-75
loss of, during heat stress,
375
phenylalanine ammonia lyase
(PAL)
induction of, synthesis,
375-76
rate of inactivation in precursor pool, 377
problems of methodology
isotopic methods, 365
precursor pools, 365-68
regulation of breakdown
and lysosomes, 385-86
and membranes, 386
and protein molecule as
a substrate, 384-85
proteolytic enzymes, 382-
83
ribulose 1, 5-diphosphate
carboxylase (RuDPCase)
interaction of synthesis and
degradation of, 377-79
RNA, 381
sulfate permease
location of specific ion uptake, 379
relation to NR and PAL,
380
senescence and cytokinins,
380
total
and abscisic acid, 374

constant infusion, 372-73
constant labeling method, 373
precursor pools, 372
pulse chase, 372
and various hormonal effects, 380-81
Proteolytic enzymes
regulation of protein break-down, 382-84, 386-89
in seed germination, 172-73
Proton gradient, 414-15
Pseudomonas phaseolicola, 559-60
Pulse procedure
to measure protein turnover, 368-69, 372

Q

Quinic acid
and aromatic compounds, 469-70
Quinones
C_6-C_1 pathways to, 475-76

R

Respiration
ATP level of, 177-79
during seed germination, 176-79
of peanut embryos, 177
redox system in, 177
Rhizobitoxine, 558
Ribulose 1, 5-diphosphate carboxylase (RuDPCase)
turnover of, 377-79
RNA
effects of ABA on, 297-99
hormones as inhibitors of, 198
isolation of, in pear, 184
and microtubule assembly, 317
protein turnover and, 381
synthesis of
in seed germination, 181-82
and syringomycin, 561
transferase activity and, 218-19
Roots
barley, 64, 66-67, 69, 72, 75
rapid response in
and hormonal regulation in growth of, 217-18
and IAA, 217

S

Saccharum, 43
Saprophytic fungi
and ectomycorrhiza, 571-72
Second Law of Thermodynamics, 7, 25

Seed coats, 169-72
diffusion pathways in, 170-71
influence of, during germination, 169-70
Seed dormancy
Went, F. W., on, 7
Seed germination
carbohydrate metabolism in, 175-76
with boron, 175
and cotyledons of peas, 175-76
interaction of gibberellic acid, 175
and loss of ability to utilize glucose, 176
control of, 167-93
and environmental factors, 167-69
enzymes in
activation, 180-83
proteolytic, 172-73
synthesis, 180-83
hormones in
and gibberellic acid, 183
and gibberellin forms, 183-84
and growth substances, 183-85
lipase activity and, 183
protein metabolism of pea cotyledons, 183
lipid metabolism and glyoxylate cycle, 173-74
membranes in, 185-87
controlling properties of, 185-86
effects of saponins on, 186
and phosphorous metabolism, 180
and phytin metabolism
formation of, and AMP, 179
formation of, and ATP, 179
and phytase activity, 179-80
protease inhibitors, 172-73
functions of, in malting process of barley, 172
functions of, in rice seeds, 172
protein activation and synthesis
of ATP, 180-81
and cytochrome reductase, 182
of DNA, 181-82
and polysome formation, 181
of RNA, 181-82
in wheat embryos, 180
redox system and
cotyledons, 177
cyanide, 177
enzyme increase, 178

respiration in
lettuce, 176, 178
rise of, 176
seed coats and
diffusion pathways, 170-71
influences of, on, 169-70
other permeability barriers, 169-72
water uptake, 170-71
ultrastructure of
as related to metabolism in organelles, 185
Senescence
and dormancy, 293
malate content and, 119
and peripheral reticulum in Portulaca oleracea, 42
photosynthesis and
C_3, 44
C_4, 44
promotion of, by ABA, 294-95
and protein turnover, 380
Sieve tubes
biodirectional movement in, 529-30
chemistry of, 520
pressure, 525-26
speed of movement in, 530
and tissue fixation, 517
turgor changes in, 517, 525-26
water movement in, 527-28
water relations of
solute concentrations, 524-25
Sink
response to removal of, 533-34
Smog
natural, 21-22
photochemical, 20-21
Starch sheath (endodermis), 31-33
formation in C_4 photosynthesis, 31-33
Stomata
localization of
in C_4 plants, 30
Sugar
and plant growth, 15-16
Sugar cane, 43, 47, 61
Sulfate permease
in protein turnover, 379
Sulfate uptake
and barley roots
as inhibited by analogs, 72
as inhibited by dinitrophenol, 63
and multiphasic kinetics, 64
and phase patterns, 69, 71-72
data on, 54-57
by higher plants, 53
and Michaelis-Menten

kinetics, 63
and multiphasic isotherms, 57
and phosphate uptake, 55-56
Synthesis
mechanisms of, in seed germination, 180-82
ATP, 181
DNA, 181-82
RNA, 181-82
Syringomycin, 561-62

T

Tabtoxins, 555-57
Temperature
influence on tissue cultures, 156-57
Tentoxin, 557-58
Terpenoid phytotoxins, 548-54
Thermoperiodicity
as control of plant environment, 11-12
Thylakoid membrane
cyclic and noncyclic flow across
and antibodies, 445
and donor sites, 445
sidedness of, 445-50
Tissue culture in plant propagation, 135-66
aseptic, 139
environment of, 156
and experiments with herbaceous genera, 137
light requirements of, 156-57
and meristem, 136-37
multiplication of propagula in, 140-46
and reestablishment in soil, 140
reproduction of selected plants in, 159-60
stages of, 138-40
tables of plants in, 141-47
temperature influence on, 157-58
Toxins
alternaria, 562
hydrogen cyanide (HCN), 563
see also specific toxins
Tracer studies
of routes of ammonia assimilation
for legumes, 96
for nonlegumes, 95-96
Tryptophan (TPP)
in biosynthesis of IAA
indoleacetaldoxime pathway, 493-94
indolepyruvic acid pathway and, 489-91
as primary precursor, 488-89
tryptamine pathway, 491-92
tryptophol pathway, 494-95
Turgor
in phloem transport, 517
and gradients of, 525-26

U

Ultrastructure
and ABA, 299-300
in seed germination, 185
Ultraviolet absorption
of abscisic acid, 262
Unicellular organisms
circadian rhythms in chloroplasts of, 118-19
ATP variations in, 118-19
RNA synthesis in, 118
Unstirred layer
and uptake mechanisms
ion uptake, 63
kinetic evidence for, 63
Uptake
models of, 63-68
compartmentation, 54, 64
dual, 54, 57, 61, 75
multiphasic series, 53-54, 62
parallel, 54, 62-63, 65
see also specific models
Uptake mechanisms, 53-79
of inorganic solutes
ATPases and binding in, 66-69, 72-73
boric acid, 57-59
Ca^{2+} and, 66
carrier mechanisms and, 65
chloride, 57-59, 63-64, 71
and compartmentation, 64
diffusion in unstirred layer, 63
and ion uptake, 63-65, 69, 71
Michaelis-Menten kinetics, 54-55, 63-65
microbial contamination and, 64
mineral cations, 57-59, 63-64, 70
multiphasic isotherms, 62
phase patterns, 66-69, 72-73
phase transitions, 71-73
phosphate, 57

plasmalemma and, 61-62
sulfate and, 56-57
variation along roots and, 64
and vessicles, 65
of organic solutes
and amino acids, 74-75
choline sulfate, 75-76
sugars, 73-74
see also Uptake

V

Variability
genetic, 16
Vein loading
in phloem transport, 520
Vessicles
role of and three-compartment model, 64
Viruses
in phloem transport
movement patterns of, 532-33

W

Went, F. W.
on air pollution, 20-24
on auxin, 4-10
on botany, 2-4
on control of plant environment, 10-17
on ecology
of desert plants, 18-19
of mycorrhiza, 19
of orchids, 18
Wheat roots
organic uptake mechanism of, and amino acids, 74
Wilting
effects of
on ABA content, 287-89

X

Xanthium
studies of protein turnover, 379-80

Z

Zea mays
chloroplast structure in, 37
and peripheral reticulum, 40
Zeitgeber
in circadian periodicity, 126
and metabolic rhythms, 130
and photoperiod, 127-28

CUMULATIVE INDEXES

CONTRIBUTING AUTHORS VOLUMES 21-25

A

Abeles, F. B., 23:259
Aleem, M. I. H., 21:67
Anderson, W. P., 23:51
Armstrong, D. J., 21:359

B

Barrs, H. D., 22:223
Bergersen, F. J., 22:121
Bidwell, R. G. S., 21:43
Bieleski, R. L., 24:225
Black, C. C. Jr., 24:253
Boardman, N. K., 21:115
Boulter, D., 21:91
Brandes, H., 24:115
Briggs, W. R., 23:293
Brown, J. S., 23:73
Burr, B., 24:493

C

Canny, M. J., 22:237
Castelfranco, P. A., 24:129
Cheniae, G. M., 21:467
Cleland, R., 22:197
Cocking, E. C., 23:29
Cook, G. M. W., 22:97
Crosby, D. G., 24:467

D

Dilworth, M. J., 25:81
Douthit, H. A., 24:311
Dugger, W. M., 21:215

E

Eschrich, W., 21:193
Evans, L. T., 22:365
Evans, M. L., 25:195

G

Goedheer, J. C., 23:87
Gunning, B. E. S., 23:173

H

Hall, A. E., 22:431
Hall, R. H., 24:415
Hampton, R. O., 23:389
Hanson, K. R., 23:335
Hatch, M. D., 21:141

Heber, U., 25:393
Hendricks, S. B., 21:1
Hepler, P. K., 25:309
Higinbotham, N., 24:25
Hodson, R. C., 24:381
Hsiao, T. C., 24:519
Huffaker, R. C., 25:363

I

Ikuma, H., 23:419

J

Jackson, W. A., 21:385
Jones, B. L., 24:47
Jones, R., 24:571

K

Kadyrov, Ch. Sh., 22:185
Kawashima, N., 21:325
Kefeli, V. I., 22:185
Kirk, J. T. O., 21:11
Kolattukudy, P. E., 21:163
Kosuge, T., 21:433
Kramer, P. J., 24:1
Kuiper, P. J. C., 23:157

L

Laetsch, W. M., 25:27
Lamport, D. T. A., 21:235
Lang, A., 21:537
Läuchli, A., 23:197
Loewus, F., 22:337
Loomis, R. S., 22:431
Lüttge, U., 22:23
Lyons, J. M., 24:445

M

MacRobbie, E. A. C., 22:75
Mahadevan, S., 24:69
Marcus, A., 22:313
Mayer, A. M., 25:167
Mazliak, P., 24:287
Mehard, C. W., 21:271
Meyer, F. H., 25:567
Milborrow, B. V., 25:259
Murakami, S., 21:271
Murashige, T., 25:135
Myers, J., 22:289

N

Nelson, O. E. Jr., 24:493
Nissen, P., 25:53
Northcote, D. H., 23:113

O

Oaks, A., 21:43

P

Packer, L., 21:271
Palevitz, B. A., 25:309
Park, R. B., 22:395
Pate, J. S., 23:173
Peterson, L. W., 25:363
Preiss, J., 21:433

Q

Queiroz, O., 25:115

R

Rains, D. W., 23:367
Rebeiz, C. A., 24:129
Rice, H. V., 23:293
Ryan, C. A., 24:173

S

Sacher, J. A., 24:197
Sane, P. V., 22:395
Saunders, P. F., 22:261
Scandalios, J. G., 25:225
Schiff, J. A., 24:381
Schneider, E. A., 25:487
Schneider, G., 21:499
Schultes, R. E., 21:571
Schwartz, M., 22:469
Scott, T. K., 23:235
Sequeira, L., 24:353
Shain, Y., 25:167
Shlyk, A. A., 22:169
Simonis, W., 24:89
Skoog, F., 21:359
Slack, C. R., 21:141
Stafford, H. A., 25:459
Steward, F. C., 22:1
Strobel, G. A., 25:541
Sussman, A. S., 24:311

T

Tewari, K. K., 22:141

Ting, I. P., 21:215
Tolbert, N. E., 22:45
Trebst, A., 25:423
Tukey, H. B. Jr., 21:305

U

Urbach, W., 24:89

V

Vickery, H. B., 23:1

Volk, R. J., 21:385
Voskresenskaya, N. P., 23: 219

W

Wardlaw, I. F., 25:515
Wareing, P. F., 22:261
Went, F. W., 25:1
Wightman, F., 25:487
Wildman, S. G., 21:325

Williams, W. A., 22: 431

Y

Yoshida, S., 23:437

Z

Zalik, S., 24:47
Zucker, M., 23:133

CHAPTER TITLES VOLUMES 21-25

PREFATORY CHAPTERS
The Passing Scene   S. B. Hendricks   21:1-10
Plant Physiology: The Changing Problems,
  the Continuing Quest   F. C. Steward   22:1-22
A Chemist Among Plants   H. B. Vickery   23:1-28
Some Reflections After 40 Years in Plant
  Physiology   P. J. Kramer   24:1-24
Reflections and Speculations   F. W. Went   25:1-26
BIOENERGETICS
Biochemical Aspects of Chloroplast Develop-
  ment   J. T. O. Kirk   21:11-42
Physical Separation of the Photosynthetic
  Photochemical Systems   N. K. Boardman   21:115-40
Photosynthetic CO_2-Fixation Pathways   M. D. Hatch, C. R. Slack   21:141-62
Ion Transport in Chloroplasts and Plant
  Mitochondria   L. Packer, S. Murakami,
                                                      C. W. Mehard   21:271-304
Photorespiration   W. A. Jackson, R. J. Volk   21:385-432
Regulation of Enzyme Activity in Photosynthetic
  Systems   J. Preiss, T. Kosuge   21:433-66
Photosystem II and O_2 Evolution   G. M. Cheniae   21:467-98
Enhancement Studies in Photosynthesis   J. Myers   22:289-312
The Relation of Ion Transport to Phosphoryla-
  tion   M. Schwartz   22:469-84
Forms of Chlorophyll in vivo   J. S. Brown   23:73-86
Fluorescence in Relation to Photosynthesis   J. C. Goedheer   23:87-112
Electron Transport in Plant Respiration   H. Ikuma   23:419-36
Photophosphorylation in vivo   W. Simonis, W. Urbach   24:89-114
Protochlorophyll and Chlorophyll Biosynthesis
  in Cell-Free Systems from Higher Plants   C. A. Rebeiz, P. A. Castel-
                                                      franco   24:129-72
Photosynthetic Carbon Fixation in Relation to
  Net CO_2 Uptake   C. C. Black Jr.   24:253-86
The C_4 Syndrome: A Structural Analysis   W. M. Laetsch   25:27-52
Metabolite Exchange Between Chloroplasts
  and Cytoplasm   U. Heber   25:393-421
Energy Conservation in Photosynthetic Electron

Transport of Chloroplasts   A. Trebst   25:423-58
CELL ORGANIZATION
Biochemical Aspects of Chloroplast Development   J. T. O. Kirk   21:11-42
Compartmentation of Intermediary Metabolites   A. Oaks, R. G. S. Bidwell   21:43-66
Physical Separation of the Photosynthetic Photochemical Systems   N. K. Boardman   21:115-40
Biochemistry and Fine Structure of Phloem in Relation to Transport   W. Eschrich   21:193-214
Cell Wall Metabolism   D. T. A. Lamport   21:235-70
Structure and Function of Plant Glands   U. Lüttge   22:23-44
Microbodies—Peroxisomes and Glyoxysomes   N. E. Tolbert   22:45-74
Cell Wall Extension   R. Cleland   22:197-222
Distribution of Function and Structure in Chloroplast Lamellae   R. B. Park, P. V. Sane   22:395-430
Plant Cell Protoplasts—Isolation and Development   E. C. Cocking   23:29-50
Chemistry of the Plant Cell Wall   D. H. Northcote   23:113-32
Transfer Cells   J. S. Pate, B. E. S. Gunning   23:173-96
The C_4 Syndrome: A Structural Analysis   W. M. Laetsch   25:27-52
Microtubules and Microfilaments   P. K. Hepler, B. A. Palevitz   25:309-62
DEVELOPMENT
Air Pollution Oxidants—Their Effects on Metabolic Processes in Plants   W. M. Dugger, I. P. Ting   21:215-34
Morphactins: Physiology and Performance   G. Schneider   21:499-536
Cytokinins   F. Skoog, D. J. Armstrong   21:359-84
Gibberellins: Structure and Metabolism   A. Lang   21:537-70
Natural Growth Inhibitors, Their Chemical and Physiological Properties   V. I. Kefeli, Ch. Sh. Kadyrov   22:185-96
Hormones and Dormancy   P. F. Wareing, P. F. Saunders   22:261-88
Flower Induction and the Florigen Concept   L. T. Evans   22:365-94
Blue Light and Carbon Metabolism   N. P. Voskresenskaya   23:219-34
Auxins and Roots   T. K. Scott   23:235-58
Biosynthesis and Mechanism of Action of Ethylene   F. B. Abeles   23:259-92
Phytochrome: Chemical and Physical Properties and Mechanism of Action   W. R. Briggs, H. V. Rice   23:293-334
Physiological Aspects of Grain Yield   S. Yoshida   23:437-64
Gametophyte Development in Ferns and Bryophytes   H. Brandes   24:115-28
Senescence and Postharvest Physiology   J. A. Sacher   24:197-224
Dormancy in Microbial Spores   A. S. Sussman, H. A. Douthit   24:311-52
Hormone Metabolism in Diseased Plants   L. Sequeira   24:353-80
Cytokinins as a Probe of Developmental Processes   R. H. Hall   24:415-44
Gibberellins: Their Physiological Role   R. L. Jones   24:571-98
Plant Propagation Through Tissue Cultures   T. Murashige   25:135-66
Control of Seed Germination   A. M. Mayer, Y. Shain   25:167-93
Rapid Responses to Plant Hormones   M. L. Evans   25:195-223
Isozymes in Development and Differentiation   J. G. Scandalios   25:225-58
The Chemistry and Physiology of Abscisic Acid   B. V. Milborrow   25:259-307
Metabolism of Auxin in Higher Plants   E. A. Schneider, F. Wightman   25:487-513
ENVIRONMENTAL PHYSIOLOGY
Cyclic Variations in Stomatal Aperture, Transpiration, and Leaf Water Potential Under Constant Environmental Conditions   H. D. Barrs   22:223-36
Agricultural Productivity   R. S. Loomis, W. A. Williams, A. E. Hall   22:431-68
Water Transport Across Membranes   P. J. C. Kuiper   23:157-72
Chilling Injury in Plants   J. M. Lyons   24:445-66
The Fate of Pesticides in the Environment   D. G. Crosby   24:467-92
Plant Responses to Water Stress   T. C. Hsiao   24:519-70
METABOLISM
Compartmentation of Intermediary Metabolites   A. Oaks, R. G. S. Bidwell   21:43-66
Oxidation of Inorganic Nitrogen Compounds   M. I. H. Aleem   21:67-90
Protein Synthesis in Plants   D. Boulter   21:91-114
Biosynthesis of Cuticular Lipids   P. E. Kolattukudy   21:163-92

Air Pollution Oxidants—Their Effects on
Metabolic Processes in Plants   W. M. Dugger, I. P. Ting   21:215-34
Cell Wall Metabolism   D. T. A. Lamport   21:235-70
Fraction I Protein   N. Kawashima, S. G. Wildman   21:325-58
Regulation of Enzyme Activity in Photosyn-
thetic Systems   J. Preiss, T. Kosuge   21:433-66
Biochemistry of Symbiotic Nitrogen Fixation
in Legumes   F. J. Bergersen   22:121-40
Genetic Autonomy of Extranuclear Organelles   K. K. Tewari   22:141-68
Biosynthesis of Chlorophyll b   A. A. Shlyk   22:169-84
Enzyme Induction in Plants   A. Marcus   22:313-36
Carbohydrate Interconversions   F. Loewus   22:337-64
Chemistry of the Plant Cell Wall   D. H. Northcote   23:113-32
Light and Enzymes   M. Zucker   23:133-56
Biosynthesis and Mechanism of Action of
Ethylene   F. B. Abeles   23:259-92
Phytochrome: Chemical and Physical Properties
and Mechanism of Action   W. R. Briggs, H. V. Rice   23:293-334
Enzyme Symmetry and Enzyme Stereospeci-
ficity   K. R. Hanson   23:335-66
Protein Biosynthesis   S. Zalik, B. L. Jones   24:47-68
Role of Oximes in Nitrogen Metabolism in
Plants   S. Mahadevan   24:69-88
Proteolytic Enzymes and Their Inhibitors in
Plants   C. A. Ryan   24:173-96
Lipid Metabolism in Plants   P. Mazliak   24:287-310
The Metabolism of Sulfate   J. A. Schiff, R. C. Hodson   24:381-414
Dinitrogen Fixation   M. J. Dilworth   25:81-114
Circadian Rhythms and Metabolic Patterns   O. Queiroz   25:115-34
Protein Turnover in Plants and Possible Means
of Its Regulation   R. C. Huffaker, L. W. Peterson   25:363-92
The Metabolism of Aromatic Compounds   H. A. Stafford   25:459-86
Metabolism of Auxin in Higher Plants   E. A. Schneider, F. Wightman   25:487-513
NUTRITION, ABSORPTION, AND TRANSPORT
Oxidation of Inorganic Nitrogen Compounds   M. I. H. Aleem   21:67-90
Biochemistry and Fine Structure of Phloem
in Relation to Transport   W. Eschrich   21:193-214
Ion Transport in Chloroplasts and Plant
Mitochondria   L. Packer, S. Murakami, C. W.
Mehard   21:271-304
The Leaching of Substances from Plants   H. B. Tukey Jr.   21:305-24
Fluxes and Compartmentation in Plant Cells   E. A. C. MacRobbie   22:75-96
Membrane Structure and Function   G. M. W. Cook   22:97-120
Translocation: Mechanisms and Kinetics   M. J. Canny   22:237-60
Ion Transport in the Cells of Higher Plant
Tissues   W. P. Anderson   23:51-72
Transfer Cells   J. S. Pate, B. E. S. Gunning   23:173-96
Translocation of Inorganic Solutes   A. Läuchli   23:197-218
Salt Transport by Plants in Relation to Salinity   D. W. Rains   23:367-88
Electropotentials of Plant Cells   N. Higinbotham   24:25-46
Phosphate Pools, Phosphate Transport, and
Phosphate Availability   R. L. Bieleski   24:225-52
Uptake Mechanisms: Inorganic and Organic   P. Nissen   25:53-79
Phloem Transport: Physical Chemical or
Impossible   I. F. Wardlaw   25:515-39
SPECIAL TOPICS
The Leaching of Substances from Plants   H. B. Tukey Jr.   21:305-24
The Botanical and Chemical Distribution of
Hallucinogens   R. E. Schultes   21:571-98
Salt Transport by Plants in Relation to Salinity   D. W. Rains   23:367-88
Mycoplasmas as Plant Pathogens: Perspectives
and Principles   R. O. Hampton   23:389-418
Electropotentials of Plant Cells   N. Higinbotham   24:25-46
Biochemical Genetics of Higher Plants   O. E. Nelson Jr., B. Burr   24:493-518
Phytotoxins Produced by Plant Parasites   G. A. Strobel   25:541-66
Physiology of Mycorrhiza   F. H. Meyer   25:567-86